THE BIRDS OF LEICESTERSHIRE AND RUTLAND

Leicestershire and Rutland Ornithological Society

The Birds of LEICESTERSHIRE AND RUTLAND

Rob Fray, Roger Davis, Dave Gamble,
Andrew Harrop and Steve Lister

CHRISTOPHER HELM
LONDON

Published 2009 by Christopher Helm, an imprint of A&C Black Publishers Ltd.,
36 Soho Square, London W1D 3QY

www.acblack.com

ISBN 978-0-7136-7233-6

A CIP catalogue record for this book is available from the British Library

This book is produced using paper that is made from wood grown in managed sustainable forests. It is natural, renewable and recyclable. The logging and manufacturing processes conform to the environmental regulations of the country of origin.

Commissioning Editor: Nigel Redman

Project Editor: Jim Martin

Design by J&L Composition, Scarborough, North Yorkshire

Printed in Great Britain by Martins the Printers, Berwick-upon-Tweed

10 9 8 7 6 5 4 3 2 1

CONTENTS

FOREWORD

by Tim Appleton

The birds of Leicestershire and Rutland were first summarised in 1889 in Montagu Browne's book entitled *The Vertebrate Animals of Leicestershire and Rutland.* Eighty-nine years later, in 1978, the late Ronald Hickling published his book *Birds in Leicestershire and Rutland.* In those intervening years, many changes to the status of the counties' avifauna occurred as so-called progress marched across the countryside altering the natural habitats once and for all. Now, 30 years on from Ronald Hickling's book, this much awaited avifauna documents yet another period of upheaval to the countryside and its wildlife. Populations of many farmland birds have plummeted as a result of agricultural intensification, while birds of prey now grace our skies in numbers probably more familiar to Montagu Browne.

During the Victorian era, several old-style concrete and brick-lined reservoirs were constructed in and around Leicester, creating a number of artificial wetlands, but the new century brought a different approach to reservoir design, namely the flooding of natural valleys. Two of these new reservoirs have had a major impact on our land-locked counties. Eyebrook Reservoir, built in 1940, featured heavily in the last avifauna, adding many new species to the county list as migratory birds following the Welland valley made Eyebrook a stopping-off point on their journeys north and south. This latest book contains many new exciting records from a much larger reservoir, Rutland Water, which filled for the first time in 1979.

But perhaps one of the most rewarding changes in the last 30 years has been the positive attitude towards the conservation of wildlife and natural heritage, although sadly too late for some species such as the Corn Crake or Common Redstart which used to breed in the counties. Fortunately many new nature reserves have been declared in Leicestershire and Rutland, providing safe refuges for a number of new breeding species including the Osprey, Gadwall, Oystercatcher and Common Tern. With more reserves planned for the future, such as Cossington in the Soar valley and a major extension to the Rutland Water Nature Reserve, the future looks even brighter for our birds. By the time the next avifauna is written there will almost certainly be more good news for the counties' birds and those that enjoy watching them.

Birdwatching has never been as popular as it is today; thousands of people take part in all types of scientific surveys, travel the length and breadth of the country and abroad to watch rare birds, or just enjoy feeding and watching birds in their own gardens. This meteoric rise in interest has without doubt spawned a multitude of very knowledgeable amateur observers, no more so than within Leicestershire and Rutland. It is their expertise and the sharing of skills that has led to the publication of this important record of our birds. The collaboration of several authors from the Leicestershire and Rutland Ornithological Society, each with their own specific knowledge, has produced an exceptional book written in their own styles. Let us hope that when the next avifauna is published it breaks the current mould of producing only one avifauna per century! For Leicestershire and Rutland comprise without doubt one of the most exciting inland areas in Britain and its birds deserve the recognition this book will create.

ACKNOWLEDGEMENTS

This book has been written on behalf of the Leicestershire and Rutland Ornithological Society (LROS) and would not have come to fruition without their generous financial support. It would also not have been possible without the contribution of many hundreds of individuals and organisations who have submitted records over the last 65 years; for a full list of contributors, see Appendix 3. All royalties from this book will be donated to LROS.

Other organisations that have been helpful in the production of this book are the British Trust for Ornithology (BTO), the British Birds Rarities Committee (BBRC) and the Rare Birds Breeding Panel (RBBP). The BTO supplied large amounts of ringing data and kindly provided a bursary to cover the costs of this data extraction. The BTO Ringing Scheme is funded by a partnership of the British Trust for Ornithology, the Joint Nature Conservation Committee (on behalf of English Nature, Scottish Natural Heritage and the Countryside Council for Wales, and also on behalf of the Environment and Heritage Service in Northern Ireland), the National Parks and Wildlife Service (Ireland) and the ringers themselves. The BBRC, and especially the late Mike Rogers, assisted in the review of several older records and kept us informed about various decisions involving Leicestershire and Rutland. Mark Holling and Judith Smith of the RBBP allowed access to previously unpublished material.

Much of the information in this book is derived from local monitoring work such as Common Birds Censuses (CBC) and Wetland Bird Survey counts (WeBS), and the following are thanked for providing data: Gerald Felstead (ringing data), Ken Goodrich (Sand Martin data from Wanlip South Gravel Pits), Tim Grove (WeBS counts and BTO gull survey data), Terry Mitcham (Rutland CBC results), Alan Rayfield (Newton Harcourt CBC results) and Chris Stoate (Loddington CBC results). This is also an opportune moment to acknowledge all those who have contributed to local survey work over the years.

Tim Appleton wrote the Foreword and contributed an introductory chapter; he also provided assistance to Andrew Harrop during research for the 'Ornithology in Leicestershire and Rutland' section, as did Peter Gamble, the late Ronald Hickling, Clifford Holt, Terry Mitcham and Frank Pickering. Steve Lister was assisted during research for the 'Migration' section by Keith Allsopp, Tim Appleton, David Barker, Terry Mitcham, Paul Powell, Eric Simms and Colin Towe. For help with compiling the Gazetteer thanks are due to Howard Bradshaw, Anona Finch, Peter Gamble, Ken Goodrich, Jim Graham and Linda Worrall. Jan Dawson provided much help and assistance at Leicester Museum.

This project has been a long time in preparation and three people deserve special thanks for their continuing help and encouragement during sometimes difficult times: Carl Baggott, Jim Graham and Frank Pickering. A number of other individuals have either read the text, provided information or assisted in some way, including Gary Bell, Richard Fray, James Fudge, Sue Graham, Andy Mackay, Tim Melling, Brian Moore, Mike Pennington, Roger Riddington, Mark Skevington and Peter Williams.

We are very grateful to all the photographers whose work is contained within this book: Tim Appleton, Carl Baggott, Adey Baker, Gary Bellingham, Dr. Brown, Jim Eaton, Pete Farbridge, Jim Graham, Danny Green, John Harriman, Andrew Harrop, Iain Leach, Brian Moore, Frank Pickering, Nigel Spencer, Keith Stone, Stephen Walton, John Wright and Steve Young. Carl Baggott provided assistance in putting together the selection of photographs. Andy Mackay and John Wright provided the illustrations, and Andy also produced the cover artwork. The maps of geology and surface deposits are reproduced with permission from Alan Strachan's 'Atlas of Leicestershire' (1985).

Jim Martin and Nigel Redman at the publishers Christopher Helm have been extraordinarily patient and thanks are due to them. Copy Editor Ernest Garcia and Project Editor Ali McNeill saw the book through to fruition.

Finally, Andrew Harrop would like to acknowledge the interest, patience and support of his wife Eleanor and his family, and Rob Fray would like to thank Rachel Sutherland for her patience and understanding.

INTRODUCTION

by Andrew Harrop

Outside the East Midlands, when members of the birdwatching community consider Leicestershire and Rutland they most probably think of Rutland Water or one of the other reservoirs. Yet these form only a small part of the counties and, as this book shows, much of our important knowledge about the birds of Leicestershire and Rutland relates to those of farmland and woodland. Although it is only 30 years since the publication of the previous county avifauna, much has altered during the intervening period. In particular, a combination of climate change and modern-day farming practices has caused some dramatic changes in the status of many of our birds, and these are documented here. The development of Rutland Water has also completely altered the status of many of our wintering and migrant birds.

The landlocked counties of Leicestershire and Rutland occupy a central position in the East Midlands. Most of the landscape is agricultural, with little woodland or high ground. The River Soar rises to the east of Hinckley, in the far south of Leicestershire, and flows northward through Leicester before emptying into the River Trent at the point where Derbyshire, Leicestershire and Nottinghamshire meet. A large part of the north-west of Leicestershire, around Coalville, forms part of the new National Forest area extending into Derbyshire and Staffordshire. The counties also border Warwickshire, Lincolnshire and Northamptonshire.

The county of Leicestershire covers an area of 2,084 square kilometres (804 square miles) and its population (including the city of Leicester, 279,921) was 889,500 at the time of the 2001 census. The population of Rutland in the 2001 census was 34,560, a rise of 4% on the 1991 total of 33,228. Rutland's greatest length north to south is only 29 kilometres (18 miles) and its greatest breadth east to west 27.4 kilometres (17 miles). It is the smallest normal unitary authority in mainland England in terms of population.

In 1974, the Local Government Act 1972 abolished the county borough status of Leicester city and the county status of neighbouring Rutland, converting both to administrative districts of Leicestershire. These actions were reversed on April 1st 1997, when Rutland and the City of Leicester became unitary authorities and Rutland became a distinct Ceremonial County once again. Bird recording has fortunately remained consistent during these periods of political change. Since its inception in 1941, and with the co-operation of both the Loughborough Naturalists' Club and the Rutland Natural History Society, LROS has published an Annual Report of records from both counties (corresponding with Watsonian Vice-county 55) which provides much of the original data on which this book is based.

This work began as a millennium project and, during the original planning stage, Richard Fray, Jim Graham, Andy Mackay and Mark Skevington provided much useful discussion with the current editorial team of Rob Fray, Roger Davis, Dave Gamble, Andrew Harrop and Steve Lister. The project took more hours and effort than any of those involved anticipated – since some single sentences are the culmination of years of careful recording and compilation, it is not surprising that it took time to complete. There were several difficult moments during the compilation of this book, but we hope that the end product does justice to all the hours committed by many people.

LANDSCAPE, MAN AND BIRDS

by Andrew Harrop

INTRODUCTION

Leicestershire has not always been as tamed and civilised as it is today, though human management of the landscape stretches back millennia. During excavations below The Shires site on High Street, Leicester, the skull of a White-tailed Eagle was found in a Roman pit (*Trans. Leics. Arch. and Hist. Soc. 67: 101–105, 1993*). Archaeological work on the medieval Austin Friars site, just west of St. Nicholas Circle in Leicester, revealed bones of Cormorant, Smew, Common Buzzard, Red Kite, Grey Partridge, crane sp., Barn Owl and Raven amongst others (Mellor & Pearce 1981). Occupied from the second half of the 13th century, on the flood-plain of the River Soar, the site provided environmental evidence with a strong waterside element represented by the flora and fauna of both wet and dry meadows (as one would expect), but also evidence of cultivated land, which was probably grazed, with small copses and thickets of oak, hazel and blackthorn. On the basis of the presence of wing-cases of a beetle (*Gyrinus strigilosus*) which has subsequently become extinct nationally as a result of climate change (in this case the so-called 'Little Ice Age') and forest clearance, the climate seems unlikely to have been colder than it is today. Marine shellfish were imported for food (probably either salted or in salt water kegs) but the birds identified are likely to have been local, with the possible exception of the crane. The scene the evidence evokes is more rural than that of today but not difficult to imagine.

Several large hunting parks were established in Charnwood Forest during this period and the early 14th century (Gamble 2001) but hunting parks then declined and by the mid-16th century only Bradgate remained. The arrival of the Black Death in the 14th century reduced the human population by about one third and the population was kept at a low level by repeated outbreaks. This reduction in population, which was a catalyst in the transition from a feudal to a capitalist economy, made room for more pasture, with the result that livestock constituted an increasingly important part of a farmer's wealth. Oak woodland had gradually been replaced by grassland since the Norman era and, by the 16th century, parts of Charnwood were becoming over-grazed by deer and domestic livestock. Subsequent increases in the human population brought further pressure on the land and disputes over enclosure, though one positive outcome was that the hedges planted during enclosure became an important habitat which improved with age. The population of Leicester increased tenfold from 23,000 to 210,000 between 1810 and 1900, as manufacturing developed, bringing with it increasing demand for water, food and space, and consequent changes in the landscape which transformed it into something like the one we know today.

GEOLOGY

The River Soar divides the counties geologically. To the west is an extensive area of Triassic Mercia mudstones with outcrops of pre-Cambrian granite and sedimentary rock on the high ground of Charnwood (reaching its highest point at Bardon Hill, 279 metres). In the far north-west there are areas of Triassic sandstone and Carboniferous coal measures close to the county boundary. To the east of the River Soar an area of Lower Lias clays (supporting rich farmland) extends from north to south. The highest points are found at Whatborough Hill (230 metres) and Robin-a-Tiptoe Hill (221 metres). Further east, in western Rutland, is an area of Middle Lias marlstones and Upper Lias clays which again supports rich farmland and grassland. The far east of Rutland is predominantly Inferior Oolitic limestone mixed with Northamptonshire ironstone.

The surface deposits of the counties are also unremarkable. Terrace gravels interspersed with alluvium are found along the valleys of the Soar, Wreake and Welland, with extensive areas of boulder clay to either side. Relatively small areas of sand and gravel are present along the river valleys, in the west, far north and east of the counties. Woodland is not extensive, covering less than 3% of the surface area, though there are relatively large areas in Charnwood, at Belvoir and to the south-west and north-east of Oakham, and there are numerous other small woods and copses.

Map of Leicestershire and Rutland showing the districts known to Browne.

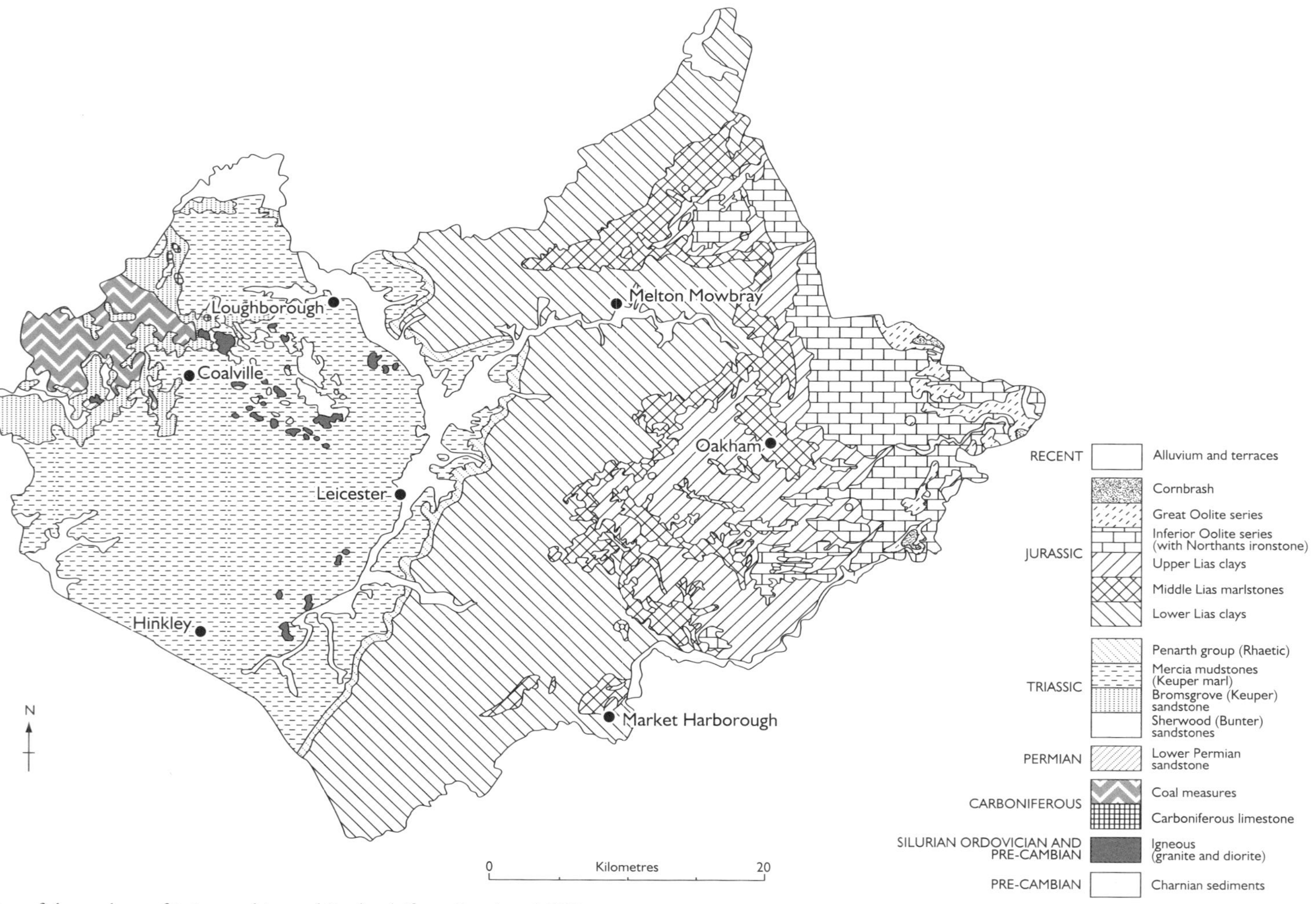

Map of the geology of Leicestershire and Rutland (from Strachan 1985).

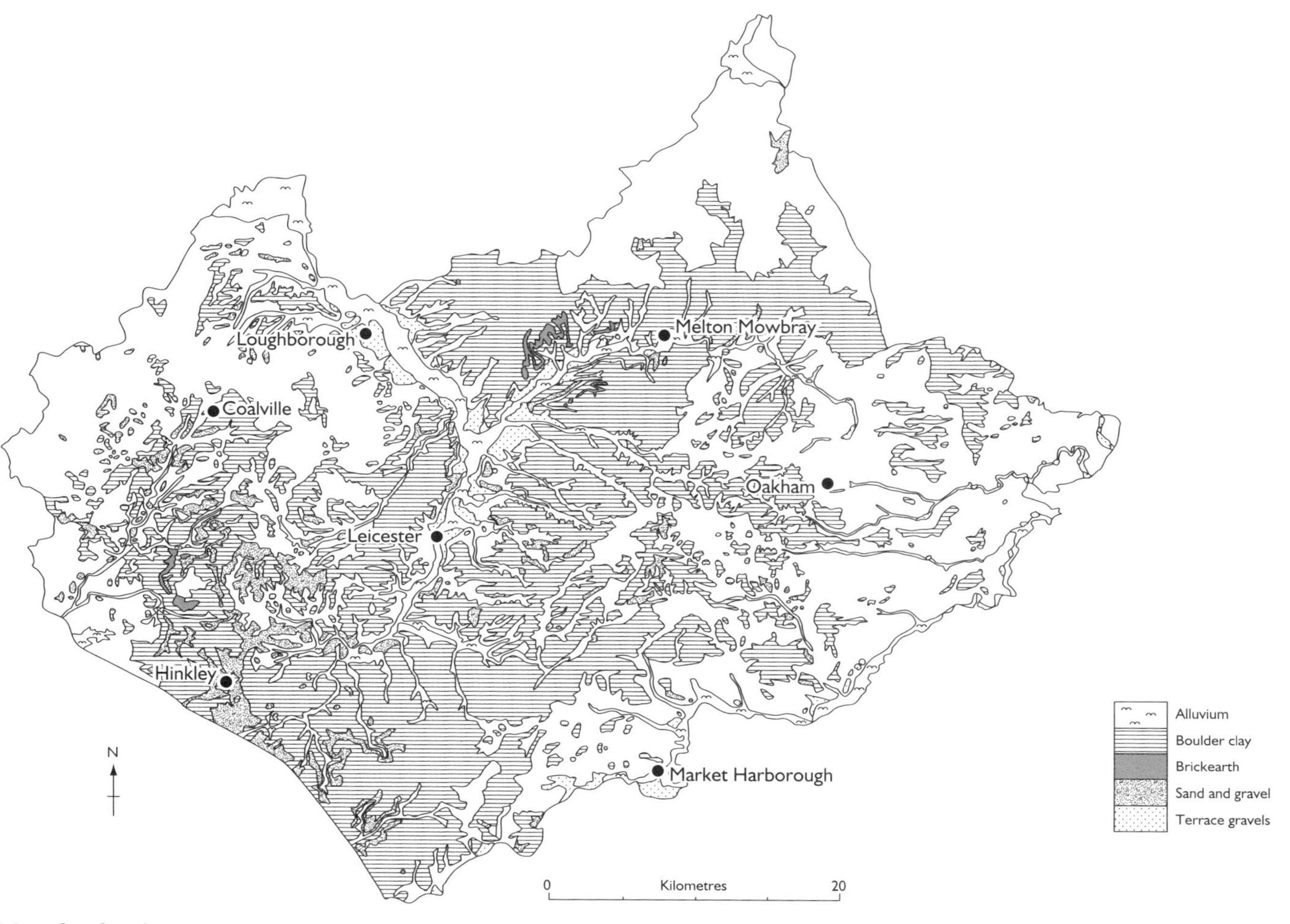

Map of surface deposits in Leicestershire and Rutland (from Strachan 1985).

HABITATS AND FARMING

The **wetland** habitats for which the counties are now best known are actually the most recent. Rutland Water, which is already an outstanding inland site of national and international importance to the extent that it merits its own chapter in this book, has been part of the landscape for just one generation. The oldest reservoirs in the counties are Blackbrook (1791), Saddington (1830) and Knipton, which was built soon afterwards. The reservoirs at Thornton, Cropston and Swithland were constructed during the second half of the 19th century. It was not until 1936 that the next reservoir was built, at Stanford, followed by Eyebrook in 1940 (just prior to the foundation of LROS) and finally Rutland Water in the mid-1970s. There is also one natural lake (Groby Pool) and there are a number of gravel pits in the Soar, Wreake and Trent valleys, which evolve as they are worked and then abandoned. There can be no doubt that these recent and, in most cases, artificial habitats have hugely increased the number and variety of wintering wildfowl and other birds, and to a lesser extent have provided productive breeding habitat. The rivers and streams of the counties are currently less studied and, since the water table of the River Soar has been lowered to assist flood control, damp meadows which formerly supported breeding Common Redshanks and Common Snipe have been lost. The Grand Union Canal and the disused Ashby and Grantham canals have stretches which support quite high densities of breeding wetland birds, notably Moorhens, Sedge and Reed Warblers and Reed Buntings.

As noted above, there is little extensive **woodland** in the counties, though this was not always the case: at the time of the Domesday survey in 1086 much of the east of the counties was still densely wooded, and the flora of Loddington Reddish leads some botanists to consider it a remnant of ancient woodland. Little of this woodland remained by the 18th century, as a consequence of enclosure, but there has been some reforestation since, mainly with coniferous plantations. The principal areas of deciduous and mixed woodland today are at Charnwood, Belvoir, in the valley of the Eye Brook and in east Rutland along the boundary with Lincolnshire. The best studied of these are the woodlands of Charnwood; none consistently holds a wide variety of woodland specialists. Woodcocks, Lesser Spotted Woodpeckers and especially Nuthatches are quite widespread (though not necessarily easy to find) but Common Redstarts, Wood Warblers and Hawfinches no longer have regular breeding sites. New conifer plantations have attracted Nightjars in recent years: this species formerly bred in some numbers in Charnwood and Rutland, but breeding populations have not yet become re-established.

Farmland has always been by far the most extensive habitat in the counties since records began. According to the 19th century classification, Leicestershire was (and is) a grazing county with relatively little arable land. The area of grassland in the two counties increased from around 50% in the early 1870s to over 70% by the 1930s. However, since the Second World War (when landowners were encouraged to 'dig for victory') the proportion of arable land has increased, especially in the east. The north-west of Leicestershire is predominantly an area of grass farming, the south-east predominantly arable and the remainder of Leicestershire and Rutland an area of mixed farming. Hickling noted that prior to 1974 there were 400,000 acres under cultivation in Leicestershire out of a total of over 530,000 acres, and that the 97,000 acres of Rutland were almost all agricultural. In 2006 in Leicestershire and Rutland there were 6,450 people working as farmers, managers and farm labourers on 2,719 farms with 475,000 acres of farmed land. The animal population was 122,284 cattle, 57,059 pigs and 314,214 sheep (DEFRA). Field sports remain an important part of the rural economy of Leicestershire, with stables, kennels and gunsmiths all based in the county. Covers grown during the 19th century continue to provide important habitat for some birds.

Many of the fields are still comparatively small, following the ten-acre model advocated by Robert Bakewell in the 18th century, and where hedges and other boundaries remain they support a rich diversity of wildlife. Between 1950 and 1987, however, more than eight metres per hectare of field boundaries were removed (Shrubb 2003). LROS began a long-term Common Birds Census survey on farmland at Stoughton in 1965, and others have followed since. This painstaking and unobtrusive work is amongst the most important the Society has undertaken and informs many of the species accounts in this book. It has revealed changes (in most cases, declines) in the populations of our farmland birds which usually also reflect national trends. It should serve as a warning about what we are doing, or allowing to be done, to our countryside. Of the species on the 'Red List' of Birds of Conservation Concern (Gregory *et al.* 2002), the Grey Partridge, Turtle Dove, Spotted Flycatcher and Corn Bunting have all declined markedly during the past 20 years and are now quite difficult to find.

Croft Hill (*Carl Baggott*). An important site for migration studies, and the quarry attracts cliff-nesting species.

Aerial photograph of the west end of Rutland Water (*Frank Pickering*).

Eyebrook Reservoir from the inflow at the north end (*Frank Pickering*).

Beacon Hill (*Carl Baggott*). A granite outcrop at one of the high points of Charnwood.

Mixed woodland near Belvoir Castle (*Frank Pickering*).

Field with hedgerows (*Carl Baggott*). Hedgerows with margins and scattered mature deciduous trees provide an important habitat for feeding, roosting and breeding, but stubble fields vary considerably in quality as a feeding habit.

Shrubb (2003) showed that despite widespread change in agricultural methods and habitats during the late 18th and 19th centuries, farmland birds were then little affected. Persecution and drainage led to the loss of fen and marshland species but farmland birds benefited from extensive new resources in addition to many old permanent grass habitats which remained relatively unaltered. High farming rotations resulted in varied habitats which provided diversity within farms and a haven in winter. Modern farming methods, especially since the 1970s, have been much more destructive: changes in grassland management from hay to silage production, the revolution in chemical weed control, the use of combine harvesters, the switch from spring-sown to autumn-sown cereals, loss of undersown ley and the loss of mixed farming have led to a collapse in farmland diversity and to a consequent steep decline in populations of a large proportion of farmland birds. As some of the species accounts make clear, sympathetic management, such as that undertaken in recent years at Loddington, can quickly reverse this trend and should be widely advocated. As well as Environmental Stewardship schemes, the planting of game-cover strips has also introduced weedy arable plots within grassland areas, thus reinstating areas of mixed farmland.

URBANISATION

By 2004 Leicester had become the tenth largest city in England, with a population of over 440,000 in the urban area. The temperature in the city is normally one or two degrees warmer than that of the surrounding countryside, which may be one reason why it is attractive to roosting Pied Wagtails, Starlings and other birds. Old city buildings provide habitat for certain specialist species (for example, the Black Redstart) and species which can adapt to living in close proximity to man. The city has a variety of green open spaces, most notably Abbey Park covering 89 acres, which support a significant variety and density of birds. Suburban gardens are also an increasingly important resource, mainly for woodland birds.

There has, however, been destructive development: extensive use of concrete and the construction of environmentally sterile tower blocks; the sealing of roofs and eaves which formerly provided breeding sites for Common Swifts, House Sparrows and other birds; and the tidying up of 'waste ground' which in fact often supports a surprising variety of life. Unsurprisingly, there is evidence that urbanisation reduces avian diversity and may contribute to taxonomic homogenisation (that is, a decline in species diversity and potentially also of the gene pool within species) by decreasing the abundance of ground-nesting species and those which prefer scrub habitats (Clergeau *et al.* 2006). The current tendencies to replace front lawns with hard standing for cars, and to plant non-native shrubs, are also having a detrimental effect. Recent research (Chamberlain *et al.* 2009) has suggested that in urban habitats food provided by man may improve adult condition during winter, leading to earlier laying dates, but paucity of natural food during the breeding season may then lead to lower productivity.

CLIMATE CHANGE

Climate change is not a new phenomenon, though the speed of change in the recent past is probably unprecedented. Since the 'Little Ice Age' mentioned above (1550 to 1700), there have been three main climatic periods in north-west Europe: a period of climatic amelioration between 1850 and 1950, a return to colder conditions until about 1980 and a subsequent return to warmer conditions.

Climate change was not yet identified as an issue of central importance by Hickling, and some scientists have been slow to accept all its implications. Research by the British Trust for Ornithology (Leech 2007) has highlighted possible benefits of climate change as well as some key areas of concern. Although an increase in mean annual temperatures in Britain is likely to increase the breeding success of some species, increased winter rainfall is likely to cause a decrease in survival rates for others (for example, the Treecreeper). Periods of drought on the African wintering grounds used by some of our breeding species may lead to a reduction in food availability and therefore to decreases in their survival rates. Perhaps to avoid this problem, in the last 20 years individuals of some species, such as Blackcaps and Chiffchaffs, that previously moved to Iberia and Africa during winter after breeding in Britain have been observed to over-winter here. It is generally considered that these individuals are birds from central Europe which have taken advantage of garden bird feeding and of progressively warmer British winters, and thus avoid having to make the longer journey to the traditional wintering grounds further south. Some continental species such as Little Egrets and more recently Cattle Egrets, which were previously occasional visitors to Britain, now winter and breed here.

The results of several studies investigating the spring arrival times of migrant species in temperate latitudes suggest that birds are reaching their breeding grounds progressively earlier in the season as temperatures in these areas increase. Advancement of arrival dates is necessary if synchrony between peak offspring demand and peak food availability is to be maintained. Using county record data from Leicestershire, Rutland and Sussex, Sparks (1999) observed that the arrival dates of 20 of the 56 migrant species analysed had become progressively earlier since 1966, and that the arrival dates of 19 of the species were related to temperatures in March and April. There is strong evidence to suggest that migrant bird species are advancing their dates of arrival at their British breeding grounds in response to increasing spring temperatures, with departure dates generally remaining constant or becoming later.

Over the period 1972 to 1991, British bird species extended their breeding ranges north by an average of 18.9km in response to increasing mean annual temperatures at the northern extent of their distribution (Thomas & Lennon 1999). There is increasing evidence to suggest that resident and some migrant birds are laying their eggs progressively earlier in the season which ensures that the peak period of nestling demand continues to coincide with the period of maximum prey abundance. It is possible that multi-brooded species may benefit from an extension of the breeding season as temperatures rise, allowing an increase in the number of broods produced per annum; but if increases in temperature have not been uniform across the breeding season, the cues used by birds to predict the timing of peak prey abundance may become increasingly unreliable. The situation may be even more serious for migrant birds, as cues used to initiate migration (for example, day-length) may not have varied in parallel with changes in prey availability. Alternatively, it may simply not be possible to advance migration dates further. The decreased period between arrival and laying may reduce breeding success or adult survival as the energy stores of the parent birds immediately prior to breeding will become increasingly depleted.

Another potential consequence of climate change is changing patterns of avian vagrancy. This will provide moments of excitement and areas for continuing research, but is perhaps unlikely to compensate for potential declines in the numbers of the resident birds and regular migrants which comprise our core avifauna.

NATURE RESERVES AND OTHER IMPORTANT SITES

We are fortunate to have a network of reserves in the counties which provide islands of protected habitat for a wide variety of species. In addition to Rutland Water, the Leicestershire and Rutland Wildlife Trust (LRWT) have 35 nature reserves in the counties, as well as a number of urban sites and roadside verges. The LRWT reserves currently most significant for birds are at Charnwood Lodge, Cossington Meadows, Ketton Quarry, Launde Woods, Narborough Bog, Prior's Coppice, Ulverscroft and Wanlip Meadows, some of which include important woodland fragments.

The most popular sites with birdwatchers tend to be the reservoirs, gravel pits and the Charnwood and Belvoir areas. Details of these can be found in Fray (2006). In terms of sheer extent, however, farmland remains the predominant habitat in the counties. It will be important for LROS to continue its important work monitoring populations of birds using our farmland, and to encourage good practice such as that at Loddington, if we are to avoid returning to the bare landscape of the early 18th century.

THE IMPACT OF RUTLAND WATER

by Tim Appleton

The late James Fisher, a highly respected British ornithologist, was one of the first people to recognise the potential of the new reservoir as a major site for birds – ten years before the first water became impounded by the huge dam at Empingham. The Leicestershire and Rutland Trust for Nature Conservation (now the Leicestershire and Rutland Wildlife Trust; LRWT), began negotiating with the Welland and Nene River division of Anglian Water Authority (now Anglian Water) in the early 1970s to develop an area of land dedicated to nature conservation at the western end of the proposed reservoir. Initially known as Empingham Reservoir, the name was later changed to Rutland Water. Although existing reservoirs were recognised as being important for waterbirds, especially wintering wildfowl, little effort up to then had been made to provide sanctuary areas for wildlife. The new reservoir would for the first time in Britain develop a plan that would take into account all forms of water-based recreation, with conservation interests on equal terms. The reservoir would be divided into zones to avoid conflict between the users. Those interested in the context of the development of Rutland Water should consult Ovens & Sleath (2007).

In 1975 Tim Appleton was appointed warden with the immediate task of planning, developing and implementing a programme of work that would eventually create a mosaic of habitats including lagoons, wader scrapes, woodlands, meadows and open water. One of the first tasks in 1975 was the construction of the three lagoons; these would have independent water controls and, most importantly, ensure that as water was extracted from the main body of the reservoir, shallow water could be retained even in the driest seasons. It was almost two years before the first waters reached the nature reserve boundaries at Gibbet Gorse but already an impressive bird list was growing, with 139 and 150 species recorded in 1975 and 1976 respectively. Some highlights included many Rutland Water 'firsts' such as Red-necked Phalarope, Hooded Crow, Red-throated Diver, Quail, White-winged Black Tern and Long-eared Owl, whilst a Great Skua on September 21st 1976 was one of many county firsts that the reservoir would produce over the next 32 years.

As a massive tree-planting programme got underway above the top water line, trees, hedgerows and houses were being cleared below to make way for the eventual inundation of the two valleys. Local farmers took a risk and planted cereals hoping the rising water levels would not flood their crops. The land clearance, along with the agricultural crops, created a vast prairie-type habitat with an abundance of seeds, insects and small mammals. Short-eared Owls, Long-eared Owls and huge flocks of passerines, including 300 Corn Buntings, 800 Reed Buntings, 250 to 300 Bramblings and several thousand Tree Sparrows, were recorded during the winter months! Breeding birds also took advantage of the transient habitats in 1976: 47 breeding Turtle Doves were noted while a single flock of 60 fed on stubble fields at Whitwell.

C. Reginald Haines, in his *Notes on the Birds of Rutland* published in 1907, regularly referred to Burley Fishponds attracting all manner of rare wetland species. In 1978 the rising water levels flooded the fishponds resulting in the loss of the largest single stand of *Phragmites* reeds in the counties. Reed from the fishponds had already been excavated and replanted on the edges of the new Lagoon III. Over 30 years later the reed has now spread and created extensive habitat, regularly attracting wintering Bitterns and Bearded Tits, while Water Rails and Reed and Sedge Warblers all breed and Marsh Harriers have been regular spring and autumn migrants. Leicestershire and Rutland's first Cetti's Warbler was caught and ringed in February 1977 in an osier bed now under several metres of water. It was another 18 years before a second bird was recorded in the Lagoon III reedbed, in November 1995. The Collared Pratincole was added to the county list in July 1977 and Rutland Water's first Bean Geese were recorded that year.

The steady inundation of the land produced an abundance of food for waterfowl. The early prediction of thousands of waterfowl wintering at the reservoir proved to be correct with numbers of Mallard, Eurasian Wigeon, Coot and Common Pochard being noticeably high. The reservoir was stocked with trout and before long Cormorants, which at the time were rarely seen inland, were attracted to this new food source; in 1978 they were present all year round for the first time in the counties. Inevitably a large body of water will attract non-native waterfowl and the first record of Egyptian Goose occurred on May 29th 1979. It was another six years before the next sighting and four years later, in 1989, a pair bred for the first time in the counties. A flock of Ruddy Ducks, numbering 18 birds in total, overwintered in 1980 and from then on numbers grew steadily, reaching a peak of 1,345 in January 2000. By 2007 the Ruddy Duck had almost disappeared from Rutland Water following a nationwide cull to eradicate the species.

The nature reserve was officially opened on a cold sunny day in January 1979. Several hides were now open and birdwatchers were able to visit either the Lyndon or Egleton sections of the reserve. A male Velvet Scoter, a new bird for Rutland Water, from January 1st to 5th got the year off to an excellent start. This was closely followed by Red-throated and Great Northern Divers and the reserve's first Waxwings. A Red-necked Grebe on February 11th was a first for Rutland Water but by the 18th a total of 13 was present, the largest number ever recorded in the county. That remarkable day also saw a Black-throated Diver and two Slavonian Grebes. On February 25th the first Sparrowhawk, a species that was still recovering from the effects of organochlorine chemicals used in agriculture, was recorded. By the beginning of the new century populations of birds of prey throughout Britain had recovered as a result of good conservation practice and a series of reintroduction schemes. A milestone in the creation of Rutland Water was reached on March 29th 1979 when the reservoir was officially declared full. Green-winged Teal and Firecrest were new species for the reserve during that year.

Although the bulk of the landscaping and planting was undertaken in the late 1970s, large numbers of native fruit-bearing trees were added in the 1980s to increase the diversity of the reserve. As both aquatic and terrestrial habitats started to show signs of maturing and providing food so the bird species increased. The opening of the nearby Cottesmore Tornado fighter-plane base in 1980 had a major impact on the numbers of roosting large gulls as all the landfill tips north of the reservoir were closed to reduce the possibility of bird-strikes. However, the smaller gulls were represented in 1980 by a county first – an adult Mediterranean Gull. This species is now not uncommon and can be seen at any time of the year; it may well breed in future amongst the colony of Black-headed Gulls. A potential new wader species for the counties was a dowitcher on Lagoon I in May; although considered to be Long-billed it was another 25 years before the first confirmed record of this species, on the same lagoon on August 9th 2005.

The reservoir was by now attracting increasing numbers of birdwatchers. More hides were constructed and some were doubled in size. Plover Hide opened in June 1980 and was one of the first in the UK to be designed primarily for disabled birdwatchers. This hide was eventually relocated to Lagoon III and the Anglian Birdwatching Centre was built in its place in 1992. In 1981 a superb Red-throated Pipit in breeding plumage was found by Lagoon I on May 9th, the same day as a Pomarine Skua was on Lagoon III; the former was the first (and to date only) record for Leicestershire and Rutland, and the latter was the first in the counties since 1906. An unusually large flock of 85 Kittiwakes was present on April 26th 1981. Over the next two years a number of notable birds were recorded: Ring Ouzel, Ring-necked Duck, Mandarin Duck, Eider, Leach's Petrel, Grey Phalarope and Nightjar were all added to the ever-growing list of species for Rutland Water.

One of the memorable avian events occurred on June 8th and 9th 1984 when a Bridled Tern was discovered on the lagoons, attracting huge numbers of twitchers. This was by far the rarest bird to date at Rutland Water and was only the eighth British record. Later in the year a first-winter Night Heron overwintered at Burley Fishponds but was eventually forced to leave as the water froze over in February 1985. It was later found dead in Whitwell Creek; the skin was mounted and resides at the Leicester Museum. Large flocks of Coot gathered that winter reaching an all-time record of 7,453, while another record, still unbroken, of 7,239 Eurasian Wigeon occurred.

Daily bird records have been kept since 1975; this continuous recording has identified changes in populations that have also been reflected elsewhere around the country. By the late 1990s huge declines were evident in many species, perhaps most noticeably the Tree Sparrow and Yellow Wagtail. A flock of 250 Yellow Wagtails on April 8th 1985 was not an uncommon occurrence at the time; 20 years later the largest flocks rarely exceed double-figures. Tree Sparrows fared even worse, with the national population declining dramatically. The Rutland Water Tree Sparrows bucked the trend and continued to increase, later becoming the subject of a four-year study into the reasons for their survival at the reserve.

In January 1987 virtually all the reservoir froze over as severe weather hit eastern Britain; the 21 Smew recorded in a single patch of ice free water is still the record count for this species to date. In October 1987 south-east Britain was hit by an unprecedented storm and several wind-blown species found their way to Rutland Water, including four Great Skuas and two Grey Phalaropes. The storms uprooted many trees, especially dead elms left standing after Dutch Elm disease, and the last Lesser Spotted Woodpeckers bred that year. Other highlights in 1987 included the first Honey Buzzard and records of Spotted Crake and Great Grey Shrike. A White-winged Black Tern on June 9th was the first to be seen in full summer plumage at the reservoir.

A Great White Egret, a county first, drew huge crowds on June 18th 1988 as it sat in the willow trees in Burley Fishponds. The Rutland Water Ringing Group, whilst operating the annual Constant Effort Ringing Site in the Lagoon III reedbed, caught and ringed the counties' second Savi's Warbler on April 19th; this male bird remained into the summer, often in full song, until July 27th. There was to be one further record, from April 13th to 24th 2005. Caspian Tern and Little Auk were new reservoir records in 1988, and the first Little Egret was present the following year from August 19th to 27th. 1989 provided another milestone as the first British Birdwatching Fair was held at the Egleton Reserve. The precursor for fairs now being held all over the world, the Birdfair has had a massive impact on international bird conservation. In 19 years, over £2,000,000 has been donated to BirdLife International's global conservation programmes from Ecuador to Madagascar, Indonesia to Brazil.

The early 1990s produced several new reserve records, including Ring-billed Gull and Ferruginous Duck, and the counties' second Great White Egret was discovered on May 26th 1990. In 1992 Rutland Water was designated both a Ramsar site and a Special Protection Area (SPA). Ramsar sites are wetlands of international importance designated under the Ramsar Convention while SPAs are classified under the EC Directive on the Conservation of Wild Birds (79/409/EEC), commonly known as the Birds Directive. The latter directive recognised the vital importance of the reservoir for internationally important populations of Gadwall and Shoveler, as well as for the 20,000 wintering wildfowl that were regularly using the site.

A superb male Red-footed Falcon, the fourth record for the counties, spent a week in mid-June 1992 hawking dragonflies over Lagoon III. The year was also significant for the counties' avifauna as Cormorants bred for the first time. Five pairs nested on Lagoon I and successfully reared seven young; a few years later the nesting colony had moved to tall willows in Burley Fishponds, where the number of breeding pairs had reached 123 by 2005. A Cattle Egret found on Lagoon I on April 3rd 1993 stayed in the area until April 15th and remains the only record for the counties. By the time the next local avifauna is written it is quite likely Cattle Egrets will be widespread in Britain, as they are following a similar movement northwards from southern Europe as Little Egrets did in the early 1990s. Another county first in 1993, and only the fifth for Britain, was a male Lesser Scaup at Barnhill Creek. In the same year 825 Cormorants, 15 Shags and 12 Eiders were all unprecedented numbers for the counties.

1994 was the year that triggered the Osprey translocation project at Rutland Water. Two Ospreys spent the summer on the reserve, fuelling speculation that they would return to breed in 1995 – sadly they did not return. But by then a project to reintroduce the Osprey to England after an absence of 150 years was gathering momentum. As it happened it was another county first that stole the limelight in 1994, with the discovery of a White-rumped Sandpiper in Manton Bay. Hundreds of birders descended on the reserve; those that missed it were rewarded with a second bird just over a year later. 1995 will be remembered for the spectacular invasion of up to 100 Common Redpolls to Rutland Water, particularly as amongst the highly mobile flock were up to six Arctic Redpolls, yet another county first. At last the seed-bearing silver birch and alder trees planted in 1970 were bearing fruit! Two more county firsts were found during 1996: a Common Crane on June 2nd and an American Golden Plover on November 2nd and 3rd. Although rather overshadowed, a Spotted Crake, a Bluethroat and a Red-backed Shrike all helped to make 1996 a special year.

It is not often that an inland site records a 'second' for the Western Palaearctic, but Lagoon I did just that when an adult drake Redhead was found on February 4th 1997. In September of that year a Long-tailed Skua made a brief pass over the north arm on the 21st and became yet another county first discovered at Rutland Water. After an absence of 18 years the counties' fifth Purple Sandpiper was found in October 1998. The following month produced the third White-rumped Sandpiper for Rutland Water. A Little Egret in May 1999 was the first to be seen away from the autumn and another unseasonal record that year was the first June sighting of a Great Northern Diver.

The new century brought the second county record of Lesser Scaup, a female which stayed from April 8th to 23rd 2000. Rutland's first Marsh Warbler was found on June 9th that year close to Fieldfare Hide. Following a nationwide influx of migrating Honey Buzzards in September four flew over on the 23rd and a further individual was seen on the 26th. Although there were no county firsts in 2001 there were several excellent sightings. A Wryneck stayed for two days in early September and later in the month six Great Skuas, the largest number ever seen in the counties, were observed. But these records were surpassed in 2001 by the first breeding of Ospreys, on private land close to the reservoir. The translocation programme had reached an all-time high and since then Ospreys have nested annually. The following year, on September 22nd, four Arctic Skuas flew over Rutland

Water, representing the largest flock ever to be seen in the counties. A Yellow Wagtail seen on March 16th, the earliest ever for the counties, might well be an early sign of climatic changes expected to occur this century.

A first-summer drake American Wigeon present from March 16th to April 13th 2003 was the first record for Rutland Water and the fifth record for the counties. Other notable records in 2003 included three Purple Sandpipers and a long staying Great Grey Shrike, which remained in the area from March 12th to April 7th. In 2004 an adult Roseate Tern, only the third for the counties, was found on August 15th and a remarkably long-staying Manx Shearwater was present from July 16th to August 7th.

The counties' third Lesser Scaup, a female, was found on April 28th 2005. The next day an adult male Montagu's Harrier flew over Lagoon I; a second bird, a female, soon followed on May 18th. This was the year that the Long-billed Dowitcher was finally added to the county list when an adult appeared on Lagoon I on August 9th. Three White-winged Black Terns stayed for four days from September 8th, an exceptional record as all previous sightings in the counties consisted of single birds. Rutland's first Yellow-browed Warbler remained for three days near the dam from October 23rd.

Rutland Water is still relatively young and as the terrestrial and aquatic habitats continue to mature so the list of new species and bird numbers will continue to expand. The water company plans to extract more water from the reservoir in the future to supply new homes anticipated for the region. This change in water management will have an impact on wildfowl and as a result of the reservoir's status as an SPA the company are under legal obligation to create alternative areas for wildfowl to roost and feed. A major project to create these new areas began in 2008 in and around land close to the nature reserve; in all, nine shallow lagoons totalling 98 hectares will be constructed. These lagoons, each with their own independent water control sluices and depths varying from a few centimetres to a maximum of one metre, will be attractive to Rutland Water's existing birds and, we hope, many new species. It is hoped that the construction of the new lagoons, along with the existing varied habitats at Rutland Water, will continue to play a major role in increasing the diversity of the avifauna of Leicestershire and Rutland.

ORNITHOLOGY IN LEICESTERSHIRE AND RUTLAND

by Andrew Harrop

On 20th January 1946, Peter Gamble and Albert Jolley visited Eyebrook Reservoir. Much of the surface water was frozen and early-morning mist was slow to clear. Eurasian Wigeon were so intent on feeding that the flock simply divided as they passed through rather than flying off. Later that day they found 21 Smew, including four adult males, though the record was never published. After 60 years it is already very difficult to imagine what birdwatching was like at a time when some observers cycled from Leicester to Norfolk to pursue their hobby and even visiting Eyebrook Reservoir could involve a camping expedition.

All those who dedicate time to this or any other discipline owe a huge and often unrecognised debt to their predecessors. There will be many observers, recorders, conservers, artists and photographers whose contribution is not acknowledged separately in what follows, though they will have contributed to the whole. There will also have been many hidden contributors: wives and partners whose support of an interest which requires much time, and can dominate lives, may never have been recognised in print.

EARLY WORKS

There is very little information about birds in Leicestershire and Rutland before 1840, with the exception of notes kept by Thomas **Barker** of Lyndon Hall, Rutland, between 1736 and 1801. Barker was Gilbert White's brother-in-law and two of the very first notes in his collection are initialled by Gilbert White. Made when White would have been about 16, they are as follows: 'March 31, 1736, a flock of Wild Geese flew N.' and 'April 6, 1736, the Cuckow heard. 'Although the notes continue without a break for 64 years, their value is limited because they mention fewer than 20 species of birds (though these do include Nightjar and Wood Lark).

Three early works provided a basis for what followed: the first account of the local avifauna was **Harley**'s 1840 '*Catalogue of the Land Birds of the County of Leicester*' which was published by MacGillivray in his '*British Birds*'; in 1842 **Babington** provided a chapter on '*Ornithology in Charnwood Forest*' as an appendix to Potter's *History and Antiquities of Charnwood Forest*'; and in 1882 **Macaulay** published a '*List of the Birds of Leicestershire*' in '*The Midland Naturalist*'. The most influential of the early works, however, was **Browne**'s 1889 '*The Vertebrate Animals of Leicestershire and Rutland*'. Though limited to 300 copies, the critical assessment of records which Browne provided became accepted as the authoritative account of the Leicestershire avifauna for the next 90 years. His section on birds comprised a systematic list of 133 pages, a table of arrival dates of summer migrants, a map and three illustrations. Both the text and illustrations (which featured Black Redstart, Pallas's Sandgrouse and Cream-coloured Courser) show that there was already considerable interest in rarities. As curator of the museum, Browne had a good working knowledge of taxidermy and was often critical in his assessment of records. His comments on a rejected Wilson's Phalarope, for example, include the statement: 'To relieve the historian of the future of any further anxiety I may say that, being behind the scenes in this matter, I can emphatically state that Wilson's Phalarope *was not obtained in the county, nor in Britain.* ' Whilst his critical judgements were often sound, he may sometimes have been too dogmatic and was criticised for this trait in an 1896 review of his work on artistic and scientific taxidermy (*Auk* XIII: 247–249). Meanwhile, the small neighbouring county of Rutland had to wait until 1907, when **Haines** published his '*Notes on the Birds of Rutland*', for the first full account of its avifauna.

RECENT PUBLICATIONS

Although the Leicestershire and Rutland Ornithological Society (LROS) published Annual Reports from 1941 onwards, the next book to describe the local avifauna was **Otter**'s '*The Birds of East Leicestershire*', published in 1965. A major milestone, and the most influential statement since Browne, was reached in 1978, when **Hickling** published his '*Birds in Leicestershire and Rutland*' on behalf of the LROS. The book's 199 pages included chapters on birds in the landscape, articles reprinted from LROS Annual Reports, four maps, 11 illustrations, 39 black-and-white photographs of habitats and a table of the arrival dates of migrants, as well as a systematic list. It provided a suitably balanced treatment of common, regular and rare species and summarised records up to 1974 (with an appendix listing unusual records up to 1977); it is therefore important as a review of the local avifauna before the development of Rutland Water. A notable strength of the work was its discussion of changes in bird numbers in relation to changes in the environment. The author's economical style, however, did result in some texts which lack descriptive detail, both for commoner species (for example Turtle Dove, to which Hickling devoted only one line of text compared with 11 lines by Browne) and some rare ones (for example Great Snipe, which is treated dismissively by Hickling even though Browne cited three specimen records, one of which is in Leicester museum and another of which he had seen personally).

One significant consequence of the publication of Hickling's book was that it stimulated a succession of more detailed local works by various authors. Of these, the most notable were two books about the birds of Rutland by **Mitcham**: '*The Birds of Rutland and its Reservoirs*' (1984) and '*Rutland Breeding Bird Atlas*' (1992). The first of these comprised the most complete statement relating to the birds of Rutland since Haines, drew extensively on records of the Rutland Natural History Society (RNHS) (founded in 1965) and underlined the huge impact which Rutland Water had on the local avifauna within ten years of its construction. The second mapped the breeding birds of Rutland in each of the smallest county's 117 tetrads, thereby providing a very useful baseline against which changes in status can be measured. One work which deserved a wider audience was **Warrilow**'s '*Atlas of Breeding Birds of Leicestershire and Rutland*' (1996). Also based on tetrads, it presented much detailed and valuable data drawn from contributions by members of all interested local societies, but its impact was limited partly because it was privately published and partly because it appeared over a decade after the fieldwork was completed.

Two other valuable recent works dealt in different ways with the avifauna of Charnwood. **Webster**'s '*Birds of Charnwood*', published in 1997, mapped the breeding birds in each 1–km square of the area and included a useful chapter on the conservation of birds in Charnwood. Finally, Peter's son Ian **Gamble** compiled '*Birdlife of Swithland Reservoir*', which was published in 2001. Although the reservoir was built in 1896, there were few records from there until the foundation of the LROS in 1941; this work also draws upon records of the Loughborough Naturalists' Club to provide a thorough account of the site and its birds. An interesting chapter on 1,000 years of change in Charnwood places recent developments in their historical context.

THE EARLY YEARS OF THE LEICESTERSHIRE AND RUTLAND ORNITHOLOGICAL SOCIETY (1940s TO 1960s)

Between the work of Browne and Haines at the beginning of the last century and the 1940s, little was published about the birds of Leicestershire and Rutland with the exception of occasional notes in *The Zoologist* and *The Field*. During the war years of 1939–1945, however, growing interest in nature conservation led to the foundation of many local societies dedicated to the study of natural history and it was in this context that the Leicestershire and Rutland Ornithological Society was formed. Following an initial informal meeting, it was decided on September 3rd 1941 to set up an Ornithological Society which would cover both Leicestershire and Rutland. To begin with the Society was affiliated to the Leicester Literary and Philosophical Society, yet by 1946 its membership exceeded that of the parent body and the decision was taken to become independent. From the beginning, the stated aims of the Society were to establish the status and study the breeding and other activities of 'more common' species and to revise the ornithological work of Browne accordingly.

It takes vigour and determination to establish and maintain satisfactory records of birds. The Society has been fortunate that in its early years, and at regular intervals since, a succession of committed individuals has maintained the high standards set at its inception. The first was **Albert Jolley**, whose strong leadership established the Society on sound lines. The publication of accurate records is of course a vital function of any ornithological society and Jolley led by example through a succession of papers in the Annual Report: in 1943 a review of the changing status of birds since the work of Browne and Haines, in 1944 a report on the Sand Martin enquiry and, in 1945, a map and discussion of proposed migratory routes through Eyebrook Reservoir. When Jolley left the area in 1946 his absence was felt and his premature death in 1952 was appropriately lamented by an obituary in the Annual Report.

Other individuals who were influential in the early years of the Society included **Eric Pochin**, **Peter Gamble** and **Ron Hickling.** Eric Pochin, the Society's first president, was an influential citizen and businessman as well as an ornithologist, yet he still found time to write articles for the Annual Report which gave accounts of visible

Peter Gamble.

Ron Hickling.

migration over Croft Hill between 1940 and 1952 and of birds in Leicester (1953). Peter Gamble's long association with the Society began in the 1940s and resulted in publication in the Annual Report of his ecological survey of Buddon (1957) and a summary of the effects of the severe 1962–63 winter. Peter has also been a mainstay of the Loughborough Naturalists' Club and until recently was a member of the LROS records committee, to which he brought useful insights into some older records. Ron Hickling has had a long association with the Society, most notably as author of '*Birds in Leicestershire and Rutland*'. In recognition of this and other contributions to ornithology he was awarded an honorary MSc by the University of Leicester in 1979. His interest in gulls and involvement with the British Trust for Ornithology resulted in him being asked to organise the wintering gulls survey and his paper on gulls in Leicestershire (1974) remains one of his most notable contributions to the Annual Reports. In 1990 he published a review of the Society through 50 years which, after clearly setting out the main aims and functions of the Society and ways in which they had been addressed, ended with an optimistic prognosis which publication of the current work shows was justified.

Clifford Holt, as well as being chairman of Cley Bird Observatory, made his mark both locally and

Jack Otter.

Frank Pickering (centre) with Tim Appleton (left) and Martyn Aspinall, Rutland Water 1996.

Terry Mitcham.

Andy Forryan (left) and Rob Fray working on the most recent review of records, 2004 (*Andrew Harrop*).

John Wright sketching the Keyhaven Lesser Sand Plover, July 2003 (*Andrew Harrop*).

The 1994 British Birdwatching Fair (*Tim Appleton*).

nationally through his involvement in early wildlife film-making. Although film was hard to obtain in the 1950s, Clifford's dedication led to his work being widely recognised and used, for example, to help the Royal Society for the Protection of Birds with its early publicity. His numerous contacts made him the ideal person to invite visiting speakers to address the Society's meetings; he did so for 20 years.

By the 1960s other individuals, notably **Jack Otter**, **Frank Pickering** and **Kath Kirton** (later Kath Potterton), were making their contribution. Jack Otter is remembered for carrying out the wildfowl count at Eyebrook Reservoir by cycling along the road with a large brass telescope balanced on his handlebars! His almost lyrical affection for the place comes across very clearly in his '*The Birds of East Leicestershire*'. A versatile man, who had carried out military service in Ceylon (now Sri Lanka) and Burma, after retiring from his work with local company Broughton and Jones he began a second career in adult education, teaching natural history. In 1977 his services to adult education were recognised by the award of an honorary MSc at the University of Leicester and he continued to teach until he was in his mid-eighties. Frank Pickering, the Society's current President, has exercised a stable and diplomatic influence on local ornithology during a period of rapid change, as well as publishing papers in the Annual Report on the birds of Leicester City Farms (1966) and artificial nest sites of Willow Tits (1969). Kath Kirton was a prolific field observer who also served as County Recorder. The quality of her observations is exemplified by notes on two vagrants, Night Heron and White-winged Black Tern, both published in the Annual Report for 1968.

THE IMPACT OF RUTLAND WATER (1970s TO 1990s)

The 1970s ushered in a period of rapid change in ornithology, both locally and nationally. First, some of the problems which had beset previous generations (rationing, limited transport and communication, scant reference material) became a fading memory as developments in technology brought previously unavailable opportunities. Second, the construction and development of the reservoir now known as Rutland Water was to have significant and largely unforeseen consequences for ornithology locally, nationally and internationally.

As observers adapted to these new circumstances, and as birding became more popular, growing numbers of contributors provided records for the Annual Report. Amongst those who guided local ornithology during this period were **Hugh Dixon**, **Fred Littlemore** and **C. F. Mason**. Hugh Dixon (whose daughter Helen was involved in setting up the Osprey project at Rutland Water) not only helped with the organisation of the LROS but also contributed to the work of the Leicestershire and Rutland Trust for Nature Conservation and for several years chaired the Rutland Water Nature Reserve Management Committee. Fred Littlemore contributed to the Society in several ways, most notably in his compilation of wildfowl figures and his study of birds and other wildlife at Stanford Reservoir. At the time of his death in 2002, he was working on a list of the birds of Stanford Reservoir which would have updated the work of Sills (1970). C. F. Mason had a special interest in the arrival dates of summer migrants, which he summarised for the period 1942–68 in the Annual Report for 1969 and later compared with those for 1969–74 (*Brit. Birds* 70: 342–343). In 1969 he also published an index of the relative abundance of waders and terns (*Brit. Birds* 62: 523–533).

By the 1980s, the volume of records required that the laborious task of compiling the Annual Report be shared between members of an editorial committee. **Roger Davis** and **Dave Gamble** both made a significant contribution to the work of the LROS, as did **Terry Mitcham** for the RNHS in Rutland. Roger Davis was County Recorder and an editor of the Annual Report for a long period during the 1980s and 1990s, and was one of the group who set up the records committee in its current role. Dave Gamble has served the Society in several ways, has developed a detailed working knowledge of a single site by keeping records of regular observations at Priory Water and has published articles in the Annual Report; most notably his 1991 summary of the survey of introduced geese. Terry Mitcham became bird recorder for the RNHS in 1982. Since then, in addition to compiling the publications previously mentioned, he has maintained regular records (notably from the Exton Estate) and supported local ornithology by leading field outings and running popular evening classes.

Arguably, the person who has made the single greatest contribution to local ornithology to date is **Tim Appleton**. Tim quickly made his mark after moving to Rutland Water from Slimbridge in 1975. Whilst not afraid to use unorthodox methods in the interests of conservation, Tim's personable management style and willingness to foster talent has involved a large number of employees and volunteers in the development of Rutland Water Nature Reserve and its designation as a RAMSAR site and Special Protection Area. Although primarily important as a refuge for wildfowl, the site has also received important publicity following the Osprey translocation project. By the late 1980s Tim's search for a new challenge was a significant factor in the initial development and subsequent success of the British Birdwatching Fair (see below). His work has received recognition in the form of an honorary MSc from the University of Leicester (1999) and more recently (2004) an MBE for services to wildlife and conservation.

The quality of recording reached new levels during the 1990s, due in large measure to the efforts of **Rob Fray** and **Andy Mackay**. In Rutland, the good work begun by Terry Mitcham has been supported by **Andrew Harrop**. Rob Fray (whose brother Richard helped to develop the LROS website) was recognised as a talented observer when he won Young Ornithologist of the Year in 1984 and 1985. He has put much time and energy into local ornithology and has even managed to combine the arduous tasks of being County Recorder and compiling the Annual Report, in which he published a pilot study of the breeding birds of Leicester's green spaces (1989). Andy Mackay has also had a significant role in local recording and has published papers in the Annual Report about winter gull roosts (1993), scarce gulls (1994) and the status of the Nightjar (1998). He is perhaps most likely to be remembered for his artwork, which has not only appeared regularly in local publications but more significantly was commissioned in 1995 for publication in *Birds of the Western Palearctic Concise Edition*. Andrew Harrop moved to Rutland from Devon in 1989. His intensive fieldwork during the 1990s led to five taxa being added to the county list and he has published articles in the Annual Report about escapes (1994), attempted breeding by Avocets (1996) and the status of the Bean Goose (1998). His work as a member of the British Ornithologists' Union Records Committee has helped to keep local ornithology in step with taxonomic developments.

The partnerships of **Dave** and **Sue Cohen**, followed by **Jim** and **Sue Graham**, have done a huge amount in recent years to promote local ornithology and the work of the LROS. Jim has also been BTO representative, whilst his technical skills have contributed to the quality of both paper and electronic publications. **Ken Goodrich** has published *Leicestershire Garden Birds* (1997) as well as contributing regular wildfowl counts and providing a focus for birdwatchers in Birstall. Having read about Eric Pochin's sightings at Croft Hill, **Carl Baggott** was encouraged to follow in his footsteps and his efforts there and elsewhere in south-west Leicestershire have helped to raise the profile of the area. His study of a pair of Peregrine Falcons resulted in articles in the Annual Report (1999, 2000).

THE NEW MILLENNIUM

The impact of increased participation on recording is illustrated by the fact that in 1944 a new record was set when 155 species were recorded during the year, yet by the 1990s it was normal for more than 200 species to be recorded during a year and the county total passed 300 species. Increasing use of digital photography, and the posting of images on the LROS website, means that news is more readily available than ever before. The challenge remains to find the best way of preserving, presenting and analysing the data. **Matthew Berriman**, whose records and images regularly appear on the website, has become a very active observer in Rutland, whilst established observers **Andy Forryan** and **Steve Lister** have both begun to combine active observation with increasing participation in the equally important analysis of records. **John Wright**, whose sketches regularly appear in *Birding World* and *British Birds*, has also produced interpretative boards for several LRWT reserves. He continues to make regular observations around Rutland Water and Eyebrook Reservoir and has dedicated countless unsocial hours to the Osprey project. **Tim Grove** has recently taken on the roles of BTO representative and WeBS organiser and has a vital role in organising surveys, which provide important data about our changing bird populations.

No history of local ornithology would be complete without reference to the **British Birdwatching Fair** which takes place annually for three days in August. When the Birdfair began in 1989, co-organisers Tim Appleton (see above) and Martin Davies of the RSPB wanted to put together activities to promote birds and birdwatching. What was at first a local event quickly became national, then international. Unifying the birdwatching community, and giving it a more compelling voice, was inspired. Their idea was also well timed: birdwatching has become popular as a hobby and has consequently generated growing commercial interest. Once it became clear how much the event contributes to global conservation initiatives, even sceptics who felt uneasy about the commercialisation of ornithology became convinced. For the first five years money raised went to conservation projects in Europe but Halmahera in Indonesia was chosen in 1994 and since then areas around the globe have benefited. The event now attracts exhibitors and visitors from several continents and has influence on political decision-making. As one of the most important events in the ornithological calendar, it has unexpectedly made Rutland a hub of global ornithology.

It would be nice to think that in January 2046, or even January 2146, the ornithological successors of Gamble and Jolley will be able to find Eyebrook Reservoir (and other important sites) a haven for wintering Eurasian Wigeon and Smew, or whatever other species climate change brings to our shores. Further developments in technology will no doubt allow them to look back with wry smiles as they correct some of the fallacies in the present work, but my guess is that they will go there, as we do, to pay homage to the astonishingly beautiful diversity of life.

BREEDING BIRDS AND COMMON BIRDS CENSUSES

by Rob Fray

BREEDING BIRDS

The Leicestershire and Rutland breeding bird list currently stands at 135, of which 102 could be classed as regular. Over the last 160 years or so 18 species have become extinct as breeding birds in the counties; 11 were lost during the 19th or early 20th century, at a time when most of these particular species were contracting their ranges due to a variety of factors (mainly human persecution). The Corn Crake ceased to breed in the counties some time around the 1960s, again in line with national trends. The remaining six (Common Snipe, Common Redstart, Whinchat, Wood Warbler, Lesser Redpoll and Hawfinch), have been lost since the late 1980s and in a number of cases the reasons for their demise are not fully understood.

Table 1: Breeding species lost in Leicestershire and Rutland

Species	Site and date of last breeding record if known
Red Grouse	Charnwood Forest c1840
Black Grouse	Charnwood Forest c1850
Spotted Crake	Late 19th century?
Corn Crake	1960s?
Stone Curlew	Ryhall Heath c1880
Common Snipe	Ulverscroft 1989
Common Sandpiper	Bradgate Park 1908
Wryneck	Market Harborough 1903
Wood Lark	Charnwood Forest c1840
Dipper	Charnwood Forest c1840
Common Redstart	Belvoir 1997
Whinchat	Stoughton Airfield and Aylestone Meadows 1989
Ring Ouzel	Whitwick 19th century
Wood Warbler	Outwoods 1994
Red-backed Shrike	Ratby 1944
Lesser Redpoll	Wigston 1996
Hawfinch	Undisclosed site 1988
Cirl Bunting	Melton Mowbray 1920

On the plus side, 20 species have commenced breeding regularly in the counties since 1941. Two of these, the Common Buzzard and the Raven, have returned naturally after becoming extinct in the 19th century whilst a third, the Red Kite, which became extinct around the same time has recolonised the counties after being reintroduced into neighbouring Northamptonshire. Human influence is also apparent in the colonisation by four species of wildfowl: Greylag Goose, Egyptian Goose, Mandarin Duck and Ruddy Duck, all of which are derived from feral or escaped stock, whilst another species, the Osprey, has been directly introduced by man. The majority of the remaining colonists have benefited from the creation of gravel pits and reservoirs in the counties.

Table 2: Breeding species gained in Leicestershire and Rutland since 1941

Species	Site and date of first breeding record
Greylag Goose	Rutland Water 1980
Egyptian Goose	Rutland Water 1989

▲ Egyptian Goose (*Nigel Spencer*). Rutland Water, April 2008. An introduced species which has developed a self-sustaining population around Rutland Water.

▼ Blue-winged Teal (*Iain Leach*). Eyebrook Reservoir, August 1998. The first record in the counties of this North American species.

▲ Smew (*Carl Baggott*). Birstall Gravel Pits, February 2004. Records of this scarce winter visitor in the counties date back to the medieval period.

▼ Great Crested Grebe (*Danny Green*). Watermead Country Park, April 2007. A typical species of new reservoirs and gravel pits, and symbol of the LROS.

▲ Shag (*Jim Graham*). Stoney Cove, 1998. A scarce autumn and winter visitor, which sometimes stays for long periods. This bird was present from November 1996 until June 1999!

▼ Gannet (*Pete Farbridge*). Eyebrook Reservoir, August 2000. A rare visitor to the counties, mainly in autumn.

▲ Little Egrets (*John Wright*). Rutland Water, October 2008. First recorded in the counties in 1982, numbers of this species have increased dramatically in recent years.

▼ Great White Egret (*Steve Young*). Stanford Reservoir, July 1992. A rare but increasing vagrant from Europe. This was the third county record.

▲ White Stork (*Iain Leach*). Bottesford, August 2001. A very rare vagrant from Europe, mainly in spring.

▼ Montagu's Harrier (*Stephen Walton*) Thornton Reservoir, May 1990. A very rare migrant through the counties, mainly in spring. All records have involved birds seen on just one day.

▲ Osprey (*John Wright*). Formerly a scarce passage migrant, Ospreys first bred in Rutland in 2001 following a successful translocation project.

▼ Red-footed Falcon (*Tim Appleton*). Rutland Water, June 1992. A very rare vagrant from eastern Europe. This was the fifth county record.

▲ Peregrine Falcon (*Carl Baggott*). A scarce resident breeder since 1994, and uncommon winter and passage visitor.

▼ Water Rail (*John Wright*). Rutland Water, May 2009. Breeding is probably more regular than records suggest. Their retiring habits make views like this of adults with young exceptional.

▲ Cream-coloured Courser (*Andrew Harrop*). Timberwood Hill, October 1827. Mounted specimen of the fourth British record.

▼ Dotterel (*Tim Appleton*). Cottesmore, April/May 1984. At least 13 were recorded at Cottesmore during this period, but otherwise this species has been a very unpredictable and rare visitor to the counties.

▲ Baird's Sandpiper (*Steve Young*). Eyebrook Reservoir, September 1994. Both records have been at this site.

▼ Pomarine Skua (*Andrew Harrop*). Near Hinckley, autumn 1878. Mounted specimen of the second record.

▲ Long-tailed Skua (*Andrew Harrop*). Near Melton Mowbray, October 1926. Mounted specimen of the first record which was rediscovered during research for this publication.

▼ Caspian Gull (*John Wright*). Rutland Water, August 2006. Since the first records in 1996, this newly recognised species has become a regular visitor in late autumn and winter.

▲ Little Auk (*Tim Appleton*). Freshly dead, Rutland Water, October 1997. A rare storm-driven vagrant from the Arctic. Many of those found inland are exhausted or dying.

▼ Puffin (*Keith Stone*). Eyebrook Reservoir, June 1995. This bird arrived in clear, calm conditions but was 25% under the average weight and later died; three of the six county records have involved birds which died following their arrival.

▲ Crag Martin (*Iain Leach*). Swithland Reservoir, April 1999. The first for the counties, and the fifth for Britain.

▲ Red-throated Pipit (*Tim Appleton*). Rutland Water, May 1981. The only county record, and an unusual inland occurrence.

▼ Grey-headed Wagtail (*Gary Bellingham*) Rutland Water, May 2001. One of two present which constitute the only confirmed record of this race in the counties. Like the Red-throated Pipit, these birds were probably on passage to Scandinavia.

▲ Black-bellied Dipper (*John Harriman*). Tolethorpe, February 1997. The second confirmed record of the nominate race in the counties.

▼ Nightingale (*John Wright*). Rutland Water, May 2006. Formerly more widespread, Nightingales are now confined almost entirely to Rutland.

▲ Bluethroat (*Jim Eaton*). Rutland Water, April 1996. The only record in the counties coincided with a national influx of white-spotted birds.

▼ Red-flanked Bluetail (*Charnwood Ringing Group*). Woodhouse Eaves, October 1997. An exceptional inland record of this vagrant from north-east Europe and Siberia.

▲ Chiffchaff (*John Wright*). Rutland Water, January 1998. A wintering bird of one of the eastern races (*abietinus*/*tristis*).

▼ Red-backed Shrike (*Iain Leach*). Egleton, September 1996. A former breeding species which is now a very rare migrant with just six modern records.

▲ Raven (*Adey Baker*). Croft Quarry, May 2008. Present in the medieval period, but died out during the early 19th century. In the early 21st century this species has returned and is again establishing a breeding population.

▼ Tree Sparrow (*Carl Baggott*). Fosse Meadows, April 2007. Formerly a common and widespread resident breeder, like many other farmland birds this species has declined and is now present in large numbers only in localised areas.

Shelduck	Rutland Water 1977
Mandarin Duck	Tixover 1991
Gadwall	Cropston Reservoir 1974
Shoveler	Eyebrook Reservoir 1941
Tufted Duck	Eyebrook Reservoir 1941
Ruddy Duck	Swithland Reservoir 1973
Cormorant	Rutland Water 1992
Red Kite	Reintroduced – Rutland 2002 (following extinction in the late 1830s)
Common Buzzard	Belvoir 1993 (following extinction in 1827)
Osprey	Introduced – Rutland Water 2001
Peregrine Falcon	Charnwood 1994
Oystercatcher	Wanlip Gravel Pits 1970
Little Ringed Plover	Hemington Gravel Pits 1955
Ringed Plover	Wanlip Gravel Pits 1965
Black-headed Gull	Moira 1943
Common Tern	Wanlip Gravel Pits 1967
Collared Dove	Fenny Drayton and Stoneygate, Leicester 1965
Raven	Breedon Quarry 2003 (following extinction in the early 19th century)

There are several species which have never established themselves as regular breeders in the counties and a few (for example Quail, Water Rail and Long-eared Owl), may nest more often than is known. Breeding attempts by species such as the Avocet, Stonechat and Pied Flycatcher will, at the time, have seemed like one-off curiosities, but could perhaps prove to be the start of more regular breeding.

Table 3: Irregular and occasional breeding species in Leicestershire and Rutland

Species	**Additional comments**
Eurasian Teal	Only one breeding record since 1985 (Rutland Water in 2002)
Garganey	Single pairs bred at Eyebrook Reservoir in 1947 and Rutland Water in 1983
Common Pochard	Three breeding records since 1991
Quail	Breeding difficult to prove due to elusive nature of this species
Black-necked Grebe	Bred at Rutland Water in four years between 1978 and 1988
Water Rail	Bred in seven years between 1947 and 2005
Avocet	Pair bred unsuccessfully at Rutland Water in 1996
Long-eared Owl	Bred in 14 years between 1941 and 2005
Nightjar	Breeding difficult to prove due to this species' nocturnal habits
Black Redstart	Six breeding records between 1974 and 1997
Stonechat	Pair bred at Sence Valley Forest Park in 2002; formerly bred in the 19th century
Northern Wheatear	Formerly bred in 19th century, six confirmed and/or probable breeding records in 20th century
Pied Flycatcher	Pair bred at Broombriggs in 1996
Siskin	Single pairs bred at Glenfield in 1998 and Newtown Linford in 2000
Common Crossbill	Confirmed and/or probable breeding recorded in five years (1960, 1962, 1991, 1998, 2003)

COMMON BIRDS CENSUSES

Common breeding birds are often neglected by birdwatchers but it is these species that are arguably the most important to monitor and record correctly. Common Birds Censuses, and their successors the Breeding Bird Surveys, have been carried out in one or more years at a number of sites in the counties, including Prior's

Coppice, Fort Henry Ponds and Loddington, whilst a pilot study of green spaces within the city boundary of Leicester in 1989 provided breeding bird data from Western Park, Abbey Park and Knighton Park (Fray 1990). The four longest-running surveys have been at Stoughton, Newton Harcourt, Aylestone Meadows and King's Hill Lodge, Uppingham, and it is from censuses such as these that we gain much of our current knowledge regarding the common breeding birds of the counties. Complete data for these four sites can be found in Appendix 5.

Stoughton

This Common Birds Census was carried out on farmland between Oadby and Stoughton by members of the Leicestershire and Rutland Ornithological Society for 36 years and was one of the longest-running such surveys in Britain. The plot covered approximately 87 hectares (215 acres) and was characterised by large fields and severely pruned hedges. In the early years large areas of barley predominated, to be replaced later by vast expanses of oilseed rape. Other features at the site included two small spinneys, several stands of mature trees, a stream with marshy areas and an area of scrub. Local and national trends are clearly illustrated in the results, including the increases in species such as Blackcap and Magpie, the depressing decline of Sky Larks, Song Thrushes and Yellowhammers and the effects of severe winter weather such as in 1978–79. This area of farmland was also representative in that it suffered from systematic habitat destruction and agricultural intensification, particularly during the 1980s and 1990s.

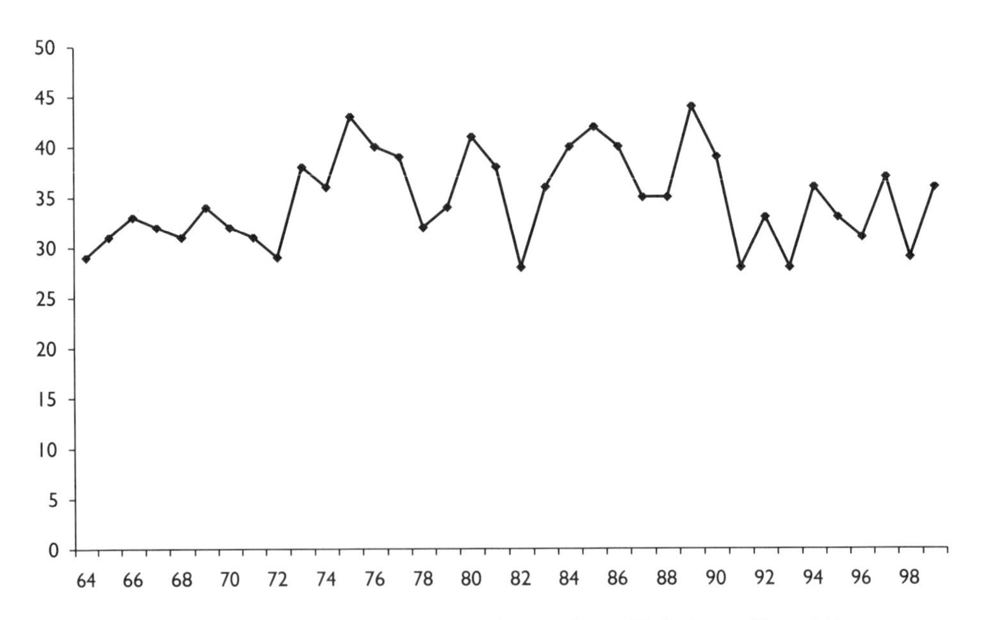

Figure 1: Total number of species holding territory at the Stoughton CBC plot 1964 to 1999.

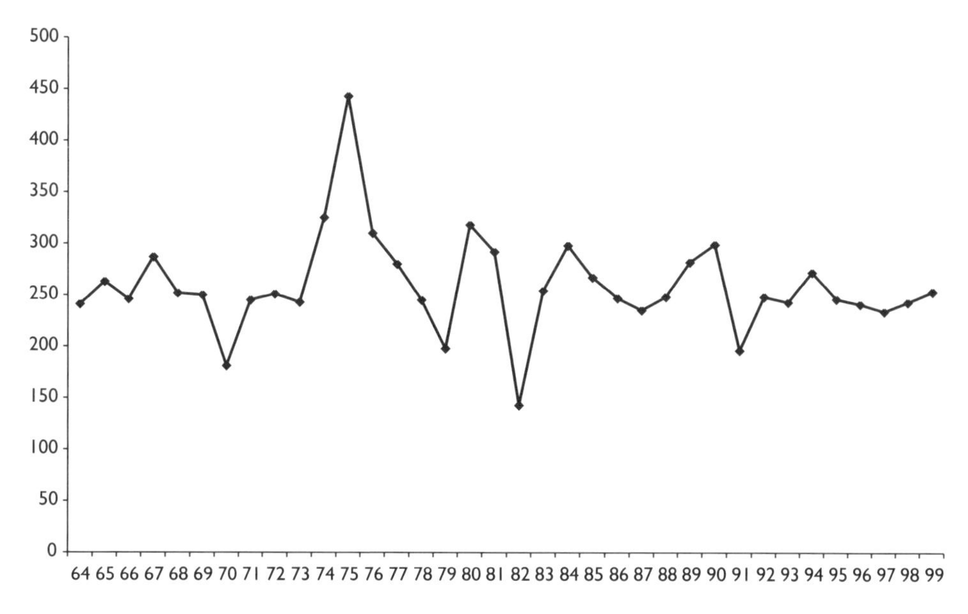

Figure 2: Total number of territories at the Stoughton CBC plot 1964 to 1999.

Newton Harcourt

This farmland plot of approximately 17 hectares (42 acres) was surveyed in most years from 1971 to 2002; field-workers were Dr. D. McNeil, Dave Scott, Dave Gamble and Alan Rayfield. The census plot consisted mainly of four large fields with mature trees and hedges along the boundaries; a stream ran through the centre of the plot. Like Stoughton, habitat destruction occurred at this site: a spinney was removed, a stream was straightened and had its banks 'improved', pasture was replaced by arable land and hedgerows were either removed or considerably reduced in height (Scott 1983). Many of the results for individual species are strikingly similar to those recorded at Stoughton.

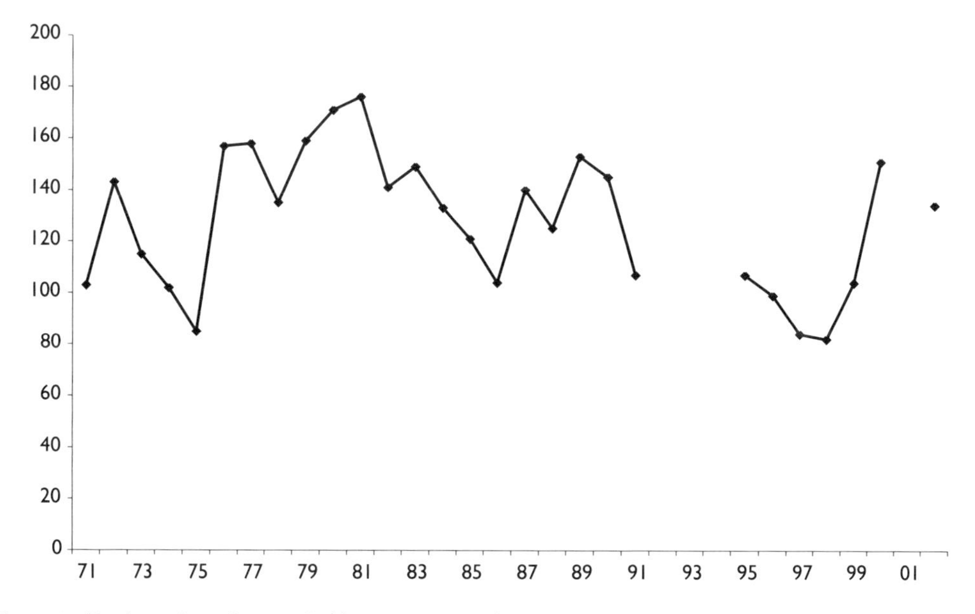

Figure 3: Total number of species holding territory at the Newton Harcourt CBC plot 1971 to 2002.

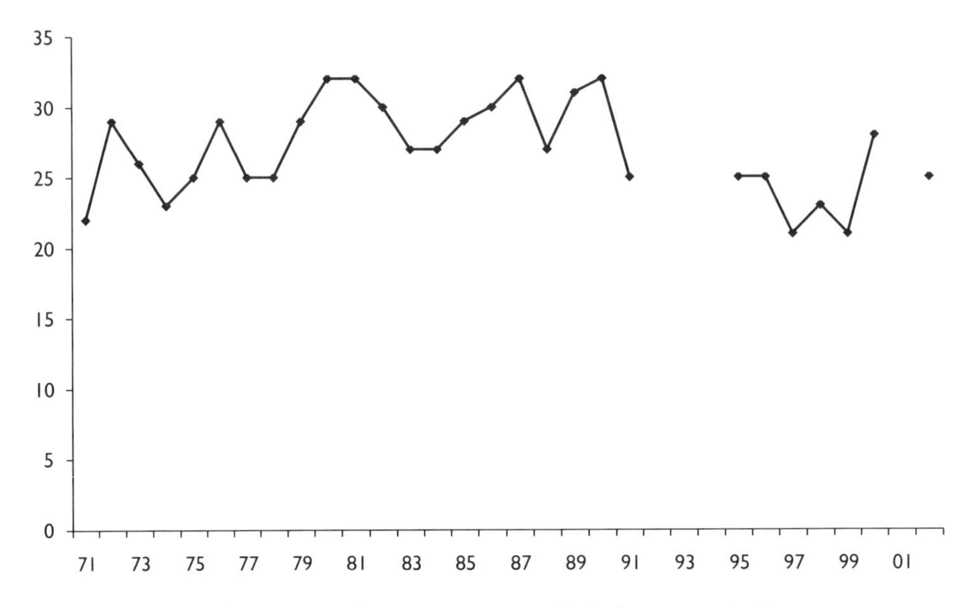

Figure 4: Total number of territories at the Newton Harcourt CBC plot 1971 to 2002.

Aylestone Meadows

This large site is located within the city boundary of Leicester and covers an area of approximately 109 acres (269 acres); around 30% of the area was surveyed by Dave Cohen, Mark Holling and Rob Fray. Unlike Stoughton and Newton Harcourt, the habitat is split between grazed pasture and areas of scrub, with the added feature of the River Biam and associated waterside vegetation.

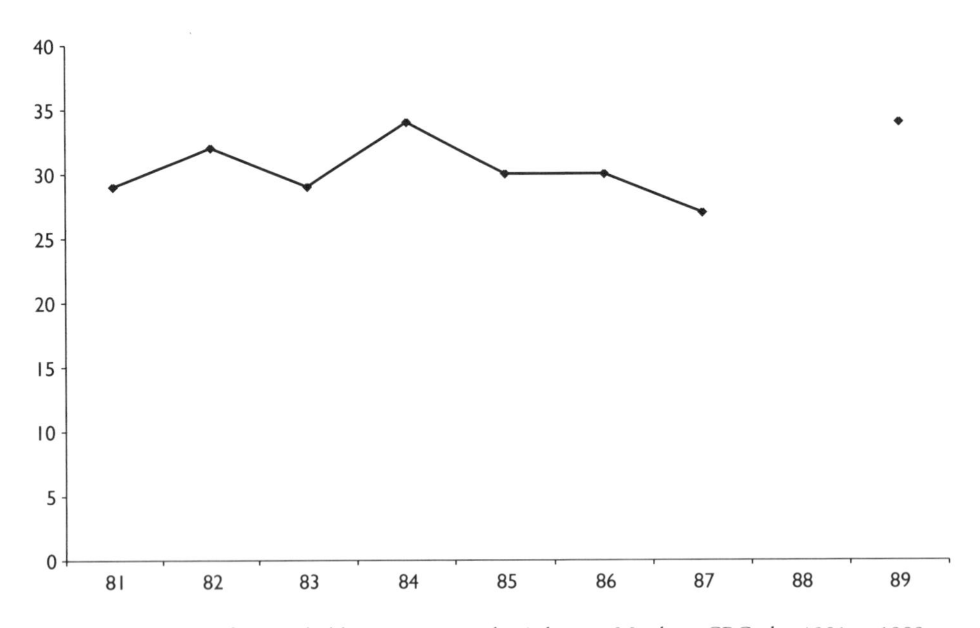

Figure 5: Total number of species holding territory at the Aylestone Meadows CBC plot 1981 to 1989.

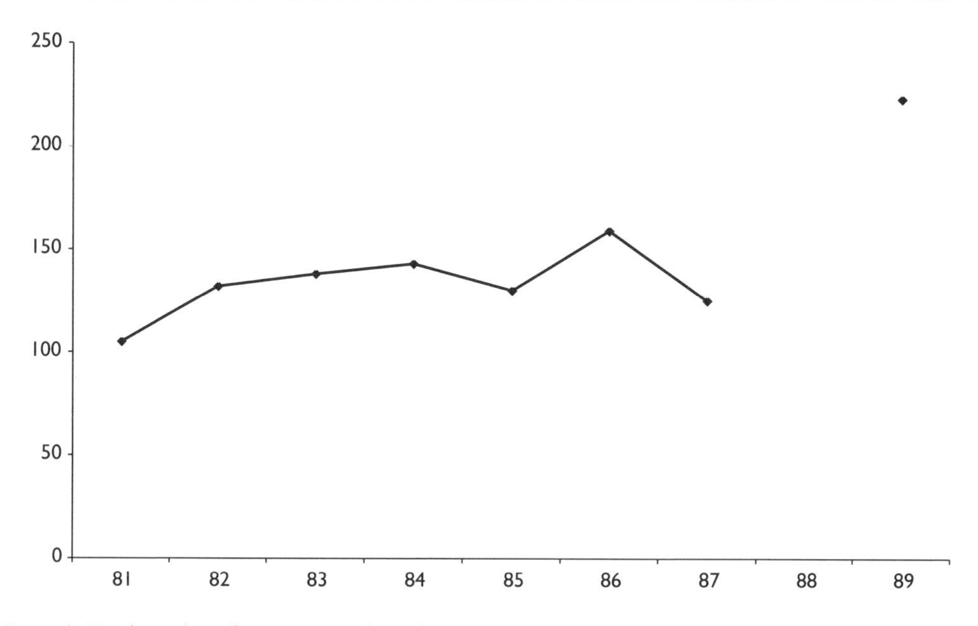

Figure 6: Total number of territories at the Aylestone Meadows CBC plot 1981 to 1989.

King's Hill Lodge, Uppingham

This farmland site in Rutland was surveyed by Terry Mitcham from 1992 to 2005. As census work here began later than at Stoughton and Newton Harcourt, the overall trends are different as by the 1990s a number of farmland species had reached their lowest ebb and had begun to stabilise or increase slightly. This is particularly evident when analysing the total number of territories which, barring a few minor fluctuations, have increased steadily since 1992.

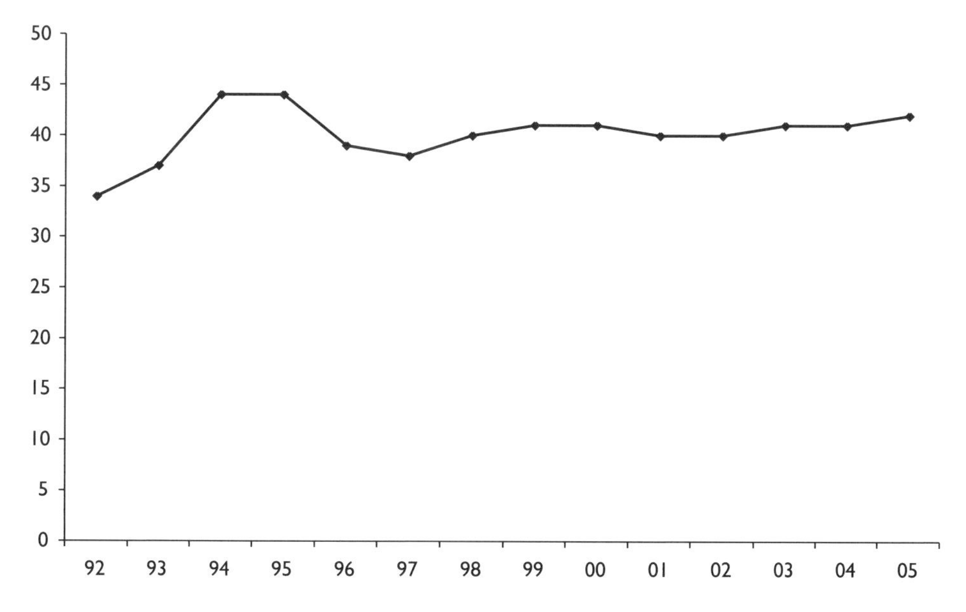

Figure 7: Total number of species holding territory at the King's Hill Lodge, Uppingham CBC plot 1992 to 2005.

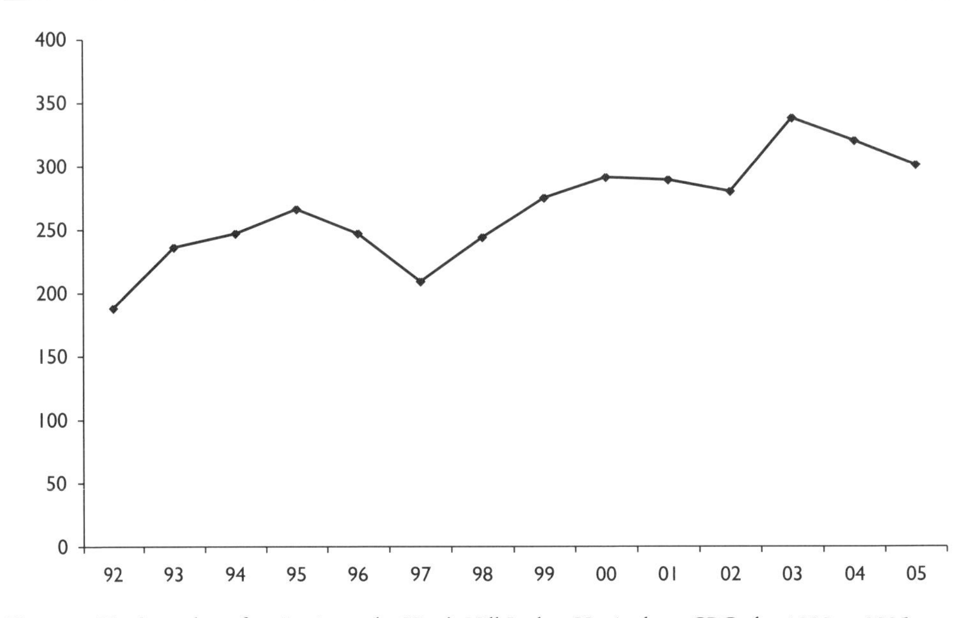

Figure 8: Total number of territories at the King's Hill Lodge, Uppingham CBC plot 1992 to 2005.

THE FUTURE

Fray (1998b), in an article in the 1997 LROS Annual Report, speculated on potential additions and re-establishments to the counties' breeding avifauna. The list of possible additions included the Siskin and Cetti's Warbler, both of which have now bred (the latter in 2007 – see Appendix 10). Of those suggested as re-establishments, the Red Kite, Osprey and Raven have consolidated their places as regular breeding birds, whilst the Eurasian Teal and the Nightjar have each bred once in recent years.

There are many species which could possibly be added to the Leicestershire and Rutland breeding list in future years: Goosander, Honey Buzzard, Marsh Harrier, Goshawk, Lesser Black-backed Gull, Yellow-legged Gull and Dartford Warbler have all been expanding their range recently, whilst the dramatic colonisation of Britain by the Little Egret over the last ten years will surely result in this species becoming a regular breeder in one or more of the counties' heronries in the not too distant future. The most likely species to recolonise the counties in future years would appear to be the Wood Lark, which is currently breeding in some numbers in neighbouring Nottinghamshire. Corn Crakes are being actively reintroduced into Cambridgeshire and, if the project is successful, it could see the return of this enigmatic species to Leicestershire and Rutland. The likely future impact of climate change could see, amongst others, the Cattle and Great White Egrets, Spoonbill, Hoopoe and European Bee-eater becoming regular British breeding species. On a more local level, plans for the development of new lagoons and an expansion of the reserve at Rutland Water may help species such as the Eurasian Teal and the Common Pochard to re-establish breeding populations.

On the negative side, the further intensification of farming is a concern and could precipitate the local extinction of declining species like the Turtle Dove and the Corn Bunting. Nightingales and Tree Pipits are both rapidly declining locally due to reasons that are not fully understood, and may soon join the likes of the Common Redstart, Whinchat and Wood Warbler as former breeding birds. Another likely local extinction is the Ruddy Duck, although this will be wholly down to human intervention; it is ironic that this species originally became established due to mankind's actions and its problematic consequences may serve as a reminder to those currently intent on introducing or reintroducing other species that caution should be exercised.

Nature reserves will continue to provide important habitat for breeding birds but it may be the condition of the countryside outside reserves, and of landscapes that include mixtures of habitats and transitional zones, which determine the state of our breeding birds of the future.

WINTERING BIRDS

by Rob Fray

INTRODUCTION

With their wealth of reservoirs and gravel pit complexes, the counties of Leicestershire and Rutland provide important wintering sites for large numbers of birds, particularly wildfowl. Several species of duck occur in nationally, or even internationally, significant numbers, and between the months of September and March one can witness massed ranks of wildfowl resting and feeding on one of the many reservoirs in the area. Add to this scene the teeming mass of one of the counties' large gull roosts and it is easy to see why many birdwatchers visit this land-locked area to view this fine spectacle.

There are currently just under 30 regularly recorded species that occur either almost entirely as winter visitors to the counties or are present in much higher numbers in winter than at other times of year. The species involved are shown in Table 4.

Table 4: Species recorded principally as winter visitors in Leicestershire and Rutland

Species	Additional comments
Bewick's Swan	
Whooper Swan	One summering record
Eurasian Wigeon	Small numbers summer
Eurasian Teal	One breeding record since 1995 (Rutland Water in 2002)
Common Pochard	Three breeding records since 1991
Greater Scaup	Occasional summer records
Goldeneye	Small numbers summer
Smew	
Goosander	Occasional summer records
Merlin	
Water Rail	Bred in seven years between 1947 and 2005
Golden Plover	
Jack Snipe	
Common Snipe	Bred until 1989
Common Gull	
Herring Gull	
Iceland Gull	
Glaucous Gull	
Great Black-backed Gull	
Short-eared Owl	
Waxwing	
Stonechat	Bred during 19th century. One recent breeding record (Sence Valley Forest Park in 2002)
Fieldfare	Occasional summer records
Redwing	
Brambling	
Siskin	Occasional summer records. Bred in 1998 and 2000
Lesser Redpoll	Bred until 1996

WATERBIRDS

Systematic counts of wildfowl have been carried out in one form or another since at least 1950, either as part of official long-term monitoring projects such as the Wetland Bird Survey (WeBS) organised jointly by the British Trust for Ornithology, the Wildfowl and Wetlands Trust, the Royal Society for the Protection of Birds and the Joint Nature Conservation Committee, or as individual studies by local observers with a particular interest in a certain area. Thus there is a wealth of data concerning wildfowl numbers in the counties.

Table 5: Maximum counts of wildfowl at regularly counted sites in Leicestershire and Rutland

	RW	EBR	StR	SwR	CrR	GrP	ThR	BLk
Mute Swan	526	129	88	86	38	52	31	2 *
Greylag Goose	367	350	370	340	35	3 *	1 *	230
Greater Canada Goose	1,539	1,178	850	1,040	602	398	235	330
Eurasian Wigeon	7,239	3,000	2,000	1,664	1,000	526	100	181
Gadwall	2,181	502	267	308	67	92	50	8 *
Eurasian Teal	2,491	831	1,661	725	650	90	42	102
Mallard	2,961	2,100	2,000	900	1,500	850	378	387
Pintail	359	500	67	32	12	15	8	0 *
Shoveler	1,154	184	548	294	130	108	38	19
Common Pochard	2,346	1,800	876	600	1,203	300	190	35
Tufted Duck	8,487	2,000	1,000	530	240	200	115	106
Goldeneye	511	76	26	95	60	2 *	23	8
Goosander	130	250	100	76	25	8	18	55
Ruddy Duck	1,345	707	274	270	156	62	26	24
Little Grebe	120	76	46	61	26	10	50	2 *
Great Crested Grebe	1,038	353	124	127	90	19	90	18
Cormorant	920	158	45	223	84	138	42	6 *
Coot	7,453	2,000	2,115	629	391	354	278	102

	KnR	WCPN	PrW	WCPS	FHP	TVP	MCP	QBP
Mute Swan	5 *	115	103	263	127	58	18	86
Greylag Goose	35	460	278	56	195	24	58	314
Greater Canada Goose	400	900	760	723	511	284	54	314
Eurasian Wigeon	300	800	1,200	400	310	200	33	328
Gadwall	9 *	136	109	38	208	73	10	45
Eurasian Teal	80	402	850	204	102	165	28	13 *
Mallard	900	502	387	163	869	153	254	67
Pintail	15	20	80	0 *	21	9	2	6
Shoveler	20	91	39	51	44	30	33	7
Common Pochard	95	154	160	118	180	111	52	210
Tufted Duck	100	454	194	249	456	171	120	56
Goldeneye	2 *	19	14	8	9	26	3	22
Goosander	59	84	48	67	13	9	18	3
Ruddy Duck	3	8	6	38	6	7	32	11
Little Grebe	1 *	34	22	34	10	9	23	31
Great Crested Grebe	36	53	22	27	19	45	9	35
Cormorant	13	71	32	60	9	101	13	5
Coot	39	830	484	257	135	359	126	283

Key to abbreviations: RW = Rutland Water; EBR = Eyebrook Reservoir; StR = Stanford Reservoir; SwR = Swithland Reservoir; CrR = Cropston Reservoir; GrP = Groby Pool; ThR = Thornton Reservoir; BLk = Belvoir Lakes; KnR = Knipton Reservoir; WCPN = Watermead Country Park North; PrW = Priory Water; WCPS = Watermead Country Park South; FHP = Fort Henry Ponds; TVP = Trent Valley Pit; MCP = Melton Country Park; QBP = Quorn Borrow Pit.

* = highest published site-count, but not necessarily the site maximum.

Several of the sites mentioned above have been counted and had their results published under different names: Priory Water was previously known as Kirby Bellars Gravel Pits and Trent Valley Pit began as Hemington Gravel Pits. The Watermead Country Park complex has suffered from a number of name changes over the years as the area has been developed but, in simple terms, Watermead Country Park North includes areas previously referred to as Wanlip Gravel Pits, Wanlip South Gravel Pits and Birstall Gravel Pits (and also includes the new reserve of Wanlip Meadows) and Watermead Country Park South includes the old sites of Watermead Gravel Pits and Watermead Park.

In addition to those included in Table 5, a number of other sites have been counted at various times. They include Frisby Gravel Pits, Saddington Reservoir, Blackbrook Reservoir, Willesley Lake, Sence Valley Forest Park, Dishley Pool, Syston Gravel Pits and the River Soar within the city boundary of Leicester. Numbers of wildfowl occurring at these sites are not usually of particular local significance (with a few notable exceptions, such as Moorhens at Frisby Gravel Pits and Little Grebes on the River Soar within Leicester).

Rutland Water has quickly established itself as a site of national and international importance for a number of species. It is now probably the single most important inland wetland in Britain and in recognition of this has been designated as both a Ramsar site and a Special Protection Area. Details of current qualifying abundance thresholds can be found in Collier *et al.* 2005.

Table 6: Species occurring in internationally important numbers at Rutland Water

	Qualifying abundance threshold	**Additional comments**
Mute Swan	380	Sixth most important site in Britain
Gadwall	600	Most important site in Britain
Shoveler	400	Third most important site in Britain

Table 7: Species occurring in nationally important numbers at Rutland Water

	Qualifying abundance threshold	**Maximum site count**	**Additional comments**
Greater Canada Goose *	600	1,539	Third most important site in Britain
Egyptian Goose *	10	70	Third most important site in Britain
Common Pochard	595	2,346	
Tufted Duck	901	8,487	Second most important site in Britain
Goldeneye	249	511	Sixth most important site in Britain
Smew	4	20	
Ruddy Duck *	30	1,345	Most important site in Britain
Little Grebe	78	120	Eighth most important site in Britain
Great Crested Grebe	159	1,038	Second most important site in Britain
Cormorant	230	920	Eleventh most important site in Britain
Coot	1,730	7,453	Third most important site in Britain

* = naturalised introduced species and so lacking official British thresholds. Figures given are those used for presentation in WeBS reports.

Other sites have qualified as being of national importance for some species at various times in recent years: Eyebrook Reservoir for Gadwall, Common Pochard, Smew, Ruddy Duck and Great Crested Grebe; Stanford Reservoir for Shoveler, Ruddy Duck and Coot; Swithland Reservoir for Gadwall, Shoveler and Ruddy Duck and the River Soar in Leicester for Little Grebe.

Inland birdwatchers often hope for scarcer wildfowl to arrive during the winter months and we are lucky in Leicestershire and Rutland to have several large reservoirs and gravel pit complexes that consistently produce such records. The construction of Rutland Water has changed the occurrence patterns of a number of species; divers and scarce grebes were previously vagrants that usually only appeared during severe weather but they are now recorded annually. Maritime species, such as the Long-tailed Duck, Velvet Scoter and Red-breasted

Merganser, are being seen with increased regularity. Smew and Goosander numbers are higher than ever, at both Rutland Water and elsewhere in the counties.

The occurrence of geese and wild swans is a little more difficult to predict, although Pink-footed Geese are now recorded in ever-increasing numbers and it has been discovered that flocks pass over the east, north-east and north-west of the counties on calm, clear January days on their annual winter movements between Norfolk and Lancashire. Other geese are still erratic in their appearances but White-fronted Geese often appear during cold weather. In the 1970s Bewick's Swans looked set to become a regular feature of the counties' avifauna when large flocks wintered annually at Eyebrook Reservoir; unfortunately numbers have declined since and their occurrence appears to have been a temporary phenomenon.

GULLS

Gull-watching, and specifically the systematic scrutiny of gull roosts, was a relatively neglected activity in Leicestershire and Rutland until the mid-1980s, when a small band of observers began concentrating their efforts at Swithland Reservoir. The presence of the nearby Mountsorrel landfill site boosted gull numbers at this site and intensive watching produced the counties' first Ring-billed and Yellow-legged Gulls, as well as several Iceland, Glaucous and Mediterranean Gulls. The closure of Mountsorrel Tip saw both gull numbers and observer interest diminish at this site, and Eyebrook Reservoir took over as the premier location in the counties for observing roosting gulls, helped by the proximity of several large landfill sites at Corby (Northamptonshire). Regular watching of this roost was largely responsible for altering the status of the Caspian Gull from that of a very rare vagrant to an uncommon but increasingly regular autumn and winter visitor. Other large roosts exist at Rutland Water and Stanford Reservoir but these do not get the coverage they perhaps deserve; the Rutland Water roost is difficult to view, due to the size of the reservoir, and Stanford Reservoir has generally been under-watched, although it has produced the counties' only Franklin's Gull.

In the 1980s and 1990s landfill sites provided opportunities for observing gulls during daylight hours, with those at Enderby, Lount and Shawell all receiving a degree of coverage and producing occasional records of Iceland and Glaucous Gulls. The majority of the counties' rubbish tips are now closed; the only large one in current operation is Bradgate Tip which, although difficult to view, has seen the number of gulls using nearby Groby Pool as a resting and bathing site increase dramatically over recent years.

The British Trust for Ornithology has organised national surveys every ten years from 1953 onwards in an attempt to gauge the national population of wintering gulls. The results from Leicestershire and Rutland show that the largest numbers were using the counties' roosts in 1983, when over 100,000 birds were present; totals in the previous years were much lower as several sites were not counted and Rutland Water was not in existence.

Table 8: BTO winter gull roost survey results 1953 to 2004

	RW	EBR	StR	CrR	SwR	ThR	WGP	Total
1953	–	25,250	nc	2,050	3,031	nc	nc	**30,331**
1963	–	37,500	nc	nc	7,351	nc	nc	**44,851**
1973	–	30,555	2,891	4,130	8,110	776	nc	**46,462**
1983	38,100	36,125	14,425	4,833	8,300	4,224	2,500	**108,507**
1993	22,863	13,800	15,952	300	4,626	1,559	6,170	**65,300**
2004	33,500	29,404	17,893	7,194	3,135	570	4,450	**96,146**

Key: RW = Rutland Water; EBR = Eyebrook Reservoir; StR = Stanford Reservoir; CrR = Cropston Reservoir; SwR = Swithland Reservoir; ThR = Thornton Reservoir; WGP = Wanlip Gravel Pits (latterly known as Watermead Country Park North). nc = not counted.

SEVERE WEATHER AND CLIMATE CHANGE

Severe winter weather can have a profound effect on birds; the most notable examples occurred during the winters of 1946–47 and 1962–63 and full details can be found in Appendix 9.

At the beginning of cold weather periods there are often movements of Lapwings, Golden Plovers, Sky Larks and thrushes, mainly to the south-west. Prolonged periods of severe weather affect different species in different ways, with some faring much worse than others. Those badly affected during the two winters mentioned above included the Moorhen, Coot, Little Owl, Kingfisher and Green Woodpecker. The winter of 1978–79 was also particularly cold and local Common Birds Census results revealed that Wrens were seriously reduced in numbers during the following breeding season. During these periods large numbers of wildfowl were forced to leave their usual haunts and seek open water: the River Soar in Leicester and the River Trent in the far north-west of Leicestershire provided such conditions and unusual species such as Greater Scaup, Smew and Red-necked and Slavonian Grebes were all recorded.

The run of milder winters since the mid-1980s has seen increased numbers of Blackcaps and Chiffchaffs wintering in the counties, the former often making use of supplementary feeding in gardens. Possibly the milder weather is also responsible for recent winter records of Common Whitethroat and Willow Warbler. Another beneficiary is the Stonechat, a bird that is susceptible to population crashes following harsh weather but which is now wintering in Leicestershire and Rutland in greater numbers than ever. And who would have thought 20 years ago that Little Egrets would be a regular sight in the counties in the winter months? These changes have all occurred in a short space of time and it will be interesting to see what new species feature regularly during the winter by the middle of the 21st century.

MIGRATION

by Steve Lister

INTRODUCTION

Leicestershire and Rutland are unlikely to feature on many birdwatchers' lists of the top counties for bird migration, given their position in the middle of England. Nevertheless, there is a mass of evidence gathered over the years that reveals substantial movement through and over the two counties. There are currently about 30 regularly recorded species that occur almost entirely as migrants, normally neither breeding nor wintering in the counties, and another four or five for which the numbers of migrants are much higher than those present at other times of year. The species involved are shown in Table 9.

Many other species that either breed or winter in the counties also occur as migrants in significant numbers. This is shown by ringing studies and also by watching visible migration, when some spectacular movements of rather unspectacular species such as Wood Pigeons and Meadow Pipits have been noted along with smaller numbers of species not normally thought of as migrants, including Greenfinch, Goldfinch and so on.

It is fair to say that there has not been a lot of attention paid to bird migration in the counties beyond searching for scarce passage birds such as Ring Ouzels. Waterbirds, and waders in particular, have been recorded comparatively thoroughly due to observers being drawn to the more attractive sites such as Eyebrook Reservoir and Rutland Water; tables of daily wader counts for selected sites were included in the LROS Annual Reports for several years.

The movements of some waterbird species are difficult to understand or explain, with the Common Scoter being a good example: small flocks can occur at almost any time of year but mainly in the summer and autumn. They are obviously on passage across the country but from where and to where? Their occurrence does not seem to be related to the weather, unlike Kittiwakes which are mainly recorded around stormy periods and hardly qualify as migrants in the counties, despite regular observations of birds heading inland from The Wash in Lincolnshire.

Grounded migrants can occur anywhere in the counties; certain areas seem to be more productive than others but the picture is greatly influenced by where observers check for them. The valley of the River Trent, generally regarded as a major cross-country migration route, follows part of the north-western border of Leicestershire and the existence of attractive habitats such as gravel pits and old-style farmland makes it a prime area. The Soar valley, especially south of Leicester, is also quite productive on a much smaller scale; small numbers of Whinchats are often a feature of riverside meadows in the autumn. The creation of Rutland Water in the mid-1970s provided a new focus for migrants and species such as the Northern Wheatear and Yellow Wagtail can be numerous there. Some of the few prominent Leicestershire hills are regularly used by migrants such as Northern Wheatears; since Bardon Hill was found to be a reliable site for seeing spring Ring Ouzels scarcer migrants such as Firecrest and Wood Lark have also been seen there. Other sites could well be discovered to be of comparable interest if they received more attention.

Table 9: Species recorded principally as migrants in Leicestershire and Rutland

Species	Additional comments
Pink-footed Goose	Occasional wintering records
Garganey	Two breeding records (1947 and 1983)
Common Scoter	Occasional wintering records
Red-breasted Merganser	Occasional wintering records
Black-necked Grebe	Occasional winter records. Bred occasionally from 1978 to 1987
Marsh Harrier	Two summering records (1995 and 1996)
Osprey	Excluding the Rutland Water introduction scheme
Avocet	One attempted breeding record (1996)
Ringed Plover	Small numbers breed
Grey Plover	Occasional winter records
Knot	Occasional winter records

Sanderling	Occasional winter records
Little Stint	Recent wintering records
Temminck's Stint	One wintering record (1982–83 and 1983–84)
Curlew Sandpiper	
Black-tailed Godwit	Recent wintering records
Bar-tailed Godwit	Occasional winter records
Whimbrel	
Greenshank	
Green Sandpiper	Small numbers regular in winter
Wood Sandpiper	
Common Sandpiper	Recent wintering records. Former breeding species in 19th century, possibly bred twice recently (1998 and 1999)
Turnstone	Occasional winter records
Little Gull	Occasional winter records
Little Tern	
Black Tern	
Sandwich Tern	
Arctic Tern	
Wryneck	Bred during the 19th century
Wood Lark	Bred during the 18th and early 19th century
Black Redstart	Six breeding records between 1974 and 1997
Common Redstart	Bred until 1997
Whinchat	Bred until 1989
Northern Wheatear	Bred during the 19th century. Confirmed or probable breeding in six years in 20th century, most recently in 1979
Ring Ouzel	Bred during the 19th century
Wood Warbler	Bred until 1994
Pied Flycatcher	One breeding record (1996)

A REVIEW OF PAST STUDIES

The pioneer of migration studies in the counties was R. Eric Pochin, who looked for evidence of passage in his observations of birds at Croft Hill between 1940 and 1952. He summarised his findings in the LROS Annual Report for 1952 (Pochin 1953), picking out clear movements of Starlings, Greenfinches, Linnets, Tree Pipits (autumn flocks of 20), Meadow Pipits, wagtails, warblers, Song Thrushes, Northern Wheatears, Common Redstarts, Robins, Dunnocks, hirundines and Common Swifts. The predominant direction of autumn passage was to the south-west.

During the same period as Eric Pochin was watching on Croft Hill, Albert Jolley was studying the comings and goings of migrant waders at Eyebrook Reservoir. He wrote up his findings and theories in an article in the 1945 Annual Report (Jolley 1946b), including these thoughts on migration routes:

'Firstly, I suggest a large proportion of the autumn migrants follow the River Humber, then the River Trent as far as Newark. Here they separate, some travelling due south through the Vale of Belvoir to the Eye valley, whilst others carry on to Nottingham (either the upper reaches of the Trent or the Sewage Farm), rest awhile, then make their way southwards picking up the Eye valley beyond Melton Mowbray. Leaving Eye valley and still travelling southwards, they skirt Northampton, Tring and the London Reservoirs, Thames valley, etc. Secondly, I believe quite a number of migrants to be seen in Eye valley have flown westward from the Norfolk coast via The Wash, then proceeding in a south-westerly direction over the Birmingham and Worcester reservoirs to the Bristol Channel. It should be remembered that Eye Brook Reservoir is less than 50 miles from the sea.'

The second of Jolley's suggested routes largely matched that described by Eric Simms, doyen of inland migration students, in his 1952 book *Bird Migrants*. This flightpath, partly based on observations made by others as early as 1891, was from The Wash to the Severn Estuary, utilising the valleys of the Rivers Welland and Nene at the north-east end and the line of the Cotswold Hills to the south-west. The Welland forms the south-east boundary of Rutland and southern Leicestershire and passes close to Eyebrook Reservoir, and the existence of a major flyway so nearby could be a reason why the reservoir has such a good reputation for waterbirds.

Jolley's other suggested route is less convincing. R. J. H. Raines was studying migration in the Trent valley at the time and his belief was that most autumn movement was south-west from the Nottingham area, towards Birmingham and the Severn, rather than south towards Eyebrook Reservoir. Certainly there is little, if any, evidence of waterbird passage through the Belvoir and Melton Mowbray areas. Rutland Water is now on the line that Jolley outlined but passage birds such as terns and Little Gulls tend to be moving on an east/west line there rather than on a north/south one.

In 1951, LROS teamed up with the Nuneaton Birdwatchers' Club and the West Midlands Bird Club for a co-ordinated migration watch along 70 miles of Watling Street on October 7th. Unfortunately the weather was unhelpful, being foggy for much of the morning, and the results were almost meaningless.

After 1952 very little was documented about migration in the counties. An exception was an article by Ian Snape in the 1976 Annual Report (Snape 1978), summarising a migration log for Frisby Gravel Pit made over 51 days in the autumn of that year. His regular observations clearly showed passage through the site, of warblers in particular, with a daily turnover of numbers.

Since 1999 there has been a revival of interest in visible-migration watching locally. First to start was Terry Mitcham at Pickworth; he had been inspired by time spent with Eric Simms on 'vismig' watches in Lincolnshire. A viewpoint on Deans Lane, Woodhouse has been used increasingly frequently, principally by Steve Lister and Andy Forryan, since about 2000 and other counts have been conducted by Rob Fray at Trent Valley Pit, Carl Baggott at Croft Hill and Steve Lister on the dam at Rutland Water. On the few occasions that there have been observers at two sites simultaneously it has been apparent that some movements have been on distinct paths, such as along the Trent valley but not over Deans Lane, whereas other movements have been broad-front. It may be hoped that with the growth of interest the study and understanding of this aspect of migration can be developed in the future. Table 10 summarises the data collected by Steve Lister at Deans Lane in autumn 2005.

Table 10: Summary of visible migration at Deans Lane, Woodhouse in autumn 2005*

Species	Days recorded	Maximum count	Total count
Bewick's Swan	1	27	27
Lapwing	1	32	32
Common Snipe	2	2	3
Stock Dove	5	29	52
Wood Pigeon	10	7,350	14,915
Great Spotted Woodpecker	2	2	3
Wood Lark	1	2	2
Sky Lark	9	25	96
Swallow	10	35	147
House Martin	8	335	780
Meadow Pipit	17	288	1,025
Yellow Wagtail	1	4	4
Pied/White Wagtail	6	32	46
Fieldfare	11	320	1,064
Song Thrush	2	2	3
Redwing	14	1,200	3,099
Starling	7	3,080	8,905
Tree Sparrow	1	2	2
Chaffinch	17	45	327
Brambling	10	95	246
Greenfinch	14	42	244
Goldfinch	11	19	91
Siskin	11	31	117
Linnet	10	76	211
Lesser Redpoll	12	23	90

Common Crossbill	5	12	19
Bullfinch	2	5	7
Hawfinch	2	2	3
Yellowhammer	3	3	7
Reed Bunting	1	1	1

* watch kept for 53 hours over 24 days between 7 September and 17 November.

SOME ASPECTS OF VISIBLE MIGRATION

Visible migration is greatly influenced by the weather, especially wind direction and strength but also cloud cover. In Leicestershire and Rutland any significant northerly element in the wind reduces the amount of movement, and wind directions from between west and south-east seem to be the most productive. Anything more than a moderate breeze gives low counts, and clear skies can cause birds to pass over too high to be identified or even seen. Movements can intensify as rain approaches but usually stop during the actual rain.

The first migration of the year is often that of Pink-footed Geese moving north-west over the northern parts of Leicestershire, especially the Belvoir area, en route from Norfolk to Lancashire and the Solway Firth. Far more are seen over Nottinghamshire, and the main flight lines are clearly a little further north than the county boundary. A northerly wind actually increases the chances of flocks being seen over Leicestershire.

The few passerine movements that have been noted in spring usually involve Meadow Pipits flying north-west either singly or in very small groups. Most other spring passage goes unseen, though flocks of Fieldfares moving north are sometimes reported and large gulls such as Lesser Black-backed Gulls flying steadily north may well be passage birds. An obvious feature of many springs is a passage of Arctic Terns, often moving east or north-east, in late April and early May: numbers are rather variable from year to year, with the 1,070 counted at four sites on May 2nd 1998 being exceptional. Smaller movements of Little Gulls and Black Terns are noted during most years.

Late spring sees small flocks of Lapwings moving west, presumably failed or early breeders arriving from the continent.

Autumn passage starts as early as late July, with Common Swifts and some hirundines moving south and south-west. This continues throughout August, with the numbers of hirundines increasing as those of Common Swifts decline. Some extremely large movements of Swallows have been observed later in the autumn, such as 5,000 an hour passing over Hinckley for three hours on September 25th 1999. The migration of many species peaks in September and October. Meadow Pipits tend to predominate from mid-September, with finches taking over in October. Starlings and Wood Pigeons can be very numerous even into early November.

Most autumn movement is to the south-west but Starlings are an exception and almost always head west, as do a proportion of winter thrushes, especially Fieldfares. Movement of Meadow Pipits to the south-east has been noted at Trent Valley Pit but not at Deans Lane, where they always head between south and south-west. Are different origins involved? Just one of many questions that 'vismig' throws up.

ARRIVAL DATES OF SUMMER MIGRANTS

C.F. Mason calculated the mean arrival dates for summer visitors using published data for 1942–68 (Mason 1970) and since 1988 a rolling ten-year mean has been included in the annual report each year; this idea was initiated by Dave Gamble and has been continued by Andy Mackay, Mark Skevington and Rob Fray. Table 11 includes a comparison of the mean arrival dates of the 21 species covered in all of the periods 1942–68, 1979–88 and 1996–2005.

It can be seen that the mean arrival dates of 15 species are now earlier than they were in 1942–68, with nine species arriving on average at least five days earlier than they did. All three hirundines show a change of ten days or more, as does the Sedge Warbler. Four of the 15 arrived significantly later in 1979–88 than in the two other periods, the most obvious being the Yellow Wagtail, and so the differences between 1988 and 2004 have been particularly marked, such as 11 days for the Yellow Wagtail and ten days for the Reed Warbler. Only four species show modern arrival dates later than in 1942–68, and these are all birds that are now much scarcer than before, with three of them (Common Redstart, Whinchat and Wood Warbler) being former breeders and now occurring purely as migrants; if larger numbers were still recorded in the counties very probably earlier individuals would be found. The Turtle Dove, Cuckoo, Lesser Whitethroat and Spotted Flycatcher have shown a remarkable consistency in their mean arrival dates: is it just a coincidence that, with the exception of the Lesser Whitethroat, these species have become much less common recently?

It is difficult to resist linking the general trend for earlier arrivals with the concept of global warming, something that could also be responsible for the autumn migration periods of some wader species becoming earlier in recent years.

Table 11: Comparison of mean first arrival dates of summer migrants in Leicestershire and Rutland

Species	**1942–1968**	**1979–1988**	**1996–2005**	**Overall change** (+ **or** –)
Turtle Dove	April 28th	April 27th	April 27th	–1 day
Cuckoo	April 13th	April 13th	April 14th	11 day
Common Swift	April 26th	April 26th	April 21st	–5 days
Sand Martin	March 28th	March 16th	March 13th	–15 days
Swallow	April 2nd	March 31st	March 22nd	–11 days
House Martin	April 11th	April 10th	April 2nd	–9 days
Tree Pipit	April 8th	April 12th	April 12th	14 days
Yellow Wagtail	April 3rd	April 9th	March 29th	–5 days
Nightingale	April 26th	April 26th	April 20th	–6 days
Common Redstart	April 13th	April 12th	April 13th	–
Whinchat	April 18th	April 23rd	April 23rd	15 days
Northern Wheatear	March 24th	March 22nd	March 16th	–8 days
Grasshopper Warbler	April 21st	April 16th	April 17th	–4 days
Sedge Warbler	April 20th	April 15th	April 7th	–13 days
Reed Warbler	April 27th	April 29th	April 19th	–8 days
Garden Warbler	April 22nd	April 25th	April 19th	–3 days
Lesser Whitethroat	April 21st	April 22nd	April 20th	–1 day
Common Whitethroat	April 17th	April 18th	April 14th	–3 days
Wood Warbler	April 25th	April 22nd	April 25th	–
Willow Warbler	April 1st	April 3rd	March 29th	–3 days
Spotted Flycatcher	May 2nd	May 4th	May 2nd	–

SYSTEMATIC LIST OF THE BIRDS OF LEICESTERSHIRE AND RUTLAND

The Systematic List only includes records up to December 31st 2005. Highlights from 2006, 2007 and 2008 are given in Appendix 10 .

Nomenclature, scientific names and the sequence of species follow the official British List, as published by the BOU (1992) and updated in their journal *Ibis*. Subspecies follow those recognised by the BOURC, with additional information from *BWP*. English names used are usually the older names given in the sixth edition of the British List, although the new BOU names, where different, are included in brackets.

Each account begins with a brief summary of the species' status in Leicestershire and Rutland. The terms used follow those found in *The Leicestershire and Rutland Bird Report 2005* (Fray 2007a) and are defined as follows:

Very rare	Fewer than ten records ever
Rare	More than ten records ever, but less than annual
Scarce	Fewer than ten birds occurring or pairs breeding annually
Uncommon	Between ten and 100 birds occurring or pairs breeding annually
Fairly common	Between 101 and 1,000 birds occurring or pairs breeding annually
Common	Between 1,001 and 10,000 birds occurring or pairs breeding annually
Abundant	More than 10,000 birds occurring or pairs breeding annually

Altogether, 307 species are included in the Systematic List. Species on Category D of the British List are listed subsequently, as are Category E species (escapes) and hybrids.

The majority of information contained within the Systematic List comes from records submitted by members of LROS and subsequently published in the Annual Reports. However, other sources have also been used, most notably the various Rutland Water bird reports. With respect to the more unusual species, only records which have been accepted by the BBRC or the LROS Records Committee have been included in the Systematic List. Therefore, many reports of scarcer species published elsewhere are not included in the official county record, as they generally have not been subjected to any kind of vetting procedure; mention is made in the various species accounts of unsubstantiated records to make it clear that they have not been overlooked. Additional unsubstantiated records from Rutland are listed on page 685. For the rarer species, the relevant BBRC report is referenced, in abbreviated form (e.g. *BB* 89:504).

Figures showing monthly occurrence patterns are based on the first sightings of the individuals involved. Data published graphically is not always complete where information is unavailable for some years.

The initials of the principal author are given at the end of each account, although all accounts have been read by each author and several have been collaborative: *RED* Roger Davis, *RMF* Rob Fray, *DJSG* Dave Gamble, *AHJH* Andrew Harrop, *SML* Steve Lister.

STANDARD REFERENCES AND ABBREVIATIONS

BB	The journal *British Birds*
BBRC	British Birds Rarities Committee
BBS	Breeding Bird Survey
BOU	British Ornithologists' Union
BOURC	British Ornithologists' Union Records Committee
Browne	Browne, M. 1889. *The Vertebrate Animals of Leicestershire and Rutland.* Midland Educational Company Ltd, Birmingham & Leicester
BTO	British Trust for Ornithology
BWP	Cramp, S. (ed.) 1977–1994. *The Birds of the Western Palearctic.* 9 volumes. OUP, Oxford
CBC	Common Birds Census
Haines	Haines, C. R. 1907. *Notes on the Birds of Rutland.* R. H. Porter, London
Hickling	Hickling, R. A. O. 1978. *Birds in Leicestershire and Rutland.* Leicestershire and Rutland Ornithological Society, Leicester.

LNC	Loughborough Naturalists' Club
LROS	Leicestershire and Rutland Ornithological Society
RBBP	Rare Breeding Birds Panel
RNHS	Rutland Natural History Society
RSPB	Royal Society for the Protection of Birds
VH	Page, W. (ed.) 1907. *The Victoria History of the County of Leicester, Volume 1.* Archibald Constable & Co. Ltd, London
Warrilow	Warrilow, G. J. 1996. *Atlas of Breeding Birds of Leicestershire and Rutland.* Privately published.
WeBS	Wetland Bird Survey

Mute Swan *Cygnus olor*

Uncommon to fairly common resident breeder, fairly common moult visitor.

Browne and Haines both described this species as domesticated or semi-wild, and by the beginning of the 20th century breeding had been recorded at Thornton Reservoir, Barrowden, Burley Fishponds and Abbey Park, Leicester. In 1941, the species was described as a common resident, though numbers were much lower than they are currently. The first significant count involved 30 at Stanford Reservoir on October 2nd 1943; by 1954 a composite total of 93 was recorded on August 1st, though this presumably excluded the flock present at the Abbey Meadows area of Leicester, which numbered 150 the following year.

Since 1950, it has been noted that numbers increase from late June or early July, as failed breeders, non-breeders and juveniles undertake moult migrations to favoured areas. Data show that numbers peak in September following moult migration, and then decline steadily during the autumn, winter and spring as birds disperse. The importance of Rutland Water (where the highest count was 526 on September 12th 1999) as a moulting site explains the threefold increase in numbers recorded during the last 25 years. Rutland Water is now of national importance for this speces, the threshold for qualification being 260 birds; by 2001, it was the fifth most important site for Mute Swans in Great Britain. Flocks of over 100 have been recorded at a further seven sites, where the maximum counts have been as follows:

- 263 at Watermead Country Park South on May 30th 2005.
- 150 at Abbey Meadows, Leicester in 1955.
- 130 by the River Soar at Sileby on April 23rd 1996.
- 129 at Eyebrook Reservoir on July 16th 2005.
- 127 at Fort Henry Ponds on December 28th 1998.
- 115 at Wanlip Gravel Pits on December 17th 1978.
- 103 at Priory Water on November 16th 1997.

For details of highest counts at individual sites see 'Wintering Birds' (pages 39–43).

The breeding population was fully censused during BTO enquiries in 1955, 1961, 1978, 1983 and 1990. The results reveal that breeding numbers appeared fairly stable during the first two surveys, but showed a notable decline in 1978, after which a recovery brought the population up to its current level. Ogilvie (1981) speculated that factors causing the 1978 decline may have included the increased utilisation of canals and rivers by leisure-craft, increased disturbance at gravel pits by recreational activities, and re-shaping of river banks as part of flood prevention schemes. However, these three factors are still at work at the present time, and in many areas disturbance is much increased in the 21st century compared to in 1978, so it is likely that the fourth theory put forward to account for this decline was the major contributing factor: lead poisoning caused by swans consuming weights discarded by anglers. It can be no coincidence that Mute Swan numbers have increased dramatically since the ban on lead weights was imposed in 1986.

Warrilow recorded confirmed breeding during 1976–84 in a total of 70 tetrads across the counties. Breeding densities at this time were low, with just one or two pairs in each occupied tetrad, giving an estimated population in the region of 70 pairs. Subsequent censuses in 1983 and 1990 suggest that this figure is probably accurate. However, it was noted in the 1990 survey that many areas of the counties, including the reservoirs at Eyebrook, Cropston and Thornton, and large stretches of the Rivers Wreake, Welland and Soar, were not apparently

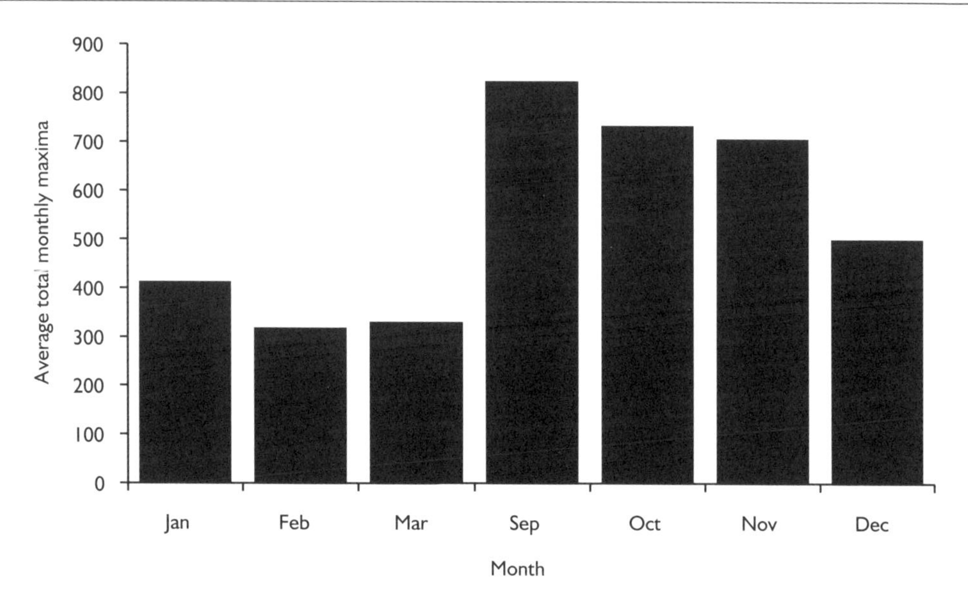

Figure 9: Average total monthly maxima of Mute Swans at the main sites in Leicestershire and Rutland 1995–2005.

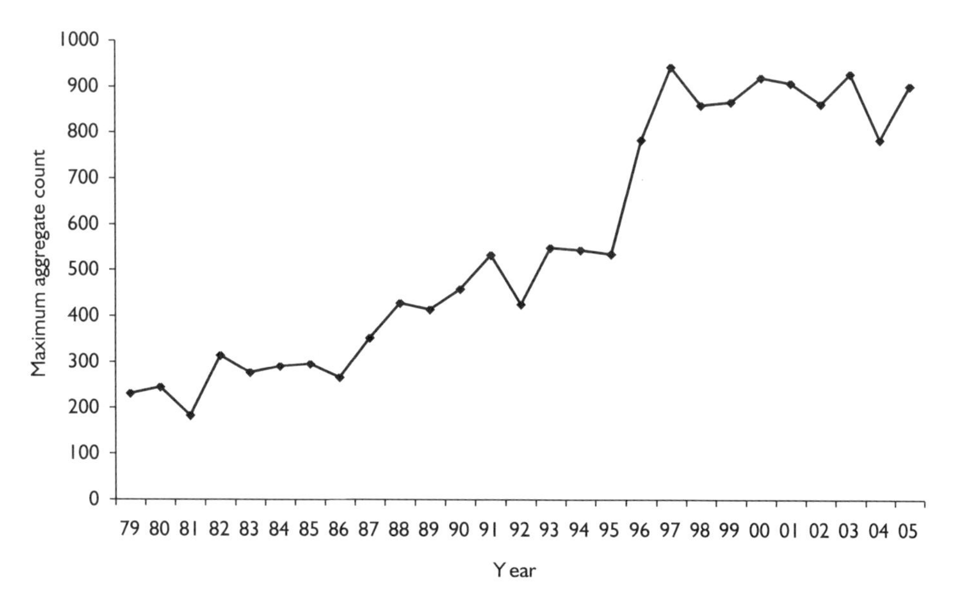

Figure 10: Maximum aggregate counts of Mute Swans at the main sites in Leicestershire and Rutland 1979–2005.

occupied by breeding Mute Swans, allowing ample scope for expansion in the population (Gamble 1991). Significant breeding concentrations in 1990 were noted in the Wreake valley between Frisby and Kirby Bellars (ten pairs), the River Soar and Grand Union Canal in Leicester (nine pairs) and the Grantham Canal between Hickling and Harlaxton (six pairs). The most important site, however, is Rutland Water. During the 1983 survey, 14 pairs nested in the undisturbed reserve areas, all successfully raising young (Measures & Hickling 1984), although in 1990, only one out of 11 pairs raised young at this site, the remainder being predated by Red Foxes (Gamble 1991).

Table 12: Numbers of Mute Swans recorded during BTO surveys

Year	Number of breeding pairs	Number of non-breeding birds
1955	58	150
1961	51	111
1978	27	102
1983	74	107
1990	70	369

Ringing recoveries shed some light on the movements of individual birds. There are several recoveries of birds ringed in the West Midlands, including most notably a pair which bred at Great Glen in 1975 of which the male had been ringed in 1972 at Alvecote (Warwickshire) before moving the following year to Draycote Water (also Warwickshire), where the female was also ringed. One at Priory Water on December 29th 1989 had been ringed as a first-year in December 1987 in Derbyshire and then recovered in Warwickshire during July 1989. From further afield, one found dead at Rutland Water in February 1995 had been ringed in Northumberland in July 1992 and another found dead at Castle Donington in March 1983 had been ringed at Caernarfon (Caernarfonshire) in February 1982. Conversely, both the longevity and more sedentary nature of this species were illustrated by a female found dead at Mountsorrel in February 1989, which had been ringed at Quorn in March 1975 when at least two years old.

In 1988 a male at Swithland Reservoir was observed killing a Mallard on July 16th. That this aggressive behaviour is not entirely atypical was shown in 1995 at Melton Country Park by a male which, after replacing another male taken into care, killed all four of its predecessor's offspring. The following year the same male twice killed Mallard ducklings in June: after shaking them violently it then ate the remains. In June 2003 a male was observed drowning a Greater Canada Goose chick at Priory Water.

'Polish' birds have been recorded on seven occasions: at Rutland Water on October 29th 1989, August 28th 2002, June 18th 2003 and May 2nd 2004, Thornton Reservoir on July 11th 2000 and from January 2nd to 30th 2005, and Cossington South Gravel Pits on April 21st 2002.

Mute Swans breed across much of Eurasia, and the European population is estimated at approximately 69,000 pairs. As more than 20% of European birds breed in Britain (in the region of 15,000 pairs), the species has recently been added to the 'Amber List' of Birds of Conservation Concern (Gregory *et al.* 2002).

AHJH

Bewick's Swan (Tundra Swan) ***Cygnus columbianus***

Uncommon to fairly common passage migrant and scarce winter visitor; recorded in all months between October and May.

Haines noted one shot in April 1870 at Tixover, whilst the only records known to Browne came from Swithland Reservoir, where there were 30 from February 27th to March 7th 1904 and six on December 28th 1906. By 1943, the Bewick's Swan was described as an 'occasional if somewhat rare visitor' (Jolley 1944); this status remained valid throughout the next two decades, evidenced by the fact that there were seven blank years during the 1940s and a further three years during the 1950s with no records.

Double-figure flocks of this species are now regular in winter at favoured localities, especially Eyebrook Reservoir and Rutland Water. Data show that numbers increased during the 1960s and 1970s, when there was a regular wintering flock at Eyebrook Reservoir which peaked at 80 in early 1979. The largest ever flock, of 101 at Rutland Water on December 27th 1976, 98 of which remained until January 3rd 1977, occurred during the same period and corresponded with a dramatic increase in the numbers of birds wintering on the Ouse Washes (Cambridgeshire). The Rutland Water flock occurred on newly flooded land and was attracted by rich feeding on winter wheat. Two other notable herds in more recent times at this site have been 95 on March 6th 1986 and 86 on March 24th 2004. Flocks of 25+ have been recorded at a further eight sites, where the maximum counts have been as follows:

- 48 at Cropston Reservoir on February 10th 1956.
- 48 at Swithland Reservoir on October 27th 1991.
- 43 at Langham on January 25th 1998.
- 39 at Saddington on March 27th 1985.
- 34 at Stanford Reservoir on January 19th 1985.
- 33 at Wanlip on January 30th 1993.
- 27 at Hugglescote on December 23rd 1971.
- 26 at Melton Mowbray on February 1st 1982.

Over 100 individuals have been recorded in 19 years since 1956, the two best years being 1976 (316) and 1979 (296). During the last two decades, however, numbers have declined, and there have been only four years since 1991 when over 100 birds have been seen; just nine were recorded in 1999. The reasons for this decline are not clear.

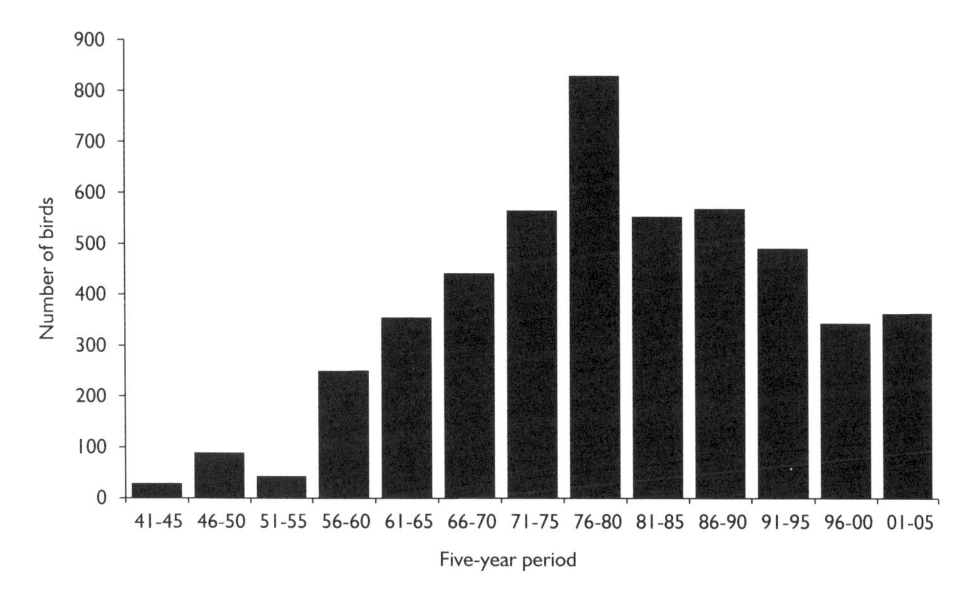

Figure 11: Number of Bewick's Swans by five-year periods 1941–2005.

Eyebrook Reservoir was traditionally the most important site for this species in the counties, and the regular wintering flock in the 1960s and 1970s was close to being of national importance, the threshold for which is currently 81 (Collier *et al.* 2005). With the creation of Rutland Water in the mid-1970s numbers at Eyebrook Reservoir dropped almost immediately, and Rutland Water took over as the most favoured site, although regular wintering there was erratic and unpredictable. Numbers at both sites have shown a continuing decline since the 1980s.

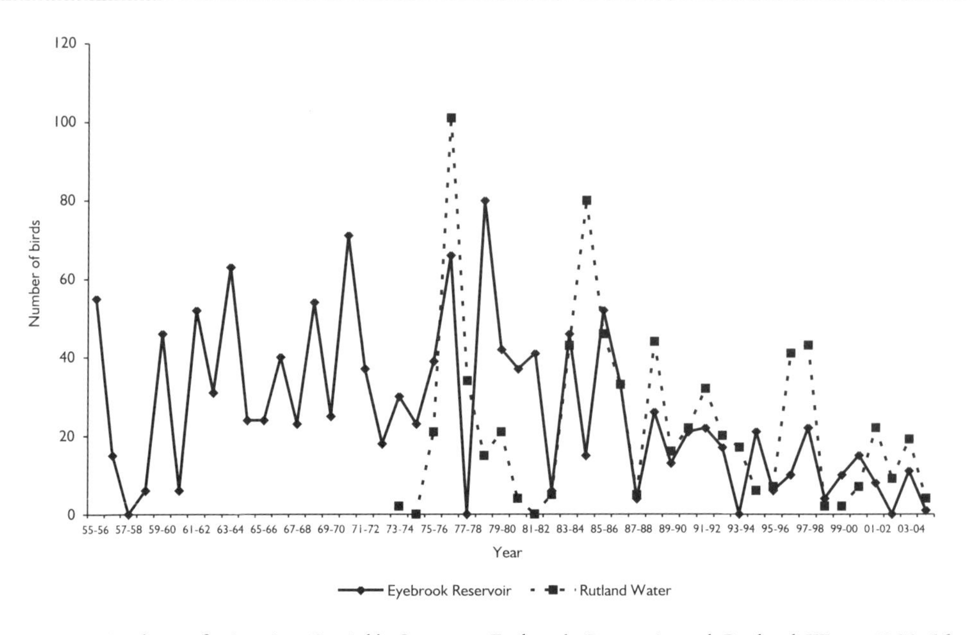

Figure 12: Numbers of wintering Bewick's Swans at Eyebrook Reservoir and Rutland Water 1955–56 to 2004–05.

Records normally fall between late October and late March. The earliest autumn arrival was one at Eyebrook Reservoir on October 5th 1974 but records before the 16th of this month are unusual, the only others being:

- an adult at Eyebrook Reservoir on October 11th 2004.
- nine adults at Rutland Water on October 11th and 12th 2002, two of which remained until November 13th.
- two at Eyebrook Reservoir on October 12th 1980.
- seven juveniles at Swithland Reservoir on October 14th 1998.
- three at Swithland Reservoir on October 15th 1990.

Small numbers have been seen during early April, although the only records later than April 10th have been:

- one at Rutland Water on April 11th 1998.
- an adult at Stanford Reservoir on April 13th 1979.
- one at Wanlip Gravel Pits on April 15th and 16th 1961.
- one at Ibstock Opencast (now Sence Valley Forest Park) on April 16th 1996.
- four at Eyebrook Reservoir from April 25th to 28th 1955 (although this record is perhaps open to debate, as four Whooper Swans were reported at this site on April 24th).

In addition, four which appeared at Cropston Reservoir on April 7th 1956 were seen regularly either here or at nearby Leicester City Farms until April 24th. The latest spring bird, however, was one at Eyebrook Reservoir on May 10th 1987.

Eyebrook Reservoir and, more latterly, Rutland Water are clearly the two most dominant sites, and account for 60% of all records. A further 25% have been recorded at the reservoirs of Swithland, Stanford, Cropston, Thornton and Saddington.

When this species was at its most frequent in the counties in the 1970s and 1980s, average arrival and departure dates remained relatively constant, but in the years before and after this period these dates have been much more erratic. Average arrival and departure dates before 1956 are not shown in the following graphs as the species was scarce prior to this and meaningful data does not exist.

One of a flock near Caldecott on February 5th 1977 had been ringed at Slimbridge (Gloucestershire) in the winter of 1971–72, whilst one with a blue neck collar at Eyebrook Reservoir on December 21st 1996 had been fitted with it on August 10th 1994 on the Khunavey River in the Pechora Delta area of north-east Russia. It was

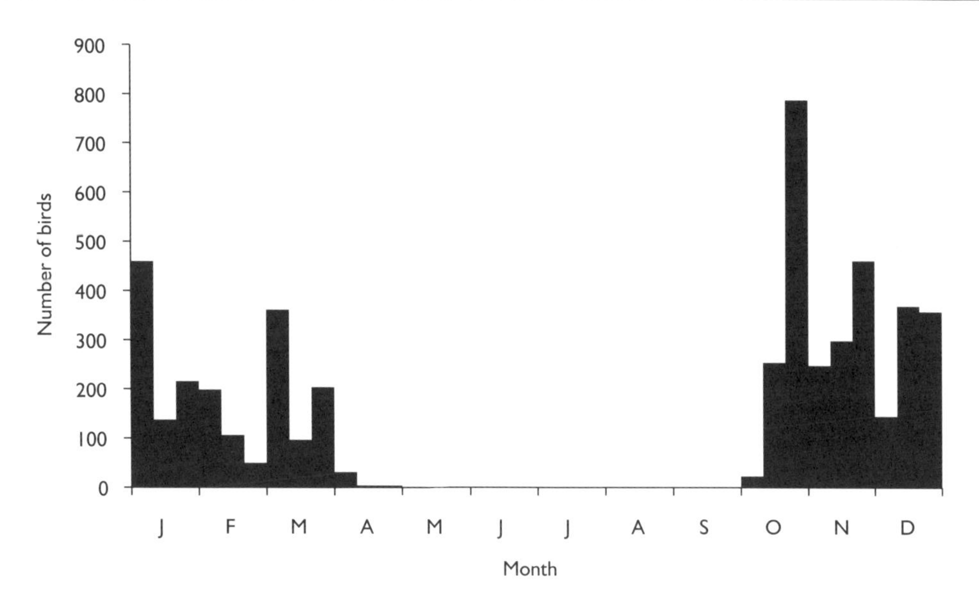

Figure 13: Monthly occurrence of Bewick's Swans 1941–2005.

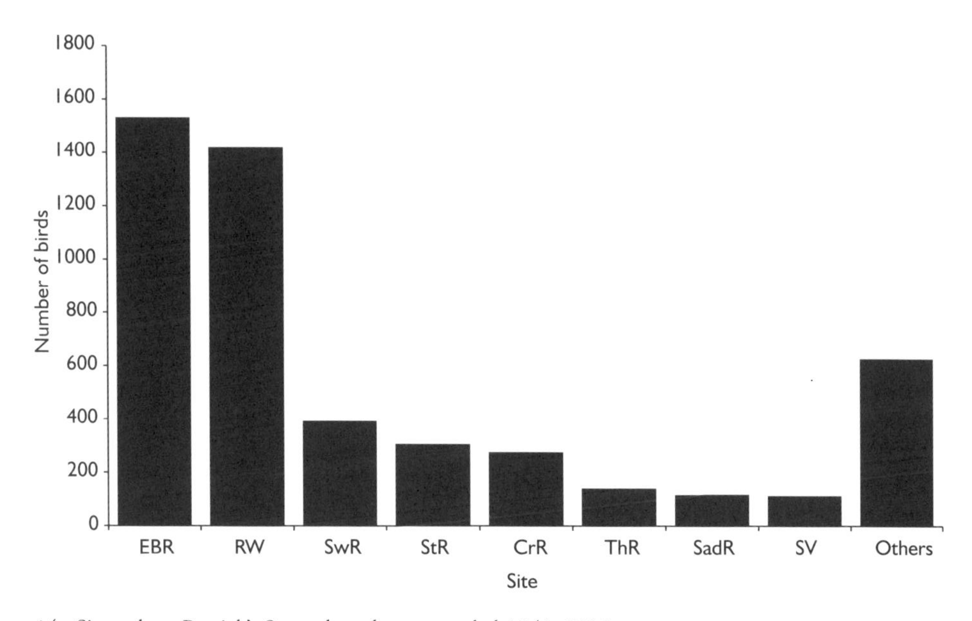

Figure 14: Sites where Bewick's Swans have been recorded 1941–2005.
Key to abbreviations: EBR = Eyebrook Reservoir; RW = Rutland Water; SwR = Swithland Reservoir; StR = Stanford Reservoir; CrR = Cropston Reservoir; ThR = Thornton Reservoir; SadR = Saddington Reservoir; SV = Soar valley

seen in the Netherlands from October to December 1996 and then in Germany in February and March 1997, as well as in Cambridgeshire and Norfolk in December 1996 and February and March 1997. These records illustrate not only that our birds originate from both the nearest large wintering populations but also how far individuals may move during a single winter.

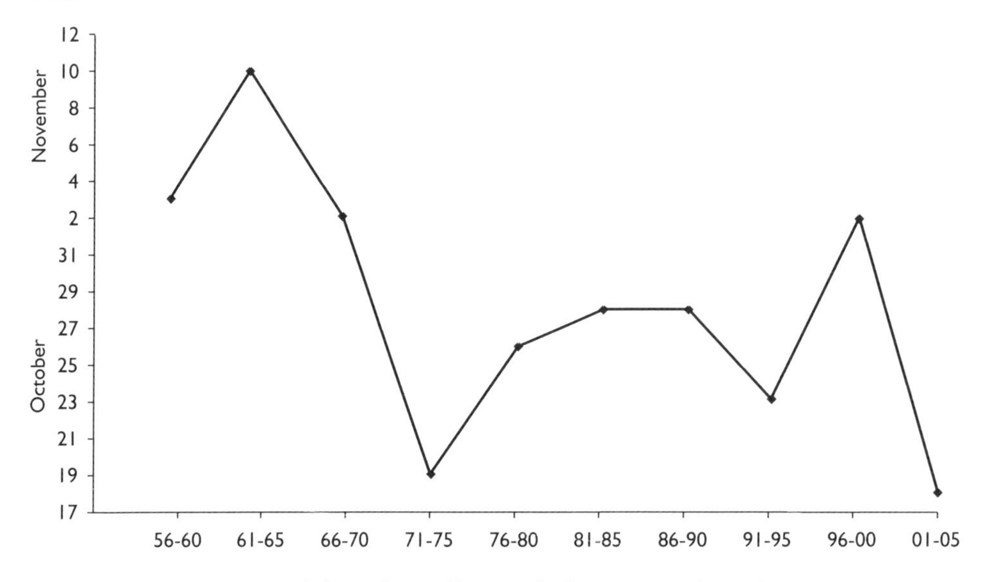

Figure 15: Average autumn arrival dates of Bewick's Swans by five-year periods 1956–2005.

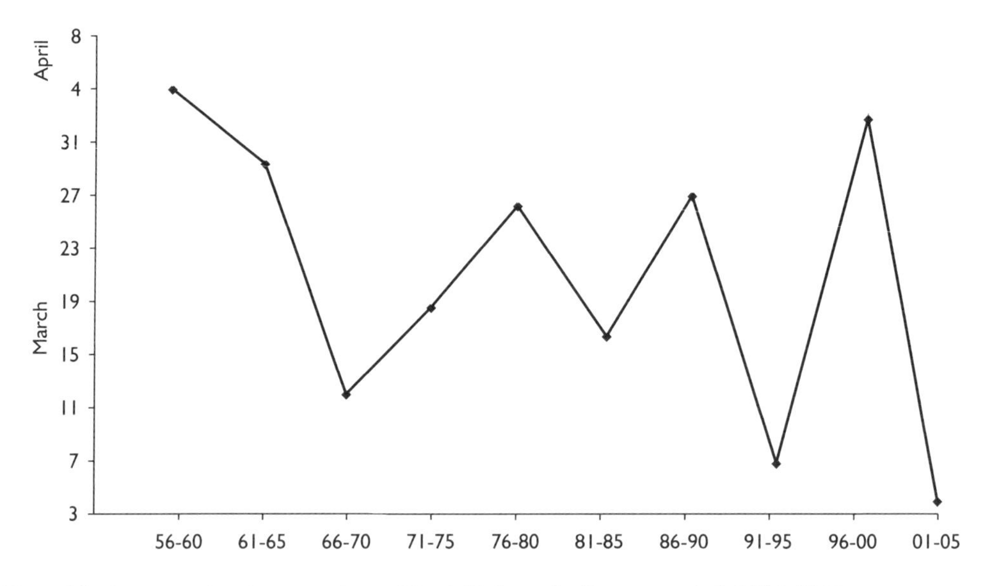

Figure 16: Average spring departure dates of Bewick's Swans by five-year periods 1956–2005.

Bewick's Swans breed across almost the full breadth of high-Arctic Siberia. Western populations (those breeding to the west of the Urals) winter in north-west Europe, chiefly Denmark, the Netherlands and Britain. The European wintering population is estimated at 17,000 birds, of which over 8,000 regularly winter in Britain (Gregory *et al.* 2002). The most important area in this country is the Ouse Washes (Cambridgeshire), where approximately 6,300 individuals can be found (Collier *et al.* 2005), and this is doubtless where the majority of birds recorded in the counties originate from. As more than 50% of the British non-breeding population is concentrated at fewer than ten sites, this species has been added to the 'Amber List' of Birds of Conservation Concern (Gregory *et al.* 2002).

AHJH

Whooper Swan *Cygnus cygnus*

Scarce passage migrant and winter visitor; recorded in all months from September to April, with the majority in October, November, January and late March.

Historically, this species was a rare winter visitor. Browne quotes Harley as saying that, in the first half of the 19th century, it had occurred at Groby Pool and on the River Soar near Loughborough. Browne also recorded a flock of ten, at least one of which was shot, in the winter of 1870–71 on floodwater near Narborough, and lists undated records at Bardon, Wanlip and Groby. Haines noted several similar records in Rutland, including seven at Burley Fishponds in 1895, one at Luffenham in 1885 and a large flock of 53 flying over Barnsdale and later Oakham on November 29th 1903. He also lists records of one shot in the 1850s and seven on February 22nd 1897, but does not mention sites. In the first part of the 20th century, the LROS archives include one at Swithland Reservoir in 1906 and a flock of 17 at the same site in 1940.

Today, as one would expect given its more northerly distribution (Lack 1986), this species is much the rarer of the two wild swans in the counties. In most years a few single-figure flocks are recorded; groups of ten or more are unusual. The largest flocks have all been at either Rutland Water or Eyebrook Reservoir. At the former site, the highest counts were 33 on March 24th 1992 and 32, in two flocks, on January 1st 1997, although the only other double-figure counts from this site were 11 on February 27th 2005 and ten on March 24th 2004. Eyebrook Reservoir has produced six flocks numbering ten or more, the largest of which were 25 on January 24th 1998 and 22 on November 5th 1974. Elsewhere, the only other double-figure groups were 19 at both Swithland Reservoir on October 28th 1991 and Kirby Lakes on February 19th 2005, 16 at both Blackbrook Reservoir on March 22nd 1942 and Huncote on November 24th 1976, and 11 at Belvoir on February 12th 1956.

The figures show an increase both in records and of large flocks since the mid-1980s, and the five best years have all been since 1991: 43 individuals in both 1997 and 2005, 38 in 1991, 36 in 1998 and 35 in 1992. This mirrors the dramatic increase in numbers wintering at the Ouse Washes (Cambridgeshire).

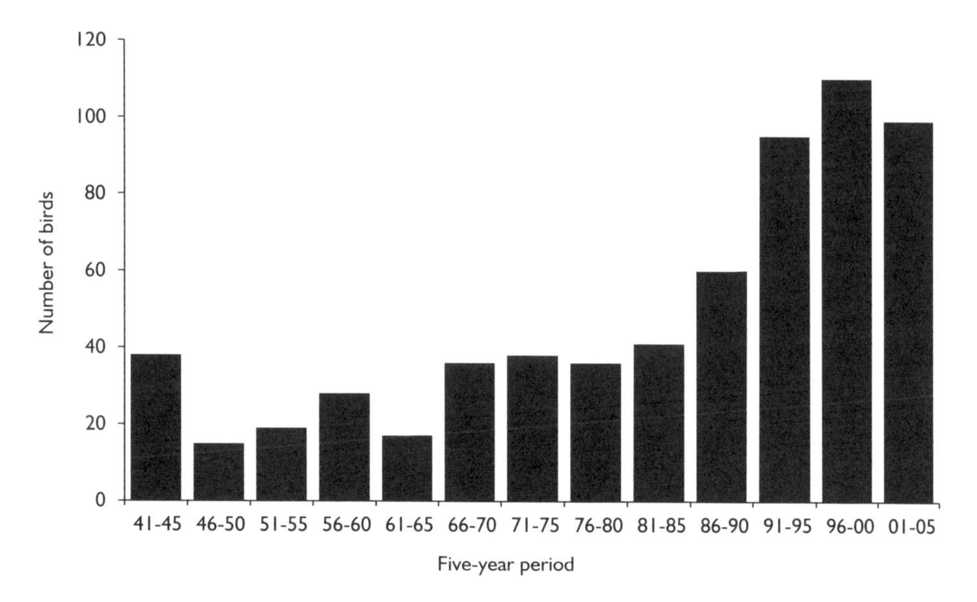

Figure 17: Numbers of Whooper Swans by five-year periods 1941–2004.

The Whooper Swan remains predominantly a passage visitor to the counties, with notable peaks in occurrences during late March and late October/early November. A single bird which arrived at Rutland Water on the exceptionally early date of September 21st 1997 and remained until March 20th 1999, before returning in 2000 from April 7th until August 1st, may have been of captive origin. Apart from this bird, the earliest to arrive in autumn was at Albert Village Lake on September 25th 2003. Records during the first ten days of October are unusual, the only ones being:

- one at Rutland Water from October 3rd 1977 to January 15th 1978.
- one at Rutland Water from October 3rd to 10th 1993, with an additional two on October 9th.
- two at Eyebrook Reservoir on October 7th 1990.
- one at Eyebrook Reservoir on October 8th 2003, with four the following day.
- two at Swithland Reservoir on October 9th 2004.
- two at Cropston Reservoir on October 10th 1992.

Small numbers have been seen during the first ten days of April but arrivals later than this are rare. The only records have all come from Eyebrook Reservoir, as follows:

- 11 on April 18th 1986.
- one on April 19th and 25th 1996.
- four on April 24th 1955 (although this record is perhaps open to debate, as four Bewick's Swans were reported at this site from April 25th to 28th).

In addition, four birds that had arrived earlier in the winter have lingered later than April 10th: one at Fort Henry Ponds from December 27th 1986 to April 12th 1987, two that had been at Woolfox from December 18th 2000 to February 24th 2001 moved to Fort Henry Ponds on April 21st and 22nd 2001, and one at Newton Harcourt from January 21st to April 14th 2004.

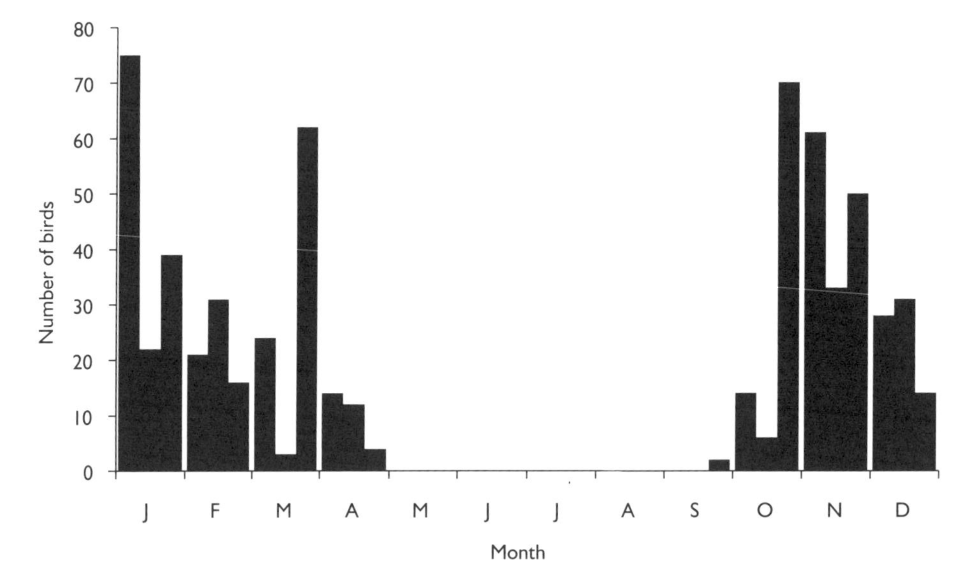

Figure 18: Monthly occurrence of Whooper Swans 1941–2005.

Although the appearance of this species is rather erratic, since the mid-1980s there has been a general trend towards earlier autumn arrivals (Figure 19).

Eyebrook Reservoir and Rutland Water are the most favoured sites and account for over 57% of all records, with another 18% having occurred at Priory Water and Swithland Reservoir. No other site has recorded over 25 individuals. The Whooper Swan is a surprisingly rare visitor to the Soar valley gravel pits, and only eight birds have been seen in this area. This species regularly accompanies Mute Swans, an unusual example being a juvenile on the Grand Union Canal in Leicester on December 9th and 10th 1980.

Whooper Swans breed across the entire breadth of the northern Palearctic, from Iceland and Scandinavia to north-east Siberia, and winter in the coastal lowlands of Europe and eastern Asia. A few pairs breed each year in Scotland. Almost 60% of the European population winters in Britain, resulting in the species being added to

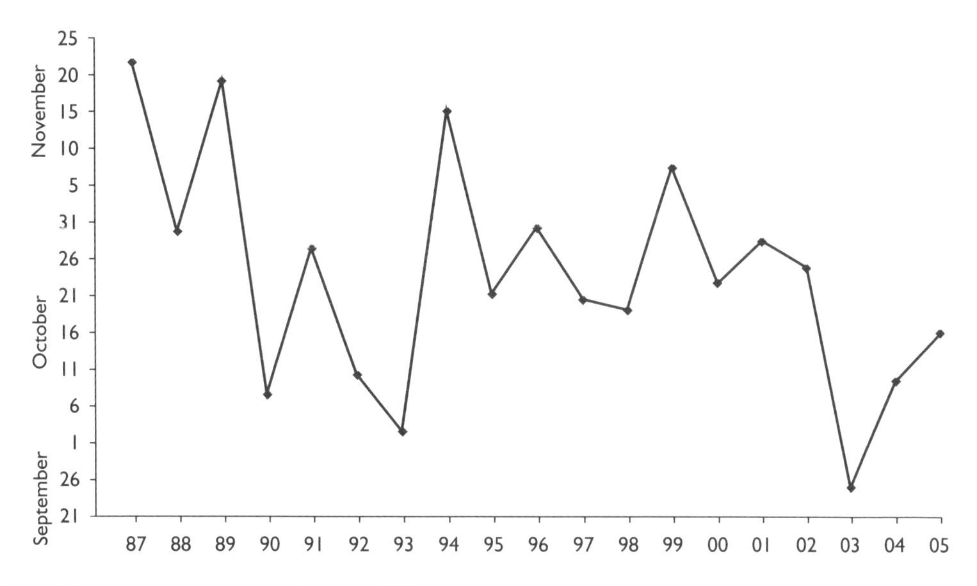

Figure 19: Average autumn arrival dates of Whooper Swans 1987–2005.

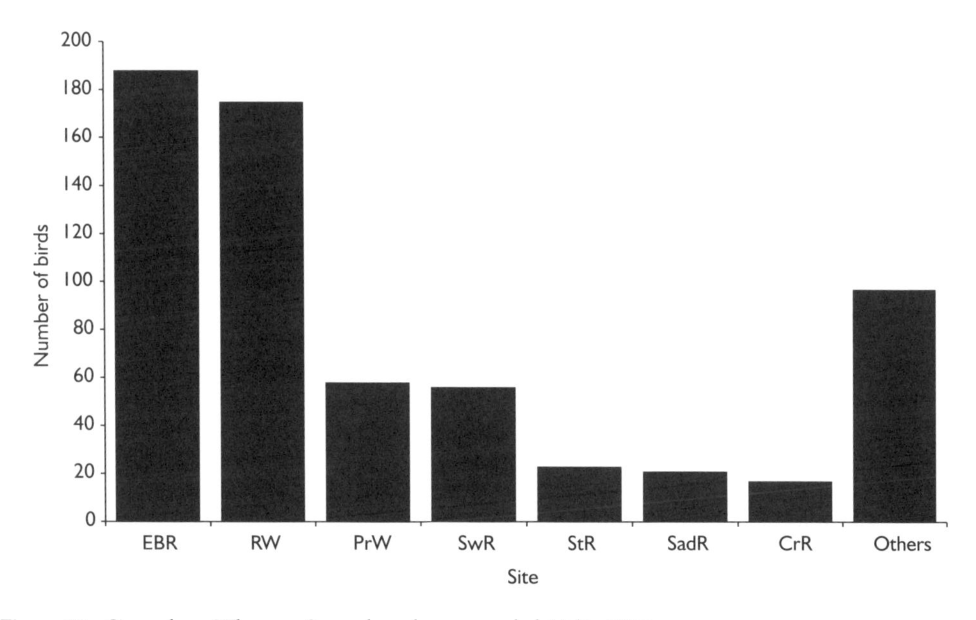

Figure 20: Sites where Whooper Swans have been recorded 1941–2005.
Key to abbreviations: EBR = Eyebrook Reservoir; RW = Rutland Water; PrW = Priory Water; SwR = Swithland Reservoir; StR = Stanford Reservoir; SadR = Saddington Reservoir; CrR = Cropston Reservoir

the 'Amber List' of Birds of Conservation Concern (Gregory *et al.* 2002). Those wintering in Britain come almost entirely from Iceland, evidenced by one of three birds at Priory Water from November 4th 1996 to April 7th 1997 which had been ringed in that country at Svartarvatn on August 11th 1995.

AHJH

Bean Goose *Anser fabalis*

Very rare winter vagrant: three records involving nine individuals.

Haines considered this species to have been abundant in the Welland valley up until the middle of the 19th century, and Browne reported large flocks flying north-west in October 1842. Browne also records single birds shot at Noseley in December 1880 and at Smeeton Westerby on December 11th 1890. A review of the nomenclature and past history in Britain of Bean and Pink-footed Geese (Bourne 2002) has, however, demonstrated that 19th century records of this species are, at best, inconclusive and in many cases refer to Pink-footed or even Greylag Geese. In these circumstances, none of the 19th century records from Leicestershire and Rutland can be regarded as conclusive.

A previous review of local records (Harrop 1999) concluded that, on examination of a photograph, a flock of 188 reported at Rutland Water on February 3rd 1977 consisted of Pink-footed Geese. Therefore, the following are the only currently accepted records:

1977 six at Rutland Water on January 30th, with one there on February 22nd and 27th; one in the Welland valley near Harringworth on February 6th was presumably one of these birds.
1992 two at Eyebrook Reservoir intermittently from February 2nd to 13th.
1993 a juvenile showing characters of Tundra Bean Goose (*A. f. rossicus*) at Eyebrook Reservoir from November 13th to February 27th 1994.

Only one of the above (the 1993 bird, which was photographed) can confidently be identified to taxon but the descriptions of the 1977 birds suggest that they were most probably Taiga Bean Geese (*A. f. fabalis*).

As with all species of goose, the escape possibility must be considered; however, the Bean Goose is uncommon in captivity, and seems to escape rarely. There have been no reports of apparent feral birds in the counties; indeed, Delany (1993) recorded only two escaped individuals in the whole of Britain during the summer of 1991. There seems to be no reason to suspect that the Bean Geese recorded in Leicestershire and Rutland are anything other than genuine wild birds.

Bean Geese occur across northern Eurasia from northern Norway to eastern Siberia. The Taiga Bean Goose *A. f. fabalis* breeds in the taiga zone of Scandinavia and Russia and winters predominantly in the Netherlands. Small numbers (around 400 birds in total) regularly winter in Britain, mainly at the Middle Yare Marshes (Norfolk) and the Slamannan Plateau (Stirling). The Tundra Bean Goose *A. f. rossicus* breeds further north, in the tundra zone, and winters in Spain, France, Italy and the Balkans. Those seen in Britain usually occur at times of severe weather on the continent. Due to the restricted nature of the British wintering population, this species is on the 'Amber List' of Birds of Conservation Concern (Gregory *et al.* 2002).

AHJH

Pink-footed Goose *Anser brachyrhynchus*

Uncommon to fairly common passage migrant and winter visitor in varying numbers; recorded in all months between September and March, with the majority in January. Frequently recorded in a feral state.

Although Haines stated that a few had been killed in the Welland valley between 1850 and 1860, it seems likely that many of the records formerly attributed to the Bean Goose were in fact of this species, which is now known to be a regular passage and winter migrant over the counties.

Since 1941, there have been reports of presumed wild birds in 25 of the 65 years up to 2005. Records are becoming more regular and there have been only five blank years since 1982. The first report of a large flock involved 400 flying north over the Rutland boundary at Harringworth on March 12th 1960 (Mitcham 1984), although big numbers were not seen regularly until the 1990s. The highest annual total was in 2005, when at least 3,293 birds were recorded, of which 3,195 passed over eight different sites between January 22nd and 30th. Overall, there have been 27 flocks which have numbered more than 50 birds, as follows:

- 400 north at Harringworth on March 12th 1960.
- 54 at Eyebrook Reservoir on December 27th 1969.
- 188 at Rutland Water on February 3rd 1977.

- 300 north-west at Castle Donington on January 18th 1987.
- 340 west at Whitwick on January 12th 1991.
- 250 west at Birstall Gravel Pits on January 13th 1992.
- 118 west at Wanlip on January 16th 1994.
- flocks of 173 and 230 south-east at Knipton on December 14th 1994.
- 850 south-west at Knipton on January 1st 2000.
- 55 north west at Branston on January 15th 2000.
- 120 north-west at Belvoir on January 15th 2000.
- 100 at Melton Country Park on January 15th 2000.
- 75 west at Stapleford on January 18th 2000.
- 56 east at Priory Water on October 6th 2002.
- 110 south-east at Rutland Water on November 9th 2002.
- 75 at Priory Water on October 19th 2003.
- 90 north-west at Deans Lane, Woodhouse on October 10th 2004.
- 187 north-east at Lockington Marshes on October 31st 2004.
- 51 at Rutland Water from October 31st to November 1st 2004.
- 80 west at Rutland Water on January 22nd 2005.
- 2,200 in four skeins, including one skein of 1,400, north-west at Trent Valley Pit on January 23rd 2005.
- 305 in four skeins north-west at Belvoir on January 23rd 2005.
- flocks of 98 and 74 west at Melton Country Park on January 23rd 2005.
- 101 north-west at Priory Water on January 23rd 2005.
- 60 north-west at Beacon Hill on January 23rd 2005.
- 250 north-west at Cossington on January 25th 2005.
- 62 west at Rutland Water on December 13th 2005.

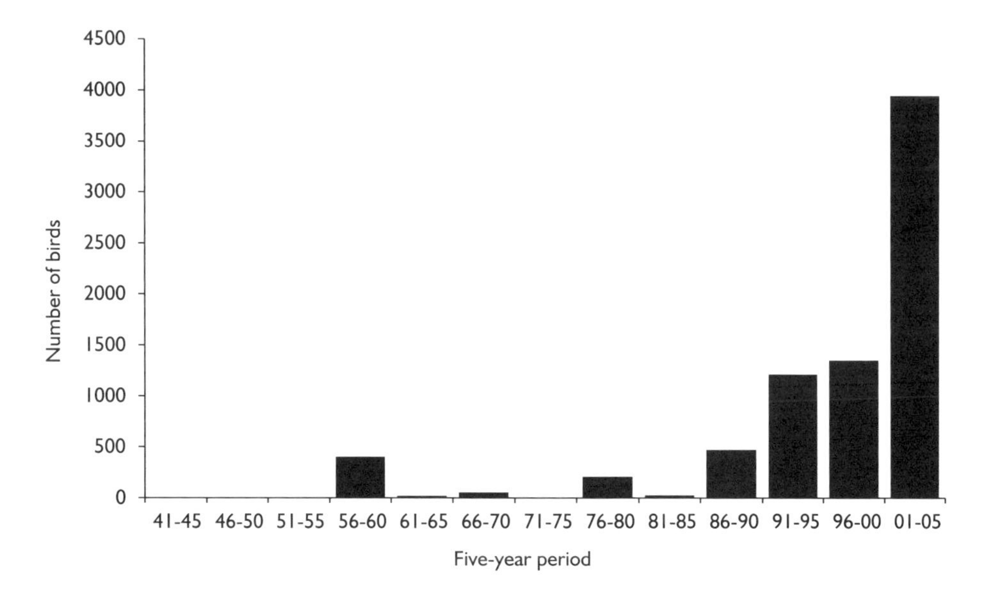

Figure 21: Numbers of Pink-footed Geese by five-year periods 1941–2005.

Flocks of this species are most regularly recorded flying over during January. At this time of year, the majority of birds have been heading west or north-west and are almost certainly groups moving between regular wintering grounds in Norfolk and Lancashire. It has also been noted that these large flocks are usually seen on calm, clear days and invariably pass over the counties during the mid-morning, suggesting that they have left Norfolk at first light. It would appear that the typical flight-line of Pink-footed Geese moving between Norfolk and Lancashire is slightly to the north of Leicestershire and Rutland, as both Nottinghamshire and Derbyshire regularly record much larger numbers. However, a pattern is now emerging to suggest that this species does frequently pass over the counties; the most regular areas are north Rutland, north-east Leicestershire from Melton Mowbray to the Vale of Belvoir, and the Trent valley in the far north-west.

The largest flocks recorded on the ground have all been at Rutland Water: an exceptional 188 on February 3rd 1977, 51 from October 31st to November 1st 2004, 14 from December 18th 1988 to March 4th 1989, and 15 on March 21st and 22nd 1994. Pink-footed Geese rarely linger for more than a day or two when they land in the counties. The flock of 14 at Rutland Water in 1988 and 1989 mentioned above is one of just three records of small flocks that have remained for any length of time, the others being up to seven at Rutland Water from January 30th to February 27th 1982 and up to four at Priory Water from January 13th to March 26th 1990.

The presence of feral birds makes it difficult to be sure of extreme dates for migrants but 26 over Rutland Water on September 16th 2005 appear to be the earliest in autumn. The only other September records occurred in 2003 (14 over Burley Wood on the 27th) and 1995 (ten over Priory Water on the 28th). The latest spring record which can confidently be assigned to wild birds is of 15 at Rutland Water on March 22nd 1994, although four which had arrived at Priory Water earlier in the winter of 1990 remained until March 26th.

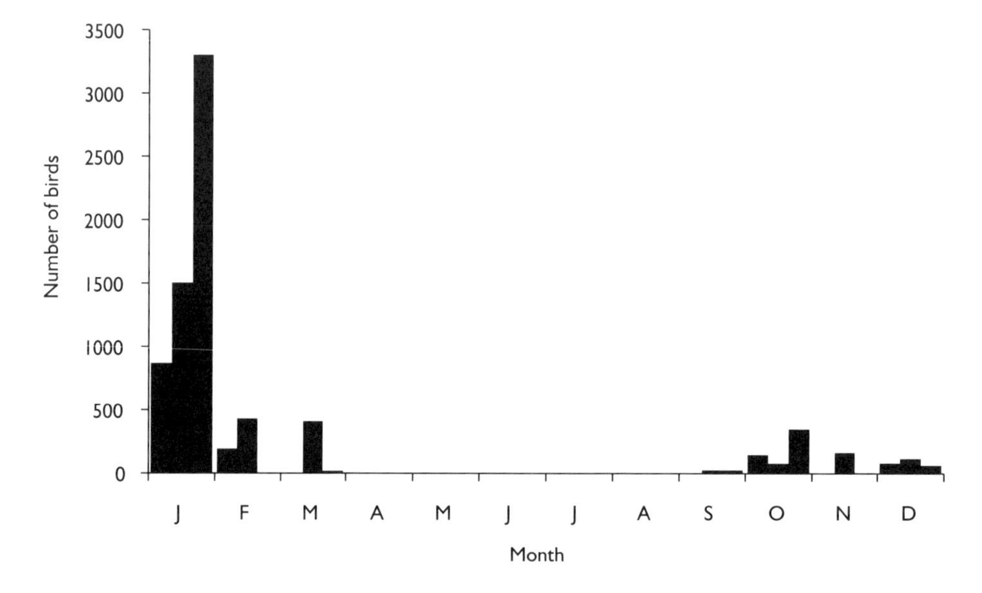

Figure 22: Monthly occurrence of Pink-footed Geese 1941–2005.

In addition to these typically large flocks of wild birds, small numbers of feral and escaped birds are frequently recorded at several sites in the counties. The first bird considered to be feral was recorded in 1969, and one or two have regularly been present at Rutland Water since 1986. During the 1990s, one or other of these birds paired with both Canada and Bar-headed Geese, but no offspring have been recorded.

Pink-footed Geese breed in Iceland, Greenland and Svalbard. Those from Iceland and Greenland winter in Britain, whilst those from Svalbard winter in the Netherlands, Belgium and Denmark. The British wintering population currently numbers approximately 275,000 birds (Collier *et al.* 2005), the majority of which are found in Scotland, Lancashire and Norfolk. Britain holds more than 75% of the world's wintering population, and as such this species has been added to the 'Amber List' of Birds of Conservation Concern (Gregory *et al.* 2002). As mentioned previously, there are a number of feral birds at large: Delany (1993) recorded 88 such individuals, at a total of 29 sites, in Britain during the summer of 1991.

AHJH

White-fronted Goose *Anser albifrons*

(Greater White-fronted Goose)

Scarce to uncommon winter visitor and passage migrant in varying numbers; recorded in all months between October and March, with the majority from December to February. Occasionally recorded in a feral state. Two distinct subspecies have occurred.

The nominate subspecies (European White-fronted Goose *A. a. albifrons)* is a winter visitor and passage migrant in varying numbers, whilst the Greenland subspecies *A.a. flavirostris* is a rare winter vagrant. Not all records have been subspecifically identified, particularly those involving flocks seen in flight, but it is assumed that the majority refer to the nominate race.

European White-fronted Goose *A. a. albifrons*

During the 19th century, Browne noted that three were seen at Tur Langton on December 18th 1879, whilst Haines recorded two small flocks in Rutland: five in the Welland valley sometime in the 1850s and 12 at Barrowden on January 27th 1888. In all three instances mentioned above, two of the flock were shot. In addition, Haines records another two shot near Caldecott on January 11th 1900, whilst Browne, writing in VH, mentions a group of six on December 28th 1906 but does not give a site. Prior to the formation of LROS in 1941, there were only another two records in the 20th century: single birds shot at Wanlip on January 11th 1924 and Wigston Sewage Farm on February 5th 1940.

Since 1941, there have been records of presumed wild birds in 45 of the 65 years up to 2005. Whilst the number of individuals recorded has not increased significantly overall, records are becoming more regular and there have been only four blank years since 1980. The highest annual total was 186 in 1992, although this was heavily influenced by the largest-ever flock recorded in the counties, of 140 flying south over Cropston Reservoir on November 13th. In most winters there are only one or two flocks recorded, although the winter of 1995–96 produced seven separate groups totalling 83 birds. Overall, there have been 19 flocks which numbered more than 15 birds, as follows:

- 50 at Eyebrook Reservoir from January 27th to March 15th 1944.
- 22 at Stanford Reservoir on January 14th 1945, with 25 from January 18th to 20th 1945.
- 20 at Leicester City Farms on February 16th 1947.
- 32 at Eyebrook Reservoir from March 4th to 18th 1956.
- 16 at Eyebrook Reservoir on October 7th 1959.
- 90 flying east over Swithland Reservoir on March 18th 1962.
- 18 at Gaulby from January 5th to 7th 1963.
- 31 flying south over Eyebrook Reservoir on January 3rd 1965.
- 20 at Stanford Reservoir on December 7th and 14th 1969, with 21 on December 18th 1969.
- 31 at Rutland Water from December 21st 1976 to February 5th 1977.
- 46 at Stanford Reservoir on January 2nd and 3rd 1977.
- 18 at Rutland Water on November 22nd 1989.
- 46 at Rutland Water from February 8th to 24th 1992, with 26 remaining until March 26th 1992.
- 140 flying south over Cropston Reservoir on November 13th 1992.
- 80 flying south-west over Bradgate Park on January 16th 1994.
- 24 at Eyebrook Reservoir on January 14th 1996.
- 29 by the River Soar near Sileby from January 21st to February 3rd 1996, with the same flock at Quorn Borrow Pit on February 8th 1996.
- 21 at Eyebrook Reservoir on December 22nd 1997.

The data show that the majority of birds have been recorded between mid-November and mid-February, although the November total is distorted by the large flock over Cropston Reservoir in 1992; in reality, the main

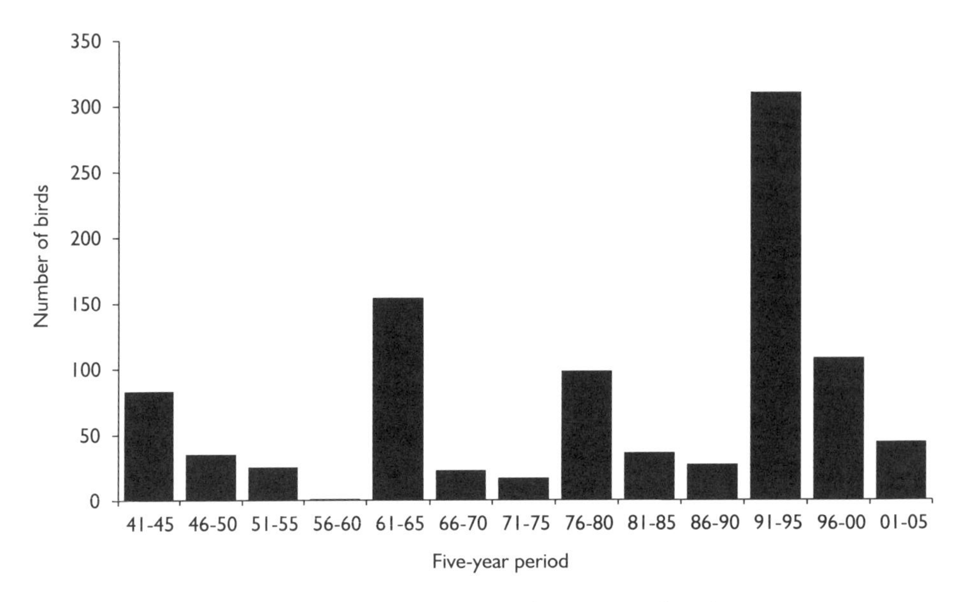

Figure 23: Numbers of European White-fronted Geese by five-year periods 1941–2005.

period is late December to mid-February. Severe weather on the continent is known to force birds to move further west and the obvious peaks in January and February correspond well with hard weather movements. The notoriously harsh winters of 1946–47 and 1962–63 produced records reflecting this: in 1947, a flock of 20 was at Leicester City Farms on February 16th, whilst in January 1963 a group of 18 spent three days feeding on rye grass protruding through the snow in a field at Gaulby. The presence of escaped or feral birds makes it difficult to be sure of extreme dates for migrants but the most plausible involve 16 at Eyebrook Reservoir on October 7th 1959 and three at Rutland Water on March 30th 1996.

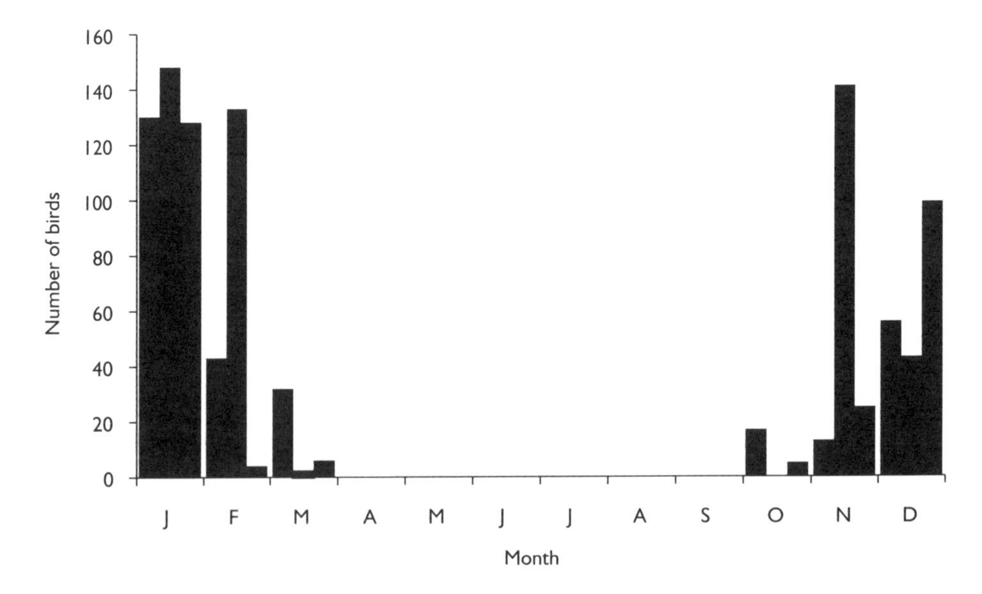

Figure 24: Monthly occurrence of European White-fronted Geese 1941–2005.

Most records involve birds flying over but on several occasions small flocks have remained for days or even weeks at favoured sites. The longest staying groups have been 12 at Ibstock Opencast (now Sence Valley Forest Park) from December 10th 1995 to March 24th 1996 and a small flock (which peaked at 31) at Rutland Water between December 11th 1976 and March 24th 1977; the coincidence in the arrival and departure dates of these flocks is noteworthy.

White fronted Geese can obviously be encountered flying over anywhere in the counties but the favoured site is Eyebrook Reservoir, which has recorded some 224 presumed wild individuals (over 20% of the overall total). Another 25% of all records have come from either Rutland Water or Stanford Reservoir. It is interesting to note, however, that the three largest flocks on record (of 140 over Cropston Reservoir in 1992, 90 over Swithland Reservoir in 1962 and 80 over Bradgate Park in 1994) have all been in the Charnwood Forest area; there have been no other records from any of these three sites.

The first record of a bird considered to be of captive origin came from Stapleford Park in 1944 and there have been several more at various sites since, although this species is found in a feral state in the counties much less frequently than either Pink-footed or Barnacle Goose. None were located in Leicestershire and Rutland during the Introduced Goose Survey in the summer of 1991 (Gamble 1992b), whilst country-wide 54 (of which 40 were in Norfolk) were found at large during this period, significantly fewer than both Pink-footed and Barnacle Geese (Delany 1993). In September 1990 an adult and two juveniles were reported from Knipton Reservoir but breeding in the counties has not yet been proved.

Hybrids with Greylag Goose, Greater Canada Goose and Barnacle Goose have all been reported: see 'Hybrids' (pages 676–684).

European White-fronted Geese breed on tundra across northern Russia and Siberia, and winter in north-west Europe, the Baltic and parts of central and southern Europe. In Britain, the most important wintering site is at Slimbridge (Gloucestershire), followed by areas in Kent and Norfolk, but numbers at these sites have been declining in recent years and the total British wintering population was estimated at approximately 2,200 birds in 2003 (Collier *et al.* 2005). On account of its moderate decline over the last 25 years and the fact that more than 50% of the British wintering population is found at fewer than ten sites, this subspecies of the White-fronted Goose has been placed on the 'Amber List' of Birds of Conservation Concern. (Gregory *et al.* 2002).

Greenland White-fronted Goose *A. a. flavirostris*

This subspecies is a very rare winter vagrant, with the following records probably attributable to wild birds:

1960 juvenile, shot near Eyebrook Reservoir, December 28th. The skin is retained at the Leicester Museum.
1969 five, Eyebrook Reservoir, November 8th to 22nd.
1991 four, Eyebrook Reservoir, October 17th.
1993 three, Cossington South Gravel Pits, March 3rd.
1998 one, Stanford Reservoir, October 10th.
2002 juvenile, Rutland Water, November 15th to December 10th.

In addition, there have been the following records of birds considered more likely to be escapes:

1975 one, Frisby Gravel Pits, May 18th and 19th.
1988 one, Rutland Water, July 20th and September 25th.
1989 one, Groby Pool, January 15th.

Greenland White-fronted Geese, as the name suggests, breed in Greenland. They generally winter in Ireland, particularly at Wexford Slobs, and on the west coast of Scotland (especially Islay). Despite the above records of birds of suspect origin (perhaps involving only two individuals), Greenland White-fronted Geese are relatively uncommon in captivity; Delany (1993) found only 23 feral birds at large in Britain during the summer of 1991, all of which were at one site in Scotland. There is a developing pattern of records from Norfolk and the Netherlands which includes ringed birds known to be wild; there is no reason to suspect that genuinely wild individuals do not occur in Leicestershire and Rutland occasionally.

AHJH

Greylag Goose *Anser anser*

Formerly a scarce visitor. Currently a fairly common to common feral resident and uncommon breeder.

The status of the Greylag Goose in Leicestershire and Rutland in the 19th century is uncertain. Browne regarded it as an uncommon winter visitor, citing only two examples: one shot in the winter of 1842 and another shot at Shangton on December 10th 1882. Haines, however, considered that this species was frequent in the Welland valley.

The first 20th century record involved a flock of up to 19 at Leicester City Farms from February 3rd to 18th 1940 (Pochin 1954), followed by five at Eyebrook Reservoir on December 13th 1941: there were no further records until 1966, 25 years later, so it would have been reasonable to assume that these were wild were it not that reintroductions began in Norfolk in 1933 (Taylor *et al.* 1999). Between 1966 and 1977, the species remained scarce, the highest count being 15 at Eyebrook Reservoir on September 30th 1973. The spring peak

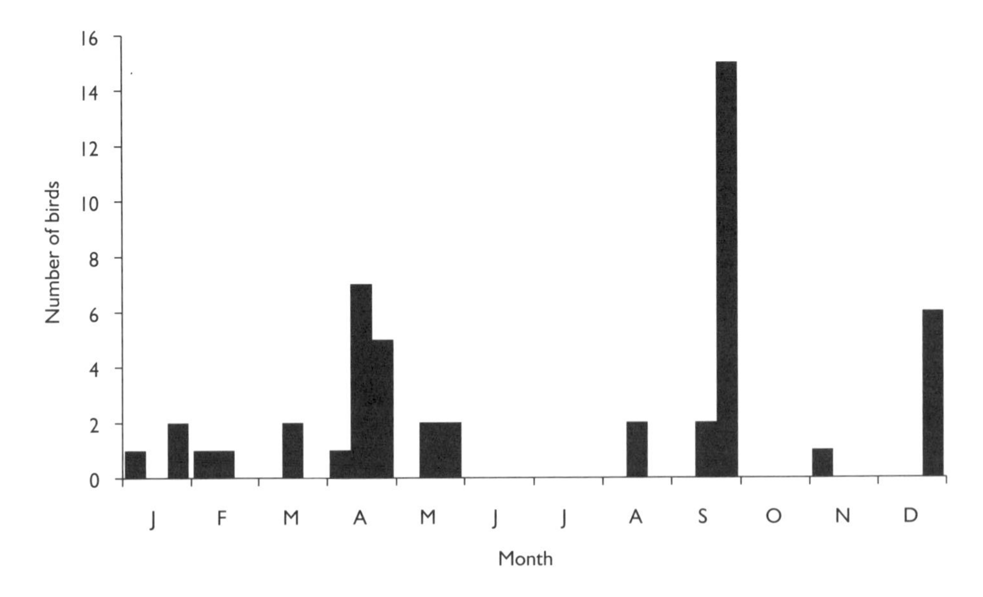

Figure 25: Monthly occurrence of Greylag Geese 1966–77.

in April and May shown by data for the period 1966 to 1977 is similar to that of the Snow Goose, so suggests that the Greylags too were of captive or feral origin.

In 1978 there were 27 records from seven localities and from then on the status of this species changed significantly. Peak counts increased rapidly from 45 at Rutland Water on December 12th 1983 to 130 at Eyebrook Reservoir on January 25th 1987. By 1990 a combined total of 344 was recorded in December. Numbers continued to rise during the 1990s, though not at the same rate as the phenomenal increase in numbers of Canada Geese. By 1999 counts of over 100 birds were recorded at seven different sites, by 2001 there were over 200 at each of six separate sites and by 2003 there were five site-counts of over 300. During the latter year, a combined total of 1,003 was recorded in January. The highest single count was 460 at Wanlip South Gravel Pits on October 24th 2003, and three-figure flocks have been recorded at a further 12 sites, where the maximum counts have been as follows:

- 450 at Cossington Meadows on August 12th 2004.
- 370 at Stanford Reservoir on October 22nd 2003.
- 367 at Rutland Water on September 19th 2004.
- 350 at Eyebrook Reservoir on January 13th 1996.
- 340 at Swithland Reservoir on December 14th 2003.
- 314 at Quorn Borrow Pit on October 27th 2001.
- 278 at Priory Water on August 15th 2004.
- 250 at Wanlip North Gravel Pits on July 6th 2002.
- 230 at Belvoir Lakes on February 3rd 2001.
- 195 at Fort Henry Ponds on October 6th 2001.
- 116 at Saddington Reservoir on January 2nd 1995.
- 107 at Syston Gravel Pits on August 9th 2005.

See 'Wintering Birds (Pages 39–43) for details of highest counts at individual sites.

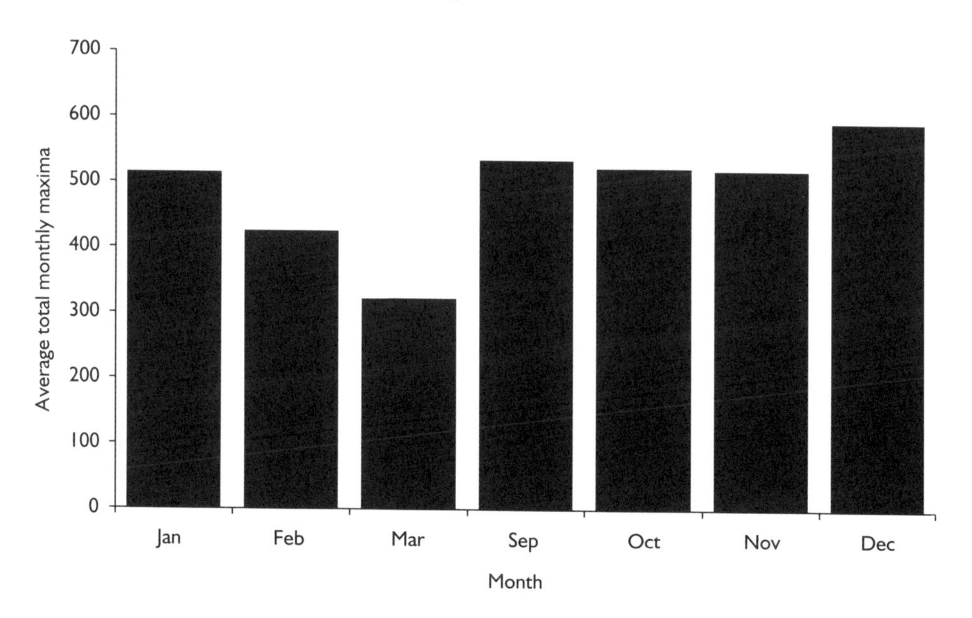

Figure 26: Average total monthly maxima of Greylag Geese at the main sites 1995–2005.

Breeding was recorded for the first time in 1980, when a pair with two young was noted at Rutland Water on May 18th. The following year two pairs bred at Rutland Water, with another pair at Frisby Gravel Pits. Breeding numbers peaked in 2004, with 32 pairs raising a total of 148 young. The core population has shifted from Rutland Water (where there were five pairs in 1984 and 1986) to Priory Water (where there were 18 pairs in

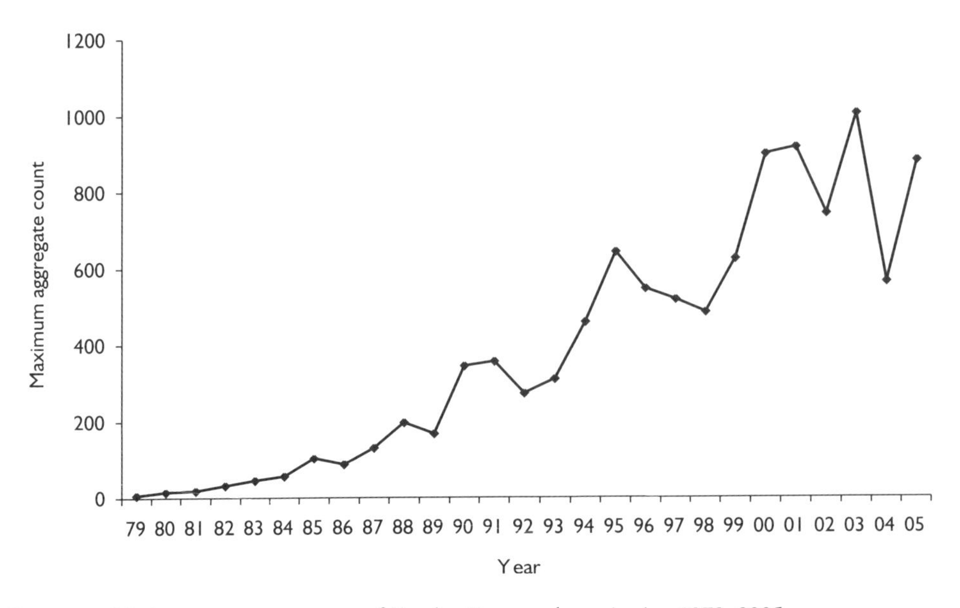

Figure 27: Maximum aggregate counts of Greylag Geese at the main sites 1979–2005.

2001 and 19 in 2002). Other sites where Greylag Geese have bred (in chronological order) are: Birstall Gravel Pits, Fort Henry Ponds, Belvoir Lakes, Stapleford Park, Kirby Lakes, Wanlip North Gravel Pits, Exton Park Lake, Quorn Borrow Pit, Syston, Branston, Saddington Reservoir, Knipton Reservoir, Swithland Reservoir and Groby Pool.

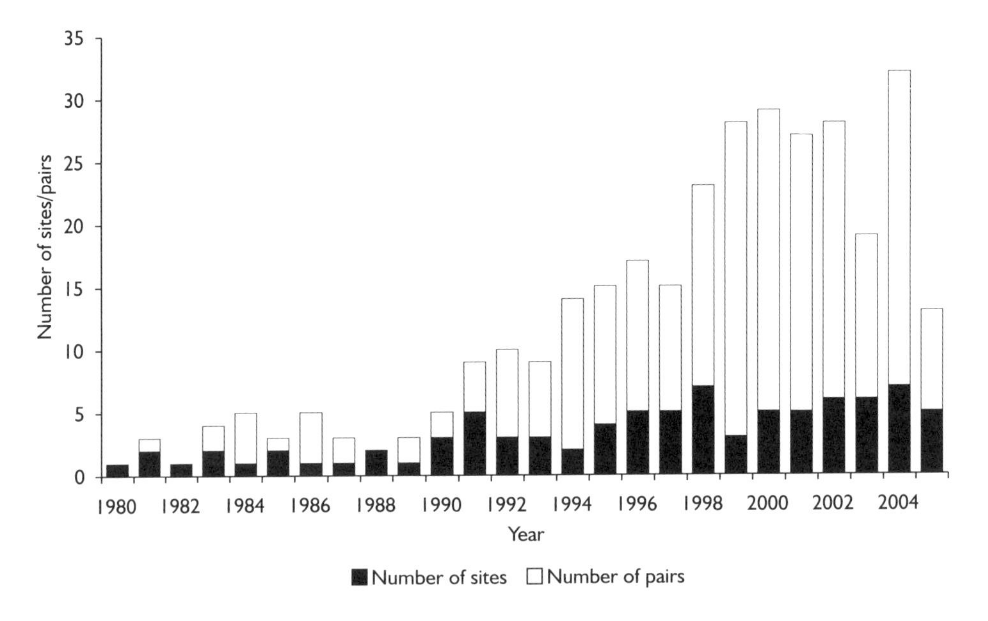

Figure 28: Breeding numbers of Greylag Geese in 1980–2005.

Hybrids with the White-fronted Goose, Swan Goose, Snow Goose and Greater Canada Goose have been recorded on several occasions: see 'Hybrids' (Pages 676–684).

The Greylag Goose has the widest distribution of any European goose. The nominate race breeds in Iceland, north-west and central Europe and Scandinavia, whilst the eastern race breeds in east and south-east Europe across Asia. In Britain, truly wild birds breed mainly in Scotland but since the 1970s there has been a gradual spread westwards of the well-established feral population in East Anglia into adjacent regions, accounting for the increased numbers now being seen in Leicestershire and Rutland. The feral population in the counties is quite sedentary with no clear pattern of movements, though numbers decline during spring as pairs move away to breed. The only ringing recoveries have involved birds from Lincolnshire and Nottinghamshire: the maximum distance involved is just 36km. The Greylag Goose has been added to the 'Amber List' of Birds of Conservation Concern; this only relates to the wild populations which, although not rare breeders, are considered vulnerable as more than 50% breed in fewer than ten areas (Gregory *et al.* 2002). The feral population is still increasing: Delany (1993) noted a total of 19,501 Greylag Geese in Britain during the summer of 1991 but by November 2003 this figure was over 27,000 (Collier *et al.* 2005).

AHJH

Greater Canada Goose *Branta canadensis*

Introduced. Common resident, fairly common breeder.

The Greater Canada Goose was introduced to Britain from North America in about 1650 and by the 19th century Browne described its status in Leicestershire as 'an introduced species often found at large, congregating in large bodies especially in winter, and flying so far afield as to give rise to the conviction that, if not now, it will soon become feral'. He noted that it had bred at a fishpond near Woodhouse and also mentioned a flock of 30 at Quorn on September 18th 1906. By contrast, Haines only reported one occurrence in Rutland during the 19th century, of a bird shot at Tixover some time before 1883; another reported by Haines as having been shot at Gretton on February 22nd 1898 has been ignored as this is actually in Northamptonshire.

By 1941, the species was regarded as resident mainly on private waters but with some colonisation elsewhere. The core population during the 1940s was at Stapleford Park, where 30 pairs were recorded in April 1945. This population had risen to 40 pairs by 1953 but in 1956 the flock was reduced to 27 birds by the Wildfowl Trust. Their intervention came too late, however, as breeding had already occurred elsewhere at Willesley Lake, Goadby Marwood Pools, Exton Park Lake, Burley and Fort Henry Ponds, and the following year was recorded at Swithland Reservoir.

During the 1960s the population grew steadily, with 55 at Fort Henry Ponds on November 12th 1967 the highest count. Numbers increased more rapidly during the 1970s: 170 were at Groby Pool on July 21st 1972 and 320 at Stanford Reservoir on September 23rd 1979. The most dramatic increases in numbers, however, occurred during the 1980s: 501 at Eyebrook Reservoir on August 29th 1982 were eclipsed by 1,181 at Rutland Water on September 13th 1987. The highest count to date is 1,539 at Rutland Water on September 17th 2000 and this site is currently ranked as the third most important in Britain for this species (Collier *et al.* 2005). Flocks of 500 or more have been recorded at a further nine sites, where the maximum counts have been as follows:

- 1,178 at Eyebrook Reservoir on September 14th 2000.
- 1,040 at Swithland Reservoir on September 20th 1992.
- 900 at Cossington South Gravel Pits on August 12th 1990.
- 850 at Stanford Reservoir on October 10th 1998.
- 760 at Priory Water on February 2nd 1991.
- 723 at Watermead Country Park South on June 26th 2005.
- 602 at Cropston Reservoir on September 24th 1991.
- 511 at Fort Henry Ponds on September 10th 1989.
- 500 at Birstall Gravel Pits on January 10th 1993.

For details of highest counts at individual sites, see 'Wintering Birds' (pages 39–43).

Numbers peak in September, then remain consistently high from October until January. During February and March numbers steadily decline as pairs disperse to breed.

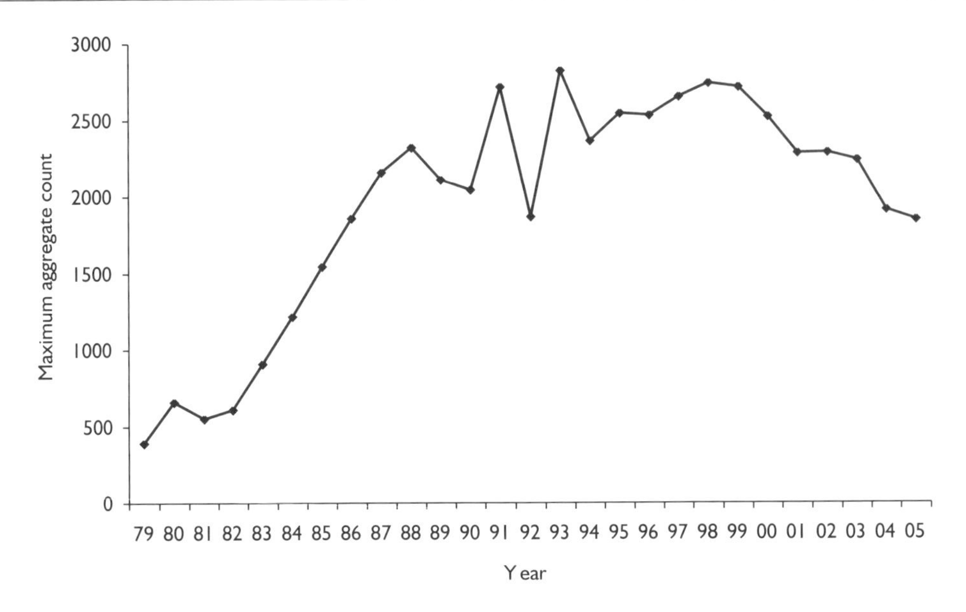

Figure 29: Maximum aggregate counts of Greater Canada Geese at the main sites 1979–2005.

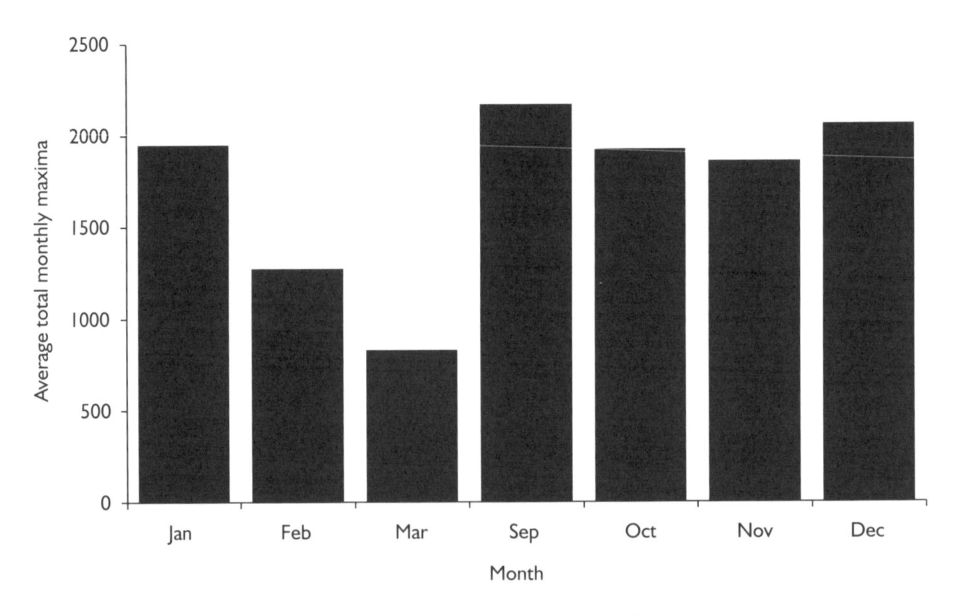

Figure 30: Average total monthly maxima of Greater Canada Geese at the main sites 1995–2005.

The breeding population also grew and spread during the same period. The Introduced Goose Survey in 1991 found 130 broods at 36 sites (Gamble 1992b) and this remains the peak year to date for breeding success. Although numbers appear to have declined since 1991, this is almost certainly due to a lack of recording effort, particularly as Warrilow found that around 40% of all breeding pairs located during 1976–84 were on ornamental ponds, a habitat rarely visited by birdwatchers.

Data show that this species is now roughly 200 times more numerous than it was in 1960, though the impact of large numbers of Greater Canada Geese on native species remains unclear. The growth in the local breeding

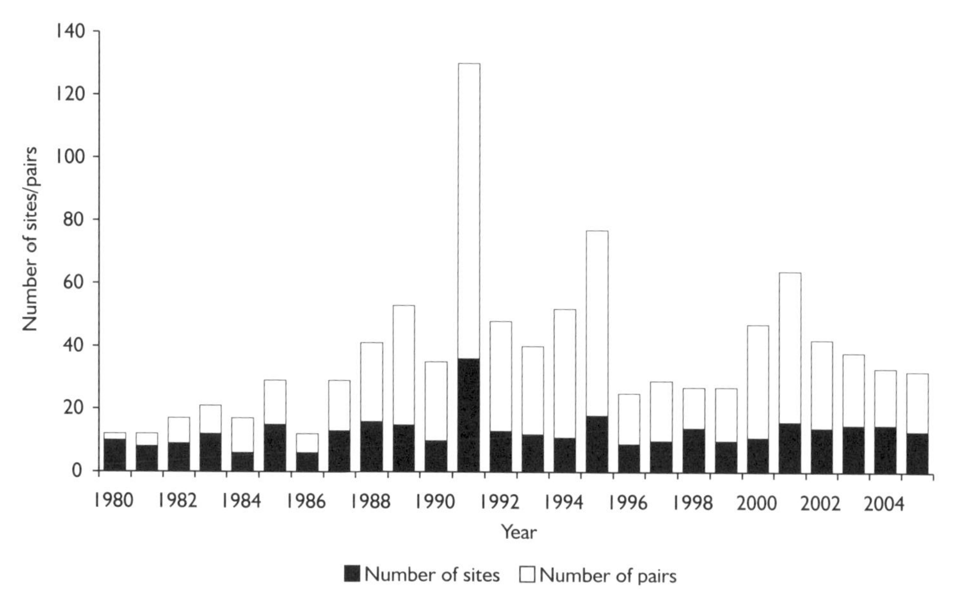

Figure 31: Breeding numbers of Greater Canada Geese 1980–2005.

population alone is insufficient to explain the overall increase in numbers, which may relate to the growing use of Rutland Water as a moulting site since the mid-1980s. Ringing recoveries indicate that the majority of birds (113 of 121 recovered) travel less than 100km, but there are also seven recoveries of birds ringed on the Beauly Firth (Highland) in July 1984 during their moult migration. These travelled up to 572km and were recovered up to six years after the date of ringing.

Hybrids with White-fronted Goose, Greylag Goose and Barnacle Goose have been recorded: see 'Hybrids' (pages 676–684).

Greater Canada Geese are found widely across England and Wales and through the southern and central lowlands of Scotland. The British population, in line with that in Leicestershire and Rutland, has increased dramatically since the 1960s and is now estimated at just under 52,000 birds (Collier *et al.* 2005). Occasional vagrants of the smaller forms (now recognised as a separate species, Lesser Canada Goose) occur in Britain and this species has been noted as an escape within Leicestershire and Rutland: see 'Category E species' (pages 659–675).

AHJH

Barnacle Goose *Branta leucopsis*

Very rare winter vagrant: two or three records of wild birds involving 65 or 72 individuals. Frequent feral individuals.

The only record in the 19th century, described by Browne in VH, was of one shot at Thornton Reservoir during the first week of April 1891. Haines included the species on the Rutland list but provided no additional details.

Although feral birds are currently a regular sight in the counties, wild birds have been recorded as rare winter vagrants on only two or three occasions. In 1981, 39 were present at Eyebrook Reservoir from February 21st until at least March 2nd. A ring carried by one of the birds indicated that it had been ringed on Spitsbergen several years earlier; it had been observed in the Netherlands during the previous two winters. This record coincided with arrivals in Kent and Norfolk which indicated a large westerly movement of birds from the Netherlands. Also in 1981, seven were seen in fields adjacent to Thornton Reservoir from March 21st to 28th and may have been part of the same movement. In 1993, a flock of 25 arived at Eyebrook Reservoir on November 7th; they were joined by another bird the next day and all 26 remained until December 4th, visiting

Rutland Water on November 13th. There was an influx of Barnacle Geese into East Anglia and the Midlands at the time and the record also coincided with that of a Bean Goose which was present at Eyebrook Reservoir.

Other records of single birds and small flocks, including colour-ringed birds, are more likely to involve feral birds. The first record of birds considered to be feral involved a pair at Stanford Reservoir on April 21st 1971. By 1987, the possibility that a small feral poulation might be establishing itself was mentioned in the LROS Annual Report, though breeding has not yet been proved. Eight colour-ringed birds believed to be from a population in north Buckinghamshire were recorded in 1990 and in 1992 a tame flock of 19 birds, some colour-ringed, was present at Priory Water from November 15th until December 13th. A flock of up to 12 has regularly been present at Rutland Water since 1996.

Hybrids with White-fronted Goose, Snow Goose, Emperor Goose and Greater Canada Goose have been recorded: see 'Hybrids' (pages 676–684).

There are three separate breeding populations of Barnacle Geese in the world and two of these winter exclusively in Britain and Ireland, using quite different areas. Birds breeding in Greenland winter on the west coast of Scotland and Ireland, whilst those from the Svalbard group of islands winter on the Solway Firth. Up to 45,000 Greenland birds and 22,000 Svalbard birds use Britain and Ireland as their wintering quarters and, due to the importance of the countries to this species, the Barnacle Goose has been added to the 'Amber List' of Birds of Conservation Concern (Gregory *et al.* 2002). A third population breeds in coastal Arctic Russia and winters in Germany and the Netherlands. As mentioned above, there are many feral birds at large in Britain: Delany (1993) recorded 925 such individuals, at a total of 89 sites, in Britain during the summer of 1991.

AHJH

Brent Goose *Branta bernicla*

Scarce winter and passage visitor; recorded in all months except June and July, with the majority from October to March: 991 individuals. Two distinct subspecies occur.

Birds of the nominate subspecies, the Dark-bellied Brent Goose , are scarce but regular winter and passage visitors in small numbers, most probably originating from the large population which winters on the Wash. The Pale-bellied Brent Goose is a very rare vagrant. Not all records have been subspecifically identified, particularly those involving birds seen in flight, but it is assumed that the majority refer to the the nominate race.

Dark-bellied Brent Goose *B. b. bernicla*

According to Browne, there were two 19th century records from Leicestershire: several were reportedly shot at Kirkby Mallory on December 31st 1844 and one that was shot at Syston was presented to Leicester Museum by the Literary and Philosophical Society on January 28th 1854. Haines mentions one shot by the River Welland near Stamford in January 1888, although this bird was unlikely to have been in Rutland. At the beginning of the 20th century, one was shot at Thurmaston in 1905.

Since 1941, there have been records in 27 of the 65 years up to 2005. This species is becoming noticeably more regular in the counties and since 1982 there have only been three blank years (1986, 1988 and 2001); by contrast, there were records in just six years between 1941 and 1982. The increase in records during the last two decades corresponds with increasing numbers wintering on the Wash. Most records involve one or two birds, although groups of three or more have been noted on seven occasions, as follows:

- six at Eyebrook Reservoir from February 25th to March 3rd 1946 (along with two Pale-bellied birds during the same period).
- three at Eyebrook Reservoir from February 15th to 17th 1966.
- four at Rutland Water on May 2nd 1983.
- three at Rutland Water on February 2nd 1987.
- six at Rutland Water from February 14th to 27th 1994.
- an exceptional 17 at Quorn Borrow Pit on March 23rd 1996.
- ten at Rutland Water on March 28th 2003, one of which remained until April 1st.

The highest annual total was in 1996, when 19 birds were recorded, although this total was heavily influenced by the flock of 17 at Quorn Borrow Pit in March. Similarly, totals of 11 in 2003 and ten in 1994 were mainly due to the small flocks mentioned above. In most years there are only one or two records, although there were four records (involving five birds) in both 1990 and 1991 and four records (involving ten birds) in 1994.

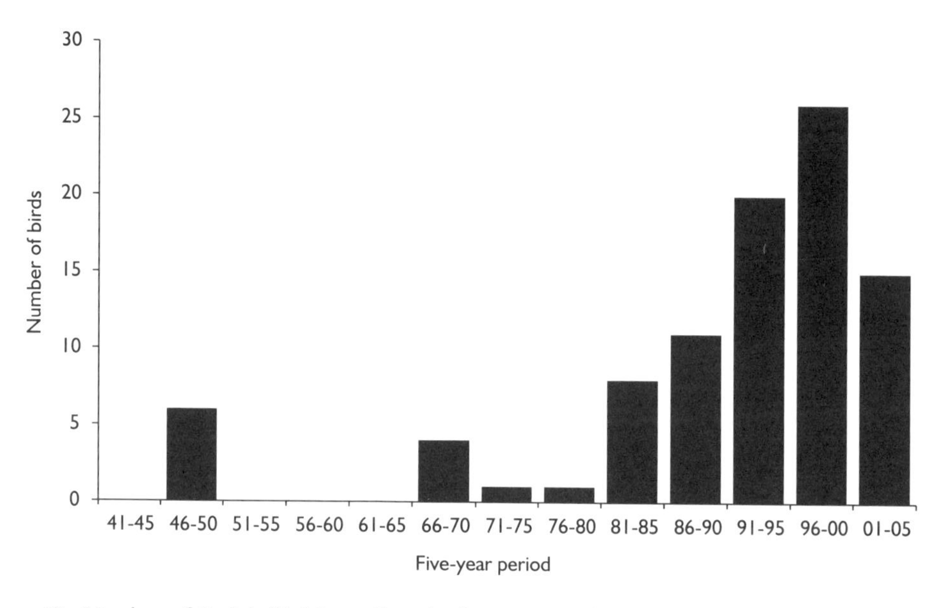

Figure 32: Numbers of Dark-bellied Brent Geese by five-year periods 1941–2005.

The data show an obvious peak in late March, although numbers in this period are distorted by the appearance of the large flocks at Quorn Borrow Pit in 1996 and Rutland Water in 2003; other favoured months are October and February. The peak in October matches this species' main autumn arrival period in Britain, whilst the peaks

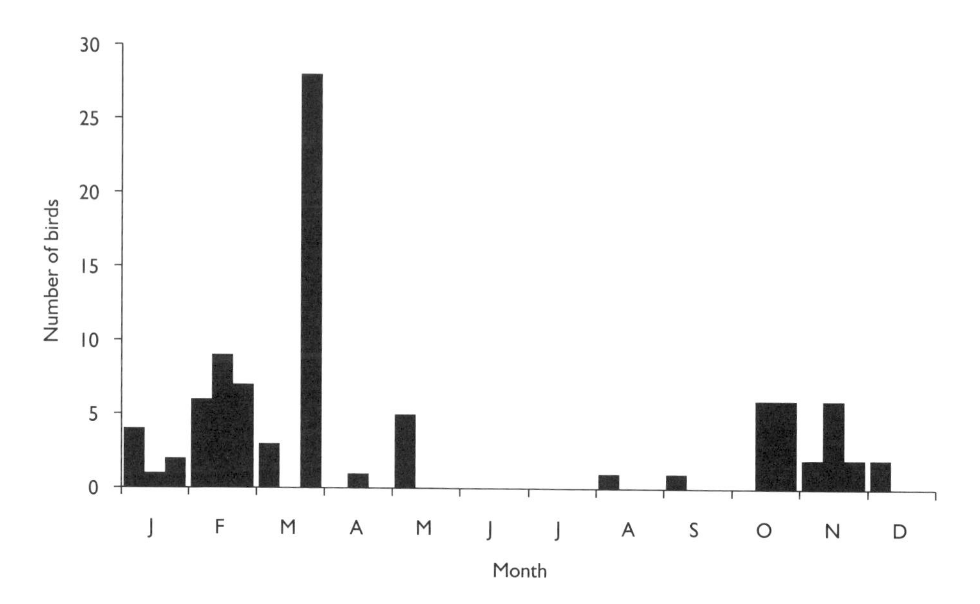

Figure 33: Monthly occurrence of Dark-bellied Brent Geese 1941–2005.

in February and March may reflect both movements following depletion of supplies of eel grass (Lack 1986) and the onset of spring passage.

The earliest autumn record relates to a first-summer bird at Rutland Water from August 4th to September 26th 2003, although arrivals prior to October 16th are rare, the only others being single birds at Eyebrook Reservoir from September 10th to 12th 1989 and Rutland Water on October 13th 1991. Despite the pronounced peak in late March, reports after the first week of this month are unusual: with the exception of the large flocks at Quorn Borrow Pit and Rutland Water previously noted, the only records later than March 8th are single birds at Saddington Reservoir on March 25th 1996 and Rutland Water on both April 18th 1994 and May 2nd and 3rd 1993, along with four at the latter site on May 2nd 1983.

Birds are normally present for just one day, although there have been four occasions when individuals have remained for over two weeks:

- one at Rutland Water from January 31st to March 28th 1987.
- a first-summer at Rutland Water from August 4th to September 26th 2003.
- one at Stanford Reservoir from November 27th to December 21st 1969.
- one at Cropston Reservoir from December 2nd to 24th 1978.

Away from Rutland Water and Eyebrook Reservoir, which between them account for almost 60% of all birds, the Brent Goose is a very rare visitor to the counties. The major reservoirs of Stanford, Thornton and Cropston have only mustered seven individuals between them, whilst remarkably there has never been a record from Swithland Reservoir.

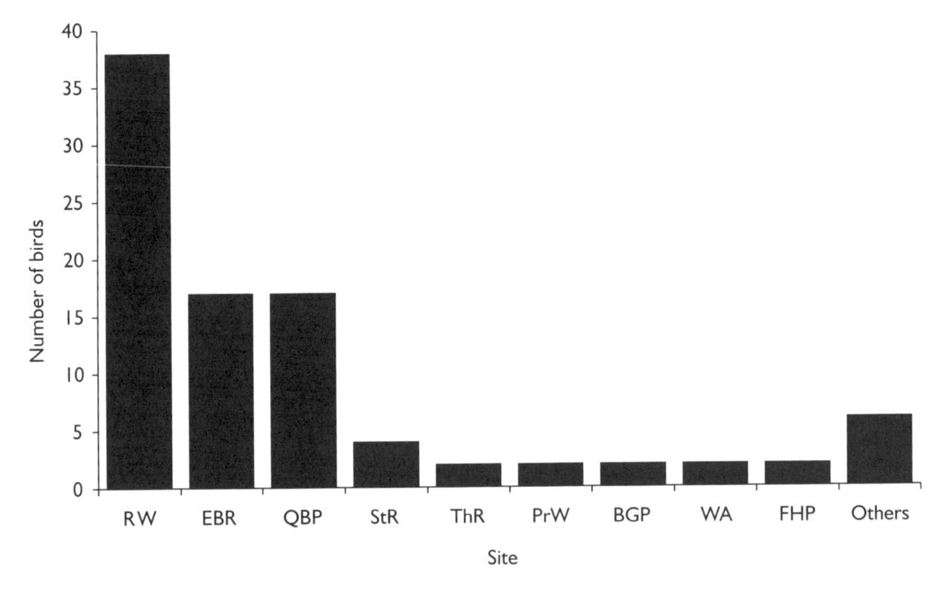

Figure 34: Sites where Dark-bellied Brent Geese have been recorded 1941–2005.
Key to abbreviations: RW = Rutland Water; EBR = Eyebrook Reservoir; QBP = Quorn Borrow Pit; StR = Stanford Reservoir; ThR = Thornton Reservoir; PrW = Priory Water; BGP = Birstall Gravel Pits; WA = Wymeswold Airfield; FHP = Fort Henry Ponds

Dark-bellied Brent Geese breed in the high Arctic tundra of Russia and winter in north-west Europe. British estuaries support approximately 98,000 birds during the winter (Baker *et al.* 2006), which equates to around one third of the world population; due to the international importance of Britain as a wintering area, this species has been added to the 'Amber List' of Birds of Conservation Concern (Gregory *et al.* 2002).

Pale-bellied Brent Goose *B.b. hrota*

There are just two records of birds considered to be this subspecies, as follows:

1946 two with six dark-bellied birds at Eyebrook Reservoir from February 25th to March 3rd.
1957 two at Eyebrook Reservoir on March 16th.

There are two populations of Pale-bellied Brent Geese, one of which breeds on the high Arctic islands of north-east Canada and Greenland and the other which breeds on Svalbard. Canadian birds winter mainly in Ireland, whilst those from Svalbard winter chiefly in Denmark and Northumberland; the latest estimates of the British wintering numbers are approximately 21,500 and 3,750 birds respectively (Collier *et al.* 2005). Although the Eyebrook Reservoir records may seem surprising, this subspecies is regularly seen in small numbers on the Wash and in north Norfolk and was formerly more common there (Taylor *et al.* 1999).

AHJH

Egyptian Goose *Alopochen aegyptiaca*

Introduced. Uncommon localised resident, scarce breeder.

The Egyptian Goose was reported on at least five occasions in the 19th century. Browne noted that one was shot out of a flock of four near Leicester on March 4th 1843 and five (one of which was shot) were at Welham on August 27th 1898, whilst in Rutland Haines recorded one on the Leicestershire/Rutland border in about 1860, one shot at Burley Fishponds in 1882 and seven at the same site in about 1895. In addition, Haines noted that one was shot 'near Stamford' in January 1805, although whether this was actually in Rutland is unknown.

The first modern record involved a bird at Eyebrook Reservoir on March 18th 1972. There were only three more reports by the end of that decade, all of single birds: at Frisby Gravel Pits from May 19th to 23rd 1975, Kegworth on May 9th 1979 and Rutland Water from May 29th to July 22nd 1979 and on December 4th 1979.

Records became more regular from 1985 onwards. The core of the population seems to have originated from a pair initially present at Tolethorpe (on the Lincolnshire boundary) from June 7th to 18th 1985, which later moved between there and Rutland Water. Although not recorded in 1987, it was probably this pair which returned to Rutland Water on August 10th 1988. During 1989 they established a territory and nested in a pollarded tree; a single young bird was seen with the parents in mid-June. A single pair was recorded breeding in each subsequent year until 1995 when four pairs with 23 young were noted. By 1999, when five pairs with 28 young and a maximum count of 69 were recorded, Rutland Water had become the sixth most important site in Britain for this species. Since then, the population at Rutland Water has continued to grow and in 2003 13 pairs raised 62 young and 70 were counted on September 14th, making Rutland Water the third most important site in Britain for Egyptian Geese (Collier *et al.* 2005).

The Rutland Water population is largely sedentary, forming a post-breeding flock in fields near Egleton where maximum counts are made in September to November. Nonetheless odd birds have been recorded at 16 other sites in the counties, with the following records of two or more together:

- 11 at Thornton Reservoir on September 21st 2005, with 13 there for the next two days, nine until September 25th and three on November 1st.
- seven at Eyebrook Reservoir on January 9th 2005.
- four at Cossington South Lakes on October 17th 2005, with three at nearby Wanlip North Lakes on October 24th and two at Wanlip Meadows on November 27th and December 11th probably relating to the same birds.

- two at Eyebrook Reservoir on May 4th 1989.
- two at Belvoir Lakes on November 12th 1989.
- two at Wanlip North Gravel Pits from January 8th to April 29th 2000, with the same two at Birstall Gravel Pits on March 3rd 2000.
- two at Swithland Reservoir on September 9th and 10th 2000.
- two at Fort Henry Ponds on March 2nd 2002.
- two at Leighfield on April 7th 2004.

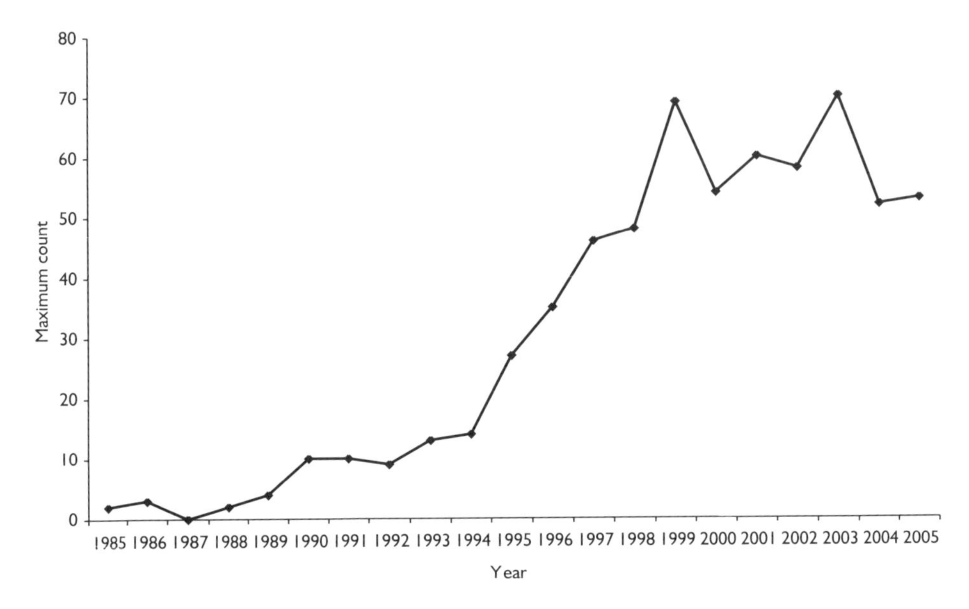

Figure 35: Maximum counts of Egyptian Geese at Rutland Water 1985–2005.

Figure 36: Breeding numbers of Egyptian Geese at Rutland Water 1989–2005.

Some of these birds are likely to have been prospecting pairs, so it is possible that a second population will become established.

Hybrids with Ruddy Shelduck and Common Shelduck have been recorded: see 'Hybrids' (pages 676–684).

All records of Egyptian Goose in Britain relate to feral or escaped birds, which have been introduced from Africa since at least the late 18th century. This species is now well established in East Anglia and has recently spread into surrounding areas such as Rutland Water. The British population is estimated at approximately 1,000 pairs (Baker *et al.* 2006).

AHJH

Common Shelduck *Tadorna tadorna*

Uncommon passage and winter visitor, uncommon breeder.

The Common Shelduck was an accidental visitor during the 19th century: Browne knew of five records from Leicestershire, involving 11 individuals and in Rutland Haines listed five records totalling six birds.

By 1942 it was considered to be an occasional visitor in very small numbers and the highest count during the 1940s was of 13 at Eyebrook Reservoir on October 10th 1948. There were 20 at the same site from December 28th 1953 into January 1954 but it was not until the mid-1970s that its status changed significantly: up to 42 were at Eyebrook Reservoir during the autumn of 1976 and the following year breeding took place for the first time when a pair reared five young at Rutland Water. The breeding population at Rutland Water increased to eight pairs which raised 59 young in 1995 and in 2000 a record 12 pairs raised 74 young.

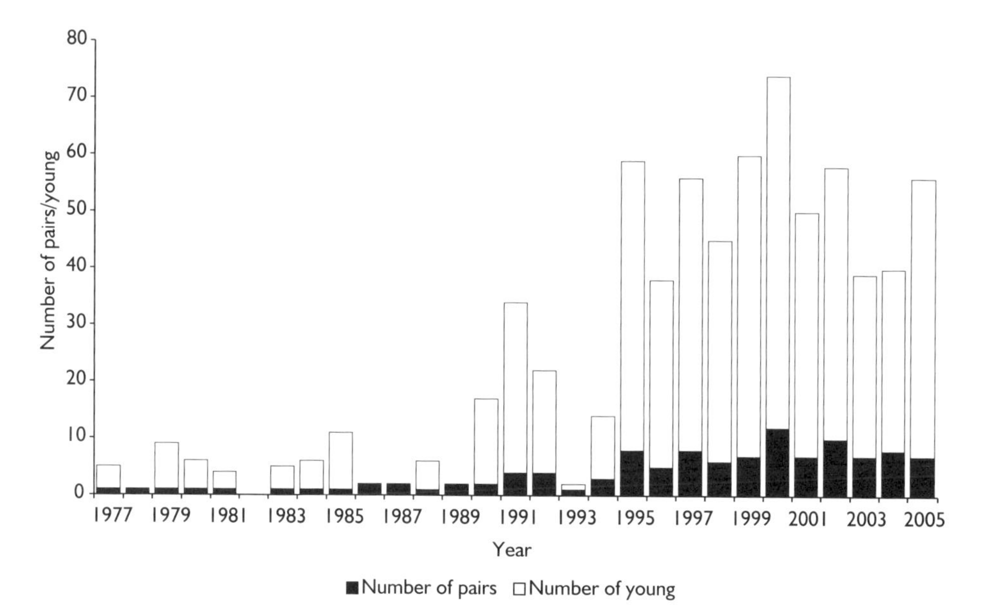

Figure 37: Breeding numbers of Common Shelducks at Rutland Water 1977–2005.

Away from Rutland Water, breeding has been confirmed or strongly suspected at 11 sites since 1980, as follows:

1980 a pair appeared to hold territory at Eyebrook Reservoir, but no proof of breeding was obtained.
1985 a pair raised two young at Fort Henry Ponds.
1988 breeding was strongly suspected at Shawell Gravel Pits.
1990 a pair raised five young at Fort Henry Ponds.
1992 a pair attempted to breed near Eyebrook Reservoir but the nest was destroyed by a predator.
1993 a pair raised ten young at Cadeby Quarry.

1994	a pair hatched 12 young at King's Hill Lodge, Uppingham and took the brood to Eyebrook Reservoir, but only one youngster survived.
1996	a pair was seen prospecting a barn near Preston in mid-April.
1997	a pair summered at Trent Valley Pit and five juveniles on July 16th may have been locally bred.
2000	a pair raised nine young at Eyebrook Reservoir.
2001	single pairs at Eyebrook Reservoir and Cossington North Gravel Pits raised eight young each and a pair at Cropston Reservoir reared seven young.
2002	a pair hatched six young at Fort Henry Ponds, but none survived.
2003	single pairs at Swithland Reservoir and Priory Water hatched three and ten young respectively, but all young from both broods perished.
2004	a pair hatched seven young at Trent Valley Pit.
2005	a pair raised ten young at Eyebrook Reservoir.

Data show that peak numbers occur in spring, with a composite total of 107 in April 2004 the highest to date. The highest counts at a single site have been at Rutland Water, where the first double-figure count was 27 on September 25th 1977. Over 70 have been counted at this site on six occasions, as follows:

- 81 on April 4th 1999.
- 76 on March 20th 2005.
- 75 on May 31st 1998.
- 74 on April 6th 2004.
- 73 on April 20th 2002.
- 72 on March 23rd 2003.

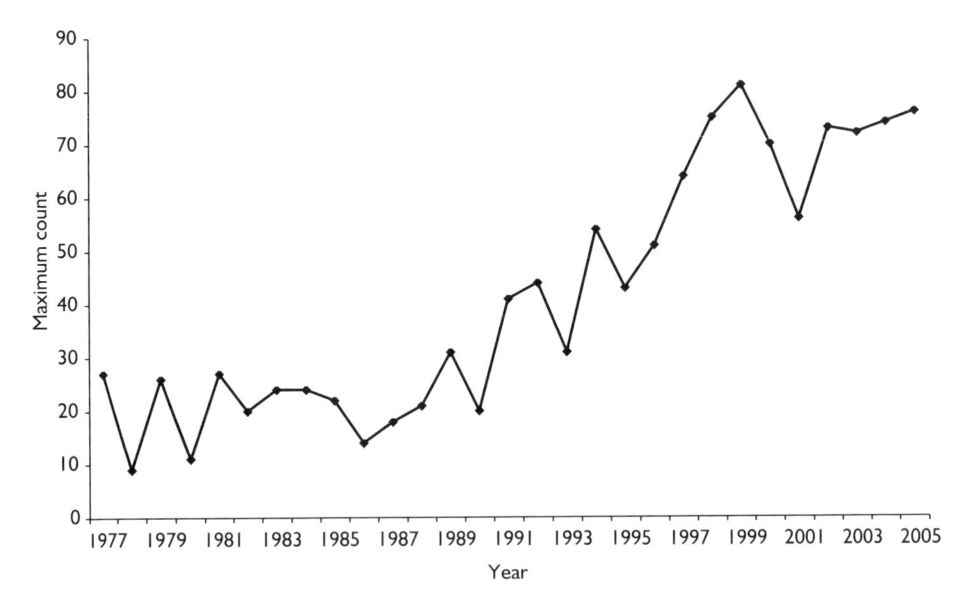

Figure 38: Maximum counts of Common Shelducks at Rutland Water 1977–2005.

Elsewhere, double-figure counts have been recorded at 11 sites, where the maxima have been:

- 46 at Swithland Reservoir on December 22nd 1981, along with one count of 11 and three of ten.
- 42 at Eyebrook Reservoir in the autumn of 1976, with other notable counts being 20 from December 28th 1953 into January 1954, 18 on both March 30th 1958 and November 15th 1968 and 17 on both July 14th 1994 and July 4th 2000. This site has recorded a further ten counts between 15 and ten.

- 24 at Stoney Stanton Jetski Centre on July 4th 2000.
- 15 flying over Bradgate Park on May 30th 1983.
- 13 at Priory Water on May 6th 1991, with 11 there on August 10th 2003.
- 12 at Saddington Reservoir on June 20th 1985.
- 12 at Trent Valley Pit on May 14th 1993, with ten there on July 2nd 2000.
- 11 flying over Sawley Marina on May 13th 2000.
- ten at Normanton Turville on February 18th 1962.
- ten at Cropston Reservoir on December 21st 1969 and April 19th 1977.
- ten at Stanford Reservoir on July 12th 1999.
- ten at Trent Farm Pool on March 30th 2000.

The growing local breeding population complicates interpretation of data but it appears that Common Shelducks have also become more numerous on spring passage following increases since 1975 in the numbers breeding at inland sites in the south of Britain (Gibbons *et.al.* 1993). After this species' well-known summer moult migration, return passage is prolonged with no clear pattern, though there is a suggestion of a first wave in September followed by a second wave in November and December.

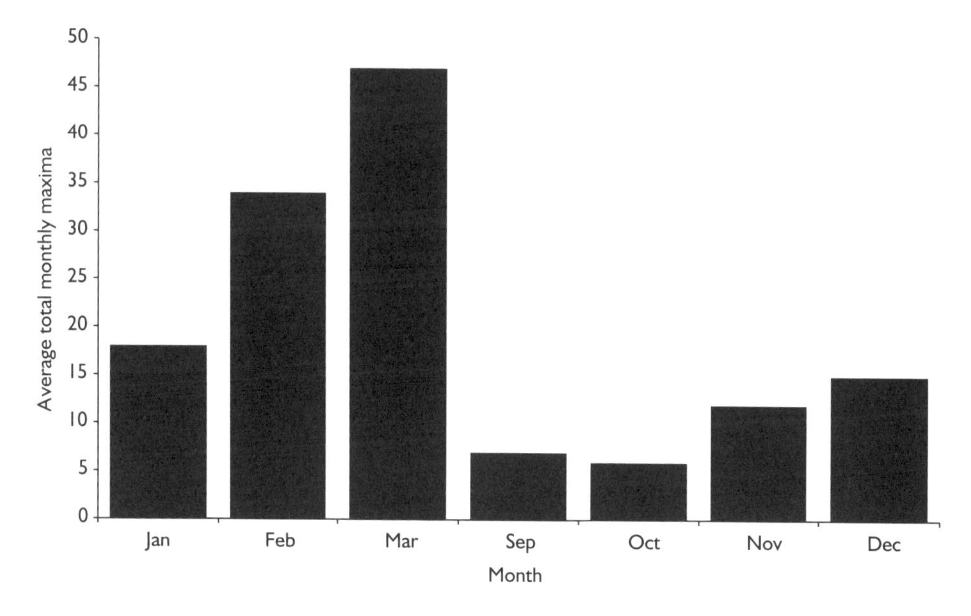

Figure 39: Average total monthly maxima of Common Shelducks at the main sites 1995–2005.

There is just one ringing recovery relating to Leicestershire and Rutland: a male ringed at Rutland Water in March 1995 was found dead 527km to the east in Germany in March of the following year.

Hybrids with Egyptian Goose and Ruddy Shelduck have been recorded: see 'Hybrids' (pages 676–684).

Common Shelducks breed across much of Europe and central Asia. After breeding they undergo a moult migration to the Heligoland Bight (Germany), the Wash (Lincolnshire/Norfolk), Bridgwater Bay (Somerset) or the estuaries of the Humber or Forth. The British breeding population showed a substantial increase from the 1960s to the 1980s, although it stabilised during the 1990s (Baillie *et al.* 2006) and is currently estimated at 10,600 pairs (Baker *et al.* 2006). More than 50% of the UK non-breeding population is found at fewer than ten sites and this, combined with the fact that over 20% of the north-west European non-breeding population uses this country, has resulted in the Common Shelduck being added to the 'Amber List' of Birds of Conservation Concern (Gregory *et al.* 2002).

AHJH

Mandarin Duck *Aix galericulata*

Introduced. Uncommon resident, scarce breeder.

All records of this species in the counties relate to feral or escaped birds. The first reports, at Ketton in April 1973 and 1974 (Mitcham 1984) may have originated from a wildfowl collection at Ketton Hall. The first record of a bird away from nearby collections involved a male at Eyebrook Reservoir on October 11th 1975. In the early 1980s it was still regarded as a scarce vagrant but records have increased since 1985 and breeding has occurred in at least five years.

In 1985, breeding was considered possible at Swithland Reservoir where, following a male and four females on January 29th and between February 23rd and March 23rd, a pair was seen displaying during April 13th to 30th. Between 1987 and 1992, birds were regularly recorded on the River Welland in the Wakerley Bridge/Barrowden area and in 1991 the first proof of breeding came from nearby, when a female with eight young was observed at Tixover. Breeding was proved again in 1996, when a female with six young was seen at Blackbrook Reservoir on June 16th. In 2002, two pairs raised a total of 17 young at an undisclosed site in Charnwood and one brood (of seven) was again recorded at Blackbrook Reservoir. The latter site provided further breeding records in 2004, when two pairs raised a total of 17 young, and 2005, when four pairs hatched a total of 15 young. Also during 2005, three pairs bred at Cropston Reservoir, raising 15 young and another pair produced 11 young from a nest in a tree at Moira. This species is unobtrusive during the breeding season, so some breeding pairs may have escaped notice: four juveniles at Fort Henry Ponds on July 29th 2000 suggest that breeding occurred nearby and a female with two well-grown young was at Cropston Reservoir on August 18th 2003.

There is a tendency for this species to favour certain sites for several years before moving elsewhere. Since 1998, Groby Pool has consistently produced records of Mandarin Ducks, with a peak of 29 there on October 25th 2003. During 2004 and 2005, however, Blackbrook and Cropston Reservoirs took over as the most regularly visited sites, with counts of 27 at the former on October 13th 2005 and 30 at the latter on November 11th

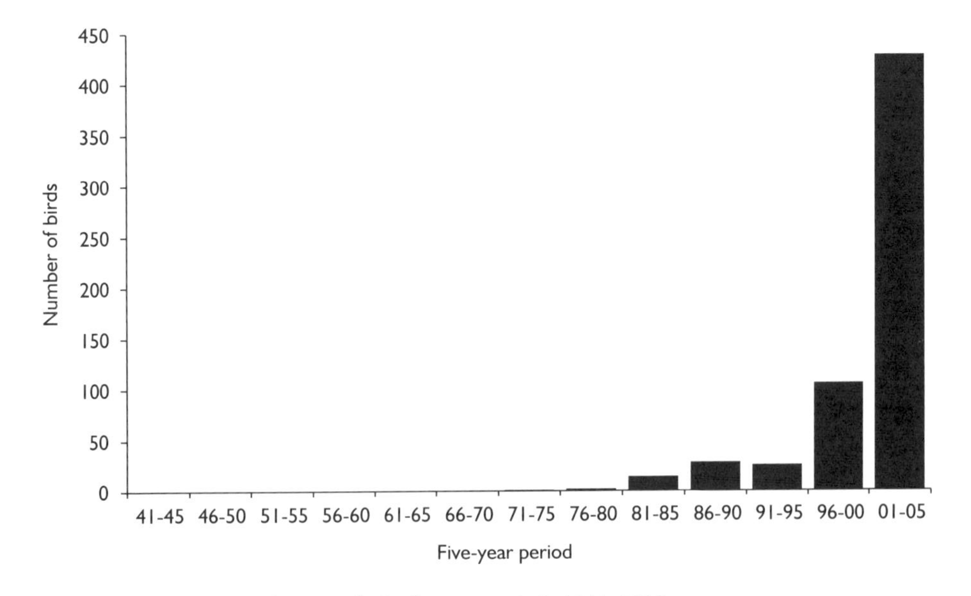

Figure 40: Numbers of Mandarin Ducks by five-year periods 1941–2005.

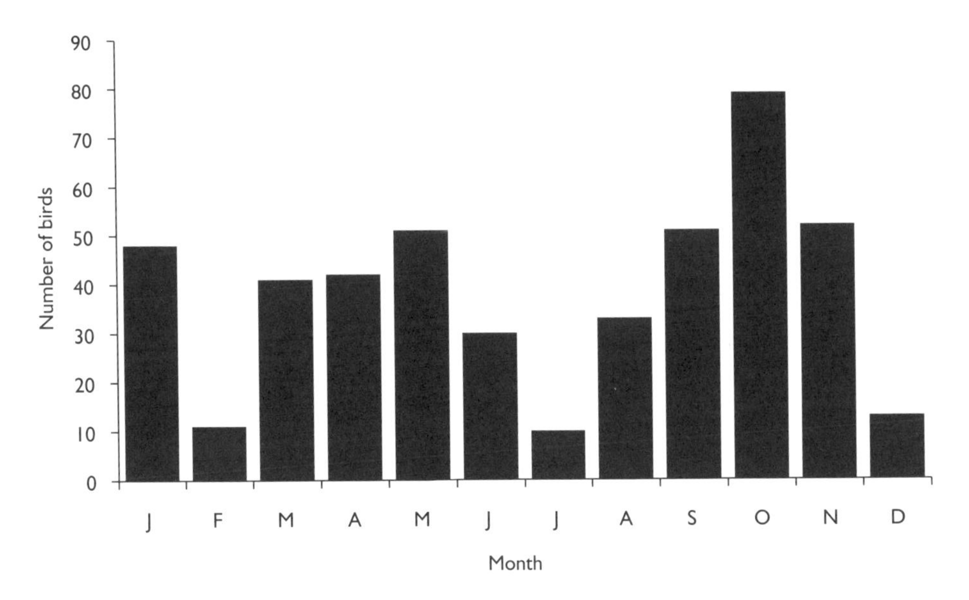

Figure 41: Monthly occurrence of Mandarin Ducks in 1941–2005.

2004. Over 30 individuals were recorded throughout the counties in both 1999 and 2001, increasing to 95 in 2002 and 117 in 2004, so further breeding records can be expected.

Hybrids with an unknown *Anas* species have been recorded: see 'Hybrids' (pages 676–684).

Mandarin Ducks are native to south-east Russia, north-east China and Japan and were introduced to England in the 18th century. The population has increased markedly in recent years and by the late 1980s numbered some 7,000 individuals (Davies 1988). Although the feral British population is generally regarded as largely sedentary, the data show that the migratory urges of its Asian ancestors have been retained.

AHJH

Eurasian Wigeon *Anas penelope*

Common winter and passage visitor, scarce in summer.

Browne described the Eurasian Wigeon as 'a winter visitant, not uncommon on the rivers Soar and Trent, as well as on large sheets of water such as Saddington and Knipton', whilst in Rutland Haines noted that it was frequently met with at Burley Fishponds and Exton and large flocks passed over the Welland valley by night in the winter months.

In the first LROS Annual Report in 1941, the Eurasian Wigeon was described as a very common winter visitor which was not known to breed. This description remains accurate, despite fluctuations in numbers and changes in seasonal status.

Data show that numbers of wintering birds declined between 1951 and 1971, then increased dramatically following the construction of Rutland Water. The first really high count at Rutland Water, of 4,518 on January 16th 1976, occurred at a time when the Ouse Washes (Cambridgeshire) were flooded: this event may have changed the habits of some of the birds involved as numbers have remained high since then and have established Rutland Water as a site of national importance for the species, the qualifying level currently being 4,060 birds (Collier *et al.* 2005). The highest single count at Rutland Water was 7,239 on January 12th 1985. Counts of 1,000 or more have been recorded at five other sites, with the maxima being:

- 3,000 at Eyebrook Reservoir on February 1st 1987.
- 2,000 at Stanford Reservoir on January 12th 1992 and November 25th 1997.
- 1,664 at Swithland Reservoir on February 15th 1987.

- 1,200 at Priory Water on March 10th 1996.
- 1,000 at Cropston Reservoir on December 26th 1946.

See 'Wintering Birds' (pages 39–43) for details of highest counts at individual sites.

From a high point in the mid-1980s and early to mid-1990s, numbers have dropped sharply since 1997 and are currently at the same level as in the late 1970s. Whether this is the start of a trend of smaller wintering numbers remains to be seen, although the recent run of mild winters may be a factor.

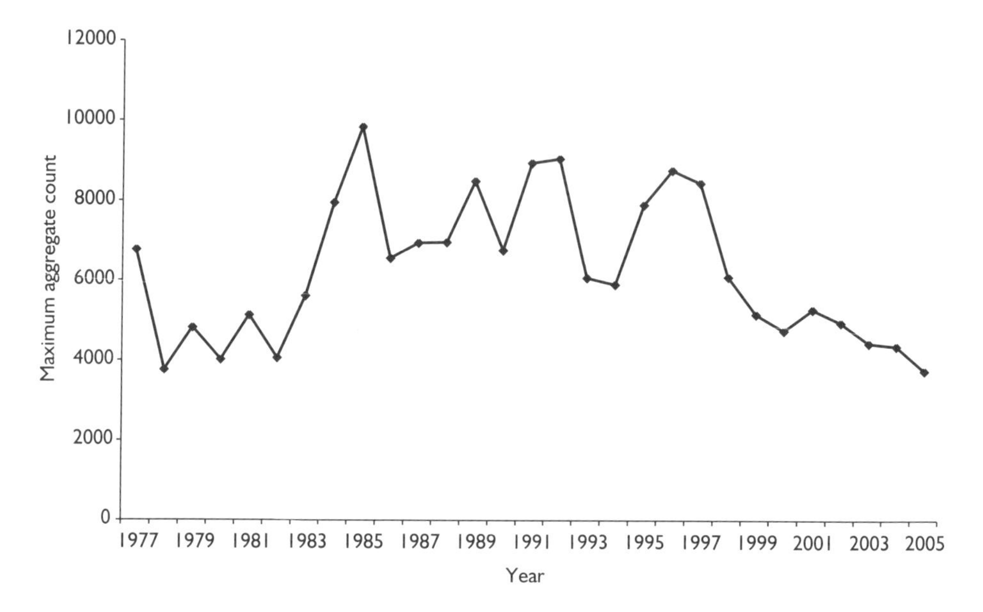

Figure 42: Maximum aggregate counts of Eurasian Wigeons at the main sites 1977–2005.

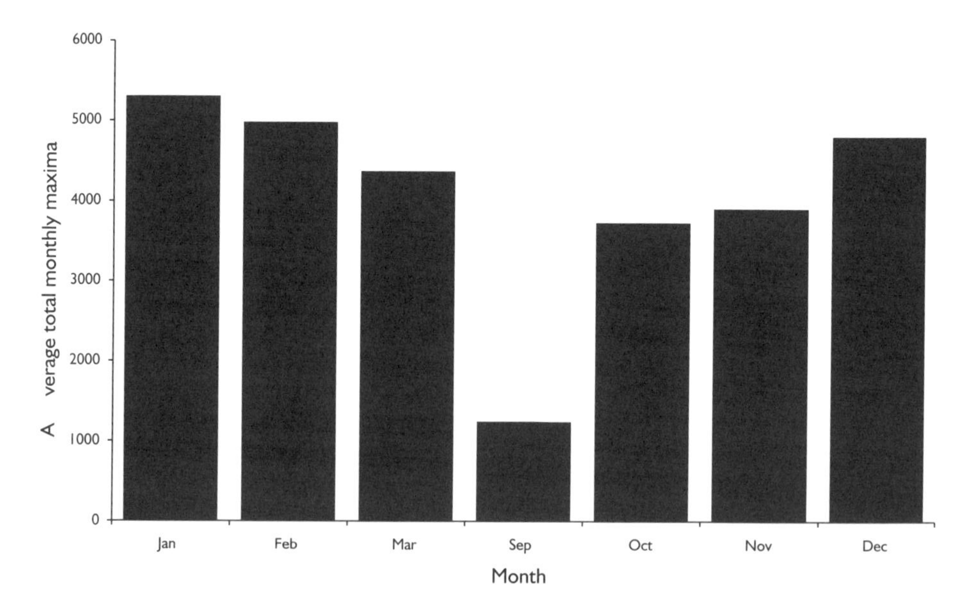

Figure 43: Average total monthly maxima of Eurasian Wigeons at the main sites 1995–2005.

Although evidence in the 1940s suggested the presence of birds on passage from mid-October until mid-November, recent data suggest that numbers increase steadily during late autumn and winter before reaching a peak in January and February; the highest aggregate WeBS count, of 9,824, was made in January 1985, although one of the next largest was 8,750 in March 1996. The number of birds arriving in September has increased significantly during the last decade: it will be interesting to see whether this trend continues.

There have been records of birds in the summer months since 1944 and in 1971 a pair was present at Wanlip Gravel Pits throughout the summer. Nonetheless, there are no records of proven breeding despite a notable increase in the numbers of summering birds since the late 1980s. The best years for summering birds have been 1996 (25 birds at four sites), 2005 (17 birds at five sites) and 2003 (15 birds at four sites).

Birds ringed in Leicestershire and Rutland have been recovered abroad in France, Greece, the Netherlands, Sweden and the former USSR (four). One of these, a female ringed at Rutland Water on December 6th 1999, was shot 3,992km to the east-north-east on May 16th of the following year. There have also been two local recoveries of birds ringed in the Netherlands.

A tendency for leucism to occur in this species has been exemplified by records of leucistic birds at Rutland Water on April 1st 1986, Priory Water on November 6th 1994 and (a female) at Swithland Reservoir on December 27th 1996.

Hybrids with Eurasian Teal have been recorded: see 'Hybrids' (pages 676–684).

Eurasian Wigeons breed from Scandinavia east to Kamchatka, as well as in Iceland, the Faroe Islands and northern Britain. Most winter in north-west Europe and on the coasts of the Mediterranean and Black Sea. The British breeding population is estimated at between 300 and 500 pairs, although over 400,000 may spend the winter in the UK (Baker *et al.* 2006). As more than 20% of the north-west European non-breeding population winters in Britain, this species has been added to the 'Amber List' of Birds of Conservation Concern (Gregory *et al.* 2002).

AHJH

American Wigeon *Anas americana*

Very rare vagrant from North America: five records.

The first county record was of an immature male, initially found by Dave Willett, at Eyebrook Reservoir from April 17th to May 17th 1974 (*BB* 68:313). It was another 18 years until the next individual was located, but since then a further four have been found; the Eyebrook Reservoir monopoly on this species has recently been broken by records from Knipton Reservoir and Rutland Water.

All records:

1974 immature male, Eyebrook Reservoir, April 17th to May 17th.

1992 an adult female, found by Andrew Harrop, was at Eyebrook Reservoir from March 26th to April 7th and a bird considered to be a juvenile female was found by the same observer at the same site on October 4th, where it remained intermittently until October 22nd (Harrop 1993a, *BB* 86:460).

2001 an adult male, initially found by John Wright, was at Eyebrook Reservoir from November 12th intermittently to January 1st 2002, although it often visited nearby Blatherwycke Lake (Northamptonshire) during this period (*BB* 95:485). It then moved to Lincolnshire, but returned to Leicestershire on February 10th 2002, when it was seen at Knipton Reservoir.

2003 a first-summer male, originally identified by Matthew Berriman, was at Rutland Water from March 16th to April 13th.

Hybrids with Chiloe Wigeon and Cinnamon Teal have been recorded: see 'Hybrids' (pages 676–684).

The American Wigeon breeds across much of Alaska, Canada and the northern United States, moving in winter to the Atlantic and Pacific coasts of the United States, as well as south through Central America into Colombia. It is a regular vagrant to Britain and was removed from the list of species considered by the BBRC at the end of 2001, by which time it had amassed approximately 350 British records; it currently averages around 20 reports a year in the country. The Leicestershire and Rutland records fit the established pattern of occurrence in Britain described by Votier *et al.* (2003), which shows a distinct peak in October/November and a smaller movement during the spring; those in autumn are likely to be newly arrived, whilst spring records probably relate to northward-bound migrants which have taken up residence on the east side of the Atlantic following earlier displacement.

AHJH

Gadwall *Anas strepera*

Common autumn and winter visitor, uncommon breeder.

Browne noted that the first record for the counties was of a female shot at Bitteswell Hall on October 25th 1890, but it is now thought that this may have been an introduced bird. The first definite modern record of Gadwall in the counties involved a male at Stanford Reservoir on November 3rd 1946, though there had been records from Holywell Hall near Stamford (Lincolnshire) since 1940 and a possible was reported at Swithland Reservoir in December 1945. Between then and 1969 there were records of 63 individuals, with no clear seasonal pattern but minor peaks in April, September, October and December suggest that most birds were on passage or wintering. There were no summer records until 1965.

From 1970 numbers increased and breeding was recorded for the first time in 1974, when a female with ten young was seen at Cropston Reservoir in mid-June. Though numbers fluctuate, the breeding population has become well established with proven records from the following 14 sites:

- Cropston Reservoir: single pairs in 1974, 1975, 1976, 1992, 1993, 2000, 2004 and 2005 and two pairs in 2002 and 2003.
- Eyebrook Reservoir: first bred in 1978 (one pair), then in all years except 1983, 1999, 2001, 2002 and 2005, with peaks of ten pairs in 1991, eight pairs in 1990, six in 2003 and five in 1980, 1989, 1992 and 1997.
- Swithland Reservoir: first bred in 1978 (one pair), then in all years from 1990 to 1997 except 1994 and 1996, with a maximum of three pairs in 1991
- Rutland Water: first bred in 1980 (one pair), then every year from 1982 to 2005 except 1987, 1993, 1994 and 1999, with peaks of 12 pairs in 2005, 11 in 2003 and 2004, ten in 2002 and five in 1985, 1989, 1990 and 1995.
- Trent Valley Pit: first bred in 1992 (two pairs), then in every year except 1997 until 2000, with peaks of seven pairs in 1993 and three in 1994 and 2000.
- Cavendish Bridge Gravel Pits: single pairs in 1993 and 1994.
- Fort Henry Ponds: single pairs in 1995, 1997 and 2002.
- Saddington Reservoir: one pair in 1996.
- Priory Water: single pairs in 1997, 2003 and 2004, three in 2000 and two in 2001.
- Cossington North Gravel Pits: one pair in 2001.
- Stanford Reservoir: one pair in 2002.
- Kirby Lakes: one pair in 2003.
- Cossington Meadows: three pairs in 2004.
- Trent Farm Pool: one pair in 2004.

The two best years have been 2003, when a total of 21 pairs bred at five sites, and 2004, when 19 pairs bred at six sites.

The non-breeding population has grown dramatically since the construction of the nutrient-rich artificial wetland at Rutland Water, which has become a site of international importance (the qualifying level being 600) and the most important site in the UK for this species (Collier *et al.* 2005). Counts from there increased as follows: 134 on October 29th 1978; 380 on December 13th 1981; 947 (a record British count at the time) on December 18th 1983; 1,577 on November 17th 1985; 1,805 on October 16th 1988 and 2,181 on November 16th 1997. Since 1997, however, the only four-figure count has been 1,529 on September 12th 1999 and the peak counts in 2004 and 2005 only numbered 630 and 670 respectively.

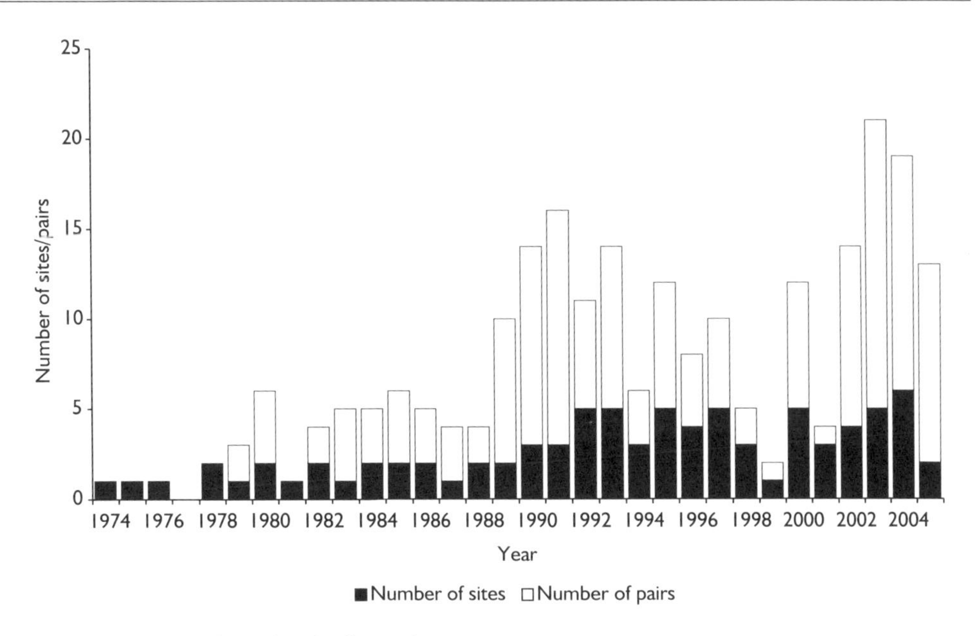

Figure 44: Breeding numbers of Gadwalls 1974–2005.

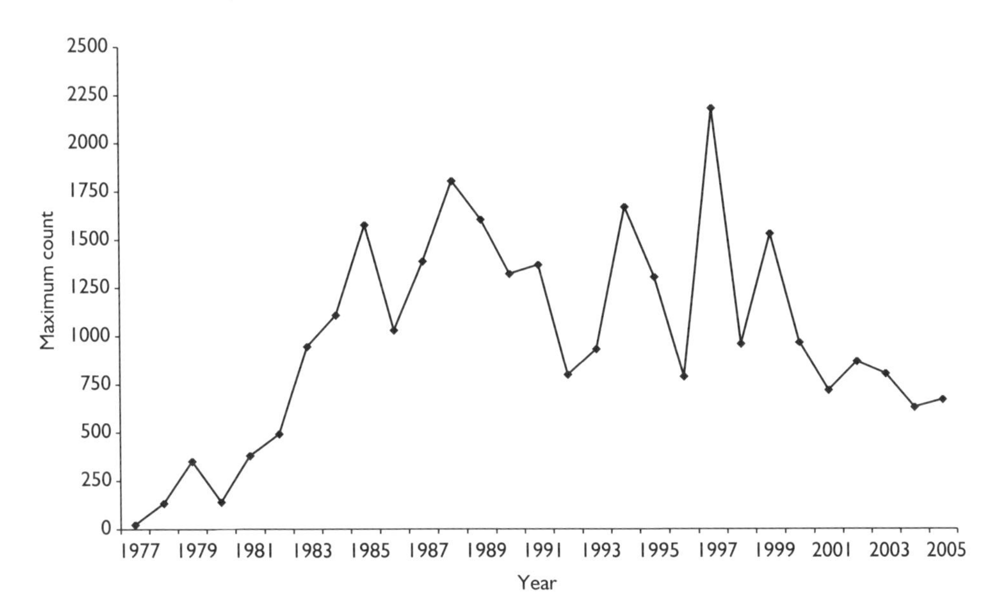

Figure 45: Maximum counts of Gadwalls at Rutland Water 1977–2005.

Numbers have increased at other local sites, with the result that Fort Henry Ponds, Stanford Reservoir, Eyebrook Reservoir and Swithland Reservoir have all reached the qualifying level of 171 to become nationally important (Collier *et al.* 2005). The highest counts at these sites have been:

- 502 at Eyebrook Reservoir on September 17th 1989
- 308 at Swithland Reservoir on December 13th 2003

- 267 at Stanford Reservoir on November 17th 1996
- 208 at Fort Henry Ponds on January 19th 1997

Counts of 100+ have been noted at a further three sites, where maxima were: 136 at Wanlip South Gravel Pits on November 24th 2002; 109 at Priory Water on November 3rd 1996 and 105 at Birstall Gravel Pits on December 20th 2005.

See 'Wintering Birds' (pages 39–43) for details of highest counts at individual sites.

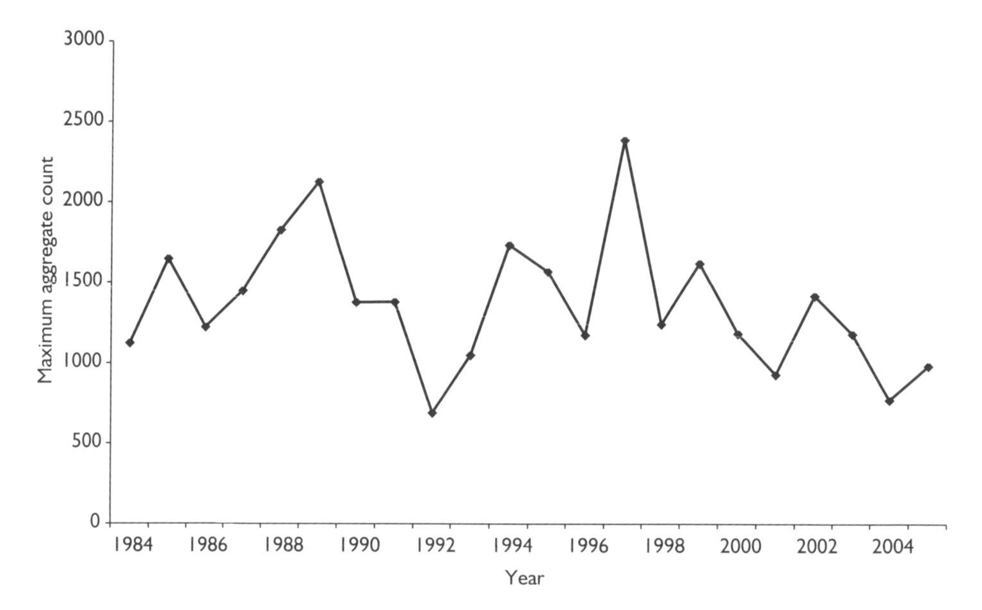

Figure 46: Maximum aggregate counts of Gadwalls at the main sites 1984–2005.

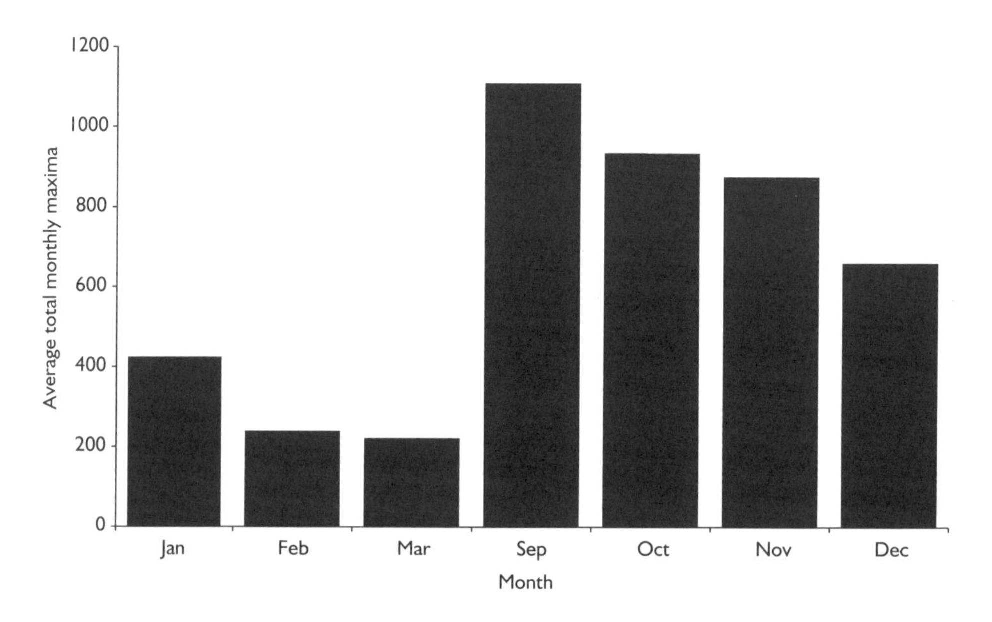

Figure 47: Average total monthly maxima of Gadwalls at the main sites 1995–2005.

Although most of the highest individual counts have been made later in the autumn and winter, data show that on average September is the month when most occur and that numbers decline rapidly during the winter. The very recent increase in numbers of passage and wintering birds is not thought to be linked to introductions which began in the mid-19th century (Wernham *et al.* 2002) and a large proportion seems likely to have originated from eastern Europe. Two males ringed at Rutland Water have been recovered abroad: one in the Netherlands and one in Portugal. The latter was ringed on October 24th 1988 and shot the following January, providing a nice example of onward movement. The local breeding population may be more sedentary.

Hybrids with Eurasian Teal, Mallard and Pintail have been recorded: see 'Hybrids' (pages 676–684).

The Gadwall breeds across Eurasia and North America, with the European stronghold in Russia. It breeds further south and east than most European dabbling ducks and extended its range in western Europe during the 20th century (Fox 1988). It was first introduced to East Anglia in the 1850s (Gibbons *et al.* 1993). As many as 1,520 pairs were recorded breeding in Britain in 2004 (Holling *et al.* 2007a) and the wintering population is estimated at approximately 17,100 birds (Baker *et al.* 2006). As more than 20% of the north-west European non-breeding population is found in Britain, this species has been added to the 'Amber List' of Birds of Conservation Concern (Gregory *et al.* 2002).

AHJH

Eurasian Teal — *Anas crecca*

Common autumn and winter visitor, scarce in summer; rare breeder.

Hickling stated that there were occasional breeding records of Eurasian Teal during the 19th century, although the only documented evidence of this is provided by Browne, who said that it nested near Dishley Mill in 1825 and a nest was found at Groby Pool in 1844. Haines could find no evidence of this species having nested in Rutland.

By 1941, the Eurasian Teal was considered to be very common as a winter visitor, with a few resident breeding birds. Since then, however, there have been breeding records in just 12 years and only one since 1985:

1947 a female was seen with young at Swithland Reservoir on July 13th.
1948 a pair with four juveniles was seen at Swithland Reservoir on June 9th and a female with two juveniles was noted at Barrow upon Soar on June 26th.
1949 single pairs with young were at Swithland Reservoir and Oakham on June 11th and 12th respectively.
1974 a brood of nine was at Cropston Reservoir on July 14th.
1975 a brood of six was at Groby Pool on May 31st and a brood of five was at Swithland Reservoir on July 8th
1977 a female with six young was at Rutland Water on July 31st.
1979 a brood of three was at Eyebrook Reservoir on July 26th.
1982 a female with six young was at Eyebrook Reservoir on July 30th and 31st.
1983 a brood of four was at Rutland Water.
1984 three pairs bred at Rutland Water.
1985 two pairs raised seven young at Rutland Water.
2002 broods of five and seven young were seen at Rutland Water during July.

Whether this species has ever been established as a breeding species is open to debate as, despite the inference in 1941 that there were a few resident breeding pairs, there is no documentary evidence to support this and it may have been that a few summering individuals each year were taken at the time to represent breeding birds. However, the reasons for the sharp decline of the breeding population which seemed stable in the mid-1980s are not clear.

Most Eurasian Teals which occur in the counties are passage or winter visitors. Data show that numbers declined between 1951 and 1971, then increased to an aggregate peak of 4,718 in November 1995. Only Rutland Water has attained national importance status for this species at any time, though the current qualifying level is 1,920 birds (Collier *et al.* 2005), a total that has not been reached at this site since 1997. More than 2,000 birds have been recorded at Rutland Water on four occasions, three of which have been since 1990:

- 2,491 on March 10th 1996.
- 2,438 on November 12th 1995.
- 2,187 on September 16th 1990.
- 2,038 on January 16th 1977.

Most other sites record much lower figures, but counts of 500+ have been recorded at five, with maxima being:

- 1,661 at Stanford Reservoir on November 18th 1990.
- 850 at Priory Water on December 15th 1991.

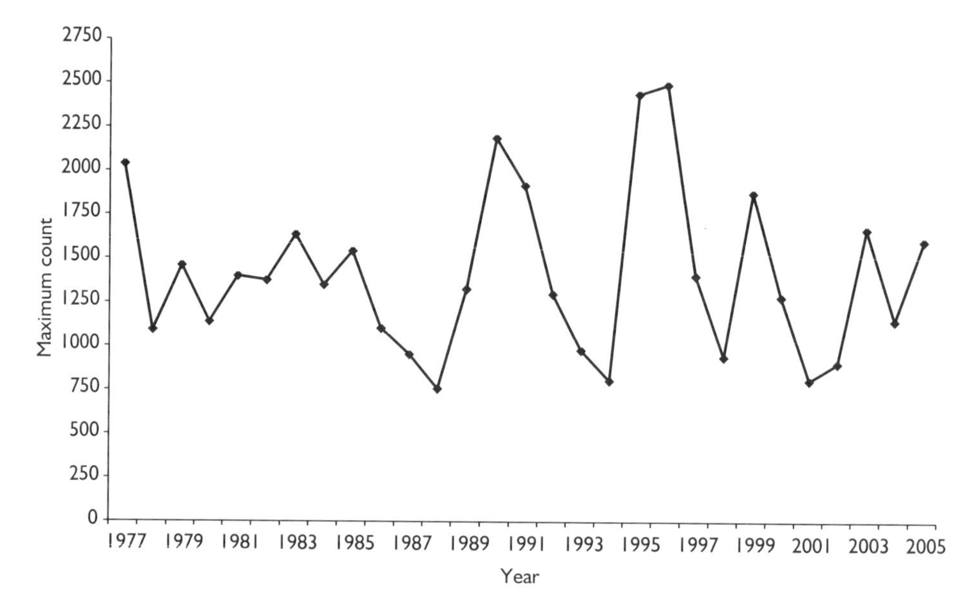

Figure 48: Maximum counts of Eurasian Teals at Rutland Water 1977–2005.

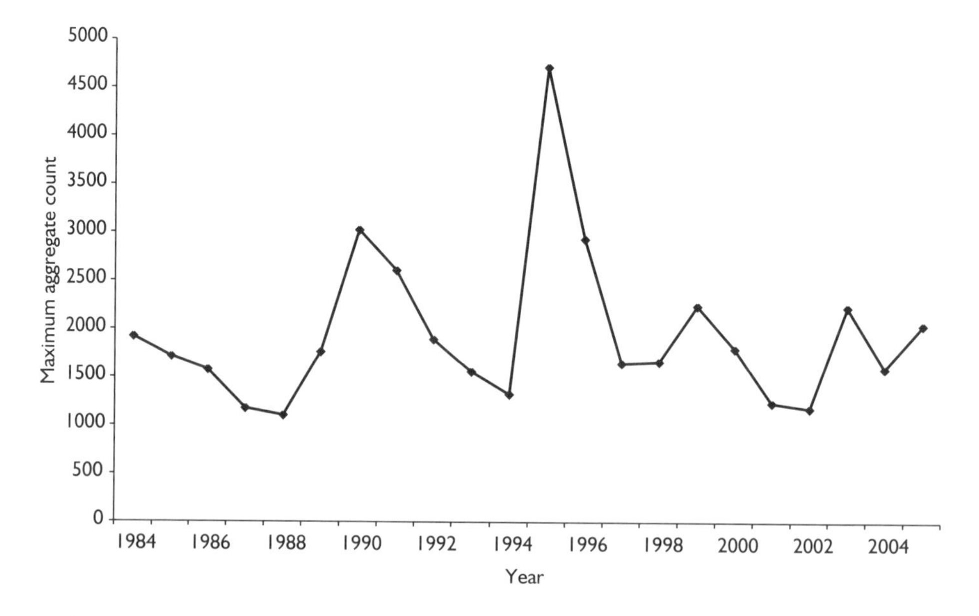

Figure 49: Maximum aggregate counts of Eurasian Teals at the main sites in 1984–2005.

- 831 at Eyebrook Reservoir on November 12th 1978.
- 725 at Swithland Reservoir on January 16th 1977.
- 650 at Cropston Reservoir on January 23rd 1955.

Other notable counts from these sites have been 1,600 at Stanford Reservoir on November 12th 1995, 801 at Eyebrook Reservoir on September 16th 2001, 600 at Cropston Reservoir in January 1949 and on January 18th 1953, 600 at Swithland Reservoir on October 13th 1990, with 510 there on October 26th 1996 and 520 at Priory Water on January 1st 1997.

See 'Wintering Birds' (pages 39–43) for details of highest counts at individual sites.

This species has a very prolonged autumn migration, with males generally moving ahead of females. Combined with hard-weather movements from the continent, this may explain the initial peak in September followed by a secondary peak in November. Numbers decline sharply in February and March following the onset of cold weather or early northward passage, although in 1995–96 higher than normal numbers remained throughout the winter until the following spring.

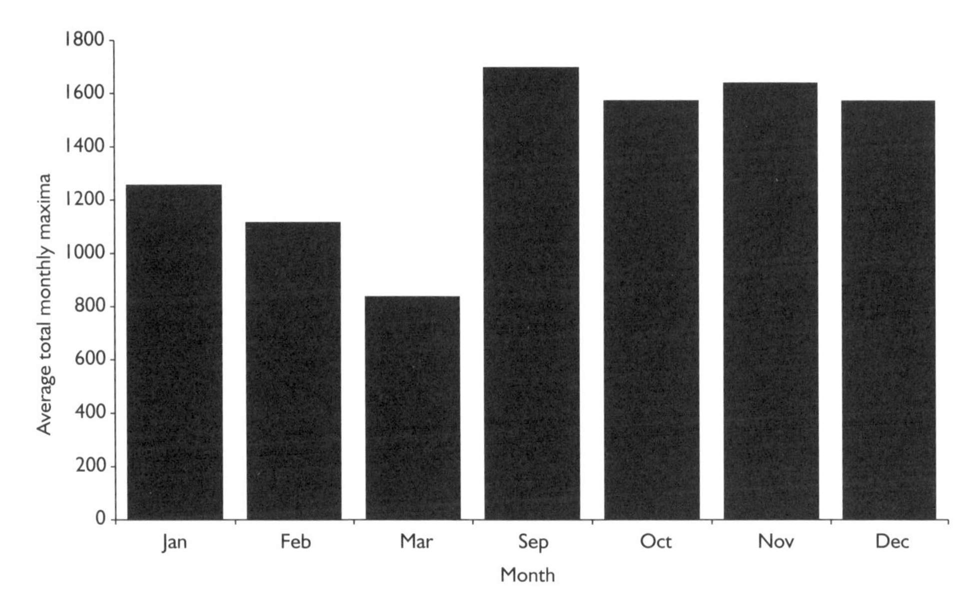

Figure 50: Average total monthly maxima of Eurasian Teals at the main sites 1995–2005.

Ringing recoveries (Table 13) show an exchange of birds with several European countries, but no clear pattern and a surprising lack of recoveries from the former USSR.

Table 13: Recoveries of Eurasian Teals moving between Europe and Leicestershire and Rutland

Country	Number of birds from Leicestershire and Rutland	Number of birds recovered in Leicestershire and Rutland	Comments
Denmark	3	3	
Finland	5	0	
France	1	0	
Germany	1	0	
Netherlands	1	1	
Norway	1	0	
Poland	0	2	Ringed in July
Sweden	0	1	Ringed in July
Turkey	1	0	

Hybrids with Eurasian Wigeon, Gadwall and Green-winged Teal have been recorded: see 'Hybrids' (pages 676–684).

Eurasian Teals breed throughout the middle latitudes of the Western Palearctic. Northern populations winter mainly in countries bordering the North Sea and, as more than 20% of the north-west European non-breeding population winters in the UK, this species has been added to the 'Amber List' of Birds of Conservation Concern (Gregory *et al.* 2002). British breeding numbers have been declining since the 1940s (Gibbons *et al.* 1996) and the latest estimate is between 1,500 and 2,600 pairs (Baker *et al.* 2006).

AHJH

Green-winged Teal *Anas carolinensis*

Very rare vagrant from North America: four records.

The first record occurred in 1979, when a male was at Rutland Water from April 18th to 28th (the dates were published incorrectly in the LROS Annual Report as April 22nd to 28th); it then moved to Eyebrook Reservoir, where it was seen from May 3rd to 13th (*BB* 73:499). The three subsequent records, all of males, have come from Rutland Water: one found by Andy Forryan on April 26th 1989 (*BB* 83:449); one seen by Keith Bindley and James Cracknell on November 17th 1989 (*BB* 83:449) and one on May 7th and 8th 1995 which was originally found by Andy Mackay and Steve Close. A male at Saddington Reservoir from December 7th to 12th 2005 was not accepted because it was thought to show some characters indicating Eurasian Teal genes.

A hybrid with Eurasian Teal has been recorded: see 'Hybrids' (pages 676–684).

The Green-winged Teal breeds in northern North America and winters across much of the USA and south into Central America and the West Indies; it was considered a race of Eurasian Teal until 2001, when it was officially split by the BOU. It was dropped from the list of species considered by the BBRC at the end of 1990. The species is a regular visitor to Britain, with 25 on average per year, mainly in winter and spring, but its occurrence patterns are clouded by the fact that eclipse males, females and juveniles are indistinguishable on current knowledge from Eurasian Teal. The four county records fit in to this established vagrancy pattern, with the November 1989 bird possibly a newly arrived individual and the other three on spring passage. As with other Nearctic wildfowl, spring records are likely to relate to birds moving north after arriving on this side of the Atlantic the previous autumn.

AHJH

Mallard *Anas platyrhynchos*

Common autumn and winter visitor, fairly common breeder.

The Mallard is one of our most familiar native birds, though not one of the best studied. Browne described it as resident and generally distributed in Leicestershire in the 19th century, to the extent that he included little information about numbers. Haines considered it a numerous resident in Rutland, breeding along the Eye and elsewhere. At times it was recorded in large flocks of hundreds, with nearly 250 at flooded meadows at Seaton on December 19th 1901.

There is little data regarding the breeding distribution and density of the Mallard in the counties with the exception of the work carried out by Warrilow between 1976 and 1984. He recorded this species in 399 tetrads in the counties (62% of all tetrads), with breeding confirmed in 196, making it the most common and widespread species of wildfowl. It was found to breed close to a wide range of wetland habitats from reservoir margins to small ponds as well as gravel pits, streams, rivers and canals. Some nests are away from water under sheltered hedgerows, along ditches or occasionally along woodland margins. There are even examples of nesting on modern housing estates. It was absent as a breeding bird from the higher ground of the Leicestershire wolds, between Loughborough and Eaton and parts of east Leicestershire between Melton Mowbray and Billesdon. Given an average of three to five pairs per occupied tetrad, he estimated a countywide population of 1,200 to 2,000 pairs. The only other recent indication of breeding distribution was provided by Mitcham (1992), who identified 59 occupied tetrads in Rutland, in 25 of which breeding was proven.

Flocks of over 1,000 birds used to be regularly recorded at the larger reservoirs during autumn, winter and spring. Aggregate counts for Leicestershire and Rutland have exceeded 5,000 in five years, the highest being 5,980 in November 1976 and 5,493 in September 1990. However, numbers have declined since the early 1990s in keeping with a national decline of 40% in wintering stock (Wernham *et al.* 2002) and the highest aggregate count has only exceeded 4,000 in one year since 1992.

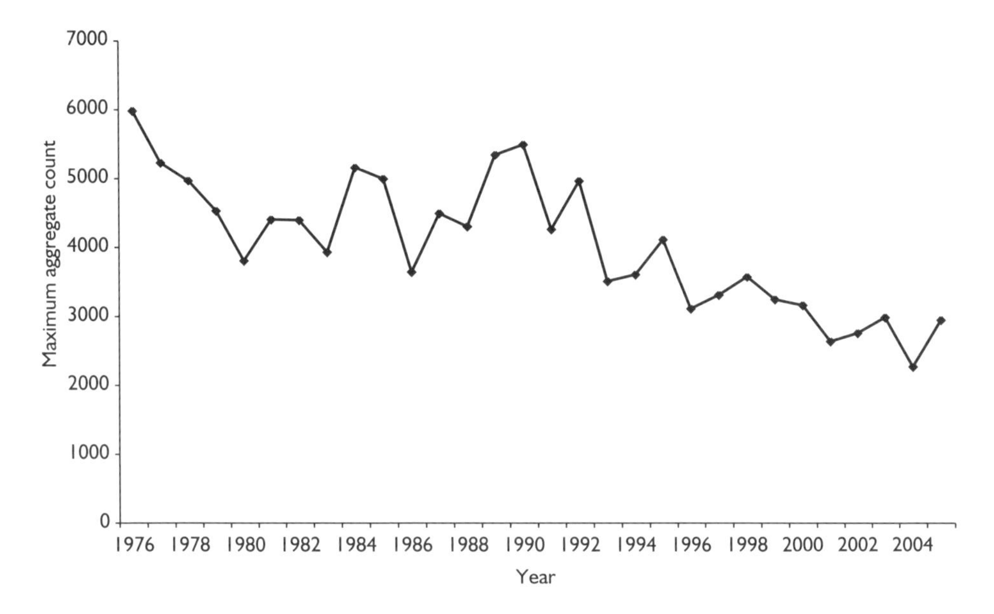

Figure 51: Maximum aggregate counts of Mallards at the main sites 1976–2005.

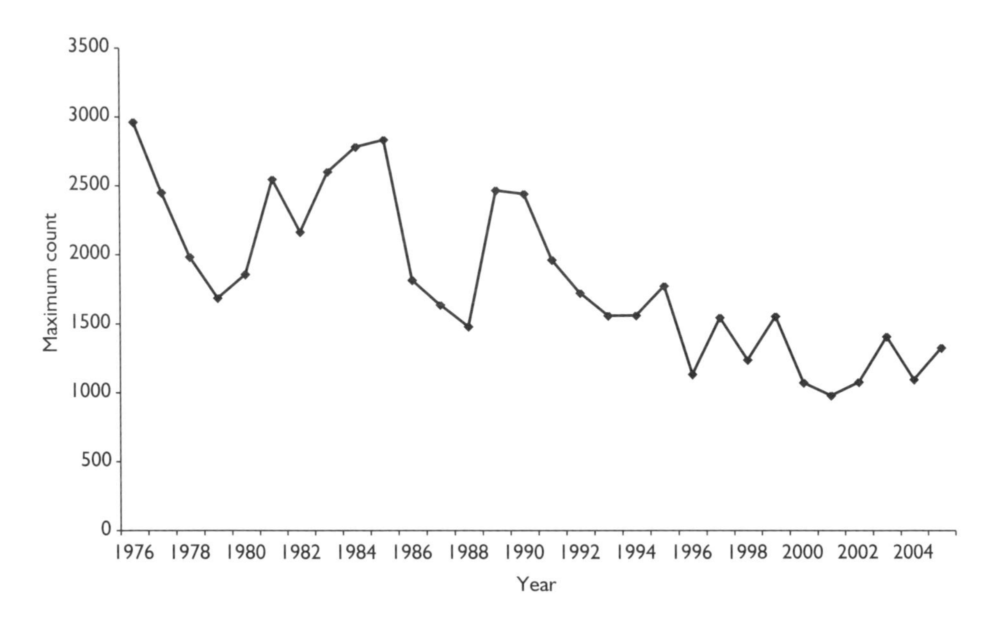

Figure 52: Maximum counts of Mallards at Rutland Water 1976–2005.

Counts at Rutland Water have exceeded 2,000 in nine years, although none of these have been since 1990: the highest have been 2,961 on December 12th 1976, 2,832 on September 15th 1985 and 2,781 on September 16th 1984. By 1996 the maximum count was 1,132, the lowest at this site since its construction; five years later the highest count only numbered 977. The current threshold for sites of national importance is 3,520 (Collier *et al.* 2005).

Counts of 1,000 or more have been recorded at a further four sites, where the maxima have been 2,100 at Eyebrook Reservoir on October 12th 1969, 2,000 at Stanford Reservoir on September 9th 1949, 1,500 at Cropston Reservoir on both December 11th 1955 and September 12th 1976 and 1,200 at Staunton Harold Reservoir on January 12th 1967; in addition, 1,120 were divided between Knipton Reservoir and Belvoir Lakes on November 21st 1954. Other notable site maxima have been 900 at both Swithland Reservoir in early January 1947 and Knipton Reservoir on December 12th 1965, 869 at Fort Henry Ponds on October 12th 1996, 850 at Groby Pool on September 13th 1970 and 600 at Blackbrook Reservoir on December 27th 1946. Significant numbers were recorded on the River Soar within the city boundary of Leicester during the 1980s and early 1990s, with several counts exceeding 350 and a maximum of 472 on February 9th 1991. See 'Wintering Birds' (pages 39–43) for details of highest counts at individual sites.

It is evident that the majority of the largest counts occurred prior to the 1970s and in recent years only Rutland Water has recorded four-figure counts. Counts of over 250 have come from the following sites since 2001: Eyebrook Reservoir, Fort Henry Ponds, Groby Pool, Lockington Marshes, Priory Water, the River Soar within the city boundary of Leicester, Stanford Reservoir and Swithland Reservoir.

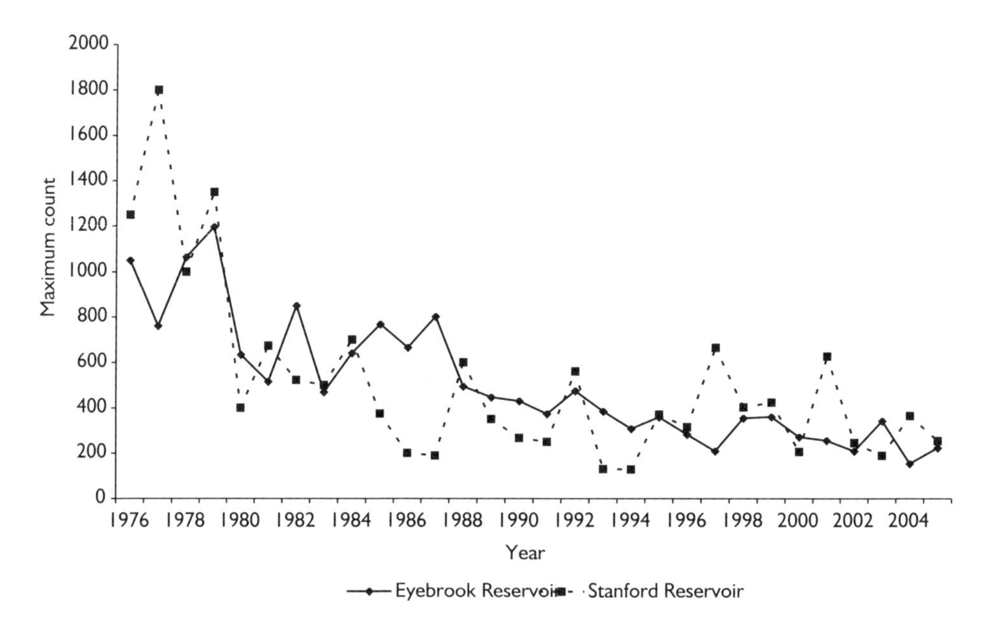

Figure 53: Maximum counts of Mallards at Eyebrook Reservoir and Stanford Reservoir 1976–2005.

There has also been a shift in the seasonal distribution of records, as more birds occur in September, which is now the peak month. Numbers remain high during the winter before declining gradually in spring as birds disperse to breed.

Ringing recoveries indicate that most birds move within the counties or to and from neighbouring counties, though there are also two foreign recoveries (from Denmark and Sweden) of birds ringed at Rutland Water and three local recoveries of birds ringed abroad (two from Belgium and one from Denmark). The most recent of the latter was from 1962: a decline in the proportion of continental immigrants may account for falling numbers of wintering birds and may explain why the autumn peak has become earlier.

Hybrids with Muscovy Duck, Gadwall, Pintail and Tufted Duck have been recorded: see 'Hybrids' (pages 676–684).

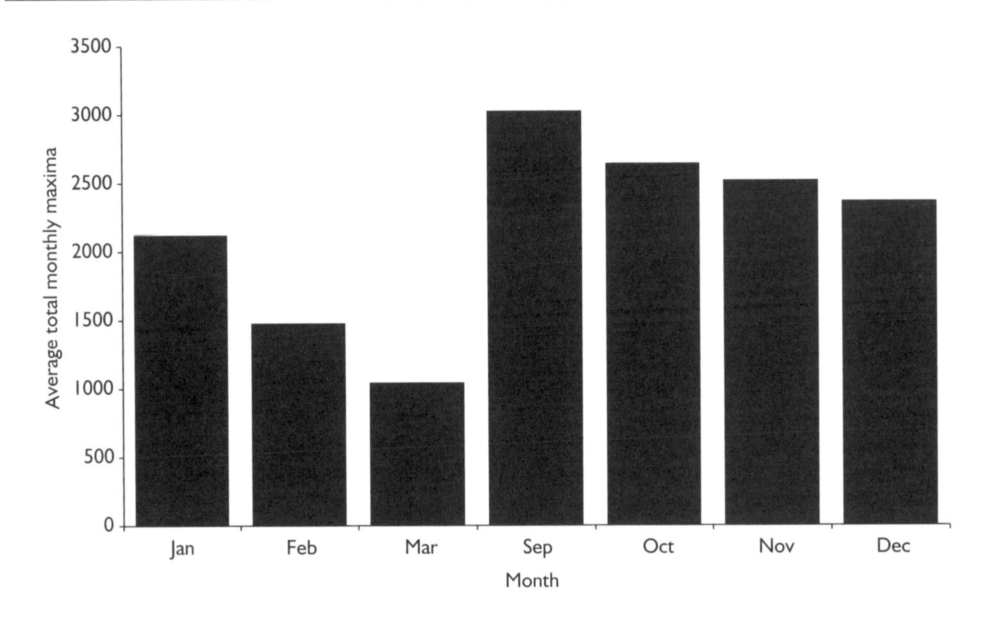

Figure 54: Average total monthly maxima of Mallards at the main sites 1995–2005.

Mallards breed throughout most of Eurasia and North America. British birds are largely resident, but numbers in winter are augmented by immigrants from Scandinavia and Iceland. Mallards have increased steadily as breeding birds in Britain since the 1960s, especially in England, an increase to which ongoing large-scale releases for shooting may have contributed. The most recent British population estimate is 47,700 to 114,400 pairs (Baker *et al.* 2006).

AHJH

Pintail (Northern Pintail) ***Anas acuta***

Fairly common autumn visitor, uncommon winter visitor.

Browne described the Pintail as an uncommon winter visitor to Leicestershire in the 19th century, citing records from Groby Pool, Kilby Bridge and Narborough Bog. Haines knew of only two records in Rutland: a pair shot at Burley in December 1883 and a female specimen at Burley House, which was probably obtained at the same locality. During the first part of the 20th century, the LROS archives refer to two records: at Narborough on May 6th 1902 and Cropston Reservoir on February 27th 1940.

The Pintail had become an uncommon winter visitor by the early 1940s but numbers increased following the flooding of Eyebrook Reservoir. In 1946 150 were present there on both January 13th and December 27th and in 1948 numbers reached 250 during January. Peak counts occurred in 1949, when 400 to 500 were recorded on February 13th and 300 on November 13th. Elsewhere during this time the only double-figure counts were 22 at Swithland Reservoir from December 26th 1946 into January 1947 and 15 at both Blackbrook Reservoir on November 5th 1942 and Groby Pool in January 1947. Numbers decreased during the next two decades; there were 150 at Eyebrook Reservoir in February 1950 and on December 27th and 28th 1953 but the highest count at this site in the 1960s was 48 on February 15th 1969. Counts of 11 at Blackbrook Reservoir on February 28th 1954 and 20 at Stanford Reservoir on December 21st 1968 were the only double-figure counts away from Eyebrook Reservoir during the 1950s and 1960s.

It is notable that the flooding of Rutland Water in the 1970s was not followed by the appearance of a stable flock which remained throughout the winter, similar to the one formerly present at Eyebrook Reservoir, although a count of 103 at Rutland Water on October 21st 1977 was the largest in the counties since 1953. From 1989 onwards, however, Rutland Water has attracted large numbers during the autumn, with peaks of

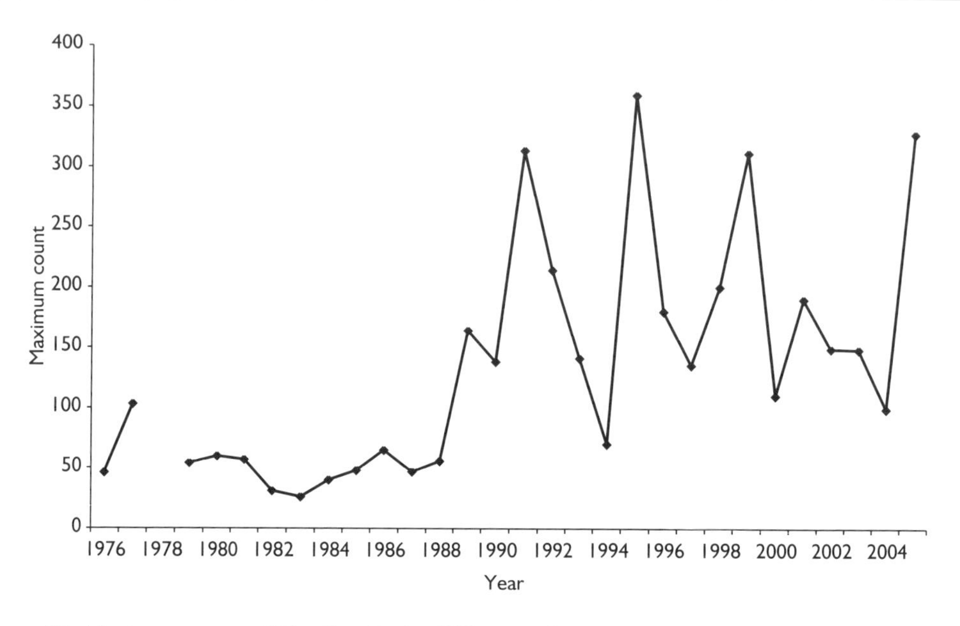

Figure 55: Maximum counts of Pintails at Rutland Water 1976–2005.

313 on October 13th 1991, 359 on October 8th 1995, 311 on September 12th 1999 and 327 on October 19th 2005. The current threshold for sites to qualify as being of national importance for this species is 279 (Collier *et al.* 2005).

Apart from 36 at Eyebrook Reservoir on November 30th 1974 numbers at this site did not exceed 30 again until 1991. The highest recent counts have been 75 on October 8th 1994, 74 on October 27th 2001, 76 on October 3rd 2002 and 90 on October 16th 2004.

Pintails are rarely recorded in significant numbers away from Rutland Water and Eyebrook Reservoir although there have been two exceptional counts: 80 flying over Priory Water on November 28th 1993 and 67

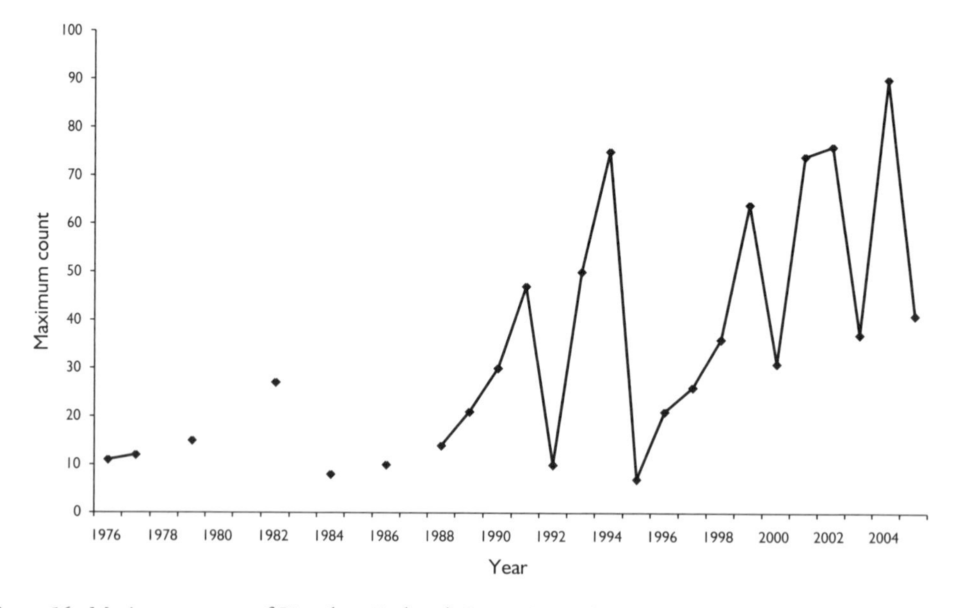

Figure 56: Maximum counts of Pintails at Eyebrook Reservoir 1976–2005.

at Stanford Reservoir on October 8th 1995. Totals of 20 or more have been recorded at another three sites, where maxima have been 32 at Swithland Reservoir on February 16th 1996, 21 at Fort Henry Ponds on October 10th 1998 and 20 at Wanlip Gravel Pits on January 2nd 1977. One or two were present in the unlikely surroundings of Abbey Park, Leicester during the winters of 2003–04 and 2004–05. See 'Wintering Birds' (pages 39–43) for details of highest counts at individual sites.

Most occur between September and April but there are occasional records of single birds during the summer months and early arrivals in autumn are sometimes present from mid-June onwards, whilst late birds in spring

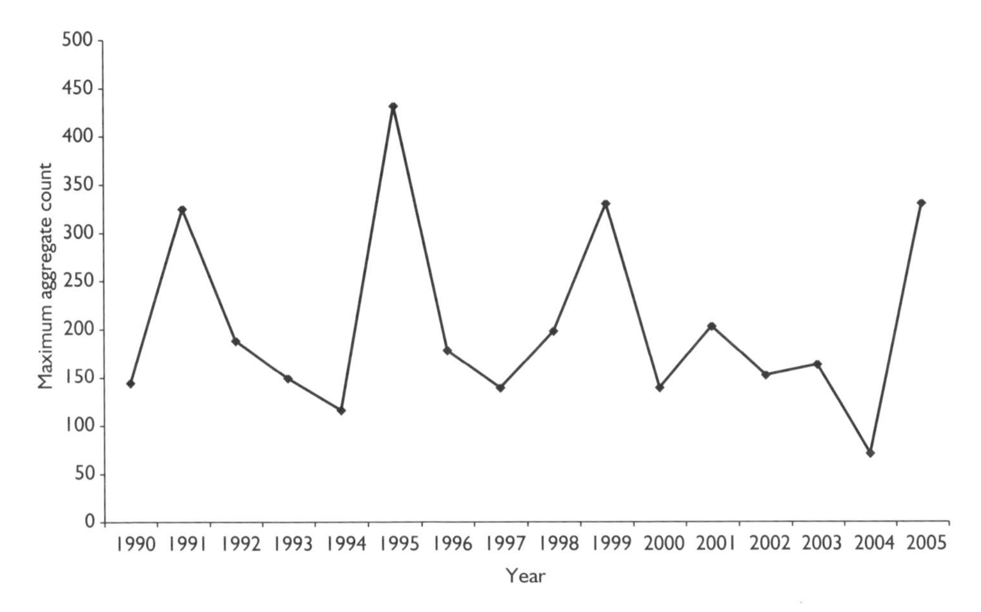

Figure 57: Maximum aggregate counts of Pintails at the main sites 1990–2005.

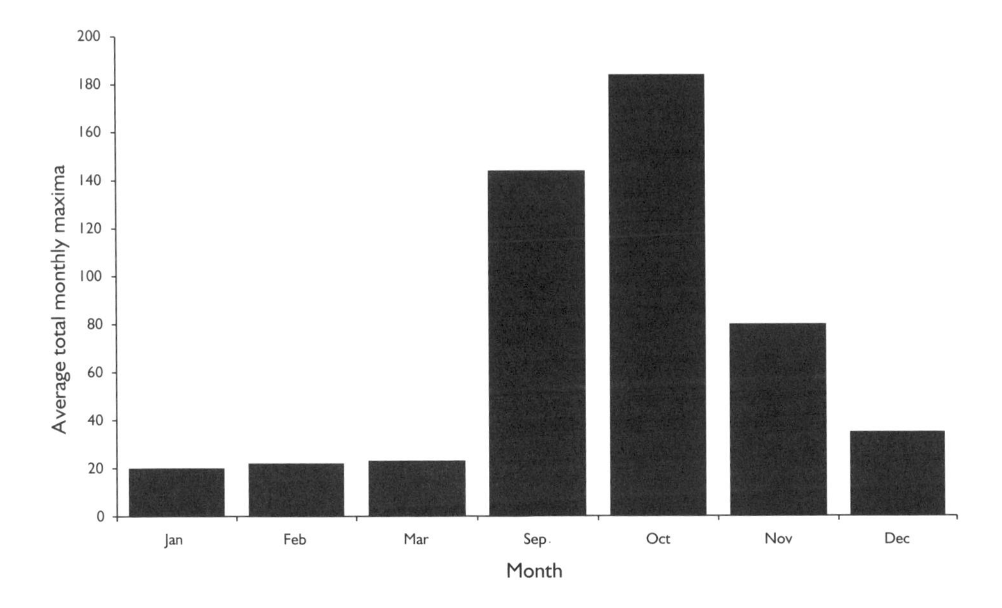

Figure 58: Average total monthly maxima of Pintails at the main sites 1995–2005.

sometimes linger into May. Recent data show that peak numbers occur during autumn passage in September and October, with the highest aggregate count being 431 in October 1995. Relatively few remain throughout the winter. In most years the majority have left by March, though an exceptional 180 were recorded at Rutland Water on March 9th 1996.

The only years in which it seemed possible that birds might remain to breed were 1996, when a pair stayed at Rutland Water until May 19th with the female present until June 2nd and 2001 when a pair was recorded at the same site from May 27th until the end of July.

Hybrids with Gadwall, Mallard and Red-crested Pochard have been recorded: see 'Hybrids' (pages 676–684).

The Pintail has a circumpolar breeding distribution. All populations winter south of the breeding areas, in western and southern Europe, west Africa and southern Asia. It is a rare breeding bird in Britain, with 30 to 40 pairs present during 1988–91 (Gibbons *et al.* 1993) and just eight to 21 pairs in 2005 (Holling *et al.* 2008). This, combined with the presence of about 47% of the European wintering population, has resulted in Pintail being added to the 'Amber List' of Birds of Conservation Concern (Gregory *et al.* 2002).

AHJH

Garganey — *Anas querquedula*

Uncommon autumn and scarce spring migrant, very rare breeder. Recorded in all months except February, with the majority from late March to May and late July to September.

The only 19th century records involved two groups of four, all of which were shot: at Saddington Reservoir in July 1868 and Burley Fishponds in August 1887. The former were all eaten! Prior to the formation of LROS in 1941, the only documented 20th century record involved a flock of 19 at Thornton Reservoir on March 25th 1940. This is a remarkable number, especially in the spring, and one that has not been exceeded since, so this record is probably best treated with a degree of caution.

The Garganey remained a scarce visitor to the counties from 1941 to the late 1960s and most records were during the spring; there were no reports in 1941, 1943, 1956, 1957 and 1959. Notable annual totals during this period were 25 in 1948 and 14 in 1952. Since 1959 this species has been recorded annually, with an increase in numbers from the early 1970s and a further increase from the early 1990s. At least ten individuals have been recorded in every year since 1981, with the highest annual totals being 33 in 1992, 35 in 1989, 36 in 2003 and an exceptional 51 in 1999. The data show that there has been an increase in the numbers recorded in autumn during the last two decades (which may reflect improvments to optical equipment and identification guides used by more observers as much as a genuine increase in numbers), but numbers in spring continue to fluctuate.

Most records involve single birds or pairs, although groups of up to four are not unusual, especially at Rutland Water and Eyebrook Reservoir. Up to seven have been seen on a number of occasions at the former site, the higher counts being:

- eight from August 30th to September 13th 1992.
- up to five males and three females during early May 1998.
- up to nine from August 20th to September 6th 2005.
- 11 on September 3rd 1995.
- 12 on August 7th and 12th 1994, with up to ten throughout the remainder of August and September.
- 12 on August 10th 1996, with ten on August 25th.
- 13 on August 20th 1983, August 27th 1984 and August 15th 1999.

At Eyebrook Reservoir there have been records of four birds together on five occasions, with five together six times. The only higher counts from this site have been six on August 18th 1974 and eight on August 14th 1963. Elsewhere, counts of four or more have come from six sites, as follows:

- Stanford Reservoir: three males and one female on March 28th 1942, two pairs on March 23rd 1952 and seven on March 18th 1962.
- Sawley Gravel Pits: two pairs from March 31st to April 22nd 1945.
- Loughborough Sewage Farm: two pairs on July 25th 1949.
- Cropston Reservoir: four on September 26th 1954.
- Swithland Reservoir: two pairs on April 21st 1968, up to four during August 1975 and five on both August 23rd 1992 and August 22nd 1995.
- Frisby Gravel Pits: four on April 29th 1974.

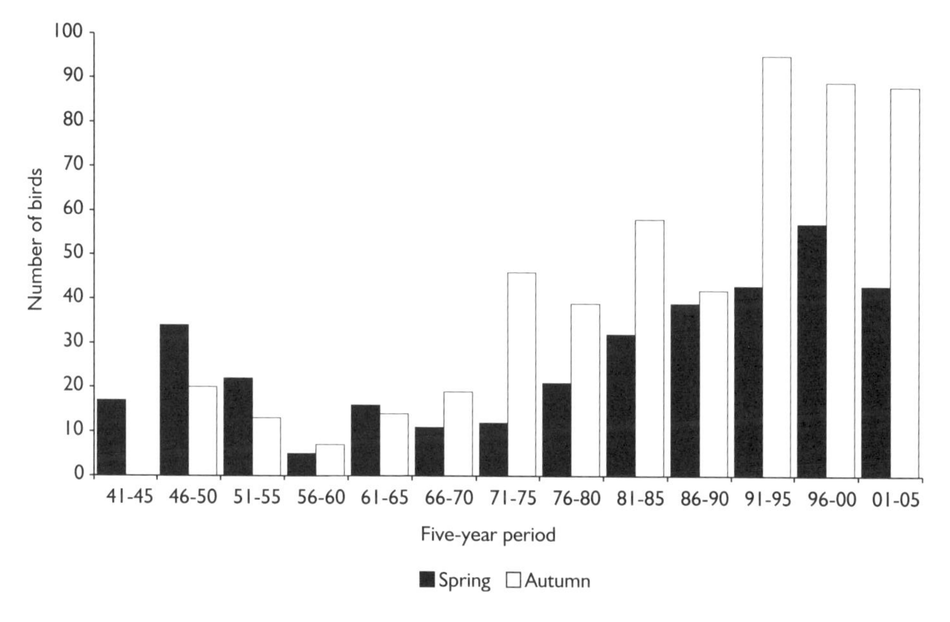

Figure 59: Numbers of Garganey by five-year periods 1941–2005.

Spring passage normally begins in late March and reaches a peak in late April and early May. The earliest spring migrant was a male at Stanford Reservoir on March 8th 1944 and another six birds have arrived on or before March 16th:

- a pair at Frisby Gravel Pits from March 9th to April 17th 1974.
- a male at Rutland Water on March 13th and 14th 1977.
- a male at Eyebrook Reservoir on March 15th 1952.
- a male at Oakthorpe from March 15th to 23rd 2004.
- a male at Trent Valley Pit on March 16th 2003.

Return passage begins in late June and reaches a distinct peak in late July and August. Numbers decline during September and the species is rare by October, though the average latest departure date in recent years has been in late October. Birds have been seen in November on seven occasions, four of which have involved individuals that arrived earlier in the autumn:

- one at Cropston Reservoir remained from October 16th to November 1st 1990.
- one at Rutland Water from November 1st to 4th 2001.
- one at Swithland Reservoir on November 7th 1976.
- one at Sence Valley Forest Park remained from October 7th to November 11th 2005.
- a juvenile female at Priory Water which was first seen on September 5th 1993 was last recorded on November 14th.

- an eclipse male at Eyebrook Reservoir from November 5th to 19th 2004.
- a juvenile at Rutland Water from November 12th to 25th 2003.

There have been two midwinter records: one at Fort Henry Ponds on December 9th 2001 and a female at Swithland Reservoir on January 9th and 20th 1977.

There are only two cases of confirmed breeding: in 1947 a pair with eight ducklings was seen at Eyebrook Reservoir in June (Bak 1948a) and in 1983 a pair with six ducklings was at Rutland Water on June 29th,

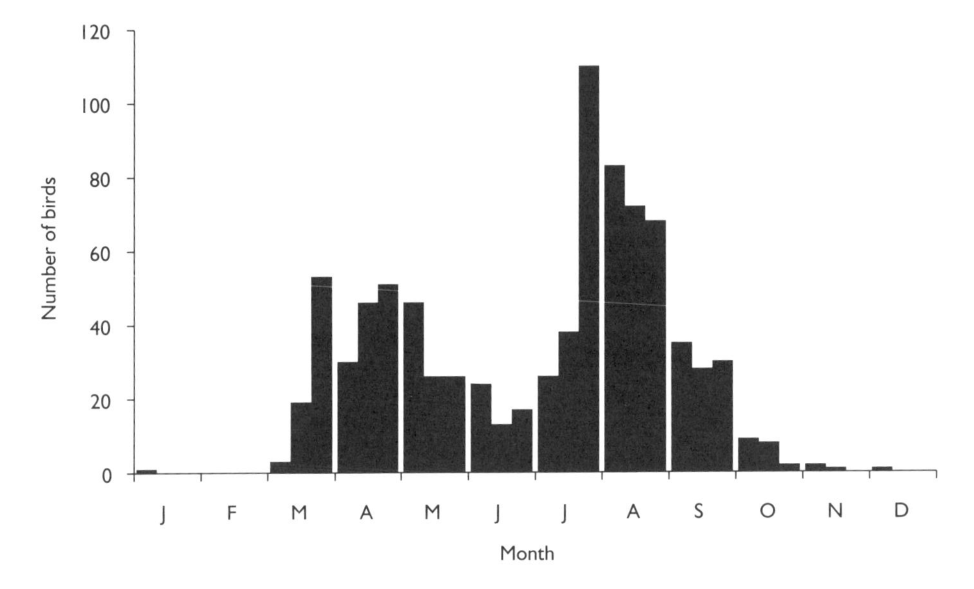

Figure 60: Monthly occurrence of Garganey 1941–2005.

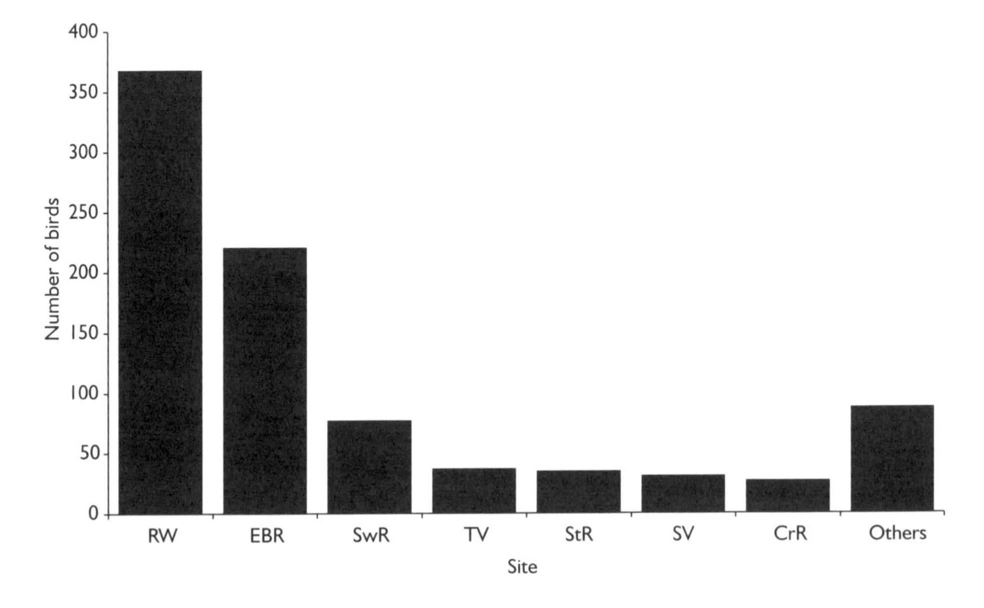

Figure 61: Sites where Garganey have been recorded 1941–2005.
Key to abbreviations: RW = Rutland Water; EBR = Eyebrook Reservoir; SwR = Swithland Reservoir; TV = Trent valley; StR = Stanford Reservoir; SV = Soar valley; CrR = Cropston Reservoir

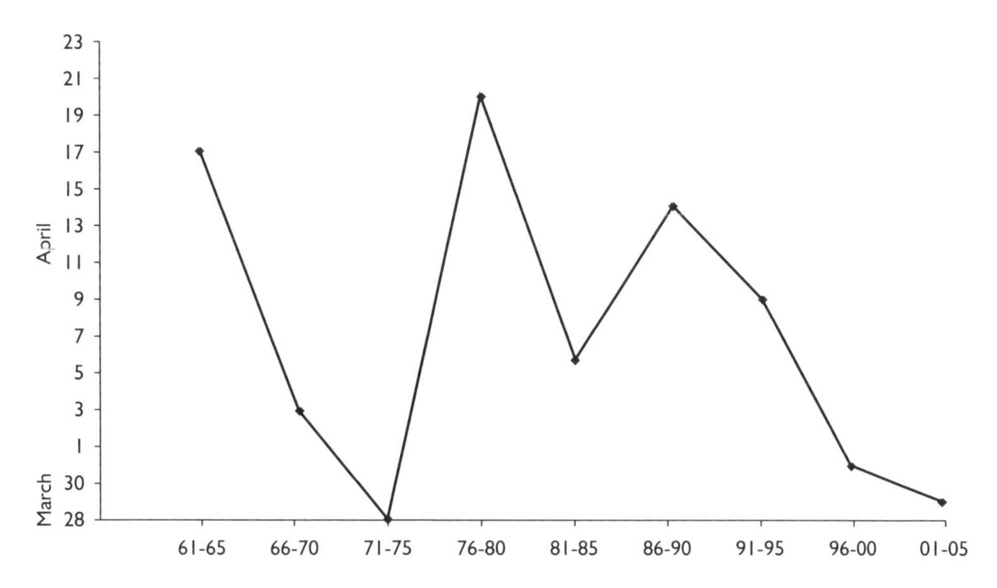

Figure 62: Average spring arrival dates of Garganey by five-year periods 1961–2005.

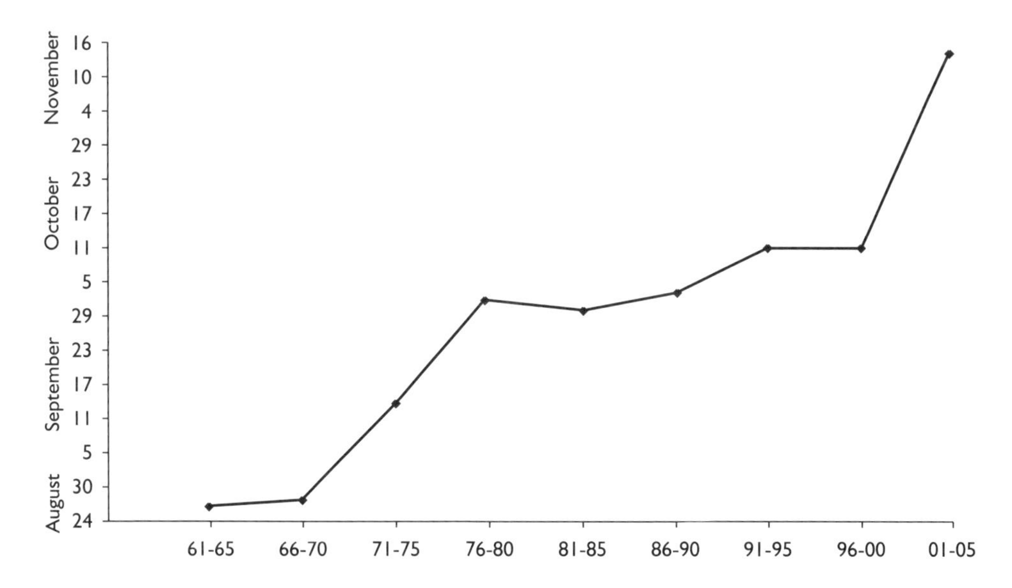

Figure 63: Average autumn departure dates of Garganey by five-year periods 1961–2005.

although the brood was reduced to two by July 3rd. In addition, a pair at Hugglescote from April 24th to June 4th 1983 may have attempted to breed, but no proof was obtained.

Rutland Water and Eyebrook Reservoir are by far the most popular sites for this species, accounting for over 66% of all records. Swithland Reservoir is also a regular site although the Garganey is rather scarce at the counties' other reservoirs: for instance, there have only been two records from Thornton Reservoir (both of single birds) and one record (of three birds) at Saddington Reservoir. The gravel pits of the Trent and Soar valleys have recorded 68 birds between them.

The average spring arrival date of Garganey is highly variable, although since the early 1990s there is a trend of earlier arrivals. Departure dates have definitely become later and it will be interesting to see whether rising temperatures lead to more late autumn and winter records.

Garganey breed from Europe east through northern Asia and most European birds winter in sub-Saharan Africa. Small numbers breed in Britain (usually around 50 to 100 pairs) and due to the small nature of this population Garganey has been added to the 'Amber List' of Birds of Conservation Concern (Gregory *et al.* 2002).

AHJH

Blue-winged Teal *Anas discors*

Very rare vagrant from North America: two records.

The first county record occurred in 1998, when an eclipse male was found by Matthew Berriman at Eyebrook Reservoir on August 29th. It remained until September 12th and was seen and photographed by many observers (Berriman 1999, *BB* 92:565). The same observer was responsible for finding the second individual, another eclipse male, this time at Rutland Water from September 22nd to October 4th 2003; like the first, it attracted many observers and photographers alike (*BB* 97:563).

In addition, a very tame, pinioned bird was at Swithland Reservoir on July 25th 1984 and is not included in the county total.

Blue-winged Teals breed from southern Alaska across much of temperate Canada to the central United States and winter from the southern United States through Central America into South America. They are frequent vagrants to Britain, with over 239 records by the end of 2005, the majority of which have appeared during the autumn. Like many species of wildfowl, there is always the possibility that escaped birds may occur, as evidenced by the Swithland Reservoir bird in 1984; however, the two county records fit neatly into the normal pattern of occurrences of this species in Britain.

AHJH

Shoveler (Northern Shoveler) *Anas clypeata*

Common autumn and fairly common winter visitor, scarce breeder.

Browne knew the Shoveler as a rare winter visitor to Leicestershire during the 19th century and noted 'Harley remarked that in his day the shoveler occurred on most of our large pools and waters, as for example Groby and Barratt, usually during severe weather'. Haines listed just nine records for Rutland; of those dated to month, two were in winter but the other was killed at Seaton on May 21st 1882. The subsequent development of larger reservoirs has resulted in a change of status: this species is now much commoner than formerly.

The Shoveler favours wetlands with abundant zooplankton, where it can remove significant proportions of its Cladoceran and Ostracod prey (Wernham *et al.* 2002). It is therefore not surprising that it is primarily a passage migrant, most numerous in autumn. Smaller numbers remain during the cold winter months. Fewer than five pairs breed in most years.

According to the LROS archives this species was said to have nested at Cropston Reservoir in 1912, but the first confirmed breeding record for the counties concerned one pair at Eyebrook Reservoir in 1941, with four broods recorded there in 1945. Nesting occurred at this site in a further 16 years between 1947 and 1991, including three broods in 1947. Breeding has been confirmed at a further ten sites:

- Swithland Reservoir: bred in 14 years between 1945 and 1991, all single pairs except for three in 1951 and two in 1953.
- Wanlip area: two pairs by the River Soar in 1947 and single pairs at Wanlip Gravel Pits in 1965 and 1976.
- River Soar between Normanton on Soar and Stanford on Soar: one pair in 1950.
- Stanford Reservoir: one pair in 1968.
- Kirby Bellars Gravel Pits: a single pair in 1973.
- Rutland Water: bred in 16 years between 1980 and 2005, including every year from 1995 onwards. The most productive years were 1986 (four broods), 2003 (five pairs hatched 24 young) and 2004 (six pairs hatched 36 young).
- Hemington Gravel Pits: one pair in 1981.

- Hemington Water Meadows: a single pair in 1985.
- Hugglescote: one pair in 1992.
- Trent Valley Pit: a single pair in 1993.

Since 1993, when a female was seen with six young at Trent Valley Pit, the only site where breeding has been confirmed is Rutland Water.

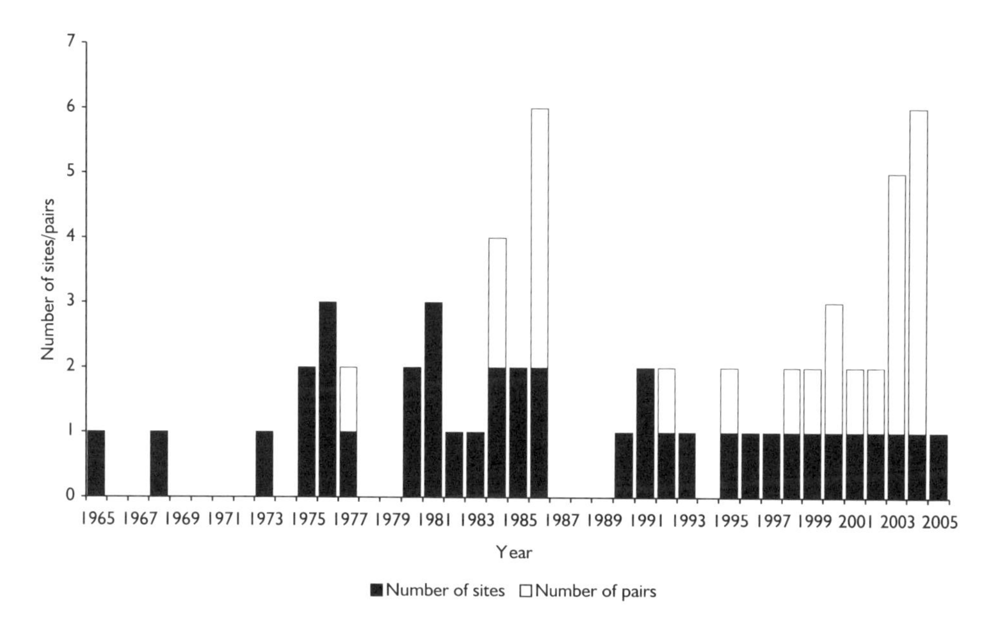

Figure 64: Breeding numbers of Shovelers 1965–2005.

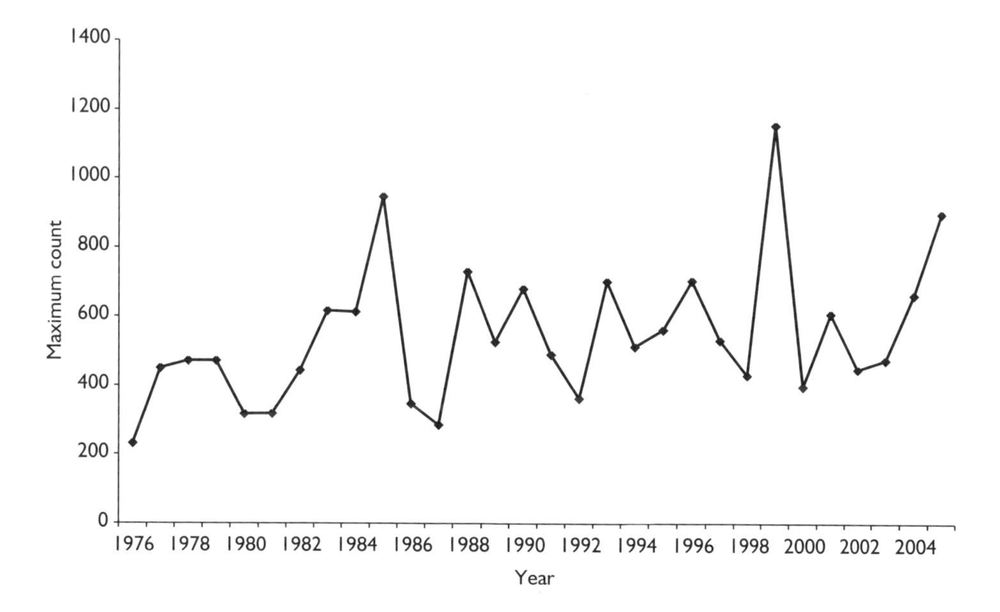

Figure 65: Maximum counts of Shovelers at Rutland Water 1976–2005.

During the 1940s and 1950s the maximum number recorded was 50 at both Stanford Reservoir on October 14th 1945 and Eyebrook Reservoir in December 1954. Numbers rose during the following decade, with 185 at Stanford Reservoir on September 30th 1969 the highest count. The status of this species changed significantly, however, following the construction of Rutland Water: 471 there on September 16th 1979 increased to 947 on October 1st 1985, an impressive 1,154 on September 12th 1999 and 899 on September 9th 2005. These numbers have resulted in Rutland Water being designated as a site of international importance for the species, the current threshold being 400 (Collier *et al.* 2005).

The current threshold for a site to be considered of national importance for the Shoveler is 148 (Collier *et al.* 2005) and two sites in the counties have qualified at various times. Counts at Stanford Reservoir have exceeded this figure in nine years, the highest counts being:

- 548 on October 6th 2001.
- 500 on November 12th 1995.
- 480 on September 17th 1978.
- 350 on November 16th 1975.
- 320 on November 25th 1997.

Numbers at Swithland Reservoir have exceeded 200 in four years, as follows:

- 294 on September 9th 2005.
- 291 on September 28th 1991.
- 222 on September 16th 2000.
- 203 on October 10th 1999.

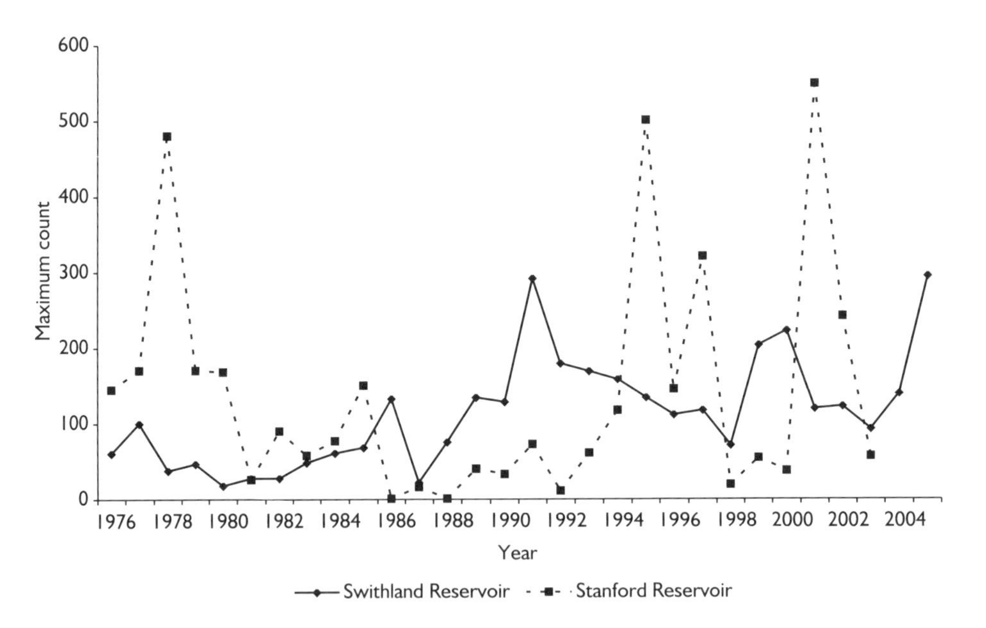

Figure 66: Maximum counts of Shovelers at Swithland Reservoir (1976–2005) and Stanford Reservoir (1976–2003).

Eyebrook Reservoir does not qualify as a site of national importance, but numbers have exceeded 100 in five years:

- 184 on October 7th 2001.
- 170 on October 15th 1978.
- 130 on November 8th 1997.
- 115 on October 14th 1979.

- 111 on October 11th 1996.
- 105 on September 7th 2002.

The only other sites which have recorded three-figure flocks are Cropston Reservoir, where the maximum count was 130 on November 16th 1975 and Groby Pool, where the highest count was 108 on October 13th 1991. Other sites which regularly attract smaller numbers include the Watermead Country Park complex, Trent Farm Pool, Melton Country Park and Fort Henry Ponds.

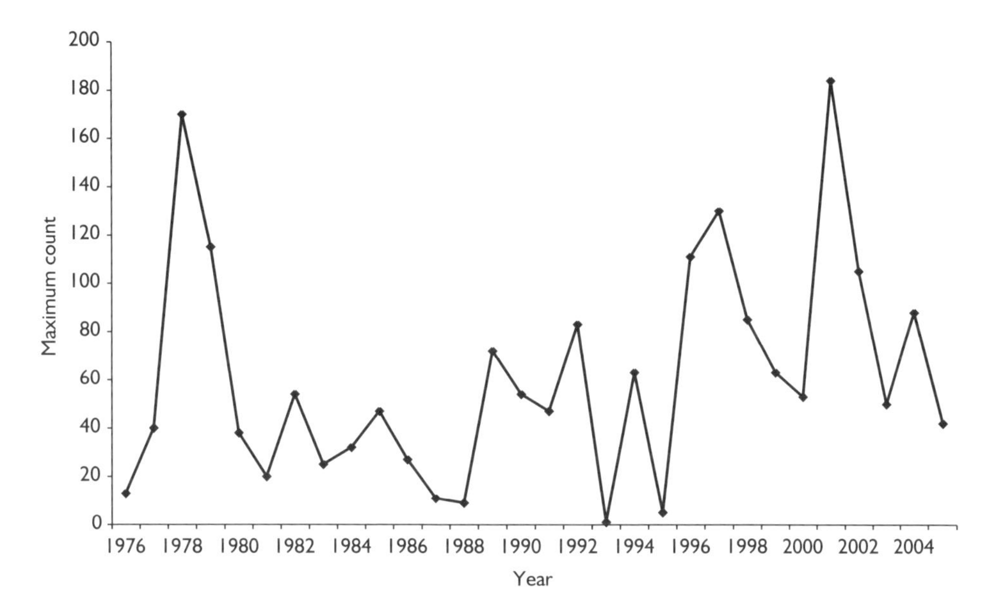

Figure 67: Maximum counts of Shovelers at Eyebrook Reservoir 1976–2005.

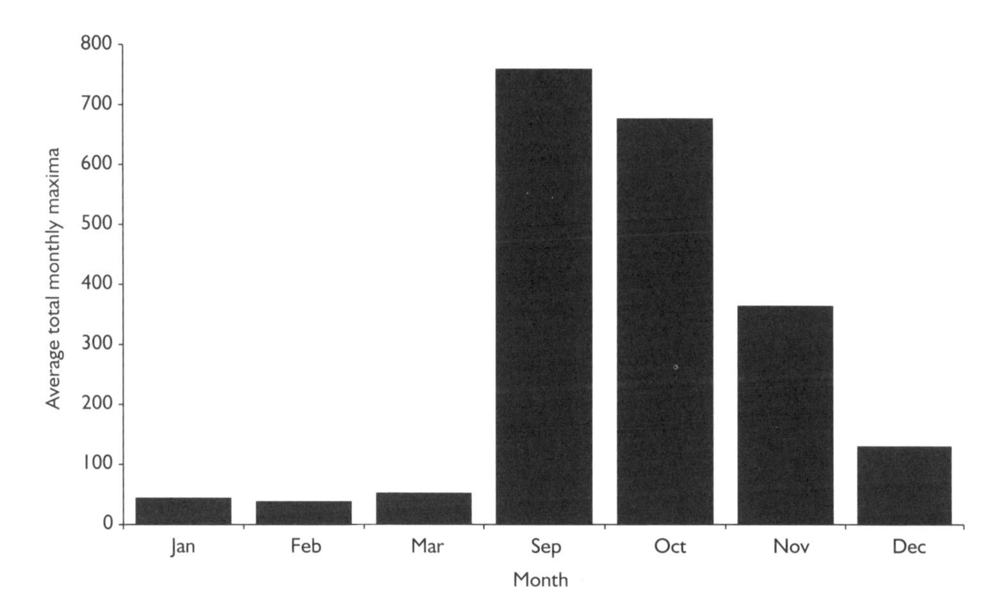

Figure 68: Average total monthly maxima of Shovelers at the main sites 1995–2005.

Data show that peak numbers occur from September to November, when four-figure aggregate counts have been recorded on four occasions:

- 1,278 in November 1995.
- 1,480 in September 1999.
- 1,127 in October 2001.
- 1,322 in September 2005.

See 'Wintering Birds' (pages 39–43) for details of highest counts at individual sites.

Numbers decrease significantly during the winter as birds move south to France, the Iberian Peninsula and North Africa. There is a small but regular and pronounced spring passage during March and April.

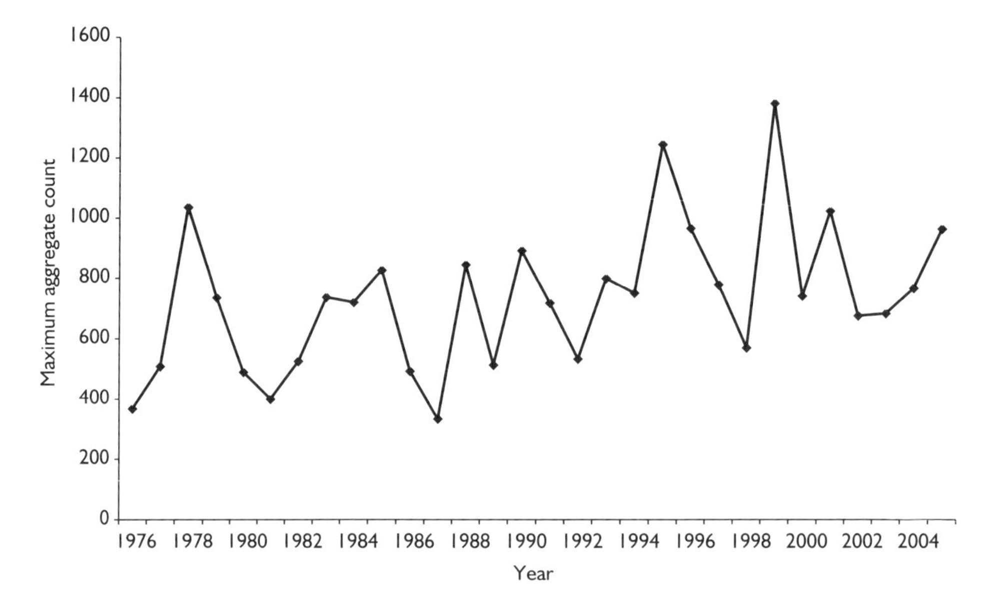

Figure 69: Maximum aggregate counts of Shovelers at the main sites 1976–2005.

There has been one recovery of a bird ringed abroad: a male ringed in Latvia on June 12th 1978 was shot at Knipton Reservoir on September 10th 1980.

A tendency for this species to exhibit leucism or partial albinism has been shown by records of two such birds at Eyebrook Reservoir on October 27th 1985, one at Rutland Water from July 17th to 31st 1988 and one again at Eyebrook Reservoir from August 6th to September 6th 1993 and August 18th to 24th 1994.

A hybrid with Chestnut Teal has been recorded: see 'Hybrids' (pages 676–684).

Shovelers breed from Iceland through northern Eurasia and from Alaska to Newfoundland. The British breeding population, the most recent estimate of which was 1,000 to 1,500 pairs (Baker *et al.* 2006), moves south to France and Iberia in autumn and is replaced by immigrants from as far east as western Siberia. The presence of almost 40% of north-west European non-breeding populations in the UK has led to this species being added to the 'Amber List' of Birds of Conservation Concern (Gregory *et al.* 2002).

AHJH

Red-crested Pochard *Netta rufina*

Scarce, probably feral, visitor; recorded in all months, with the majority from July to November.

The first record of Red-crested Pochard in the counties involved three males at Stanford Reservoir from September 30th until October 2nd 1943, with one remaining until November 7th. Although it was removed

from the list of species considered by the BBRC in 1963 (at the same time as Pectoral Sandpiper and Mediterranean Gull amongst others), the Red-crested Pochard remained a rare vagrant in the counties until the mid-1970s, the only records prior to 1976 being:

- two males, Stanford Reservoir, March 15th 1958 (*BB* 53:161).
- two males, Groby Pool, August 23rd to 30th 1961.
- female, Eyebrook Reservoir, November 16th 1968.
- female, Stanford Reservoir, September 6th 1971.
- female, Eyebrook Reservoir, July 13th 1972.
- eclipse male, Eyebrook Reservoir, July 21st to 22nd 1973.
- male, Swithland Reservoir, September 1st and 15th 1974; same, Cropston Reservoir, September 9th 1974.

This species has been recorded annually since 1976, although it remained rare until the mid-1980s. In all, 28 individuals had been seen in the counties by 1982, so the total of 16 in 1983 was remarkable. Since then, this annual total has been exceeded on eight occasions, the best years being 2004 (30 individuals), 2002 (24), 1987 (21), 1997 (21) and 2005 (20). This trend of larger numbers seems likely to continue.

Most records involve single birds or small groups of up to five, although six have been seen together on two occasions and larger flocks have been recorded as follows:

- six males and a female at Rutland Water on July 17th 2005.
- eight at Rutland Water on September 17th 1987.
- eight (three males and five female/juveniles) at Rutland Water on November 5th and 19th 1995.
- eight (four males and four females) at Stanford Reservoir on October 24th 2004.
- nine (four males and five females) at Rutland Water on November 9th 1997, with five males on November 15th and six males on November 16th.
- nine (six males and three females) at Rutland Water on November 9th 2003.
- ten (all males) at Rutland Water on July 10th 2004.

Although the monthly pattern of records, with a distinct peak in September and October following earlier arrivals during July and August, is compatible with movements of wild birds from continental populations, Harrop (1991) argued that since continental populations have declined the recent dramatic increase in British records is in most cases more likely to be attributable to the growing numbers of birds of captive or feral origin. This view is supported by the recorded presence of up to 19 breeding pairs in the UK in 2004 (Holling *et al.* 2007b), by the growing numbers of the naturalised population in the upper Thames valley and by the fact that large numbers have been released for shooting in north Suffolk from 2005 onwards (Musgrove *et al.* 2007).

Most records come from Rutland Water, which has accounted for 60% of all sightings. A further 19% have been found at Eyebrook Reservoir, meaning that this is still a relatively scarce species in the counties away from the two main sites. It is a surprisingly rare visitor to the Soar valley gravel pits, where the only records have been of a male at Thurmaston Gravel Pits on October 22nd 1983 and a female/juvenile at Birstall Gravel Pits on November 19th 1988, which was seen at Cossington South Gravel Pits eight days later. The only records from Saddington Reservoir are of a male from November 14th to 28th 1992 and a female on July 16th 1996, whilst Thornton Reservoir has produced just one record, of a pair on October 20th 2002. Several of the counties' larger

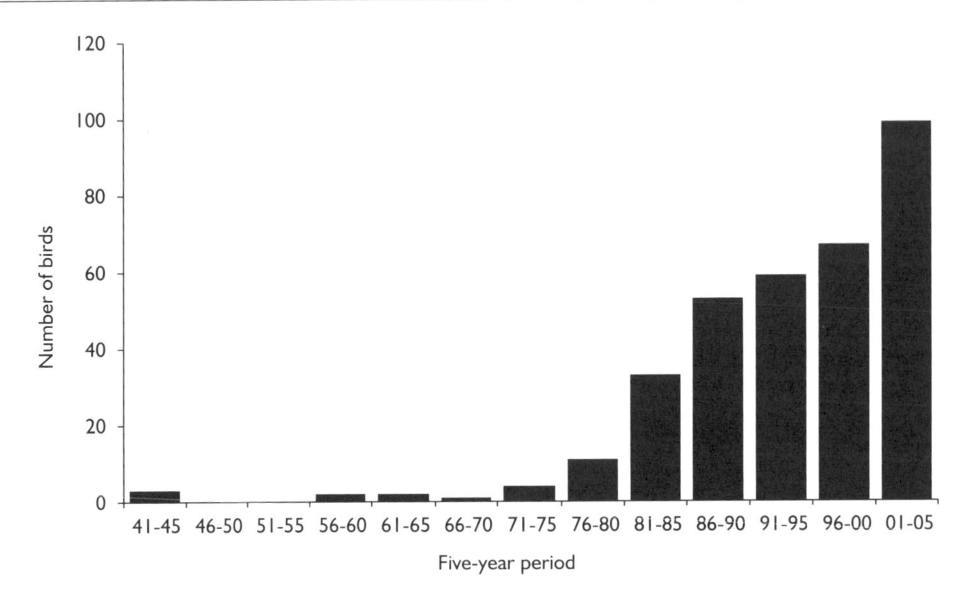

Figure 70: Numbers of Red-crested Pochards by five-year periods 1941–2005.

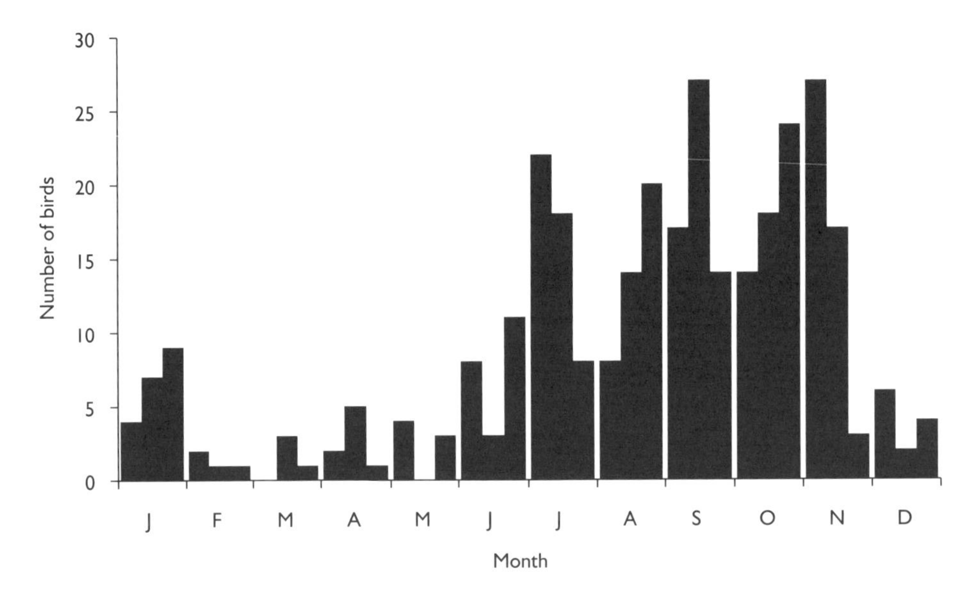

Figure 71: Monthly occurrence of Red-crested Pochards 1941–2005.

areas of water, such as Belvoir Lakes, Trent Valley Pit and the reservoirs at Knipton and Blackbrook, have never recorded this species. The most noteworthy of the more unusual sites that Red-crested Pochards have visited are Enderby Pool (a female from January 22nd to March 10th 1995 and a male from February 10th to May 6th 1996), Frolesworth Manor Lake (two males on August 27th 2001), Sence Valley Forest Park (four juveniles on August 7th 2004) and Ratby Meadows (a first-winter male on September 12th 2004).

Since 1998 there has been a tendency for one or two birds to remain throughout the year. The longest-stayer by far is a male originally seen at Groby Pool on December 24th 1997 which was seen intermittently until at least the end of 2005. On April 30th 2000 a female was observed building a nest at Rutland Water. There has

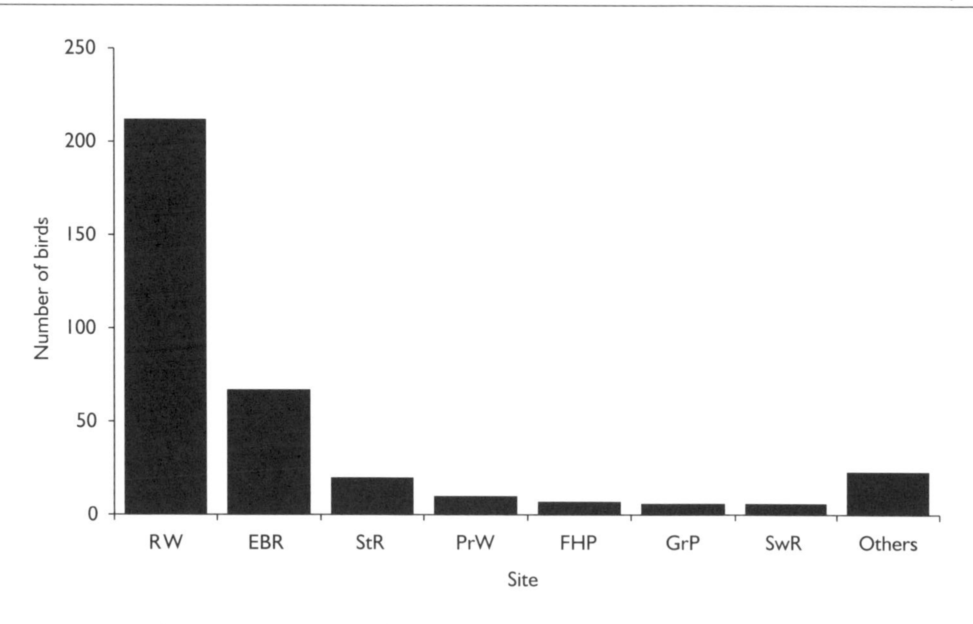

Figure 72: Sites where Red-crested Pochards have been recorded 1941–2005.
Key to abbreviations: RW = Rutland Water; EBR = Eyebrook Reservoir; StR = Stanford Reservoir; PrW = Priory Water; FHP = Fort Henry Ponds; GrP = Groby Pool; SwR = Swithland Reservoir

been a small feral breeding population just 20 miles to the east in Lincolnshire since 1996 and 11 pairs probably bred at two sites in that county in 2004 (Holling *et al.* 2007b), so future breeding records would not be surprising.

Leucistic males were recorded at Rutland Water and Eyebrook Reservoir between August 22nd and November 20th 2004 and at Ratby Meadows on September 12th 2004.

Hybrids with Pintail and Common Pochard have been recorded: see 'Hybrids' (pages 676–684).

Red-crested Pochards breed in Europe, principally east of the Black Sea as far as central Asia. European populations are scattered and relatively small, though there was a range extension into central Europe during the last century. About 20 to 30 pairs nested in the Netherlands in the early 1990s. Most European birds winter either in Spain or around the Danube delta and Black Sea. As no British thresholds have been set, a qualifying level of ten has been chosen for presentation of data in WeBS reports (Musgrove *et al.* 2007).

AHJH

Common Pochard *Aythya ferina*

Fairly common to common autumn and winter visitor, rare breeder.

During the 19th century Browne and Haines gave slightly different versions of the status of this species, Browne describing it as 'a winter visitant, occurring occasionally' in Leicestershire, whilst Haines considered it a frequent visitor to the Burley and Exton Ponds. In fact, Browne was able to list numerous records, including a report that it had been 'fairly abundant recently' in December 1906. He also gave details of a breeding record: in June 1902 a pair nested on the island at Saddington Reservoir; the female was sitting on seven eggs on Whit Sunday but a Mr. Evans camped on the island for two or three days, causing her to desert; the keeper, Stafford, placed the eggs under a hen but they did not hatch.

Subsequent to the 1902 record, breeding was first proved in 1962 when a brood of three was seen at Wanlip Gravel Pits. The *Phragmites* beds of Burley Fishponds were used as a breeding site by two pairs which raised 12 young in 1970 and one pair which hatched seven ducklings in 1974. Breeding was last recorded there in 1976, when two pairs raised eight young, before Rutland Water subsequently flooded this site. From 1981 to 1986 breeding occurred annually at Rutland Water, with two pairs in 1984 and 1985 and single pairs in the other years, though brood sizes tended to be small. In 1985, single pairs bred at Groby Pool and Swithland Reservoir, with breeding proved again the following year at the latter site.

Since then the breeding population has almost disappeared: in 2000 a pair bred at Rutland Water, raising five young and in 2005 a female with two small ducklings was again seen at Rutland Water on July 8th. In addition, a female was seen at Kirby Lakes on June 16th 1991 leading one young Common Pochard and one young Tufted Duck; either both ducklings were in fact hybrids, or a Tufted Duck had laid in the Common Pochard's nest or an early Tufted Duck brood had become mixed with the Common Pochard brood (Gamble 1992a).

The difference in opinion about the status of this species in the 19th century may have been caused because numbers fluctuate from year to year. Over 1,000 were reported as present during November 1941, but apart from counts at Eyebrook Reservoir of 750 on December 9th 1945 and 600 on January 12th 1957 numbers did not reach four-figures at any one site until the construction of Rutland Water in the 1970s. The winter of 1976–77 produced counts of 1,444 in November 1976 and 1,556 on January 16th 1977 and since then flocks exceeding 1,000 have been recorded in a further four winters, with maxima of 2,346 on October 9th 1994, 1,776 on September 10th 1995, 1,218 on October 14th 1990 and 1,032 in August 1983. As well as the three counts listed above, the 1990s also produced notable totals of 855 on September 15th 1996 and 920 on October 31st 1998, but subsequently numbers of this species have declined noticeably and counts have exceeded 425 in only three years since 1998; these figures unfortunately reflect a marked decline nationally (Musgrove *et al.* 2007). Despite this, Rutland Water qualifies as being of national importance for Common Pochard, the current threshold being 595 (Collier *et al.* 2005).

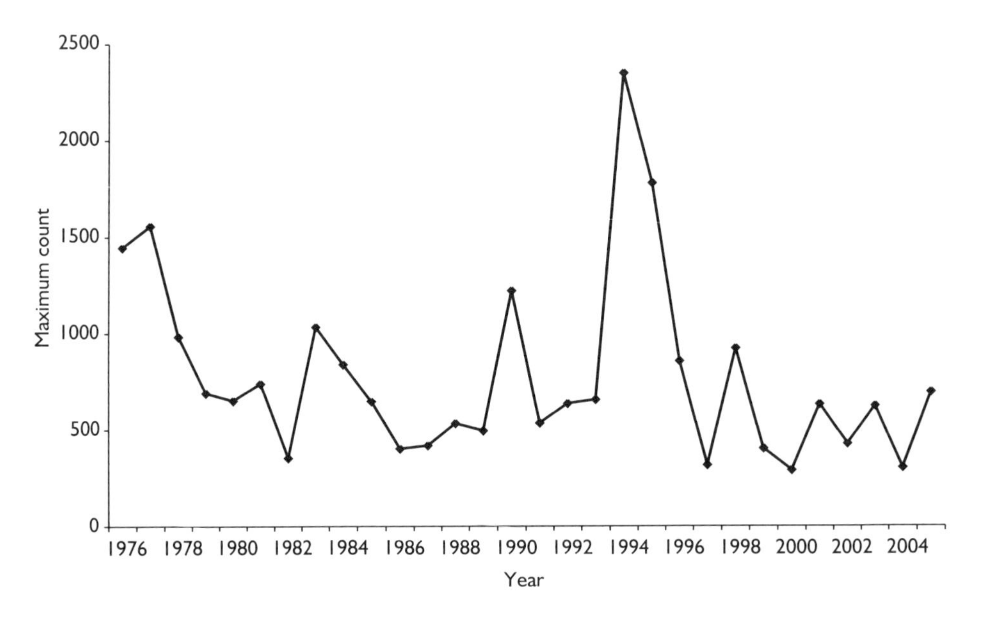

Figure 73: Maximum counts of Common Pochards at Rutland Water 1976–2005.

Away from Rutland Water the highest counts have come from Eyebrook Reservoir, with numbers exceeding 1,000 on three occasions: 1,260 on October 15th 1978, 1,313 on September 13th 1992 and 1,800 on September 30th 1995. Apart from the two counts of 750 in 1945 and 600 in 1957, flocks of over 500 have been recorded at this reservoir on six occasions:

- 531 on both September 15th 1985 and January 12th 1986.
- 574 on September 19th 1989.
- 630 on November 13th 1994.
- 799 on October 9th 1999.
- 742 on October 11th 2003.

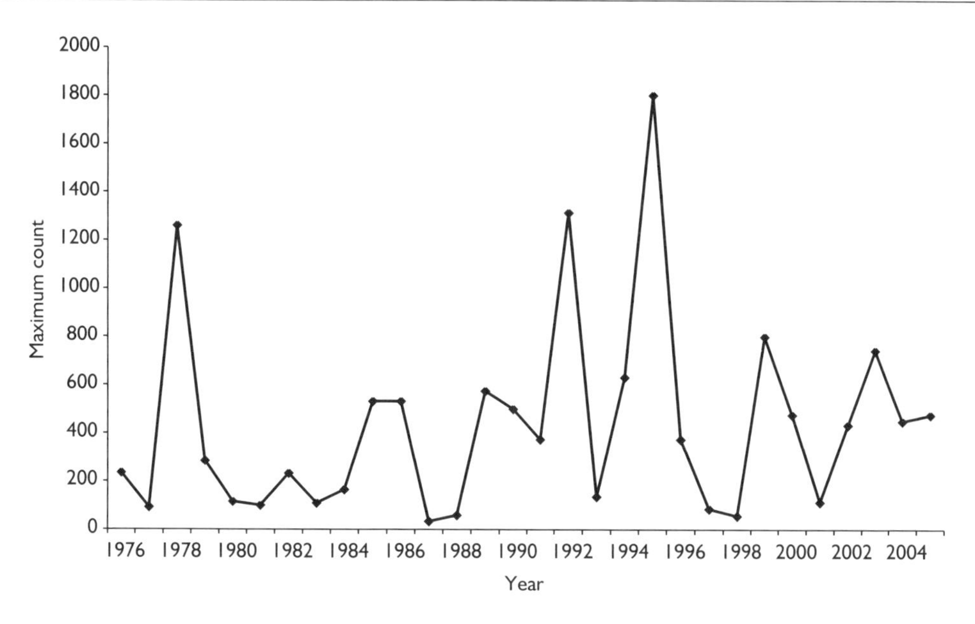

Figure 74: Maximum counts of Common Pochards at Eyebrook Reservoir 1976–2005.

The latter two counts are the highest anywhere in the counties since 1998, a measure of the reduced numbers currently appearing in Leicestershire and Rutland.

Swithland Reservoir and Stanford Reservoir have consistently produced three-figure totals over the years. At Swithland Reservoir, the largest count is 600 on January 26th 1989; counts of more than 250 have been recorded on a further four occasions, as follows:

- 510 on February 10th 1996.
- 450 in early January 1950.
- 435 on January 16th 1977.
- 285 on December 18th 1983.

The highest count at Stanford Reservoir is 876 on February 27th 1977; flocks exceeding 250 have been recorded on a further three occasions, as follows:

- 330 on November 9th 1975.
- 295 on October 18th 1992.
- 269 on December 1st 1999.

Counts of 200 or more have been recorded at another five sites in the counties. By far the largest was 1,203 at Cropston Reservoir on February 19th 1989, at a time when the reservoir was being refilled after being drained; the following winter 700 were there on December 18th 1989. Elsewhere the maximum counts have been 300 at Groby Pool on January 15th 1989, 210 at Quorn Borrow Pit on December 12th 1993 and 200 at both Blackbrook Reservoir in late January 1949 and Staunton Harold Reservoir on January 12th 1967. A further seven sites have recorded flocks into three figures. See 'Wintering Birds' (pages 39–43) for details of highest counts at individual sites.

During periods of severe weather, this species is often encountered in small numbers on the River Soar within the city boundary of Leicester. Notable totals, all at Abbey Park, have been 30 in mid-February 1947, 13 on February 12th and 23rd 1963, 40 on December 29th 1981, up to 30 during January and February 1985 and 44 on March 4th 1986.

Passage birds, predominantly moulting males, begin to arrive during July and August. Data show that numbers peak in September and remain high until November. The wintering population is on average roughly 25% smaller than that present during autumn and declines rapidly during late winter and early spring. There is little evidence of spring passage.

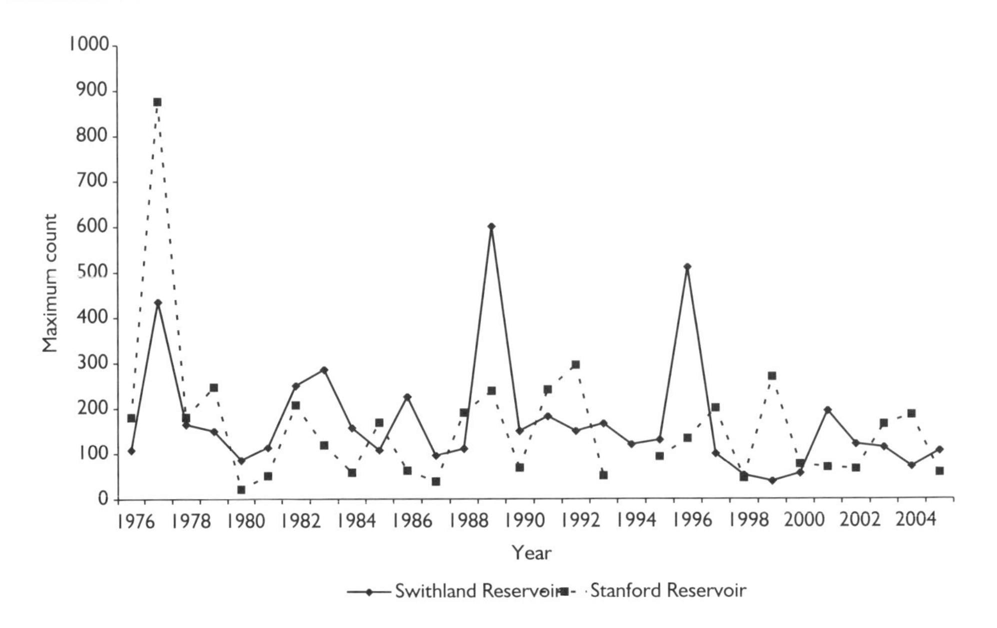

Figure 75: Maximum counts of Common Pochards at Swithland Reservoir and Stanford Reservoir 1976–2005.

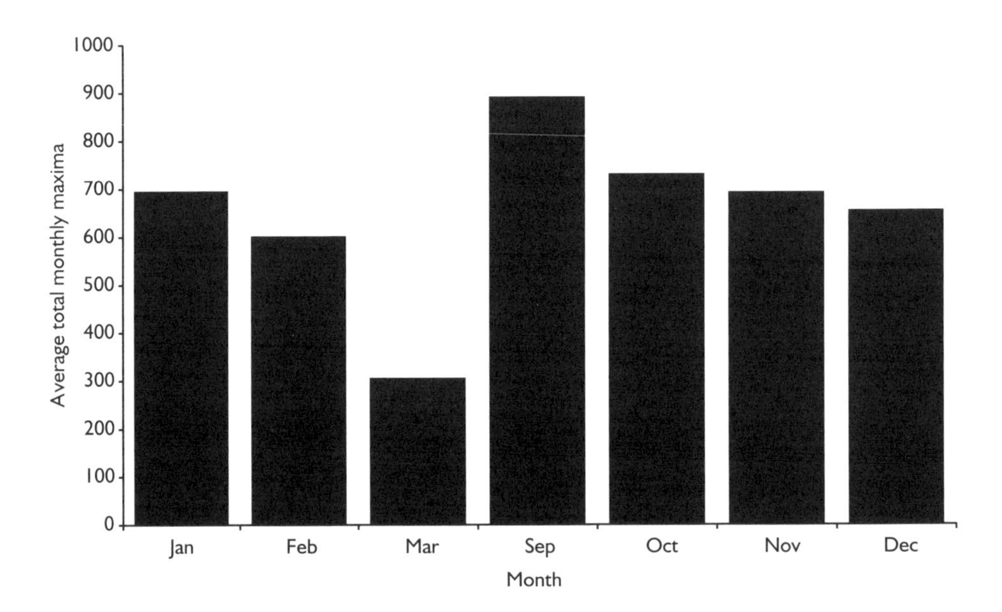

Figure 76: Average total monthly maxima of Common Pochards at the main sites 1995–2005.

There are three foreign recoveries of birds ringed at Rutland Water: from the Czech Republic, Poland and Russia. The last of these was shot near Novgorod (2,105km to the east-north-east) in April 2000, four years after it had been ringed.

Hybrids with Red-crested Pochard, Ring-necked Duck, Ferruginous Duck and Tufted Duck have been recorded: see 'Hybrids' (pages 676–684).

The Common Pochard breeds from Iceland, Ireland and Spain in the west to Lake Baikal in central Asia. Numbers in Britain are augmented in the winter by birds from the Baltic. It became established as a breeding

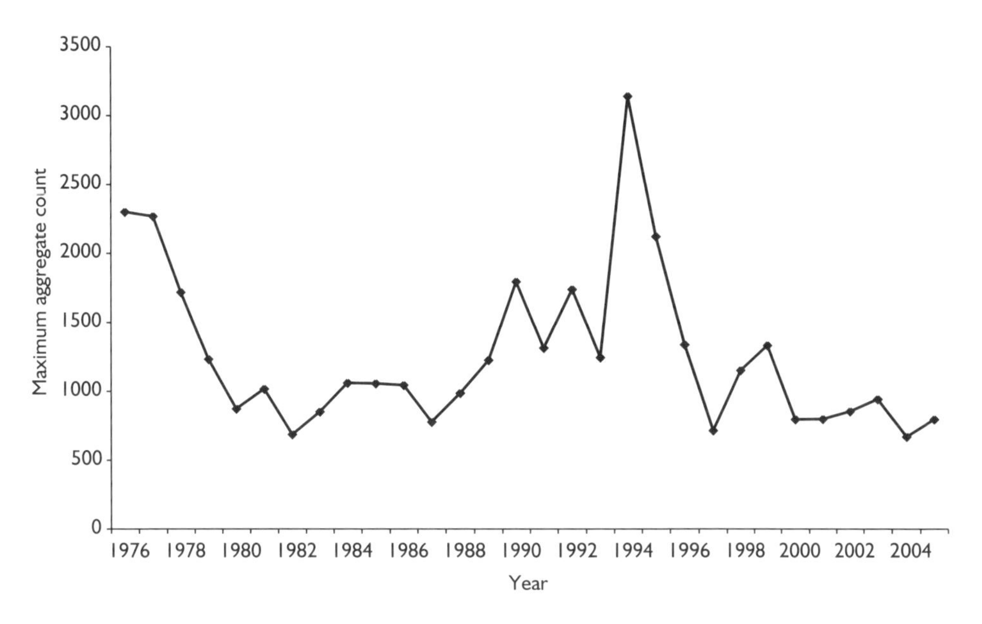

Figure 77: Maximum aggregate counts of Common Pochards at the main sites 1976–2005.

species in Britain in the 19th century and around 500 pairs have been reported in recent years (Holling *et al.* 2008). This species has been added to the 'Amber List' of Birds of Conservation Concern because the UK holds almost 25% of the European non-breeding population (Gregory *et al.* 2002).

AHJH

Redhead *Aythya americana*

Very rare vagrant from North America: one record.

An adult male was found by Robert Mills on Lagoon I at Rutland Water on February 4th 1997, where it remained until February 23rd (Mills 1998, *BB* 91:467). It was only the second British record, following one in Nottinghamshire the previous year which probably involved the same individual. Since then, there have been a further two birds found in the country. This is therefore the rarest bird on the county list.

Redheads breed mainly in the prairie regions in central and western North America, with small populations north and west to Alaska and winter south to central Mexico and Cuba.

AHJH

Ring-necked Duck *Aythya collaris*

Rare vagrant from North America: 13 records involving up to 14 individuals.

The first county record was of a male, found by P.H. Johnson and E.T. Lamb, at Eyebrook Reservoir on January 2nd 1978 (*BB* 72:515). At the time, this was around the 50th British record and it arrived as part of a major influx of at least 22 birds between November 1977 and March 1978.

All records:

1978 male, Eyebrook Reservoir, January 2nd.
1980 male, Eyebrook Reservoir, March 16th to 23rd (*BB* 74:462).
1982 male, Rutland Water, August 11th to 18th (*BB* 78:538).
1994 male, Priory Water, April 24th.

1995 male, Rutland Water, September 2nd to 16th; same bird, Eyebrook Reservoir, September 23rd.
1996 male, Fort Henry Ponds, April 28th.
male, Rutland Water, June 27th, July 9th and from August 9th to September 10th.
female, Rutland Water, October 13th.
1997 male, Rutland Water, August 3rd intermittently to September 7th.
2000 female, Groby Pool, December 6th to 16th.
2001 male, River Trent adjacent to Trent Valley Pit, January 20th and 21st.
male and female, Eyebrook Reservoir, April 3rd.
2003 male, Eyebrook Reservoir, April 11th to 23rd.

The records of a male between 1994 and 1997 may all relate to one individual, which complicates interpretation, but the general pattern of reports matches an increase nationally. This species has arrived in the counties in eight different months, with four found in April; the high proportion of birds on spring passage, or presumed to be returning, is typical of the region.

A hybrid with Common Pochard has been recorded: see 'Hybrids' (pages 676–684).

Ring-necked Ducks breed across northern North America, where there has been a recent expansion eastwards, and winter mainly in coastal states of the USA south into Central America and the West Indies. The first British record was as recent as March 1955 and the species remained a major rarity in this country until the mid-1970s; records then increased dramatically and Ring-necked Duck was removed from the list of species considered by the BBRC at the end of 1993. By the end of 2005 the British total was well over 500 records.

AHJH

Ferruginous Duck *Aythya nyroca*

Rare visitor, mainly in autumn: between 13 and 24 individuals.

The first county record involved one seen by Peter Gamble on the River Soar at Barrow upon Soar on November 30th 1947; the occurrence was documented in *BB* (Gamble 1948). There then followed a series of records over the next four years, which may have related to a total of just five birds, as follows:

1949 five, Barrow upon Soar Gravel Pits, December 4th.
pair, Eyebrook Reservoir, December 28th.
1950 pair, Stanford Reservoir, March 12th, male to March 14th.
1951 male, Stanford Reservoir, March 12th.

The party of five at Barrow upon Soar Gravel Pits in December 1949 was an extraordinary record, especially as Witherby *et al.* (1939) described the species as a rare vagrant. In this context it is perhaps significant that two flocks of ten were recorded in Norfolk in April 1903 and a flock of five in October 1920 (Taylor *et al.* 1999), so the species does seem to have been more numerous early in the last century. Given the sites and dates involved, it seems perfectly plausible that all records between 1947 and 1951 could have involved birds from the flock of five in 1949. There were no further records until 1964, when one was at Thornton Reservoir on October 18th and this was followed by a male at Stanford Reservoir on three dates between October 29th and December 12th 1972.

All early records of this species have been reviewed twice (Mackay 1995a, Fray 2005) and this resulted in the rejection of six reports between December 3rd 1949 and April 2nd 1951; all of these records came from either Barrow upon Soar, Swithland Reservoir or Cropston Reservoir. It is also worth noting that several of the other early records do not appear ever to have been fully documented.

Since 1990, this species has been recorded in nine years, as follows:

1990 male, Priory Water, August 26th; same, Cropston and Swithland Reservoirs, September 10th to November 2nd.
1992 male, Rutland Water, July 12th to 19th.
1994 juvenile male, Rutland Water, October 21st to 22nd.
1995 male, Eyebrook Reservoir, August 18th to September 21st.

1997	adult female, Priory Water, September 14th.
	juvenile female, Rutland Water, November 22nd to 30th.
1998	male, Rutland Water, March 7th to 14th.
	male, Dishley Pool, September 6th to 27th.
1999	female, Rutland Water, August 22nd to September 11th (*BB* 93: 523).
2002	male, Swithland Reservoir, October 5th to 15th (*BB* 96:557).
2003	male, Eyebrook Reservoir, September 20th to October 12th (*BB* 97:564).

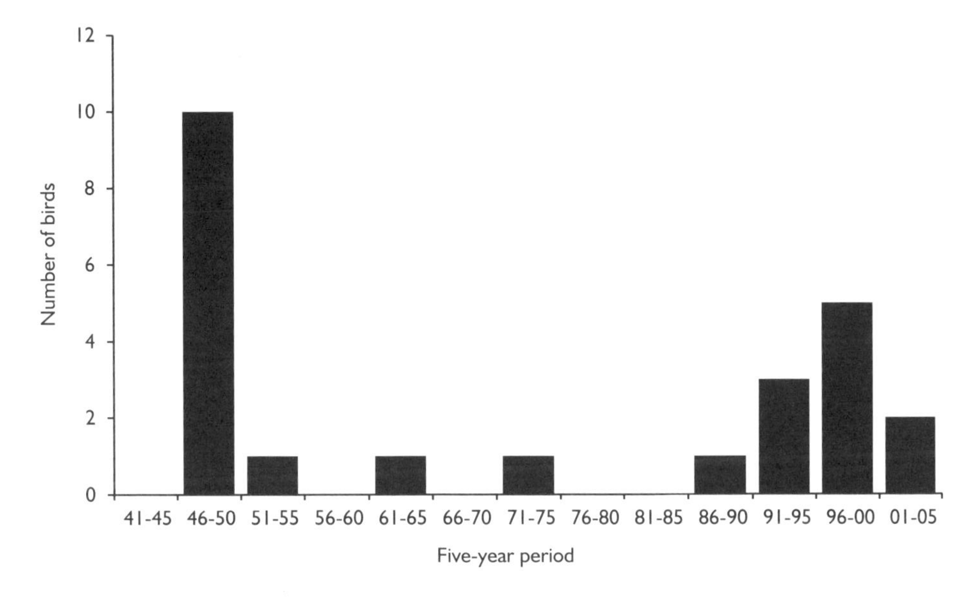

Figure 78: Numbers of Ferruginous Ducks by five-year periods 1941–2005.

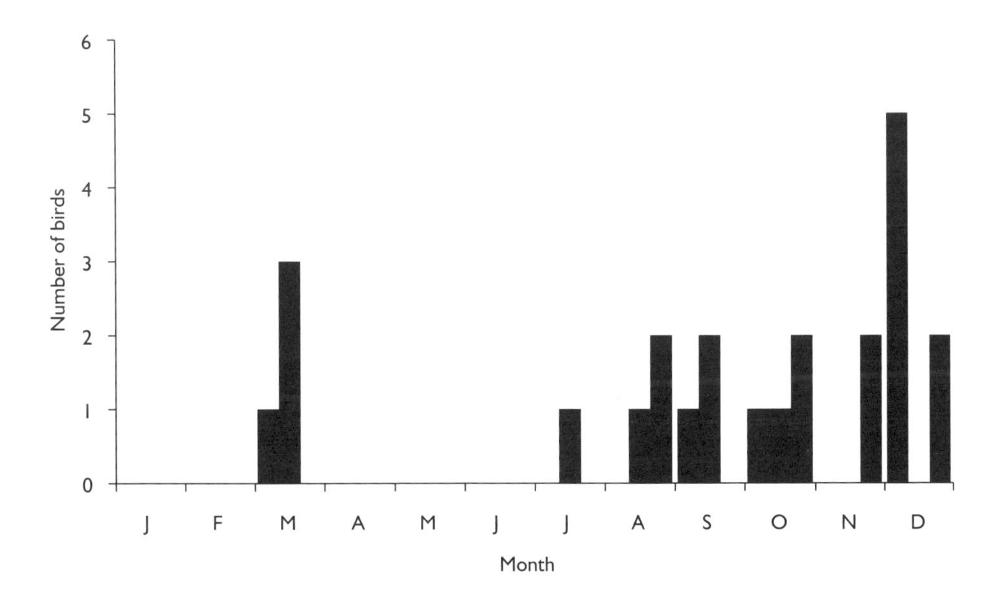

Figure 79: Monthly occurrence of Ferruginous Ducks 1941–2005.

The series of records of an adult male at various localities in the 1990s may have involved just one returning individual. The same could be said of the male in 2002 and 2003. A conservative interpretation might therefore conclude that no more than six individuals were recorded during 1990–2004.

The pattern of records is broadly similar to that described by Vinicombe (2000), who argued that most British records are likely to relate to wild birds, though it is notable that the higher proportion of records in early autumn in recent years corresponds more closely with the species' main autumn migration period.

Hybrids with Common Pochard and Tufted Duck have been recorded: see 'Hybrids' (pages 676–684).

The main breeding range of the Ferruginous Duck is in the temperate steppe-forest from Poland and Hungary east through Ukraine to the Caspian Sea, with other populations in southern Spain, Kazakhstan, western Mongolia and the Tibetan Plateau. Most spend the winter in the eastern Mediterranean, Black and Caspian Seas, north-east Africa and the Indian subcontinent. The Ferruginous Duck was dropped from the the list of species considered by the BBRC in 1968 as they were concerned about the 'large number of escapes', but it became clear that this was still a rare vagrant to Britain and it was reinstated to the BBRC list in 1999, only to be dropped again at the end of 2005. It currently averages between ten and 15 reports per year and by the end of 2005 there had been around 470 accepted British records.

AHJH

Tufted Duck *Aythya fuligula*

Common autumn and winter visitor, uncommon to fairly common breeder.

Browne described the Tufted Duck as not uncommon in winter in Leicestershire during the 19th century, though it did not appear to remain to breed. Haines agreed, describing it as 'the commonest of our occasional ducks and a regular visitor to the Ponds.' An influx was recorded as early as the winter of 1840 and there were records from the River Soar and other streams during a cold snap in March 1845. Despite the lack of proof, a record from Belvoir Lakes dated June 19th 1884 suggests that breeding possibly occurred.

Although the LROS archives describe it as 'possibly breeding occasionally', the first definite breeding record involved two pairs at Eyebrook Reservoir in 1941 and since then there have been published records of proven breeding from a further 34 sites (in chronological order): Stanford Reservoir, Fort Henry Ponds, Swithland Reservoir, Groby Pool, Market Bosworth, Cropston Reservoir, Wanlip Gravel Pits, Asfordby Gravel Pits (later referred to as Kirby Bellars Gravel Pits and now Priory Water), Frisby Gravel Pits, Coleorton Hall, Burley Fishponds, Hemington Gravel Pits, Dimminsdale, Market Overton, Rutland Water, Clipsham Ford, Ketton Hall Lake, Wanlip, Shacklewell Hollow, Banthorpe, Foxton Locks, Tinwell, Belmesthorpe, Wistow, Woodhouse, Priory Water, Watermead Park, the River Soar within Leicester at each of Abbey Meadows, Abbey Park and Belgrave Marina, Quorn Borrow Pit, Melton Country Park, Trent Valley Pit and Cossington Meadows. The breeding population therefore both increased in numbers and expanded in range during the latter half of the 20th century and it is likely that there are unpublished breeding records from other sites. Notable concentrations of breeding pairs have been recorded at the following sites:

- Priory Water/Kirby Bellars Gravel Pits: 17 broods in 2002, 16 in 1989, 15 in 1990, 13 in 1977 and 2004 and ten in 1974.
- Watermead Park: 16 broods in 1995 and 2000 and eight in 2003.
- Rutland Water: 13 broods in 2005, ten in 1984 and eight in 1976 and 1980.
- Wanlip Gravel Pits: eight broods in 1964 and 1977.
- Quorn Borrow Pit: eight broods in 2002.
- Cropston Reservoir: eight broods in 2003 and six in 2002.
- Melton Country Park: seven broods in 2003.
- Frisby Gravel Pits: six broods in 1974.

During 1976–1984 Warrilow found Tufted Ducks in 101 tetrads in the counties (16% of the total number of tetrads), with breeding confirmed in 48. They bred at a relatively high density on large undisturbed flooded gravel pits with deep pools and abundant fringing vegetation; he estimated a countywide population of 130 to 200 pairs. In recent years, the highest numbers of breeding pairs reported to LROS have been 53 pairs at 12 sites in 2003, 52 pairs at 14 sites in 2002, 41 pairs at 11 sites in 2004 and 40 pairs at 12 sites in 1995.

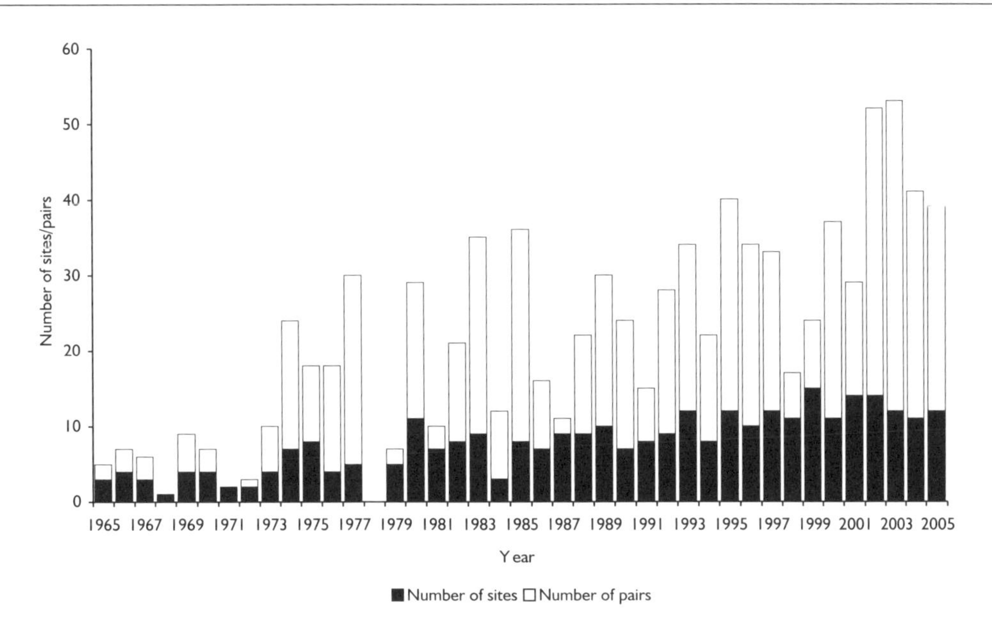

Figure 80: Breeding numbers of Tufted Ducks 1965–2005.

2,000 Tufted Ducks were recorded at Eyebrook Reservoir on December 13th 1941 but this figure was not equalled until the late 1970s, after the construction of Rutland Water. In 1945 it was reported that there were 'not often more than six' at Eyebrook Reservoir and the peak number in winter at any site later in the same decade was 100. Numbers increased slightly during the following two decades, when 180 were at Swithland Reservoir in February 1954, 150 at Staunton Harold Reservoir on January 12th 1967 and 164 at Wanlip Gravel Pits on November 16th 1969. During the 1970s, however, this species became significantly more numerous: 480 were at Swithland Reservoir on October 14th 1974, 1,000 at Stanford Reservoir on September 30th 1979 and, most notably, 2,287 at Rutland Water on November 12th 1978.

The current threshold for a site to be considered of national importance is 901 (Collier *et al.* 2005) and Rutland Water has now become the second most important site in Britain for Tufted Ducks. The peak annual count has exceeded 1,500 every year since 1978 and has topped 3,000 annually since 1994. Over 5,000 have been seen in six years, including every year since 2001, the highest count being a phenomenal 8,487 on October 19th 2005; the first time a British site has held over 8,000 Tufted Ducks. Other counts of over 5,000 have been:

- 7,496 on October 6th 2002.
- 6,618 on September 14th 2003.
- 6,488 on October 17th 2004.
- 5,582 on September 18th 1988.
- 5,115 on September 16th 2001.

Numbers at Eyebrook Reservoir have never since approached the count of 2,000 recorded there in December 1941 and have only reached 400 or more in six years, when maxima have been:

- 623 on September 10th 1995.
- 469 on September 18th 1983.
- 440 on September 16th 1990.
- 438 on December 15th 1985.
- 400 on July 21st and 22nd 1997.
- 400 on July 16th 1998.

The only site away from Rutland Water to have held over 500 birds since 1995 is Stanford Reservoir, where there were 511 on August 30th 2003. The highest count at this site is 1,000 on September 30th 1979; 500 or more have been recorded in another six years, as follows:

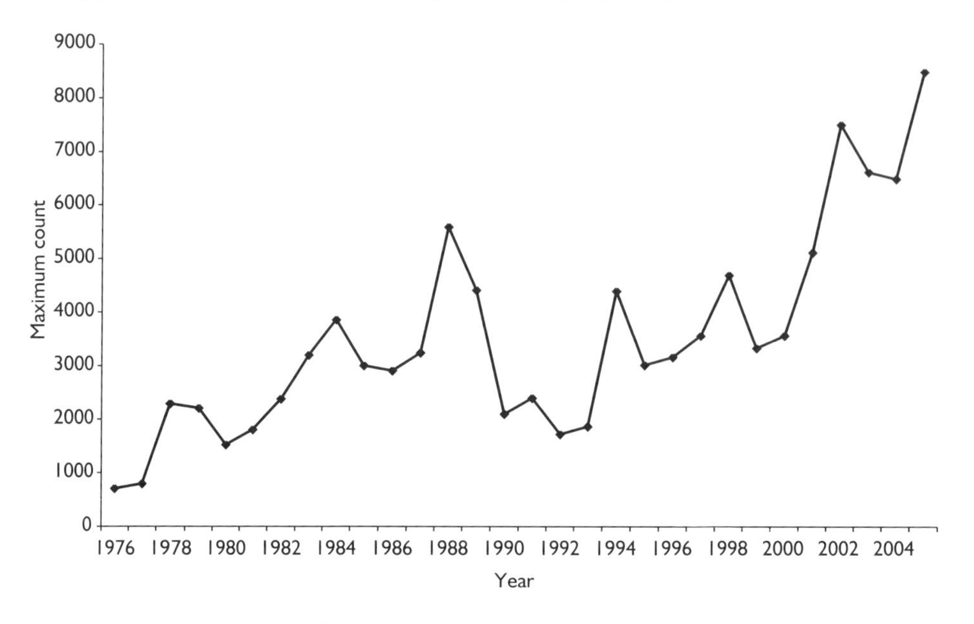

Figure 81: Maximum counts of Tufted Ducks at Rutland Water 1976–2005.

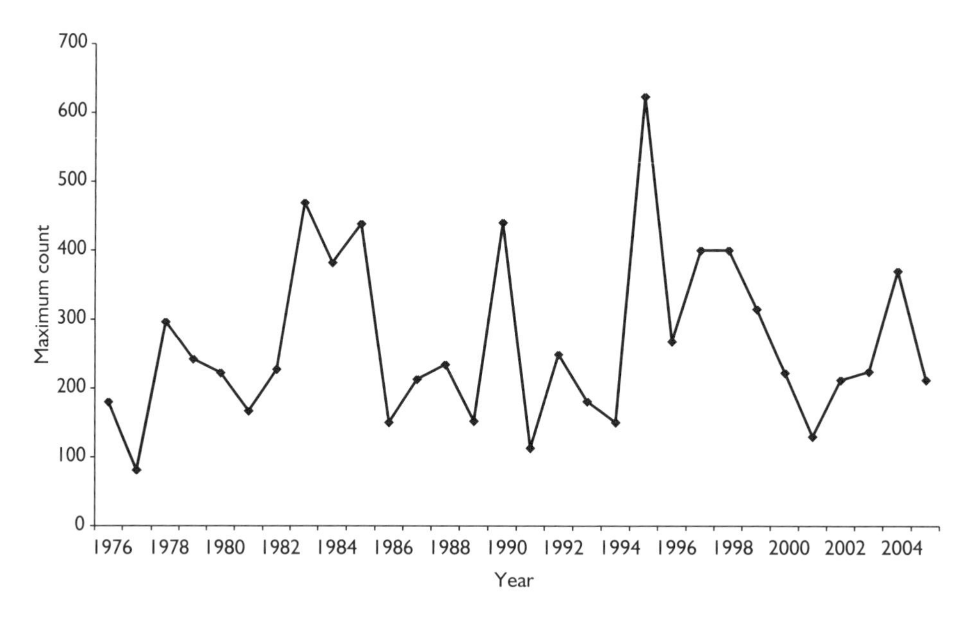

Figure 82: Maximum counts of Tufted Ducks at Eyebrook Reservoir 1976–2005.

- 900 on November 13th 1977.
- 750 on September 17th 1978.
- 700 on September 13th 1987.
- 504 on August 18th 1985.
- 500 on September 18th 1983.
- 500 on October 12th and November 16th 1986.

The maximum count at Swithland Reservoir is 530 on August 10th 1986 and this site has recorded over 400 birds on another five occasions:

- 480 on October 14th 1974.
- 480 on August 19th 2004.
- 460 on July 29th 1991.
- 420 on August 29th 2005.
- 405 on September 2nd 1989.

It is interesting to note that the majority of the highest counts at Swithland Reservoir have occurred earlier in the autumn in July and August than at the other major waters, where the largest numbers have tended to be in September and October.

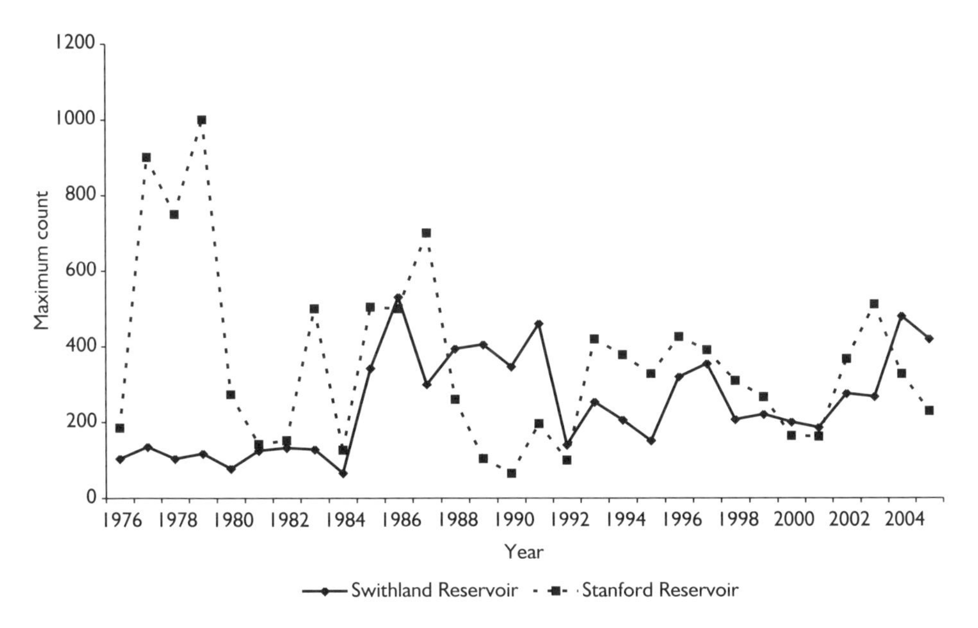

Figure 83: Maximum counts of Tufted Ducks at Swithland Reservoir and Stanford Reservoir 1976–2005.

Within Leicester itself, some notable counts have been made on the River Soar at Abbey Park, usually during freezing conditions. Three-figure totals have been recorded in four winters, with maxima being 130 on February 22nd 1963, 191 on December 30th 1981, an exceptional 412 on February 25th 1986 and 166 on January 4th 2002.

Elsewhere there have been counts of 200 or more at six sites, where the maxima have been:

- 456 at Fort Henry Ponds on January 5th 1997.
- 454 at Wanlip Gravel Pits on February 13th 1983.
- 273 at Albert Village Lake on August 6th 2004.
- 249 at Watermead Park on January 12th 1997.
- 240 at Cropston Reservoir on September 17th 1989.
- 200 at Groby Pool on January 15th 1989.

See 'Wintering Birds' (pages 39–43) for details of highest counts at other individual sites.

Data show that numbers of this species have been increasing steadily in the counties since the early 1990s and that the highest numbers occur in September and October. Although peak numbers in the UK occur during the winter months of December and January (Wernham *et al.* 2002), the local wintering population is roughly 30% smaller than that present during the early autumn.

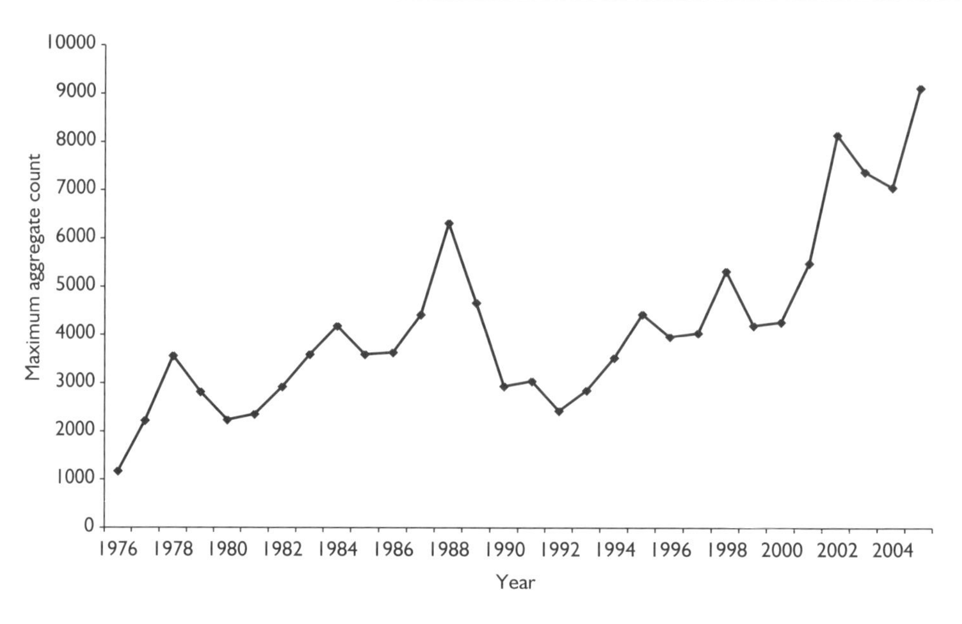

Figure 84: Maximum aggregate counts of Tufted Ducks at the main sites 1976–2005.

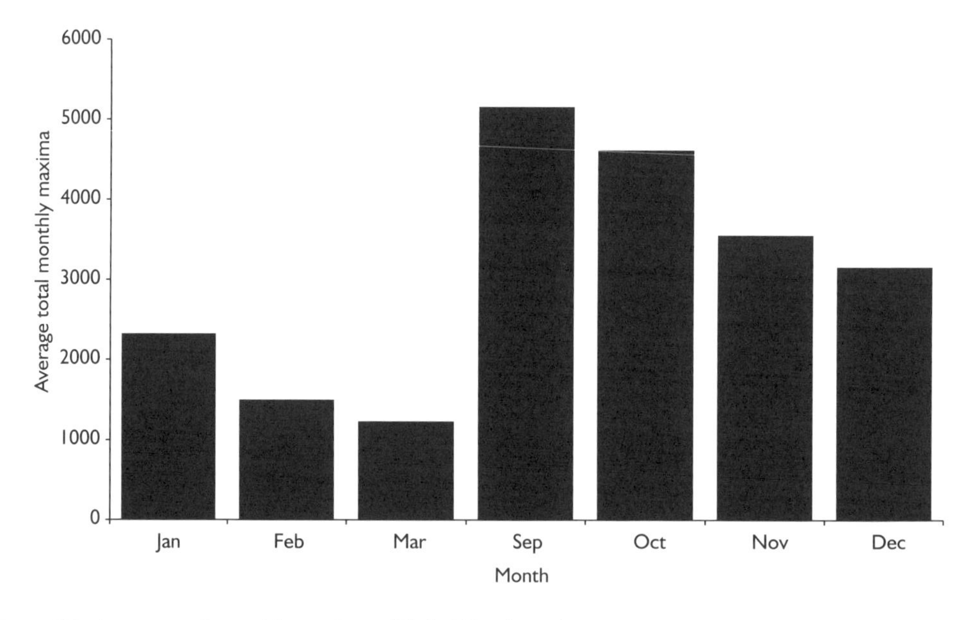

Figure 85: Average total monthly maxima of Tufted Ducks at the main sites 1995–2005.

Birds ringed at Rutland Water have been recovered abroad in Denmark, Finland, France (three) and the former USSR (five). The furthest distance travelled involved a female ringed on February 11th 1997 which was shot 3,324km to the east-north-east near Ust-Tsilemskiy (Russia) on June 3rd 1999. There have also been two Leicestershire recoveries of birds ringed in the Baltic States.

Hybrids with Mallard, Common Pochard, Ferruginous Duck and Greater Scaup have been recorded: see 'Hybrids' (pages 676–684).

Tufted Ducks breed from Iceland, Britain and Ireland east to eastern Siberia. British wintering numbers are supplemented by immigrants from Iceland, Scandinavia and Russia. The Tufted Duck is the species considered to have undergone the greatest population increase in Britain since 1800 although the rate of increase has slowed somewhat since the 1970s (Gibbons *et al.* 1996); the latest population estimate is 10,200 to 11,500 pairs (Baillie *et al.* 2006). WeBS counts reveal that wintering numbers have also increased since the 1960s (Collier *et al.* 2005) and the British wintering population is put at 90,100 birds (Baker *et al.* 2006).

AHJH

Greater Scaup *Aythya marila*

Uncommon winter and passage visitor; recorded in all months, with the majority from January to March and October to December.

Browne considered the Greater Scaup to be a winter visitor, rarer than Tufted Duck and was able to cite just eight records. Haines described it as 'occasional, chiefly at the Ponds, where several have been shot', though he cited just three records. The LROS archives include a further two records prior to 1941: single birds at Wanlip in 1922 and Normanton on January 4th 1940. It appears therefore this species has consistently been an uncommon visitor in the counties.

Since 1941, the Greater Scaup has been recorded in all but eight years, the last blank year being as long ago as 1975. Numbers have increased consistently since the early 1970s and the five best years have all occurred since the early 1990s: 1991 (46 individuals), 2002 (31), 2001 (30), 2005 (30) and 1996 (28). Most records are of single birds or small groups but larger flocks are unusual and have exceeded 15 on only four occasions:

- 26 (11 males and 15 females) at Eyebrook Reservoir on March 21st 1961.
- 18 (eight males and ten females) at Swithland Reservoir on March 23rd 1963.
- 16 at Rutland Water on February 9th 1997.
- 16 (seven males and nine females) at Eyebrook Reservoir on February 4th 2001.

Most birds arrive from October onwards following movements into British coastal waters and the January peak corresponds with the highest numbers at sea (Lack 1986). Numbers then decline during late winter before

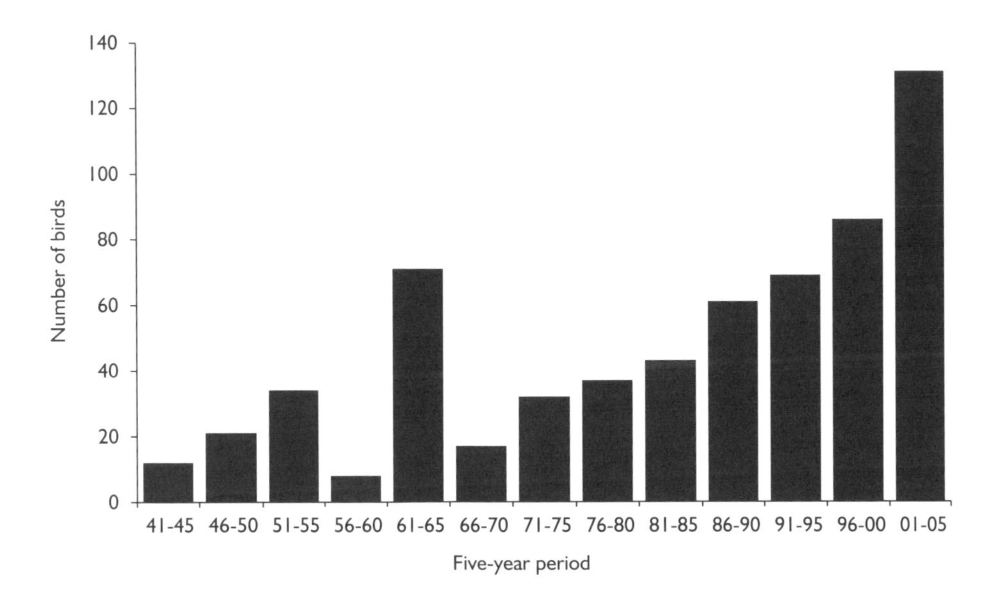

Figure 86: Number of Greater Scaups by five-year periods 1941–2005.

increasing in March at the time of spring passage. Few are recorded in late spring and summer; the month with the least new arrivals is June, with just five birds found, as follows:

- a female at Eyebrook Reservoir on June 4th and 5th 1949.
- two males at Rutland Water on June 7th 1995.
- a female at Swithland Reservoir on June 23rd 1990.
- a male at Rutland Water on June 28th 1987.

Eight have been found during July:

- an adult male at Rutland Water from July 6th to 9th 2003.
- an adult male at Swithland Reservoir from July 7th to 16th 2001.
- two males at Eyebrook Reservoir on July 10th 1965.
- a male at Eyebrook Reservoir on July 10th 1971.
- two males at Swithland Reservoir from July 15th to 21st 1980.
- a male at Eyebrook Reservoir on July 30th 1962.

There have been two records of oversummering birds: a male at Fort Henry Ponds in 1995 remained for an exceptional six months from February 12th until August 17th, before returning for a further month from September 17th to October 24th and a male was at Rutland Water from May 1st to September 18th 2005.

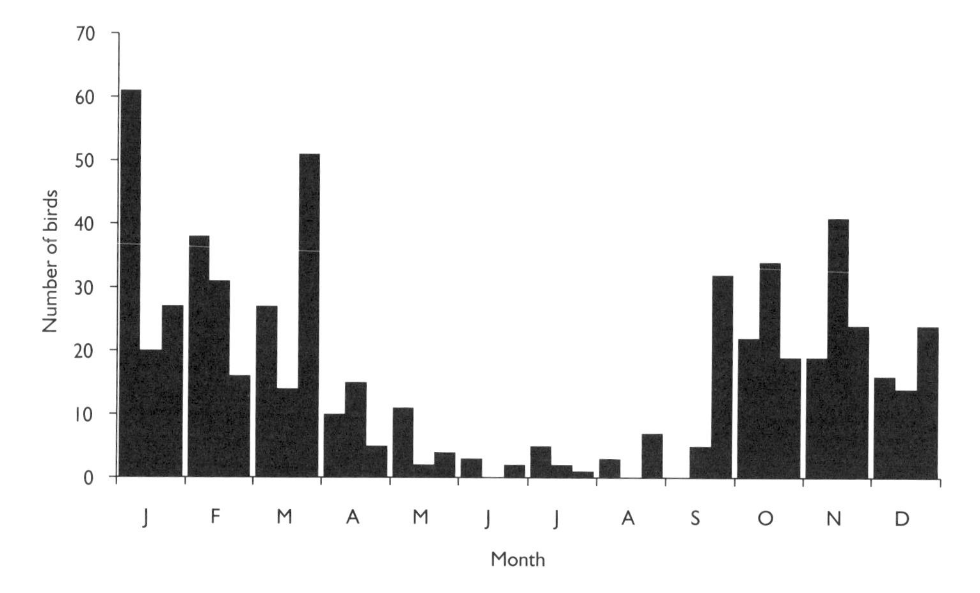

Figure 87: Monthly occurrence of Greater Scaups 1941–2005.

Rutland Water is the dominant site, accounting for almost 40% of all records and a further 24% have occurred at Eyebrook Reservoir, although Greater Scaups have occurred at the majority of the counties' reservoirs, lakes and gravel pits. During the severe winter of 1946–47, up to four were present on the River Soar within the city of Leicester, at Abbey Park, from February 6th to March 12th 1947; during the same period, a pair was on the River Soar at Kegworth on February 16th. Likewise, during the harsh winter of 1962–63, up to four frequented the River Trent at Castle Donington from January 27th to March 12th 1963. A further two birds have been seen on the River Soar within Leicester: single females at Frog Island on February 16th 1985 and Freemen's Weir from February 25th to March 11th 1991.

70% of all records have referred to adult birds and a further 14% have been unaged and unsexed, leaving just 16% of individuals aged as juvenile or first-winter.

When interpreting the data it should be noted that during the 1980s it became fashionable for records committees to take a very hard line with records of this species, so it is likely that several good records were rejected.

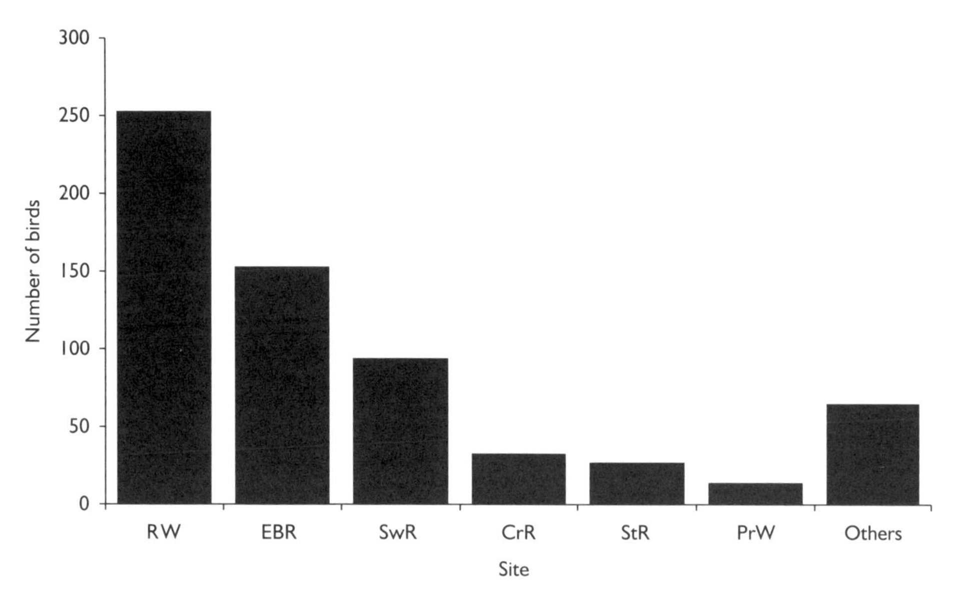

Figure 88: Sites where Greater Scaups have been recorded 1941–2005.
Key to abbreviations: RW = Rutland Water; EBR = Eyebrook Reservoir; SwR = Swithland Reservoir; CrR = Cropston Reservoir; StR = Stanford Reservoir; PrW = Priory Water

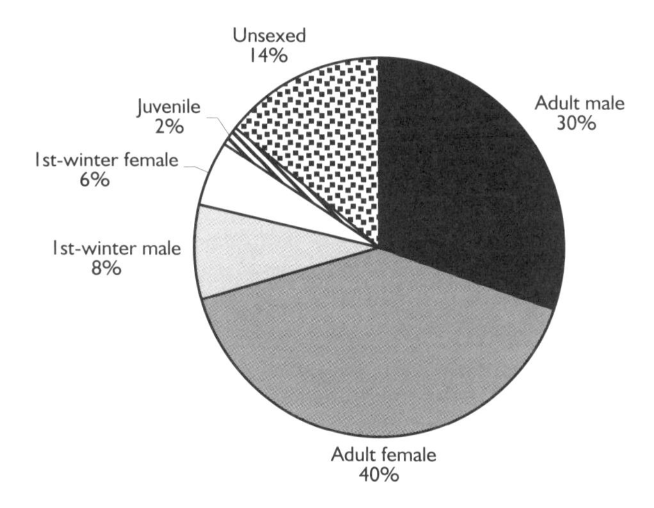

Figure 89: Ages and sexes of Greater Scaups 1941–2005.

Between 1988 and 1999 there were 19 records of birds considered to be hybrids between Greater Scaup and Tufted Duck, compared with 199 records of Greater Scaup. Greater Scaup are therefore ten times more frequent than closely similar hybrids, a higher proportion than that proposed by Smallshire (1986a).

There is one ringing recovery: a bird ringed at Lake Myvatn (Iceland) on August 6th 1947 was recovered near Ashby-de-la-Zouch on December 22nd 1948.

Hybrids with Tufted Duck have been recorded: see 'Hybrids' (pages 676–684).

The Greater Scaup has a circumpolar breeding distribution in Arctic and sub-Arctic regions. It winters to the south of the breeding range. Always rare, it has almost disappeared from Britain as a breeding bird, which makes the recent summer records from Leicestershire and Rutland intriguing; perhaps they are males which have chosen to moult here rather than with the large flock on the Ijsselmeer in the Netherlands. On account of its tiny British breeding population and relatively concentrated wintering population, this species has been added to the 'Amber List' of Birds of Conservation Concern (Gregory *et al.* 2002).

AHJH

Lesser Scaup *Aythya affinis*

Very rare vagrant from North America: three records.

All three records have occurred at Rutland Water. The first was of a first-winter male, found by Andy Forryan, in the Barnhill Creek area on February 14th 1993. It was subsequently seen by many observers and remained until February 17th (Forryan 1994, *BB* 87:516). Leicestershire and Rutland's second record involved a female, found by Matthew Berriman, in the north arm from April 8th to 23rd 2000; this too was seen by many observers during its stay (*BB* 94:465). In 2005, a female was originally located by John Wright on Lagoon I on April 28th. It remained until May 11th, mainly favouring Lagoon III, and towards the end of its stay appeared to be paired with a male Tufted Duck (*BB* 100:22).

Lesser Scaups breed across northern North America and winter mainly down the west and east coasts of the USA, across the southern states and through Central America, as well as in the West Indies. The first British record occurred as recently as 1987 and the 1993 Rutland Water individual was only the fifth for Britain; it was, however, not entirely unexpected, as two of the previous four had occurred in the nearby counties of Staffordshire and Nottinghamshire. They are now increasingly frequent vagrants to this country, evidenced by the fact that the 2000 individual was the 41st British record and a total of 86 had been seen by the end of 2005. The majority occur between October and April and both county records conform to this established pattern of occurrence. Diligent observers who habitually check diving ducks are likely to turn up more individuals of this species in future.

AHJH

Eider (Common Eider) *Somateria mollissima*

Rare vagrant, mainly between October and February: 15 records involving 33 individuals.

The first record of this maritime duck was a female, seen by many observers, at Eyebrook Reservoir from February 7th to 16th 1976. By the end of 2005 there had been a total of 15 records, involving 33 individuals. Although Eiders have appeared in Leicestershire and Rutland in seven different months, they are essentially very rare winter vagrants, the vast majority having arrived between late October and early December.

All records:

1976	female, Eyebrook Reservoir, February 7th to 16th.
1982	two males and three immatures, Cropston Reservoir, December 3rd, with one female and one immature male until December 5th.
1983	immature male, Rutland Water, November 16th to May 29th 1984.
1988	adult male and immature male, Rutland Water, October 23rd and 24th, with the immature male until October 30th.
1989	male, Priory Water, May 21st.
	female, Swithland Reservoir, December 15th.
1993	two males and ten females/immatures, Rutland Water, October 31st, with one immature male and three females to November 7th, two females on November 28th and one immature male on November 29th.
	female, Watermead Park, October 31st.
	female, Fort Henry Ponds, October 31st to November 1st.
	two females, Quorn Borrow Pit, November 1st.
	male, Saddington Reservoir, November 3rd to 10th.
	female, Melton Country Park, November 6th.

2000	male, Eyebrook Reservoir, April 22nd to May 16th.
2003	male and female, Rutland Water, April 19th.
2005	male, Rutland Water, March 7th to 13th.

Most records have been of birds remaining for a short period only, with the notable exception of the Rutland Water bird over the winter of 1983–84 and the Eyebrook Reservoir individual of spring 2000. The remarkable influx during late October and early November 1993, which was mirrored in other Midlands counties, followed strong north to north-east winds over Denmark and extensive low cloud over England and the North Sea which apparently disorientated birds returning from Baltic moulting areas. The distribution of birds in the counties

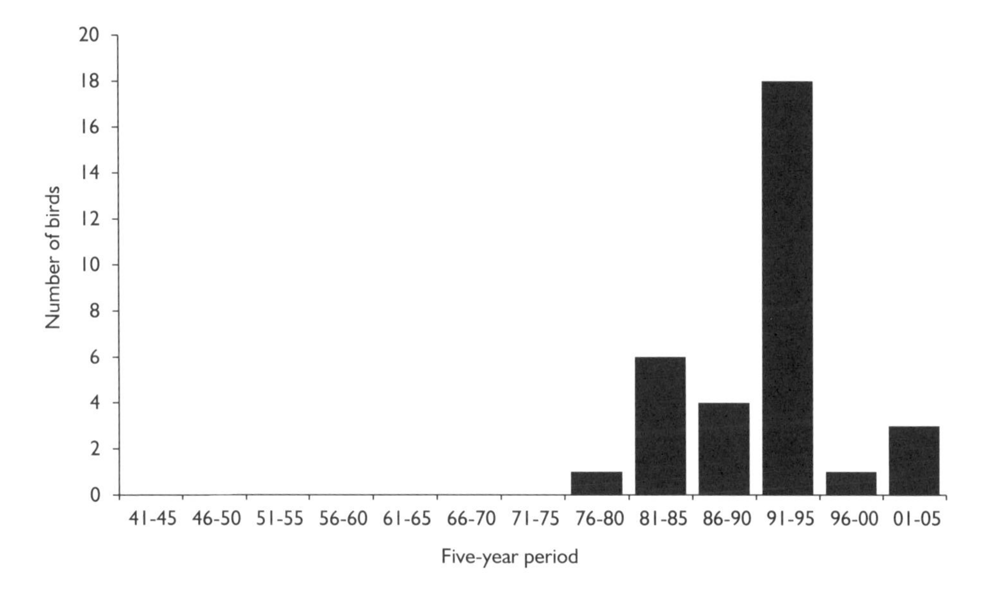

Figure 90: Number of Eiders by five-year periods 1941–2005.

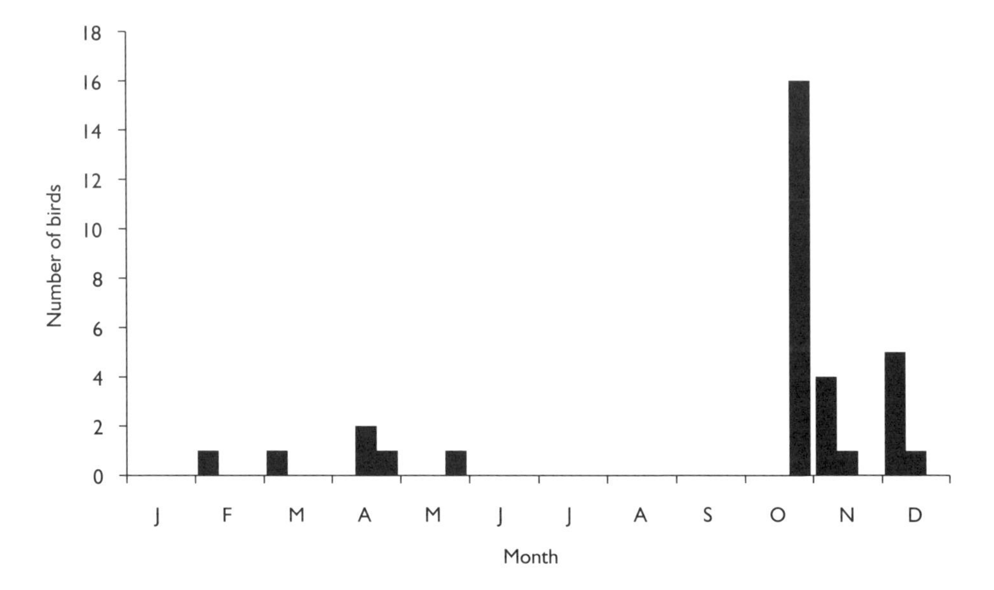

Figure 91: Monthly occurrence of Eiders 1941–2005.

during this influx was rather unexpected; with the exception of the flock of 12 at Rutland Water, all other records came from small waters and none were seen at the large reservoirs of Eyebrook, Swithland, Stanford, Cropston or Thornton. The total of 18 seen during this period accounts for over half of all records in the counties.

The marked increase in records during the last two decades matches a dramatic increase in numbers of birds wintering around the Wash, following a spectacular increase in the Dutch population (Taylor *et.al.* 1999).

The Common Eider breeds throughout coastal Arctic and sub-Arctic zones. Britain is at the southern limit of its breeding range and it is restricted to northern England, Scotland and Northern Ireland. Nevertheless, with a total British population of over 31,000 pairs, this species is the second commonest duck in Britain, its population being exceeded only by that of the Mallard. With the exception of the Tufted Duck, the Eider is the species which was considered to have undergone the greatest population increase in Britain during 1800–1995 (Gibbons *et al.* 1996), although there is evidence of a recent decline in numbers, particularly in Shetland (Pennington *et al.* 2004). As in excess of 50% of the British non-breeding population winters at less than ten sites, this species has been added to the 'Amber List' of Birds of Conservation Concern (Gregory *et al.* 2002).

AHJH

Long-tailed Duck *Clangula hyemalis*

Rare visitor; recorded in all months except June, August and September, with the majority between November and February: 36 records involving 51 individuals.

The only historical record of a Long-tailed Duck is mentioned by Haines, who reported that one was shot at Burley Fishponds in February 1900. It was not until 1951 that the next record occurred, when two females were at Stanford Reservoir from December 2nd to 9th, with one remaining until December 27th. There have been records in a total of 32 years since 1951 although, due to a number of long-staying birds, new arrivals have only been found in 24 of these years. Of the 50 individuals seen in the counties since the 1900 bird, 36 (or 72%) have occurred since 1980; in common with a number of other species of seaduck, the marked increase in records during the last two decades can be explained by the construction of Rutland Water, which has attracted most birds in recent years.

Most records are provided by single birds, although two have been seen together on eight occasions. There have been two instances where three have been recorded together: a male at Rutland Water from November 26th 1985 was joined by two females on December 1st, with all three remaining until January 18th 1986, and three females were at the same site from February 12th to March 29th 1989. A first-winter at Rutland Water from November 3rd 1991 was joined by two of a similar age on November 23rd, with a fourth bird arriving on

December 6th; they all remained until April 12th 1992, representing the only time that four have been recorded together. This small flock resulted in 1991 being one of only four years when a total of four birds were recorded in the counties, the others being 1980, 1983 and 1989; three were found in 1985, 1988 and 1993 but there have only been one or two records in all other years.

The pattern of records shows a pronounced peak in November and December, with 60% of all arrivals occurring in these two months, reflecting southward dispersal following the main arrival into northern British waters during October. A very similar pattern was described for the West Midlands by Harrison *et al.* (1982). Arrivals prior to late October are rare, the only ones being an immature at Eyebrook Reservoir from October 6th to 13th

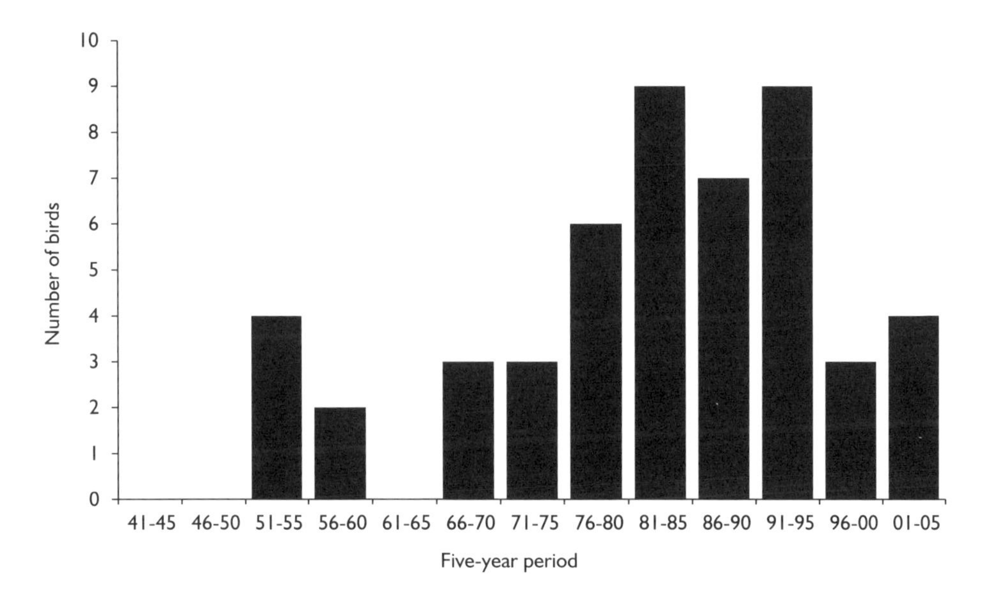

Figure 92: Numbers of Long-tailed Ducks by five-year periods 1941–2005.

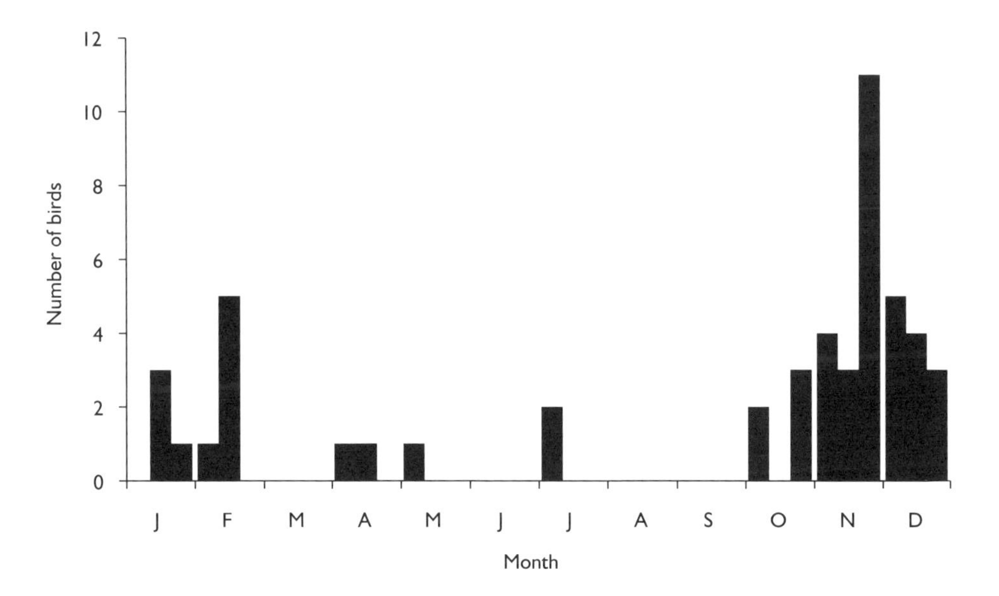

Figure 93: Monthly occurrence of Long-tailed Ducks 1941–2005.

1974 and a female at Rutland Water which was initially seen on October 2nd 1993 and remained until April 17th 1994. Records of new birds are unusual during the early part of the year, although there have been two arrivals in April and one in May: a male at Eyebrook Reservoir on April 19th 1955, one at Burley Fishponds on an unspecified date in April 1974 and a male at Eyebrook Reservoir from May 1st to 10th 2004. In addition, a total of ten long-staying birds have lingered into April, with another four remaining into May; the latest date this species has been seen in the counties during the spring is May 31st, when a female at Stanford Reservoir was last seen during 2004. There are also two midsummer records which presumably involve non-breeding birds: a first-summer male at Rutland Water from July 2nd to 9th 1995 and an adult female at Cropston Reservoir on July 2nd 2000.

This species regularly embarks on lengthy stays when it appears in the counties; the average duration of a visit is 57 days. Eleven individuals have remained for over 100 days, with five lingering for over 150 days, as follows:

- a female at Rutland Water from October 2nd 1993 to April 17th 1994 (198 days).
- a first-winter female at Trent Valley Pit from November 22nd 1995 to May 12th 1996 (172 days).
- a male at Rutland Water from October 31st 1993 to April 17th 1994 (169 days).
- a first-winter female at Rutland Water from November 3rd 1991 to April 12th 1992.
- a male at Rutland Water from November 29th 1980 to May 2nd 1981.

The Long-tailed Duck is a very rare bird in the counties away from the two major reservoirs; Rutland Water and Eyebrook Reservoir account for 74% of all records. Elsewhere, three birds have been found at both Stanford Reservoir (the two females in 1951 previously mentioned, along with a female from January 17th to May 31st 2004) and Cropston Reservoir (two females from December 12th 1980 to February 20th 1981 and the mid-summer record in 2000 mentioned above). Swithland Reservoir has recorded an immature from November 15th to 30th 1969 and an adult male from November 18th to 20th 1984, although one of the females from Cropston Reservoir during the winter of 1980–81 visited this site on February 1st and 3rd 1981. Priory Water is the only other site where more than one bird has been seen; two females were present here on November 27th 1988. Apart from single birds at Burley Fishponds and Trent Valley Pit previously mentioned, the only other record is of an adult female at Fort Henry Ponds from January 15th to 22nd 1989.

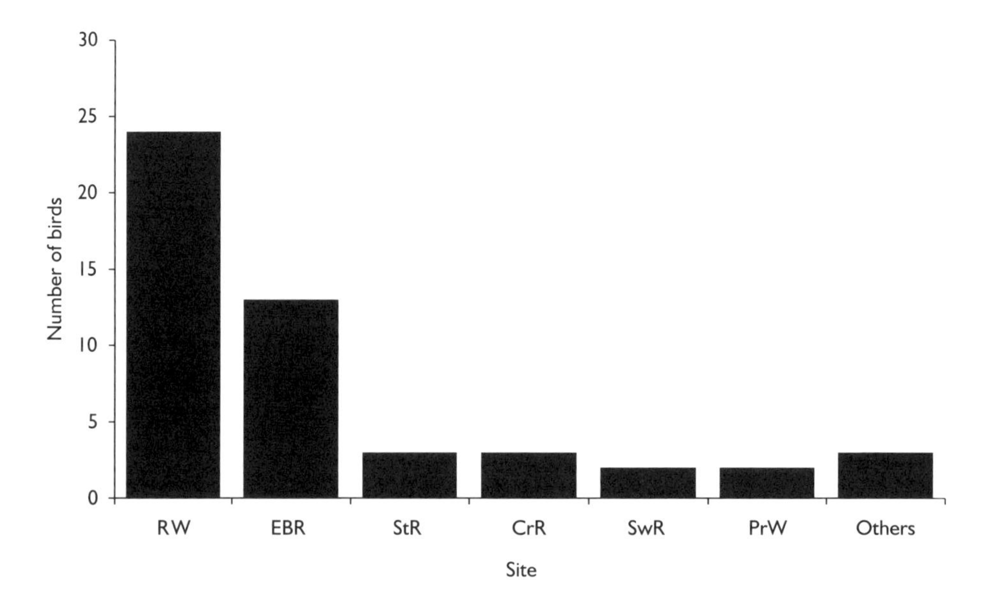

Figure 94: Sites where Long-tailed Ducks have been recorded 1941–2004.
Key to abbreviations: RW = Rutland Water; EBR = Eyebrook Reservoir; StR = Stanford Reservoir; CrR = Cropston Reservoir; SwR = Swithland Reservoir; PrW = Priory Water

Long-tailed Ducks are circumpolar breeders, the majority of European birds nesting on islands and coasts of high Arctic western Russia. They winter south of the breeding range. The British wintering population is estimated at approximately 16,000 birds (Baker *et al.* 2006), with the Moray Firth being of particular importance; as more than 50% of wintering birds in Britain are found in fewer than ten defined areas, this species has been added to the 'Amber List' of Birds of Conservation Concern (Gregory *et al.* 2002).

AHJH

Common Scoter *Melanitta nigra*

Uncommon passage and scarce winter visitor; recorded in all months, with the majority in April, October and November.

Browne described the Common Scoter as a 'not uncommon winter visitant' during the 19th century and knew of four certain records: two males shot out of a flock at Thornton Reservoir on September 18th 1879; three obtained at Saddington Reservoir during August and September 1881, one of which was shot on September 3rd out of a flock of 20; one shot at Abbey Meadows, Leicester on February 9th 1882 and two seen at Swithland Reservoir on October 16th 1906. Browne also mentioned undated reports from Groby Pool, Melton Mowbray and Bosworth Park. Around the same, Haines recorded one shot at Burley Fishponds around 1885 and four at Exton in 1889, with it being recorded 'once since' at the latter site.

Prior to 1941, the only 20th century records were one at Stanford Res on October 18th 1936 and a male on the River Soar near Kegworth on May 1st and 2nd 1940. Following the formation of LROS in 1941, this species has been recorded in all but six years, the last blank year being 1959. It remained rather scarce until the mid-1970s, with only nine years before 1975 producing ten or more birds, but since then there have been just three years that have yielded fewer than ten birds, the last being in 1982. More birds have been seen since the mid-1980s than ever before and the five best years have all occurred since 1986: 1992 (131 individuals), 1998 (128), 1986 (109), 2004 (77) and 1994 (72). The reasons for the steady increase in numbers recorded during the last four decades are not clear but may be attributable to an increase in the number of suitable bodies of water combined with a consequent willingness by this species to follow overland routes. The growing number of active observers may also be a secondary factor.

Most records relate to single birds or small flocks but larger groups are occasionally recorded during the main passage periods. Double-figure flocks have been recorded on 40 occasions and from eight sites, with the majority at Rutland Water, Eyebrook Reservoir and Swithland Reservoir. Counts of over 15 at these sites have been:

- Rutland Water: 107 (60 males and 47 females) on November 19th 1988, with 32 females the following day; 26 on April 7th 1979, with 37 the following day; 32 (19 males and 13 females) on April 6th 2003; 29 on September 26th 1992; 25 (16 males and nine females) on April 27th 1986; 24 females on November 17th 2002; 22 females on November 18th 2005.
- Eyebrook Reservoir: 44 females/juveniles on November 6th 1995; 19 on April 11th 1980; 18 on October 29th 1976; 16 (11 males and five females) on August 4th 1951.
- Swithland Reservoir: 33 on August 9th 1992; 30 females/juveniles on November 15th 1989; 21 (15 males and six females) on July 12th 1986.

Elsewhere there have been nine double-figure flocks, as follows:

- 16 males at Cropston Reservoir on June 22nd 1986.
- 15 at Stanford Reservoir on May 15th 1994.
- 13 at Stanford Reservoir on October 26th 1968.
- 13 (12 males and one female) at Thornton Reservoir on June 8th 2002.
- 11 (three males and eight females) at Cropston Reservoir on May 19th 1972.
- 11 females/juveniles at Cropston Reservoir on November 19th 2004.
- ten (two males and eight females) at Cossington South Gravel Pits on November 20th 1988.
- ten (three males and seven females) at Thornton Reservoir on June 3rd 1991.
- ten at Wanlip South Gravel Pits on March 24th 1996.

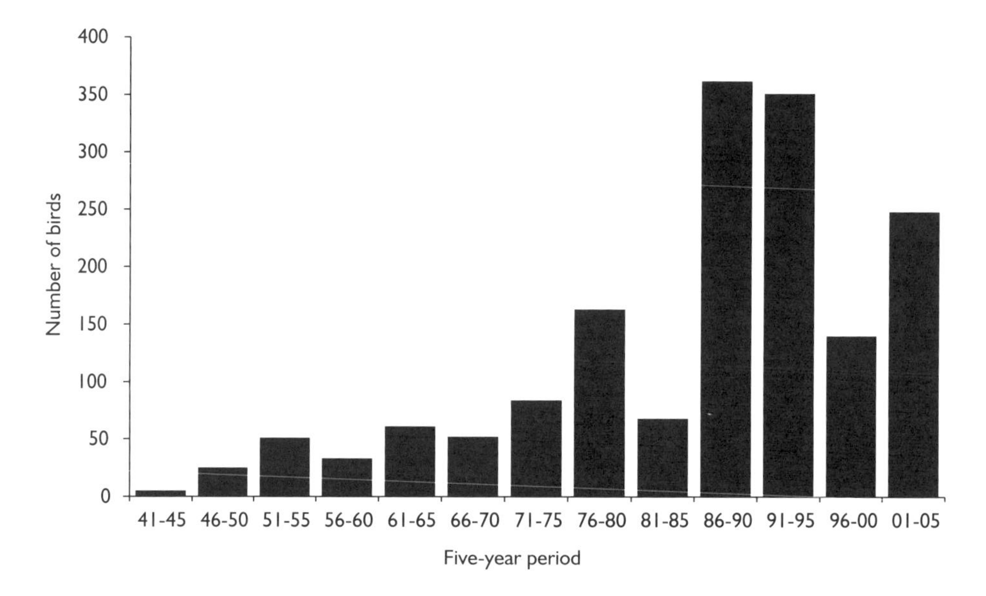

Figure 95: Numbers of Common Scoters by five-year periods 1941–2005.

Although primarily a maritime species, the Common Scoter is well known for its overland passage and moult migrations. Spencer (1969) recognised three distinct peaks in east to west movements, in April/May, July/August and October/November; records in Leicestershire and Rutland show the same pattern. It is not unusual for this species to appear on several of the counties' waters on the same day; notable examples of this include:

- on April 7th 1979, there were 26 at Rutland Water and 15 at Eyebrook Reservoir; the following day there were 37 at Rutland Water, 11 at Eyebrook Reservoir, four at Cropston Reservoir and one at Swithland Reservoir.
- on July 12th 1986, 21 were at Swithland Reservoir, 13 at Eyebrook Reservoir and six at Groby Pool.
- March 24th 1996 saw ten at Wanlip South Gravel Pits, eight at Watermead Park, six at Rutland Water and three at Eyebrook Reservoir.

Although it was considered a not uncommon winter visitor in the 19th century, modern data show that this species is least common in winter.

Common Scoters are clearly attracted to the larger areas of water in the counties. Rutland Water (41%), Eyebrook Reservoir (25%) and Swithland Reservoir (15%) account for over 80% of all records, with Cropston, Stanford and Thornton reservoirs producing a further 13% between them. The Common Scoter is a rare visitor to the counties' well-watched gravel pit sites: the Soar valley has managed just six records (involving 32 birds), Trent Valley Pit has four records (11 individuals) and Priory Water three records (five birds). In this con-

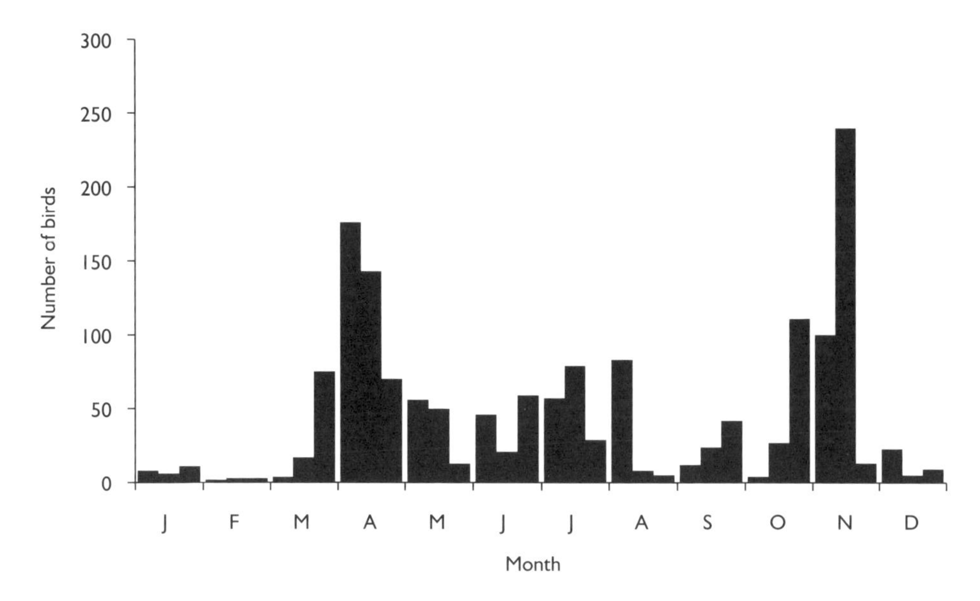

Figure 96: Monthly occurrence of Common Scoters 1941–2005.

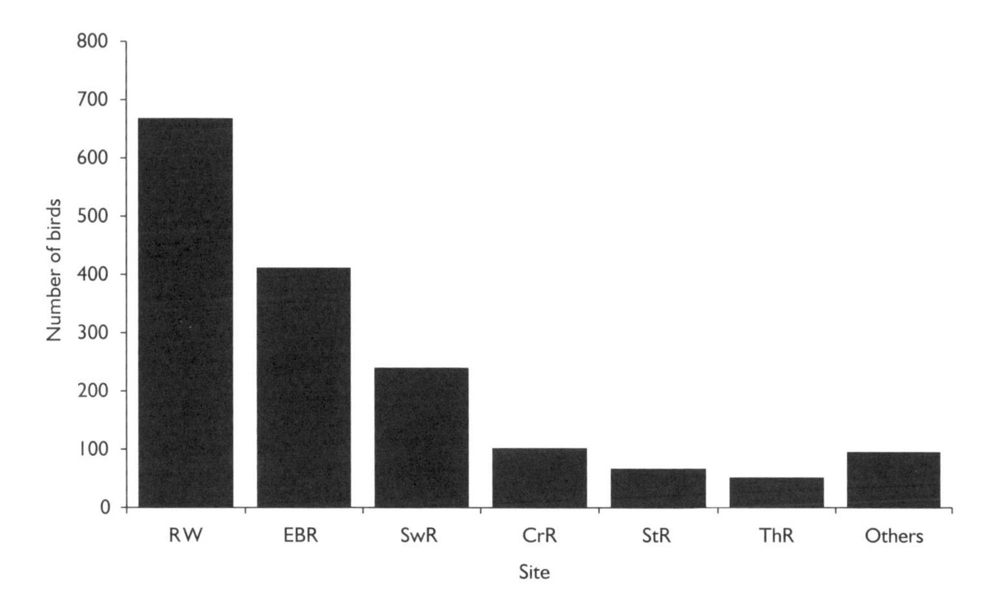

Figure 97: Sites where Common Scoters have been recorded 1941–2005.
Key to abbreviations: RW = Rutland Water; EBR = Eyebrook Reservoir; SwR = Swithland Reservoir; CrR = Cropston Reservoir; StR = Stanford Reservoir; ThR = Thornton Reservoir

text, records of a first-winter male on a small pool at Kaye's Plantation, Quorn fom February 8th to 13th 1995 and a male at Newton Harcourt Pool on March 28th 2005 are notable.

24% of all birds that have occurred in Leicestershire and Rutland have not been sexed, making analysis difficult, although as adult males are such distinctive birds it is possible that many of the unsexed records relate to females or juveniles. Of those that have been sexed, 48% have referred to males. Spring and in particular late summer movements contain a high proportion of males, whilst in late autumn females and immatures tend to predominate.

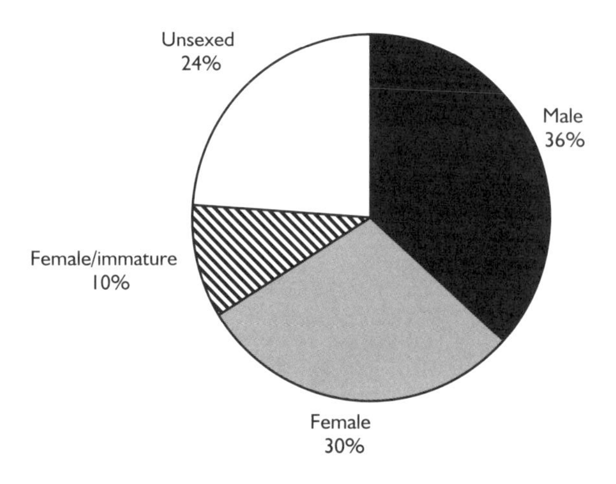

Figure 98: Sexes of Common Scoters 1941–2005.

Common Scoters breed in open tundra areas of Arctic and sub-Arctic Eurasia as far south as northern Britain. They winter on European coasts. The British breeding population is confined to northern Scotland and has declined markedly since the mid-1970s (Gibbons *et al.* 1996); in 2005 there were probably fewer than 20 pairs thought to have bred (Holling *et al.* 2008). Up to 50,000 birds winter in Britain (Baker *et al.* 2006), a large proportion of these being off the coast of north-west England and north Wales. Due to the small, declining nature of the British breeding population, this species has been added to the 'Red List' of Birds of Conservation Concern (Gregory *et al.* 2002).

AHJH

Velvet Scoter *Melanitta fusca*

Rare autumn and winter visitor; recorded in all months between October and April: 31 records involving 52 individuals.

Browne recorded one shot on either November 11th or 12th 1889 at Saddington Reservoir, the specimen of which was sent to the Leicester Museum. There were no further records until 1947 and by the end of 2005 there had been reports in a total of 21 years.

All records:

1889	shot, Saddington Reservoir, November 11th or 12th.
1947	Eyebrook Reservoir, November 16th.
1950	three females, Eyebrook Reservoir, April 8th.
1953	Swithland Reservoir, December 5th.
1963	female/immature, Cropston Reservoir, December 15th to January 12th 1964.
1964	immature, Cropston Reservoir, November 8th to 21st.
1968	male, Stanford Reservoir, November 16th to 23rd.
1971	two females, Thornton Reservoir, November 13th.
1974	male, Cropston Reservoir, December 24th.
1976	Stanford Reservoir, February 1st.
	Eyebrook Reservoir, March 21st.
	Wanlip Gravel Pits, October 31st.
	Cropston Reservoir, December 12th.
1978	Eyebrook Reservoir, December 3rd to 17th.
1979	male, Rutland Water, January 1st to 5th.

	two adult males and one immature male, Rutland Water, February 10th.
	female, Rutland Water, February 18th.
1980	male, Rutland Water, November 1st.
1982	female, Rutland Water, November 13th to 27th.
1985	two adult males and one first-year male, Rutland Water, January 12th to 23rd.
	female, Rutland Water, January 22nd to 23rd.
1987	male, Swithland Reservoir, February 20th.
1988	seven males, Rutland Water, November 19th.
1991	first-winter male, Rutland Water, December 6th to 10th.
1993	female, Fort Henry Ponds, November 3rd; same, Rutland Water, November 7th.
2001	female, Rutland Water, April 13th.
	female, Rutland Water, November 22nd to December 15th.
	first-winter male, Rutland Water, December 15th.
2002	female, Rutland Water, October 26th to November 4th.
	six females and three juveniles, Rutland Water, November 9th, with two females until December 4th.
	female, Cossington Meadows, December 28th to January 20th 2003.

All records have been between October 26th and April 13th. Most have related to single birds, notable exceptions being the flocks of seven and nine at Rutland Water in November 1988 and November 2002 respectively; the former group occurred on the same day as an unprecedented flock of 107 Common Scoters at Rutland Water.

The pattern of records suggests that birds are most likely to occur during the period of peak autumn passage, particularly in the first half of November, or subsequently during hard weather movements in winter. The series of records at Rutland Water in early 1979 was an example of the latter; following several spells of strong easterly winds and snow in the first two months of the year, three separate influxes of this species onto inland waters were noted during January 1st–7th, January 22nd–28th and February 12th–18th, corresponding almost perfectly with the Rutland Water records (Chandler 1981). Unlike the Common Scoter, this species is very rare in spring and has not yet been recorded in summer.

As with the majority of scarce wildfowl recorded in the counties, Rutland Water is the favoured site, with 32 individuals recorded there. Eyebrook Reservoir has had a total of six birds, whilst the only other water with more

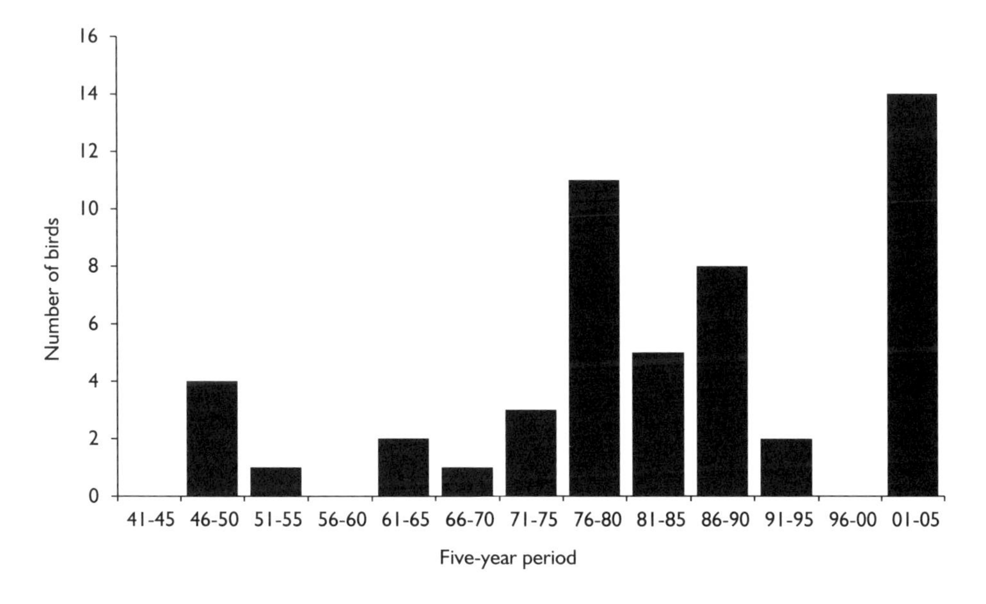

Figure 99: Number of Velvet Scoters by five-year periods 1941–2005.

than two records is Cropston Reservoir, with four. Rutland Water's dominance is shown by the fact that, prior to the first bird there in 1979, there were 13 records of 16 individuals from a total of six sites in the preceding 32 years, but there have been only three reports (all of single birds) away from Rutland Water in the 26 years since. The record from the relatively small site of Fort Henry Ponds in 1993 is noteworthy for a seaduck, whilst the female at Cossington Meadows in December 2002 and January 2003 frequented a very small pool, making its long stay even more remarkable.

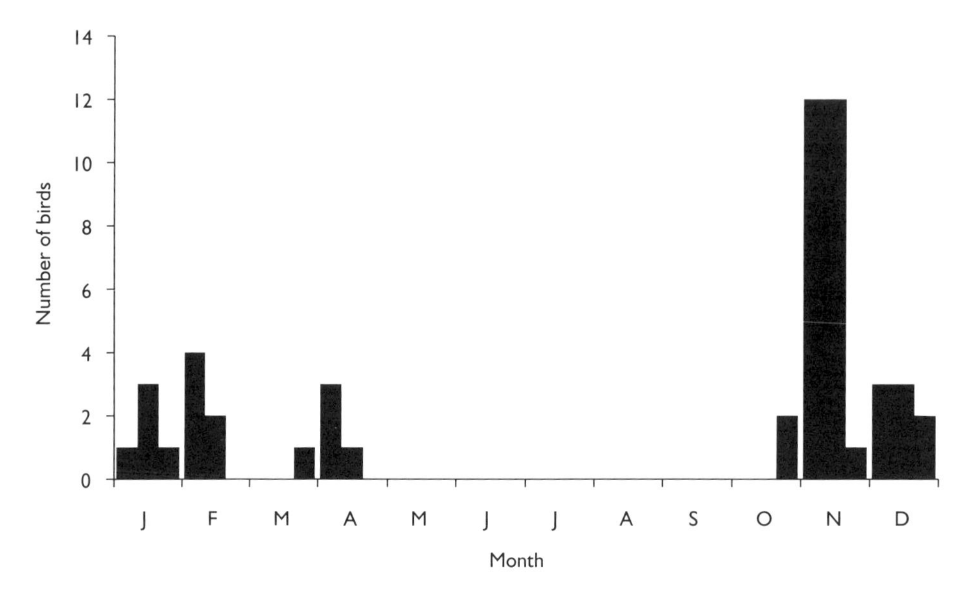

Figure 100: Monthly occurrence of Velvet Scoters 1941–2005.

Velvet Scoters have a circumpolar distribution, breeding in the Arctic and northern boreal zones, but are absent from eastern North America, Greenland and Iceland. The major known wintering areas in Europe are off the eastern Danish and southern Norwegian coasts. The British wintering population varies considerably from year to year, but usually numbers between 2,500 and 5,000 individuals, with the most important areas being the Firths of Forth and Moray in Scotland. As more than 50% of the British wintering population is found at less than ten sites, it is considered vulnerable and has therefore been added to the 'Amber List' of Birds of Conservation Concern (Gregory *et al.* 2002).

AHJH

Goldeneye (Common Goldeneye) ***Bucephala clangula***

Fairly common winter and passage visitor, scarce in summer.

Browne and Haines both considered this species to be an uncommon winter visitor in the 19th century. During the severe winter of 1845 it appeared in fairly large numbers and several were obtained at Groby Pool. Since then, numbers have increased significantly following the development of the larger reservoirs.

During the 1940s the Goldeneye was a regular winter visitor between October and March, with 15 at Swithland Reservoir on March 6th 1948 constituting the largest flock. By the 1960s flock sizes had tripled with notable counts including 46 at Eyebrook Reservoir on January 28th 1968 and 40 at Swithland Reservoir on

March 18th 1967. A marked spring passage began to be noted during April, when peak numbers occurred in many years. On April 4th 1969, for example, 45 were at Swithland Reservoir and 43 were at Eyebrook Reservoir.

During the early 1970s up to 75 were regularly recorded on spring passage in March or April yet the highest winter count was 58 at Eyebrook Reservoir in December 1974. Following the construction of Rutland Water, however, the status of this species changed significantly. Peak counts began to be made during the winter, increasing from 147 on January 14th 1979 to 303 on February 17th 1985, then reaching a peak of 505 on February 17th 1991 which was not exceeded until 511 were recorded there on February 22nd 2004. The threshold for a site to be classed of national importance for Goldeneye is 249, making Rutland Water the sixth most important site in Britain for this species (Collier *et al.* 2005). Once this large wintering population was established, spring flocks were no longer so noticeable. It is clear from wildfowl count data that most of our wintering birds arrive during November and that numbers increase during the winter before reaching a peak in February. Numbers recorded during October and March are variable, presumably reflecting movements of birds on passage.

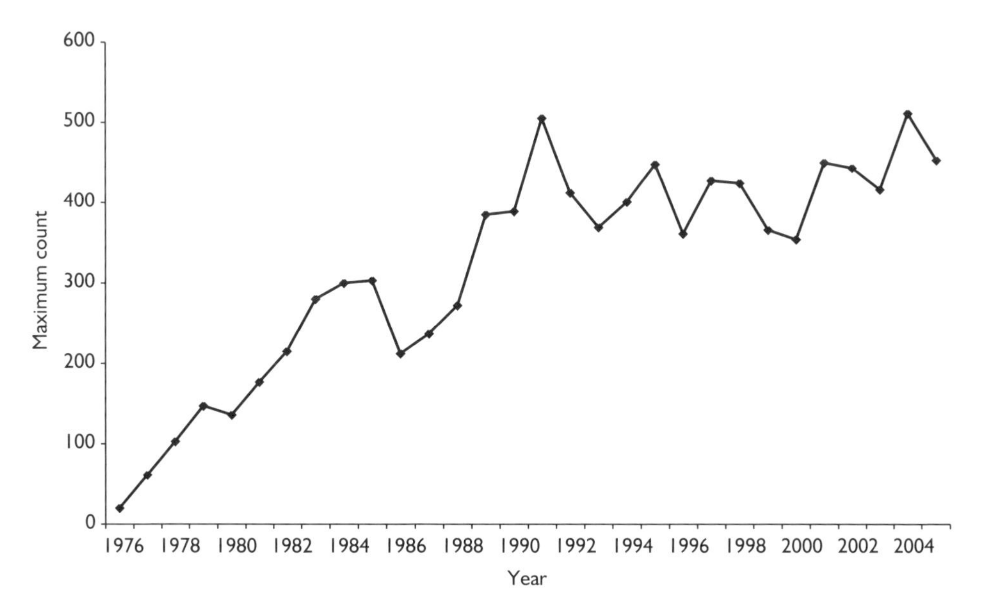

Figure 101: Maximum counts of Goldeneye at Rutland Water 1976–2005.

The next most important sites after Rutland Water are Swithland Reservoir and Eyebrook Reservoir. Counts at Swithland Reservoir have exceeded 70 in seven years, the maxima being:

- 95 on March 5th 1989.
- 95 on April 1st and 2nd 2004.
- 94 on February 22nd 2005.
- 87 on March 7th 1985.
- 73 on March 14th 1998.
- 72 on December 14th 2003.
- 71 on February 19th 2000.

Numbers at Eyebrook Reservoir are generally smaller, but have reached 60 or more in four years:

- 76 on March 25th 2004.
- 75 on February 25th 2005.
- 64 on February 25th 1994.
- 60 in December 1976.

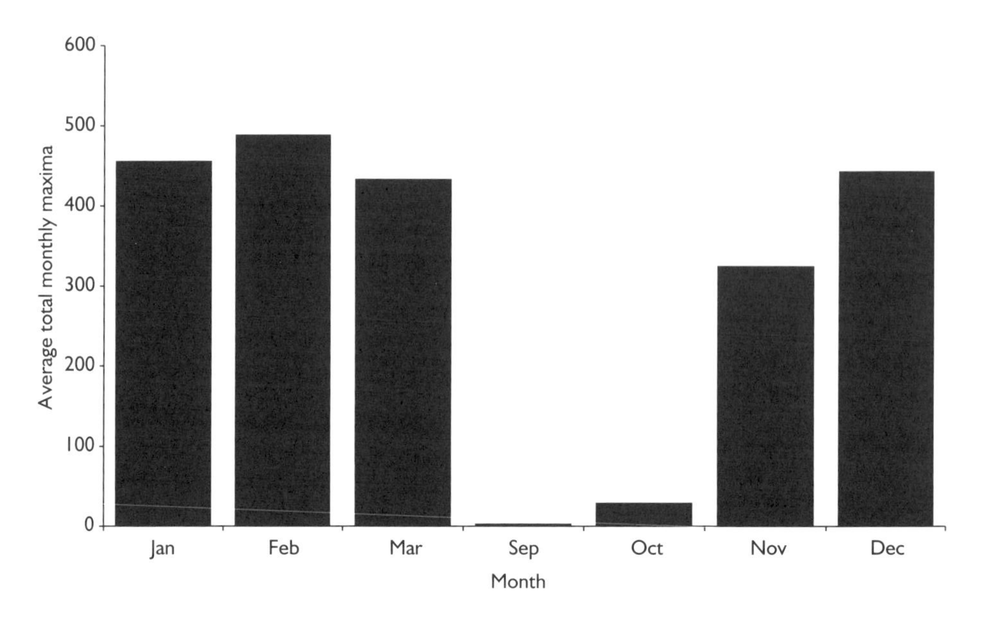

Figure 102: Average total monthly maxima of Goldeneye at the main sites 1995–2005.

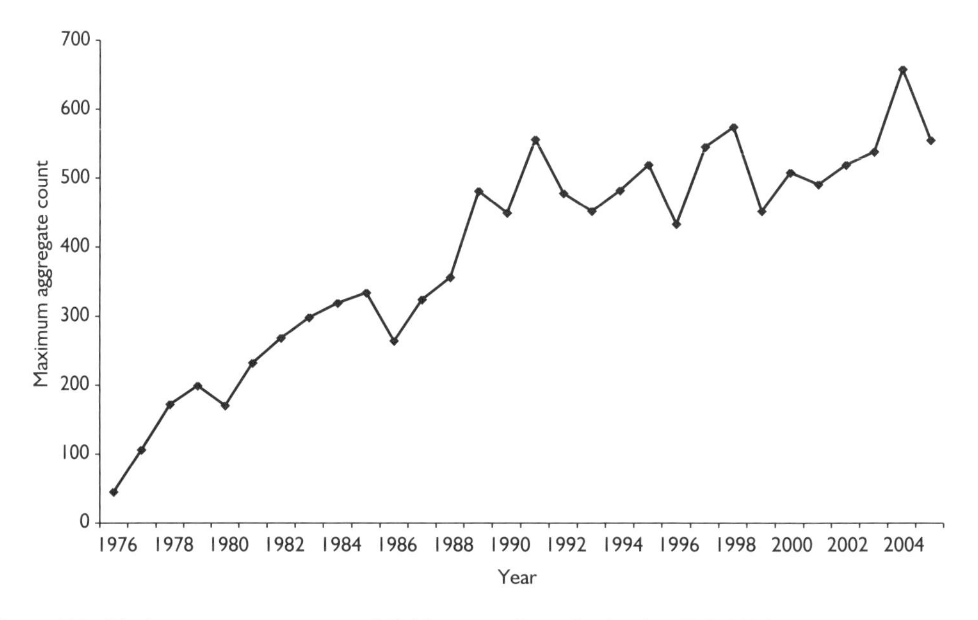

Figure 103: Maximum aggregate counts of Goldeneye at the main sites in 1976–2005.

Elsewhere counts have exceeded 25 at four sites, where maxima were 60 at Cropston Reservoir on April 3rd 1977, 29 on the River Trent at Castle Donington on February 28th 2004 and 26 at both Stanford Reservoir on March 15th 1998 and Trent Valley Pit on March 27th 1999. See 'Wintering Birds' (pages 39–43) for details of highest counts at other individual sites.

During periods of extreme weather a few birds have been seen on the River Soar within the city boundary of Leicester, including four at Abbey Park from January 15th to February 21st 1963; up to seven frequented the River Soar at Kegworth in the harsh winter of 1946–47.

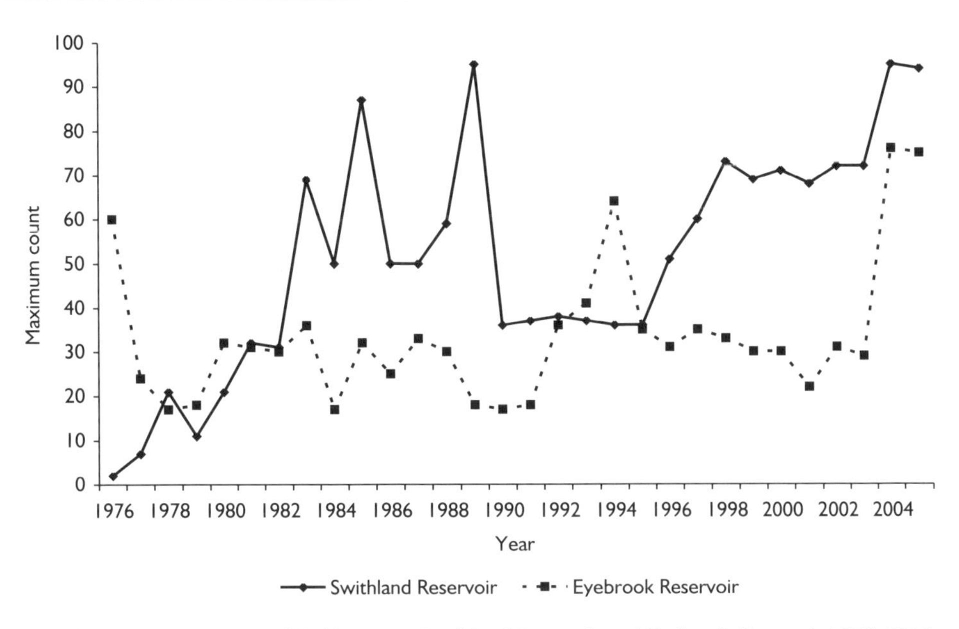

Figure 104: Maximum counts of Goldeneye at Swithland Reservoir and Eyebrook Reservoir 1976–2005.

A tendency for some non-breeding individuals to summer in the counties was first noted in 1960, when a male was recorded at Swithland Reservoir on June 5th and July 3rd. Such records remained unusual until the mid 1980s, but have become regular since then. In 2001, for example, a male and two females were present at Rutland Water during May and June, with a single female present during July and August; summering birds were also noted in 2003 and 2005. Though not conclusive, field observations suggest that some of these birds are returning individuals.

The origin of our birds is uncertain but most of those in winter probably come from Scandinavia or Russia. Groups of four at Rutland Water from the last week of July 1988 and five there during July 15th–17th 1990, however, are perhaps more likely to originate from the rapidly expanding British population.

A female at Rutland Water on October 27th 2002 was a rare variant with an orange-yellow bill lacking dark pigment.

Goldeneyes have a circumpolar breeding distribution. There is a small expanding population in Scotland, which has grown from 90 pairs during 1988–91 (Gibbons *et al.* 1993) to 145 to 149 pairs in 2005 (Holling *et al.* 2008). Summering birds have also been noted in several English counties. Because the breeding population remains small and the wintering population is relatively concentrated, this species is on the 'Amber List' of Birds of Conservation Concern (Gregory *et al.* 2002).

AHJH

Smew — *Mergellus albellus*

Uncommon winter visitor.

During the 19th century Browne recorded this species as a rare winter visitor to Leicestershire, though it was not mentioned by Haines as occurring in Rutland. Its first recorded occurrence was during the severe weather of February and March 1845, when according to Harley 'it was frequently met with in the society of scoters, pochards and wigeon.' Browne also knew of four specimen records. These early records seem to have come from widely scattered sites, those mentioned being Groby Pool, Syston, Thornton Reservoir, the River Trent at Castle Donington and the River Eye near Wyfordby. The LROS archives include regular records from Swithland Reservoir in January 1928, December 1933, February 1934 and March 1935.

Since systematic recording began in 1941, when it was considered to be an occasional winter visitor between December and March, the Smew has been recorded annually except in 1960 and 1965. Numbers during the 1940s and early 1950s were high, with annual totals of 20 in 1944, 29 in 1946, 23 in 1947 and 35 in 1948. Notable groups during this period were:

- 13 at Eyebrook Reservoir on February 10th 1946.
- 11 at Eyebrook Reservoir in late December 1950 and early January 1951.
- ten at Eyebrook Reservoir in early 1944.
- ten at Stanford Reservoir on January 26th 1947.
- ten at Blackbrook Reservoir on March 6th 1948.
- ten at Eyebrook Reservoir on March 7th 1948.
- nine at Swithland Reservoir on February 12th 1956.
- eight at Groby Pool on December 19th 1948.
- seven at Stanford Reservoir in early 1944.
- seven at Stanford Reservoir on December 3rd 1953 and March 7th 1954.

Flocks of this size were not exceeded until the late 1980s and numbers at Stanford Reservoir, Swithland Reservoir, Blackbrook Reservoir and Groby Pool have never again reached these levels.

Numbers recorded between 1957 and 1984 were considerably smaller, the largest counts being of six at Stanford Reservoir on December 13th 1959 and Eyebrook Reservoir on both January 9th 1963 and January 3rd 1979. From 1985 onwards, however, numbers increased significantly and have included annual totals of 66 in 1997, 58 in 2003, 56 in 1998 and 54 in 2002. A flock of 12 at Rutland Water on January 11th and 12th 1986 was the first double-figure count since 1951, but such flocks are now regular at the two main sites of Eyebrook Reservoir and Rutland Water. The highest counts at these two sites have been:

- 22 (including three adult males) at Eyebrook Reservoir on March 9th 1997.
- 20 (including four adult males) at Rutland Water on January 31st 1987.
- 19 (including four adult males) at Rutland Water on December 6th 1998.
- 18 (including seven adult males) at Rutland Water on January 18th 1998.
- 17 (including four adult males) at Eyebrook Reservoir on February 9th 1999.

The current threshold for sites of national importance has been set at just four (Collier *et al.* 2005), so Rutland Water and Eyebrook Reservoir both qualify.

This species has appeared at most of the counties' reservoirs, lakes and gravel pit complexes over the years, although only Eyebrook Reservoir and Rutland Water could be classed as regular wintering sites. During the last ten years, other sites where Smew have appeared with some degree of frequency have included the Soar valley gravel pits, Swithland Reservoir, Trent Valley Pit and Saddington Reservoir. Numbers at these sites rarely exceed two, although four have been seen together in the Soar valley on three occasions (at Watermead Park on December 28th 1997, Wanlip South Gravel Pits from January 29th to March 2nd 1999 and Birstall Gravel Pits from January 17th to March 11th 2004), four were at Trent Valley Pit on January 12th 1997 and five were at Saddington Reservoir on February 27th 1999, with four there from February 9th to 13th 2002. There have been several records of Smew from the River Soar within the city boundary of Leicester, usually during severe weather. In the notoriously cold winter of 1946–47 one was at Abbey Park from January 2nd to February 16th, whilst in the equally severe winter of 1962–63 one or two were in the same area from January 1st to February 4th. More recently, single 'redheads' have been at Abbey Park from February 16th to March 4th 1986, Freemen's Weir from January 5th to 9th 1997 and Evans' Weir on January 9th 1997and a drake was at Abbey Park in February 1998. Other unusual sites that have attracted it include a small pool at Theddingworth on January 1st 1963, Shawell Gravel Pits on February 12th 1989 and Froleworth Manor Lake on December 9th 2003.

The first autumn birds normally arrive in mid-November, although there have been six October records, all of single 'redheads', as follows:

- Rutland Water, October 20th 1991.
- Albert Village Lake, October 20th 2003.
- Eyebrook Reservoir, October 22nd 2002.
- Rutland Water, October 25th 2005.

- Eyebrook Reservoir, October 30th 1981.
- Swithland Reservoir, October 31st 1992.

Average arrival dates for 1956–80 are not calculated as appearances were scarce and erratic during this period.

WeBS count data show that relatively few are recorded before December and that peak numbers occur in January and February. These are also the months with the highest ratios of older males to redheads, although in recent years adult males have been recorded with increasing frequency during March. Occurrence patterns have

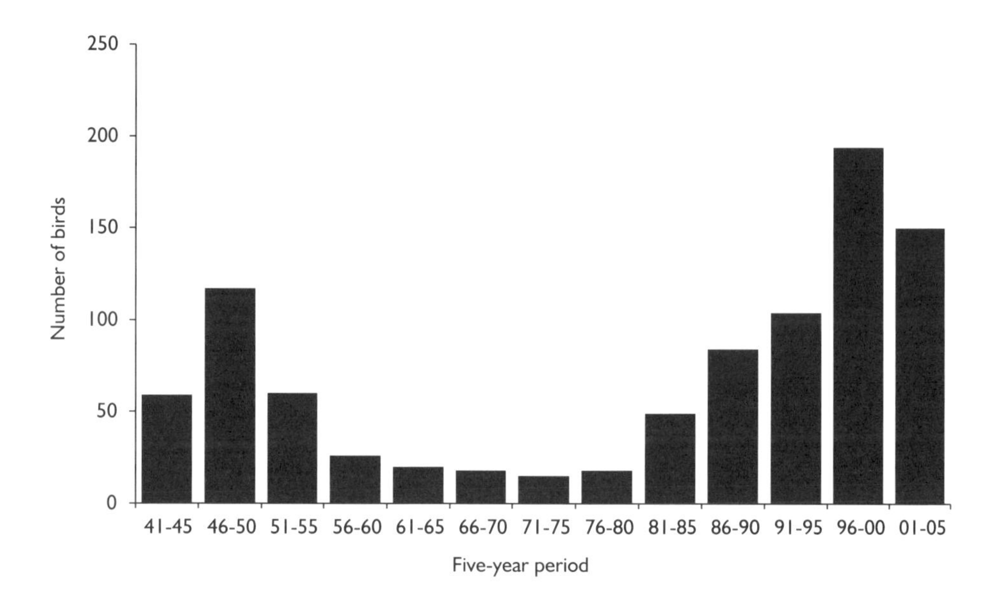

Figure 105: Numbers of Smew by five-year periods 1941–2005.

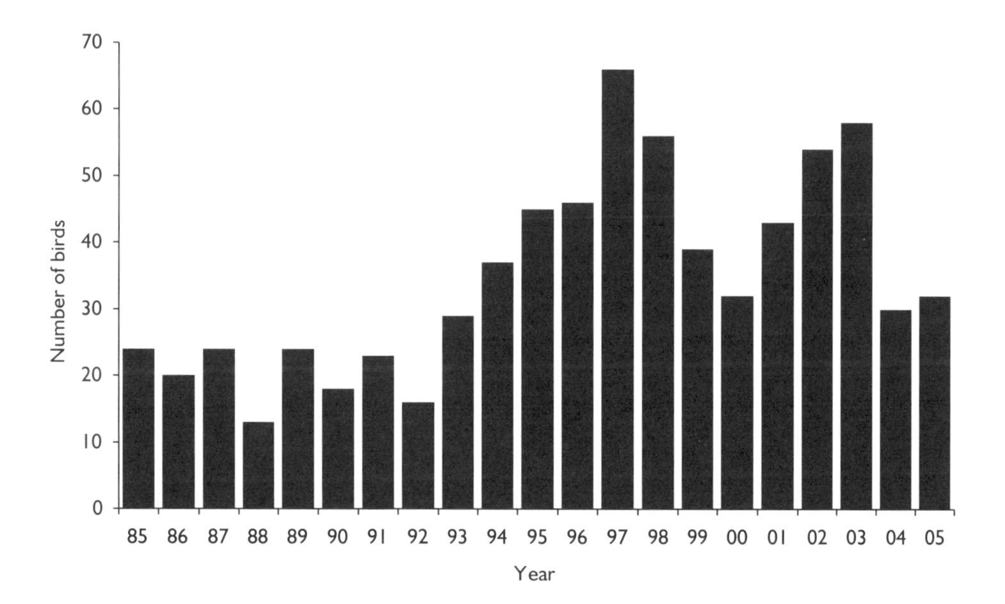

Figure 106: Numbers of Smew 1985–2005.

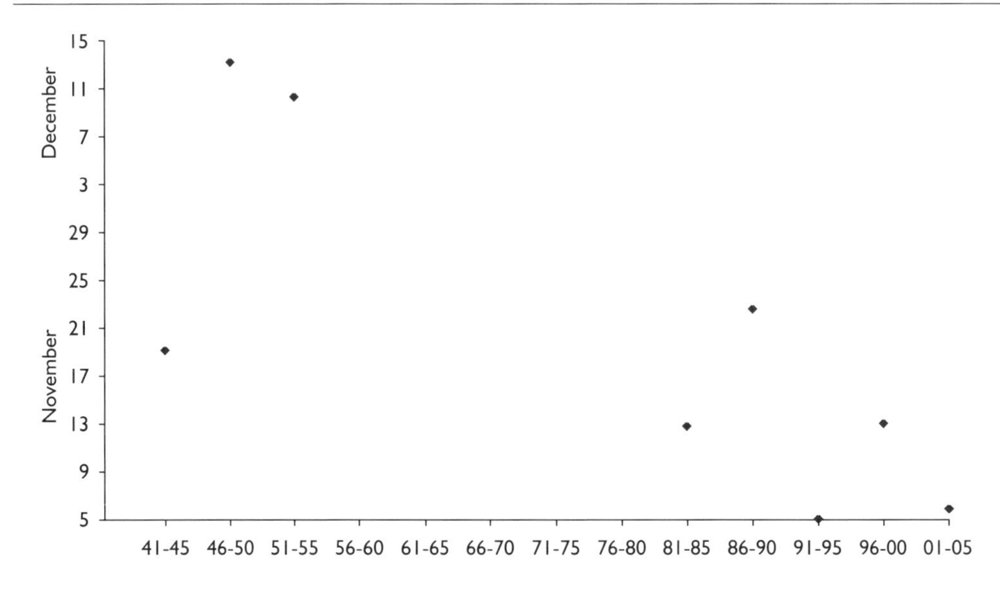

Figure 107: Average autumn arrival dates of Smew by five-year periods 1941–2005.

changed significantly since 1995, with more birds than previously arriving during November and remaining until March. It will be interesting to see whether this trend continues in the long term.

Table 14: Average monthly ratio of older males to 'redheads' in 1997–2005

January	February	March	November	December
1 : 2.6	1 : 1.8	1 : 2.4	1 : 4.1	1 : 3

The last birds of the spring are usually seen in mid to late March although there have been records of lingering individuals in April in 13 years. Most of these have involved birds seen during the first few days of the month,

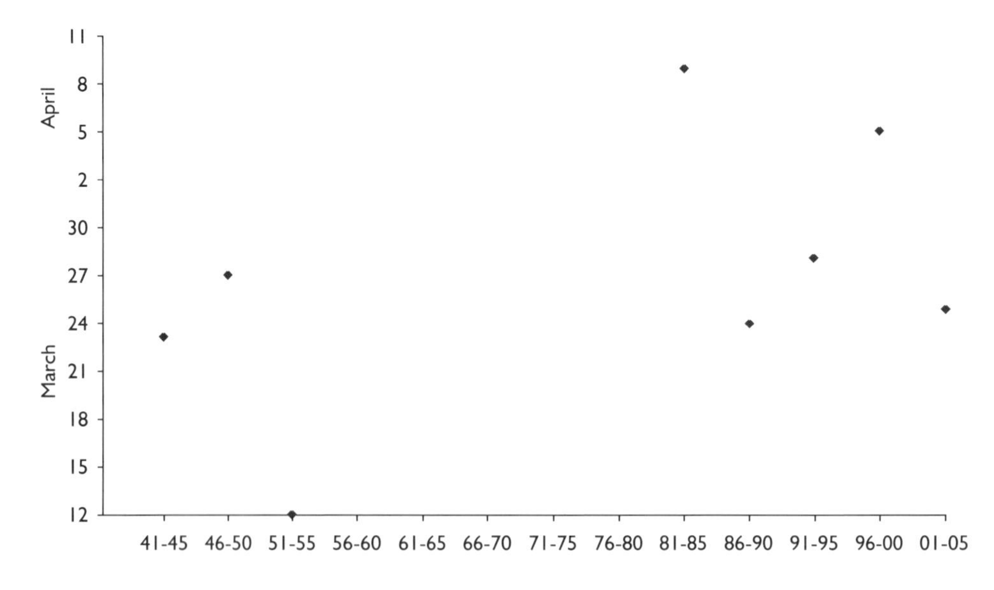

Figure 108: Average spring departure dates of Smew by five-year periods 1941–2005.

although a male remained at Swithland Reservoir on April 30th 1979 and single 'redheads' stayed at Blackbrook Reservoir until April 18th 1945 and Rutland Water until April 13th 1982. A 'redhead' at Swithland Reservoir in the 1990s regularly lingered into late April, remaining until the 23rd in 1994, the 28th in 1995, the 26th in 1996 and the 27th in 1997. A female stayed at Rutland Water until May 2nd 1981 and, exceptionally, a female arrived at Eyebrook Reservoir on May 27th 1973 and was still present the following day.

Note that, in the graph above, average spring departure dates from 1956 to 1980 are not calculated as this species was scarce and erratic in its appearances during this time.

Average departure dates for 1956–80 are not calculated as appearances were scarce and erratic during this period.

Smew breed in boreal zones of Eurasia, from northern Scandinavia to eastern Siberia. They winter in Eurasia south of the breeding range, when small numbers reach Britain. 'Redheads' move further than males, making the so-called 'white nuns' a prized sight for birdwatchers.

AHJH

Red-breasted Merganser *Mergus serrator*

Scarce winter and passage visitor; recorded in all months except August, with the majority from October to February.

The Red-breasted Merganser was a rare visitor in the 19th century. Browne knew of just one occurrence, one shot at Coleorton Hall in about 1860 which was preserved in the collection of Sir G. Beaumont, whilst in Rutland Haines gave five or six records involving eight to ten birds: three immatures shot at Burley Fishponds in about 1878, with two or three there in about 1888 and 'one or two others since', one killed at Ketton in 1882 and an undated record from Withcote Hall Lake. Prior to the formation of LROS in 1941, the only other known occurrences were at Stanford Reservoir, where there were two on November 23rd 1934 and a pair on December 19th 1938.

There were records in 19 of the 35 years between 1941 and 1975. In most years just one bird was recorded, although two to four were seen in five years, six were noted in 1969 and 1974 and there were seven in 1956. This species has become more frequent since 1976, with records in every year since then and it is now a regular winter visitor and migrant in small numbers. This may be the result of expansion of the breeding range into north-west England and north Wales, though winter records are thought to include birds from the Baltic (Lack 1986). Double-figure annual totals have been recorded in 11 years, eight of them since 1992, although the two highest totals were 25 in 1979 and 18 in 1985.

Most records involve single birds or groups of up to three, but a few larger flocks have appeared, as follows:

- four (two males and two females) at Eyebrook Reservoir on March 3rd 1957.
- five at Rutland Water on both December 13th 1982 and November 13th 1983.
- five females/juveniles at Swithland Reservoir on September 23rd 2001.
- six males at Groby Pool on January 29th 1969.
- six females at Rutland Water on November 10th 1979.
- an exceptional 11 at Rutland Water on February 18th 1979, with seven until February 24th. These birds were associated with a nationwide influx following hard weather, when over 500 Red-breasted Mergansers were seen inland in mid-February (Chandler 1981).

In addition, at least six and possibly as many as 13, were at Rutland Water between January 16th and February 17th 1985.

All records have occurred between September and May except for single females at both Market Bosworth on June 18th 1983 and Eyebrook Reservoir on June 6th 1987 and a male at Eyebrook Reservoir on July 8th 1995. The earliest autumn record is of a female at Eyebrook Reservoir on September 7th 2004, although there have been only another seven occurrences in this month, as follows:

- a male at Swithland Reservoir on September 19th 2001.
- a female/juvenile at Rutland Water on September 22nd 2001.
- five females/juveniles at Swithland Reservoir on September 23rd 2001.

- three eclipse males at Swithland Reservoir on September 25th 1977.
- single birds at both Swithland Reservoir and Eyebrook Reservoir on September 30th 1979.
- a female at Rutland Water on September 30th 1997.

There have been several records in early May but only four later than the 4th: a female at Rutland Water from May 9th to 30th 1984, a male at the same site on May 14th 1998, a pair at Swithland Reservoir on May 15th 1993 and a pair at Stanford Reservoir on May 30th 1968. The peaks in December, January and February coincide with maximum numbers in British coastal waters, which decline in March, whilst those recorded in April and early May (often in pairs) are likely to have wintered further south.

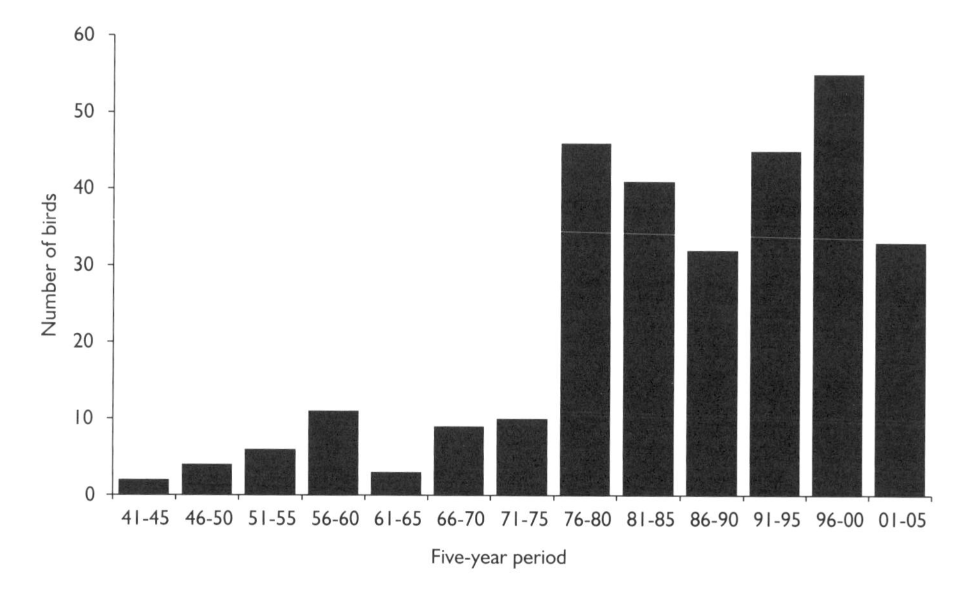

Figure 109: Number of Red-breasted Mergansers by five-year periods 1941–2005.

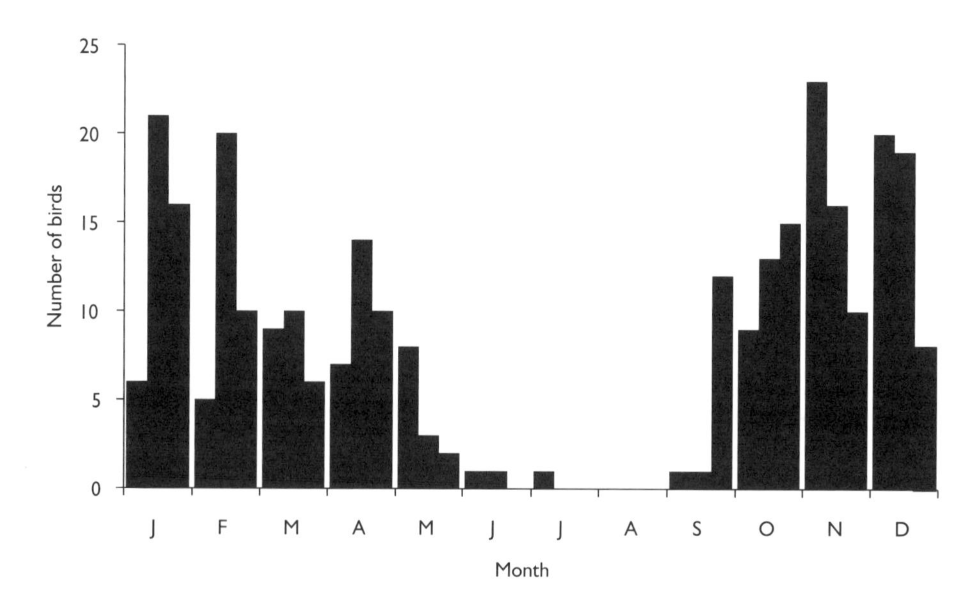

Figure 110: Monthly occurrence of Red-breasted Mergansers 1941–2005.

Rutland Water is by far the most popular site, with almost 50% of all individuals having occurred here. Eyebrook Reservoir accounts for a further 22% of records. Red-breasted Mergansers in Leicestershire and Rutland are clearly attracted to reservoirs and only 26 individuals have occurred away from such sites, nine of which have been at Priory Water and eight at Groby Pool. There has only ever been one record from the Soar valley gravel pits (a female in the Wanlip South Gravel Pits/Birstall Gravel Pits area from December 19th 1999 to February 22nd 2000) and the Red-breasted Merganser is missing from the list of species recorded at a number of likely-looking sites such as Fort Henry Ponds, Trent Valley Pit, Blackbrook Reservoir, Knipton Reservoir and Belvoir Lakes. Two birds have been recorded on the River Soar within the city of Leicester: single females at Freemen's Weir on October 15th 1998 and Abbey Park on December 24th 1999.

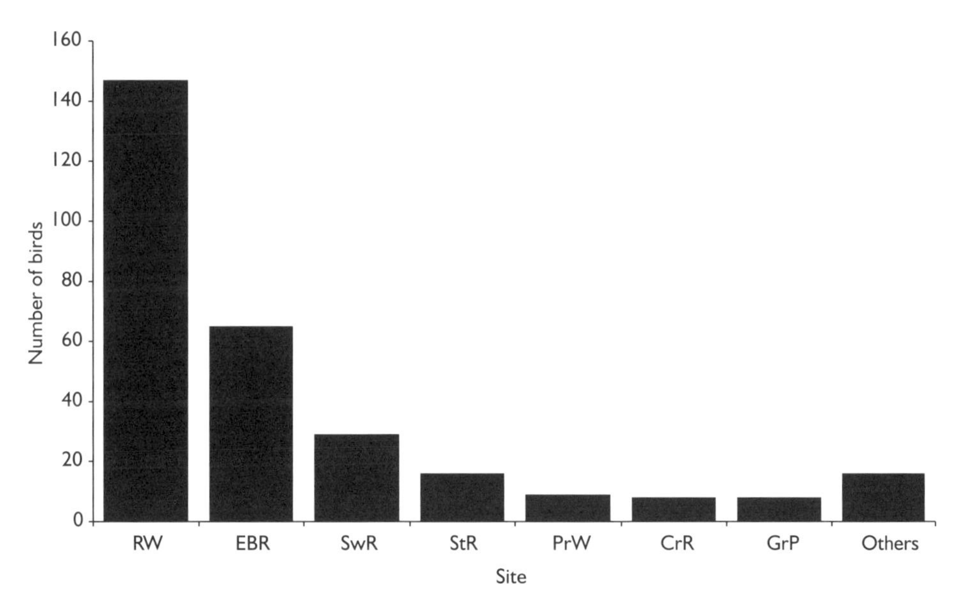

Figure 111: Sites where Red-breasted Mergansers have been recorded 1941–2005.
Key to abbreviations: RW = Rutland Water; EBR = Eyebrook Reservoir; SwR = Swithland Reservoir; StR = Stanford Reservoir; PrW = Priory Water; CrR = Cropston Reservoir; GrP = Groby Pool

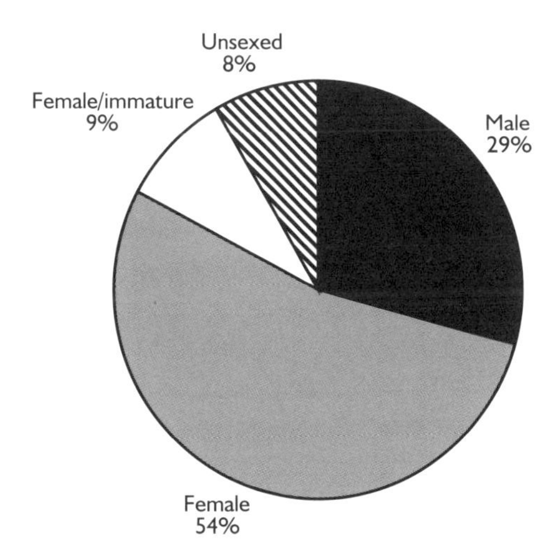

Figure 112: Sexes of Red-breasted Mergansers 1941–2005.

The majority (62%) of records have referred to females or juveniles, with another 8% being unsexed. Adult males account for only 30% of all individuals recorded.

Red-breasted Mergansers breed from the low Arctic to northern temperate zones. Northern populations are migratory, whilst southern birds are resident. They are widespread breeders in Scotland and parts of Northern Ireland, Wales and northern England, with almost all birds moving to the coast in the autumn. The British breeding population estimate is 2,150 pairs and the wintering population is believed just under 10,000 birds (Baker *et al.* 2006). National WeBS data show that this species increased greatly during the winter since the 1960s, followed by a slight decline since the late 1990s (Collier *et al.* 2005), mirroring the occurrence patterns in Leicestershire and Rutland.

AHJH

Goosander *Mergus merganser*

Fairly common winter visitor, rare in summer.

Numbers of this species in the counties seem to have increased steadily since records began. In the 19th century it was described as a rare winter visitor to Leicestershire by Browne and Haines knew of just two Rutland records, both from Burley Fishponds. The only early record which involved a lengthy stay involved one at Swithland Reservoir from November 29th 1903 until February 1st 1904. In the first half of the 20th century Goosanders were regarded as occasional winter visitors, with the following records noted in the LROS archives: single birds at Aylestone in 1923, Wanlip in 1932, Cropston Reservoir on November 20th 1937 and Thornton Reservoir on January 17th 1939.

By the time of the first LROS Annual Report in 1941, this species was described as an occasional winter visitor. A flock of 11 at Swithland Reservoir from March 1st to 10th 1942 was, at the time, the largest ever recorded in the counties, although from 1945 onwards a wider spread of records and greater numbers than previously were noted. Eyebrook Reservoir became a regular wintering site, with peak counts in the 1940s and 1950s of 27 on December 27th 1946 and February 13th 1949 and 48 on February 24th 1957. Numbers in the 1960s and early 1970s increased further; 93 were present on March 10th 1965, with 100 on December 22nd 1967 and a record flock of 230–250 was seen in late December 1973. The construction of Rutland Water in the mid-

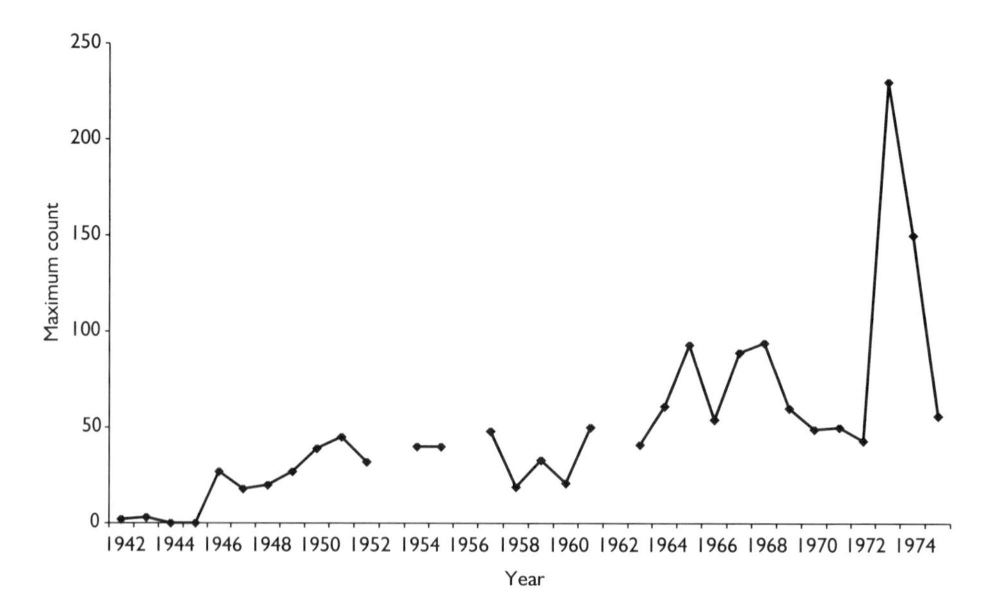

Figure 113: Maximum counts of Goosanders at Eyebrook Reservoir 1942–75.

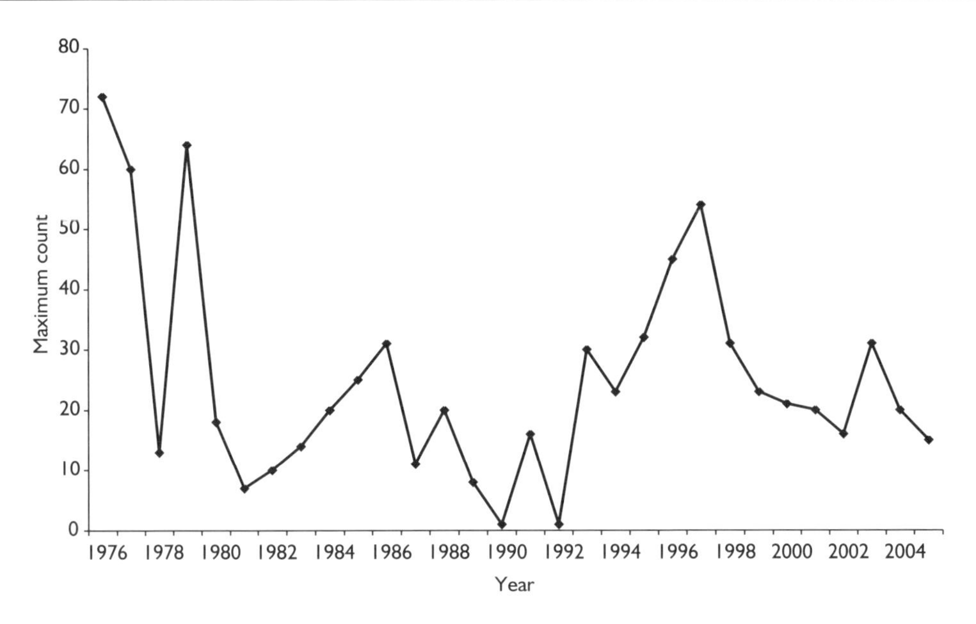

Figure 114: Maximum counts of Goosanders at Eyebrook Reservoir 1976–2005.

1970s, however, had a profound effect on numbers at this site; apart from counts of 45 in February 1996 and 54 on February 2nd 1997, numbers have not exceeded 32 in any winter after 1979.

Elsewhere during the period from the 1940s to the mid-1970s, double-figure counts were recorded at four sites, all of which were the highest ever recorded at these waters:

- 100 at Stanford Reservoir in January 1974.
- 76 at Swithland Reservoir on January 20th 1972.
- 25 at Cropston Reservoir in February 1972.
- 14 at Blackbrook Reservoir on March 6th 1948.

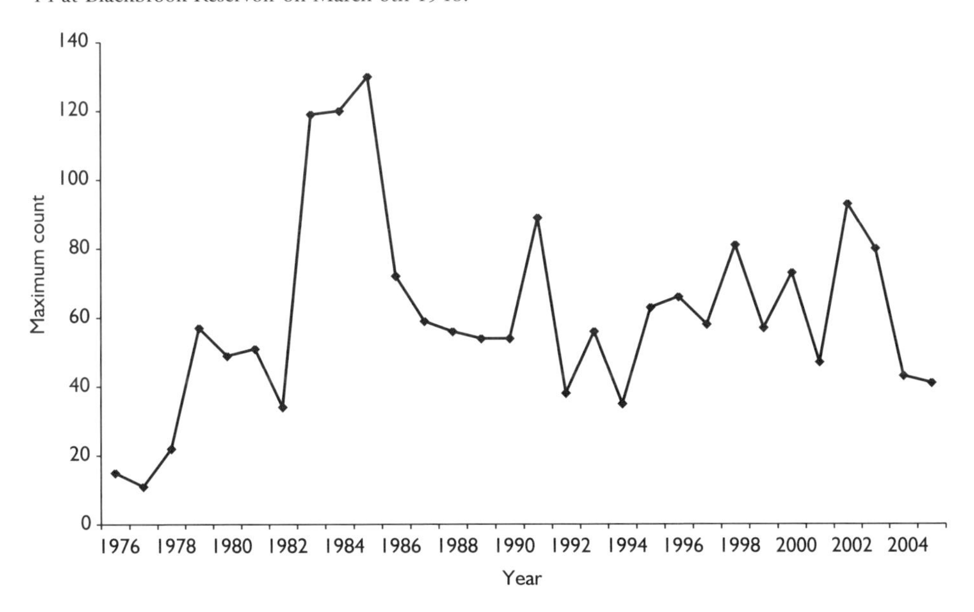

Figure 115: Maximum counts of Goosanders at Rutland Water 1976–2005.

It took several years for a regular wintering flock to be a feature at the newly-constructed Rutland Water. The mid-1980s produced the peak numbers, with 120 in early January 1984 and 130 on January 26th 1985 being the highest ever at this site. Since then numbers have fluctuated from year to year, but as yet no obvious trend or pattern has emerged; continental weather patterns are as likely to influence these fluctuations as local factors. The highest totals in recent years have been 89 on February 17th 1991, 81 on February 15th 1998, 87 on January 5th 2002 and 93 on December 28th 2002. The current qualifying level for a site to be considered of national importance is 70 (Collier *et al.* 2005), so although counts at Rutland Water have exceeded this figure on a number of occasions the site does not consistently meet the qualifying criteria.

The Watermead Country Park complex has become a regular wintering area since the early 1990s, with the highest counts being 84 at Birstall Gravel Pits on February 22nd 1991, 67 at Watermead Park on February 4th 1996 and 68 at Wanlip South Gravel Pits on January 24th 2002.

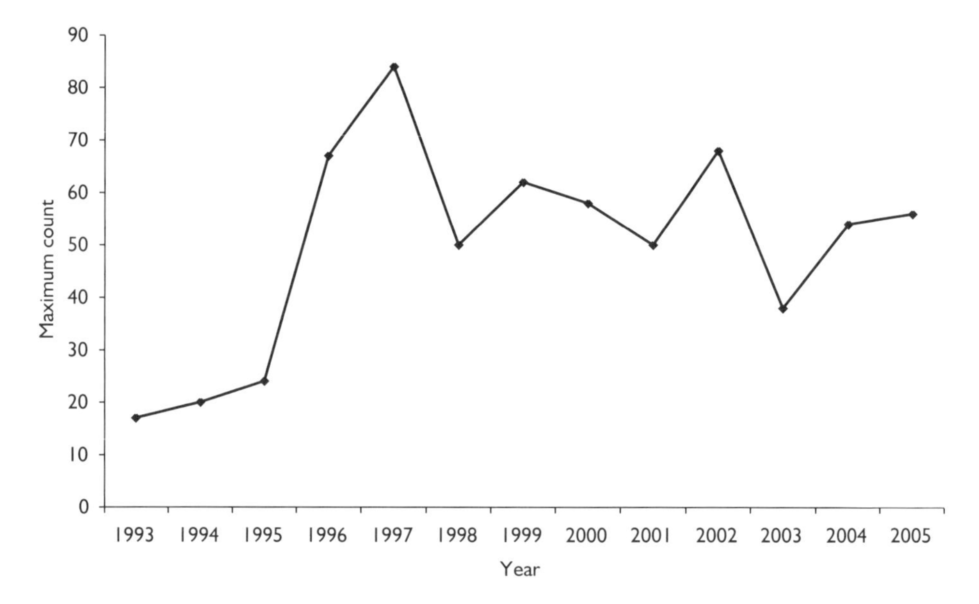

Figure 116: Maximum counts of Goosanders at the Watermead Country Park complex 1993–2005.

Other than those areas already mentioned, counts of 40 or more have come from four sites, where maxima have been:

- 59 at Knipton Reservoir on January 25th 1997.
- 55 at Belvoir Lakes on February 18th 1996.
- 48 at Priory Water on January 19th 1997.
- 40 at Staunton Harold Reservoir on December 7th 1980.

In recent years, small numbers have wintered at the unlikely-looking site of Abbey Park, Leicester, where the highest counts have been 35 on January 27th 1998, 20 in late December 1998, 14 on February 2nd 2000 and in December 2002 and 12 on December 30th 2005. See 'Wintering Birds' (pages 39–43) for details of highest counts at other individual sites.

The majority of wintering birds, probably from northern Fennoscandia and western Russia, arrive between November and January, later than other wintering ducks (Wernham *et al.* 2002). WeBS count data show a distinct peak in January and February. Those recorded in late spring, during the summer or in early autumn are more likely to originate from the expanding British breeding population. The last spring birds are usually seen during April, although there have been May records in 16 years since 1941, nine of which have been since 1991. Birds have been seen during the second half of the month in six years, as follows:

- a pair at Rutland Water on May 31st 1975.
- a male at King's Mills on May 31st 1999.
- a female at Trent Valley Pit on May 31st 2003.
- a male at Cropston Reservoir on May 24th 1994.
- a male at Stanford Reservoir on May 20th 1999.
- a female at Rutland Water on May 19th 1984.
- a male at Swithland Reservoir on May 16th 1993.

The earliest autumn record was four at Eyebrook Reservoir on August 25th 1951, the only ever arrival in this month. Birds have been recorded in September in six years, three of which have been since 2001; all refer to single birds unless stated:

- Staunton Harold Reservoir, September 12th 1965.
- four, Rutland Water, September 16th 2001.
- Eyebrook Reservoir, September 19th 1973.
- five, Rutland Water, September 23rd 2001.
- Rutland Water, September 24th 2005.
- Rutland Water, September 25th 1993.
- Rutland Water, September 29th 2002.

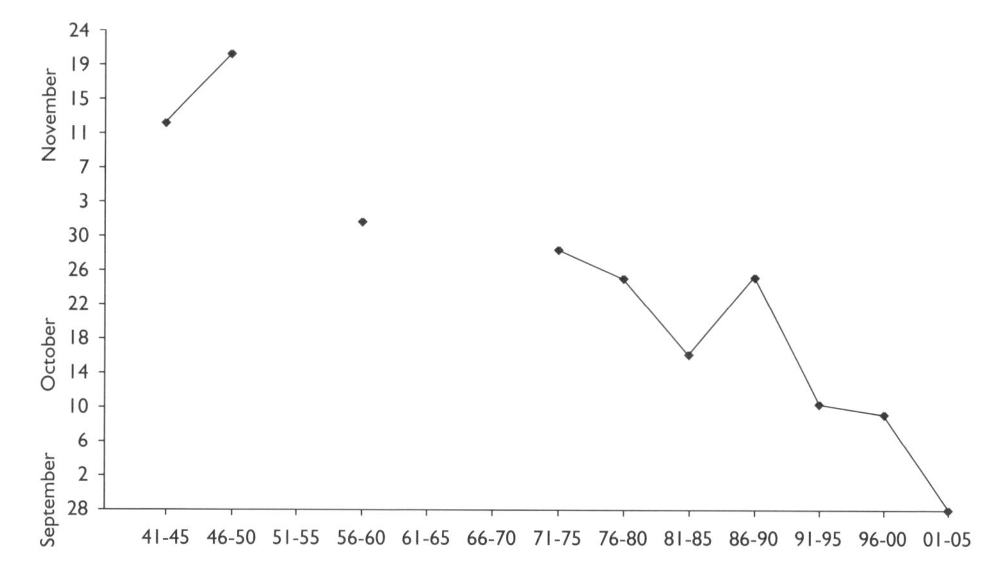

Figure 117: Average autumn arrival dates of Goosanders by five-year periods 1941–2005.

In 1960 a female was recorded at Stanford Reservoir on July 26th. There were no further summer records until 1987, when a female was present at Eyebrook Reservoir from May 10th until August 1st. Since then such records have become more frequent:

- nine juveniles at Trent Valley Pit on July 26th 1994 were thought likely to have come from the nearby Derbyshire breeding population.
- a juvenile was at Frisby Gravel Pits on July 7th 1995.
- a male at Frisby Gravel Pits on June 21st 1996 was truly extraordinary since adult males undertake a moult migration to Tana Fjord in northernmost Norway during June to October.
- a female was on the River Soar at Freemen's Weir, Leicester from May 21st until June 1st 1998.
- an injured male (which had possibly flown into power lines) remained on the River Soar within the city boundary of Leicester from March 21st until December 31st 2002 and was then at Birstall Gravel Pits until July 20th 2003.
- three juveniles were at Trent Valley Pit on July 28th 2005.

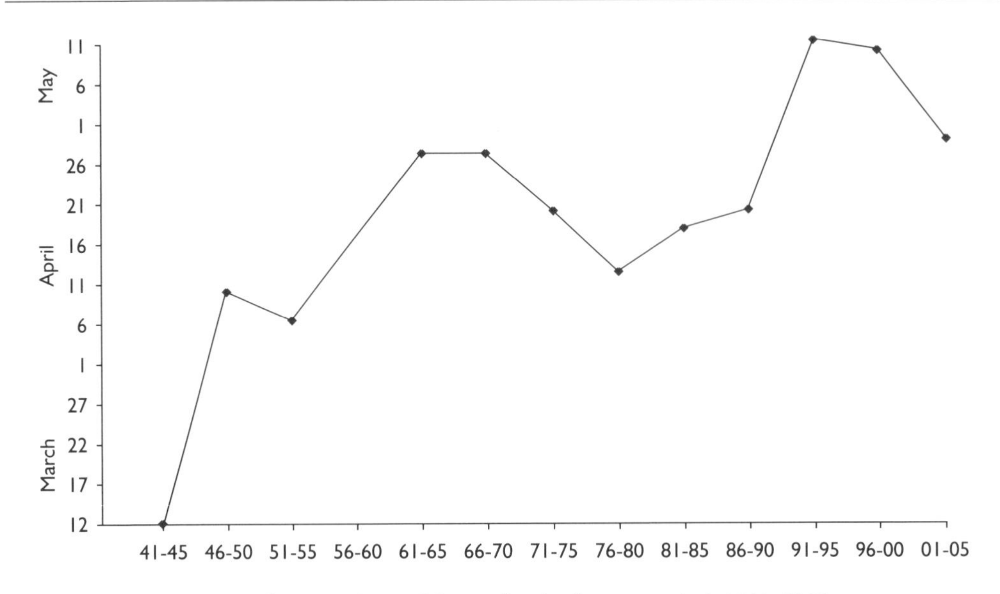

Figure 118: Average spring departure dates of Goosanders by five-year periods 1941–2005.

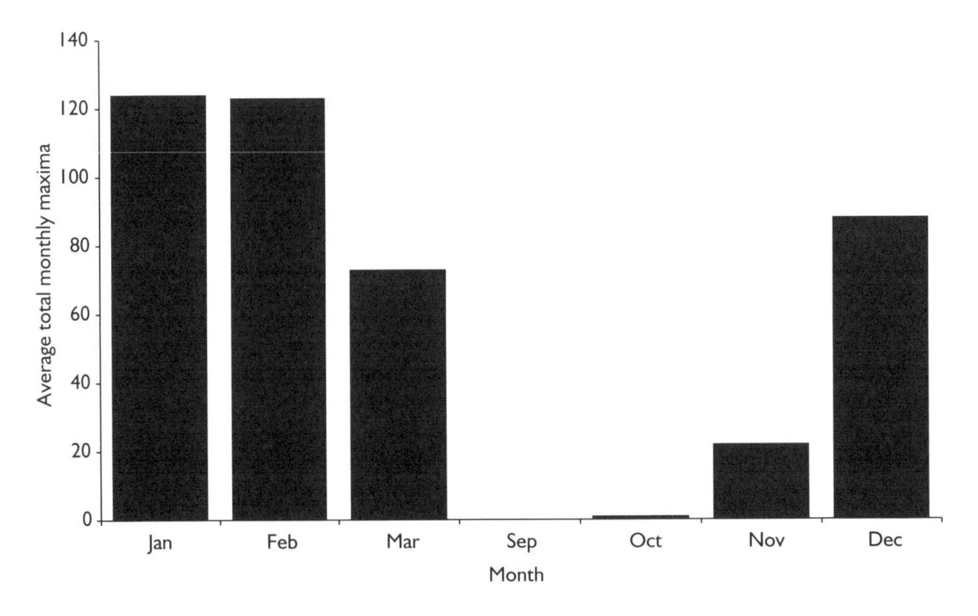

Figure 119: Average total monthly maxima of Goosanders at the main sites 1995–2005.

Goosanders have a circumpolar breeding distribution, from the low Arctic to temperate zones. Most populations are migratory, wintering to the south of the breeding area. Influxes into Britain from the near continent and Scandinavia often occur during severe weather. The British breeding population is mainly found on upland rivers in the west and north and was estimated at 2,700 pairs during 1988–91 (Gibbons *et al.* 1993). There has been a recent range expansion in the Pennines, where breeding was first recorded in Derbyshire in 1981, which neatly explains the subsequent increase in summer records in Leicestershire and Rutland.

AHJH

Ruddy Duck *Oxyura jamaicensis*

Feral. Fairly common to common winter visitor, uncommon breeder.

Of all the birds introduced into Britain, the Ruddy Duck has caused most controversy. It also provides a graphic example of how human activity affects avian populations. After being introduced from North America to private collections during the 1930s, birds escaped from 1953 onwards and in 1960 breeding was recorded in the wild at Chew Valley Lake (Somerset). The first published record in Leicestershire involved a bird at Swithland Reservoir on April 16th 1967, though unpublished reports suggest that some may have been present at Charnwood reservoirs since 1961.

Numbers did not increase significantly until the late 1970s, when the first double-figure count was 11 at Groby Pool on December 7th 1975, followed by 56 at Cropston Reservoir on December 27th 1979 and then 100 at nearby Swithland Reservoir on December 20th 1980. Numbers continued to rise steadily during the 1980s and 1990s; Swithland Reservoir was traditionally the favoured site, the highest counts here being 224 on November 27th 1983, 245 on February 26th 1992 and 270 on March 6th 1993. From the mid-1980s the largest numbers were found in the east of the counties, notable examples being 400 at Eyebrook Reservoir on January 20th 1988, 756 at Rutland Water on December 15th 1991 and 1,170 at Rutland Water on December 6th 1998. This last figure was the highest ever recorded at a single site in the UK, but was exceeded by 1,345, again at Rutland Water, on January 16th 2000. Counts of 500+ have been recorded at the latter site in a total of nine years and have reached four-figures on another three occasions: 1,078 on January 12th 1997, 1,161 on December 19th 1999 and 1,187 on January 14th 2001. At Eyebrook Reservoir counts of 250 or more have been recorded in 11 years since 1985, with a maximum of 707 on January 26th 1992; other notable totals there have included 318 on January 12th 1985, 325 on January 14th 1990, 442 on January 20th 1994 and 380 on March 10th 1997.

The current qualifying level for publication in the annual WeBS Report is 30 (Collier *et al.* 2005) and as well as Rutland Water, Eyebrook Reservoir and Swithland Reservoir, the other site that traditionally qualifies is Stanford Reservoir, where counts have exceeded 200 on four occasions: 221 on March 9th 1997, 223 on December 1st 1999, 274 on December 17th 2001 and 270 on December 18th 2003. Away from the four major sites, other notable counts have been 103 at Cropston Reservoir on January 30th 1984, 156 at the same site on March 9th 1997 and 62 at Groby Pool on March 26th 1990. Numbers in the counties therefore increased 100 times during the last 25 years of the 20th century. See 'Wintering Birds' (pages 39–43) for details of highest counts at individual sites.

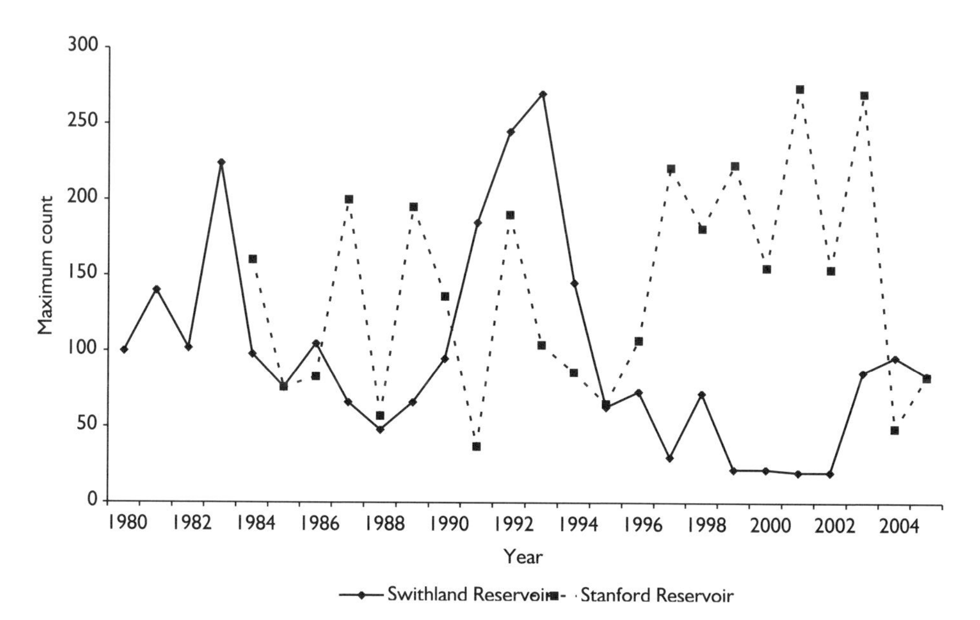

Figure 120: Maximum counts of Ruddy Ducks at Swithland Reservoir and Stanford Reservoir 1980–2005.

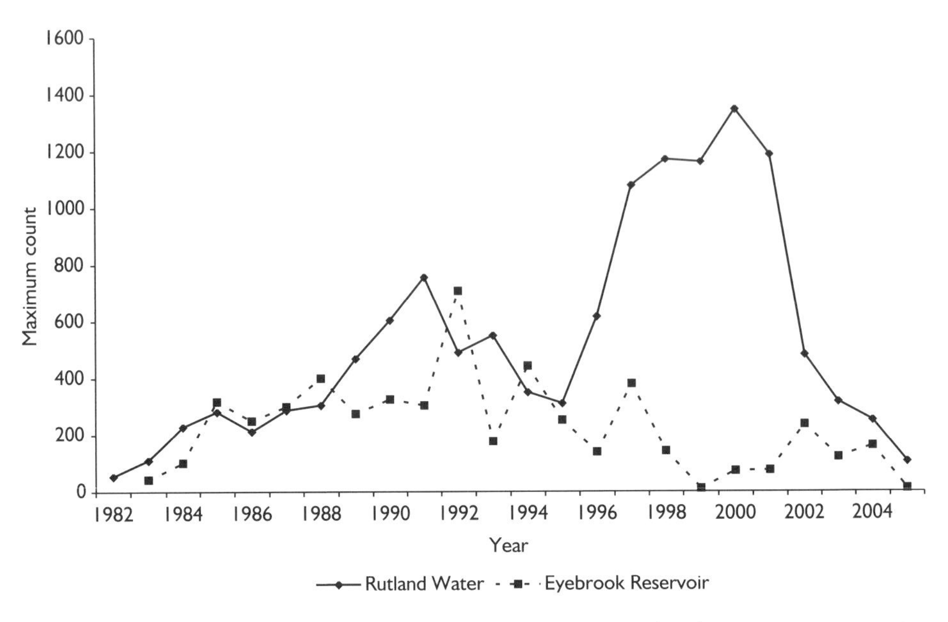

Figure 121: Maximum counts of Ruddy Ducks at Rutland Water and Eyebrook Reservoir 1982–2005.

Measures to control the spread of Ruddy Ducks with the aim of aiding the conservation of the White-headed Duck in southern Europe were implemented by the Wildfowl and Wetlands Trust in 1994, when 21 were shot at Eyebrook Reservoir and ten shot at Stanford Reservoir during January to March. These measures did result in a reduction in numbers over the following two seasons, but freezing conditions in early 1997 concentrated birds at Rutland Water and four-figure counts remained annual until 2002. Since then, however, there have not been any single counts of 500+and by 2005 the Rutland Water maximum (105 in March) was the lowest there since 1982, whilst this species had almost completely abandoned Eyebrook Reservoir.

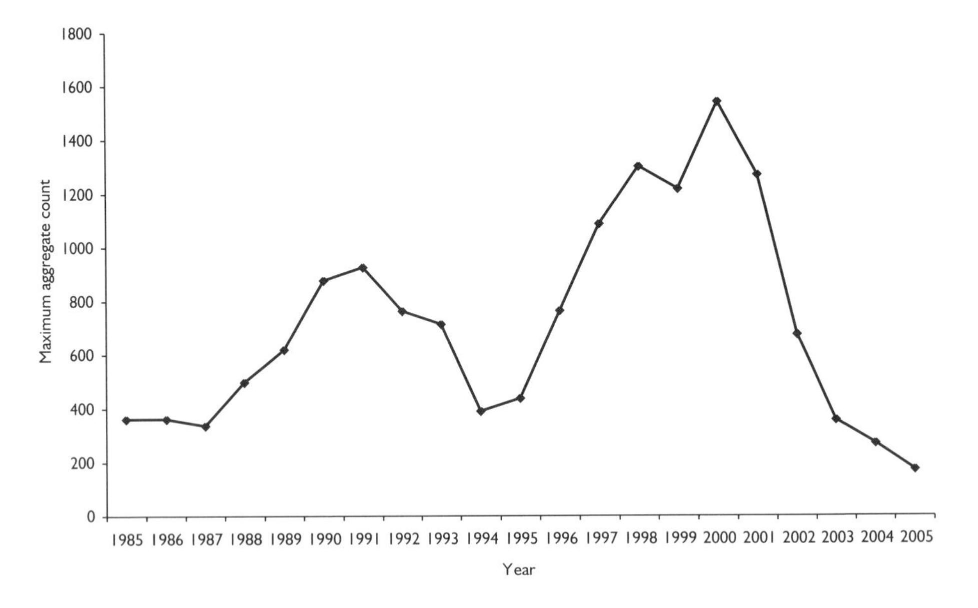

Figure 122: Maximum aggregate counts of Ruddy Ducks at the main sites 1985–2005.

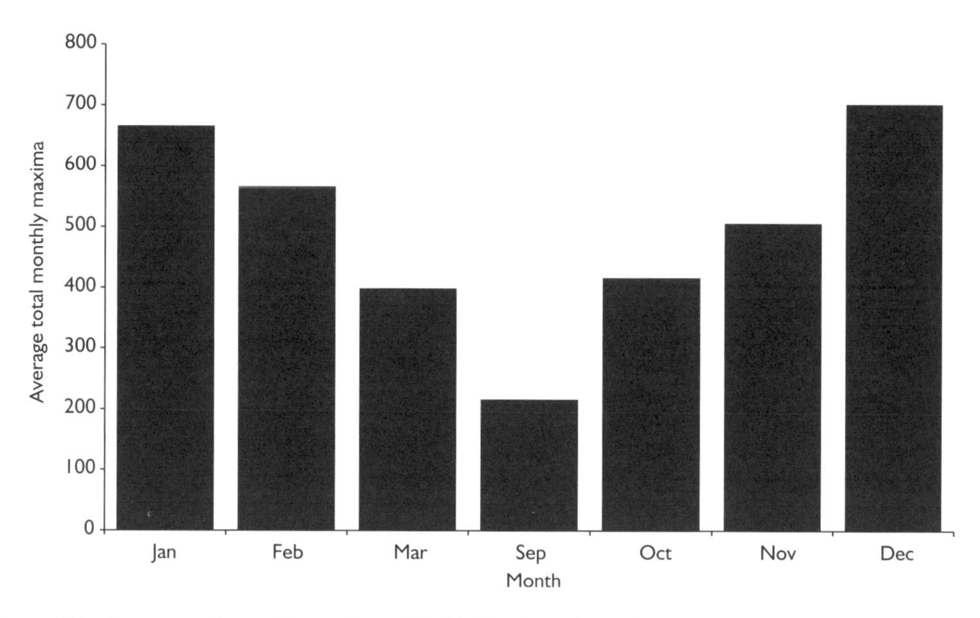

Figure 123: Average total monthly maxima of Ruddy Ducks at the main sites 1995–2005.

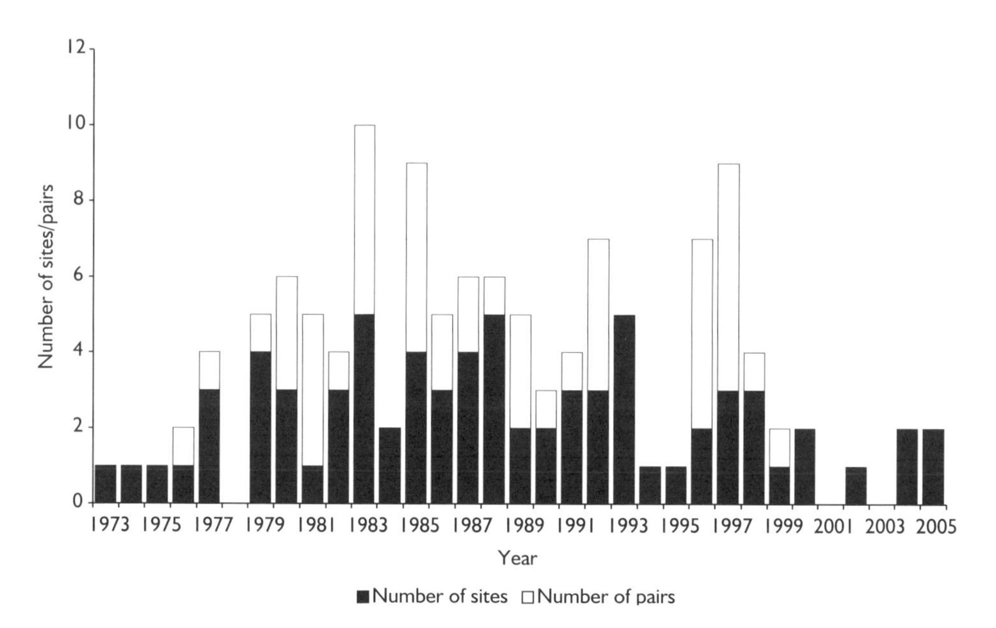

Figure 124: Breeding numbers of Ruddy Ducks 1973–2005.

Data show that numbers are lowest in September and reach a peak in December and January as birds move in from elsewhere in the region.

Breeding was first recorded at Swithland Reservoir, where a pair raised two broods in July and then September 1973. Breeding has subsequently been recorded (in chronological order) at Groby Pool, Cropston Reservoir, Sutton Cheney, Willesley Lake, Market Bosworth, Wanlip Gravel Pits, Rutland Water, Kirby Bellars Gravel Pits, Fort Henry Ponds, Birstall Gravel Pits, Stanford Reservoir, Thornton Reservoir, Blackbrook Reservoir, Kirby Lakes, Cadeby Quarry, Watermead Park, Melton Country Park and Priory Water. The highest numbers of broods have been recorded at Swithland Reservoir (six in 1985) and Rutland Water (five in 1997). There were no confirmed breeding records in either 2001 or 2003, though breeding was noted at two sites in both 2004 and 2005 and it is known that some observers no longer report breeding records.

A dark-headed male (or males) was recorded at Thornton Reservoir from August 31st to September 29th 1995 then at Swithland Reservoir on October 7th of the same year and in 1996 at Swithland Reservoir from March 16th to 23rd, Rutland Water from June 23rd to 30th and Eyebrook Reservoir from September 7th to 11th.

A hybrid with White-headed Duck has been recorded: see 'Hybrids' (pages 676–684).

A number of Ruddy Ducks escaped from Slimbridge (Gloucestershire) in 1953 and soon established a breeding population. The species increased rapidly and by 1991 there were 750 breeding pairs in Britain; others had spread to much of northern Europe, including Iceland. British birds are of the nominate race, which breeds in western North America, with isolated populations in eastern North America. It winters from the southern United States to central America. Other races breed in South America.

AHJH

Red Grouse (Willow Ptarmigan) ***Lagopus lagopus***

Extinct. Formerly a scarce to uncommon, localised, breeder.

Hickling stated that the Red Grouse bred in Charnwood Forest until the early 1820s, but became extinct around this time. Browne quotes Harley as saying 'the Red Ptarmigan occurs in the county in much the same ratio, as regards its distribution and its numerical diffusion, as its congener the Black Grouse. This species of Ptarmigan, moreover, appears to affect alike the same locality – Charnwood Forest – a situation as yet the only one known to the author where it occurs in the county'. Harley also added that it 'well nigh become extinct'. The fact that Harley's diaries, so extensively quoted by Browne, covered the period 1840 to 1855 perhaps suggests that the Red Grouse was still hanging on in Charnwood Forest to at least the 1840s, although it would appear that some effort to reintroduce the species to Charnwood was made earlier than this, as Browne quotes a Mr Babington, writing in 1842, as saying that 'Mr Gisborne attempted to introduce the bird from Scotland and the Derbyshire moors, but without success, it being unable to bear the dust of the journey.'

There appear to have been only three records in the second half of the 19th century. One which was apparently feeding on hips in a hedgerow was shot by the Rev. J. C. Davenport at Skeffington in the winter of 1860, whilst the only record for Rutland is of one shot in deep snow near Ridlington in the winter of 1870 or thereabouts; this latter bird was purchased by a Mr Healey of Uppingham. Finally, a mounted specimen in the Leicester Museum was apparently shot at Noseley in 1878; this specimen was viewed by Browne, who stated that it had been shot by Sir Arthur Hazelrigg 'whilst it was sitting on a whitethorn eating the haws. It had been previously observed sitting on the top of a large ash tree.' This record, however, was ignored by Hickling.

The Red Grouse is resident in northern Eurasia, Alaska and northern Canada. In Britain, it is widespread in Scotland, Wales and northern England, but largely absent from central, eastern and southern England. A long-term decline in the British population has been evident since the 1940s, mainly due to loss of heather moorlands through overgrazing and afforestation. The latest estimate is 15,700 breeding pairs (Baker *et al.* 2006), and as the population has decreased markedly since the mid-1980s, the species was included on the 'Amber List' of Birds of Conservation Concern by Gregory *et al.* (2002). The nearest birds to Leicestershire and Rutland are only about 30 miles from the county border, on the Staffordshire and Derbyshire moors; however, as this species is not known to wander away from its specialised breeding grounds, it seems very unlikely that Red Grouse will ever be recorded again in the county.

RMF

Black Grouse ***Tetrao tetrix***

Extinct. Formerly a scarce to uncommon, localised, breeder.

Hickling stated that the Black Grouse bred in Charnwood Forest until the middle of the 19th century, being last seen in 1850 but, as with his summary of Red Grouse, this may not be entirely accurate. Browne quotes a

Mr Babington, writing in 1842, as saying that the species was present 'near Charnwood Forest, Sharpley etc in tolerable numbers until the last two years. They are now nearly extinct.' Harley, whose diaries covered the period 1840 to 1855, wrote: 'We meet with this fine bird on the summits and flanks of Charnwood Forest. The species breeds there annually, but in sparing numbers only, since the ancient forest exists only in small patches of a few hundred acres in extent; consequently, the range of the Black Grouse is circumscribed to such spots. On the flanks of the wild hills overlying the lordship of Whitwick there remain a few birds still protected.' Browne also quotes Sir G. Beaumont, who remembered 'killing Black Game on Charnwood Forest about 1847 or 1848, and during the next ten years shooting several Grey Hens near Coleorton.'

Haines mentions only two records from Rutland. A female shot at Burley Wood in January 1851 was presented to Burley House, and another female was shot on September 24th 1896 in Greetham Parish by Mr Evan Hanbury of Braunston. The latter bird was 'feeding with Pheasants in a stubble field and its crop contained acorns.'

The Black Grouse occurs across much of northern Europe, with the greatest densities found in the boreal forests of Scandinavia and Russia. In Britain, its distribution shrank dramatically in the 20th century, and it is currently restricted to parts of Scotland, Wales and northern England. The species was previously common throughout southern counties of England from Lincolnshire and Norfolk south to Hampshire and Cornwall, and in the late 19th century it was still described as 'occasional' in Nottinghamshire, and 'rare' in counties such as Surrey, Berkshire and Worcestershire (Holloway 1996). It disappeared from Nottinghamshire and Norfolk in the early 20th century, and from Lincolnshire around 1935 (Parslow 1967), although there were still populations in south-west England on Dartmoor, Exmoor and the Quantocks in the early 1970s (Wernham *et al.* 2002). By the late 20th century, the only area where Black Grouse could be found south of Yorkshire was on the north Staffordshire moors, but this small, isolated population died out in the 1990s; however, a reintroduction programme began in October 2003 in the Upper Derwent valley, Derbyshire. The main cause of decline appears to be loss of habitat through agricultural intensification, although overgrazing is also a problem, whilst the ancient Leicestershire population appeared also to be seriously affected by human persecution. British numbers were estimated at 25,000 pairs in the early 1990s (Stone *et al.* 1997), but by 1995 had fallen to 6,510 pairs (Baker *et al.* 2006); this rapid decline, along with the substantial range contraction experienced by this species in Britain, resulted in it being added to the 'Red List' of Birds of Conservation Concern (Gregory *et al.* 2002). As with Red Grouse, it seems extremely unlikely that Black Grouse will be recorded in Leicestershire and Rutland in the future.

RMF

Red-legged Partridge *Alectoris rufa*

Introduced. Fairly common resident breeder supplemented by frequent releases.

The Red-legged Partridge was introduced into Britain from about 1770 onwards and by the 19th century it was described as 'resident but sparingly distributed' in Leicestershire by Browne. According to Haines, the species was introduced to Rutland around 1850 by Sir Gilbert Heathcote of Normanton; it first nested near Uppingham in about 1858 and by 1880 it had increased considerably but was still not as common as the Grey Partridge.

There is little information on the status of the Red-legged Partridge in Leicestershire and Rutland during the first part of the 20th century, although the LROS archives state that it was commonest in the east of the counties and scarce in Charnwood. The first LROS Annual Report, in 1941, described it as 'resident and local', although this was upgraded to 'fairly common and widespread' the following year, when it was thought to be nearly as common as the Grey Partridge in Rutland and south-east Leicestershire. Throughout the remainder of the 1940s the LROS Annual Reports consistently refer to an increase in numbers, particularly in Charnwood, where there was an estimated 25% increase around Quorn, Swithland and Woodhouse in 1945. Conversely, a marked decrease was noted in the Soar valley in 1946 and by the following year it had apparently been 'almost wiped out' from this area. Mitcham (1984) stated that it was locally distributed and less common than Grey Partridge in Rutland in 1941, but was as common as this species by 1949.

Since the 1940s, there has been little comment in LROS Annual Reports on the status of this species. In 1964 it was described as 'fairly common with local distribution in suitable habitat', with most reports from Rutland

and south-east and east Leicestershire. By 1969 it was considered the commoner of the two partridges in east Leicestershire, particularly on high ground. Mason & Pickering (1968) noted that it became widespread at Leicester City Farms in the 1950s and was commoner than the Grey Partridge by the 1960s. In 1986, records were received from a total of 105 1-km squares and subsequently some effort has been made to list reports similarly. The highest total since then was in 2000, when there were records from 87 1-km squares, although there were reports from fewer than 35 1-km squares in 1989, 1990, 1992 and 1993. Clearly, as with the Pheasant, the fact that birds are obviously not 'wild' results in many observers ignoring Red-legged Partridges.

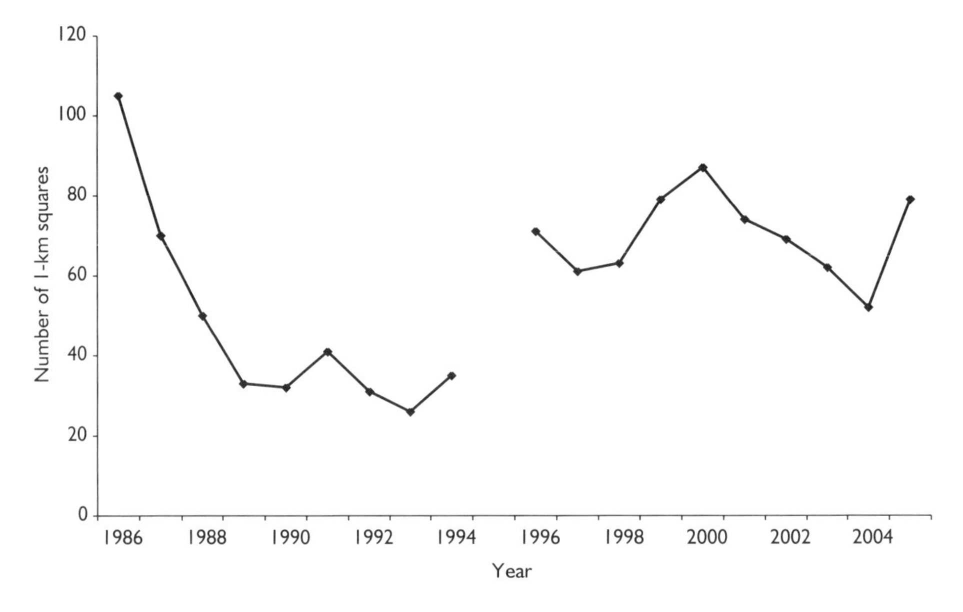

Figure 125: Number of 1-km squares with records of Red-legged Partridges 1986–2005.

The most useful work on the status of Red-legged Partridge in Leicestershire and Rutland was provided by Warrilow. During 1976–84 he recorded this species in 412 tetrads in the counties (64% of the total number of tetrads), with breeding confirmed in 109. It was closely associated with pastoral and arable farmland and preferred lighter, better-drained soils; the general absence recorded from parts of east Leicestershire and west Rutland may have been related to the heavier poorly-drained soils in these areas. Warrilow proposed a county-wide population estimate of between 1,600 and 3,000 pairs based on four to eight pairs per occupied tetrad.

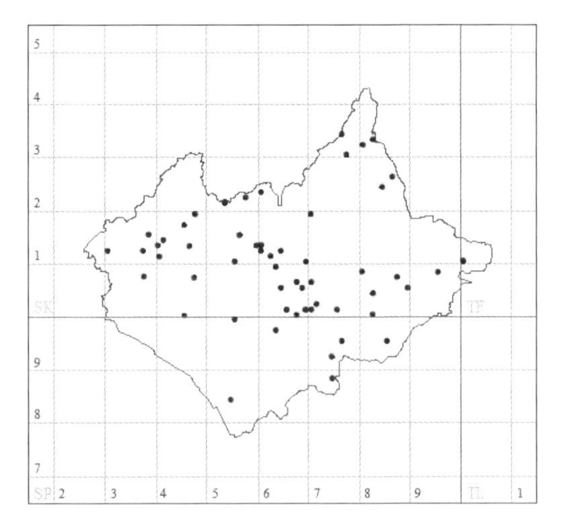

Figure 126: Distribution of Red-legged Partridges in 2005.

Local CBC data does not reveal a significant amount about the fortunes of this species. At both Newton Harcourt and King's Hill Lodge, Uppingham, up to three territories were located each year, with no obvious pattern emerging. Similarly, one or two territories were found annually at Stoughton from 1964 to 1988, although the Red-legged Partridge was not thought to have bred at this site from 1989 to 1999. At Loddington, territories increased from two in 1992 to 16 in 1998, although this is an atypical site as it is managed with gamebirds in mind and benefits from frequent releases.

Figure 126 shows the distribution of all records received of this species during 2005.

Large flocks of this species are a not-uncommon sight, especially during the autumn and obviously consist of recently released birds. There have been 26 documented records of groups of 50 or more, with another 36 involving flocks of between 25 and 50. The largest have been:

- 1,200 near Greetham on August 28th 2002.
- 730 in the Knipton/Branston/Harston area on September 15th 2002.
- 191 at Belvoir on August 1st 2003.
- 156 at Branston on September 1st 2001.
- 120 at Lubbesthorpe in September 1999.
- 100 at Whetstone Pastures in early January 1986.
- 100 at Lubbesthorpe in October 2000.
- 97 at Branston on September 25th 1994.
- 93 at Barkby Holt on November 26th 2005.
- 90 at Belvoir on September 17th 1999.

The fact that the majority of these big flocks have been recorded since 1999 suggests that larger numbers than ever are currently being released.

Red-legged Partridges have a habit of appearing in unusual places. There have been records of single birds in gardens at Somerville Road, Leicester on April 20th 1969 and Oadby in March 1980, as well as two at Birstall in March 1992. Birds have occasionally been seen in Leicester city centre and have included individuals at St. Margaret's Bus Station on March 26th 1982, Carlton Street/Oxford Street on March 15th 1994 and the forecourt of a Great Central Street petrol station on November 28th 1998.

Hybrids with Chukar Partridges have been recorded: see 'Hybrids' (pages 676–684).

The natural range of the Red-legged Partridge is south-western Europe, through Italy, France and the Iberian peninsula. The British population is estimated at between 72,000 and 200,000 pairs (Baker *et al.* 2006); this figure is necessarily somewhat vague due to the frequent releases of this species by gamekeepers. National data show that there has been a significant increase in numbers since 1994, again linked to deliberate releases (Baillie *et al.* 2006).

RMF

Grey Partridge *Perdix perdix*

Formerly a common resident breeder, now an uncommon resident breeder.

During the 19th century, the Grey Partridge was a common and widespread bird; it was described by Browne as 'resident and common' in Leicestershire and by Haines as 'abundant everywhere' in Rutland. There is little data on its status during the early part of the 20th century, the LROS archives merely stating that it was 'common' around this time.

The first LROS Annual Report, in 1941, described the Grey Partridge as, once again, 'resident and common'. Throughout the remainder of this decade there were contradictory statements in the Annual Reports. In 1943 there was a marked increase in the Quorn area and 70 pairs were found within six kilometres of here the following year. Another 'substantial increase' was noted in this area in 1948, as well as at Lockington and a 'general increase' was reported county-wide in 1949. Conversely, this species suffered a 'disastrous breeding season due to wet weather' in 1946 and a 'general decrease' was noted county-wide in 1947. Mitcham (1984) considered that Grey Partridges started declining gradually in Rutland from 1941 onwards.

Grey Partridges were still considered to be 'common and widespread' in 1960 but by 1964 a 'steady decline following a series of poor breeding seasons' was noted. The first suggestion that farming practices may have been responsible for a decline came in 1969, when a statement in the Annual Report said that this species was 'considered to prefer small fields and will suffer due to the trend towards prairie farming'. In the same year, a survey by the RNHS found 34 pairs breeding in Rutland.

It is known that the national population of the Grey Partridge declined by 57% between 1973 and 1998 (Chamberlain & Vickery 2002), although there was very little comment in the LROS Annual Reports regarding reduced numbers until 1989, when it was stated that the 'former even spread of the species across the county seems to have become increasingly fragmented'.

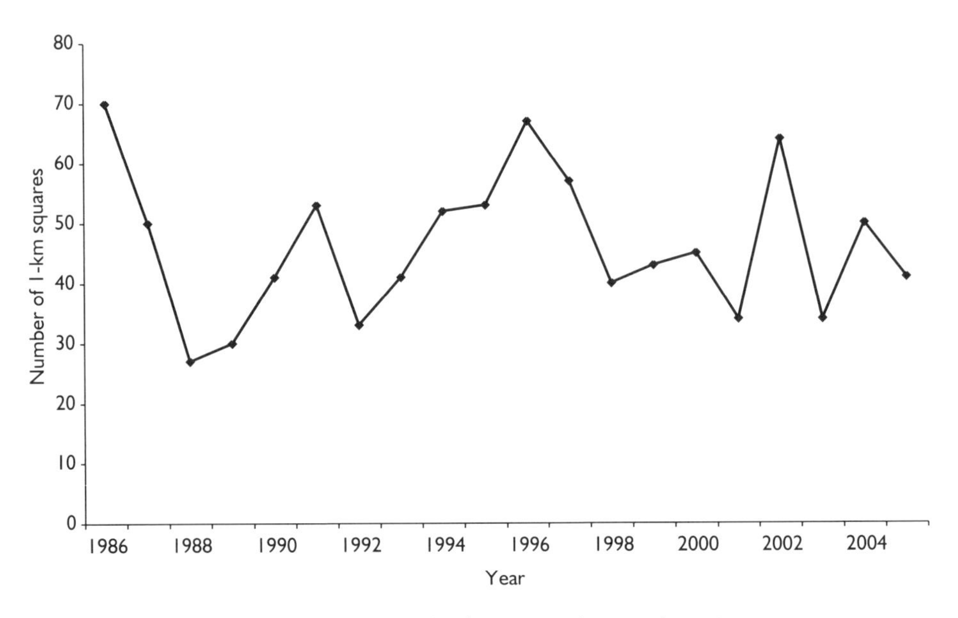

Figure 127: Number of 1-km squares with records of Grey Partridges 1986–2005.

In 1986, records were received from a total of 70 1–km squares, with blank areas along the northern and western edge of Leicestershire and west Rutland. The highest total since 1986 was in 1996, when there were records from 67 1–km squares, although there were reports from fewer than 35 1–km squares in 1988, 1989, 1992, 2001 and 2003.

During 1976–84, Warrilow recorded this species in 420 tetrads in the counties (66% of the total number of tetrads), with breeding confirmed in 113. It was absent from large tracts of east Leicestershire, where intensive farming predominates. Compared to the Red-legged Partridge, it was less widespread in Rutland but slightly commoner in west Leicestershire. Warrilow proposed a county-wide population of 2,100 to 4,200 pairs, based on an average of five to ten pairs per occupied tetrad. It seems certain that this is now a serious overestimate, although there is no data to confirm this. Confirmed breeding records have always been hard to come by, in part due to the fact that this species favours habitat not often visited by birdwatchers. Breeding has been confirmed at 33 sites since 1987, although only at Trent Valley Pit (six years) and Kelham Bridge (four years) has it occurred more than twice during this period.

The map shows the distribution of all records received during 2005.

CBC data show a decrease in numbers at both Stoughton and Newton Harcourt. At the former, three or four pairs were regularly recorded from 1964 to 1978, with one or two from 1979 to 1986 and a single pair in just three years thereafter, whilst at Newton Harcourt two or three pairs were present from 1971 to 1980 but just one pair was recorded in only three years subsequently.

There have been 27 documented records of coveys of 20 or more and a further 79 instances of double-figure groups up to 19. The largest counts have been:

- 75 at Rowley Fields, Leicester on January 21st 1979.

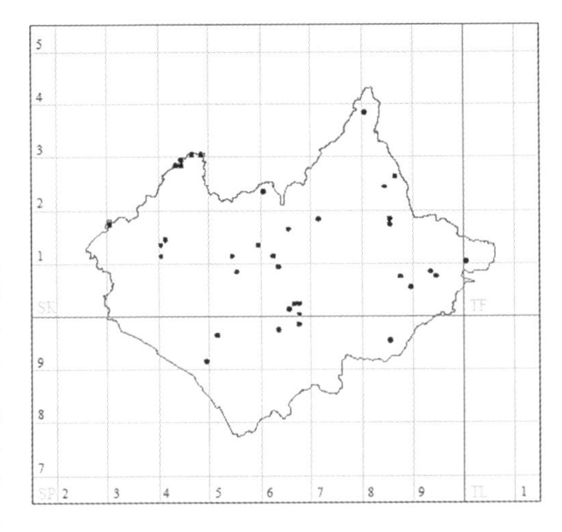

Figure 128: Distribution of Grey Partridges in 2005.

- 44 at Stoughton Airfield on January 28th 2005.
- 38 at Waltham on the Wolds on November 29th 1944.
- 36 at Enderby on October 10th 1979.
- 33 at Hathern on December 2nd 1985.
- 30 at Hoby on January 25th 1984.
- 30 at Rutland Water during the autumn of 1990.

It is noticeable that only one of these counts has been since 1990, despite the ever-increasing number of observers in the counties. Since 2000, nearly two-thirds of all double-figure flocks have been recorded from just three areas: Trent Valley Pit and neighbouring sites, Stoughton Airfield and the Edmondthorpe area.

The Grey Partridge occurs widely throughout North America (where introduced), Europe and Asia. It began declining in Britain during the early part of the 20th century; this accelerated from 1940 and became even more pronounced from around 1970 (Gibbons *et al.* 1996). The decline has been attributed to the effects of agricultural intensification (specifically herbicides) on the food plants of young chicks (Baillie *et al.* 2006). The British population is now estimated at 70,000 to 75,000 pairs (Baker *et al.* 2006) and, due to the rapid decline in numbers, this species has been added to the 'Red List' of Birds of Conservation Concern (Gregory *et al.* 2002).

RMF

Quail (Common Quail) ***Coturnix coturnix***

Scarce to uncommon summer migrant in varying numbers; recorded between April and September with most from late May to July. Breeding difficult to prove.

Occasionally heard, but rarely seen, the Quail is one of Leicestershire and Rutland's most unpredictable and enigmatic visitors. Today it is a scarce to uncommon summer visitor in varying numbers and the story appears to have been similar in the 19th century, although it was perhaps slightly commoner at that time. Browne quotes Harley as saying 'visits are only irregular and uncertain and appear confined to meadow-lands and fields lying contiguous to our streams.' However, Harley also stated that Quails bred annually in small numbers in the Soar valley around Cossington, Sileby and Barrow upon Soar, a situation which it cannot be said to apply in the 21st century. In addition, Browne reported that this species bred occasionally in the Vale of Belvoir and had also bred near Melton Mowbray. Of the other records mentioned by Browne (which involved at least 23 birds at a total 12 sites), the most noteworthy were three winter occurrences: one captured in Leicester Market Place on November 15th 1846, one shot at Braunstone, Leicester five days later and one flushed at Edmondthorpe on December 24th 1856. Without any further evidence or the existence of specimens, it is difficult to know what to make of these three records. One other report detailed by Browne worth mentioning is that of a bevy of nine at Husband's Bosworth in 1845, five of which were shot.

It would seem from the records mentioned by Haines that the Quail was more frequent in Rutland in the 19th century. He describes it as 'not so common as in old days', but 'appears regularly every spring and certainly stays to breed.' Haines knew of records from 21 sites in Rutland; it apparently bred regularly in the Great Casterton and Edith Weston areas and nests were found at Uppingham between 1845 and 1850, Lyddington in 1872 and near Seaton in 1897 or 1898. One apparently shot at Egleton during the first week of January 1887 represented the fourth reported winter occurrence in the counties during the 19th century. Another noteworthy record was of nine (six of which were shot) at Bisbrooke in 1870, a year that produced large numbers of Quails in Britain (Gibbons *et al.* 1993). In addition, Haines noted that 15 were recorded during 1904, a good total even by today's standards when there are a lot more observers actively searching for birds.

There is little information available on the status of the Quail in Leicestershire and Rutland during the first 40 years of the 20th century. Since the formation of LROS in 1941, there have been records in 47 of the 65 years up to 2005, the last blank year being as long ago as 1981. Although its occurrence in the counties can be highly unpredictable, it is noticeable that larger numbers have been appearing since the early 1980s; three times as many birds were recorded in the 23 years following 1982 than in the preceding 41 years.

As previously mentioned, this species is prone to good and bad years, both locally and nationally. There have been six years in which over 15 birds have been recorded, as follows:

1953	17 individuals at a total of eight sites, including up to six at Shenton between May 28th and July 7th and up to five at Croft in June and July.
1983	26 individuals at a total of 11 sites, including up to ten in the Packington area during July.
1989	the best year on record, with at least 31 birds at a total of 11 sites, including up to ten at Bruntingthorpe Airfield from June 4th to July 18th.
1995	23 birds at a total of nine sites, including up to ten in the Orton-on-the-Hill area from July 3rd to 19th.
1997	although not a record year in terms of numbers (22 individuals), this influx was the most widespread, with records from a total of 14 sites. No more than three birds were located at any one site.
1998	18 individuals at a total of 13 sites, with no more than two in any one area.

These six years in Leicestershire and Rutland, which between them account for over 40% of all records in the counties between 1941 and 2004, coincided with widespread national influxes (Gibbons *et al.* 1993, Ogilvie *et al.* 2004). The record year of 1989 was mirrored over the rest of Britain, when a remarkable 1,655 singing birds were found nationally (Spencer 1991).

Most records of Quails involve one or two singing birds, although three or four birds have been located singing in close proximity on 12 occasions. Excluding those mentioned above at Shenton, Croft, Packington, Bruntingthorpe Airfield and Orton-on-the-Hill, the only other count of more than four is five at Cottesmore Airfield on July 27th 2001.

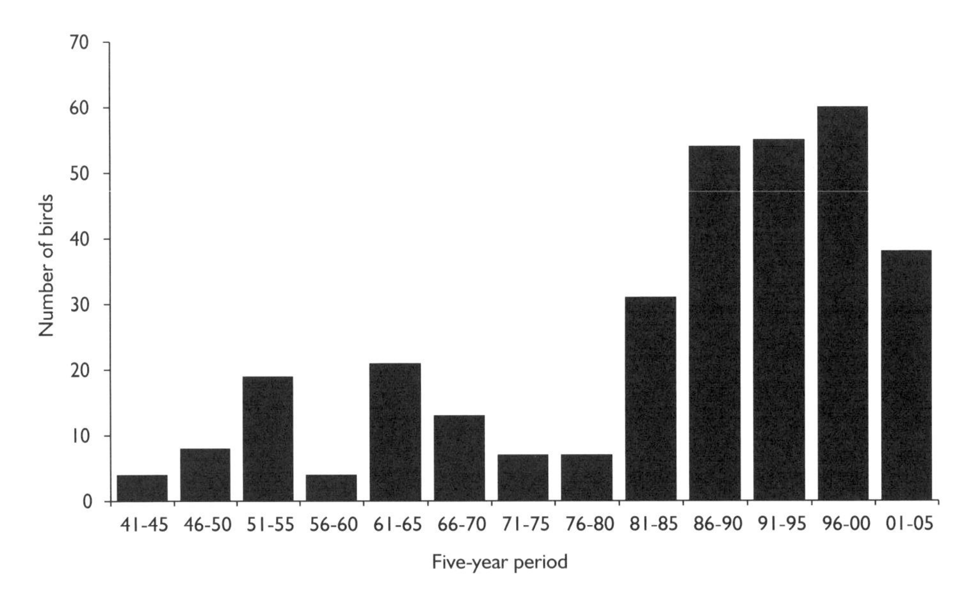

Figure 129: Number of Quails by five-year periods 1941–2005.

Quails are one of the latest summer migrants to arrive. The earliest record was of one singing at Little Casterton on April 25th 1998, but the only other records prior to May 6th have been single birds at Exton Park on May 2nd 1999 and Wellsborough on May 3rd 1960. The peak arrival time is late May and early June, although the data show another apparent arrival during late June and early July, which could be a result of observers specifically looking for Quails at this time of year or an influx of birds hatched earlier in the year around the Mediterranean. The majority seem to depart during early August, although once this species stops singing it is incredibly difficult to locate and many birds may well pass through the counties unnoticed. Since 1941, there have been only five records later than August 25th, all of single birds, as follows:

- Tilton on the Hill, August 28th 1947.
- Thornton Reservoir, August 28th and 29th 1989.

- Eyebrook Reservoir, August 31st 1947.
- Snarestone, September 1st 1945.
- Barkby, September 1st 1947.

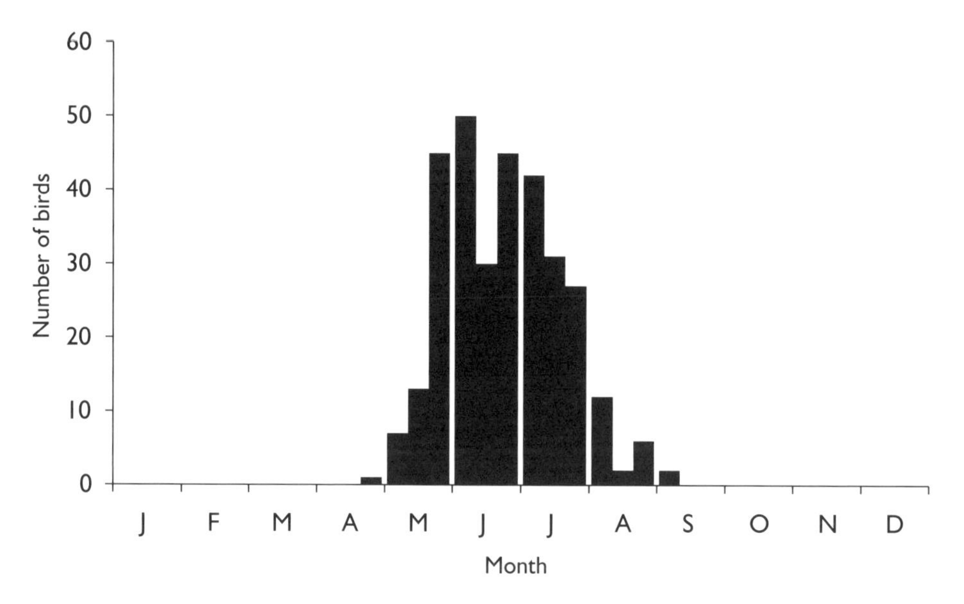

Figure 130: Monthly occurrence of Quails 1941–2005.

In addition, two were recorded at Oakham during August and September 1958, although the correct dates are unknown. Also, one was apparently shot at Barrowden on the late date of September 21st 1940.

The distribution map shows a wide scatter of records over the counties, although there are several areas which have proved more attractive to Quails than others, specifically eastern Rutland (particularly the Great Casterton area and Exton Park), the Vale of Belvoir and the far west of Leicestershire around Wellsborough and Orton-on-the-Hill. Other sites where it has occurred with some regularity include Bruntingthorpe Airfield, Eyebrook Reservoir and, more recently, Sence Valley Forest Park.

Quails breed over much of Europe, north-west Africa and the Middle East. European birds winter mainly in sub-Saharan Africa and as such are the region's only migratory game bird. There are marked annual fluctuations in the north of the range, including Britain, where in non-invasion years the population is usually in the region of 100 to 300 pairs. A very marked decrease was apparent from the early 19th century to the middle of the 20th century, although since about 1940 numbers have, on average, shown a small increase (Gibbons *et al.* 1996). The decrease has been attributed to changed methods of agriculture (Parslow 1967), although the fact that this species was mercilessly trapped along the Mediterranean coast until the regulation of spring hunting in 1937 may also have been a major factor (Gibbons *et al.* 1993). Due to the major historical decline in the numbers of Quails occurring in Britain, this species has been added to the 'Red List' of Birds of Conservation Concern (Gregory *et al.* 2002).

RMF

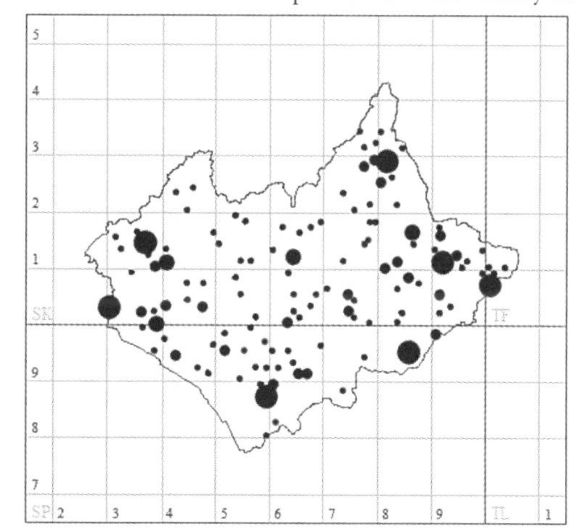

Dot = number of birds, 4 sizes of dot
1–2 (smallest), 3–4, 5–9, 10+ (largest)

Figure 131: Distribution of Quails 1941–2005.

Pheasant (Common Pheasant) *Phasianus colchicus*

Introduced. Common resident breeder supplemented by frequent releases.

The Pheasant is a typical bird of Leicestershire and Rutland farmland, preferring areas with scattered woods and shrubby cover. It has been a part of the counties' avifauna for at least 300 years and probably longer; Hickling mentioned that during the Middle Ages the Priory of Ulverscroft had hunting rights for Pheasants over 1,700 acres of land in the Charnwood Forest region. By the time of Browne and Haines, the species was resident and commonly distributed over both counties.

Today, despite being one of the commonest and most widespread birds in the counties, the Pheasant is one of the most poorly studied. Large numbers are released each autumn for shooting purposes and the fact that such birds are clearly not 'wild' is perhaps the major reason why most observers ignore this species. Groups exceeding 50 have been noted on ten occasions, with four counts of 100 or more, as follows:

- 200 at Terrace Hills, Belvoir on December 22nd 1998.
- 150 at Harston on September 16th 2002.
- 117 at Exton Park on December 30th 1996.
- 100 near Swithland Reservoir on September 7th 1986.

Warrilow recorded Pheasants in 526 tetrads in the counties (82% of the total number of tetrads) during 1976–84, with breeding confirmed in 155. A tentative county-wide population of 5,200 territorial males, 3,500 non-territorial males and 7,800 females was proposed, with the caveat that these numbers may easily be distorted by large-scale releases for shooting. The species was absent from built-up areas or those with limited woodland cover, although Pochin (1954) mentioned that 'odd birds were reported from time to time' within the city boundary of Leicester and Fray *et al.* (1990) found four pairs apparently holding territory at Aylestone Meadows in 1989. The first reference to Pheasants visiting urban gardens was in 1982, when a female was seen in the Narborough Road area of Leicester during cold weather on January 4th and since 1988 this habit has become regular; perhaps the most extreme example of this was a female on an upstairs window sill of a house on East Park Road, Leicester on January 22nd 1991.

CBC data from farmland plots in both Leicestershire and Rutland show that numbers have remained fairly stable, with occasional small fluctuations, at least in these four areas. However, results from the Allerton Research and Educational Trust site at Loddington show substantial gains, with 37 pairs in 1992 increasing to

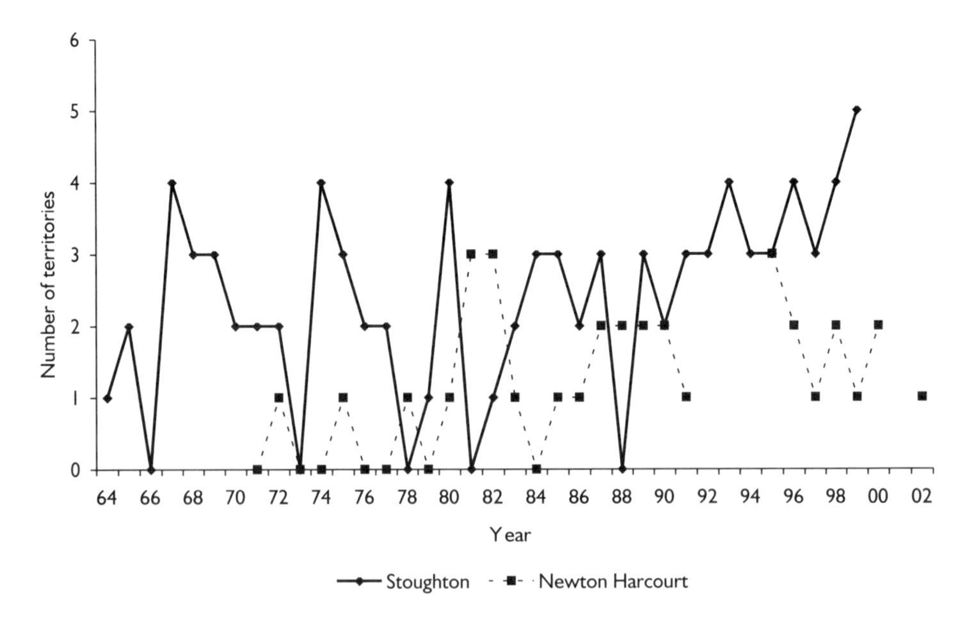

Figure 132: Numbers of breeding pairs of Pheasants on two Leicestershire CBC plots 1964–2002.

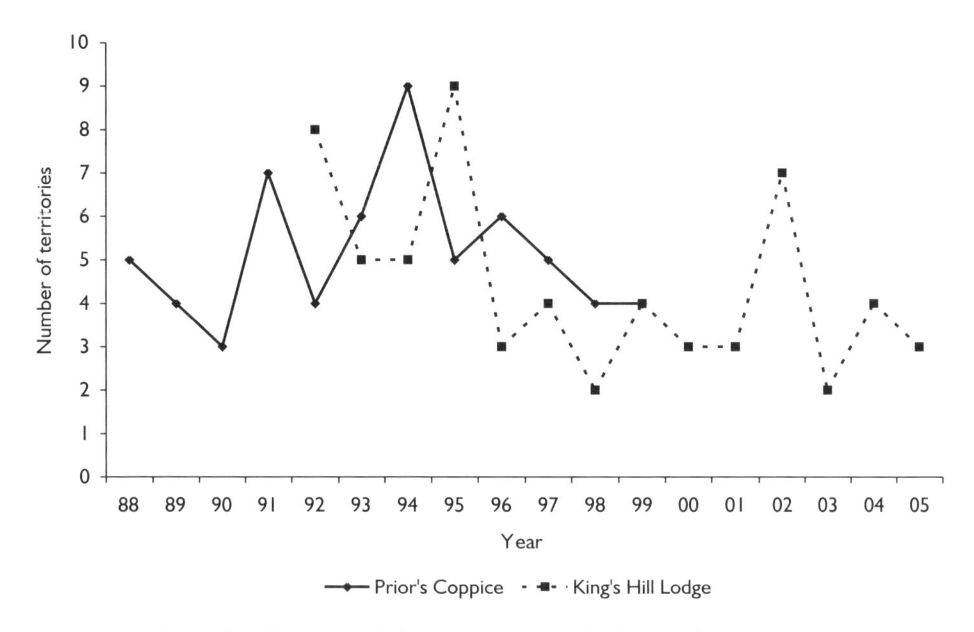

Figure 133: Numbers of breeding pairs of Pheasants on two Rutland CBC plots 1988–2005.

78 in 1998 and 87 in 2001; these figures are not entirely surprising though, as the site is managed with the conservation of game birds in mind.

Haines makes reference to an albino bird shot at Uppingham in 1893 and since 1946 there have been records of 12 similar birds. Individuals described as melanistic have been recorded on five occasions since 1947. Both of these colour forms are likely to be more common than reports suggest, although in the case of birds described as melanistic the situation is confused by the presence of hybrids with the Green Pheasant *Phasianus versicolor* (Harrop 2008).

Pheasants were introduced into Britain in the 16th century and Gibbons *et al.* (1993) estimated the population to be in the region of 850,000 territorial males, 650,000 non-territorial males and 1,600,000 females. As previously mentioned, autumn numbers are greatly increased by the release of hand-reared birds for shooting.

RMF

Red-throated Diver *Gavia stellata*

Rare to scarce winter visitor, very rare at other seasons; recorded in all months between September and April with most from November to March: 63 individuals since 1941 and an unknown number previously.

In the 19th century, the Red-throated Diver was the most frequent diver species to appear in Leicestershire by some considerable margin. Browne quotes Harley as saying that it was 'frequently met with on the Soar about Loughborough and also on the Trent' and that various specimens had been shot on the Wreake and at Groby, Saddington and Dishley. Furthermore, according to Harley, Red-throated Divers were 'captured during the storm of January 4th 1854 in several parts of the county'. Browne knew of a further three certain 19th century records; an immature shot at Saddington Reservoir on December 16th 1840, an adult in summer plumage shot on the Grand Union Canal near West Bridge, Leicester on September 10th 1869 and one found dying at Burton Overy on March 2nd 1889. The latter specimen was donated to Leicester Museum. In addition, Browne mentions undated records of one shot at

Groby and two shot at Cropston Reservoir. The only record known to Haines from Rutland at this time was of one shot at Exton in about 1858.

Prior to the formation of LROS in 1941 there were five 20th century records, beginning with an immature shot at Swithland Reservoir on January 10th 1907; the specimen was sent to Leicester Museum. Subsequently, one was shot at Thornton Reservoir in February 1918, single birds were at Cosby on November 26th 1936 and Stanford Reservoir on January 23rd 1937 and three were at the latter site from January 29th to February 15th 1938. Since 1941, there has been a total of 63 individuals found, making it the most numerous diver in the counties. However, unlike both the Black-throated and Great Northern Divers, this species is currently appearing less frequently than in the past, with only 19 birds recorded in the 25 years from 1981 to 2005 compared to 27 during the preceding 25 years.

The Red-throated Diver has been recorded in a total of 32 years since 1941. In most of these years, only one or two individuals were noted, although three were seen in 1948 and 1976, four in 1945, 1965 and 1985 and five in 1979. In the latter year, four of these birds were found between January 7th and March 14th and were part of a widespread influx onto inland waters following strong easterly winds and snow (Chandler 1981). With the exception of two at Swithland Reservoir from March 14th to 26th 1945 and three at Eyebrook Reservoir on January 25th 1948, all records have been of single birds.

All birds have arrived between September and April, although one which appeared at Swithland Reservoir on March 14th 1979 remained until May 4th. The earliest autumn record was of one, still in summer plumage, at Eyebrook Reservoir from September 19th to 26th 1954, although records before November are rare and the only others are single birds at Eyebrook Reservoir on September 23rd 1985 and from October 28th to 29th 1976 and Swithland Reservoir on October 31st 1964. The majority of records occur between late November and mid-March, with particular peaks during mid-February (usually coinciding with hard weather) and mid-March (which may represent early passage birds beginning to return north). There have been seven April arrivals, the latest being one at Rutland Water on April 30th 1988.

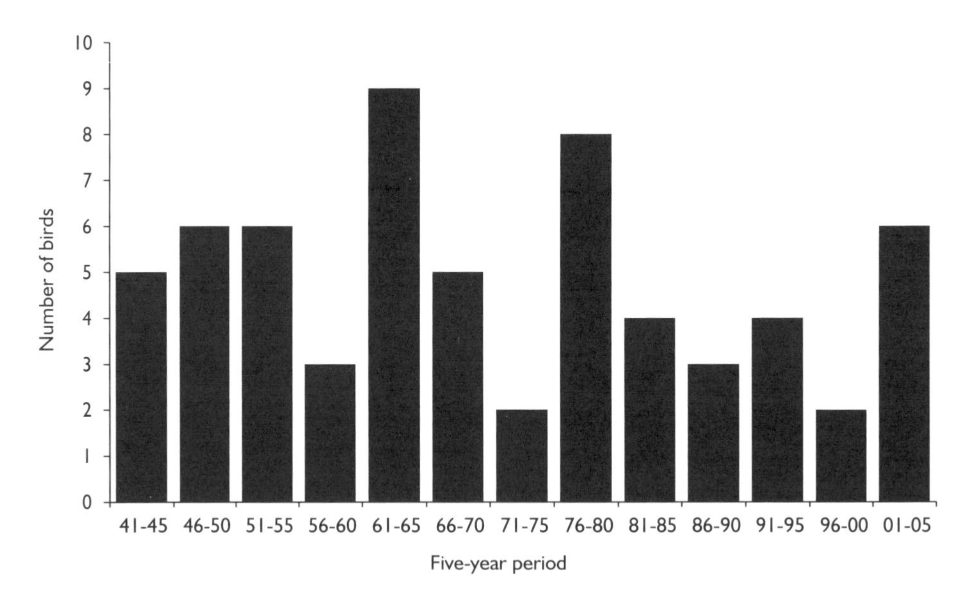

Figure 134: Numbers of Red-throated Divers by five-year periods 1941–2005.

The favoured site has been Eyebrook Reservoir, which has 21 records to its name, although Rutland Water is catching up fast and has recorded this species on 15 occasions. The importance of Rutland Water is shown by the fact that, since 1986, only four birds have been found away from this site. Elsewhere, records have come from a further ten areas, with the reservoirs at Swithland, Cropston and Stanford accounting for the majority of reports. Apart from single birds at Kegworth on February 19th 1947, Wanlip Gravel Pits from February 18th to 26th 1979 and Stoney Cove from March 14th to 21st 1996, all other records have been of individuals found

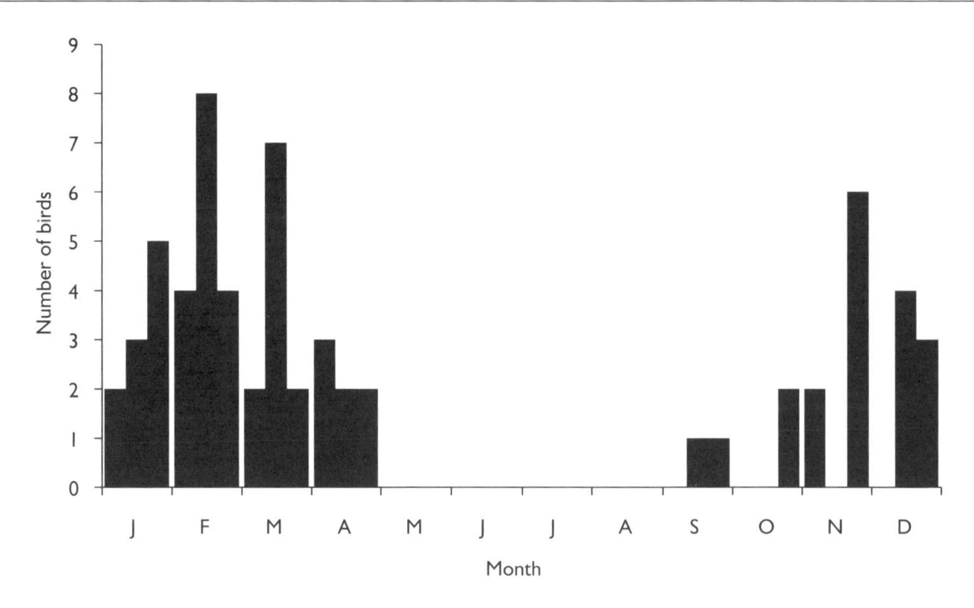

Figure 135: Monthly occurrence of Red-throated Divers 1941–2005.

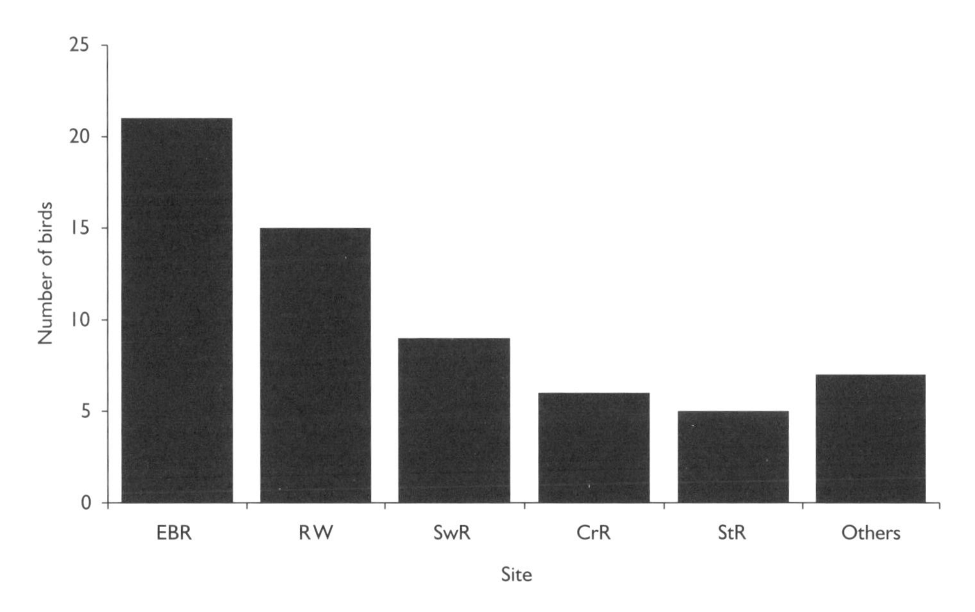

Figure 136: Sites where Red-throated Divers have been recorded 1941–2005.
Key to abbreviations: EBR = Eyebrook Reservoir; RW = Rutland Water; SwR = Swithland Reservoir; CrR = Cropston Reservoir; StR = Stanford Reservoir

away from water; this species often fares badly when it reaches the counties and birds have been found either dead or exhausted on eight occasions.

In contrast to the other two diver species occurring in the counties, Red-throated Divers are often brief visitors and many have been seen on just one day; the average duration of a stay is ten days, compared to 16 for Black-throated and 32 for Great Northern Diver. The longest stayer was a first-winter at Rutland Water from January 23rd to March 26th 1994 and a further four have remained for periods of over six weeks:

- Cropston Reservoir, January 7th to February 25th 1961.
- first-winter, Swithland Reservoir, March 14th to May 4th 1979.
- Rutland Water, January 13th to February 28th 1985.
- juvenile, Rutland Water, December 17th 2002 to February 20th 2003.

One noted in the LROS Annual Report for 1957 as occurring at Stanford Reservoir on February 17th was actually recorded on February 2nd.

Red-throated Divers breed from the high Arctic in Greenland, Siberia and North America south to northern temperate areas. In Europe, they breed from northern Russia, through most of Fennoscandia, in Iceland and northern Scotland. The major stronghold in Britain is in Shetland, Orkney and the Outer Hebrides and the total British breeding population is estimated at 935 to 1,500 pairs (Baker *et al.* 2006). It is thought that a moderate decline in the British breeding population has occurred over the last 25 years, resulting in this species being added to the 'Amber List' of Birds of Conservation Concern (Gregory *et al.* 2002). In Europe, most Red-throated Divers winter along north-western coasts south of the breeding range, with a few as far south as the Mediterranean and Black Seas. The British wintering population is augmented by arrivals from northern Europe and Red-throated Divers are relatively widespread around the coast of Britain at this time of year.

RMF

Black-throated Diver *Gavia arctica*

Rare winter visitor, very rare at other seasons; recorded in all months between October and April with most from November to February: 29 individuals since 1941 and eight previously.

Browne details six 19th century records, three of which occurred on the River Soar in Leicester during January 1854: one 'procured' in a meadow below Leicester Castle on the 4th, one shot at Abbey Meadows the same day and another shot at Aylestone on the 10th. The latter two were mentioned in the donation book at Leicester Museum. Browne considered that these three birds were 'driven inland by the gale which prevailed on January 4th and the severity of the north-east wind, which brought a hurricane of snow.' One was apparently shot at Saddington Reservoir in February 1874 and Browne mentions two undated records, at Donington Park and Mountsorrel. The only record known to Haines in Rutland during the 19th century was of one shot at Exton in about 1850; the specimen was set up for the Right Honourable Gerard Noeland and was seen by Browne who 'pronounced it an immature bird or an adult in autumnal plumage.'

The only record in the first half of the 20th century was of one shot at Thornton Reservoir in February 1917 and there were no further occurrences of this species in Leicestershire and Rutland until 1962, when one was at Swithland Reservoir on March 3rd and 4th. Since then, there have been records in a total of 18 years, as follows:

1978	two, Rutland Water, March 3rd to 4th.
1979	Rutland Water, January 4th to 5th.
	Rutland Water, February 18th to 24th.
	Staunton Harold Reservoir, February 22nd.
1983	juvenile, Eyebrook Reservoir, December 19th to January 18th 1984.
1984	Rutland Water, December 29th to January 5th 1985.
1985	Cropston Reservoir, January 5th.
	adult and first-winter, Rutland Water, January 13th to February 6th, with one remaining until February 16th.
	Rutland Water, November 24th to December 22nd.
1986	Rutland Water, January 5th to 19th.
1988	adult, Rutland Water, October 29th to November 5th.
	Rutland Water, December 9th.
1993	juvenile, Rutland Water, April 5th to 15th.
1994	first-winter, Rutland Water, February 24th to March 28th.
1995	first-winter, Eyebrook Reservoir, January 7th to 10th, with the same bird then at Rutland Water from January 13th to April 15th.

1996	juvenile, Eyebrook Reservoir, November 27th to December 23rd, with an additional juvenile from December 17th to 20th.
1997	second-winter, Rutland Water, January 5th to 12th.
1999	adult, Rutland Water, April 30th to May 5th.
2000	first-winter, Rutland Water, December 21st to January 19th 2001.
2001	first-winter, Rutland Water, December 23rd to January 1st 2002.
2002	juvenile, Eyebrook Reservoir, October 16th.
	juvenile, Cropston Reservoir, December 8th.
2003	juvenile, Cropston Reservoir, February 16th to 21st, with the same bird then at Rutland Water from February 22nd to March 29th.
	adult, Albert Village Lake, November 20th to 25th.
2005	first-winter, Trent Valley Pit, March 3rd to 6th.

This is the scarcest of the three diver species in the counties by some margin, but is now appearing more frequently than ever before. The upturn in reports can be almost exclusively attributed to the construction of Rutland Water, which has accounted for almost 60% of all records since 1978 (a total of 17 individuals). Eyebrook and Cropston Reservoirs are the only other sites to have hosted Black-throated Divers on more than one occasion, although it is worth noting that the five most recent records have all involved birds found away from Rutland Water.

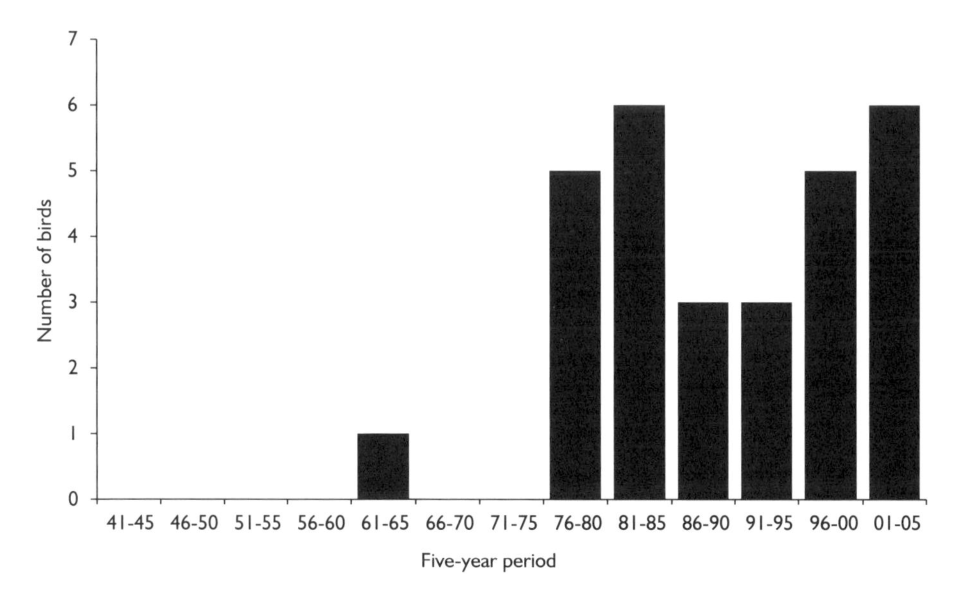

Figure 137: Numbers of Black-throated Divers by five-year periods 1941–2005.

Extreme arrival dates are October 16th and April 30th, although the majority of records have occurred between late November and mid-February and are often linked to hard weather. The most notable example of this was in 1979, when the two individuals in February were part of a widespread inland influx of this species and other waterbirds following high pressure over Scandinavia and bitterly cold north-easterly winds (Chandler 1981).

Lengthy stays are less frequent by this species than by Great Northern Divers, the average length of a visit being 16 days (compared to 32 days for Great Northern Diver). The most obvious exception to this is the 1995 individual, which was present for 98 days.

Black-throated Divers breed in the tundra and boreal zones of Eurasia, although are absent from Iceland and Greenland. In Britain, the breeding population numbers approximately 150 pairs and is restricted almost exclusively to larger lochs in the Outer Hebrides and the mainland of north and west Scotland. Due to the small size of the British population, this species has been added to the 'Amber List' of Birds of Conservation Concern

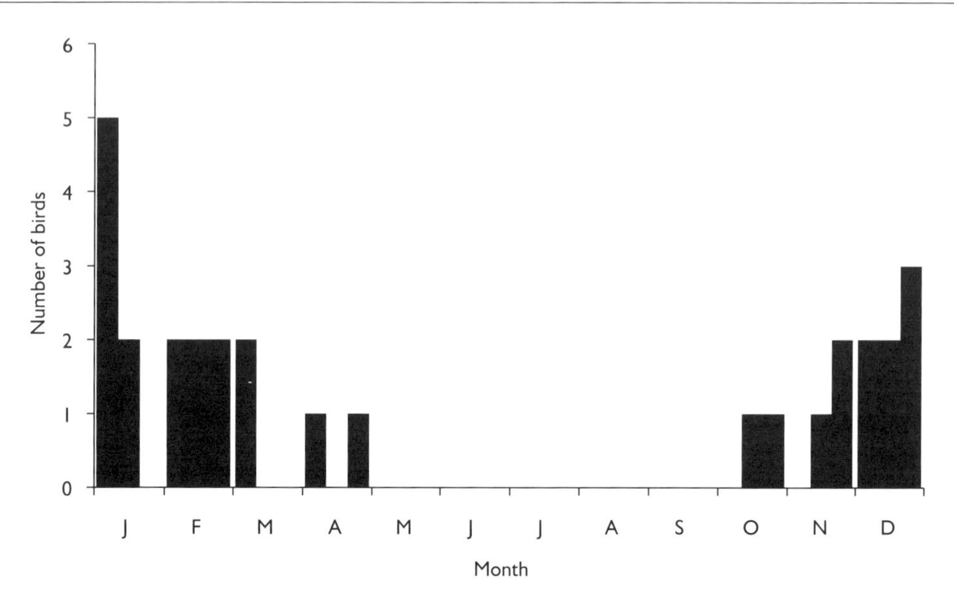

Figure 138: Monthly occurrence of Black-throated Divers 1941–2005.

(Gregory *et al.* 2002). The main wintering grounds lie along the Norwegian coast, along continental coasts of the North Sea and south into the Bay of Biscay; the Baltic is also important as a wintering area. It is the scarcest of the three regular wintering divers off the British coast, with an estimated 700 birds being the usual number (Baker *et al.* 2006).

RMF

Great Northern Diver *Gavia immer*

Rare to scarce winter visitor, very rare at other seasons; recorded in all months except June and August with most from November to January: 56 individuals.

Browne knew of one record of this species, but was less than impressed, stating that 'the only authority I have for including this species in the present list is a statement by the late Mr Widdowson, that it 'has been killed here in immature plumage', but as both of the following species (Red-throated Diver and Black-throated Diver) so often do duty for this much rarer bird, I am inclined to think that the species have become confused with one another.'

The first acceptable county record, therefore, occurred in 1933, when two were at Swithland Reservoir on December 9th. A further 54 individuals have been found since, although prior to the 1970s this species was still something of a rarity in the counties, with records in only nine years between 1933 and 1973, involving 13 birds. Despite the all-time county total for the Red-throated Diver still being higher, the Great Northern is now the most frequently occurring diver in Leicestershire and Rutland; since 1976, there have been 42 Great Northern compared to 27 Red-throated Divers. The construction of Rutland Water must be a contributing factor, as this species in general prefers deeper water than the other two divers, a habitat that this site most certainly offers in abundance. Rutland Water has now accounted for 33 individuals and the importance of this site is shown by the fact that, since the first for the reservoir on November 7th 1977, there have been only nine records from other waters. In total, Great Northern Divers have been recorded at nine sites within the counties; after Rutland Water, the next most favoured reservoirs have been Eyebrook and Swithland, with ten and seven records respectively. Thornton Reservoir has been visited twice (on

March 12th 1978 and from November 11th to 18th 1979), as has Cropston Reservoir (from January 2nd to 24th 1958 and March 3rd to 5th 1962) and Stanford Reservoir (from January 1st to February 3rd 2005 and on March 11th 1978); the latter bird was assumed to be the same as the one seen at Thornton Reservoir the following day. The most unusual sites have been in the Soar valley: one was at Cossington South Gravel Pits from January 22nd to 25th 1995 and then moved to Charnwood Water from February 1st to 25th and another frequented Watermead Park from December 11th to 17th 2002. All three of these water bodies were rather small for this species to visit, especially Charnwood Water, where the occurrence of a Great Northern Diver on a small lake in Loughborough, frequented by very little other than semi-domesticated Mallards, presented rather an incongruous sight.

This species has been recorded in a total of 32 years since the first county record in 1933. As noted, it is now more frequent than ever and the only blank years since 1984 have been 1992, 1993, 1997 and 2004. In most years, there are only one or two records, but three were found in 1986, 1998, 2000 and 2005 and four were noted in 1979. The majority of records have involved single birds, although two have been seen together on seven occasions and up to three were present at Rutland Water from November 27th 1977 to February 18th 1978. Of those that have been aged, 19 have been first-winters and six have been adults; it is likely that the majority of un-aged birds would also have been first-winters and it has been speculated that a contributory factor in the rather frequent inland occurrences of Great Northern Divers is migratory overshooting by immature birds (Lack 1986).

There have been new arrivals in every month except June and August, but there is a clear peak during the late autumn/early winter period, with 23 of the 56 individuals (41%) recorded thus far having been found between November 16th and December 15th. Autumn records prior to November are unusual; the earliest was of two at Eyebrook Reservoir on September 7th 1947, whilst the only other autumn reports before November were single birds at Rutland Water on September 17th 2000 and October 26th 1996. New birds after January are quite scarce; only four have arrived in February and just two during March. There have been two spring records, at Eyebrook Reservoir on April 13th 1980 and Rutland Water on May 23rd 1994; both of these were adults seen on one day only and presumably involved northbound migrants taking an overland route. More difficult to explain was a summer plumaged adult at Rutland Water from July 17th to 21st 1990.

This species is renowned for its often extended stays once it arrives on the counties reservoirs; the average duration of a visit is 32 days. Three individuals have clocked up over 100 days, all at Rutland Water: from November 20th 1988 to April 13th 1989 (114 days), November 29th 1998 to June 1st 1999 (185 days) and November 5th 2003 to May 16th 2004 (193 days). The 1998/99 bird was the only individual ever to be seen in June in the counties.

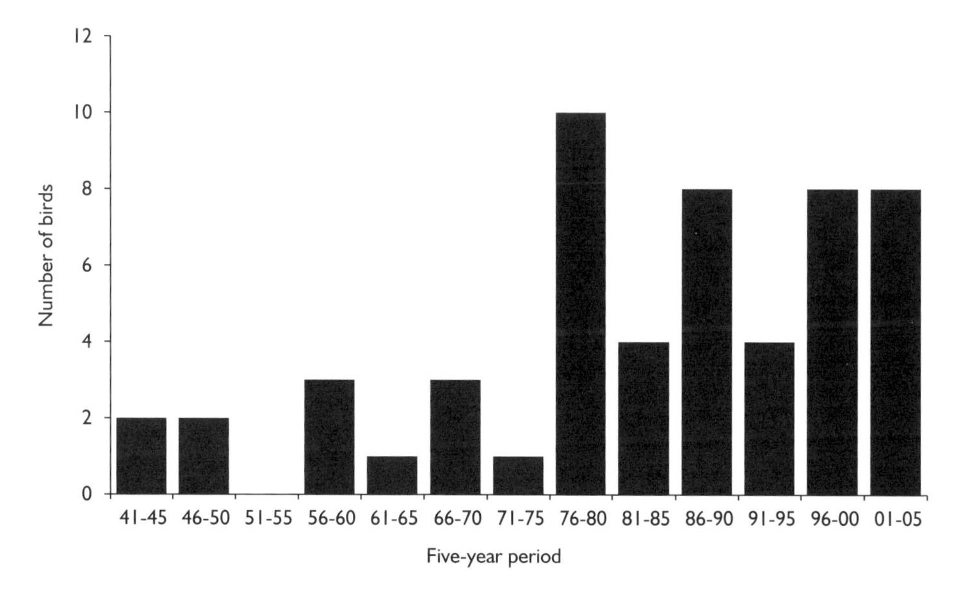

Figure 139: Numbers of Great Northern Divers by five-year periods 1941–2005.

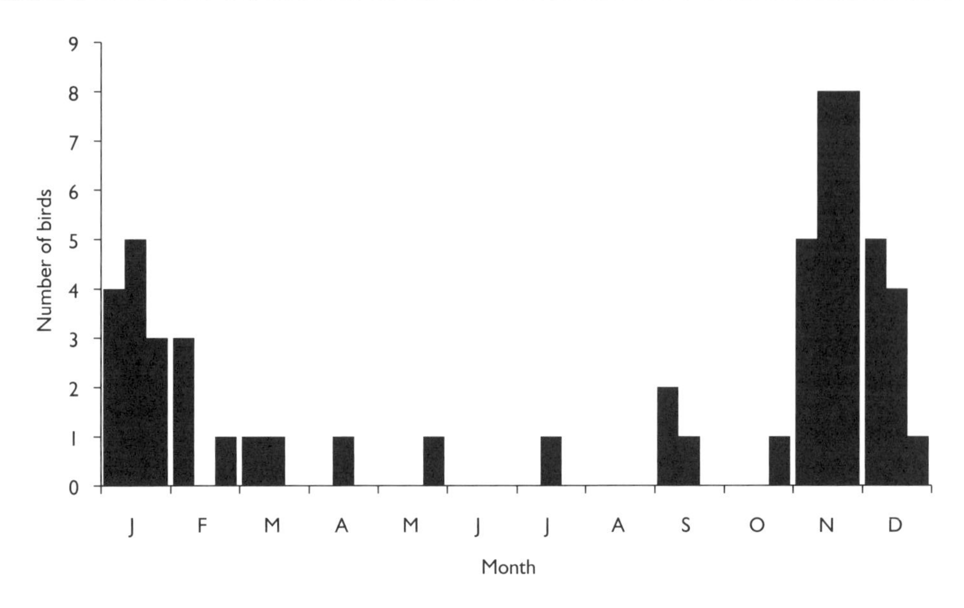

Figure 140: Monthly occurrence of Great Northern Divers 1933–2005.

A report of one at Frolesworth Manor Lake on March 1st 1995 was published in the LROS Annual Report but found to be unacceptable on review in 2004 (Fray 2005).

Great Northern Divers breed in Iceland, west Greenland, throughout Canada and Alaska and along the fringes of the northernmost United States. Large numbers winter off both the Atlantic and Pacific coasts of North America. In Europe, the wintering population is estimated at 6,000 birds, which occur from northern Norway south to northern Spain. Over 3,000 of these regularly winter off the coasts of Britain and Ireland, particularly off north-west Scotland and the north and west of Ireland. Due to the importance of British and Irish waters on the north-west European non-breeding population, the species is currently on the 'Amber List' of Birds of Conservation Concern (Gregory *et al.* 2002)

RMF

Little Grebe *Tachybaptus ruficollis*

Uncommon to fairly common resident breeder, uncommon winter visitor.

During the 19th century, Browne described the Little Grebe as 'resident but sparingly distributed' in Leicestershire, whilst in Rutland Haines considered it to be 'somewhat scarce' except at Burley Fishponds and Exton. The first LROS Annual Report, in 1941, summed up the status of this species as 'much more widespread but not so locally common as Great Crested Grebe. Breeds on most reservoirs and patches of water, even on ornamental lakes in the city parks.'

The current status of the Little Grebe remains much as that stated in 1941, although there is some evidence of a decline in breeding numbers. In recent times the best year was 1991, when 40 pairs bred at a total of 16 sites; by 2005, only seven pairs were confirmed to have bred. This apparent decline may be in some part due to lack of observer effort, as Little Grebes breed in habitats rarely visited by birdwatchers such as small rivers and ponds. The best estimate of the county-wide breeding population was provided by Warrilow who, during 1976–84, recorded this species in 121 tetrads (19% of the total number of tetrads), with breeding confirmed in 68. It was found to be more numerous in lower-lying areas where slow-flowing rivers, reservoirs and flooded gravel pits are concentrated and was absent from most areas to the east of Leicester. Of those birds found breeding, 40% were on rivers and canals, 25% used ornamental lakes, 20% were on reservoirs and 13% utilised gravel pits. Warrilow estimated a total breeding population of between 120 and 360 pairs.

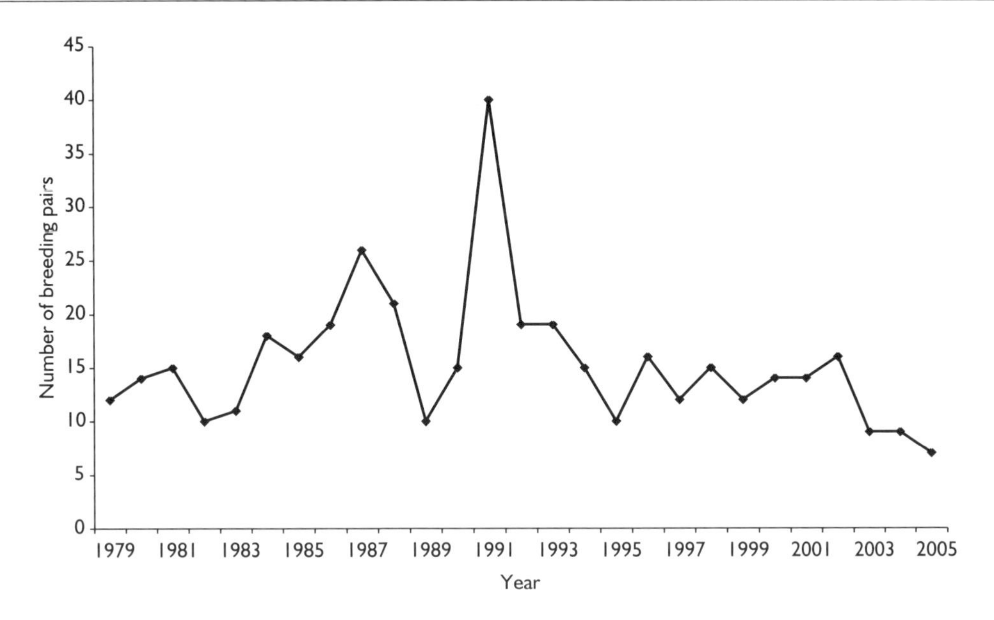

Figure 141: Number of breeding pairs of Little Grebes 1979–2005.

The Little Grebe is more numerous in the counties during autumn and winter. Rutland Water is currently a site of national importance for this species and counts over the qualifying threshold of 78 have been recorded in ten years, as follows:

- 120 on September 12th 1999.
- 113 on November 15th 1991.
- 103 on November 19th 1984.
- 99 on September 7th 1976.
- 96 on September 18th 2005.
- 91 on November 13th 1983.
- 88 on October 13th 1985.
- 87 on both October 12th 2003 and October 22nd 2000.
- 83 on November 12th 1995.

During the mid-1980s to early 1990s, the River Soar within the city of Leicester was also of national importance for Little Grebes. Counts exceeding 50 were regular, with the highest totals being 83 on February 9th 1991, 68 on December 16th 1990 and 62 on December 17th 1988. Numbers since then have declined rapidly, although a reduction in recording effort may be partly responsible for this. Many of the largest counts were during periods of severe weather, when the warmer water of the river in the industrialised centre of Leicester remained ice-free whilst nearby lakes and reservoirs were frozen; the recent run of milder winters may also be a contributing factor to the current lower counts.

Eyebrook Reservoir has produced counts of 50+ in six years, the highest being 76 on September 14th 1996. The only other site to record more than 50 Little Grebes is Swithland Reservoir, where there were 61 on October 23rd 2003. Elsewhere, counts of 30+ have been recorded at five sites, the maxima being:

- 50 at Thornton Reservoir on September 14th 1980.
- 46 at Stanford Reservoir on September 16th 1984.
- 34 at Wanlip Gravel Pits on November 13th 1976.
- 34 at Watermead Park on September 15th 1990.
- 31 at Quorn Borrow Pit on both August 12th 2002 and September 14th 2004.

See 'Wintering Birds' (pages 39–43) for details of highest counts at individual sites.

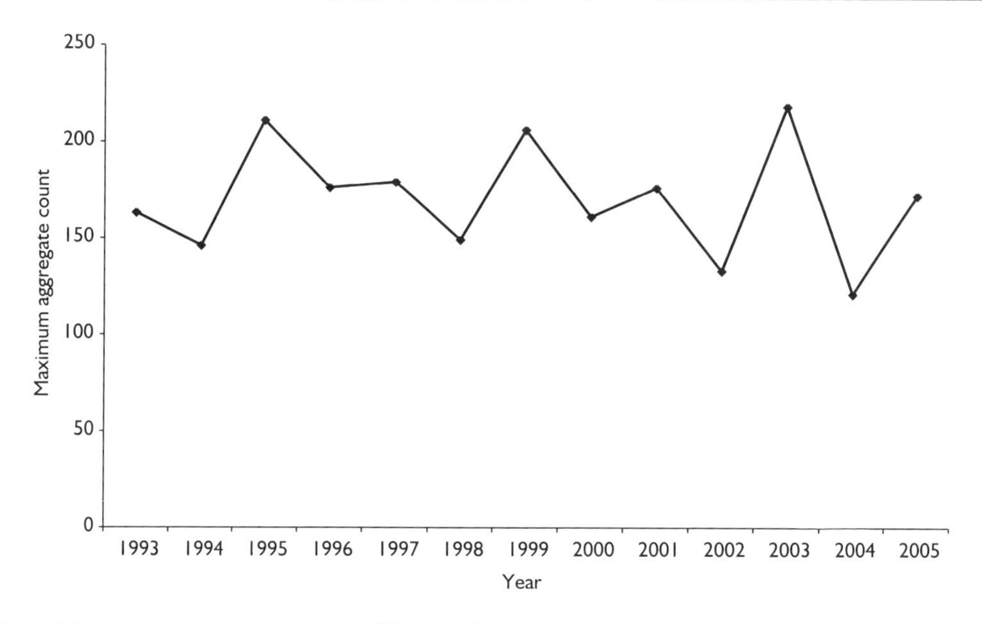

Figure 142: Maximum aggregate counts of Little Grebes at the main sites 1993–2005.

Little Grebes breed in many parts of the Old World except Australasia. Most populations are resident but birds in northern and eastern Europe are migratory. The British breeding population is currently estimated at 5,000 to 10,000 pairs (Baker *et al.* 2006).

RMF

Great Crested Grebe *Podiceps cristatus*

Fairly common to common passage and winter visitor, uncommon breeder.

The Great Crested Grebe was believed to be on the verge of extinction in Britain around 1860, when only 32 to 72 pairs were known in England (Holloway 1996), but a reduction in persecution by humans resulted in numbers of this species gradually increasing at the end of the century. This pattern was reflected in the comments made by the 19th century authors. Browne described it as a spring visitor to Leicestershire which sometimes remained until winter and noted that the first breeding record for the counties occurred at Saddington Reservoir in 1874. It then bred regularly at this site from 1883 onwards and by 1886 there were several pairs nesting there. Breeding was recorded at Cropston Reservoir in 1879 and Swithland Reservoir in 1906, when there were eight pairs present. By 1907 Browne considered that the Great Crested Grebe was greatly increasing in numbers. The first record for Rutland known to Haines was of one killed at Tixover on November 28th 1883 and by the end of the century it was to be found regularly in Rutland although did not remain through the winter. It bred at Exton in 1885 and then annually there from 1898 and was also known to have nested at Burley Fishponds.

During the first part of the 20th century the LROS archives describe the Great Crested Grebe as resident, with some leaving for the winter, whilst the first LROS Annual Report, in 1941, put this species' status as 'common as a breeding species on all reservoirs, not so common in winter'. These status descriptions represented a subtle change in occurrence from the late 19th century, when Great Crested Grebes did not regularly remain into the winter months.

The Great Crested Grebe was one of the best-studied birds in Leicestershire and Rutland during the 1940s. A summary in the 1946 Annual Report, a year when there was a 'great effort by a large number of observers to census this species', noted three main findings:

- a few grebes are present on most of the larger sheets of water throughout the winter.
- there is an influx of passage migrants in March and April and again in September and October, the autumn movement being much the heavier.
- a very large non-breeding population is present throughout the summer at Eyebrook Reservoir.

Spring passage during the 1940s was evidenced by records from Eyebrook Reservoir of 50 in March 1944, 37 in April 1945, 58 in early April 1946 and 80 in early March 1949. The same site also produced the largest autumn flocks during this period, with counts of 150 in October 1946 and October 1947, 200 in early October 1943, August and October 1948, November and December 1949 and August 1952 and 250–300 on September 29th 1951. Numbers at other waters were much smaller, but included 15 at Swithland Reservoir on September 15th 1943 and 30 at Thornton Reservoir on September 14th 1943. The non-breeding population at Eyebrook Reservoir referred to above peaked at 115 in June 1951, with other counts including 70 in July 1944 and 60 in July 1945.

A full breeding census was carried out in 1947, when a total of 52 pairs were recorded at 14 sites; this included concentrations of eight pairs at Swithland Reservoir, five at both Stanford and Thornton Reservoirs and four at Cropston Reservoir. At Eyebrook Reservoir 17 nests were located early in the season but falling water levels left many high and dry and the majority were robbed by Carrion Crows. 'Colonies' in other years during the 1940s and early 1950s included 15 pairs at Stanford Reservoir in 1944, with 12 there the following year, eight pairs at Cropston Reservoir in 1948, seven pairs at Swithland Reservoir in 1944 and 1951 and six at both Thornton Reservoir in 1944 and Saddington Reservoir in 1951.

Table 15: Number of breeding pairs of Great Crested Grebes 1944–1951

	1944	**1945**	**1946**	**1947**	**1948**	**1949**	**1950**	**1951**
Number of sites	9	5	7	14	?	6	13	5
Number of pairs	40	28	20	52	35	13	24	22

There is little information on breeding numbers of Great Crested Grebes in the counties during the 1950s and 1960s, although there were 20 nests at Eyebrook Reservoir in 1965 and 18 there the following year. In 1967, nine nests at this site were trampled by cattle. A more complete picture is available from 1970 onwards. During 1976–84 Warrilow recorded this species in 58 tetrads in the counties (9% of the total number of tetrads), with breeding confirmed in 43. The distribution mainly matched the location of the counties' reservoir and gravel pit complexes, although 10% of breeding records were on canals and rivers; Warrilow estimated a county-wide breeding population of 85 to 130 pairs. In recent years the highest numbers of breeding pairs reported to LROS have been 92 in 1984, 87 in 1985, 66 in 2005 and 58 in 1991. Large 'colonies' have included 33 at Rutland Water in 2005 and 26 at Eyebrook Reservoir in 1991, whilst 62 nests at Rutland Water in 2003 were abandoned due to falling water levels. This is a conspicuous species when nesting and haunts many sites favoured by birdwatchers, so breeding numbers reported to LROS are likely to represent a good proportion of the counties' population.

Numbers wintering in Leicestershire and Rutland were small in the 1940s and 1950s; in 1948 12 at Eyebrook Reservoir and eight at Swithland Reservoir in January were considered 'more than usual'. The first large winter count was 200 at Eyebrook Reservoir on January 13th 1952, but apart from 100 at the same site on December 13th 1959 there were no subsequent three-figure winter counts until the early 1970s. More recent data show that this species is still more numerous as an autumn migrant, with peak numbers in September, although numbers remain high until December after which they decline rapidly. In severely cold weather this species may all but abandon the counties: during the famous freezing spell between mid-January and mid-March 1947 the only bird that remained in the counties was one on the River Soar at Abbey Park, Leicester, whilst in 1982 only two birds were recorded in the whole of the counties on the January WeBS count.

As with a number of other waterbirds, the construction of Rutland Water in the mid-1970s dramatically altered this species' status in the counties. The first large count at this site was 222 on January 14th 1979, a total

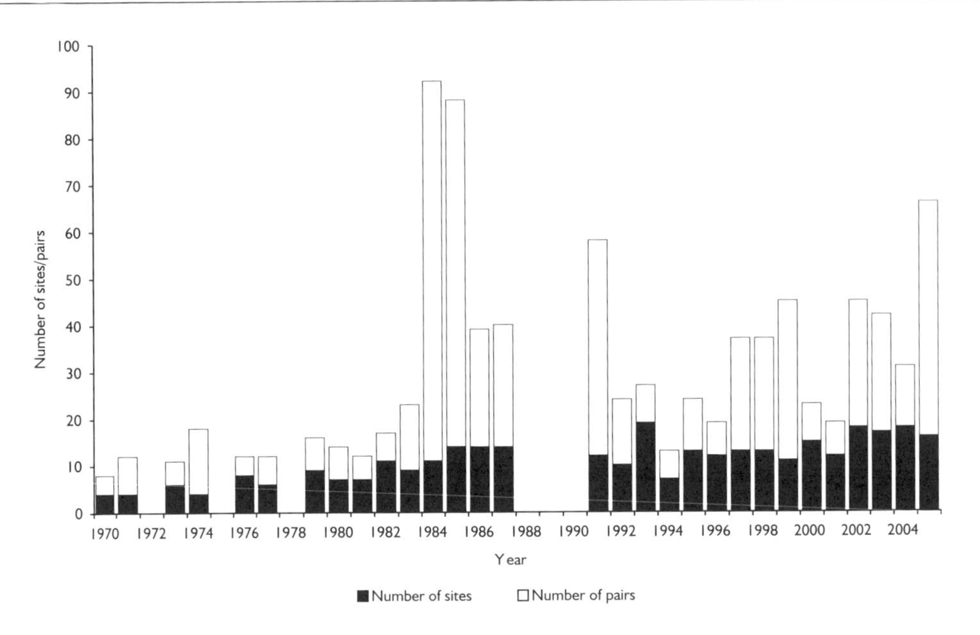

Figure 143: Number of breeding pairs of Great Crested Grebes 1970–2005.

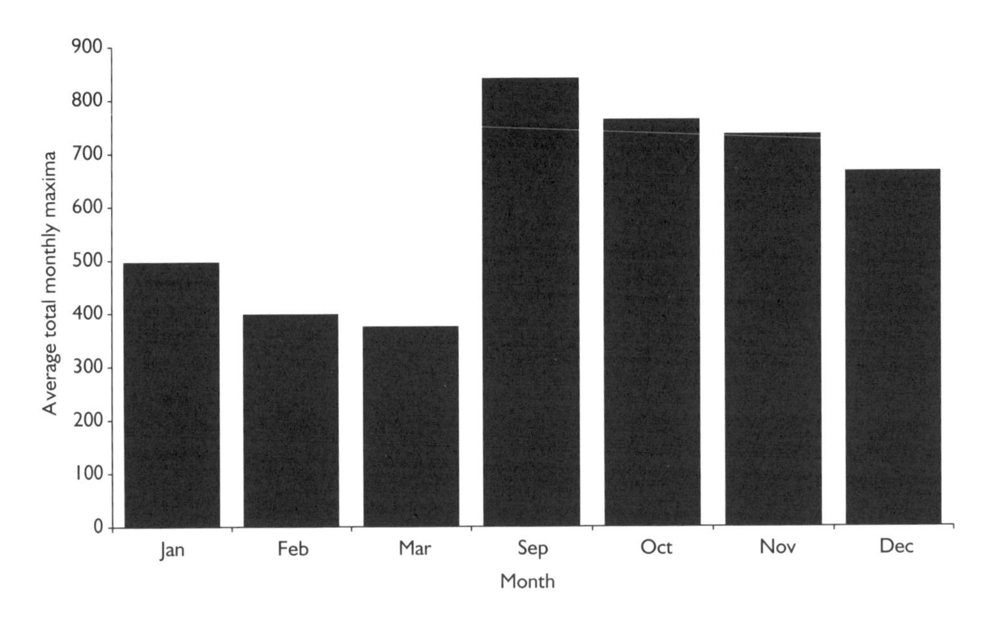

Figure 144: Average total monthly maxima of Great Crested Grebes at the main sites 1995–2005.

which coincided with a widespread national influx of other waterbirds, including Red-necked Grebes, following high pressure over Scandinavia and bitterly cold north-easterly winds (Chandler 1981). This total was not bettered until 1983, when 520 on December 18th was an unprecedented number in the counties; since then, however, the maximum count has exceeded this total in all but four years. The qualifying threshold for a site to be considered of national importance for the Great Crested Grebe is 159 and Rutland Water is now the second most important site in Britain for this species (Collier *et al.* 2005). Counts of 966 on October 14th 1984 and 1,038 on January 17th 1991 were, at the time, the highest individual totals at one site ever recorded in the United Kingdom. Numbers have exceeded 800 in a further five years, as follows:

- 997 on October 22nd 2000.
- 900 on January 22nd 1985.
- 894 on October 17th 1993.
- 843 on September 6th 1998.
- 815 on November 14th 2004.

Since the construction of Rutland Water the maximum aggregate counts have showed a steady increase, in line with national WeBS totals which have shown a sustained increase in recent years (Collier *et al.* 2005).

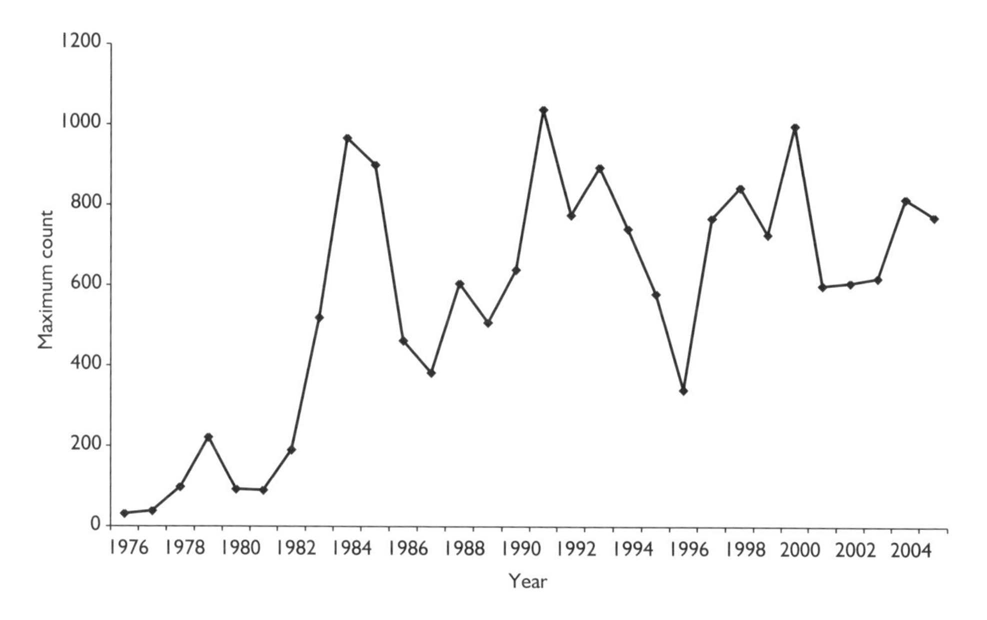

Figure 145: Maximum counts of Great Crested Grebes at Rutland Water 1976–2005.

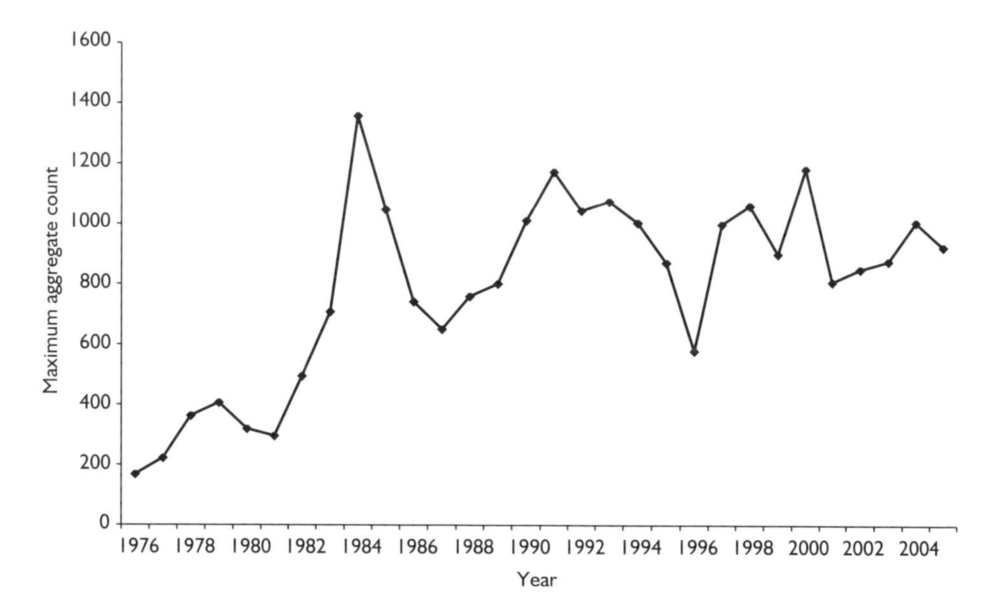

Figure 146: Maximum aggregate counts of Great Crested Grebes at the main sites 1976–2005.

Eyebrook Reservoir has qualified in the past as a site of national importance, although numbers here have dropped considerably since the mid-1990s. The largest total was 353 on November 18th 1984 and other than the counts of 200 or more in the 1940s and 1950s already mentioned numbers have exceeded 175 on a further six occasions, as follows:

- 300 on August 2nd and 4th 1991.
- 268 on November 16th 1975.
- 197 on November 12th 1978.
- 185 on October 26th 1974.
- 180 on June 6th 1968.
- 180 on October 16th 1983.

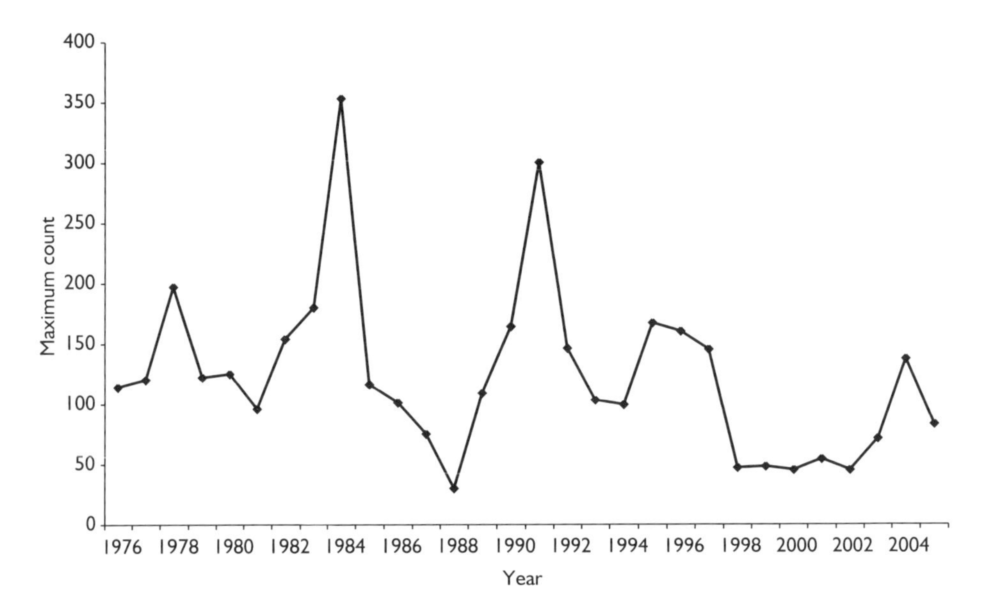

Figure 147: Maximum counts of Great Crested Grebes at Eyebrook Reservoir 1976–2005.

Swithland Reservoir and Stanford Reservoir have both achieved three-figure counts. At the former site the maximum was 127 on November 7th 2002, with other notable totals being 125 on July 27th 1969, 102 on October 13th 1990 and 88 on October 23rd 1970. At Stanford Reservoir the largest flock was 124 on October 5th 1971, with 121 on November 13th 1983, 112 on October 7th 1979 and 98 on October 13th 1985 also being of note. Counts of 40+ have been recorded at a further five sites, the maxima being:

- 90 at Thornton Reservoir on September 17th 1972.
- 90 at Cropston Reservoir on January 20th 2001.
- 64 at Staunton Harold Reservoir on August 14th 1971.
- 53 at Wanlip Gravel Pits on March 15th 1987.
- 45 at Trent Valley Pit on both November 30th 1999 and December 29th 2001.

See 'Wintering Birds' (pages 39–43) for details of highest counts at individual sites.

Three leucistic birds have been reported, at Rutland Water on August 30th 1985 and December 22nd 1999 and Eyebrook Reservoir on September 9th and 23rd 1995. Two individuals have died in unusual circumstances: on March 7th 1999 one at Trent Valley Pit flew into a barbed wire fence and hung itself, whilst one found dead at Swithland Reservoir on June 19th 2000 appeared to have its bill trapped in the stonework of the dam.

The only ringing recovery of note involving Leicestershire and Rutland concerned an adult ringed at Borth (Dyfed) on January 29th 1992 which was found dead at Nanpantan Reservoir on June 14th 1992, a movement of 193km to the east.

The nominate race of the Great Crested Grebe breeds over most of Europe as well as in central Asia. Other races are found in Africa and Australasia. Most European populations winter to the south and west of the breeding range. The British population is currently increasing slowly and the latest estimate is 8,000 pairs (Baker *et al.* 2006). Numbers as monitored by WeBS counts have also shown a sustained shallow increase (Collier *et al.* 2005) and the British wintering population is put at 15,900 birds (Baker *et al.* 2006).

RMF

Red-necked Grebe *Podiceps grisegena*

Scarce winter and passage visitor; recorded in all months, with the majority from September to March.

This species was virtually unknown in the counties prior to the 1940s. Browne reported that 'according to Mr Macaulay, one was shot at Saddington Reservoir in 1874 by Mr Kemp . . . but Kemp visited Leicester Museum in January 1888 and on looking at the specimens he could not see one like his own and said it certainly was not Red-necked Grebe but thought it might be Slavonian.' This record has subsequently been ignored by later authors, leaving the first generally accepted record for the counties being of a bird found dying at Stoneygate, Leicester in March 1924. Two further individuals were noted prior to the formation of LROS in 1941: single birds at Swithland Reservoir on March 6th 1926 and Stanford Reservoir some time in 1935.

Since 1940, 137 birds have been found in Leicestershire and Rutland, although the species remained very rare until the 1970s. Between 1940 and 1969 there were records in 16 years, involving 21 individuals, but since 1970 there have been only four years with no new arrivals and a total of 116 birds in this time. During 1940–69, eight birds occurred between September 5th 1945, when one was at Cropston Reservoir and April 14th 1947, when one was found dead at Ashby-de-la-Zouch; otherwise, this species went long periods without being recorded in the counties, including a spell with just one bird between 1956 and 1965. As with a number of other waterbirds, the noticeable increase in records from the mid-1970s onwards can be directly attributed to the creation of Rutland Water. After the first at this site, in February 1979, the Red-necked Grebe has been recorded there in all but four years since, involving 64 individuals. Only 41 birds have been found elsewhere in the same period, meaning this species has only marginally increased as a visitor to the counties' other waters over the last 26 years. Oddly, records dropped off considerably from the late 1990s and there were only ten new individuals recorded between December 1998 and the end of 2005.

Most years see between one and five records, although there were six in 1986, 1988, 1989 and 1993, and seven in 1985 and 1996. However, these totals were completely eclipsed by an impressive 18 in 1979, all of which occurred between January 26th and March 25th and were part of an unprecedented influx into Britain following high pressure over Scandinavia and bitterly cold north-easterly winds (Chandler 1981). Numbers at Rutland Water at this time were remarkable: after one from February 11th to 14th, 13 were present on the 18th, with smaller numbers remaining until March 25th. These numbers were obviously exceptional and the majority of records usually involve single birds. Two have been seen together on eight occasions, all at Rutland Water apart from two at Eyebrook Reservoir on January 11th 1975. Higher counts, all of which occurred at Rutland Water, have been up to five from January 11th to February 20th 1985 and three from March 7th to 21st 1993.

The pattern of records shows that this species is most frequent in the counties during January and February, with notable peaks during the middle ten days of both of these months, reflecting cold weather movements. There is another minor peak in occurrences in late November and birds arriving at this time often remain for much of the winter. Small numbers have occurred during both the spring and autumn passage periods and the only month with no new arrivals is June. In the spring, there have been six new arrivals in April, although none have been after the 14th; however, six birds have arrived in May:

- Rutland Water, May 1st and 2nd 1988.
- Swithland Reservoir, May 12th 1993.
- Priory Water, May 13th 1989.
- Rutland Water, May 14th 1989.
- Rutland Water, May 18th to September 19th 1985.
- Eyebrook Reservoir, May 25th 1980.

The earliest returning bird was one at Eyebrook Reservoir on July 12th 1980, which remained until September 20th. The only other July record came from the same site in 1995, when one arrived on the 25th and remained until December 31st. This species remains scarce during August, the only records being a juvenile at Thornton Reservoir from August 9th to September 10th 1992 and single birds at Rutland Water from August 14th to September 27th 1992, August 25th to October 26th 1997 and August 26th to October 22nd 1993.

Red-necked Grebes have a propensity to remain for long periods once they arrive in the counties and 42 birds have stayed for more than four weeks. The longest residence was by one which was at Rutland Water for nearly

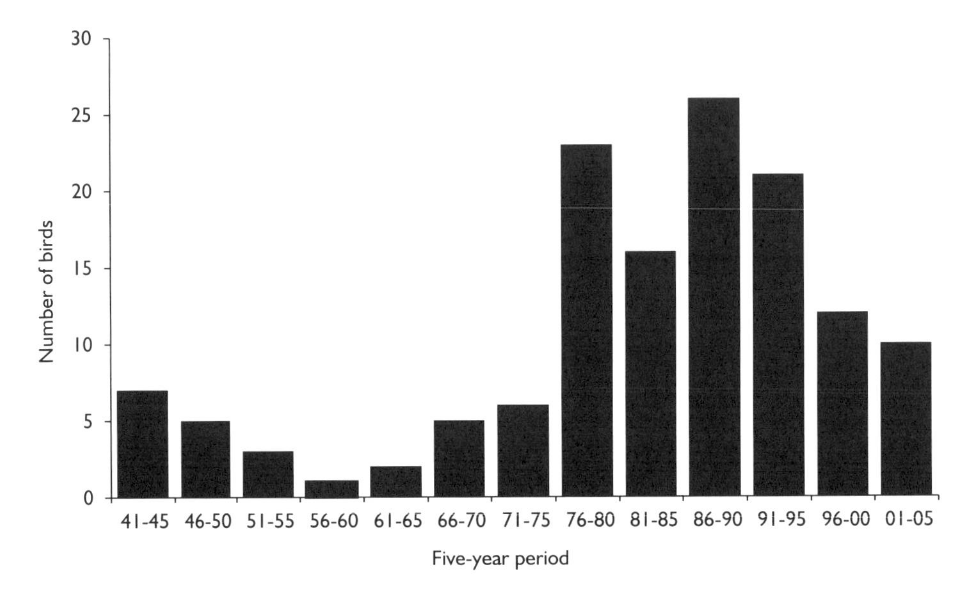

Figure 148: Numbers of Red-necked Grebes by five-year periods 1941–2005.

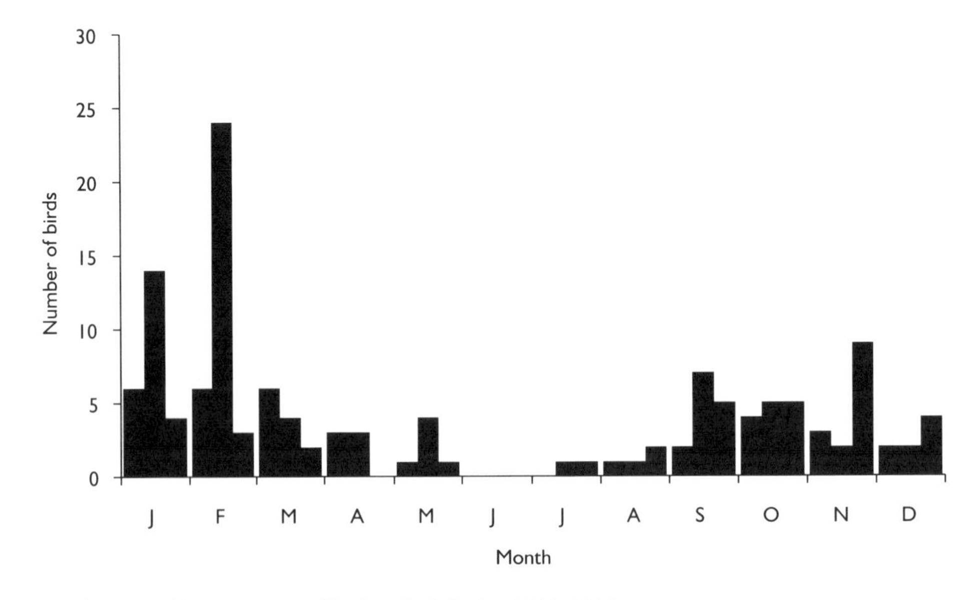

Figure 149: Monthly occurrence of Red-necked Grebes 1941–2005.

18 months, from November 29th 1998 to May 13th 2000. A further seven birds have remained for periods greater than four months:

- Cropston Reservoir, October 1940 to March 1941.
- Eyebrook Reservoir, October 5th 1974 to April 13th 1975.
- Rutland Water, May 18th to September 19th 1985.
- Rutland Water, October 2nd 1988 to March 12th 1989.
- Eyebrook Reservoir, July 25th to December 31st 1995.
- Rutland Water, December 10th 1995 to May 5th 1996.
- Rutland Water, October 11th 2003 to May 14th 2004.

As mentioned previously, Rutland Water is the dominant site, with 64 individuals recorded (47% of the county total). Eyebrook Reservoir has 27 records to its name, followed by Swithland Reservoir with 15, Thornton Reservoir with nine and Cropston Reservoir with eight. Away from these five sites, this is a very rare bird in the counties: Saddington Reservoir has recorded four birds whilst, rather strangely, the Red-necked Grebe has been seen at the large Stanford Reservoir on just two occasions. There have been no records from the counties' other main reservoirs at Knipton and Blackbrook, whilst this species is also missing from the list of birds recorded at several other likely-looking sites, including Fort Henry Ponds, Trent Valley Pit and Watermead Country Park North. In total, there have been 17 records away from the five main sites, all of single birds:

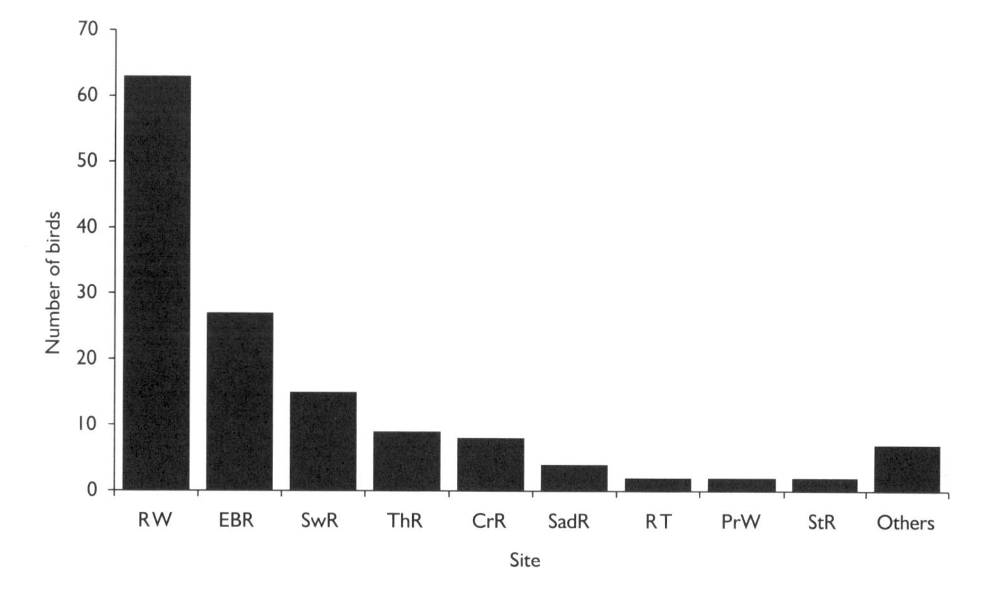

Figure 150: Sites where Red-necked Grebes have been recorded 1924 –2005.
Key to abbreviations: RW = Rutland Water; EBR = Eyebrook Reservoir; SwR = Swithland Reservoir; CrR = Cropston Reservoir; ThR = Thornton Reservoir; SadR = Saddington Reservoir; RT = River Trent; StR = Stanford Reservoir

- picked up dying, Stoneygate, Leicester, March 1924.
- Stanford Reservoir, some time during 1935.
- Stanford Reservoir, September 28th to October 10th 1944.
- found dead, Ashby-de-la-Zouch, April 14th 1947.
- Saddington Reservoir, January 13th to February 13th 1967.
- Saddington Reservoir, December 25th 1969 to January 3rd 1970.
- River Trent, Trent Lock, February 24th and 25th 1979.
- Staunton Harold Reservoir, March 25th 1979.
- Frisby Gravel Pits, November 29th to 30th 1984.

- River Trent, King's Mills, February 14th to March 3rd 1986.
- Thurmaston Gravel Pits/Watermead Gravel Pits, February 6th to March 11th 1987.
- Priory Water, May 13th 1989.
- Saddington Reservoir, February 18th to March 2nd 1996.
- Birstall Gravel Pits, March 27th 1996.
- Priory Water, September 29th 1996.
- Saddington Reservoir, February 4th 2003.

The three records from the Rivers Soar and Trent are especially notable. All three occurred during periods of particularly cold weather, when many other areas of water in the counties were frozen: the Abbey Park individual was obviously associated with the famous severe winter of 1963, whilst the bird at Trent Lock in 1979 was part of the large influx previously discussed.

One record that has previously been published in LROS Annual Reports is now considered unacceptable: a single bird at Eyebrook Reservoir on December 8th 1963 (Fray 2005).

Red-necked Grebes breed in eastern Europe, Siberia, Alaska and eastern Canada. European birds winter on coasts to the south and west of breeding areas. They are scarce winter visitors in Britain, with approximately 200 birds recorded each year. Unsuccessful breeding attempts were made in both Scotland and Cambridgeshire in 1988 (Parslow-Otsu & Elliott 1991) and a pair successfully raised young in Scotland in 2001 (Ogilvie *et al.* 2003). Due to the fact that more than 50% of the United Kingdom's non-breeding population winters at fewer than ten sites, this species has been added to the 'Amber List' of Birds of Conservation Concern (Gregory *et al.* 2002).

RMF

Slavonian Grebe — *Podiceps auritus*

Scarce winter and passage visitor; recorded in all months except June, with the majority from September to April.

During the 19th century, Browne described this species as a 'rare winter visitant', although the only certain record appears to be one shot at Groby Pool during the winter of 1844–45. It had also apparently been 'met with by gunners and sportsmen on the Soar, Trent and Wreake' and another supposedly occurred at Melton Mowbray, although there is no further evidence to substantiate these claims. Around the same time, Haines quoted Mr A.C. Elliot as saying it was 'not very scarce in Rutland', although again the only apparently definite record was of one killed at Great Casterton on February 27th 1881. Another was said to have occurred at Fort Henry in 1897.

In the 20th century, there were five records prior to the formation of LROS in 1941, all of single birds:

- Wanlip, January 1919. The skin is retained at the Leicester Museum.
- Wanlip, January 1922.
- Swithland Reservoir, October 13th 1928.
- Stanford Reservoir, some time in 1935.
- Cropston Reservoir, October 21st 1940.

Since 1941, 181 birds have been found in Leicestershire and Rutland. A noticeable increase in numbers is detectable from the late 1960s onwards, with another increase occurring from the early 1990s. Between 1941 and 1965, this species was recorded in just 11 of the 24 years and was particularly scarce throughout most of the 1950s, with only seven birds seen during this decade after October 28th 1950. Since 1965 the only blank year has been 1976 and, as with many other waterbirds, the creation of Rutland Water in the mid-1970s has benefited this species. Following the first record at this site, on February 28th 1977, a further 60 individuals have been found there; the importance of Rutland Water is demonstrated by the fact that, during the same period, all other sites in the counties have a combined total of 56 records.

Between 1940 and 1992, one or two records per year were the norm, although there were notable totals of six in both 1947 and 1987 and eight in 1950. 1947 was, of course, famous for its exceptionally severe weather during the first few months and four birds were found between February 2nd and 21st, of which only the individual at Cropston Reservoir on the 13th was at an expected site. Others were located at Abbey Park, Leicester on the 2nd, Glen Parva on the 12th and Kegworth on the 21st, the latter bird succumbing to the weather on the 25th. The other notoriously cold winter, of 1962–63, only produced two birds during January and February, both similarly at unusual sites: one again at Abbey Park and another on the River Trent at King's Mills. Since 1993, there have been only three years (1999, 2000 and 2005) which have produced fewer than four records. Eight birds were found in both 1997 and 1998, there were nine in 1996 and a remarkable 14 in 2002. The majority of records have involved one or two birds, but three have been recorded together on six occasions:

- Cropston Reservoir, September 5th to 19th 1945.
- Eyebrook Reservoir, February 12th to 19th 1950.
- Rutland Water, November 7th 1993.
- Rutland Water, November 22nd to December 31st 1997.
- Rutland Water, February 6th to March 30th 2003.
- Rutland Water, February 24th to March 28th 2004.

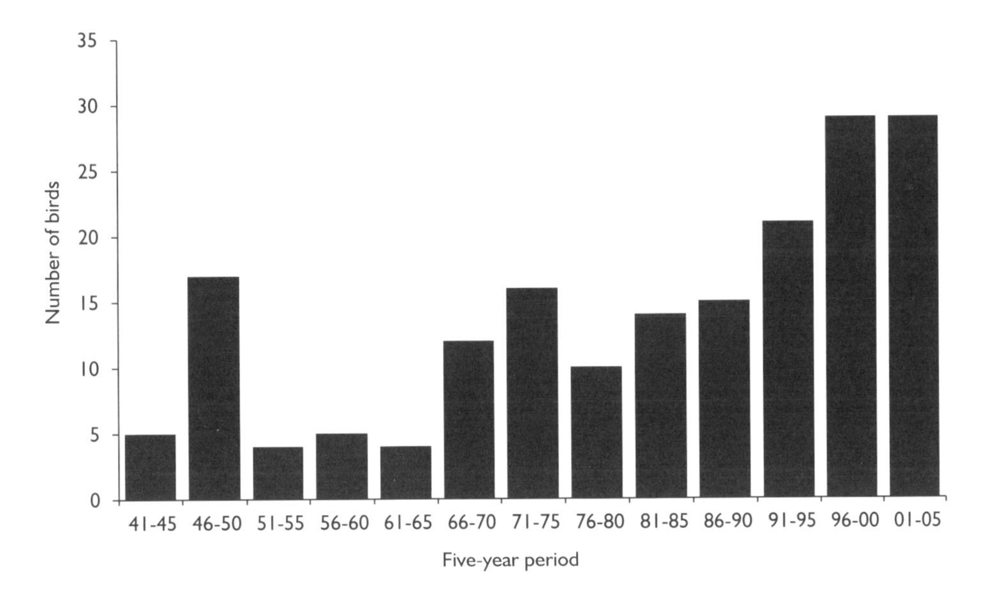

Figure 151: Number of Slavonian Grebes by five-year periods 1941–2005.

The data show that this species occurs mainly between September and early April, with the main period for arrivals being between mid-October and late November. There is also a peak in mid-February, which probably coincides with cold weather movements, whilst another small peak in early April relates to passage birds moving north towards their breeding grounds. However, only five spring birds have arrived after April 11th:

- Thornton Reservoir, April 19th 1999.
- Swithland Reservoir, April 26th 1971.
- Eyebrook Reservoir, April 27th to 29th 1968.
- Rutland Water, May 9th 1981.
- Stanford Reservoir, May 15th 1947.

These spring records have invariably involved birds in their spectacular breeding plumage and pairs have even been seen displaying at Rutland Water on April 4th 1993 and March 23rd 2004. A record of one at Eyebrook Reservoir on May 5th 1950 was published incorrectly, the actual date being March 5th.

During the autumn, this species is rare before September. One at Eyebrook Reservoir on July 17th and 26th 1952 was a remarkable record, whilst there have only been three others before September: single birds at Eyebrook Reservoir on August 17th 1978 and August 31st 1948 and at Rutland Water on August 23rd 1987.

The pattern of records during the early autumn has altered markedly over recent years; of the eight records in September that have occurred before the 15th, only two have been since 1967. In these earlier days, the identification criteria of this species had not been fully resolved and there is a risk that some of these records may have been confused with Black-necked Grebes. A review of the earlier records was attempted in 2004 (Fray 2005), but as documentation was lacking for the majority they were all allowed to stand; it is perhaps wise, however, to treat some of these earlier records with a degree of caution.

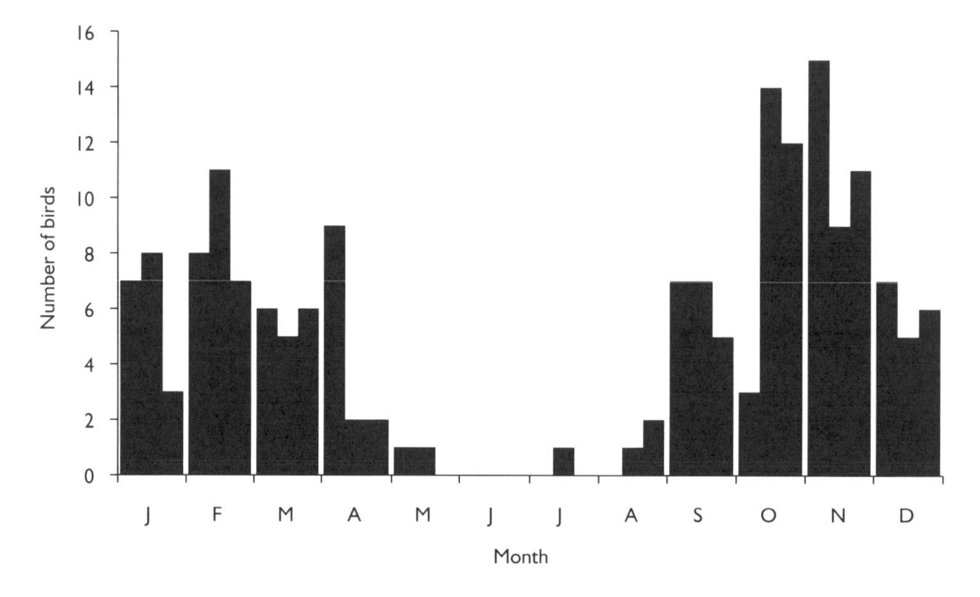

Figure 152: Monthly occurrence of Slavonian Grebes 1941–2005.

There has been a recent trend for Slavonian Grebes to remain in the counties for longer periods. In total, 27 have lingered for more than four weeks, all since 1966. Six have remained for over 100 days, all at Rutland Water:

- November 10th 2002 to April 8th 2003.
- November 8th 2003 to April 4th 2004.
- November 24th 2002 to April 8th 2003.
- November 26th 2000 to April 1st 2001.
- December 18th 1994 to April 10th 1995.
- December 7th 2003 to March 28th 2004.

Away from Rutland Water, only seven birds have remained for more than four weeks:

- Eyebrook Reservoir, September 2nd to November 8th 1981.
- Eyebrook Reservoir, September 18th to November 2nd 1966.
- Groby Pool, March 3rd to April 13th 1993.
- Eyebrook Reservoir, February 19th to March 27th 1966.
- Eyebrook Reservoir, December 8th 1995 to January 13th 1996.
- Trent Valley Pit, December 27th 1997 to February 1st 1998.
- Saddington Reservoir, February 27th to April 2nd 1996.

Rutland Water and Eyebrook Reservoir are by far the most favoured sites for this species, with 61 and 57 individuals recorded respectively (nearly 65% of the county total). Elsewhere, only Swithland Reservoir has amassed a double-figure total (19 records). Of all the scarce grebes, this one is the most likely to appear on some of the counties' smaller waters, with records having come from, amongst others, Sawley Gravel Pits (October 27th and 28th 1950), Belvoir Lakes (October 16th 1988), Fort Henry Ponds (November 1st to 3rd 1993) and Stoney

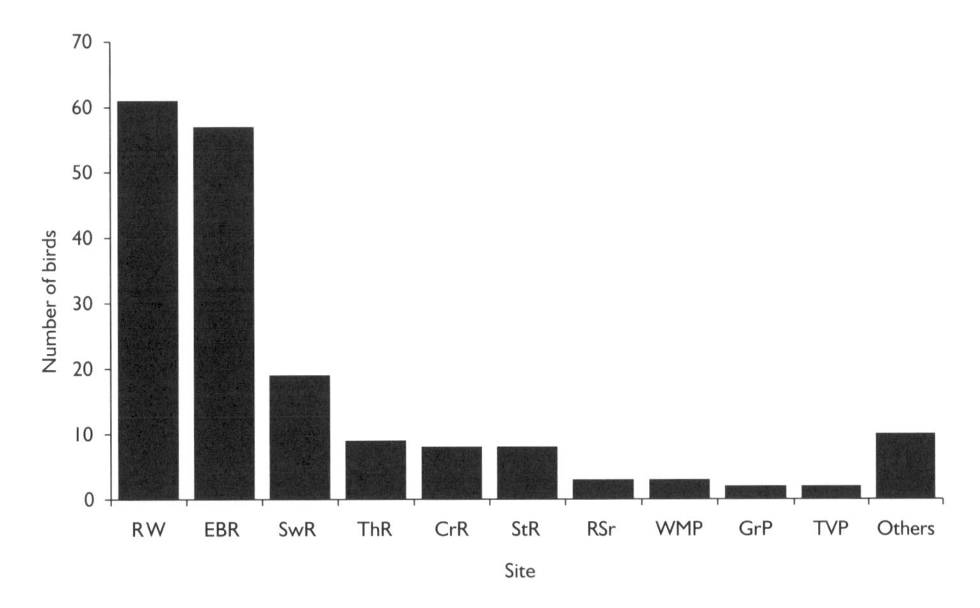

Figure 153: Sites where Slavonian Grebes have been recorded 1941–2005.
Key to abbreviations: RW = Rutland Water; EBR = Eyebrook Reservoir; SwR = Swithland Reservoir; ThR = Thornton Reservoir; CrR = Cropston Reservoir; StR = Stanford Reservoir; RSr = River Soar, Leicester; WMP = Watermead Park; GrP = Groby Pool; TVP = Trent Valley Pit

Cove (February 7th 1996). It has also been found three times on the River Soar within Leicester (in the winters of 1946–47 and 1962–63 as mentioned previously, as well as at Abbey Meadows from January 28th to February 5th 1977).

A record of one at Eyebrook Reservoir on February 19th 1944 was published in the LROS Annual Report but is now considered unacceptable (Fray 2005).

Slavonian Grebes breed in the boreal and sub-Arctic zones of the Old and New Worlds. In Europe, the population is centred on Finland, Sweden, Norway and Iceland. Small numbers have bred in the Scottish Highlands since the first nest was found in 1908; numbers peaked at around 80 pairs in 1979 and 1980, but had declined to 46 by 2002. Due to this decline and the fact that the small Scottish population is considered vulnerable, this species has been added to the 'Amber List' of Birds of Conservation Concern (Gregory *et al.* 2002). The wintering population in Britain is estimated at 400 individuals (Lack 1986), the majority of which are to be found off the coasts of Scotland and eastern England.

RMF

Black-necked Grebe — *Podiceps nigricollis*

Uncommon passage migrant and rare winter visitor; former breeder.

Browne described the Black-necked Grebe as 'a rare visitant, usually in spring' although the only certain record was of one shot at Groby Pool in the winter of 1844. Haines knew of no records in Rutland during the 19th century. Prior to the formation of LROS in 1941, the only 20th century records were of three at Stanford Reservoir from February 6th to March 17th 1937 and another three at the same site on November 2nd 1937.

From 1941 to the mid-1970s this species was a rare to scarce visitor to the counties. It was recorded in 25 of the 35 years between 1941 and 1975 and was particularly scarce between 1956 and 1975, with records in only ten of the 20 years in this period, involving 15 birds in total. Notable annual totals prior to the mid-1970s included nine in 1944, six in 1950 and five in four other years. Since 1975 the Black-necked Grebe has been recorded annually in the counties; the highest numbers occurred during the 1980s and 1990s, with an average of 11 per year in the 1980s and 18 per year in the 1990s. Peak annual totals have been 23 in 1997, 22 in 1993, 21 in 1992 and 1998 and 19 in 1983 and 1990. Since 2000 numbers have taken an unexplained downturn and during 2000–05 averaged just nine per year.

Most records involve one or two birds, although small parties are sometimes seen. The largest counts have come from Rutland Water, where three or four have been seen on ten occasions and higher counts have been:

- 12 on September 16th 1989, with ten on August 27th and seven on August 15th, September 23rd and November 11th.
- 11 on September 16th 1984.
- ten on August 29th and September 4th 1988.
- eight on August 29th 1990, with seven on August 26th and six on August 4th.
- eight on August 25th 1991.
- seven on September 20th 1997.
- five in mid-September 1983, on April 4th 1988 and July 17th 1992.

Elsewhere there have been 12 counts of three or more:

- eight at Swithland Reservoir on October 18th 1997, with seven there from September 21st to October 21st.
- five at Cropston Reservoir on April 13th 2003.
- four at Swithland Reservoir on April 20th 1944.
- four at Swithland Reservoir on September 6th 1999, with three until September 11th.
- three at Stanford Reservoir from October 17th to 24th 1976.
- three at Swithland Reservoir from July 24th to 27th 1983, on August 30th and 31st 1998 and November 14th 1998.
- three at Eyebrook Reservoir from April 29th to May 1st 1988, on September 9th and 10th 1995 and October 31st 1999.
- three at Saddington Reservoir on July 22nd 1993.

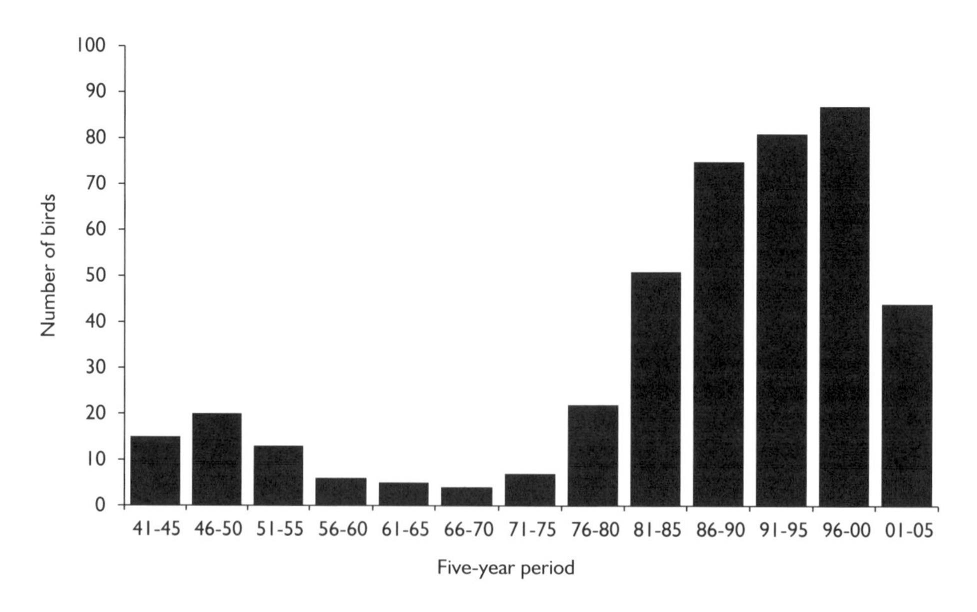

Figure 154: Numbers of Black-necked Grebes by five-year periods 1941–2005.

The pattern of records shows that there are two distinct peaks in occurrence. Spring passage is mainly concentrated from late March to late April, with fewer in May, whilst autumn passage is more prolonged and extends mainly from late July to late September. Winter records, defined as birds that have arrived from November to February, are currently rare but were much more prevalent from the 1940s to the mid-1960s: in the 27 years between 1941 and 1967 there were reports of 24 birds arriving in these months (equating to 40% of all records during this period), but since 1967 the proportion of winter records has fallen to below 9%. It is interesting to compare this pattern with the Slavonian Grebe, which prior to 1967 apparently arrived far more frequently in early autumn. As mentioned under that species, a review of the earlier records of Black-necked and Slavonian Grebes was attempted in 2004 (Fray 2005), but as documentation was lacking for the majority they were all allowed to stand; it is perhaps wise, however, to treat some of these earlier records with a degree of caution.

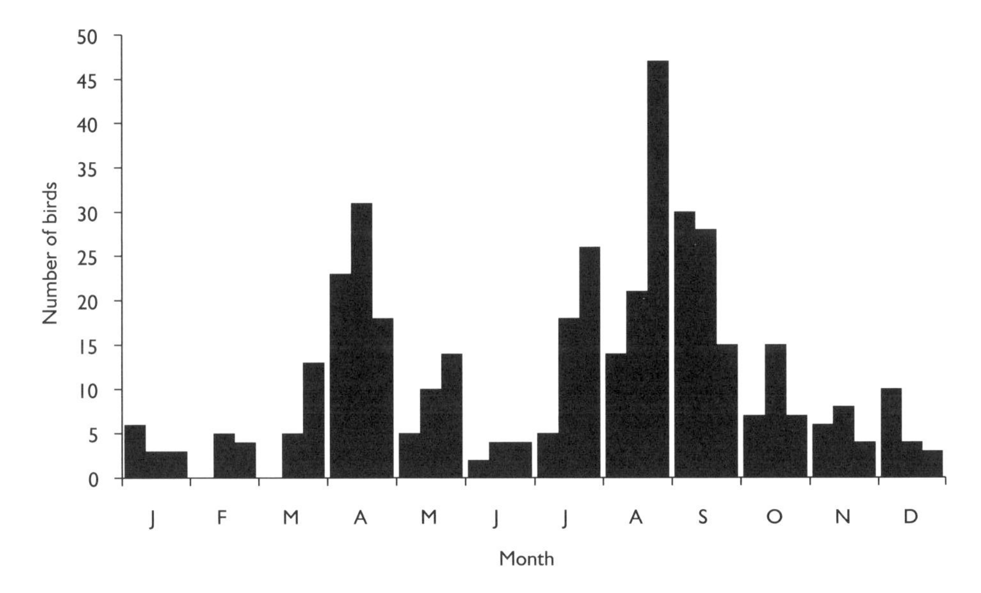

Figure 155: Monthly occurrence of Black-necked Grebes 1941–2005.

As with many other waterbirds, the Black-necked Grebe has benefited from the creation of Rutland Water and this site accounts for over 42% of all records. Eyebrook Reservoir and Swithland Reservoir are also favoured and are responsible 21% and 16% of all records respectively. Away from the three main sites, this species is relatively scarce: Stanford Reservoir has recorded 27 birds since 1941, whilst the other major reservoirs at Thornton and Cropston have 13 and 12 individuals to their name respectively. Other sites with more than one record are the Soar valley gravel pits (eight records of single birds), Kirby Bellars Gravel Pits/Priory Water (seven records of single birds), Quorn Borrow Pit (six single birds), Groby Pool (five records totalling seven birds) and Melton Country Park (two single birds). There has only been one record at Saddington Reservoir (of three on July 22nd 1993), whilst this species has never been recorded at several likely-looking localities such as Trent Valley Pit, Blackbrook Reservoir, Knipton Reservoir and Belvoir Lakes. The only other sites where this species has been seen are Loughborough Sewage Farm (one on July 19th and 20th 1947), Sawley Gravel Pits (two from October 2nd to 5th 1948), Fort Henry Ponds (an extraordinarily long-staying bird from December 26th 1993 to November 6th 1994) and Glen Parva Gravel Pits (one on April 6th 2002).

Breeding was confirmed at Rutland Water in at least four years between 1978 and 1988, although the occurrences were (and still are) shrouded in secrecy and details are a little sketchy. The details that are known are as follows:

1978	one pair raised two young in the Burley Fishponds area.
1979	one pair probably bred.
1980	one pair possibly bred.

1983	two pairs bred, raising broods of two and one.
1987	one pair raised one young.
1988	one pair raised two young, another three pairs probably bred and a further pair possibly bred.

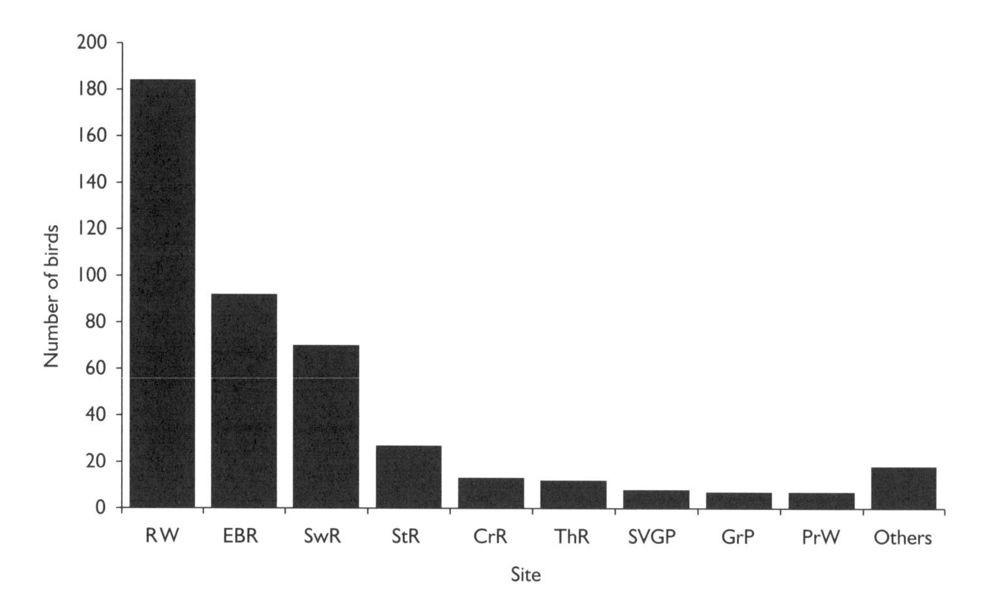

Figure 156: Sites where Black-necked Grebes have been recorded 1941–2005.
Key to abbreviations: RW = Rutland Water; EBR = Eyebrook Reservoir; SwR = Swithland Reservoir; StR = Stanford Reservoir; CrR = Cropston Reservoir; ThR = Thornton Reservoir; SVGP = Soar valley gravel pits; GrP = Groby Pool; PrW = Priory Water

The nominate race of Black-necked Grebe breeds patchily from south-western Europe to central Asia, with other subspecies in Africa and North America. European birds winter on both fresh and salt water to the south and west of the breeding range. Small numbers breed in Britain; in 2003 and 2004 there were 44 confirmed pairs but this had dropped to 38 in 2005, the lowest number since 1997 (Holling *et al.* 2008). Due to the small nature of the British breeding population, the Black-necked Grebe has been added to the 'Amber List' of Birds of Conservation Concern (Gregory *et al.* 2002).

RMF

Fulmar (Northern Fulmar) *Fulmarus glacialis*

Rare vagrant; recorded in all months except March, October and November: 17 records.

The first County record occurred in 1975 when, following strong winds, one was found exhausted at Barrowden by J. Metcalfe on April 5th. It was taken into care and subsequently released, apparently none the worse for its ordeal, at Cromer (Norfolk) on May 1st.

All records:

1975	picked up, Barrowden, April 5th (released at Cromer, Norfolk on May 1st).
1979	Eyebrook Reservoir, August 9th.
1983	Cropston Reservoir, June 14th.
1984	Rutland Water, May 12th.
1986	Rutland Water, February 8th to 9th.
1989	Rutland Water, September 9th to 10th.
	Ashby Folville, September 11th.

	picked up, Leicester, September 11th.
	picked up, Rothley, September 12th.
	long dead, Rutland Water, December 8th.
1993	picked up, Thistleton, July 19th (released at Hunstanton, Norfolk on July 22nd).
1994	Rutland Water, May 19th.
	two, near Tinwell, September 1st.
1997	Rutland Water, January 1st, 2nd and 5th.
2001	Rutland Water, June 10th.
2004	Rutland Water, February 29th.

Unlike the majority of inland seabirds, which usually appear in autumn following gales, Fulmars show a curious and rather haphazard pattern of occurrence in Leicestershire and Rutland. There have been records in all months except March, October and November and several birds (such as those at Cropston Reservoir in 1983 and Rutland Water in 1984 and 2001) have arrived in dry and settled conditions, making their appearance inland all the more odd. Where weather conditions seem to have played a part in the occurrence of this species, it is noticeable that northerly or north-easterly winds feature prominently: the birds in 1979, 1986 and 1997 were all found in these conditions, whilst the remarkable run of four individuals in four days in September 1989 followed a strong north-easterly gale which brought several other seabirds (such as Leach's Petrel, Gannet and Great Skua) to the counties. The 2004 individual was part of a 'wreck' in the southern North Sea, when many thousands of birds were found dead or moribund on the coasts of Britain, the Netherlands, Belgium and France and several appeared inland in England (van Franeker 2005).

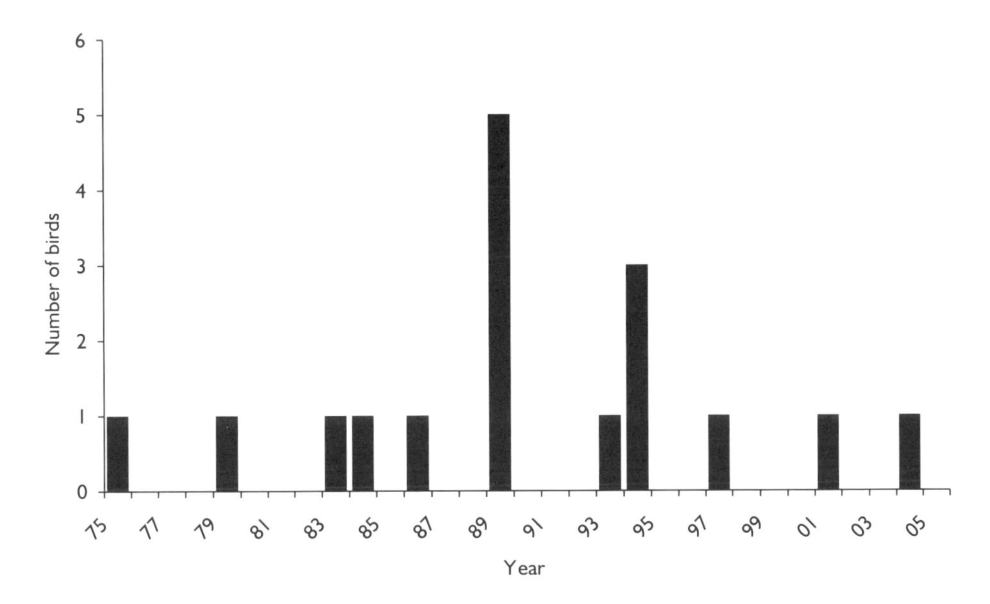

Figure 157: Numbers of Fulmars 1975–2005.

Rutland Water has proved to be the favoured site for this species, with eight records to its name; this is no doubt due to its size and the fact that it is nearer to the coast than other areas of water in the county. A further four have been found in agricultural Rutland, with another at Eyebrook Reservoir; this is therefore a truly rare vagrant to Leicestershire, with just four individuals recorded.

Fulmars breed around the coasts of northern Europe, including Britain and winter at sea. From 1850 to 1940, the UK population enjoyed a spectacular increase and continued to grow over the next 50 years (Gibbons *et al.* 1996), resulting in an estimated total of 543,000 breeding pairs by the mid-1980s (Stone *et al.* 1997). The latest UK population estimate is just over 500,000 pairs (Mitchell *et al.* 2004), although as more than 50% of the

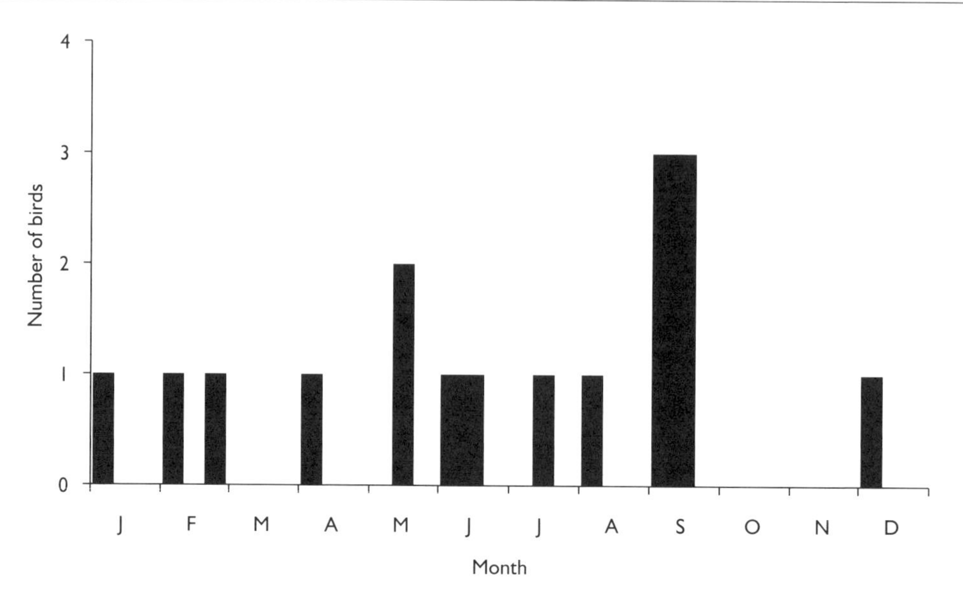

Figure 158: Monthly occurrence of Fulmars 1975–2005.

population nests in fewer than ten defined areas, the species is considered vulnerable and has been added to the 'Amber List' of Birds of Conservation Concern (Gregory *et al.* 2002).

RMF

Manx Shearwater *Puffinus puffinus*

Rare storm-driven vagrant; recorded from July to October, with the majority in September: 26 individuals since 1941 and 13 previously.

Browne cites seven records from the 19th century, with a further occurrence noted in VH at the beginning of the 20th century, as follows:

1840	captured by a dog in a turnip field by the River Soar at Cossington, undated.
1867	picked up dying at Gumley, November.
1877	caught by a dog at Billesdon, undated.
1879	captured alive at Nether Broughton, September 2nd.
1888	found dead at New Walk, Leicester, August 30th.
1891	picked up alive at Barwell, September 1st.
	caught by a dog at Smeeton Westerby, September 7th.
1904	found dead at Bradgate Park, undated. The specimen was purchased by the Leicester Museum.

In addition, the LROS archives give one found dead at Bagworth Park on September 8th 1893, which was sent to the Leicester Museum and another at Arnesby in July 1898. During the same period, the only record from Rutland known to Haines was of one picked up at Empingham, although the year of occurrence was unknown. In the early part of the 20th century, single birds were found at Hinckley in 1910, Humberstone Road, Leicester on October 31st 1920 and Desford in September 1926.

Since 1941, there have been a further 26 individuals, as follows:

1941	found dead at Little Stretton, September 1st.
1960	picked up dying at Orton-on-the-Hill, October 1st.
1963	found dying at Narborough Road, Leicester. The specimen was sent to the Leicester Museum.

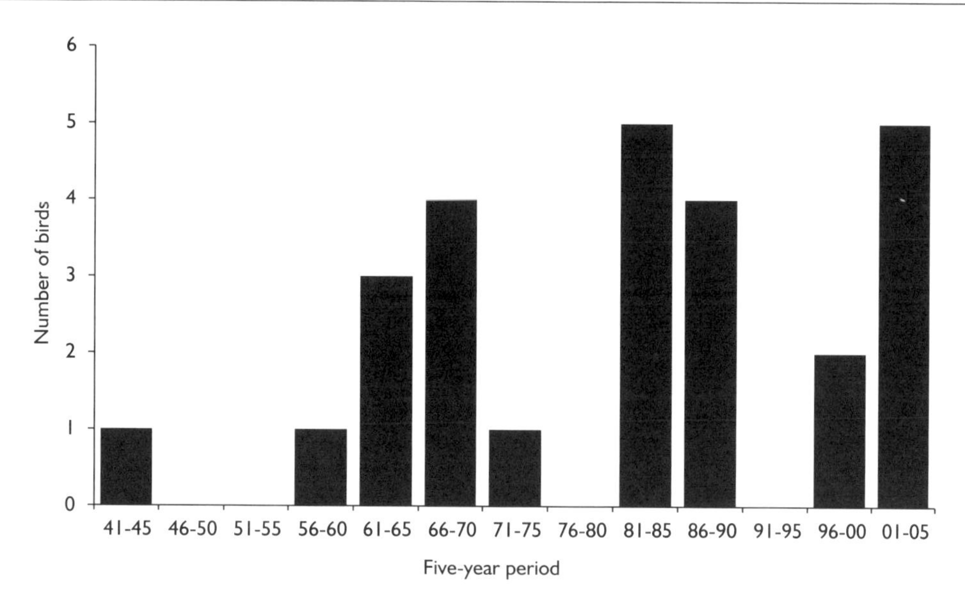

Figure 159: Numbers of Manx Shearwaters by five-year periods 1941–2005.

	picked up exhausted at Braunstone, September 28th. The bird recovered in care and was later released, although the locality is unknown.
1965	picked up exhausted at Glenfield, September 2nd and later released off the coast of Wales.
1966	picked up exhausted at Somerville Road, Leicester, September 14th. The bird was later released at Groby Pool on September 19th.
	picked up exhausted at Scraptoft, September 17th. Also released at Groby Pool, on September 18th.
1970	picked up exhausted at Leicester University, September 10th.
	picked up exhausted at Wistow, September 12th. Both this and the bird above recovered in care and were later released, although the locality is unknown.
1971	found dying at Uppingham, September 3rd.
1981	two found exhausted at Leicester during late September or early October. Both were released at Holme (Norfolk) on October 17th.
1983	one watched for 40 minutes at Rutland Water, September 4th.
1984	picked up exhausted at Desford, September 2nd.
	picked up exhausted at Stoney Stanton, September 9th and released at Rutland Water the following day.
1988	picked up exhausted at Rutland Water, September 4th and released there later the same day.
	found exhausted at Ashby-de-la-Zouch, September 6th.
	found exhausted at Oadby, early September. Both this and the bird above were later released off the south Wales coast.
	picked up dying, early September. The bird was handed to the Tropical Bird Gardens at Desford, although it is not known where it was originally found.
1997	found exhausted at Enderby, September 5th and later released at Sheringham (Norfolk).
1998	an apparently healthy individual was found at Saddington Reservoir on July 11th and remained until early the following morning before flying off east-north-east.
2004	one at Rutland Water on July 16th was joined by a second bird the following day, with both remaining until July 19th. One was found dead on July 20th, but the other bird remained until August 7th.
	one at Trent Valley Pit on July 17th and 18th was found dead the next day.

an apparently healthy individual was at Rutland Water on August 30th.
another apparently healthy individual was at Albert Village Lake on September 15th.

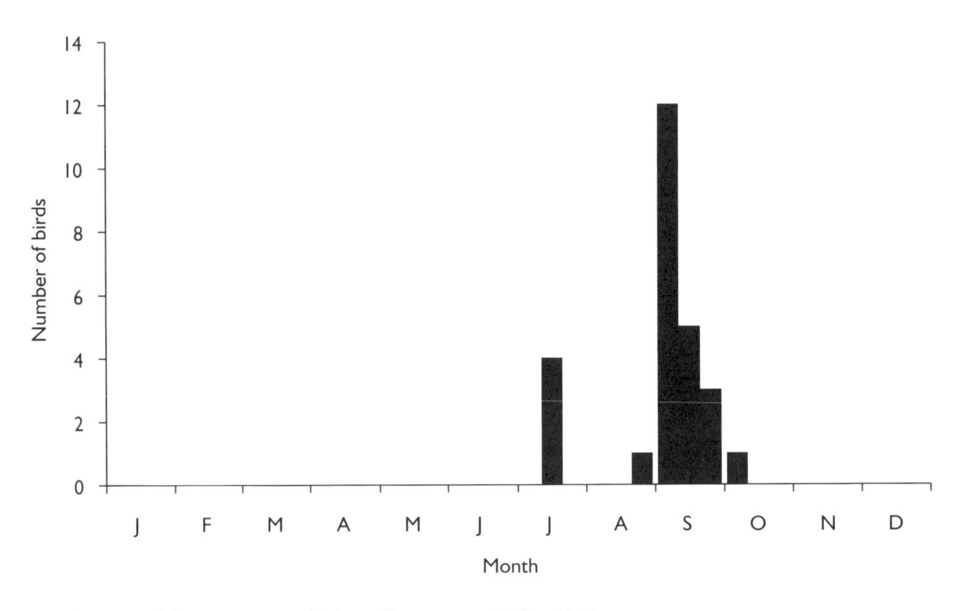

Figure 160: Monthly occurrence of Manx Shearwaters 1941–2005.

The pattern of records is as one would expect from a seabird, with the majority occurring during September (particularly the first ten days) after severe gales. The four individuals found in mid-July in recent years do not conform to this pattern, although several seabird species (such as Fulmar, Storm Petrel and Puffin) have also been recorded at this time of year. It is clear that Manx Shearwaters fare rather badly when they appear in the counties; all but seven birds have been found dead, dying or exhausted and of these seven, two have subsequently succumbed.

A bird picked up exhausted at Grendon (Warwickshire) was released at Eyebrook Reservoir on October 10th 1958.

Manx Shearwaters breed in colonies in the north Atlantic, with a large proportion of the population nesting on islands along the coast of western Britain. Smaller colonies occur elsewhere in western Europe and in the north-eastern United States. The main wintering area is off the coast of Brazil. The British population is estimated at approximately 295,000 pairs (Mitchell *et al.* 2004) and, although the species is not classed as a rare breeder, it has been added to the 'Amber List' of Birds of Conservation Concern as more than 50% of the UK breeding population is confined to fewer than ten sites.

RMF

Storm Petrel (European Storm-petrel) *Hydrobates pelagicus*

Rare storm-driven vagrant, mainly in autumn: 11 records.

Browne cites four 19th century records from Leicestershire, as follows:

1846 shot on October 23rd 'close to Leicester, on the River Soar, a few yards below West Bridge.'
1862 dead, Gumley, undated. The specimen was 'in the possession of Rev A. Matthews.'
1875 found dead 'in a field near Anstey after very stormy weather', undated.
c1882 caught in Dover Street, Leicester, 'having flown against a wall', undated.

In addition, one was found dead at Earl Shilton on November 24th 1892 and the skin is still retained at the Leicester Museum today.

Haines records two 19th century Rutland occurrences: one picked up at Empingham in 1879 after a storm and another killed against telegraph wires at Burley. The latter record is undated, although the bird was apparently preserved at Burley House.

There were just four records of this highly pelagic species during the 20th century. In 1953, one was found exhausted by A.E. Williams at Loughborough and later died; the skin was presented to the Leicester Museum. The 1953 LROS Annual Report states that the bird was found during October, although the Museum specimen is labelled September 22nd. The next record was not until 1987, when one was seen by W.D. Mudie, J. Withall and and R. Spiers flying over Lagoon II at Rutland Water in the early afternoon of September 19th. It was knocked into the water by a mobbing Lapwing, but recovered and flew off to the south. Following severe westerly gales, one was seen by at least five observers at Eyebrook Reservoir on the afternoon of October 29th 1989 and finally another was seen by four observers at the same site during the evening of July 9th 1990, remaining until 05:50 the next morning. The latter record would, at first glance, appear to be on a most unusual date for this species to be inland, especially given that all details available of the previous ten individuals suggest it only occurs as a storm-driven vagrant in autumn; however, several other seabirds (including Fulmar, Manx Shearwater and Puffin) have appeared in the counties in late June and July.

Storm Petrels breed colonially along the coasts of the north-east Atlantic and the Mediterranean; they are commonest in Iceland, Norway, the Faroe Islands and along the north and west coasts of Britain and Ireland. The majority spend the winter in the southern oceans off South Africa. The latest British population estimate is 25,500 pairs (Mitchell *et al.* 2004) and the species is currently on the 'Amber List' of Birds of Conservation Concern as, although numbers have remained stable since the 19th century, it is considered vulnerable because over 50% of the breeding population is contained within fewer than ten sites (Gregory *et al.* 2002).

RMF

Leach's Petrel (Leach's Storm-petrel) ***Oceanodroma leucorhoa***

Rare storm-driven vagrant, mainly in September and October: 21 or 22 records.

Browne and Haines detail three records from the 19th century, as follows:

1876 picked up dead at Sketchley, Hinckley, undated. The specimen was deposited at the Leicester Museum and is still there today.

picked up 'dead and dirty' at Empingham, undated.

1899 picked up dead at Cosby, November. The specimen is retained at the Leicester Museum.

In addition, Browne mentions an undated record of one found dead at Gopsall Park. Furthermore, one 'collected by the Leicester Literary and Philosophical Society was obtained in the county, but the precise locality is unknown.' It is unclear whether this latter record relates to one of the birds previously mentioned.

The 20th century saw records in ten years, involving 17 individuals:

1929	picked up dead at Peckleton, December. This bird was subsequently identified by the London Natural History Museum.
1938	found dead at Oadby, November 23rd.
1943	picked up exhausted at Melton Mowbray, April 6th.
1952	in flight, being mobbed by Rooks, at Congerstone on October 27th.
	found dead at Gwendolen Road, Leicester on October 30th. The skin is retained at the Leicester Museum.
	two found dead at Loughborough at the end of October.
	found dead at Measham, November 2nd.
1974	Eyebrook Reservoir, September 21st.
1978	Eyebrook Reservoir, September 30th
	Swithland Reservoir, October 2nd and 3rd.
1983	Rutland Water, September 3rd.
1988	Priory Water, September 18th.
	Rutland Water, October 8th. This bird was subsequently killed by a Carrion Crow.
1989	Rutland Water, September 9th and 10th.
	Thornton Reservoir, October 29th.
1998	Eyebrook Reservoir, December 21st.

The general pattern of occurrence conforms to that expected for a seabird which is only occasionally driven inland during the most severe autumn storms. Of the 16 fully dated records since 1938, 13 have occurred between September 3rd and November 2nd, coinciding with the period when this species is usually heading south from its breeding grounds. The Eyebrook Reservoir individual in December 1998 was on a very late date, as the majority of Leach's Petrels have usually left British waters by late November. The bird found exhausted at Melton Mowbray on April 6th 1943 was even more remarkable, as British breeding colonies are not usually occupied until late April at the very earliest.

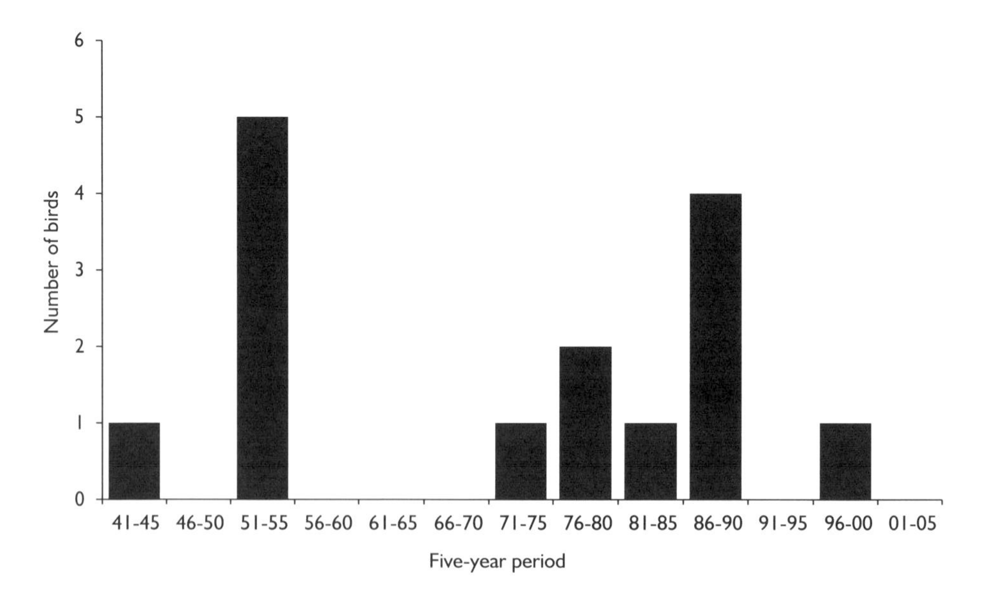

Figure 161: Numbers of Leach's Petrels by five-year periods 1941–2005.

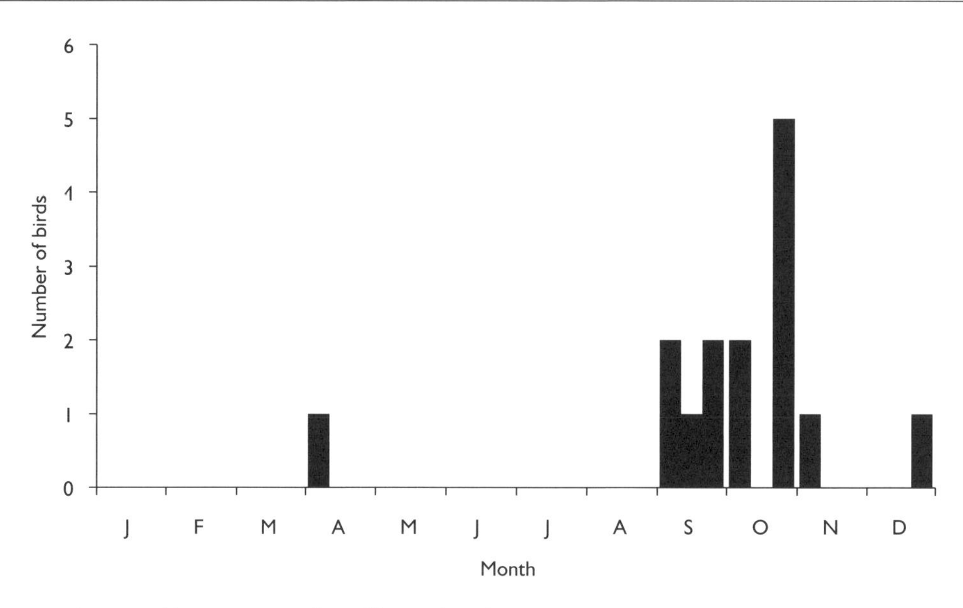

Figure 162: Monthly occurrence of Leach's Petrels 1941–2005.

The records in 1952 coincided with a huge 'wreck' of this species following widespread and persistent westerly gales at the end of October. At least 6,700 birds were found in Britain at this time, with records in every English county except Rutland. Other neighbouring counties recorded extraordinary numbers, including at least 14 in Nottinghamshire, 22 in Warwickshire and 23 in Staffordshire (Boyd 1954).

Leach's Petrels breed on remote islands in both the north Pacific and north Atlantic oceans. They winter at sea, mainly in tropical waters of the Atlantic. There are seven known colonies in Britain, all on islands off the north-west coast of Scotland and the latest British population estimate is 49,000 pairs (Mitchell *et al.* 2004). As the whole British breeding population is restricted to fewer than ten sites, this species is considered vulnerable and has been added to the 'Amber List' of Birds of Conservation Concern (Gregory *et al.* 2002).

RMF

Gannet (Northern Gannet) *Morus bassanus*

Rare vagrant, mostly in autumn: 42 records involving 65 individuals.

Browne and Haines detail 12 records of 13 individuals during the 19th century, the majority of which were either shot or found exhausted (or in some cases, both!). Three of these were undated: a juvenile at Buddon Wood, an immature near Bottesford and one killed at Somerby. In addition, Browne and Haines contradict each other on the dates of two: a juvenile at Edith Weston in either 1870 or 1876 and one killed at Empingham in either 1878 or 1879. The remaining six 19th century records were as follows:

1869 one caught alive, Houghton on the Hill, September.
1878 immature, Shangton, no date.
1886 one caught alive, Uppingham, no date.
1891 immature shot, Thistleton, October 14th.
1896 immature found alive at Tonge, January 26th; it died a few days later.
1897 one found exhausted, Ashwell, 'winter'.
1898 remains of two found dead, Luffenham Heath, November 5th.

With the exception of one found dead at Barkby in February 1927, the skin of which is still at the Leicester Museum, all further records have occurred since 1942, as follows:

1942	first-year, Burbage, for several days prior to October 28th when it was shot. The skin is retained at the Leicester Museum.
1950	immature, Stanford Reservoir, September 7th.
1965	immature found dead, Desford, October 18th.
1970	nine adults and two immatures, Stanford Reservoir, September 11th, with one immature until September 12th and one adult until September 13th. Single dead adults were found on September 12th and 20th.
1972	adult, Eyebrook Reservoir, May 26th.
1973	adult, New Parks, Leicester, October 8th.
1976	two immatures, Eyebrook Reservoir, September 19th.
	found exhausted, Loughborough, September 26th (later released at Cropston Reservoir).
1979	immature found exhausted, Belton, September 4th.
1981	found exhausted, Birstall, April 27th.
	three, Rutland Water, April 27th. Two were taken into care but later died, the other remained until April 29th.
	found dead, Wymeswold Airfield, August 30th.
	adult found exhausted, Sapcote, October (later released at Holme, Norfolk on October 17th).
1983	sub-adult, Rutland Water, September 6th to 7th.
1986	third-year, Rutland Water, February 4th to 9th.
	second- or third-year, Rutland Water, June 7th.
1988	eight immatures, Rutland Water, September 14th.
1989	first-year, Rutland Water, September 10th to 11th.
1996	first-winter, Rutland Water, October 27th.
1997	fourth-year, Rutland Water, September 16th (found dead on September 20th).
2000	adult, Eyebrook Reservoir, August 7th to 8th.
2001	juvenile, Tickencote, September 19th.
	juvenile, Stanford Reservoir, September 20th.
	juvenile, Staunton Harold Reservoir, September 21st.
2002	third-year, Knipton Reservoir, May 26th.
	immature, Rutland Water, September 23rd.
	juvenile, Trent Valley Pit, October 27th.
2004	juvenile, near Castle Donington, October 17th.
	three juveniles, Trent Valley Pit, October 26th.

Records show the expected pattern for an inland seabird, with a noticeable peak during the autumn. 80% of all individuals since 1942 have occurred in either September or October; the first two weeks of September is the favoured period, during when nearly half of all birds have arrived. Gannets only usually appear in the counties after the most severe autumn storms and the fact that 11 have been found either dead, dying or exhausted shows that even such apparently hardy birds are often unable to cope with these conditions. Records during the winter and spring are a little more difficult to explain, although the May 1972 individual appeared after a gale, whilst those found in April 1981 were part of a widespread 'wreck' of inland seabirds following a severe north-easterly gale and blizzards; at least 57 Gannets were found inland at this time, many of which were in a poor condition, including one found on a motorway in south-east England which was treated as a hazard by the local police and 'fenced off' with traffic cones (Nightingale & Sharrock 1982).

Birds have been seen at five county reservoirs, with the most individuals found at Rutland Water (18) and Stanford Reservoir (13). Both of these figures are strongly influenced by the two remarkable flocks, of eight at Rutland Water in September 1988 and 11 at Stanford Reservoir in September 1970. Of the other reservoirs, Eyebrook has four records to its name, whilst Staunton Harold and Knipton have both recorded single birds; some of the other larger reservoirs, such as Swithland, Cropston and Thornton, have yet to record a Gannet. The only other area of water where this species has been found is Trent Valley Pit, which has had four individuals, the first of which (in 2002) provided the slightly bizarre spectacle of a Gannet plunge-diving into a relatively small gravel pit. Nine birds have been found either dead or in a poor condition away from water.

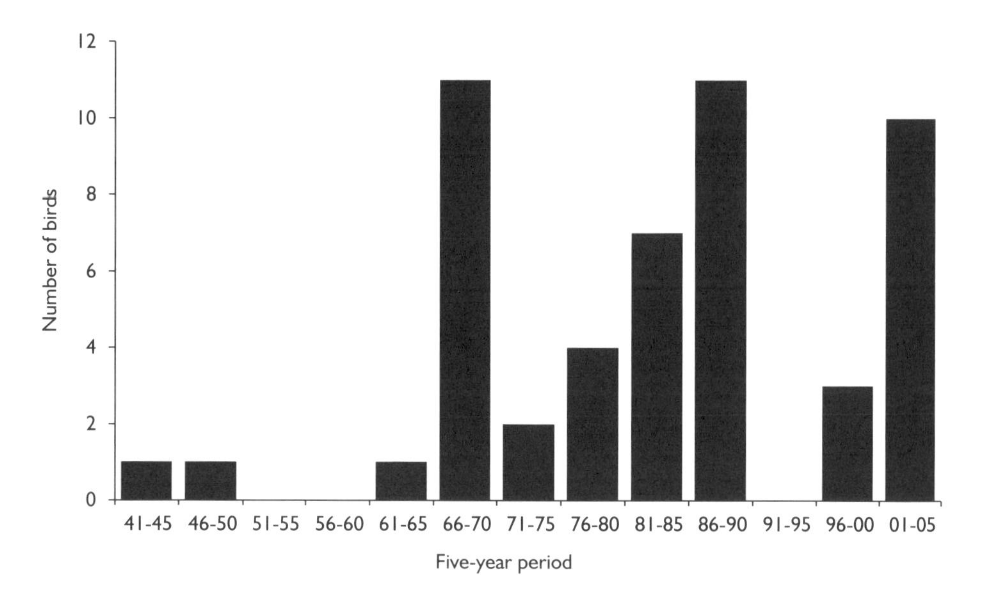

Figure 163: Numbers of Gannets by five-year periods 1941–2005.

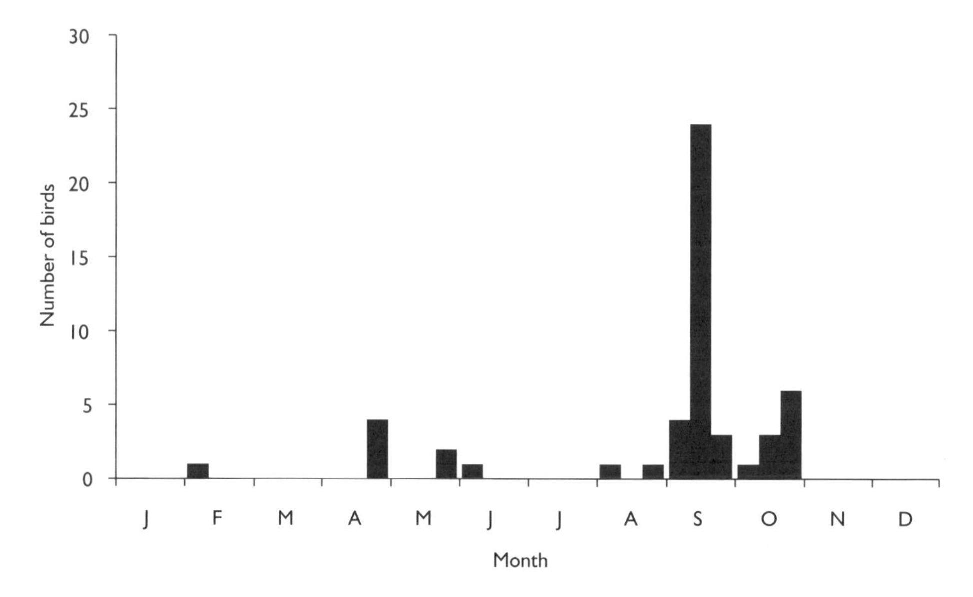

Figure 164: Monthly occurrence of Gannets 1941–2005.

The Gannet's breeding range extends from north-west France north to Iceland and east to the Murman coast of Russia and from the Gulf of St Lawrence to Labrador in the west Atlantic. The total world population is currently estimated at approximately 417,000 pairs, of which over 225,000 (54%) are in Britain; there has been a steady increase in the number of breeding pairs over the last 100 years following excessive harvesting of eggs and young for human consumption in the 19th century (Wanless *et al.* 2005). Outside the breeding season, Gannets wander widely in the north Atlantic as far south as west Africa. Despite the current healthy status of this species, it has been added to the 'Amber List' of Birds of Conservation Concern as more than 50% of the British breeding population nests at fewer than ten sites and it is therefore considered vulnerable (Gregory *et al.* 2002).

RMF

Cormorant (Great Cormorant) *Phalacrocorax carbo*

Fairly common localised resident breeder and passage migrant.

During the 19th century, the Cormorant was a vagrant to the counties. Browne knew of only four records: one caught near Langton Hall on September 6th 1883, three at Ratcliffe on the Wreake during late August 1890, one at Saddington Reservoir on April 7th 1891 and one caught in the grounds of Belvoir Castle in the middle of August 1893. In Rutland, the only record known to Haines was of two or three at Burley Fishponds in about 1896. In the first part of the 20th century, there were single birds at Swithland Reservoir on April 17th 1904 and September 7th 1905, with two there from October 10th to 18th 1906 and one was at Cropston Reservoir on October 30th 1938.

From the time of the formation of LROS in 1941 through to the mid-1970s, this species remained a scarce visitor to the counties. During this period, the majority of records occurred during March to May and August to October, with very few during the summer and winter. Most reports were of single birds or of small groups up to six, the only higher counts being:

- 12 at Eyebrook Reservoir on August 24th 1952.
- nine at Eyebrook Reservoir on September 16th 1950.
- nine at Swithland Reservoir on April 21st 1973.
- eight at Eyebrook Reservoir on September 24th 1948.

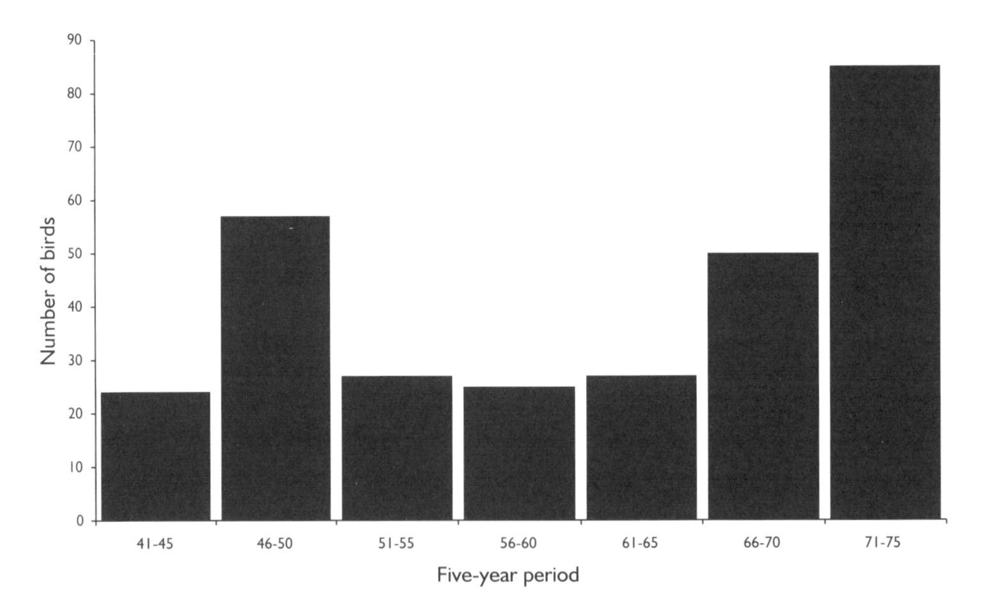

Figure 165: Numbers of Cormorants 1941–1975.

From the mid-1970s the status of the Cormorant changed significantly, coinciding with the construction of Rutland Water. In September 1976 there were three double-figure counts, including 25 at Stanford Reservoir on the 13th and 24 at Rutland Water on the 25th. 98 were at Rutland Water on December 24th 1983 and the first three-figure count was recorded at this site the following year, of 181 on October 28th. Since then there have been counts of 200+ at Rutland Water in every year except 1987 and since 1992 there has been only one

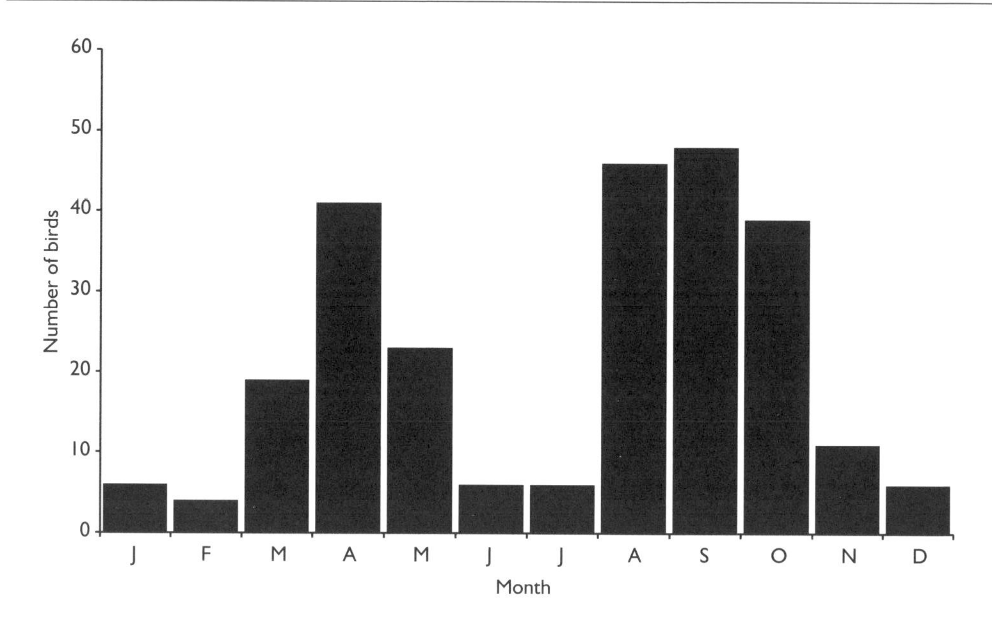

Figure 166: Monthly occurrence of Cormorants 1941–1975.

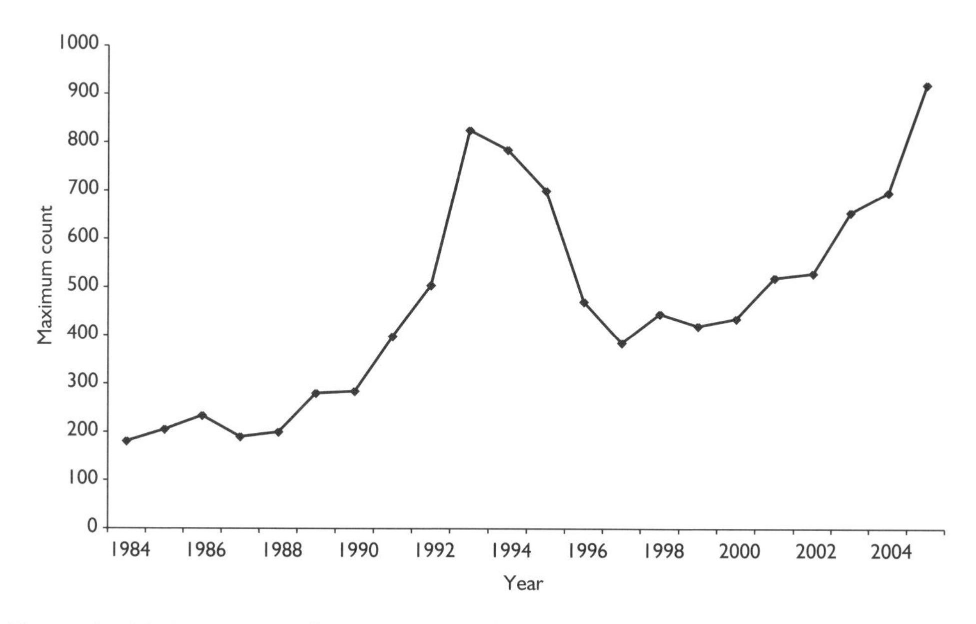

Figure 167: Maximum counts of Cormorants at Rutland Water 1984–2005.

year where the maximum count has not exceeded 400. Numbers have exceeded 700 on three occasions: 785 on September 3rd 1994, 825 on September 25th 1993 and 920 on September 23rd 2005. Rutland Water is now one of the most important sites in Britain for this species; the current threshold for a site to be considered of national importance is 230 (Collier *et al.* 2005).

Swithland Reservoir and Eyebrook Reservoir have consistently produced siginificant counts. At the former site, three-figure counts have been recorded every year since 1996, the maximum being 223 on September 25th and 27th 2005. The largest gathering at Eyebrook Reservoir has been 158 on November 16th 1997; counts exceeding 100 have been recorded in another two years.

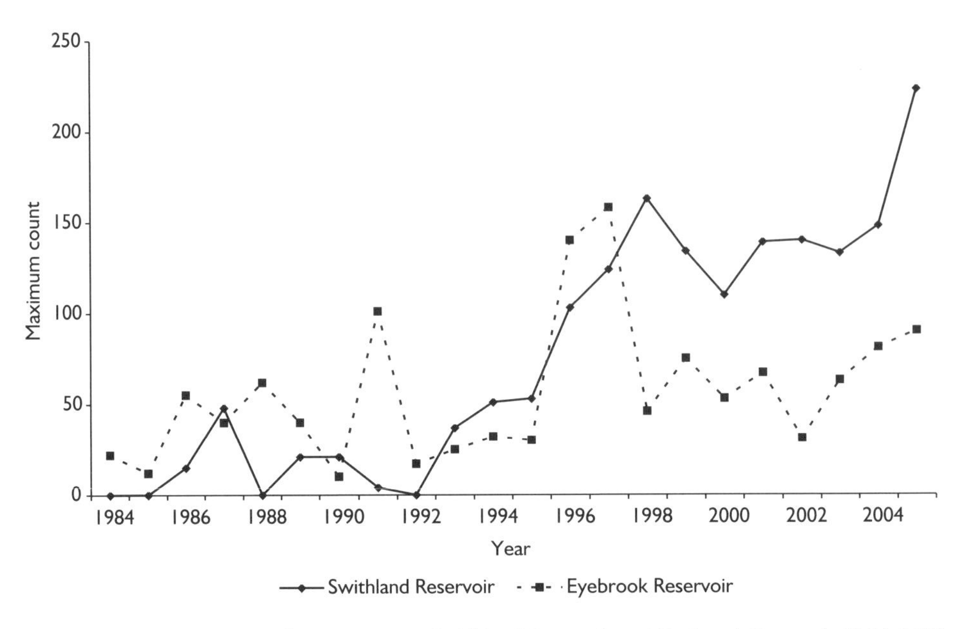

Figure 168: Maximum counts of Cormorants at Swithland Reservoir and Eyebrook Reservoir 1984–2005.

Away from the three main reservoirs, a further eight sites have recorded flocks exceeding 50, with the maxima at each being:

- 138 at Groby Pool on September 29th 2005.
- 118 at Frolesworth Manor Lake on December 21st 1995.
- 101 at Trent Valley Pit on November 23rd 1996.
- 84 at Cropston Reservoir on September 26th 2005.
- 71 at Birstall Gravel Pits on October 20th and 22nd 2001.
- 60 at Watermead Park on October 30th 1996.
- 56 at Wanlip North Gravel Pits on December 10th 1995.
- 53 at Dishley Pool on January 13th 1991.

See 'Wintering Birds' (pages 39–43) for details of highest counts at individual sites.

A bird was seen carrying twigs at Rutland Water on March 11th 1978 but it was not until 1992 that Cormorants first bred at this site, with five pairs nesting that year. The colony rapidly increased in size and by 2003 there were an estimated 150 pairs breeding; numbers had declined slightly, to 123 pairs, in 2005. Two pairs nested at Swithland Reservoir in 1997 and, as at Rutland Water, this colony quickly expanded, reaching a peak of 53 pairs in 2003.

The first mention of birds of the continental race *P. c. sinensis* was of 'several' at Rutland Water on April 11th 1982, although at that time the identification features of this race were not fully understood. However, undoubted *sinensis* birds do occur: DNA evidence from the Rutland Water colony has showed that this race makes up a proportion of the birds present (Lister 2002) and various colour-ringed individuals originating from the Netherlands, France and Denmark will also have been *sinensis*. The Rutland Water colony has been well-studied and a number of interesting observations have been made. In 2001, a bird ringed as a pullus in 1999 was found breeding at the colony; breeding by two-year-old birds is common in developing colonies, whereas in more established colonies birds usually first breed at three years old (Lister 2002). By 2004, only one of the 22 colour-ringed birds that fledged from the colony in 2003 was seen at Rutland Water and four of 21 colour-ringed birds from 2002 were noted, suggesting that most immature birds were spending at least their first two years away from the colony. This may be an indication that the Rutland Water colony has now passed the 'developing' stage (Lister 2006).

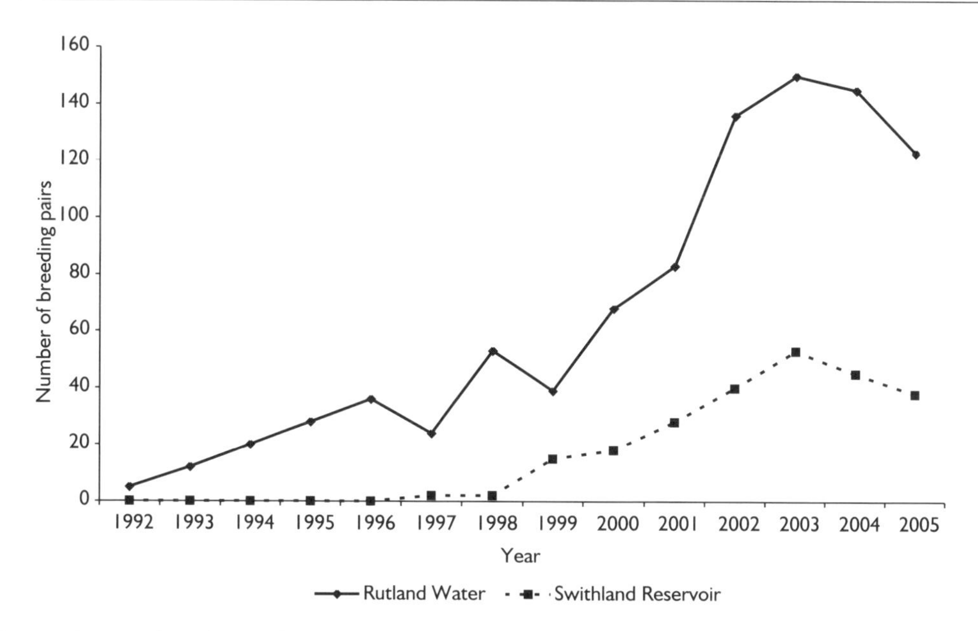

Figure 169: Number of pairs of Cormorants breeding at Rutland Water and Swithland Reservoir 1992–2005.

There is a wealth of ringing data involving Leicestershire and Rutland. Colour-ringed birds from various British colonies (especially Abberton Reservoir in Essex) are regularly seen in the counties, whilst four colour-ringed birds from foreign colonies have appeared locally:

- ringed on June 9th 1993 in the Netherlands, ring read at Rutland Water on August 28th 1994.
- ringed as a pullus at Haringvliet, Zuid-Holland (Netherlands) on June 8th 1999, ring read at Rutland Water on June 9th 2001.
- ringed as a pullus at Lac de Grand-Lieu (France) on May 11th 2001, present at Rutland Water from May 4th to September 4th 2002.
- ringed as a pullus in Sweden in June 2001, ring read at Rutland Water on January 14th 2003.

There have been five instances of birds ringed as pulli at Rutland Water which have moved abroad, as follows:

- ringed on July 3rd 1993, found dead at Favières (France) on November 5th 1993, a movement of 315km south-south-east.
- ringed on July 3rd 1993, found dead (shot) in the Loire-Atlantique region (France) on August 22nd 1995, a movement of 605km south.
- ringed on June 6th 1995, found dead at Muros (Spain) on February 19th 1996, a movement of 1,262km south-south-west.
- ringed on June 13th 1995, found dead at Benodet (France) on October 30th 1995, a movement of 586km south-south-west.
- ringed on May 31st 1999, found dead at Fouesnant (France) on March 23rd 2000, a movement of 581km south-south-west.

Cormorants are distributed widely throughout Eurasia, Australia, Africa and eastern North America. The nominate race *P. c. carbo* breeds around the coasts of Britain, Ireland, France, Norway and Iceland, whilst the continental race *P. c. sinensis* breeds from north central Europe to southern China. Historically the Cormorant was a coastal-breeding seabird in Britain, but since 1980 a number of inland colonies have been established and these now hold 15% of the British breeding population, which in total numbers 8,355 pairs (Baker *et al.* 2006). As more than 50% of the UK breeding population is found at fewer than ten sites and more than 20% of the north-west European population winters in Britain, this species has been added to the 'Amber List' of Birds of Conservation Concern (Gregory *et al.* 2002).

RMF

Shag (European Shag) ***Phalacrocorax aristotelis***

Scarce autumn and winter visitor; recorded in all months, with the majority from August to February: 120 individuals.

Browne, writing in VH, mentions two records, the first of which was 'founded upon the head and neck of an immature specimen presented to the Museum in 1890' which had apparently been caught about 30 years previously in a meadow by the River Wreake near Ratcliffe on the Wreake. Browne then reported that a second individual was shot at Saddington Reservoir on August 20th 1892. Browne seemed satisfied that both of these records were genuine and given his scepticism about many other reports during the 19th century, it is odd that these two records were ignored by subsequent authors, who state that the first county record occurred in 1946, when a Mr Mee of Ibstock caught one 'fluttering about his house' on September 5th. It was taken into captivity and then released at Thornton Reservoir on the 8th, but was picked up dead on September 13th.

Since this bird at Ibstock, a further 117 individuals have been recorded, with new arrivals in 34 of the 60 years between 1946 and 2005. Records have shown a distinct increase since the early 1980s and there have been only three blank years since 1982. Like many waterbirds, this increase in numbers corresponds with the creation of Rutland Water; following the first at this site, on September 10th 1983, there have been a further 45 birds recorded there up to the end of 2005, compared to 42 elsewhere in the counties during the same period.

One or two records are the norm in most years, although five were recorded in both 1983 and 1996, six were found in 1992 and 2004 and seven arrived in 1998. The three best years, however, were 1965 and 1984, each with 13 individuals and 1993, when at least 19 birds were found. These three years account for nearly 40% of all records of the Shag in the counties.

The majority of records involve single birds, but two have been seen together on 11 occasions. Higher numbers have been:

- up to 15 at Rutland Water from February 6th to March 6th 1993, with 12 until May 14th and smaller numbers remaining to July 6th.
- 11 first-winters landed on the main street at Saddington on November 21st 1965 during a hail storm. They were caught and later released at the nearby reservoir.
- up to five at Rutland Water from November 1st to 22nd 1998.
- three first-years at Eyebrook Reservoir on August 18th 1992.
- up to three at Rutland Water from January 12th to May 21st 1984.

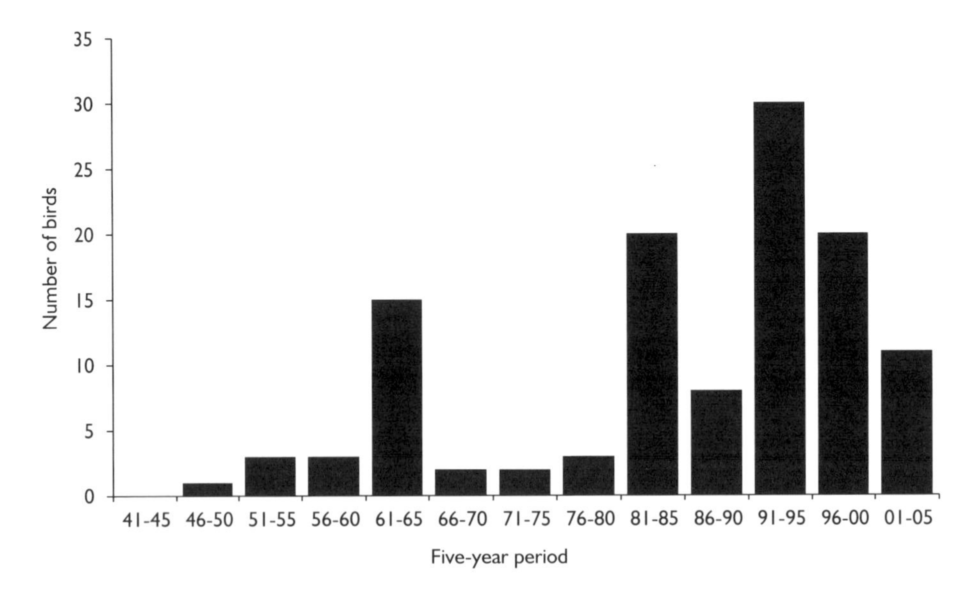

Figure 170: Numbers of Shags by five-year periods 1941–2005.

This species is considered a scarce autumn and winter visitor; the peak months are clearly November and February, which account for almost half of all records. It is curious how few birds have arrived in October and December. Early autumn, from mid-August to late September, has produced the majority of other records. The earliest autumn bird was a juvenile at Swithland Reservoir on August 10th 1957, although there have been only four further records, involving eight individuals, prior to August 20th, all of which were juveniles/first-winters:

- two at Rutland Water on August 13th 2000, one of which remained until August 21st.
- two at Rutland Water on August 16th 1992.
- three at Eyebrook Reservoir on August 18th 1992.
- one at Belvoir on August 19th 1952.

During the late winter and spring, new arrivals are scarce after the end of February. Three birds have appeared in March, with single birds in April and May:

- a first-winter on the River Soar at Frog Island, Leicester from March 3rd to June 6th 1984.
- two first-winters at Stoney Cove from March 19th to July 15th 1990.
- an adult at Trent Valley Pit on April 8th 1995.
- one at Leighfield on May 1st 1999.

There have been no new arrivals in either June or July, but several long-staying birds have remained throughout these months. Although the majority of sightings are of birds on one day only, 25 have stayed for more than four weeks, including the records mentioned above of up to three at Rutland Water in 1984, up to 15 at the same site in 1993, one at Frog Island, Leicester in 1984 and two at Stoney Cove in 1990. In addition, other long-stayers have included single second-winters at Rutland Water from December 30th 1990 to February 11th 1991 and February 13th to June 19th 1994, but the record is held by a first-winter which arrived at Stoney Cove on November 1st 1996 and finally departed over two and half years later on June 22nd 1999.

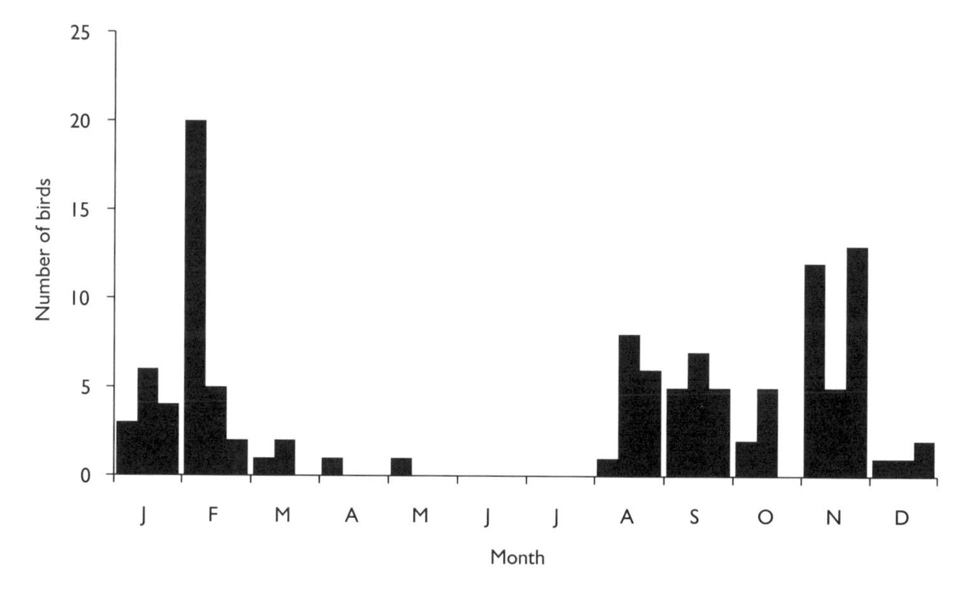

Figure 171: Monthly occurrence of Shags 1941–2005.

As mentioned previously, Rutland Water is by far the most favoured site, with 46 individuals having been recorded there. Swithland and Eyebrook reservoirs have 13 and ten records to their names respectively, but the only other site to have recorded a double-figure total of individuals is the main street in Saddington, thanks to the grounded flock there in 1965. Records have come from a further 20 scattered sites, the series of records at Stoney Cove being noteworthy. In addition to the records previously mentioned in 1990 and from 1996 to 1999, one was present from October 11th to 31st 1980; all four birds recorded at this site have found the cliff faces surrounding the cove to their liking and this is likely to be the closest to their natural habitat they will find at an inland site. The industrialised River Soar within Leicester city centre has produced a surprising total of six records, whilst birds have also been seen on the River Wreake at Asfordby on September 19th 2004 and the Grand Union Canal at Kilby Bridge the following day. A number of birds have proved to be extremely tame once they have arrived in the counties, the most famous being the long-staying birds at Frog Island in 1984 and Stoney Cove from 1996 to 1999; the former spent three months sitting on a weir under a footbridge, staring at passers-by, whilst the latter became attached to a flock of domesticated Mallards and regularly took bread!

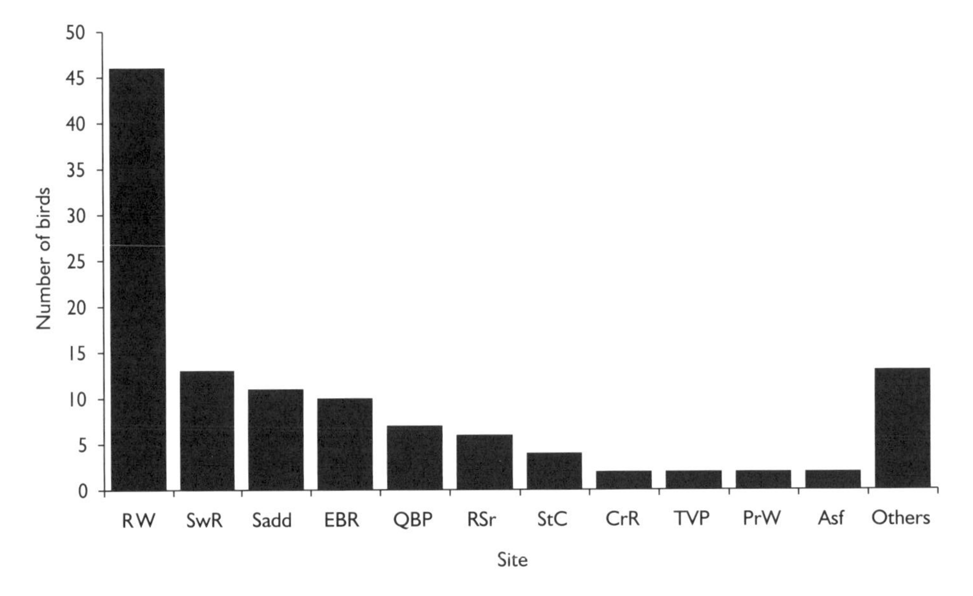

Figure 172: Sites where Shags have been recorded 1941 to 2005.
Key to abbreviations: RW = Rutland Water; SwR = Swithland Reservoir; Sadd = Saddington; EBR = Eyebrook Reservoir; QBP = Quorn Borrow Pit; RSr = River Soar, Leicester; StC = Stoney Cove; CrR = Cropston Reservoir; TVP = Trent Valley Pit; PrW = Priory Water; Asf = Asfordby

This species is ringed in large numbers on its breeding grounds and this gives a good indication of where Shags appearing in Leicestershire and Rutland come from. Of ten birds noted carrying rings, six originated from the Isle of May (Fife), where they had all been ringed as nestlings:

- a first-winter caught and released at Market Harborough on January 26th 1984 had been ringed on June 7th 1983.
- one found dead at Rutland Water on February 24th 1993 had been ringed on June 28th 1991.
- a first-winter caught and released near Welham on January 28th 1984 had been ringed on July 27th 1983.
- two first-winters at Rutland Water on November 21st 1998 had been ringed on June 24th 1998 and July 8th 1998 respectively.
- a first-winter found long dead at Rutland Water on January 3rd 1999 had been ringed on June 24th 1998.

The remaining four ringed individuals also originated from the north-east coast of Britain, where they were all ringed as nestlings:

- a first-winter found freshly dead at Castle Donington on February 26th 1953 had been ringed at the Bass Rock (East Lothian) on July 6th 1952.
- one of the group of 11 first-winters which landed on Saddington main street on November 21st 1965 had been ringed on the Farne Islands (Northumberland) on July 1st 1965.
- a first-winter caught and released at Ketton on December 8th 1965 had also been ringed on the Farne Islands (Northumberland) on June 29th 1965.

- a first-winter found freshly dead at Rutland Water on January 26th 1984 had been ringed at Craigleith (East Lothian) on June 18th 1983.

Shags are confined to the north-east Atlantic and the Mediterranean and Black Seas. They are essentially resident, but are dispersive (rather than migratory), especially in their first winter. In Britain, they breed mainly on the north and west coasts, although there are scattered colonies along the east coasts of Scotland and England. After a marked increase in the British population from 1940 to 1970 (Gibbons *et al.* 1996), breeding numbers peaked at around 38,500 pairs in the late 1980s (Gibbons *et al.* 1993), although since then numbers have dropped and the current estimate is 26,000 pairs (Mitchell *et al.* 2004). Britain is, however, still a very important area for Shags and as over 20% of the European breeding population is found in the United Kingdom, this species has been added to the 'Amber List' of Birds of Conservation Concern (Gregory *et al.* 2002).

RMF

Bittern (Great Bittern) ***Botaurus stellaris***

Rare to scarce winter visitor; recorded in all months except May, June and July, with the majority from November to February: at least 47 individuals since 1941 and 29 previously.

Browne, writing in VH, mentioned 20 records, although only ten of these have details relating to both year and site, as follows:

1834	shot near Ashby-de-la-Zouch, undated.
1844	Croft, winter.
1847	Swithland, January.
c1848	shot, Elmesthorpe, undated.
1854/55	Carlton Curlieu, winter.
1868	shot, Groby Pool, March.
1871	shot, Enderby, undated (specimen sent to Leicester Museum).
1878	shot, Thurmaston, December 28th.
1885	shot, Cropston Reservoir.
1892	River Wreake between Rearsby and Ratcliffe on the Wreake, January 26th.

Of Browne's other ten records, undated birds were seen at Market Bosworth and Swithland, with another shot near Wanlip, one was noted at an unknown site in December 1855 and six further reports of birds shot contain no details regarding either date or site.

Haines refers to five records from Rutland in the 19th century, as follows:

1850/51	shot, Pickworth, undated.
c1855	shot, Welland valley, winter.
1876	shot, Greetham, November.
1887	shot, Exton, undated.
1898	Exton, April 10th.

The LROS archives contain details of four birds shot between 1925 and 1930, at Wanlip in December 1925, Saddington in 1928, Hungarton in 1929 and Market Bosworth in 1930.

Since the formation of LROS in 1941, there have been records in a total of 33 years involving at least 47 individuals. Reports have been annual since 1994 and over half of all modern records have occurred since that year. This may be connected to increased observer coverage, but a recent resurgence in the British population, along with improved areas of habitat in the counties for this species (most notably at Rutland Water) are also likely to be factors. One or two birds are recorded in most years, although four were found in 2003 and five were located in 2002.

As to be expected, the majority of birds have been seen during the winter, with over 72% of records having occurred between late November and mid-February. A noticeable peak can be seen during the second half of December, when 14 birds have arrived, perhaps corresponding with the first spell of hard weather on the near continent. Only four individuals have been seen prior to October 27th, as follows:

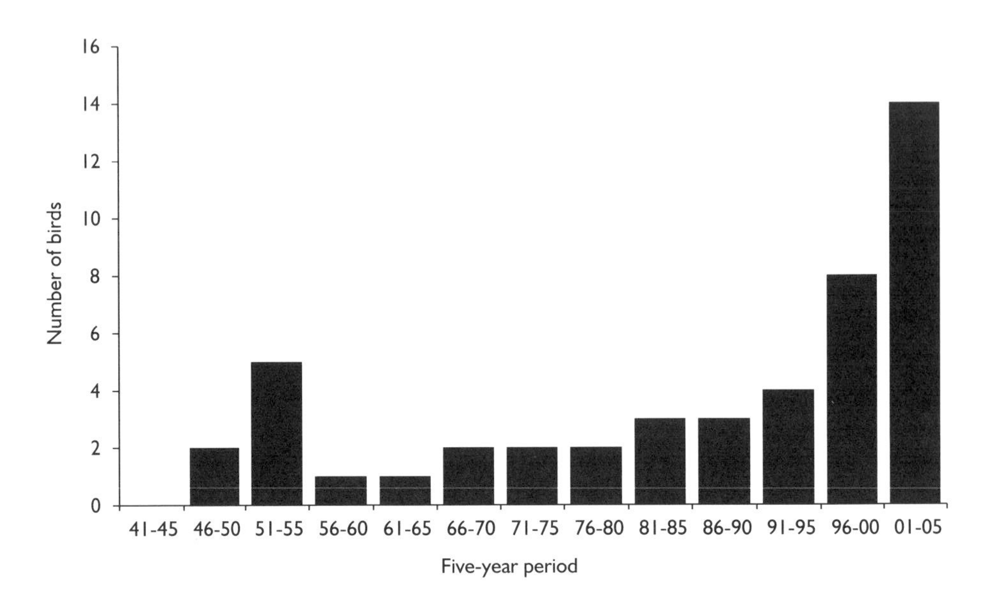

Figure 173: Number of Bitterns by five-year periods 1941–2005.

- a juvenile at Rutland Water on August 22nd 1999.
- one at Stanford Reservoir on September 9th 1999.
- one at Eyebrook Reservoir on September 22nd 1952.
- one by the River Welland near Market Harborough on October 19th 1952.

It is worth noting that only two years are involved in these four records and given how scarce Bitterns are in the counties this early in the autumn it is not inconceivable that only two birds were involved in these records.

True wintering has only been recorded at two sites, with the most well-known being a bird which was first seen at Swithland Reservoir between February 24th and March 19th 1986. It then returned for four of the following five winters: from December 1986 to March 8th 1987, November 22nd 1988 to February 12th 1989, December 19th 1989 to February 21st 1990 and late November 1990 to January 19th 1991. One was at Oadby from December 16th 1990 to March 4th 1991, being seen at nearby Newton Harcourt in February 1991 and returning to Oadby in December 1991. This record was extraordinary in that the bird frequented small suburban gardens, feeding from ornamental fish ponds. The majority of other records involve birds seen on just one date, although this may be a reflection on the species' elusive habits rather than anything else. With the exception of the wintering individuals mentioned above, only four birds have remained for more than two weeks, as follows:

- one between Manton and Preston from March 4th to April 19th 1971.
- one at Trent Valley Pit from December 22nd 2002 to January 25th 2003.
- one at Stanford Reservoir from January 11th to 31st 2003.
- one at Rutland Water from October 29th to November 17th 1994.

Records after early March are unusual, although the returning Swithland Reservoir bird lingered twice into this month, as did the Oadby one, whilst the long-staying individual between Manton and Preston in 1971 mentioned above is the only bird to be seen into April. The only times that presumed 'new' individuals have been seen later than March 4th are single birds at Stanford Reservoir on March 12th 2005 and Rutland Water on March 23rd 2002 and one found dead at Groby Pool on March 31st 1955.

Although still a scarce visitor to the counties, Bitterns can be encountered almost anywhere and have been seen at a total of 27 sites since 1941. Of these, only five sites have recorded this species on more than one occasion; Rutland Water leads the way, with ten records, followed by Stanford Reservoir (six), Groby Pool (five) and Swithland and Eyebrook Reservoirs (three each).

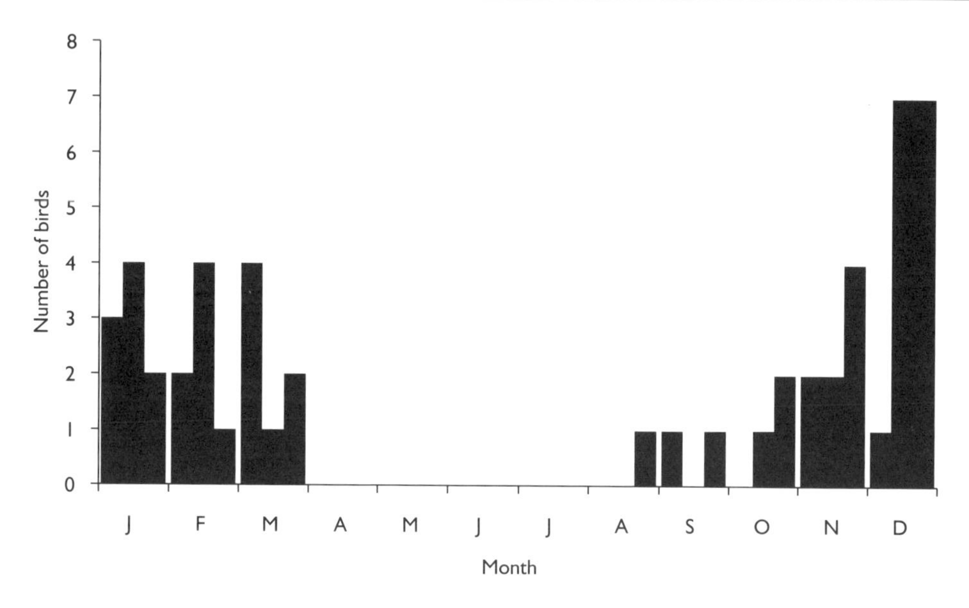

Figure 174: Monthly occurrence of Bitterns 1941–2005.

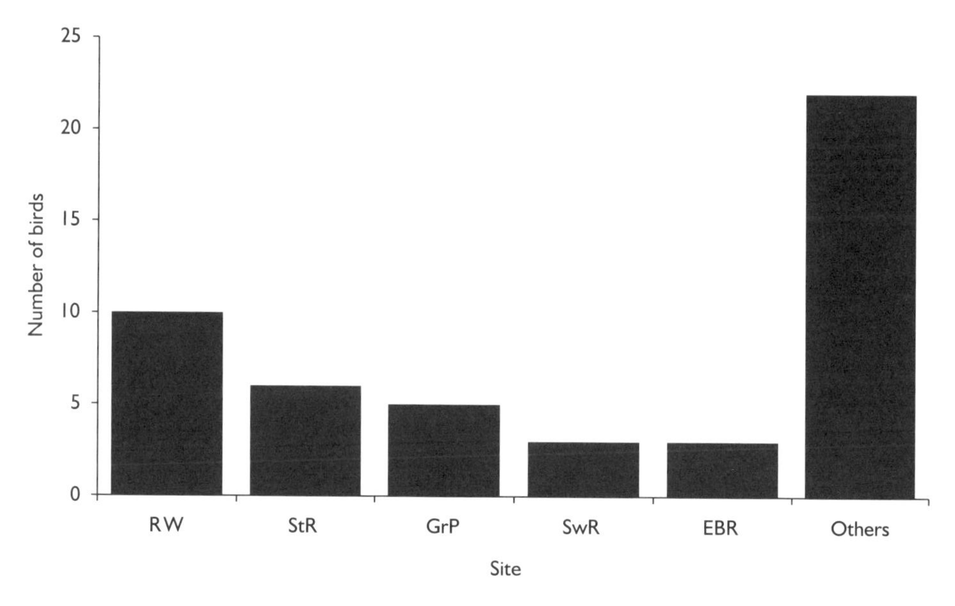

Figure 175: Sites where Bitterns have been recorded 1941–2005.
Key to abbreviations: RW = Rutland Water; StR = Stanford Reservoir; GrP = Groby Pool; SwR = Swithland Reservoir; EBR = Eyebrook Reservoir

Bitterns are known to be susceptible to periods of harsh weather (Bibby 1981) and five have been found dead: at Swithland Reservoir in February 1947, Stanford Reservoir on February 17th 1954, Groby Pool on March 31st 1955, Rutland Water on January 8th 1979 and Enderby on December 23rd 1981.

Two previous records published in LROS Annual Reports, at Rutland Water on July 20th 1984 and September 24th 1984, were found to be unacceptable on review in 2004 (Fray 2005).

Bitterns breed from western Europe across Asia and in southern Africa. Populations in the south are mainly sedentary, but those in the north and east of the range are migratory, moving from their breeding quarters to areas with unfrozen water. Drainage and persecution drove the Bittern to extinction as a breeding bird in Britain by 1886, but following recolonisation early in the 20th century a breeding population slowly built up to approximately 80 pairs by the early 1950s. However, another decline set in during the 1950s and 1960s and reached a low point in 1997, when only 11 booming males were located. Since then, active habitat management and creation has resulted in the population recovering to over 50 booming males in 2004. Due to the historical population decline and small breeding population, this species has been added to the 'Red List' of Birds of Conservation Concern (Gregory *et al.* 2002). In Britain, the number of wintering Bitterns is linked to the severity of weather on the near continent and it is presumed that most birds recorded in the counties are continental birds rather than from the small British breeding population. However, a juvenile at Rutland Water on August 22nd 1999 had been fitted with a radio transmitter at Minsmere (Suffolk) earlier the same year, an encouraging sign of a British-born bird perhaps searching for potential new breeding areas. With ongoing habitat creation at Rutland Water and in the Soar valley and the recent upturn in fortunes for the British population, we may one day have this species breeding in Leicestershire and Rutland.

RMF

Little Bittern *Ixobrychus minutus*

Very rare vagrant from southern Europe: three records.

Browne refers to two 19th century records, the first being one shot 'at the close of the summer of 1853' at Groby Pool. The second bird was also shot, at Great Glen, although the date is rather confused: according to Browne, a Mr Davenport wrote in January 1886 that it was shot 'some dozen years ago by a Mr Allen of Glenn and sold by him to Potter', which would place the occurrence some time around 1874. However, Browne also states that 'Potter gives the date as November 1867' and this would appear to be more accurate as the event was apparently recorded in *The Field* on January 4th 1868. There is no such doubt regarding the third county record, which involved a juvenile shot at Thornton Reservoir on August 21st 1954; the specimen was sent to the Leicester Museum, where it remains to this day.

Little Bitterns breed across much of southern and central Europe, western Asia and tropical Africa, as well as parts of Australasia. The European population winters in sub-Saharan Africa. The majority of sightings in this country are of spring overshoots from April to June, although surprisingly there have been records for every month of the year. This species formerly appeared in Britain much more frequently; there were well over 250 occurrences prior to 1958, but even with the huge increase in birdwatchers since then, there have only been around 200 subsequent records. Most British sightings are in southern and eastern England; this is a very rare bird in the Midlands, with the only reports from the region in the last 50 years being three in Warwickshire and two in Northamptonshire, the most recent of which was in 1981. Remarkably, however, a pair bred at Potteric Carr, South Yorkshire, in 1984, raising three young (Allport & Carroll 1989), so it is perhaps not unreasonable to expect this species to occur in Leicestershire and Rutland again in the future.

RMF

Night Heron (Black-crowned Night Heron) *Nycticorax nycticorax*

Very rare vagrant from Europe: seven records involving eight individuals.

Browne cites two 19th century records, the first being 'a fine example shot by a countryman in Anstey as it was sitting on the top of a pollard willow by a pool.' No mention is made of the date of this occurrence, although Hickling states that it was during 1840. Of the subsequent six records, five have been since 1968.

All records:

1840	shot, Anstey, date unknown.
1846	shot, Castle Donington, date unknown.

1968 one was seen by S.J.R. Jones perched in a horse chestnut tree in a garden adjacent to the River Soar at Kegworth on April 11th. What was presumed to be the same bird was then noted by members of the Trent Valley Bird Watchers on the Leicestershire side of the River Soar near Ratcliffe on Soar on April 28th (*BB* 62:462–463).
an adult was watched by Kath Kirton flying around a pool at Welham on June 2nd (Kirton 1969, *BB* 62:463).
1973 a juvenile was at Eyebrook Reservoir from November 17th to 24th (*BB* 67:315).
1983 two adults frequented Aylestone Meadows from April 25th to 28th (*BB* 77:510 & 78:533).
1984 a first-winter was seen briefly at Burley Fishponds, Rutland Water on December 27th. It was noted again on two further occasions in the same area in January 1985 and was then relocated at Whitwell Creek on February 16th, where it was seen by several observers during the next few days. Unfortunately, it was found dead on February 19th and had presumably been unable to find enough food during what was a particularly cold spell of weather (*BB* 80:521). The skin is retained at the Leicester Museum.

Two additional records are not included in the county total. Haines mentions a heron species at Clipsham on August 16th and 22nd 1885 that 'from its grey and moping look was taken to be a Night Heron'; however, disbelief was expressed at the time and Haines only included this report in square brackets. An escaped adult, with colour-rings on its legs, was at Staunton Harold Lakes for at least a week up to February 6th 2000; this species is quite commonly held in captivity and there are free-flying colonies at Edinburgh Zoo and in Norfolk (Vinicombe *et al.* 1993).

The Night Heron has a huge world range and breeds on all continents except Australasia and Antarctica. The majority of the European population winters in sub-Saharan Africa, although a few remain in southern Europe. Prior to the 1980s, records averaged around five a year in Britain, but a notable influx of 21 in 1983 (which included the two birds at Aylestone Meadows) heralded the beginning of a marked increase in numbers occurring in this country; two extraordinary arrivals in 1987 and 1990 resulted in annual totals of 53 and 61 respectively and by the end of 2001 Night Herons were occurring frequently enough in Britain for them to cease being considered by BBRC. Most British records occur between late March and mid-May and involve overshooting adults, such as the county records in 1968 and 1983. Autumn records are rarer and usually involve juveniles; these sometimes remain to overwinter, such as the Rutland Water bird of 1984/85.

RMF

Squacco Heron *Ardeola ralloides*

Very rare vagrant from southern Europe: one record.

The only county record is of an adult, initially found by Ken Spriggs, at Eyebrook Reservoir from June 15th to July 17th 1971. It became the subject of the first major 'twitch' in Leicestershire and was subsequently seen by several hundred observers as it fed along the old course of the Eye Brook at the northern end of the reservoir (Allsopp 1972, *BB* 65:326).

Squacco Herons are birds of warm Mediterranean, sub-tropical and tropical climates. In the Western Palearctic, they have a patchy distribution from Morocco across southern Europe to south-west Asia, with the greatest numbers breeding around the Mediterranean basin. The European population is largely migratory, wintering in Africa, where the species is also resident and relatively widespread. A major decline in the 20th century, caused mainly by habitat destruction and hunting, was reflected in the species' occurrence in Britain; there were approximately 75 records prior to 1950, but only a further six up to 1970. The Eyebrook Reservoir bird was just the ninth to be found in Britain since 1950, explaining the interest it caused at the time. A distinct upturn in records since has resulted in the British total reaching almost 140 by the end of 2005. Most occurrences in this country are of late spring overshoots, with the favoured month being June: the Leicestershire individual thus fits this established pattern.

RMF

Cattle Egret *Bubulcus ibis*

Very rare vagrant from Europe: one record.

The only county record concerns an adult found by L. Rowley, Mr and Mrs H.V. Higgins and Mr and Mrs D. Charles on the Egleton Reserve at Rutland Water on the evening of April 3rd 1993. After a somewhat extended tour of the western end of the reservoir, it finally settled down in a sheep field near Egleton church, where it remained until April 15th. The bird was seen by many hundreds of observers and was well photographed (Fray 1994, *BB* 87:511).

Cattle Egrets are widespread throughout much of Africa, Asia, Australia and the Americas. In Europe, they are common in southern Spain and Portugal, with small expanding populations in France and Italy and recent instances of breeding in England. Hitherto, vagrants to the UK have usually occurred as winter visitors or, like the Rutland Water bird, spring overshoots. Although the British total is now almost 140 (compared to just 14 prior to 1970), this species is still rather erratic in its appearances here; notable influxes of 14 in 1986, 21 in 1992, 13 in both 1998 and 2005 and 12 in 2001 have accounted for over half of the British total.

RMF

Little Egret *Egretta garzetta*

Uncommon but increasing visitor; recorded in all months, with the majority in July and August: at least 124 individuals.

One seen by Neil Hagley at Eyebrook Reservoir during the evening of June 5th 1982 was the first county record (*BB* 76:481); at the time, this bird fitted in neatly with the general occurrence pattern of Little Egrets being mainly spring overshoots to Britain. The species remained a true rarity in Leicestershire and Rutland until the mid-1990s, with the only subsequent records prior to 1994 being one at Eyebrook Reservoir on August 22nd 1987 (*BB* 81:543) and two which were originally seen at the same site on August 16th 1989 and then wandered to Rutland Water and Wakerley Bridge later in the month (*BB* 83:445). The latter two records demonstrated the rather sudden changing status of this species in Britain from spring overshoot to late summer visitor, brought about by juvenile dispersal from the expanding breeding colonies in Europe, whilst the two birds in 1989 were part of an unprecedented (at the time) influx involving well over 120 individuals (Combridge & Parr 1992).

In line with many other parts of Britain, records of this attractive species have increased dramatically since the mid-1990s. There have been reports in every year since 1996, in ever increasing numbers; the best year so far has been 2005, with at least 30 individuals found, although this figure will doubtless be beaten in the near future. There have been records in every month, although a clear peak is apparent in July and August, with over 60% of all birds having arrived in these two months. Reports between October and May are still rather scarce; it was not until 2002 that the first winter records occurred, when single birds were at Horn Mill on January 5th and Groby Pool from January 12th to 27th.

Most records have been of one or two birds, with the highest counts coming from Rutland Water, where there were nine on July 25th 2004 and five from August 10th to September 3rd 2001. Elsewhere, the largest number seen together has been four at Trent Farm Pool on August 7th and 8th 1999. Most areas of water in the counties have now been graced by this species; the favoured site, rather predictably, is Rutland Water, where at least 42 individuals have been noted, with the Trent Valley Pit/Trent Farm Pool area being next, with 21 records. Eyebrook Reservoir accounts for 15 reports, but no other site in the county has yet recorded more than five birds in total. Of these, perhaps the most unusual to date was an adult in full summer plumage at Freemen's Weir, in Leicester city centre, on June 3rd and 4th 2001, which during its stay often frequented waste ground that had been cleared for the construction of Leicester City Football Club's new stadium.

As alluded to above, the Little Egret has undergone a remarkable range expansion following the large influx in 1989. Formerly a rare vagrant, it was removed from the list of species considered by BBRC at the end of 1990 and by 1998, the first single-site count of 200+ was made (Musgrove 2002). The species first nested in Britain in 1996, on Brownsea Island in Dorset (Lock & Cook 1998), although it has been suggested that it may have formerly bred in the Middle Ages (Bourne 2003). By 2005, over 391 pairs were breeding at 52 localities in Britain; most were on the south or east coast, but recent nesting attempts have been made in Cambridgeshire,

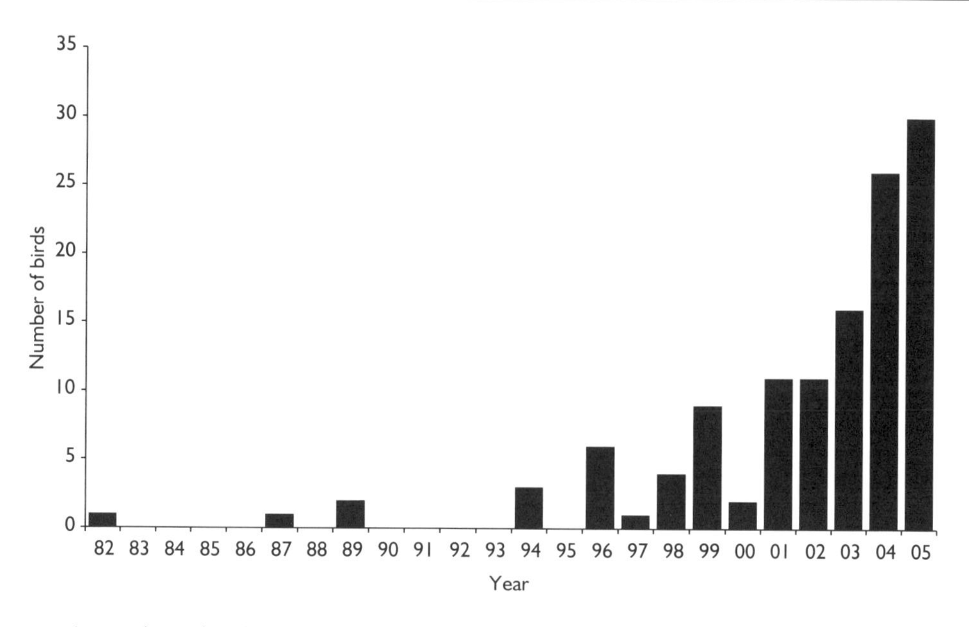

Figure 176: Numbers of Little Egrets 1982–2005.

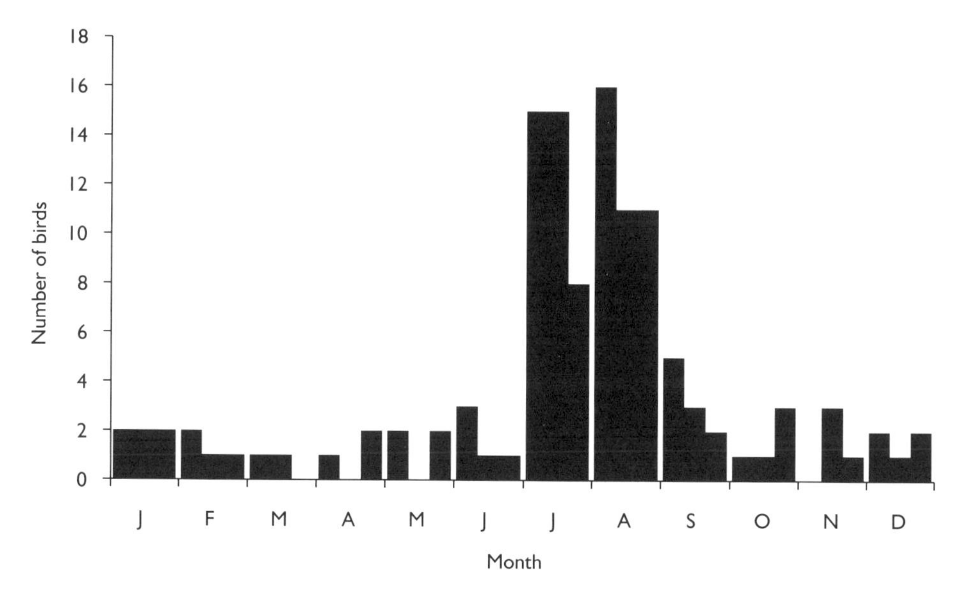

Figure 177: Monthly occurrence of Little Egrets 1982 –2005.

Lancashire, Cheshire, north Wales and Buckinghamshire (Holling *et al.* 2008). As the British breeding population is currently relatively small, the Little Egret is on the 'Amber List' of Birds of Conservation Concern (Gregory *et al.* 2002), but given the rate of increase it seems likely that this will be merely a temporary measure. The only vague sign of any breeding behaviour in Leicestershire and Rutland came in 2003, when three birds on the River Trent at King's Mills on August 30th were seen indulging in some half-hearted display; however, future colonisation by this species is surely a strong possibility.

RMF

Great White Egret (Great Egret) ***Ardea alba***

Very rare vagrant from Europe: eight records.

The first county record was of one found roosting in a willow tree at Saddington Reservoir by Neil Sturgess and J. Mason during the evening of June 14th 1988. It was seen again briefly a couple of times over the following two days and was relocated at Thornton Reservoir on the evening of June 16th, where it remained for just over an hour before flying off to the south-east. Remarkably, it then appeared at Rutland Water on June 18th, where it frequented Lagoon I and the Burley Fishponds area until flying off east in the evening (*BB* 82:513).

All records:

1988 Saddington Reservoir, June 14th to 16th; same, Thornton Reservoir, June 16th; same, Rutland Water, June 18th.

1990 one seen by many observers at Rutland Water on May 26th was initially located on Lagoon I during the afternoon before moving to the Burley Fishponds area; it remained until late evening before flying off to the north (*BB* 84:457).

1992 an adult, initially located by Simon Tilley and I.M. Wilson, was at Stanford Reservoir from July 5th to 19th, where it was seen and photographed by large numbers of observers. It spent much of its time feeding in the bays in Northamptonshire, but often roosted in trees to the north of the reservoir, about a quarter of a mile into Leicestershire (*BB* 86:457).

2002 one was present at Eyebrook Reservoir for just ten minutes during the morning of August 12th, where it was witnessed by Eric Locker and J.D. Periam (*BB* 96:552). Later the same year, one was seen briefly by Terry Mitcham at Fort Henry Ponds on October 24th before it flew off to the north (*BB* 96:552).

2003 one was located by Jim Sharpe on a small flash near Oakthorpe during the afternoon of July 24th, where it was seen by several other observers (*BB* 97:570). What was considered to be a different bird, aged as an adult, was present at Eyebrook Reservoir from August 9th to 12th; it was seen to fly off high to the north-west during the late morning and was relocated at Rutland Water a couple of hours later, where it remained until September 23rd (*BB* 97:570).

2005 a wandering individual in the Soar valley was first seen briefly by Peter Williams at Wanlip Meadows on October 8th. It flew over Watermead Country Park North two days later and was then seen at Wanlip North Lakes on October 24th. It was relocated at Cossington Mill on November 3rd, where it remained until November 11th and was seen by many observers (*BB* 100:29).

Great White Egrets are cosmopolitan, occurring in almost all temperate and tropical regions of the world. In Europe, there is a small, but increasing, breeding population in the Netherlands; elsewhere in Europe, the breeding range is highly fragmented from Spain to Ukraine. The Western Palearctic population is generally migratory, wintering south of the breeding range, but there has been a recent trend for this species to overwinter in north-west Europe (including Britain). Records in the UK are on the increase; the wandering 1988 individual was only the 39th to be recorded in Britain, but by the end of 2005 over 300 had been seen in the country and this species was removed from the list of birds considered by the BBRC. The two individuals seen in Leicestershire and Rutland in 2003 were part of a record influx of at least 49 into Britain that year.

RMF

Grey Heron ***Ardea cinerea***

Fairly common resident breeder.

During the 19th century, Browne described the Grey Heron as 'resident, sparingly distributed'. The only active heronries known were at Stapleford Park, where six nests in about 1840 increased to 40–50 by 1884 and Belvoir, from where no numbers were provided. Breeding was reported sporadically at other sites in the 19th century: at Martinshaw Wood in 1840, Buddon Wood and Bradgate in 1885 and at Bosworth Park in an unknown year. This species also formerly bred near Cotes. Haines noted that the only breeding location in Rutland was Burley, although nesting ceased here in approximately 1830.

The LROS archives state that this species bred again at Bradgate in 1938, but by the time of the formation of LROS in 1941 the only two known heronries were those at Stapleford Park and Belvoir. The former has been monitored on a fairly regular basis; in most years there have been between eight and 15 pairs, the peak counts being 19 pairs in 1952, 18 in both 1954 and 1956, 17 in 1953 and 16 in 1988. The colony at Belvoir (in Briery Wood) has not been monitored regularly but has produced one of the highest ever nest counts in Leicestershire and Rutland, of 47 in both 1986 and 1987. There were still 34 nests at this site in 1991 and 25 in 1993, but since then details have only been forthcoming in two years and have shown a sharp drop in numbers to only five nests in 1995 and eight or nine in 2003.

By 2005 a further eight heronries were known to be established in the counties, as follows:

- Gopsall Park: first reported in 1971, the number of nests at this site remained at between four and seven until 1986, when 12 were recorded, with 14 the following year. Details have been lacking for most years since, although in 2003 there were 16 nests and in 2005 there were 20.
- Groby Pool: two pairs bred in 1981 and 1982 and breeding behaviour was noted over the following three years, but apart from an isolated attempt by one pair in 1993 breeding did not take place at this site again until 1997. From then on this heronry became quickly established, reaching a peak of 20 pairs in 2003.
- Rutland Water (Burley Fishponds): single pairs bred in 1987 and 1993, with five in 1995 and 11 in 2003. Unfortunately, no further information is available on numbers.
- Great Glen Lake: breeding was first noted at this site in 1988, when one pair nested, after which small numbers bred regularly; the highest nest count was eight in 2000.
- Wanlip South Gravel Pits: breeding was first noted in 1990, when three pairs nested. This heronry quickly became established and peaked at 24 pairs in 1998. By 2005 numbers had reduced to 11 pairs.
- Birstall Gravel Pits: a pair bred in 1990 and 1991, following which numbers built up quickly to reach a peak of 53 pairs in 2003. 41 pairs were present in 2004 and 2005, making this currently the largest heronry in the counties.
- Stoke Dry Wood: three pairs bred in 1992, followed by six the following year and smaller numbers thereafter. Like the Rutland Water heronry, little further information is available on numbers at this site.
- Swithland Reservoir: breeding was first noted at this site in 1995, when one pair nested. As at nearby Groby Pool, this heronry quickly became established and reached a peak of 19 pairs in 2003.

Sporadic breeding attempts have taken place at a further six sites since 1941, as follows:

- Thurcaston: a pair nested in 1944 but the eggs were robbed.
- near Loughborough: a 'small colony' was found in 1948 and at least one pair probably nested in 1949.
- Tonge: a pair nested in 1949 and probably did so again the following year.
- Saddington Reservoir: single pairs nested successfully in 1951 (raising four young) and 1982 and a pair attempted to breed in 1984 but the nest was robbed.
- near Blackbrook Reservoir: a pair bred in 1972.
- Ulverscroft: a pair nested successfully in 1995.

In addition, several pulli were ringed at Donington Park in 1986 and 1987, although no further details are known about this heronry.

Late summer/autumn congregations of Grey Herons are a feature at several sites in the counties. The largest counts have all come from areas close to heronries and presumably involve birds bred at the site: 72 at Rutland Water on July 2nd 1994, 49 at the same site on September 18th 2005 and 44 at Swithland Reservoir on September 25th 2005. Away from the heronries, the largest gatherings have been:

- 32 at Stanford Reservoir on September 3rd 1968, with 28 there on September 15th 1968.
- 30 at Staunton Harold Reservoir on August 28th 1995.
- 27 at Sawley Gravel Pits on July 16th 1950.
- 26 at Stanford Reservoir on both October 14th 1990 and November 8th 1995.

- 25 at Oakthorpe on July 26th 2003.
- 21 at Lockington on March 3rd 1970.
- 21 at Thornton Reservoir on July 13th 1997.
- 21 at Trent Farm Pool on September 5th 2004.

A melanistic individual was recorded at Cropston Reservoir on August 27th 1983 and a leucistic bird was seen at several sites in the Charnwood area from July 3rd 2002 to May 1st 2004.

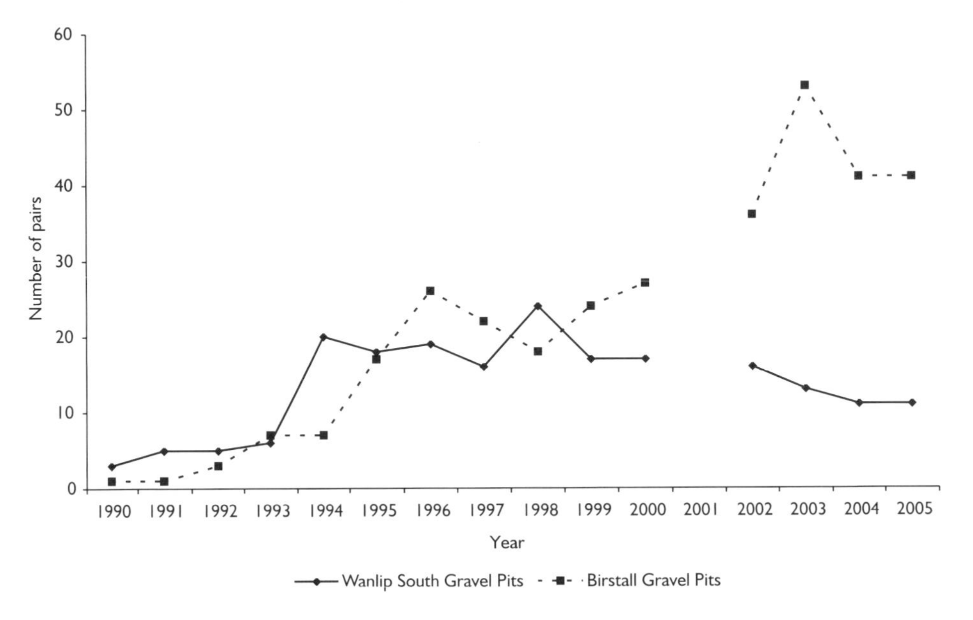

Figure 178: Number of pairs of Grey Herons breeding at Wanlip South Gravel Pits and Birstall Gravel Pits 1990–2005.
(Note that data is unavailable for 2001)

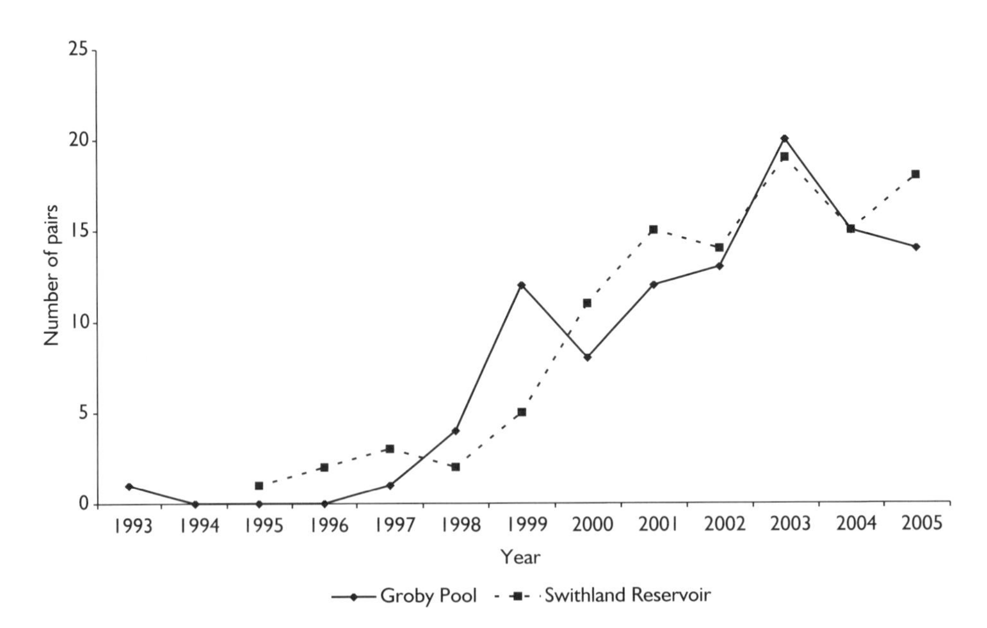

Figure 179: Number of pairs of Grey Herons breeding at Groby Pool and Swithland Reservoir 1993–2005.

The nominate race of the Grey Heron breeds over most of Eurasia and Africa, with other races in Asia and Madagascar. A total of 14,200 nests was estimated in Britain in 2003 (Baillie *et al.* 2006). The Scandinavian population is migratory as evidenced by a number of foreign-ringed recoveries in Leicestershire and Rutland, as follows:

Table 16: Recoveries of Grey Herons moving from Europe to Leicestershire and Rutland

Ringing site	Ringing date	Recovery site	Recovery date	Distance (km)	Direction
Amsterdam, Netherlands	April 11th 1961	Belvoir	April 22nd 1963	391	West
Kvale, Norway	June 13th 1970	Langham	January 9th 1971	775	South-west
Lake Yxningen, Sweden	May 27th 1973	Ashwell	December 6th 1973	1,231	West-south-west
Rasso, Sweden	May 15th 1974	Shepshed	December 22nd 1974	1,029	South-west
Edam, Netherlands	July 1st 1978	Wistow	November 7th 1978	412	West
Dalavik, Norway	May 21st 1984	Eyebrook Reservoir	January 6th 1985	865	South-south-west
Osterild Plantage, Denmark	April 28th 1988	Enderby	January 1st 1989	814	South-west
Westerbroek, Netherlands	May 9th 1988	Broughton Astley	September 17th 1988	534	West

In addition, birds ringed in Leicestershire and Rutland have been recovered in seven English counties, as well as one ringed at Wanlip South Gravel Pits on May 8th 1999 which was found dead near Dublin (Ireland) on April 7th 2001, a west-north-westerly movement of 341km. Individuals ringed in Norfolk, Cambridgeshire, Gloucestershire, Oxfordshire and North Yorkshire have been found dead in Leicestershire and Rutland.

RMF

Purple Heron *Ardea purpurea*

Very rare vagrant from southern Europe: four records.

The first three records all occurred in the Trent valley in the north-western corner of the county, beginning with one which was seen by T.G. Smith and Rod Key flying from the direction of Sawley towards Shardlow on April 19th 1968. It appeared to alight in an extensive reedbed at Hemington Gravel Pits but could not be relocated (*BB* 62:461). In 1975, one was flushed by Roy Frost at Hemington Water Meadows on August 27th (*BB* 69:328), whilst in 1989 one was found dead by Rob and Richard Fray at Sawley Marina on July 9th. The only individual to be seen by any number of observers was a juvenile found by Barry Raine at Saddington Reservoir on August 27th 2001. It was not seen again until September 8th, but fortunately remained in the area until September 20th; it usually roosted at the reservoir but ranged widely during the day, often visiting the nearby Grand Union Canal to the north-east of the reservoir.

Haines mentions that one was 'said to have been killed at Burley in 1888', but as he had 'no further particulars of it' the record was placed in square brackets.

Purple Herons have a wide range across southern Europe through the Middle East to India, south-east Asia and Indonesia, as well as Africa. European birds mainly winter in sub-Saharan Africa. In Britain, most Purple Herons occur in spring as a result of northbound migrants overshooting or being displaced westwards in settled anticyclonic conditions; a smaller peak in autumn usually involves juveniles, which are prone to random dispersive movements prior to the onset of migration proper. The Leicestershire records broadly follow this pattern, although the dead bird in midsummer in 1989 was intriguing; where had it been lurking prior to its untimely end? By 1982, the Purple Heron was occurring regularly enough in Britain for it to be removed from the list of species considered by the BBRC and despite a serious decline in the nearest breeding colonies (in the Netherlands), numbers occurring here have remained relatively stable (Fraser & Ryan 1992, Fraser & Rogers 2003). Both 1968 and 1975 were influx years into Britain, nicely corresponding with the first two Leicestershire records. In contrast, 2001 was a poor year, with just 13 reported in Britain; the Saddington Reservoir bird was the only autumn record in the country that year (Fraser & Rogers 2003).

RMF

Black Stork *Ciconia nigra*

Very rare vagrant from southern or eastern Europe: one record involving two individuals.

Two adults were seen by Neil Hagley in the Husband's Bosworth area on July 18th 1991. They were originally noted in low flight south of the village, having seemingly just taken off from nearby fields and were then watched for 15 minutes circling on a thermal before they continued to the west (Hagley 1992, *BB* 85:512).

Black Storks breed from Iberia and eastern France through central Europe to Russia and across Asia to the Pacific. Most are migratory, wintering in Africa and south-east Asia. The European population is currently increasing and expanding its range, with a corresponding increase in records in Britain. The total at the end of 2005 stood at 162 individuals; spring overshoots are responsible for many of these records, although wandering birds (such as those seen in Leicestershire) are sometimes found during the summer and autumn. The two at Husband's Bosworth were part of a record influx of 23 birds into Britain in 1991.

RMF

White Stork *Ciconia ciconia*

Very rare vagrant from Europe, mainly in spring: nine or ten records.

Hickling briefly mentions three 19th century reports, in 1849, 1851 and 1873, but it may be that there were only actually two records involved. It appears Harley recorded that one was obtained near Melton Mowbray in 1849, whilst Browne states that 'one in the possession of Mr T. Morris of Wycomb, near Melton, was shot by his brother early one morning as it sat on one of his farm buildings at Scalford Lodge in 1851. I believe this to be the one alluded to by Harley.' There is no such confusion over the 1873 record, or the seven birds found between 1971 and 2002.

All records:

1849 'obtained', near Melton Mowbray, date unknown.

1851 shot, Scalford Lodge, date unknown (but see text above).

1873 shot, West Leigh, Narborough Road, Leicester, March 6th.

1971 one was watched feeding in a field by R.K. Butler and M. Broome at Thorpe Langton during the afternoon of May 7th. It was later seen roosting in a tree during the evening, but had gone by the following morning (*BB* 65:327). Just over a month later, Sir Henry and Lady Nairne Tate located one feeding in a field at Belton-in-Rutland on June 9th (*BB* 65:327).

1998 an adult was found by Peter Gamble in the 'Little Matlock' area of Bradgate Park during the evening of May 1st. It was still present early the following morning, when it was seen by a number of other observers, but flew off at 08:45; it was later seen flying over Thurmaston, Syston and Wanlip.

2001 one was seen by M.D. Thomas as it circled Fosse Meadows at 09:00 on March 27th before appearing to land in an inaccessible area. Another was seen in flight, and superbly photographed, by Iain Leach just south of Bottesford on August 19th.

2002 one spent half an hour following a plough being driven by J.W. Nourish near Preston on July 7th before flying off north-west.

2004 one was seen by Andy Smith and others as it flew north over Swithland Reservoir on March 27th.

In addition, Haines mentions a second-hand report of one seen at Ketton on August 4th 1886, but as there was no mention of it in Lilford (1895) the record was square-bracketed and has never gained widespread credence.

White Storks breed in much of Europe, as well as in north-west Africa, parts of the Middle East and central Asia. Western Palearctic breeders winter in Spain and Africa. There were dramatic decreases in the European population during the 20th century, although there have been recent signs of a recovery (e.g. 16,463 breeding pairs in Spain in 1994, compared to just 6,753 in 1984) (*BB* 88:265); British records have shown a corresponding increase. Prior to the mid-1970s, there were generally only a handful of reports each year, although there was a notable influx of 22 in 1971 (nicely corresponding with the birds seen at Thorpe Langton and Belton-in-Rutland); White Storks then began occurring more frequently and the species was removed from the list considered by the BBRC at the end of 1982. The average annual total is now 30 and the two best years on record are 1998 and 2002, with 55 and 53 individuals respectively (Fraser & Rogers 2005); again, two more of the county records occurred in these influx years.

White Storks are notorious for their propensity to break out from captivity and two obvious escapes have been noted at large in the county. One at Rutland Water on June 28th and 29th 1978 bore a ring inscribed A070 on its left leg, showing that it had escaped from Nieupoort Zoo in the Netherlands; this bird then wandered to Berkshire and East Sussex, where it was found dead in January 1979 (*BB*: 72:511). Another individual at Rutland Water on April 20th and 21st 2002 carried a metal ring, not of the style usually associated with ringing programmes, on its left leg; the same bird was seen flying over Nanpantan later in the day on the 21st. Some of the other county records may have involved escaped individuals; the Bradgate Park bird, for instance, was rather approachable, although White Storks are naturally quite tame. However, the general pattern of records – spring overshoots in influx years – suggests that a wild origin is more likely.

RMF

Spoonbill (Eurasian Spoonbill) ***Platalea leucorodia***

Rare vagrant from Europe; recorded in all months between April and November, with the majority in May and June: 22 records involving 26 individuals.

The first county record is described by Browne, writing in VH and involved a specimen he purchased for the Leicester Museum which had been shot at Cropston Reservoir on July 6th 1892 by the splendidly-named Gervasse Reckless. Since then, there have been a further 21 records, involving 25 individuals.

All records:

1892	shot, Cropston Reservoir, July 6th.
1954	adult, Eyebrook Reservoir, November 7th.
1965	Wanlip Gravel Pits, May 26th to 31st.
1974	Frisby Gravel Pits and Kirby Bellars Gravel Pits, April 7th.
1975	immature, Eyebrook Reservoir, October 19th to 23rd.
1977	Stanford Reservoir, July 17th.
1982	adult, Eyebrook Reservoir, June 12th.
1983	immature, Tooley Park, Desford, October 20th.
1987	Rutland Water, June 10th.
1988	juvenile, Rutland Water, September 16th to 18th.
1989	Stanford Reservoir, June 15th.
	Rutland Water, August 4th.
	adult, Swithland Reservoir, August 14th.
1993	Rutland Water, June 7th.
1995	second-year, Rutland Water, May 7th.
1996	adult, Rutland Water, May 4th.
	adult and two first-summers, Rutland Water, May 25th to 28th, with one first-summer until June 2nd.
1997	Rutland Water, April 12th.
	first-summer, Rutland Water, June 25th.

1999	adult, Rutland Water, July 25th.
2001	first-summer, Rutland Water, June 7th to 18th; joined by a second bird of similar age from June 16th to 18th.
	first-summer, Rutland Water, August 9th to September 21st; joined by a second bird of similar age from August 15th to September 21st.

Of the 26 individuals recorded, 18 have occurred since 1987, when Rutland Water had its first record. In this period, only two have been found away from this site, both in 1989; thus there have been no records away from

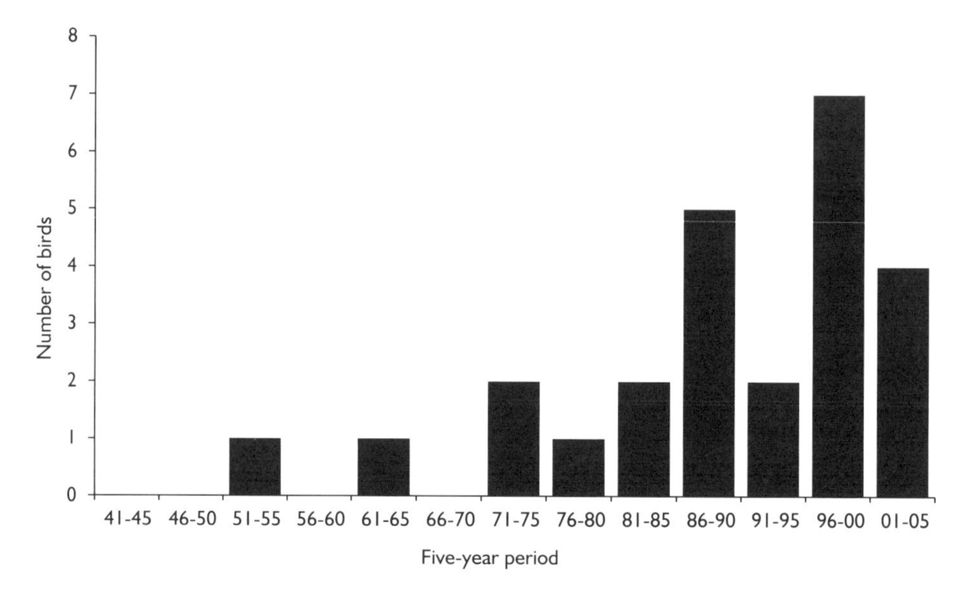

Figure 180: Numbers of Spoonbills by five-year periods 1941–2005.

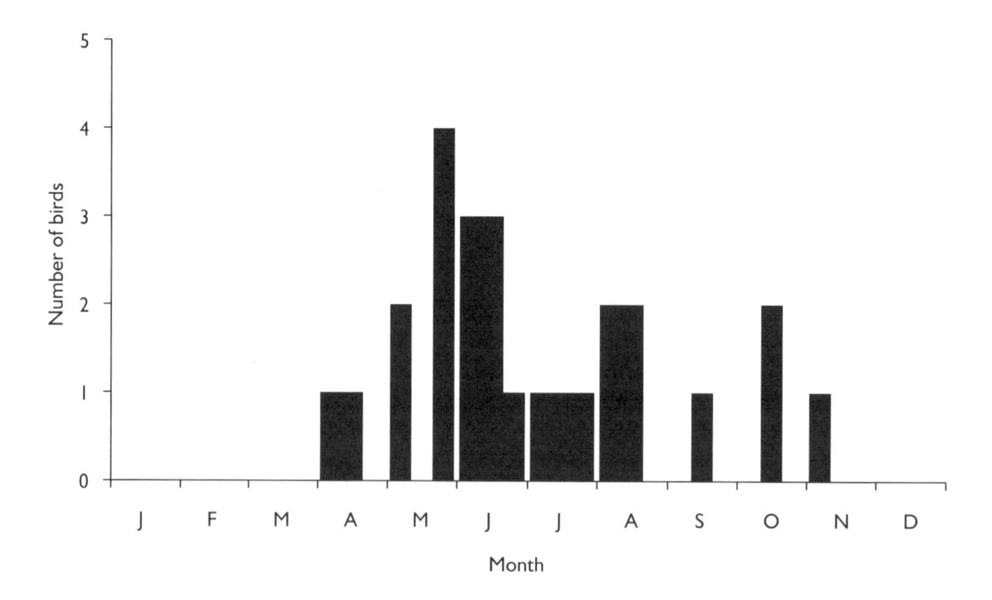

Figure 181: Monthly occurrence of Spoonbills 1892–2005.

Rutland Water for 16 years. This is therefore a true rarity elsewhere in the counties and only Eyebrook Reservoir, with three records and Stanford Reservoir, with two, have recorded this species on more than one occasion.

Spoonbills have appeared in every month between April and November, although exactly half have been found between May 25th and June 15th. The majority of birds, especially those in the spring, have been short-stayers, although autumn birds, particularly those recorded as juveniles or 'immatures', may remain for a few days. In this context, the stay of over six weeks by one of the 2001 individuals is unusual.

Spoonbills breed over large parts of Europe, Asia and Africa, although in western Europe breeding is restricted to just a few colonies; birds from these populations winter in Spain and west Africa. The nearest colonies to Britain, in the Netherlands, increased in size markedly over the latter part of the 20th century and by 2002 there were 1,586 pairs nesting in that country (Ogilvie *et al.* 2004). Many of the birds seen in Britain originate from here; indeed, the adult at Rutland Water in July 1999 was sporting several colour-rings proving it had originated from a colony at Terschelling in the Netherlands, where it had been ringed as a nestling on July 15th 1994. As is often the case with Spoonbills when they reach Britain, this particular bird had rather nomadic tendencies and was also seen in Norfolk, Suffolk, Grampian and Cleveland in June and July 1999. The two adults seen at Rutland Water in May 1996 were also colour-ringed and they too were thought to have originated from Dutch colonies. Although this species is, at present, chiefly a regular visitor to Britain, mainly in spring and summer, future colonisation of this country is possible and a pair bred in Suffolk in 1998, the first confirmed breeding in Britain since the 17th century (Ogilvie *et al.* 2000); since then, one or two pairs have shown signs of attempting again at various sites each year. Due to this very small potential breeding population, the species has been added to the 'Amber List' of Birds of Conservation Concern (Gregory *et al.* 2002).

RMF

Honey Buzzard (European Honey-buzzard) ***Pernis apivorus***

Rare passage migrant; recorded in all months between May and October, with the majority in September: 29 records involving 38 individuals.

Browne and Haines list eight certain records from the 19th century, as follows:

1841	shot at Martinshaw Wood, October 28th 1841. The skin is still retained at the Leicester Museum.
	shot at Lea Wood 'shortly after' October 28th.
1859	'light-coloured specimen' shot at Tunneley Wood, undated (this record was erroneously noted by Hickling as occurring in 1854).
1872	shot at Coney Hill Plantation, Noseley, undated. The specimen is still retained at the Leicester Museum.
1879	shot at Theddingworth, June 18th.
1881	'dark specimen' killed after flying into telegraph wires at Twyford, September. The skin is still retained at the Leicester Museum.
1884	shot at Croxton Park, June 13th (this record was erroneously noted by Hickling as occurring at Twyford).
1890	female shot at Arnesby, September 19th.

In addition, Haines recounts a somewhat unbelievable tale of one wounded and captured at Burley in May 1905, 'but its mate discovered the captive and between them they broke a hole in the net which covered the pheasant pen in which the prisoner was confined so that it escaped.' Subsequent authors have, probably wisely, ignored this record.

There were no records in the 20th century until 1987, since when this species has been noted in ten years. In total, 30 individuals have been recorded, as follows:

1987	pale-phase adult south over Rutland Water, July 18th.
1989	adult west over Stoughton Airfield, October 6th.
1991	intermediate-phase adult flew out of Coppice Plantation, Bradgate Park and left to the south, October 1st.

1996	pale-phase adult landed in Greetham Wood, August 16th.
1998	female over Windsor Hill, Belvoir, June 7th.
	one south-west over Tunneley Wood, June 28th.
	one over Langton Caudle, September 29th.
1999	one north over Rothley Park Golf Course, June 19th.
2000	juvenile west over Markfield, September 21st.
	four, including at least one adult and one juvenile, over Rutland Water, September 23rd.
	dark juvenile over Birstall Gravel Pits, September 23rd.
	dark individual south over Groby Pool, September 24th.
	five (three south-west and two west) over Pickworth, September 25th.
	two juveniles landed in a pine plantation at Bardon Hill, September 25th.
	dark juvenile south over Rutland Water, September 26th.
	two (both probably juveniles) over Beacon Hill, September 28th.
	one south-east over Asfordby, October 1st.
	dark juvenile over Newbold Verdon, October 4th.
2001	one over Narborough, May 7th.
2002	adult female flew out of Burley Wood and headed south-east, August 4th.
2004	one south over Swithland Reservoir, September 17th.

Most have appeared between September 17th and October 6th, including the remarkable series of reports in 2000 involving 19 individuals. These were part of an unprecedented influx of this species into Britain in late September, which involved an estimated 1,900 birds (Fraser & Rogers 2002). Away from the late autumn period, a few birds have been seen on spring passage, the most notable being the one in 2001 over Narborough on the extremely early date of May 7th. With a small population established in the neighbouring county of Nottinghamshire it is somewhat surprising how rare Honey Buzzards are in Leicestershire and Rutland.

A further record, of one at Owston Wood on June 6th 1976, was originally accepted but later rejected on review (Mackay 1995a).

Honey Buzzards breed throughout the temperate and boreal regions of Europe and eastwards into the boreal zone of western Asia. They migrate to winter largely in sub-Saharan Africa. They are scarce breeding birds in Britain; a full survey carried out in 2000 estimated the British breeding population to be just over 60 pairs

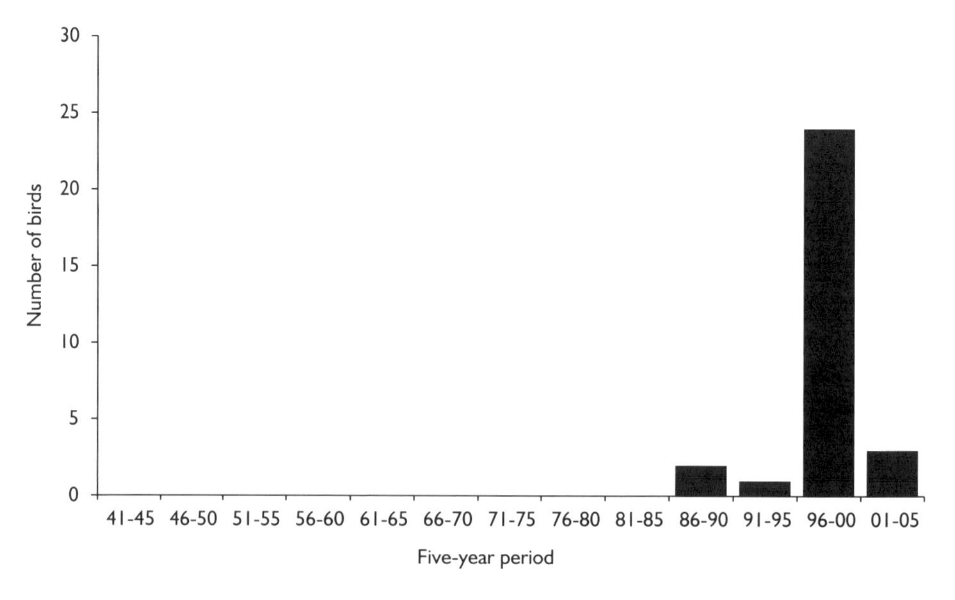

Figure 182: Numbers of Honey Buzzards by five-year periods 1941–2005.

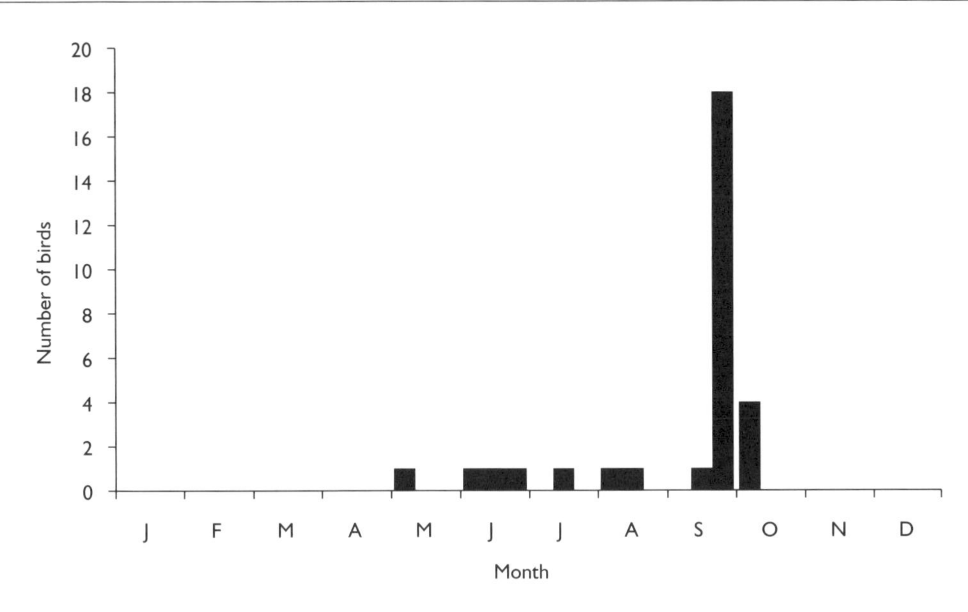

Figure 183: Monthly occurrence of Honey Buzzards 1941–2005.

(Batten 2001). Due to the small size of the breeding population, this species was added to the 'Amber List' of Birds of Conservation Concern (Gregory *et al.* 2002).

RMF

Red Kite *Milvus milvus*

Formerly a fairly common or common resident breeder prior to extinction in the mid-19th century; now an uncommon visitor and very rare breeder following recent reintroductions.

The Red Kite was a common and widespread species in the counties until the early 19th century. In Leicestershire Browne reported that it was 'previously widely known in the county' but the last authentic record was at Belvoir in 1850. A similar distribution was described in Rutland by Haines: this species was abundant in the Uppingham area in the early 19th century and at this time it was not uncommon to see 20 or 30 together in the Eye valley. It disappeared as a resident in Rutland between about 1835 and 1840; the last three nests were found in the late 1830s, one of which was at Stoke Dry Wood. The only records after this were at Barrowden Heath in about 1840 and Beaumont Chase in 1852.

Following the extinction of the Red Kite in Leicestershire and Rutland it was well over 100 years before this species next made an appearance in the counties. The first 20th century record was one at Oadby on September 24th 1969 but it was another nine years until the next sighting, of one at Sileby on November 26th 1978.

Following this there were records in ten of the 15 years between 1980 and 1994, involving 15 individuals, as follows:

1980	Saddington Reservoir, April 17th.
1981	Eastwell, December 31st.
1982	between Prestwold and Barrow upon Soar, January 8th.
	near Empingham, February 13th to March 2nd.
1983	dead, near Stamford (but within the Rutland border), some time in May.
1984	near Lutterworth, August 13th and 21st; same, Stanford Reservoir, August 18th.
	dead, near Melton Mowbray, November 21st.
1986	Ibstock, May 6th.
1988	Cropston, March 19th.
	Hugglescote, April 18th.
1989	Dunton Bassett, February 13th.
	Shoby, August 16th.
1991	Birstall Gravel Pits, January 2nd; presumed same, Newbold Verdon, January 3rd.
1993	Egleton, March 24th.
	Beacon Hill, June 26th.

No clear pattern emerges from these sightings, with records in all months except July and October and no more than two seen in any month. The source of these birds is unclear; some may have been from the then small but increasing Welsh population, although direct evidence of continental origin is provided by the bird found dead near Melton Mowbray in 1984, which had been ringed as a pullus at Olganitz (Germany) on June 8th 1983.

A reintroduction programme began in 1995 in the Rockingham Forest region of Northamptonshire, close to the Leicestershire and Rutland borders and by 1998 70 birds had been translocated to the area from Spain. This had an almost immediate impact on the occurrence of the Red Kite in Leicestershire and Rutland and its status changed quickly from that of a rare vagrant to an uncommon visitor. Annual totals in the mid to late 1990s increased from two in 1995, five in 1996 and seven in 1997 to at least 24 in 1998 and 22 in 1999. In 1998 up to three were present in the Knipton/Belvoir area from February 1st to June 28th and two were seen regularly at Eyebrook Reservoir and Stoke Dry Wood from March 30th to May 31st, whilst up to five frequented Buckminster from July 23rd until March 13th 1999. By the early part of the 21st century small numbers were resident in three areas: the Vale of Belvoir and the woods around both Rutland Water and Eyebrook Reservoir.

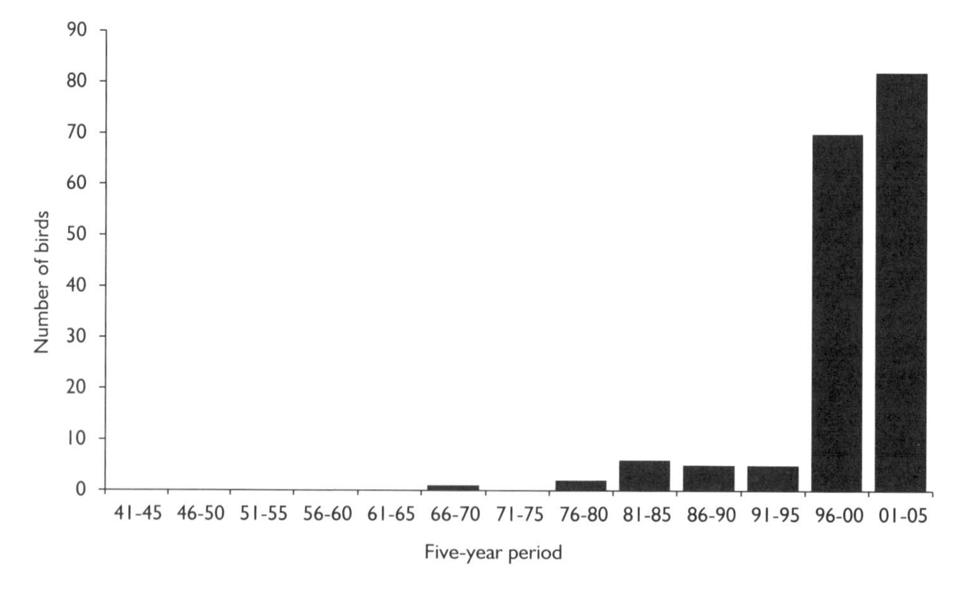

Figure 184: Numbers of Red Kites by five-year periods 194–2005.

Breeding occurred in 2002 when a pair raised three young at a site in Rutland, providing the counties with their first breeding record since the middle of the 19th century. In 2003 and 2004 the same site was used again; one young was raised in 2003 although their success or otherwise was unknown in 2004. In 2005 two pairs reared a total of four young with probable breeding by a third pair (Holling *et al.* 2008).

Today Red Kites can be encountered in almost any part of the counties, although there is an obvious easterly bias on the accompanying maps which show the distribution of all records since 1996 and all records in 2005. A cluster of records is also apparent around Charnwood, which would seem to be the most likely area for this species to colonise next.

The monthly occurrence pattern of Red Kites in the counties is now complicated by resident birds although over 40% of all records have occurred between early March and mid-May, perhaps indicating that the occasional passage bird still reaches the counties.

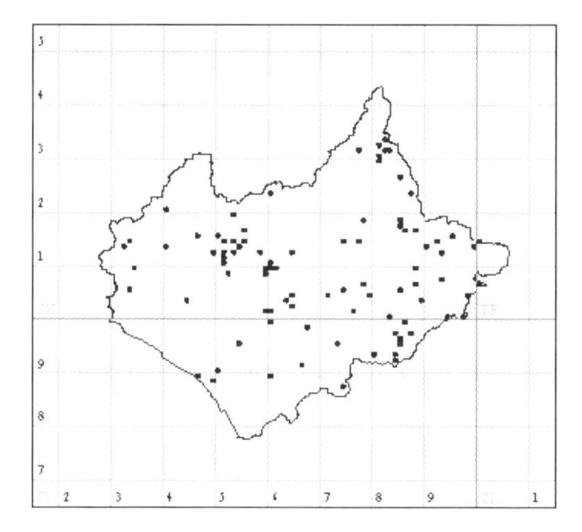

Figure 185: Distribution of Red Kites 1996–2005.

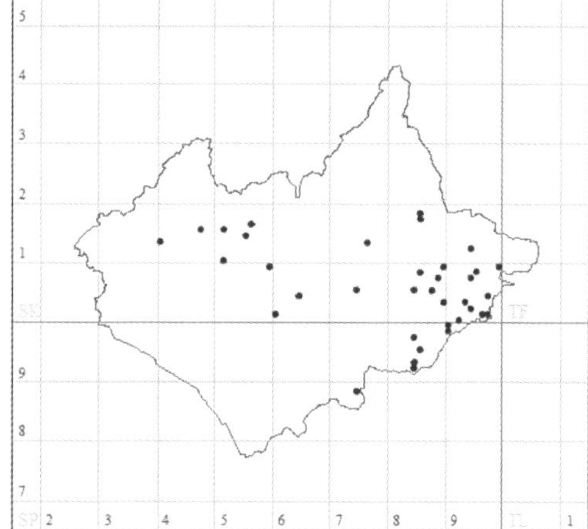

Figure 186: Distribution of Red Kites 2005.

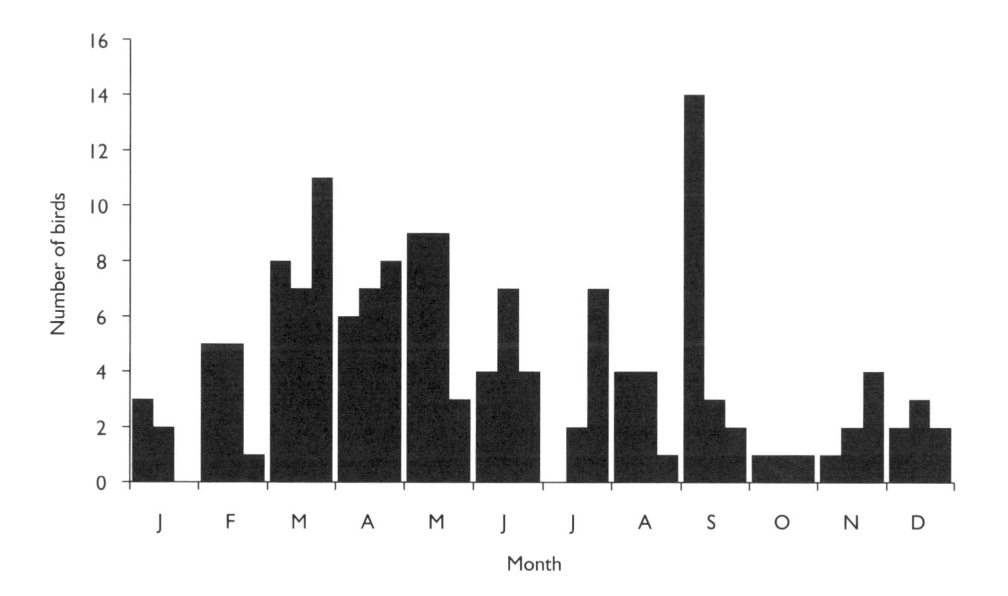

Figure 187: Monthly occurrence of Red Kites 1941–2005.

Many birds that have been seen in the counties have been carrying wing-tags proving that they have originated from the reintroduction scheme in Northamptonshire; however, an individual that wandered the Charnwood Forest area between April 29th and July 14th 2001 was from the population in the Chilterns (Oxfordshire/Buckinghamshire), where it had been tagged as a pullus in 1999. One of the young from the counties' breeding pair in 2002 was ringed and was found near Aberystwyth (Dyfed) on December 6th of the same year.

Red Kites breed locally in southern and central Europe, with small populations in north-west Africa, the Canary Islands and the Cape Verde Islands. Central and northern European birds move south to winter. This species was once widespread in Britain, but persecution wiped it out completely from England and Scotland by the end of the 19th century and left only a small population in central Wales by the early 20th century. Reintroduction programmes began in 1989 in the Chilterns (Oxfordshire/Buckinghamshire) and northern Scotland; the East Midlands programme responsible for the sudden increase in records in Leicestershire and Rutland began in 1995 and was followed by similar schemes in West Yorkshire, central Scotland, south-western Scotland and north-eastern England. By 2005 the British population of the Red Kite was estimated at between 900 and 970 pairs, including 52 in the East Midlands (mainly Northamptonshire) (Holling *et al.* 2008). Due to the historical population decline of this species it was added to the 'Amber List' of Birds of Conservation Concern (Gregory *et al.* 2002).

RMF

White-tailed Eagle *Haliaeetus albicilla*

Very rare vagrant from Europe: four records.

All four records of this species occurred more than 100 years ago. Browne reports two occurrences in Leicestershire, the first of which was a 'fine example' captured by a Mr Adams at Bradgate Park on December 26th 1840. A second bird was shot at Coleorton on November 6th 1879; it had been seen several days previously feeding on a rabbit. Haines lists a further two records in Rutland: an eagle 'without reasonable doubt an Erne' was at Exton Ponds from February 3rd to 5th 1891 and another was shot at, but missed, near Empingham in about 1900.

The White-tailed Eagle breeds in Greenland, Iceland, northern, central and eastern Europe and across northern Asia to the Pacific. It was widespread throughout Scotland and Ireland in the 18th century but years of persecution wiped it out in the early 20th century; it was then reduced to an extreme vagrant, with only two British records between 1958 and 1972. A successful reintroduction programme has re-established the species in the west of Scotland since 1975 and numbers have gradually built up from six pairs in 1993 to 33 in 2005 (Holling *et al.* 2008). Due to the small size of the Scottish population, this species was included on the 'Red List' of Birds of Conservation Concern (Gregory *et al.* 2002). There has also been a marked upturn in sightings of presumed European vagrants in more recent times, with 20 records between 1982 and 1998, mainly of immatures on the east coast. One wintered well inland on the Buckinghamshire/Oxfordshire border in 1983/84 and another was seen in north Derbyshire in January 2005, so future records are conceivable.

RMF

Marsh Harrier (Eurasian Marsh Harrier) *Circus aeruginosus*

Uncommon passage migrant; recorded in all months between February and October, with the majority in April, May, August and September.

Browne stated that this species used to be taken frequently in vermin traps before the enclosure of Charnwood Forest in 1811 but, with the exception of two at Buddon Wood in 1841, one of which was killed, there were apparently no further records in the 19th century.

The first 20th century record was of a juvenile at Stanford Reservoir on September 16th 1948 but it was not recorded again until 1967, when a female was at Burley Fishponds on May 13th and one visited Swithland Reservoir on August 13th. Since then, the Marsh Harrier has been found in all but six years, the last blank year

being 1981 and its status has changed from that of a rare visitor to an uncommon passage migrant. Between 1967 and 1986, no more than three were seen in any one year, with the exception of five in 1983. However, 1987 saw ten individuals recorded and double-figure yearly totals have been regular since then. Numbers have continued to increase during the early part of the 21st century, with an average of 20 per year in the period 2000 to 2005. The highest annual totals have all occurred since 1998, with 30 in 2000, 21 in 2002 and 2005, 19 in 2001 and 16 in 1998 and 1999.

The data show that it is most regular from late April to late May and again from early August to early September. Between 1980 and 1995, Marsh Harriers occurred with almost equal frequency in spring (41 individuals) and autumn (40 individuals), but since 1996 a noticeable change has occurred, with almost twice as many autumn records (113) as spring (60). The increasing number of autumn birds probably relate to dispersing juveniles from the expanding British breeding population.

The earliest migrant is a female at Rutland Water on February 15th 2005, but this species is rare prior to the middle of April, with only eight other records before April 11th:

- a male at Rutland Water on February 18th 2005.
- a female at Beeby on February 26th 1997.
- an immature male at Rutland Water on March 19th 2001.
- a female at Knipton on March 22nd 1998.
- a male at Rutland Water on March 29th 2005.
- a female at Rutland Water on April 1st and 2nd 1999.
- a male at Rutland Water on April 2nd 2004.
- one at Rutland Water on April 4th 2000.

Spring passage peaks during the first three weeks of May but tails off by the end of the month and there have only been six records during June:

- a female at Nailstone on June 4th 1990.
- a female at Stanford Reservoir on June 5th and 6th 1971.
- a male at Rutland Water on June 7th 1987.

- a male at Rutland Water on June 8th 1992.
- one at Rutland Water and a female at Melton Country Park, both on June 10th 2000.

The earliest autumn migrant is one at Rutland Water on July 12th 1990, although records before the last four days of this month remain unusual, the only ones being a female at Eyebrook Reservoir on July 16th 2005, a female at Rutland Water on July 18th 2002, one at the same site on July 21st 1989 and a female/juvenile at Trent Lock on July 25th 1999. August is by far the peak month, accounting for almost 40% of all Marsh Harrier records in Leicestershire and Rutland. Records diminish considerably in September and there have been seven individuals found in October, four of which have occurred after the 12th:

- a female at Beeby on October 13th 2000.
- one at Rutland Water on October 14th 2003.
- one at Rutland Water from October 25th to 31st 1976.
- a female/juvenile at Belmesthorpe on October 27th 1983.

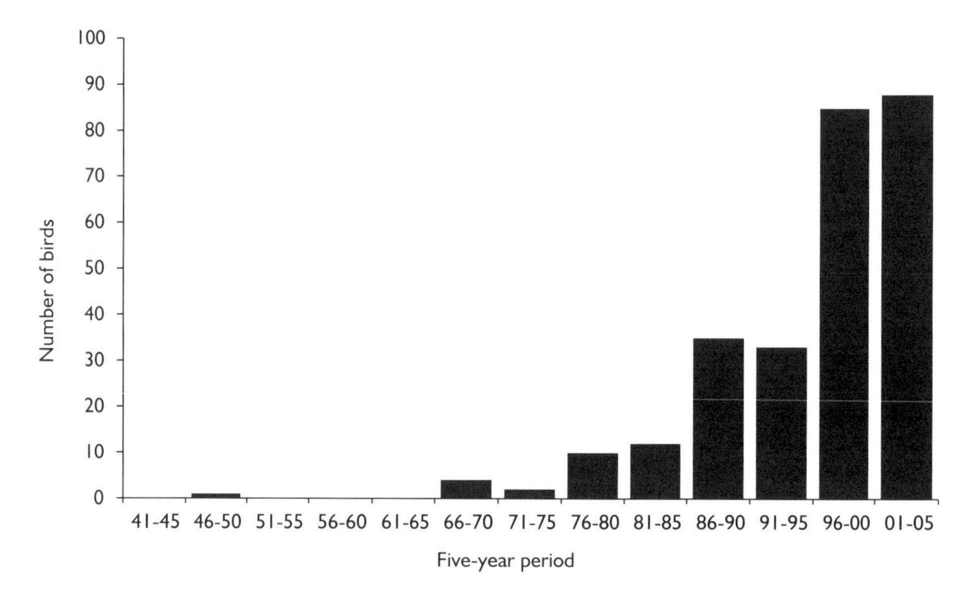

Figure 188: Numbers of Marsh Harriers by five-year periods 1941–2005.

As is to be expected with a passage migrant in the counties, the majority of birds have been seen on one date only. Just 31 individuals (11%) have lingered for two days or more, with nine remaining for over a week. Most of these long-stayers have involved juveniles at Rutland Water during the autumn, although single adult females remained at this site from April 17th to 30th 1994 and May 6th to 16th 1999. Of even greater interest was a female which summered at Loddington in both 1995 and 1996.

The distribution of records shows a noticeable bias towards the eastern half of the counties, 78% of all records having occurred to the east of Leicester. Rutland Water is the dominant site and accounts for 49% of all reports, with a further 15% having occurred at Eyebrook Reservoir. Only six other sites have recorded this species on more than two occasions: Stanford Reservoir (ten individuals), Priory Water (eight), Groby Pool (seven), Fort Henry Ponds and Swithland Reservoir (five each) and Sence Valley Forest Park (four).

The majority of records involve adult females during the spring and juveniles during the autumn. A large number of birds reported during the autumn have been described as 'female/juvenile' and a number have been unsexed and it is likely that many of these individuals have actually been juveniles. Adult males are very much in the minority and account for only 7% of all records.

Marsh Harriers breed patchily in western Europe and more widely across eastern Europe and central Eurasia, with localised populations in north-west Africa; most northern birds winter to the south of the breeding range. The species has a chequered history in Britain, being quite widespread in the 1800s before declining significantly dur-

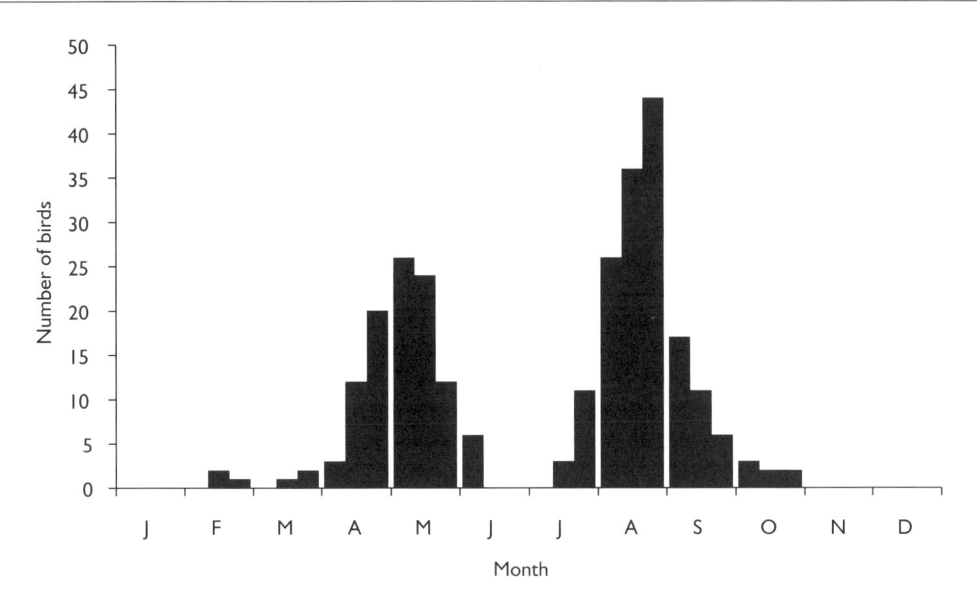

Figure 189: Monthly occurrence of Marsh Harriers 1941–2005.

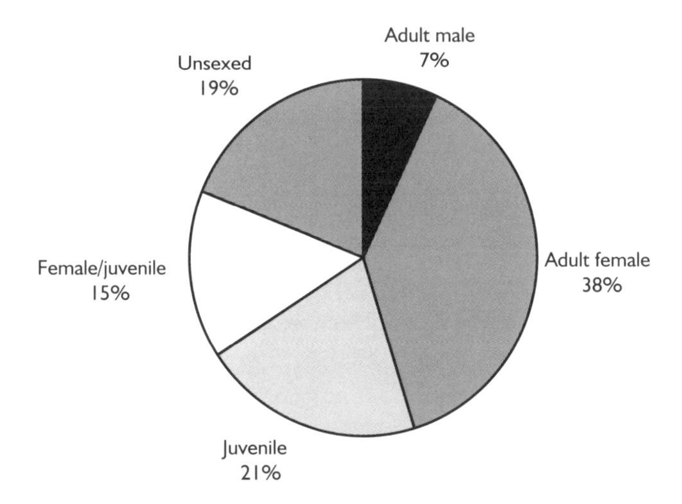

Figure 190: Ages and sexes of Marsh Harriers recorded 1941–2005.

ing the 19th century (in line with the Leicestershire status during this period). It became extinct as a breeding species in Britain in 1899, but recolonisation occurred from 1927 and breeding has been recorded every year since (Holloway 1996). However, another serious decline throughout the 1960s, linked to the use of organochlorine pesticides, resulted in the population plummeting to just one pair in 1971, at Minsmere (Suffolk). Numbers have recovered spectacularly since then and reached a 200–year high of 360 breeding females in 2005 (*BB* 99:382). The Leicestershire and Rutland records follow this pattern, with very few prior to 1970 and a noticeable and sustained increase in numbers following this, particularly since the mid-1980s. The majority of the British population is found in East Anglia, but nesting now occurs regularly in both Cambridgeshire and Lincolnshire and it is not unreasonable to suggest that Marsh Harrier may well be added to the Leicestershire and Rutland breeding list in the not-too-distant future. The species was included from Amber List' of Birds of Conservation Concern, due to its historical decline and relatively small breeding population (Gregory *et al.* 2002).

RMF

Hen Harrier *Circus cyaneus*

Scarce winter and passage visitor; recorded in all months between September and April, with the majority from October to December: 72 modern records involving 73 individuals. Probably a former rare breeding resident.

According to Browne, a keeper named Adams reported that this species used to nest in the Charnwood region regularly before the enclosure of the Forest in 1811. Haines thought that it 'no doubt occurred often enough in Rutland in the days of the Raven and Kite', although he had no evidence to substantiate this statement. The Hen Harrier obviously died out as both a breeding bird and winter visitor to the counties rather rapidly, as the only record known to Browne subsequent to the enclosure of Charnwood Forest was of one seen at Thringstone in 1841, whilst Haines had no definite records for Rutland during the same period.

Today, the Hen Harrier is a scarce passage and winter visitor to the counties. The only mention in the LROS archives is of one shot at Normanton le Heath in 1921 and, contrary to the statement of Hickling, who said there were records for most years, the next Hen Harrier of the 20th century was not convincingly documented until 1971. Since then, there have been records in every year except 1988 and 2000, although there were no new arrivals in 1972. In most years there have been just one or two records, although three have been noted in seven years, four in four years and a record six were found in 2004. In the latter year, an adult male at Market Bosworth on November 12th was joined by a second-winter male three days later, with both remaining until November 20th; this is the only occasion that two birds have been seen together in the counties.

The data show that it is most regular from late October to mid-December, with the peak period being from October 26th to November 20th. The earliest autumn migrant was a female/juvenile at Narborough Bog on September 9th 1979, but sightings before late October are rare and only a further six have been recorded prior to October 26th:

- a female/juvenile at Eyebrook Reservoir on September 20th 2005.
- a male at Stoney Stanton on September 21st 1981.
- a juvenile male at Rutland Water on September 30th 1984.
- a female/juvenile at Saddington Reservoir on October 20th 1980.
- a first-winter male at Rutland Water from October 22nd to November 4th 1987.
- a female at Billesdon Coplow on October 23rd 1983.
- an adult male at Lockington Marshes on October 25th 2003.

Records of new arrivals tail off during January and February, although a slight peak is detectable in late March as passage birds move through the area on their return to the breeding grounds. There have been seven April records, including a relatively high proportion of adult males, as follows:

- a female at Rutland Water on April 6th 1983.
- a female at Pickworth on April 7th 1985.
- an adult male between Langham and Whissendine on April 13th 2003.
- a female/immature at Frolesworth on April 17th 1979.
- a female at Stanford Reservoir on April 25th and 26th 1971.
- an adult male at Scraptoft on April 25th 1992.
- an adult male at Dunton Bassett on April 30th 1983.

As a large percentage of birds seen in the counties are on passage, it is no surprise to learn that the majority of records refer to single birds seen on one date only. Of the 73 individuals recorded since 1971, just 17 have lingered for more than one day. Five have remained for more than two weeks:

- a female/juvenile at Rutland Water from October 31st 1976 to May 4th 1977.
- a first-winter female at Cossington Meadows from November 22nd 2002 to February 14th 2003.
- a female/juvenile at Luffenham Airfield from January 3rd to February 28th 2005.
- a female/juvenile at Rutland Water from December 12th 2004 to January 28th 2005.
- a first-winter male at Rutland Water from January 28th to February 26th 1978.

The distribution of records shows a noticeable bias towards the eastern half of the area, with 71% of all records having occurred to the east of Leicester. Rutland Water is the dominant site, with 16 individuals, whilst there

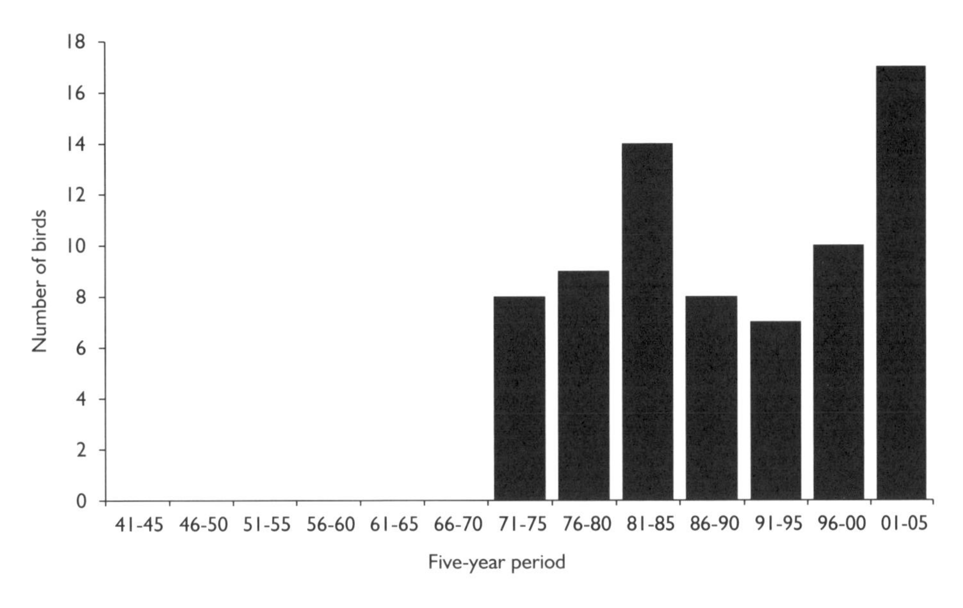

Figure 191: Numbers of Hen Harriers by five-year periods 1941–2005.

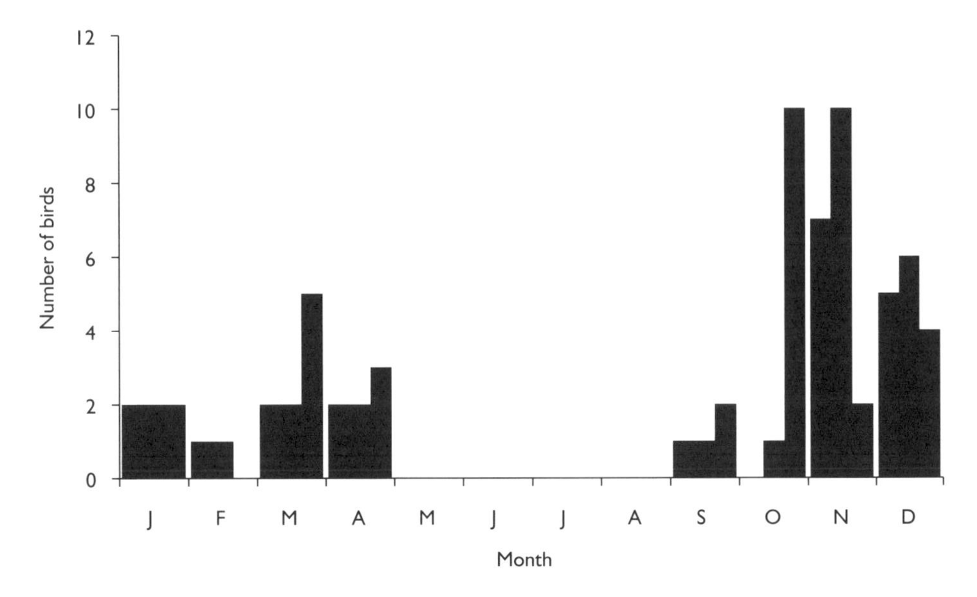

Figure 192: Monthly occurrence of Hen Harriers 1941–2005.

have been a further 21 records from other sites in Rutland, including four at Clipsham and three at both Eyebrook Reservoir and Pickworth. Away from Rutland, only four sites (Saddington Reservoir, Cossington, Lockington Marshes and Market Bosworth) have recorded this species on more than one occasion. The supposed ancient breeding area of Charnwood Forest is now almost completely shunned, with just five records from this region since 1971.

As with several other scarce raptor species, adult males are relatively scarce in the counties, with only 26% of records referring to this age and sex. 'Ringtails' have accounted for 66% of all records, with the remaining 8% of unsexed individuals presumably also relating to either females or juveniles.

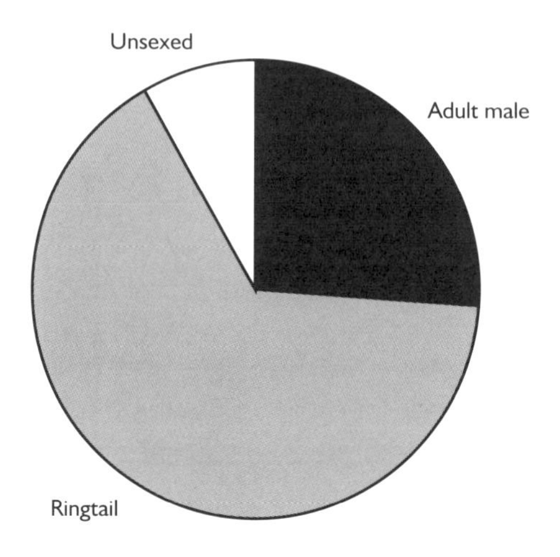

Figure 193: Sexes of Hen Harriers recorded 1941–2005.

The total number of Hen Harrier records currently accepted is probably an underestimate of the actual numbers that may have occurred. There have been 19 records that have been accepted only as unidentified harrier species, the majority of which were probably Hen Harriers. A further three records previously accepted and published, of two at Pickworth on September 29th 1976 and singles at Rutland Water on April 21st 1984 and Burley Wood on August 30th 1989, were rejected following review in 2004 (Fray 2005).

Hen Harriers breed across wide areas of Europe, Asia and North America. Some European birds winter within or near the breeding range but others move south, though very few actually cross the Mediterranean Sea. In Britain, the breeding population was estimated at 570 pairs in 1998 (Sim *et al.* 2001) and is restricted to the north and west (particularly Scotland), as well as the Isle of Man and Ireland. Birds leave their moorland nesting areas in the winter and move to the lowlands, particularly the east coast of England and a clue to where at least some of the birds found in Leicestershire and Rutland originate from is provided by the record of a first-winter male at Pickworth on December 13th 1998 and then Thorpe by Water on January 24th 1999 which was carrying a wing-tag showing it had been marked as a chick in the summer of 1998 at Langholm (Dumfries and Galloway). There has been a long term decline in the British breeding numbers and this species is unfortunately still persecuted relentlessly in some areas, giving genuine grounds for concern for its future as a breeding bird in this country. These factors have resulted in the Hen Harrier being added to the 'Red List' of Birds of Conservation Concern (Gregory *et al.* 2002).

RMF

Pallid Harrier *Circus macrourus*

Very rare vagrant from south-east Europe or Asia: one record.

An adult male was seen by Dave Gamble at Saddington Reservoir on September 15th 1993. It originally appeared at 15:15, being pursued by two Rooks and eventually drifted off to the south about 15 minutes later (Gamble 1995, *BB* 88:505).

Pallid Harriers breed on steppe grasslands from Ukraine through central Asia to north-west China and winter mainly in Africa south of the Sahara and in the Indian subcontinent, with smaller numbers in south-west Asia and China. By the end of 2005 there had been 23 British records, all except three since 1993. The Leicestershire bird was only the seventh seen in this country and arrived the same day as a juvenile in Shetland. The weather conditions on September 15th 1993 were perhaps responsible for their appearance, being rather murky with a strong easterly airflow; there was an arrival of other birds of prey (most notably Honey Buzzards) along the east coast of Britain the same day.

RMF

Montagu's Harrier *Circus pygargus*

Very rare vagrant from Europe, mostly in May: nine records.

Browne, writing in VH, describes 'a stuffed specimen I purchased for the Museum in 1893, which had been shot at Heath Farm, Earl Shilton, some years ago.' Since then, there have been a further eight records, all since 1982.

All records:

pre-1893	shot, Earl Shilton.
1982	an adult female was seen by Jonathan Starie near Enderby on May 27th. This record was originally only accepted as a 'harrier sp.', but a recent review found the description to be thoroughly acceptable and it retrospectively became the first Montagu's Harrier in the counties for at least 89 years (Fray 2005).
1990	an adult male was seen being mobbed by corvids over Thornton Reservoir during the evening of May 1st, before it flew off west. The fortunate observer, Stephen Walton, managed to obtain several excellent photographs of the bird.
1991	a female was watched by Rob Fray and Andy Lawson over the northern end of Eyebrook Reservoir for five minutes from 18:35 on May 25th, before it flew off to the north-east.
1995	a juvenile was seen by Dave Gray and Richard Watkins on August 1st; remarkably, it was in the very same area of Eyebrook Reservoir as the 1991 individual. To date, this is the only autumn record.
2000	a first-summer male flew north-west over Trent Valley Pit at 06:34 on May 13th, witnessed by Dave Gamble, Tim Grove and Howard Orridge.
	a ringtail was seen heading east at Owston Wood on May 15th by Andy Forryan.
2005	an adult male, seen by Tim Appleton and Steve Lister, flew south over the Egleton Reserve at Rutland Water on April 29th.
	a female was noted heading north-east over the north arm at Rutland Water by Andy Forryan on May 18th.

Haines mentions two possible records from Rutland in the 19th century, neither of which are particularly convincing: 'a large hawk so grey-looking as almost to be called white' was seen in 1860 (although Haines omits to say where this was) and an egg found at Bisbrooke Gorse in 1865 which was purported to have been of this species.

Montagu's Harriers breed across much of western Europe as far north as Denmark and eastwards to central Asia, wintering in sub-Saharan Africa and the Indian subcontinent. Small numbers (usually between ten and 15 pairs) also breed in southern England; this is one of the rarest breeding birds in the country and, due to the small size of the population, the species was included on the 'Amber List' of Birds of Conservation Concern (Gregory *et al.* 2002). It is more frequent as a passage migrant, especially in the spring and all eight of the modern county records conform to this pattern.

RMF

Goshawk (Northern Goshawk) *Accipiter gentilis*

Rare visitor, possibly scarce resident: 18 modern records.

Browne quotes Harley, writing in 1841, as saying Goshawks 'used to occur not infrequently in our woodlands and forest wilds', but had become exceedingly rare. The species had apparently been captured at Oakley and Gopsall Woods and another was supposedly shot at Allexton in 1881, although Browne was far from convinced by the authenticity of these claims, commenting that he was 'in doubt whether a large female Sparrowhawk has not done duty in this, as in many similar cases, for the Goshawk.' Haines notes two records from Rutland: a male shot near Barrowden in 1856 and an undated individual picked up on the 'Rutland side of Stamford'.

Browne's scepticism lives on in the 21st century; the status of this species today is uncertain, being clouded by misidentification and suppression and it is probably a rare visitor at best. Following a major review in 2004, all records prior to 1992 were considered inadequately documented, including a run of nine reports from various sites in 1950 and 1951 (Fray 2005). There are currently 18 accepted records, as follows:

1993	female, Knipton Reservoir, February 7th.
	immature male, Burley Wood, June 5th.
	immature, Knipton Reservoir, June 19th.
	adult, Belvoir, June 19th.
1994	adult, Belvoir, March 12th.
	adult male, Burbage, September 14th.
	adult, Burley Wood, September 23rd.
1997	adult female, Shenton, November 22nd.
1998	female, Pickworth, March 20th.
	female, Harston/Knipton, March 28th and September 20th.
	male, Knipton, April 14th.
1999	male, Exton Park, April 10th.
	female, Stoke Dry Wood/Great Merrible Wood, September 26th.
2000	adult female, Swithland Wood, December 27th.
2001	adult female, Burley Wood, May 10th.
2003	adult, Blakeshay Wood, June 7th.
	adult male, Burley Wood, August 22nd.
2005	male, Wymeswold, December 13th.

The pattern of records shows a mixture of birds in potential breeding habitat in early spring (such as those in the Knipton/Belvoir area in 1994, 1995 and 1998) and others which are possibly on passage, particularly those recorded in April, August and September. It is interesting to note that four of the presumed passage birds have occurred in the east of the county, which perhaps strengthens the case for a continental origin of these individuals.

Not only is this species notoriously problematical for observers to describe adequately, the situation is further clouded by potential escaped falconers' birds. One such example may have been a male at Burbage in 1995 which was filmed eating a Collared Dove in a small suburban garden. In addition, five obvious escapes have been recorded, all of which carried jesses or other signs of previous confinement:

1981	Market Bosworth, April 20th.
1985	female, Carlton Curlieu, April 4th and 7th.
	female, Stoughton Airfield, August 22nd.
1989	Rutland Water, October 23rd.
2004	Charnwood Lodge, April 12th; presumed same, Oaks in Charnwood, October 18th.
2005	Blackbrook Reservoir, February 27th (presumed same as the 2004 individual).

Goshawks breed throughout much of Europe, northern Asia and North America. Most populations are resident, although those in northern Fennoscandia are partially migratory. In Britain, the species breeds at low density in suitable habitat; the population only amounts to around 400 pairs (Holling *et al.* 2008), although numbers have shown a marked increase from 1970 onwards (Gibbons *et al.* 1996). It is thought that Goshawks currently breeding in Britain are not derived from continental immigrants, but rather from birds which have escaped from falconers or been deliberately released (Marquiss & Newton 1982).

RMF

Sparrowhawk (Eurasian Sparrowhawk) ***Accipiter nisus***

Fairly common resident breeder.

The Sparrowhawk was described by Browne as resident and generally distributed in Leicestershire in the 19th century and breeding was recorded within the city boundary of Leicester at Knighton. Haines' assessment in Rutland during the same period was 'this conspicuous and rapacious bird still maintains its existence against the gamekeeper's gun and as compared in numbers with the Kestrel may perhaps be described as one in seven'.

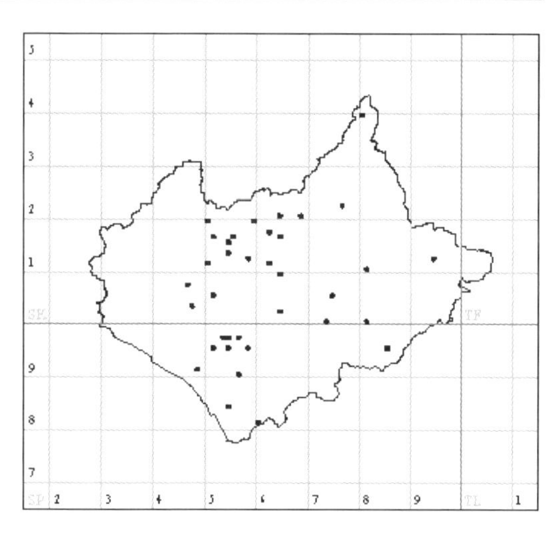

Figure 194: Distribution of confirmed and probable breeding records of Sparrowhawks 1941–49.

The LROS archives describe this species as being thinly distributed during the first 40 years of the 20th century and an identical status was used in the first LROS Annual Report in 1941. The following year it was 'just about maintaining its status despite attention of keepers', but in 1943 it was thought to be probably increasing and in 1944 was steadily increasing its range. In 1949 it was considered to be exceptionally numerous during the early months of the year. Confirmed or probable breeding was recorded at 36 sites during the 1940s; the majority were in the western half of the counties, with particular clusters in Charnwood Forest (including nine pairs in the Quorn area in 1948) and to the south-west of Leicester. It was very scarce in Rutland at this time, with the only breeding records being from Eyebrook Reservoir in 1947 and 1948 and Exton Park in 1948.

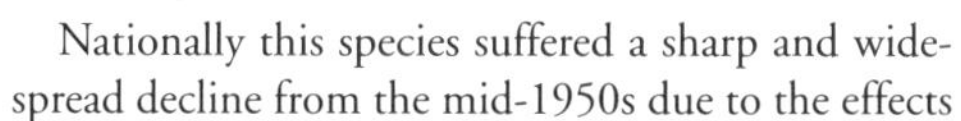

Nationally this species suffered a sharp and widespread decline from the mid-1950s due to the effects of the widespread use of organochlorine pesticides. This decline was first mentioned locally in 1960, when it was noted that the Sparrowhawk was 'now rare as a breeding species' and that it had 'declined seriously in the last few years'. During the 1960s it was only a scarce winter visitor, with very few records in some years (such as 1967, when the only reports were single birds at Eyebrook Reservoir and Loughborough). Two pairs bred in 1969, at Tooley Spinney and Seagrave, and during the 1970s there was a slow increase in the number of winter sightings. The majority of records came from the western half of Leicestershire, particularly Charnwood Forest, and in 1979 a pair which nested in the north of Leicestershire was the first confirmed breeding record for the counties since 1969.

Since 1979 breeding has been confirmed every year. The first cluster of breeding records came from the Market Bosworth and Charnwood Forest areas, suggesting the origin of these early colonists was from further west where the species had already expanded its range. By 1985 this species was widespread throughout the counties, with records from 90 sites; the majority were in the west and north, although 26% were in the east.

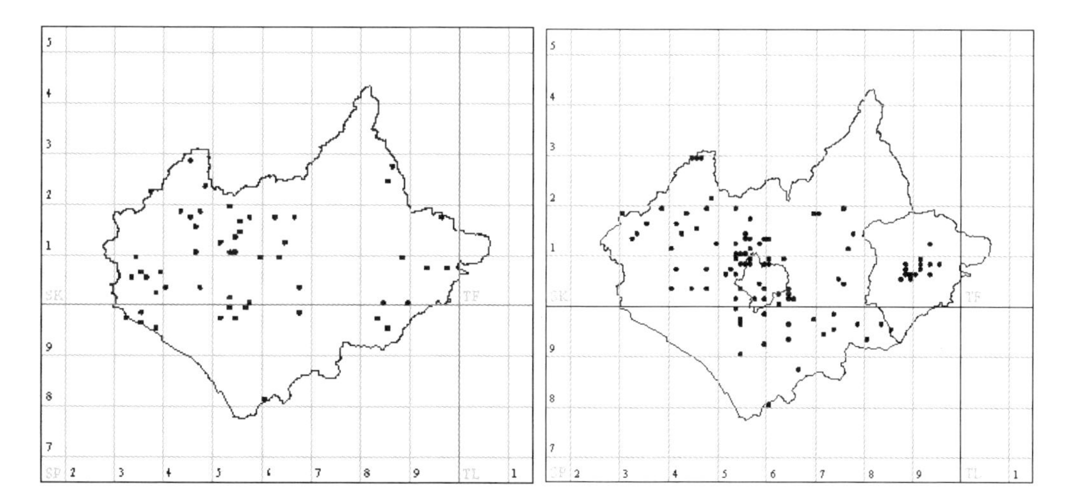

Figure 195: Distribution of Sparrowhawks 1959–79.

Figure 196: Distribution of Sparrowhawks 1985.

Warrilow carried out his tetrad survey in the counties during 1976–84, at a time when this species was still recovering its numbers. His estimate of 50 pairs is now completely out of date. Mitcham (1992) found 42% of Rutland tetrads occupied and commented that the species had made a good recovery following near extinction in the 1960s and 1970s; the main gaps in distribution were in north-west Rutland, where there is little woodland. Webster recorded confirmed or probable breeding in a surprisingly low 13% of one-kilometre squares in Charnwood during his 1992 to 1994 survey, but commented that they are difficult to prove breeding so were perhaps more common than the results indicated.

Since 1995 LROS Annual Reports have noted the number of sites at which this species has been recorded. The highest number was 192 in 1990, although subsequent drops in numbers are probably not significant as many birds are now not reported. The accompanying maps show little change in distribution between 1995 and

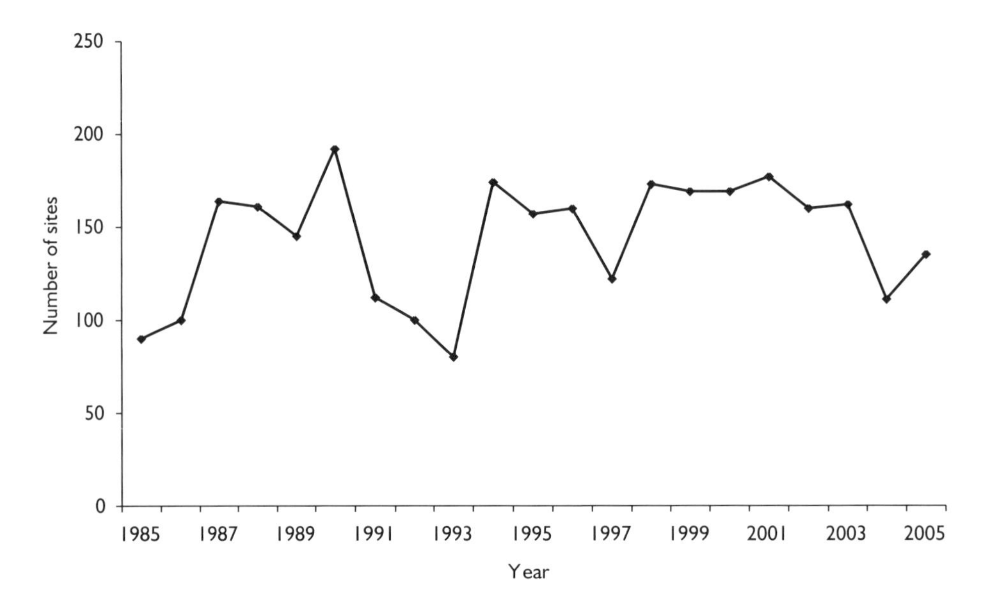

Figure 197: Number of sites with records of Sparrowhawks 1985–2005.

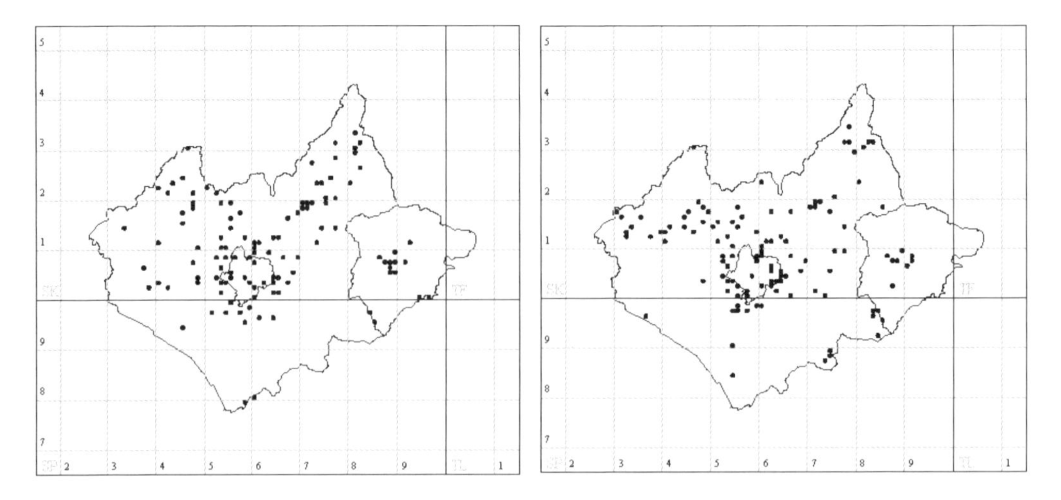

Figure 198: Distribution of Sparrowhawks 1995.

Figure 199: Distribution of Sparrowhawks 2005.

2005; the large areas of south Leicestershire which are apparently unoccupied are probably not representative and are likely to reflect the distribution of observers.

Sparrowhawks are usually reported singly or in pairs, although four to six together have been recorded on a number of occasions. Higher counts have come from the Belvoir/Knipton area, including seven on December 13th 1998, eight on April 28th 1998 and 11 on February 26th 1995. A total of 12 birds flew south-east over Enderby on October 21st 1997.

An interesting record in 1986 concerned two females which shared the same nest and were often seen brooding side by side; they laid a total of nine eggs, six of which hatched and three young fledged. What were presumably the same two females were seen sharing the same nest again in 1987.

Local ringing recoveries demonstrate the generally sedentary nature of this species: of a total of 106 birds either ringed or recovered in the counties, only four had moved more than 100km, as follows:

- a pullus ringed at Swithland Reservoir on June 26th 1981 was found dead 116km to the south-south-east at Hemel Hempstead (Hertfordshire) on March 5th 1983.
- a pullus female ringed at Sutton-in-Craven (North Yorkshire) on July 1st 1986 was controlled at Burton on the Wolds on September 26th 1988, a movement of 136km to the south-south-east.
- a pullus male ringed at Eyebrook Reservoir on July 6th 1990 was found dead 253km to the south-west at Holcombe Regis (Devon) on December 6th 1990.
- a pullus female ringed at Langsett (South Yorkshire) on July 12th 1992 was found dead at Hinckley on April 10th 1993, a movement of 110km to the south-south-east.

The nominate race of Sparrowhawk breeds from Europe east to western Siberia, with other subspecies in Siberia, central Asia, north-west Africa and islands in the Mediterranean and North Atlantic. Southern and western populations are sedentary, although northern birds move south to winter. As mentioned above, there was a marked decline in Britain in the 1950s and 1960s due to the effects of organochlorine pesticides but it has increased strongly since and the latest British population estimate is 38,600 pairs (Baker *et al.* 2006).

RMF

Common Buzzard *Buteo buteo*

Uncommon to fairly common resident breeder and passage migrant; formerly a scarce passage and rare winter visitor following extinction as a breeding bird in the 19th century.

Browne described the Common Buzzard as being of accidental occurrence in Leicestershire during the late 19th century, although it had formerly been resident and had bred at Martinshaw Wood, Bardon, Oakley Wood, Piper Wood, Belvoir, Castle Donington and Gopsall Wood. A similar status was reported in Rutland by Haines, who described it as 'formerly resident and common, now a rare straggler'. The last nest in Rutland was near Uppingham in about 1827 and this was the latest dated breeding record in the counties during the 19th century. The extinction of this species in Leicestershire and Rutland was mirrored across much of eastern and central England during the 19th century, when the Common Buzzard was exterminated as a breeding species due to human persecution (Clements 2000).

During the early part of the 20th century this species was described in the LROS archives as an 'occasional wanderer', although the only records specifically mentioned were of single birds at Thurnby in both April 1934 and April 1935. From the formation of LROS, in 1941, to the late 1980s, the Common Buzzard remained a scarce visitor to the counties. Approximately 200 birds were reported during this period, with a slump in records during the 1950s and 1960s coinciding with reduced numbers nationally due to the effects of myxomatosis in the rabbit population and the deleterious effects of organochlorine pesticides (Baillie *et al.* 2006). A noticeable increase occurred from the 1970s onwards, again in line with national trends. The only blank years during this time were 1941 and 1962, although there was only one record in each of 1952, 1953, 1965 and 1985. By contrast, at least 11 individuals were seen in both 1971 and 1977 and ten were noted in 1944 and 1976. Most records concerned single birds, although two were seen together on 11 occasions and three were at Ragdale on September 8th 1944.

Between 1941 and 1990 Common Buzzards were seen in all months, with a distinct passage in spring and autumn, particularly April and September which between them accounted for almost half of all records during

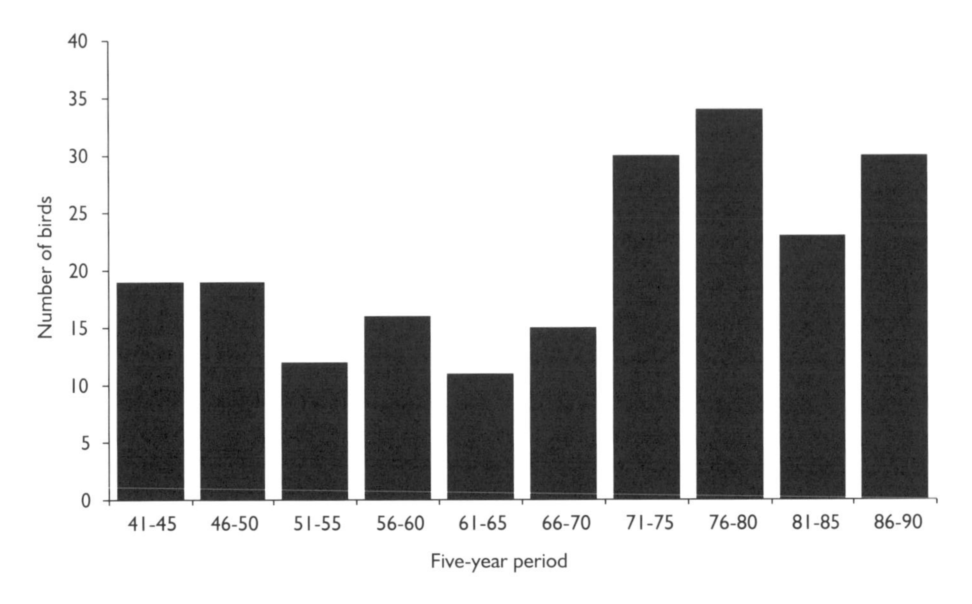

Figure 200: Numbers of Common Buzzards by five-year periods 1941–90.

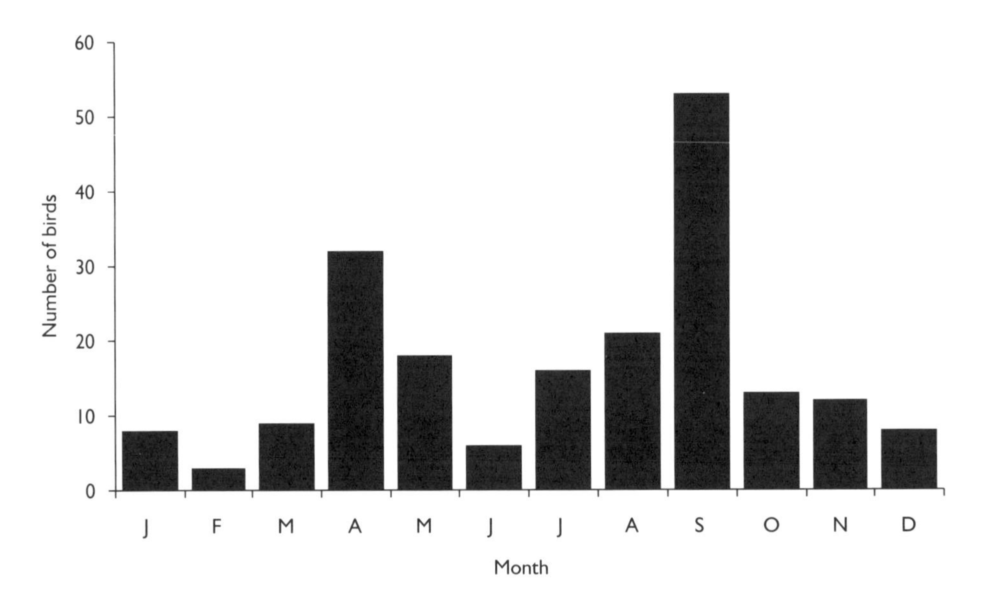

Figure 201: Monthly occurrence of Common Buzzards 1941–90.

this period. Sightings between December and March were infrequent, although single birds wintered at Market Bosworth in 1981–82 and Tooley Park, Desford in 1986–87.

Records during this period came from many widely-scattered sites, with a preponderance of sightings in the Charnwood Forest area and a distinct lack of records from large parts of the east and north-east of the counties.

Since 1991 the status of the Common Buzzard in Leicestershire and Rutland has changed dramatically from that of a scarce visitor to an uncommon or fairly common resident breeder. In 1991 at least 16 birds were seen, a record total at the time and there was an unsubstantiated report that up to seven were present in the Belvoir area, prompting the suggestion that breeding may already have been taking place. Up to three were present at

Belvoir during 1992 and the following year breeding was confirmed for the first time since 1827, with different juveniles noted on August 1st and 16th. Three pairs held territory at Belvoir in 1994, with at least one pair breeding; display was noted in the west of Leicestershire during the same year, the first indication of breeding away from Belvoir. 1995 saw Rutland's first breeding record since the 19th century and from then on the breeding population in both Leicestershire and Rutland has gone from strength to strength. A co-ordinated census would be required to arrive at a population estimate, but it is known that the Common Buzzard is now more widespread than Sparrowhawk and may even be as numerous as Kestrel. Some idea of population densities can be gained from recent counts in known breeding areas:

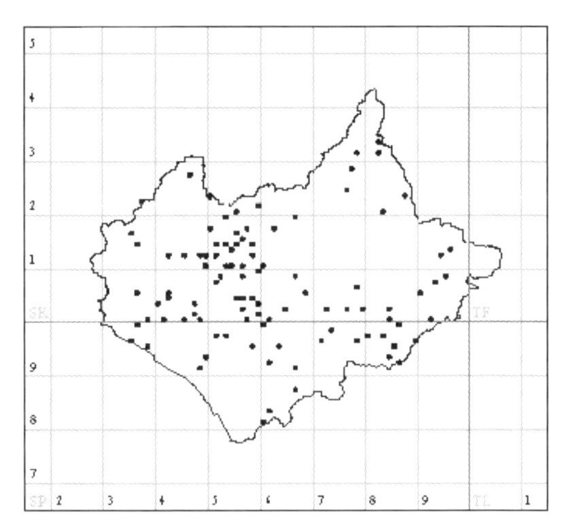

Figure 202: Distribution of Common Buzzards 1941–90.

- 27 resident birds in the Charnwood Forest area in 2004, including 11 territorial pairs.
- 23 at Belvoir on both April 14th 1998 and February 13th 2000.
- 20 at Gopsall Park on April 3rd 2001.
- ten at Stretton on May 17th 1998.
- ten at Loddington Reddish on February 14th 2002.
- nine at Oakthorpe on August 29th 2001.
- nine at Lubbesthorpe on both February 28th and August 22nd 2004.
- nine at Burley Wood on September 2nd 2005.

The accompanying map shows the distribution of all records received of this species during 2005. Although some of these records will refer to passage migrants it is clear that most suitable areas of the counties are now occupied. The absence from parts of Rutland and east Leicestershire is probably a reflection on the intensively-farmed nature of these areas.

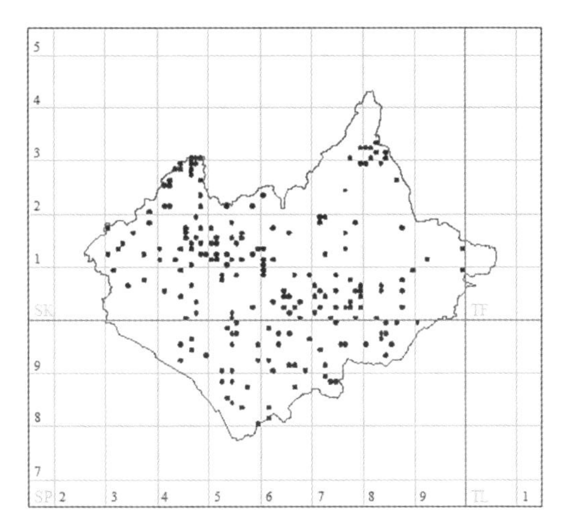

Figure 203: Distribution of Common Buzzards 2005.

From 1991 to 2004 an attempt was made to calculate the number of birds recorded each year in the counties; by 2004 the figure was estimated to be 338 individuals. This was almost certainly an underestimate, as by now the species was so widespread that most observers had stopped reporting them. Nonetheless, from the records received it is clear that the Common Buzzard has continued to increase year on year.

It has become increasingly difficult to differentiate between resident and passage birds although analysis of the records from 1991 to 2004 reveals an obvious peak in September, a similar pattern to that shown during 1941–90. In 2002 and 2003 the estimated totals for September were 144 and 113 individuals respectively, suggesting that passage birds do still occur in the counties; records such as eight over Priory Water on September 8th 1996 and ten over Thornton Reservoir on September 15th 2002 tend to confirm this. Another noticeable peak occurs in April, as it did before 1991, although almost as many birds are now seen in March and it is likely that the upsurge in this month relates to resident birds becoming more obvious as they indulge in their aerial displays.

Common Buzzards breed throughout most of Europe and northern Asia. Most are sedentary, although populations in Scandinavia and Asia are largely migratory and winter as far south as eastern and southern Africa and

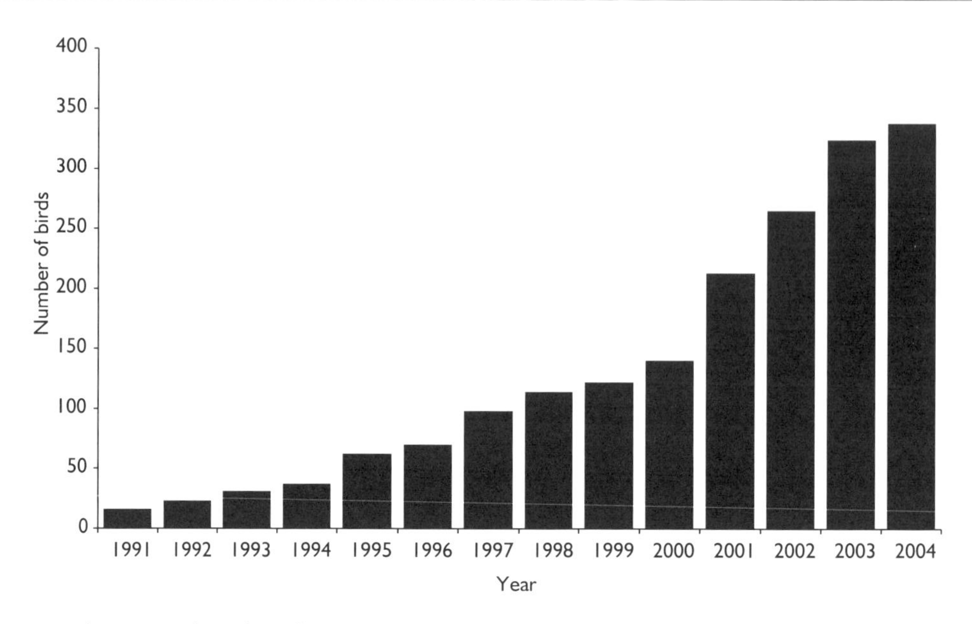

Figure 204: Estimated number of Common Buzzards 1991–2004.

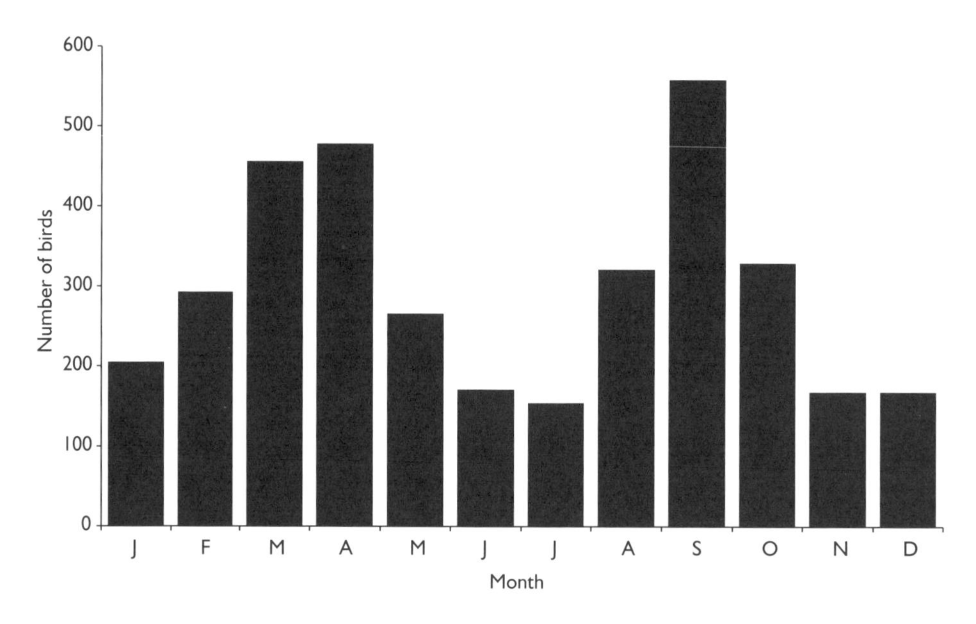

Figure 205: Monthly occurrence of Common Buzzards 1991–2004.

southern Asia. In Britain they have expanded their range eastwards at a rapid rate since 1991 (Clements 2000), corresponding with the recolonisation of Leicestershire and Rutland. A bird at Knipton Reservoir between April 25th and August 27th 2000 closely resembled the 'fox-red' morph of *vulpinus*, but because it is impossible to distinguish such birds from intergrades (or even exceptional nominate birds) this subspecies is not on the British List (Harrop & Collinson 2003). The British population was estimated at 12,000 to 17,000 pairs during 1988–91 (Gibbons *et al.* 1993) but this had increased almost four-fold, to between 43,930 and 60,820 pairs, by 1997, making it probably the most abundant diurnal raptor in Britain (Clements 2002).

RMF

Rough-legged Buzzard *Buteo lagopus*

Rare winter visitor from Europe; recorded in all months between October and April: 22 or 23 records.

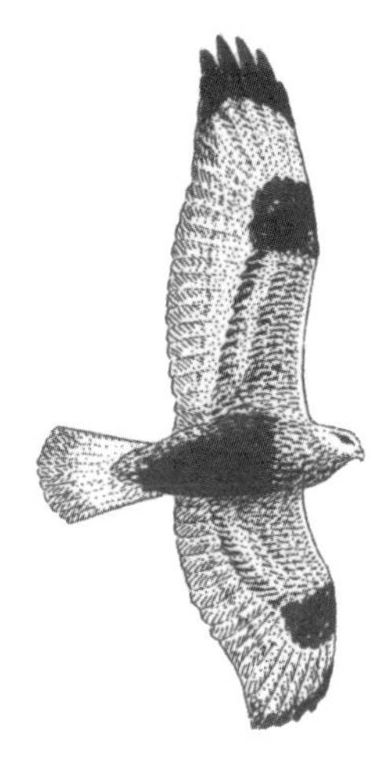

The number of 19th century records of this species has been consistently over-estimated by previous authors, who have noted that there were approximately 37 individuals recorded in that period. This confusion arose following a statement in the 1946 LROS Annual Report that, in the winter of 1839–40, approximately 30 birds were 'procured'. However, Browne notes that 30 birds were captured or shot during this winter in the two counties of Leicestershire and Nottinghamshire and it appears that only nine of these were actually in Leicestershire. Of these, three were shot at Bradgate Park, all in November: a female on the 12th, a male on the 14th and another on the 15th. The latter specimen is still retained at Leicester Museum today. Another five were captured at various sites in Charnwood Forest and a further specimen which was found residing in the Bickley Collection was thought to have been shot at Stathern. Browne details an additional five 19th century records, all of which were shot, as follows:

1854	Holywell Wood, undated.
1876	Lockington Hall, November.
1880	near Ashby-de-la-Zouch, February 21st.
1888	Leicester Forest East, November.
1891	female, Thornton, November 2nd.

Haines also makes reference to the 1854 record but casts doubt on whether the bird was actually in Rutland, as Holywell Wood is just over the county border in Lincolnshire. As this is the only known Rutland record, it is debatable whether the Rough-legged Buzzard has ever occurred in this county. The LROS archives make reference to a bird shot at Bardon in 1876, whilst Hickling mentions two early 20th century records: single birds shot at Bradgate Park in 1910 and Swithland in 1925, the latter of which is still retained at Leicester Museum. It is worthwhile noting that Witherby *et al.* (1938) mention 1839/40, 1875/76, 1880/81, 1891/92 and 1910/11 as notable influx winters, corresponding with the majority of records listed above.

Since the formation of LROS in 1941, there have been a further six records, as follows:

1946	one was seen by Harold Hunt at Swithland Reservoir on October 24th, with what was presumably the same bird shot the following day nearby at Nanpantan. The skin was identified by staff at the Leicester Museum.
1974	one was recorded by A. Mattocks at Swithland Reservoir on February 16th.
1979	one flew north-west over Cropston Reservoir on March 15th, seen by Jean Ironside.
1994	a juvenile remained in the Belvoir area from November 19th to April 9th 1995 and was seen by large numbers of observers. It may have been present for up to two weeks before its identity was confirmed by Andy Mackay and Steve Close.
1995	a juvenile was watched for 30 minutes by Ralph Lockwood and Alex Lees at Belvoir on April 6th, where it was seen together with the long-staying individual mentioned above.
1996	one was seen for 15 minutes by Dave Gamble and Mark Rossell near Knipton Reservoir on March 10th.

The record in 1974 followed one of the largest ever influxes into Britain, when approximately 170 individuals arrived during October 1973 (Scott 1978); likewise, the 1979 bird occurred after an unusual midwinter influx on the east coast in January following severe weather (Davenport 1982). The long-staying and often very obliging Belvoir juvenile of 1994/95 similarly arrived following a large irruption (Fraser *et al.* 1997).

All records of the Rough-legged Buzzard in Leicestershire and Rutland were reviewed in 1994 and 2004 and whilst the above remained acceptable, three other previously published reports were considered inadequately documented: single birds at Rutland Water in July and August 1976 and December 1st 1984 and Swithland Reservoir on September 22nd 1988 (Mackay 1995a, Fray 2005).

Rough-legged Buzzards are circumpolar breeders from Scandinavia to north-eastern Canada, mainly occupying the arctic and subarctic zones. They winter chiefly from the Low Countries and eastern Europe across Asia north of the Himalayas and in southern Canada and the United States. Britain lies at the extreme north-western edge of the normal wintering range and usually only small numbers occur in this country as autumn migrants, with some birds remaining to winter. Fennoscandian populations of Rough-legged Buzzards, the origin of British birds, fluctuate in response to population levels of arctic rodents and larger than usual autumn influxes in Britain are thought to reflect a south and westwards shift of the Fennoscandian breeding range when small mammals in northern latitudes are in short supply.

RMF

Golden Eagle *Aquila chrysaetos*

Very rare vagrant from Europe: one record.

The only record was in 1895, although the details are a little confused. Browne, writing in VH, states one was recorded in *The Field* of November 16th 1895 by Mr H.S. Davenport, as having been seen at Skeffington on October 24th. Haines, however, recorded it as having been seen on October 27th and then being shot at Slate Wood, Easton (presumably Great Easton) on October 29th.

Golden Eagles breed over large parts of Europe, north-west Africa, the Middle East, Asia and North America. In Britain, they are mainly restricted to Scotland, although a pair regularly breeds in Cumbria; numbers declined seriously in the 19th century, but remained fairly stable during the 20th century (Gibbons *et al.* 1996) and a complete census in 1992 estimated a total British breeding population of 422 pairs (Stone *et al.* 1997). The species was included on the 'Amber List' of Birds of Conservation Concern (Gregory *et al.* 2002). Most are resident and sedentary and the chances of another Golden Eagle appearing in Leicestershire and Rutland are extremely remote; given the rather vague details of the only county record and lack of supporting evidence in the form of a specimen, its place on the county list is perhaps a little debatable.

RMF

Osprey *Pandion haliaetus*

Scarce introduced migrant breeder and scarce to uncommon passage migrant; formerly a rare to scarce passage migrant.

During the 19th century the Osprey was a rare visitor to the counties. Browne knew of eight records in Leicestershire, including one apparently shot at Edmondthorpe on the very late date of November 13th 1858;

the others, most of which were shot, were single birds at Sileby in 1840, Donington Park in October 1841, within the county boundary near Overseal in the autumn of 1841, Bradgate Park on both September 18th 1879 and in March 1887, Saddington Reservoir and Gumley from October 13th to 22nd 1882 and an undated record from Groby Pool. A similar pattern of occurrence was reported in Rutland by Haines, with several reports from Burley Fishponds and Exton Park including one at the latter site on the unlikely dates of February 21st and March 5th 1898. There was never any indication that breeding had taken place in the counties.

In the first part of the 20th century the only records mentioned in the LROS archives are of single birds at Cropston Reservoir on September 27th 1913 and Knipton Reservoir in October 1930. The Osprey remained a rare visitor to the counties from the 1940s to the mid-1970s, with records in just 13 of the 34 years between 1941 and 1974 involving a total of 23 individuals. All records during this period were of single birds except for two at Swithland Reservoir from May 30th to June 3rd 1967 and the only year in which more than two birds were seen was 1966, when five were noted. The vast majority occurred during the peak passage periods of April/May and August/September, although one was at Stanford Reservoir on July 12th and 13th 1966. Most records involved short-staying birds seen on one date only, but three autumn juveniles lingered for lengthy periods of time: at Cropston Reservoir from September 15th to 29th 1951 and September 16th to 28th 1956 and Fort Henry Ponds from October 1st to November 1st 1969. This species was particularly scarce during the late 1950s and early 1960s, the only record between 1956 and 1965 being one at Eyebrook Reservoir on May 28th 1959; likewise, the early 1970s was a lean period, with a single bird at Swithland Reservoir on May 20th 1973 being the only one between 1970 and 1975.

1974 was the last blank year in the counties for the Osprey and since then the number of birds occurring has increased significantly. The record annual total of five in 1966 was broken in 1984 when six were recorded; since 1988 there have only been three years in which numbers have not reached double figures. The best years have been 2002 (29 individuals), 2004 (28 birds), 1998 (23) and 1999 (21), although whether these higher numbers reflect an increase in 'natural' migrants rather than translocated introduced birds (see below) is doubtful.

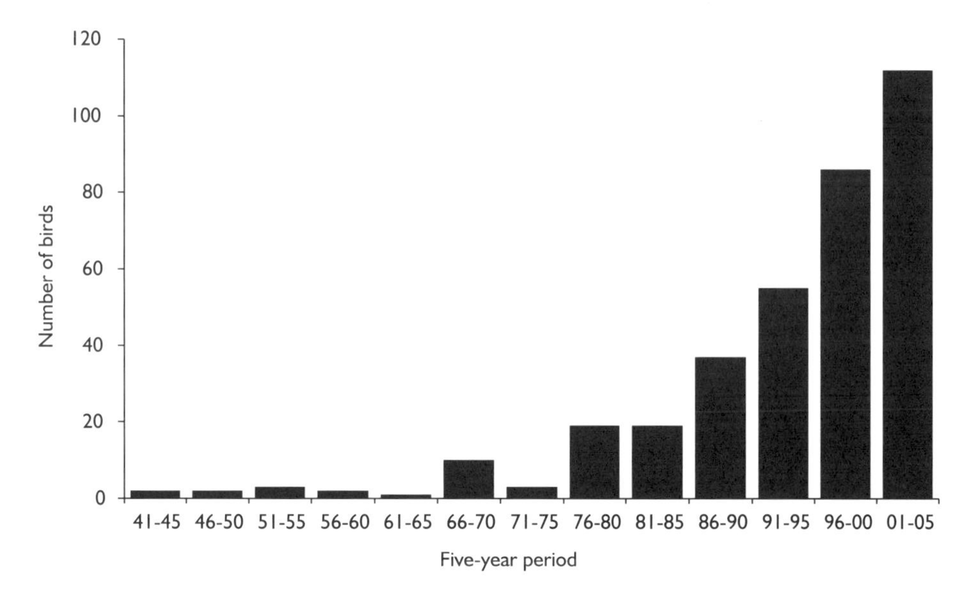

Figure 206: Numbers of Ospreys by five-year periods 1941–2005.

In 1994 a pair (probably a first-summer male and a first-summer female) summered at Rutland Water, raising the possibility that breeding might occur naturally at the site in the future. However, before natural recolonisation could be realised, a translocation project, organised jointly by English Nature, Scottish Natural Heritage, Anglian Water and the Leicestershire and Rutland Wildlife Trust, was implemented. Between 1996 and 2001 a total of 64 Osprey chicks were taken from nests in Scotland and raised at Rutland Water, with another 11 translocated in 2005. In 2001, a translocated male from 1997 ('03(97)') bred with an unringed female at a site close to Rutland Water, raising one chick, thus providing the first (albeit not totally natural) breeding record of

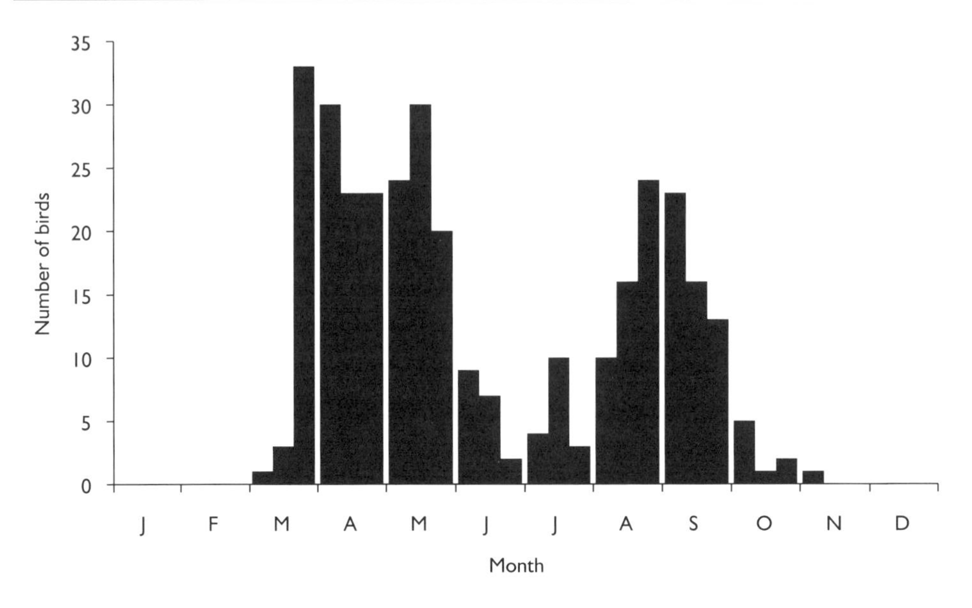

Figure 207: Monthly occurrence of Ospreys 1941–2005.

Osprey in England for over 150 years (Dixon 2002). Breeding has been attempted at Rutland Water each year since, as follows:

2002	translocated male '03(97)' and the unringed female attempted to breed but the chick(s) died during a prolonged period of heavy rain.
2003	translocated male '03(97)' and a translocated female '05(00)' raised three young and a translocated male '03(98)' and a translocated female '06(01)' raised two young. The female of the latter pair was the first known two year-old female to breed successfully in Britain.
2004	male '03(97)' and female '05(00)' raised two young.
2005	male '03(97)' and female '05(00)' raised three young.
2006	male '03(97)' and female '05(00)' raised two young
2007	male '03(97)' and female '05(00)' raised three young; a second pair in Manton Bay – male '08(97)' and female 5N which fledged from the 2004 brood – raised two young
2008	male '03(97)' and female '05(00)' raised two young; a second pair in Manton Bay – male '08(97)' and female 5N which fledged from the 2004 brood – failed during incubation
2009	two pairs incubating at the time of writing; the female '05(00)' of the original pair was replaced by an unringed bird (presumably Scottish)

Prior to the establishment of the small breeding population in the counties, spring passage extended from early April to late May, with late April to mid-May being the peak period. Prior to 1998, the only March records were of single birds at Eyebrook Reservoir on March 5th 1966 and Rutland Water on March 22nd 1987, March 27th 1989 and March 31st 1995. Since 1998, however, the first arrivals have been recorded in March every year, usually at Rutland Water during the last few days of the month. Despite this, none have come close to beating the individual at Eyebrook Reservoir on the March 5th in 1966 and the only arrivals prior to the 21st have been single birds at Eyebrook Reservoir on March 14th 2004, Thornton Reservoir on March 17th 2005 and Pickworth on March 20th 1998.

Departure dates have become significantly later since the mid-1990s. In most years the final birds are seen in mid to late September although there have been eight records of birds seen in October:

- juvenile, Fort Henry Ponds, October 1st to November 1st 1969.
- juvenile, Priory Water, October 23rd 1988.

- adult, Wanlip South Gravel Pits, October 22nd 1988.
- Groby Pool, October 15th and 16th 1944.
- two, Frolesworth Manor Lake, October 5th 2002.
- juvenile, Kirby Bellars Gravel Pits, September 23rd to October 3rd 1983, with presumably the same bird at Cropston Reservoir on October 2nd 1983.
- Sence Valley Forest Park, October 2nd 1999.
- Aylestone Meadows, October 1st 1998.

The latest record, however, involved a juvenile at Oakthorpe on November 8th 2005. It is interesting that there has never been an October record from Rutland Water, suggesting that these late individuals are passage migrants rather than birds from the local breeding population.

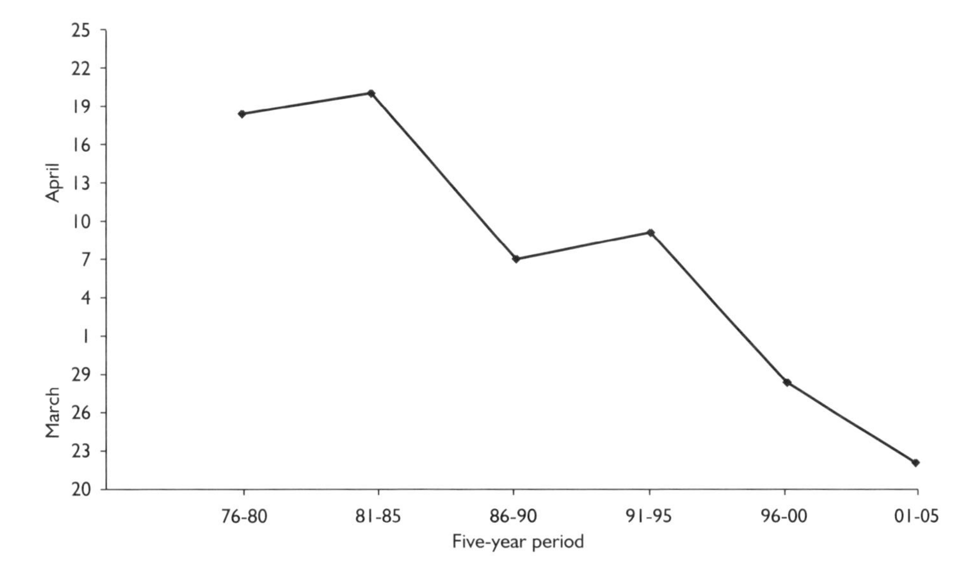

Figure 208: Average spring arrival dates of Ospreys by five-year periods 1976–2005.

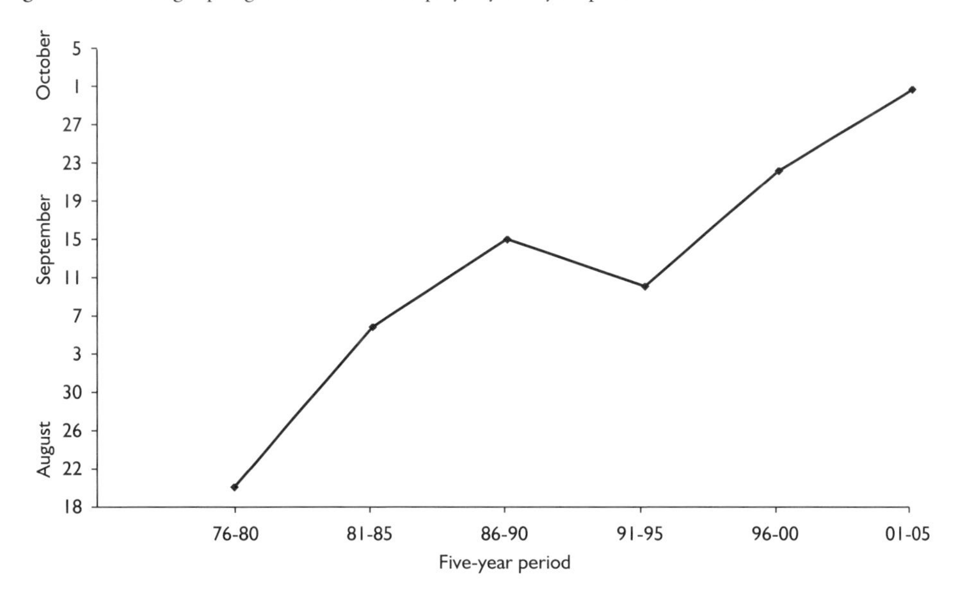

Figure 209: Average autumn departure dates of Ospreys by five-year periods 1976–2005.

There is a wealth of data regarding the movement of translocated juveniles from Rutland Water. The following had all been fitted with radio transmitters:

- one which left on August 21st 1999 was tracked to Segou (Mali) by November 1st 1999.
- one left on August 21st 1999 and spent the winter in Senegal, where it was still present on March 8th 2000.
- one left on August 30th 1999 and was south of Marrakech (Morocco) by September 9th and south of Saint-Louis (Senegal) by September 17th 1999.
- one left on August 23rd 2000 and stayed near Cádiz (Spain) until December 9th 2000 before spending the remainder of the winter near Saint-Louis (Senegal).
- one which left on August 30th 2000 was last tracked at sea north-west of Freetown (Sierra Leone) on November 12th 2000.
- one which left on September 3rd 2000 was in Mali by September 13th 2000.
- one left on August 23rd 2001 and was found dead at Tuineje, Fuerteventura (Canary Islands) on September 14th 2001.
- a female which left on September 2nd 2001 wintered by the River Tejo (Portugal) and then spent the summer of 2002 wandering between Wensleydale (North Yorkshire), Masham (North Yorkshire) and Berwick-upon-Tweed (Northumberland). This bird then returned to breed at Rutland Water in 2003.

In addition, one ringed at Rutland Water on July 9th 1999 had its ring read at Welbeck (Nottinghamshire) on June 7th 2001, whilst one ringed in Scotland on July 1st 1985 was found shot at Somerby on August 22nd 1985, providing a stark reminder of the difficulties raptors face from human persecution.

Ospreys breed patchily throughout Eurasia, northern and central America and Australia. Most European birds winter in west Africa, with some in India and south-east Asia. Intensive human persecution in the 19th century led to the extinction of this species as a breeding bird in England in the 1840s, with the last known nest being in Somerset in 1847, although small numbers continued to breed in Scotland until 1916. Ospreys returned to Scotland as a breeding species in 1954 when a pair attempted to breed at Loch Garten (Highland); numbers have steadily increased since then and in 2005 158 pairs were known to have laid eggs in Scotland (Holling *et al.* 2008). A pair from the Scottish population has nested at Bassenthwaite Lake (Cumbria) since 2001. In 2004 two pairs nested in Wales; the males were both birds that had been translocated from Scotland to Rutland Water in previous years. As the British breeding population is still under 300 pairs, the Osprey was added to the 'Amber List' of Birds of Conservation Concern (Gregory *et al.* 2002).

RMF

Kestrel (Common Kestrel) — ***Falco tinnunculus***

Fairly common resident breeder.

The Kestrel is Leicestershire and Rutland's commonest and most widespread raptor, as always appears to have been the case. During the 19th century, Browne described it as 'resident and generally distributed' in Leicestershire, although Haines considered it to be 'much persecuted by gamekeepers' in Rutland; he also thought that it was migratory, with comparatively few remaining through December and January.

The next comment on this species' status appeared in the first LROS Annual Report, in 1941, when it was described as 'resident and common'. The following year, it was considered that numbers were 'being maintained despite the attitude of some keepers' and comments in the Annual Reports for 1943, 1944 and 1946 indicated that Kestrels were increasing in the counties. It is known that, nationally, this species suffered a marked decrease between 1959 and 1963 due to toxic chemicals (Parslow 1967), although the only indication of this taking place in the counties was a statement in the 1960 Annual Report that the Kestrel was 'probably decreasing'. In 1961, it was thought that this species had not suffered the disastrous crash which had affected the Sparrowhawk at the time. It is worth remembering, however, that there were many fewer active observers in the early 1960s than today and population trends would have been difficult to monitor effectively. Fortunately, Griffiths (1967) carried out work on Kestrels in 1963 and 1964 and estimated a county-wide population of between 180 and 210 pairs, providing a useful baseline figure for future studies.

The most significant data on Kestrels in Leicestershire and Rutland was provided by Warrilow. During 1976–84, this species was recorded in 455 tetrads in the counties (71% of the total number of tetrads), with breeding confirmed in 106. The highest densities were in west and central Leicestershire and central Rutland, it being absent from parts of north Rutland and east and north-east Leicestershire; the latter areas are the main arable farming regions of the counties, where rough ground has been eliminated and outbuildings and other potential nest sites removed. Warrilow estimated a county-wide population during the period of this survey of 250–450 pairs, showing that it appeared to have made a recovery from the lower numbers in the 1960s estimated by Griffiths.

Local CBC data does not reveal much information about the fortunes of the Kestrel since Warrilow's work. At Newton Harcourt, Prior's Coppice and King's Hill Lodge, Uppingham, numbers have varied between none and two pairs throughout the period of each census, with no obvious patterns emerging. However, at Stoughton, Kestrels were not thought to have nested in any year between 1964 and 1974, but from 1975 onwards there were only four years without a confirmed breeding record, perhaps indicating that the population became more stable from the mid-1970s.

Kestrels nest in a broad range of habitats, including urban and suburban areas. Pochin (1954) stated that it was 'commonly reported as haunting the church spires' within the city of Leicester, whilst a survey in 1989 of four green spaces within the city boundary (Abbey Park, Aylestone Meadows, Knighton Park and Western Park) found this species to be present at all four sites, with breeding confirmed at three of them (Fray *et al.* 1990). Another habitat which the Kestrel uses is quarries and an interesting breeding record at Stoney Cove in 1999 saw two nests within ten metres of each other, fledging three and two young. The same male attended both nests; bigamy is exceptional behaviour in Kestrels as they are usually monogamous.

This species is usually seen singly or in pairs, although occasionally larger groups are recorded. Eight have been seen together twice (at Enderby on September 10th 1993 and Cossington Meadows on July 31st 2004) and nine were at Knipton on September 16th 2002. The largest numbers, however, were recorded at Leicester City Farms, where there were up to 15 in August and September 1967 and 'abnormal numbers . . . attracted by a plague of voles' in 1946.

Kestrels breed widely in Eurasia and Africa and the British population is estimated at approximately 35,400 pairs (Baker *et al.* 2006). National CBC data shows a decrease in numbers of 26% between 1973 and 1998 (Chamberlain & Vickery 2002) and this decline has resulted in the Kestrel being added to the 'Amber List' of Birds of Conservation Concern (Gregory *et al.* 2002). British birds are largely resident, although juveniles often disperse widely and there is a wealth of ringing data from Leicestershire and Rutland to back this up. A total of 13 birds originally ringed in the counties had moved over 100km when recovered; 12 of them were ringed as nestlings and were found later the same year. Eight had moved in a generally south-easterly direction, with the remaining four all heading between north-west and north. There have been four continental recoveries, all involving chicks ringed in Rutland:

- one ringed at an unspecified site in Rutland on June 17th 1968 was found shot at Eure-et-Loire (France) on September 29th 1968, a movement of 464km south-south-east.
- one ringed at Ketton on July 8th 1981 was found dead in France on October 27th 1981, a distance of 334km south-south-east.
- one ringed at Rutland Water on June 23rd 1992 was found dead at Paris (France) on June 12th 1993, a movement of 473km south-south-east.
- one ringed at Ketton Quarry on June 17th 1999 was retrapped at Brecht (Belgium) on an unspecified date later the same year, a distance of 383km east-south-east.

Populations in north and east Europe are migratory and although the Kestrel is not generally thought of as a passage or winter visitor to the counties, two ringing recoveries reveal that some birds in Leicestershire and Rutland are of Scandinavian origin: one ringed as a pullus in Norway on July 16th 1989 was found dead at Lutterworth on September 15th of the same year, having travelled 1,300km south-west and one ringed as a pullus at Lilballe (Denmark) on July 16th 1976 was found dead at Long Whatton on January 12th 1997, a movement of 764km west-south-west.

RMF

Red-footed Falcon *Falco vespertinus*

Very rare vagrant from eastern Europe or western Asia: six records.

The first county record was an immature male at Belgrave, Leicester on July 1st 1865, mentioned by Browne. It was shot by a Thomas Adcock who, according to Browne, 'was so nervous when he first saw it, thinking it was something rare, that he shot at it twice without effect. . .at the third attempt, he succeeded in shooting it.' The specimen was sold to the Leicester Museum and some years later was examined by Browne himself, who was satisfied with the authenticity of the record. It was not for another 91 years that this species occurred again but two were seen in 1956, beginning with a first-summer male found by Ron Hickling at Rothley Sand Pit on June 18th. This bird frequented a Sand Martin colony and arrived following heavy rain which had washed away the cliff-face, leaving nests containing chicks exposed; it remained until June 23rd. Later the same year, a juvenile was well seen and described by Peter Gamble at Loughborough Sewage Farm on September 25th; for some unknown reason this record was not accepted at the time and only came to light during a major review of past records in 2004 (Fray 2005). The three most recent records all occurred in the 1990s, the first of which was an adult male watched by Dave Gamble for ten minutes at Thornton Reservoir during the evening of June 28th 1991 (*BB* 85:520). In 1992, John Watts and Jim Sharpe found an adult male on the Egleton Reserve at Rutland Water on June 7th; this bird remained until June 13th and was seen and photographed by many observers (*BB* 86:467). Finally, a first-summer male, originally found by Ian Merrill, was present at Kelham Bridge on June 9th and 10th 1997 (*BB* 91:471).

Red-footed Falcons breed from eastern Europe through Russia and eastwards across southern Siberia and winter in south-west Africa. They are annual vagrants to Britain, being much more frequent in spring than autumn; this seasonal dichotomy is due to their spring migration route being much further west than that taken in the autumn. Spring records are often rather late in the season, the peak being late May to mid-June; five of the six county records have occurred between June 7th and July 1st, neatly matching this established vagrancy pattern. Numbers recorded in Britain vary considerably each year, the annual total usually being between five and 15, although periodic spring invasions have taken place, including 42 in 1973, 40 in 1989 and a remarkable 125 in 1992. The latter influx (which included the male at Rutland Water) was linked to the weather conditions at the time: a persistent anyticyclone over Scandinavia in late May and early June resulting in warm temperatures and light easterly winds (Nightingale & Allsopp 1994). By the end of 2005 this species had amassed almost 780 British records and consequently was removed from those assessed by the BBRC.

RMF

Merlin *Falco columbarius*

Scarce winter and passage visitor; recorded in all months between August and May, with the majority from October to February.

Browne and Haines both described the Merlin as an uncommon winter visitor in the 19th century. Browne cites at least seven individuals that had been shot in Leicestershire and stated that it had been 'taken occasionally at Belvoir', whilst Haines mentions at least 20 records known to him in Rutland, most of which also fell to the gun. Given the comparative lack of observers at this time, it seems reasonable to assume that this species occurred more frequently in the 19th century than it does today.

There is no local data on records during the early part of the 20th century, but it is known that this small dashing falcon suffered a drastic decline nationally in this period. This is reflected in the pattern of records from the formation of LROS in 1941 to the mid-1970s. Between 1941 and 1975 there were reports in just 14 years, involving 15 individuals, including a complete lack of records between December 11th 1962 and November 9th 1970. Numbers increased markedly through the late 1970s and 1980s and reached a peak in the 1990s, when 80 individuals were seen. The three best years all occurred in this decade, when there were 16 records in 1998, 11 in 1997 and ten in 1995. The early part of the 21st century looks set to continue in a similar vein, with 35 records between 2000 and 2005.

The majority of records occur between mid-October and mid-February, with smaller numbers during the passage periods in March, April and September. The earliest autumn migrant was a juvenile at Cropston

Reservoir on August 31st 1995, but occurrences during the first half of September are unusual. The only other autumn records prior to September 15th are:

- a first-winter male at Eyebrook Reservoir on September 2nd 1998.
- one at Stanford Reservoir on September 9th 1945.
- a female/juvenile at Frisby Gravel Pits on September 10th 1997.
- a female/juvenile at Ibstock Opencast (now Sence Valley Forest Park) from September 11th to October 5th 1997.

The data show that reports of this species drop off considerably in late February, before picking up again during March and early April as passage birds begin to return to their breeding grounds. There are few records after April 20th, the only ones being:

- a female at Enderby on April 23rd 1981.
- a female/immature at Cosby on April 25th 1985.
- one at Little Casterton on April 25th 1998.
- one at Eyebrook Reservoir on April 27th 1952.
- a female at Blakeshay Wood on May 7th 2002, with probably the same bird at Thornton Reservoir three days later.
- a female at Eyebrook Reservoir on May 13th 2001.

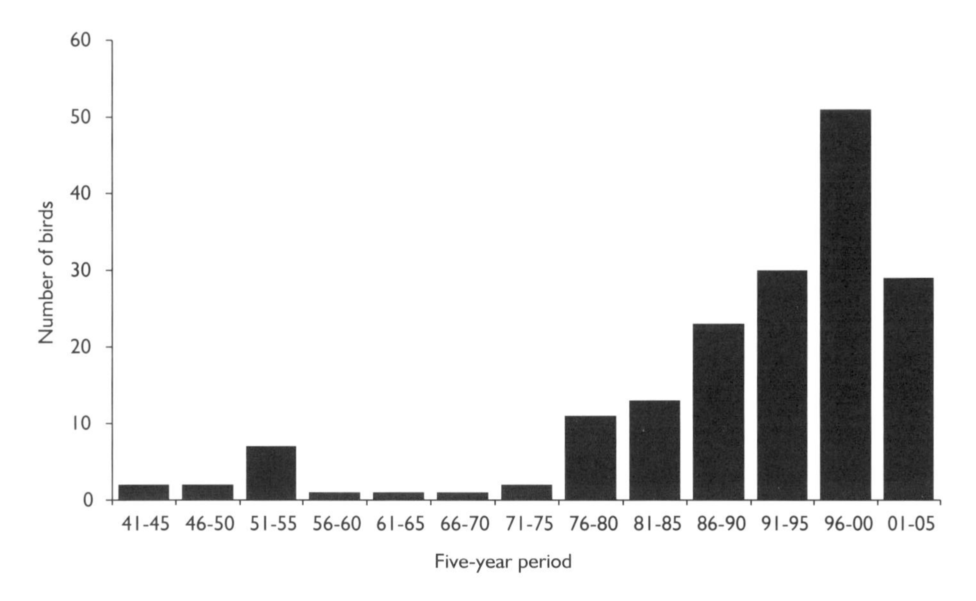

Figure 210: Numbers of Merlins by five-year periods 1941–2005.

A typical sighting of a Merlin in the counties is a brief view of a bird zipping across open countryside and the majority of records are of single birds seen on one date only. Only 20 of the 173 individuals reported since 1941 have been seen on more than one day, although there have been five which have embarked on exceptionally long stays:

- a female/immature in the Knipton Reservoir and Belvoir areas from October 9th 1994 to April 2nd 1995.
- a first-winter female at Oakthorpe from November 3rd 1996 to February 7th 1997.
- a male at Rutland Water and Eyebrook Reservoir from November 11th 1995 to January 27th 1996.
- a female/immature at Rutland Water and Eyebrook Reservoir from September 24th to November 24th 1995.
- a male at Branston from December 27th 1994 to February 26th 1995.

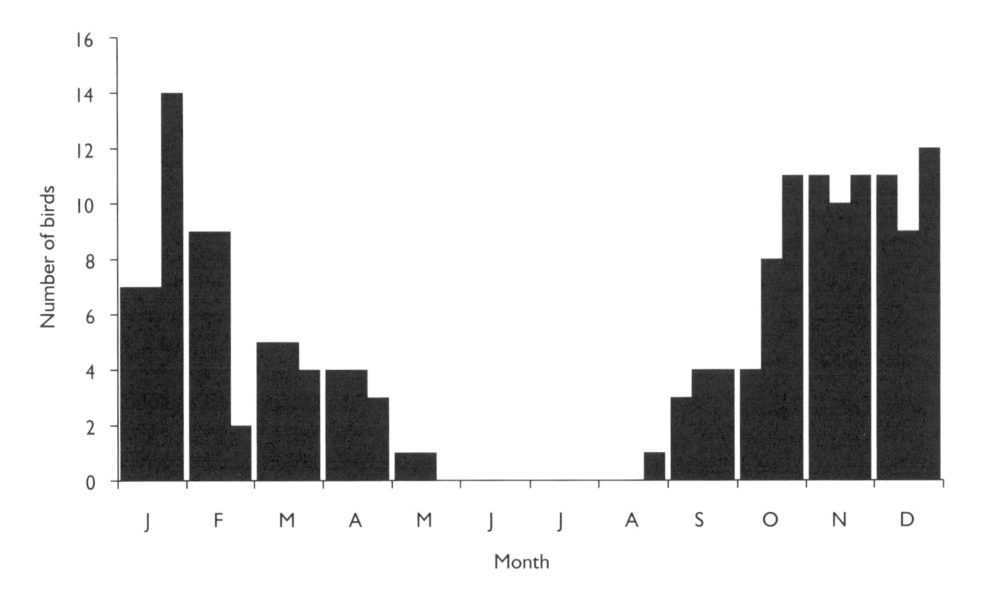

Figure 211: Monthly occurrence of Merlins 1941–2005.

Even these long-staying birds have, however, proved elusive: the Knipton Reservoir bird of 1994/1995, for instance, was only seen on five dates during its stay of almost six months.

Merlins can occur almost anywhere in the counties and have even been seen as close to Leicester city centre as Castle Hill Park and Beaumont Leys. Another unusual record was of one attempting to catch captive birds from an aviary in a suburban garden at Oadby on September 27th 1989, but these occurrences are the exceptions. Open countryside, old airfields and reservoir surrounds have provided the majority of records, especially in areas where large flocks of finches or other small birds are found. The most favoured site is Eyebrook Reservoir, which has 27 records to its name. The east and north-east of the counties have also provided many records, with particular concentrations around Rutland Water, Exton Park and the Vale of Belvoir. Elsewhere, Charnwood Forest fares well, as does the north-west of Leicestershire around Ibstock and Oakthorpe.

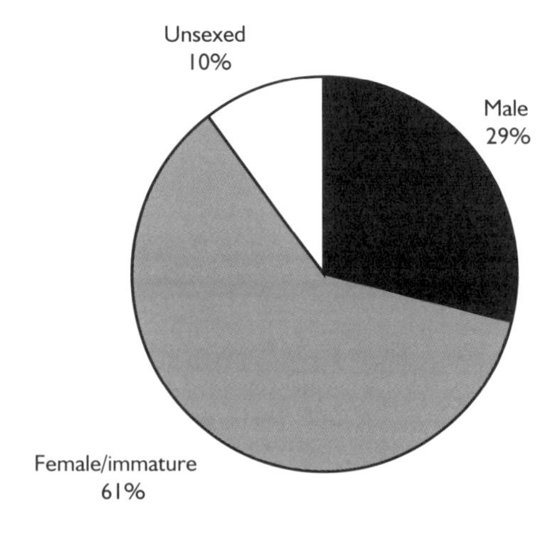

Figure 212: Sexes of Merlins recorded in Leicestershire and Rutland 1941–2005.

Most Merlins seen in Leicestershire and Rutland have been identified as females or immatures. It is likely that a good proportion of these will have been young birds rather than adult females, as it has been shown that young birds generally move further from the breeding sites in the winter months than the adults (Lack 1986). Adult males are very much in the minority, with only 29% of records referring to these. The remaining 11% have been unsexed.

Following review in 2004, two previously accepted records, both on exceptional dates, were found to be inadequately documented and are no longer considered acceptable: single birds at Quorn on July 3rd 1948 and Rutland Water on May 12th 1984 (Fray 2005). Merlin records suffer from a very high rejection rate and it is possible that a number previously considered unacceptable did in fact relate to this species.

Merlins breed throughout northern Eurasia and northern North America. Most populations are migratory and in winter this species can be found throughout Europe south of the breeding range, with a few reaching North Africa and the Middle East. In Britain, they breed thinly across most major areas of heather moorland, the nearest population to Leicestershire and Rutland being in the Peak District area of Staffordshire and Derbyshire. It is thought that the majority of British Merlins do not leave the country during the winter but move into the lowlands from their moorland breeding habitat (Lack 1986). This assumption is borne out in some way by the three ringing recoveries involving Leicestershire and Rutland: a first-winter male found dead at Earl Shilton in November 2004 had been ringed as a chick in County Durham on July 4th 2004, one ringed as a pullus at a Derbyshire breeding site on June 24th 1994 was found injured near Leicester on February 6th 1995 and a female ringed at a breeding site in Powys on June 2nd 1987 was found dead just inside the Rutland border near Stamford on February 20th 1992. The British breeding population is currently estimated at 1,300 pairs (Baker *et al.* 2006) and has shown an increase over the last 30 years following a drastic decline in the late 1800s and early 1900s (Gibbons *et al.* 1996). This historical population decline has resulted in the species being added to the 'Amber List' of Birds of Conservation Concern (Gregory *et al.* 2002).

RMF

Hobby (Eurasian Hobby) ***Falco subbuteo***

Uncommon to fairly common migrant visitor and scarce to uncommon breeder; formerly a rare vagrant.

During the 19th century the Hobby was a rare visitor to the counties. Browne described it as an uncommon summer visitant to Leicestershire which had bred, although the only breeding report he mentioned was at Houghton on the Hill in 1840. In Rutland Haines reported that it had been first recorded in the county in about 1858 when one was shot at Wardley Wood. Breeding appeared to be more regular than in Leicestershire, with nests reported at both Pickworth Great Wood and Casterton in about 1883, Burley in 1889 and 1890, Barnsdale in about 1890, Ayston in 1893 and Greetham in 1900. Both Browne and Haines mentioned records on unlikely dates: one apparently shot at Smeeton Westerby in January 1888 and one seen at Greetham on February 22nd and March 18th 1901. Neither of these reports can be regarded as reliable. The LROS archives mention a few records during the early part of the 20th century, including single birds at Stoughton in 1901, Barkby Holt in 1932, Uppingham in September 1938 and a pair shot at a nest at Oakham on June 17th 1935.

In the 30 years from 1941 to 1970, this species was recorded in 21 years. It was particularly scarce between 1954 and 1962, with the only records being single birds at Loughborough on September 9th 1956, Barrow upon Soar on October 4th 1956, Leicester on August 19th 1957 and Quorn on May 23rd 1958. In most years there were just one or two sightings, although up to eight were seen in 1968. Given the rarity of the Hobby in the counties during this period it must have been something of a surprise that a pair nested in an old Carrion Crow's nest near Shenton in 1953, successfully raising two young (Lapworth 1954). Breeding may have occurred in the Rothley/Swithland area in 1965 and 1967, when one or two were seen regularly throughout the spring and summer in both years, whilst in 1968 two adults and a juvenile were seen at Swithland Reservoir on August 3rd. During the first half of the 1970s numbers of this diminutive falcon increased, with at least 35 individuals seen between 1971 and 1975. A pair bred at a site in the south of Leicestershire in both 1974 and 1975 and another pair raised two young in the east of the counties in the latter year. Display was also noted at Stanford Reservoir in 1975.

During 1941–75 the majority of records occurred during May and August, with smaller numbers in June, July and September. The only April report was of one at Woolfox on the early date of April 7th 1950, whilst

October records were also scarce, the only ones being single birds at Barrow upon Soar on October 4th 1956, Eyebrook Reservoir on October 24th 1965 and Quorn on October 8th 1974. Records came from 42 sites during the period, concentrated mainly in two distinct areas: the south of Leicestershire, particularly Stanford Reservoir, where at least 12 birds were seen between 1949 and 1975 and Charnwood Forest, where Swithland Reservoir was particularly favoured. It was surprisingly scarce in Rutland, the only records away from Eyebrook Reservoir being the early bird at Woolfox in April 1950 and one at Wardley Wood on May 18th 1969.

Since the mid-1970s the status of the Hobby in Leicestershire and Rutland has changed to that of a scarce to uncommon breeder and an uncommon to fairly common migrant visitor. Breeding was confirmed in every year

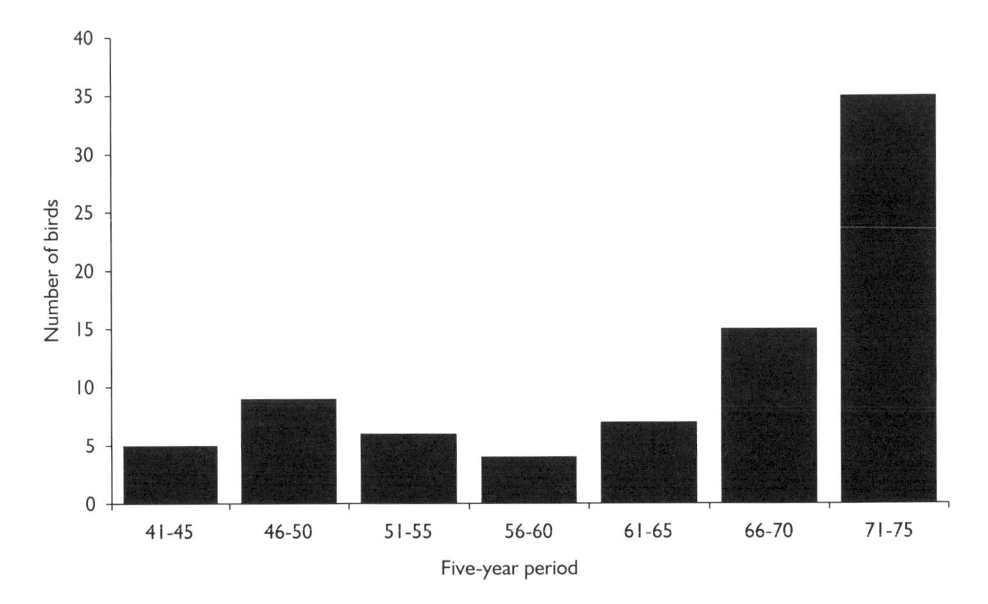

Figure 213: Numbers of Hobbies by five-year periods 1941–75.

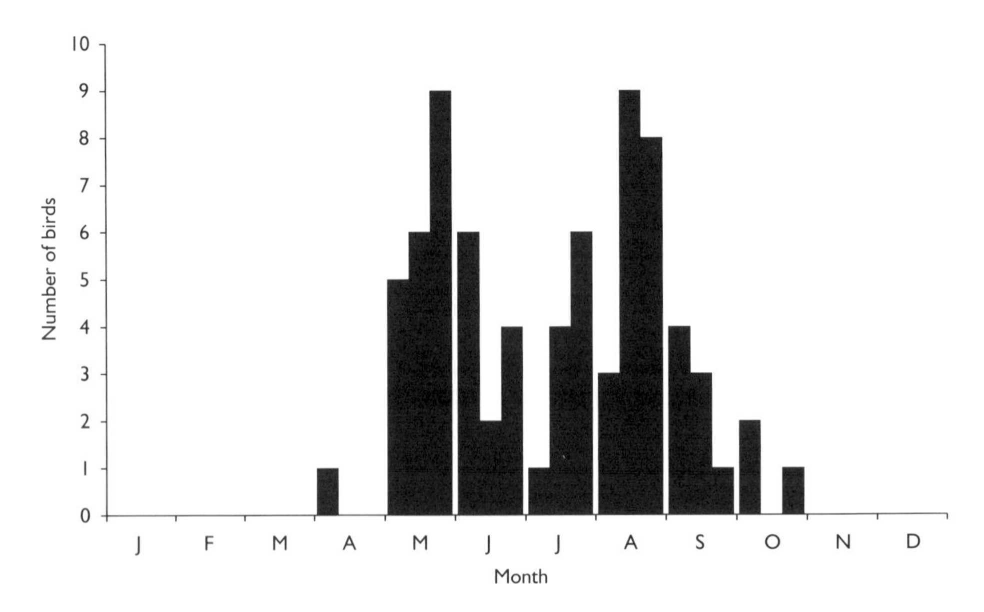

Figure 214: Monthly occurrence of Hobbies 1941–75.

between 1976 and 2002 except 1985, although it was not confirmed in 2003, 2004 and 2005. Hobbies are often very secretive when breeding and usually frequent areas of undistinguished farmland rarely visited by birdwatchers, so often the presence of fledged juveniles during the early autumn is the first indication that local breeding has taken place. The best year for confirmed breeding was 1988, when seven nests were found, although there were potentially as many as 19 pairs in 1998 and 17 pairs in 1990. Breeding was confirmed within the city boundary of Leicester in 1992.

The number of sites at which this species has been recorded has increased dramatically since the mid-1980s, peaking at 100 in 1990.

The average spring arrival date of this species has remained consistent at April 17th/18th since the early 1980s. There have been six records prior to April 10th, all of single birds, including the previously mentioned bird at Woolfox on April 7th 1950; other early arrivals are as follows:

- Enderby, March 27th 1982.
- Enderby, April 3rd 1988.
- Priory Water, April 8th 2000.
- Newbold Verdon, April 9th 1994.
- Groby/Anstey, April 9th 2000.

By contrast, the average autumn departure date of the Hobby has become later in recent years; prior to 1983 there had been only four records in October, but the final record has been in October every year since 1988.

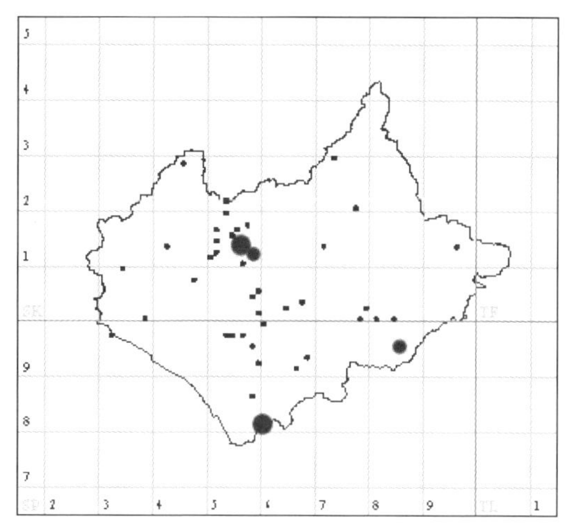

Dot = number of birds, 3 sizes of dot
1–2 (smallest), 3–5 (medium), 5+ (largest)

Figure 215: Distribution of Hobbies 1941–75.

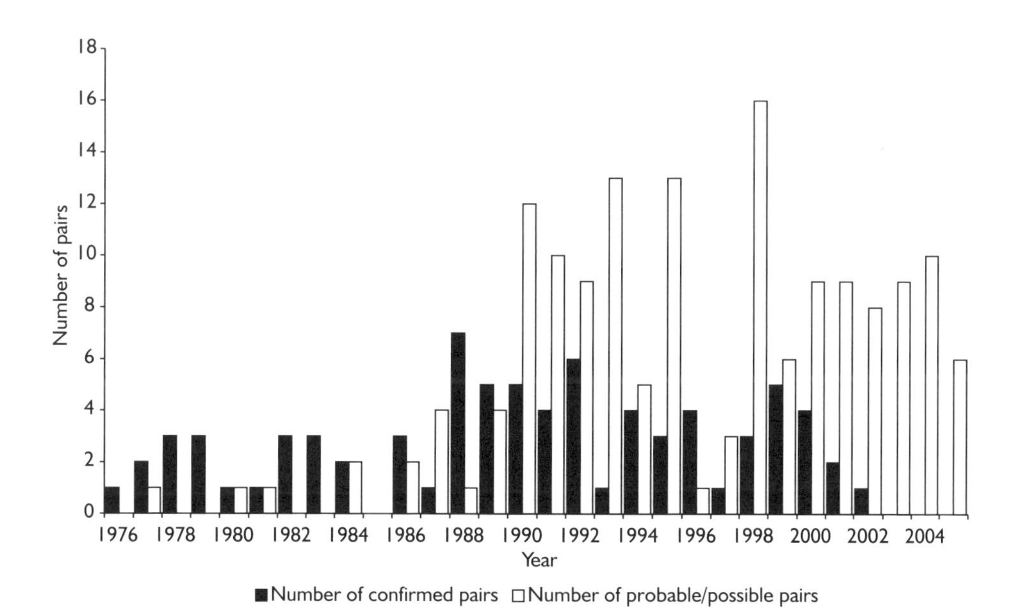

Figure 216: Breeding numbers of Hobbies 1976–2005.

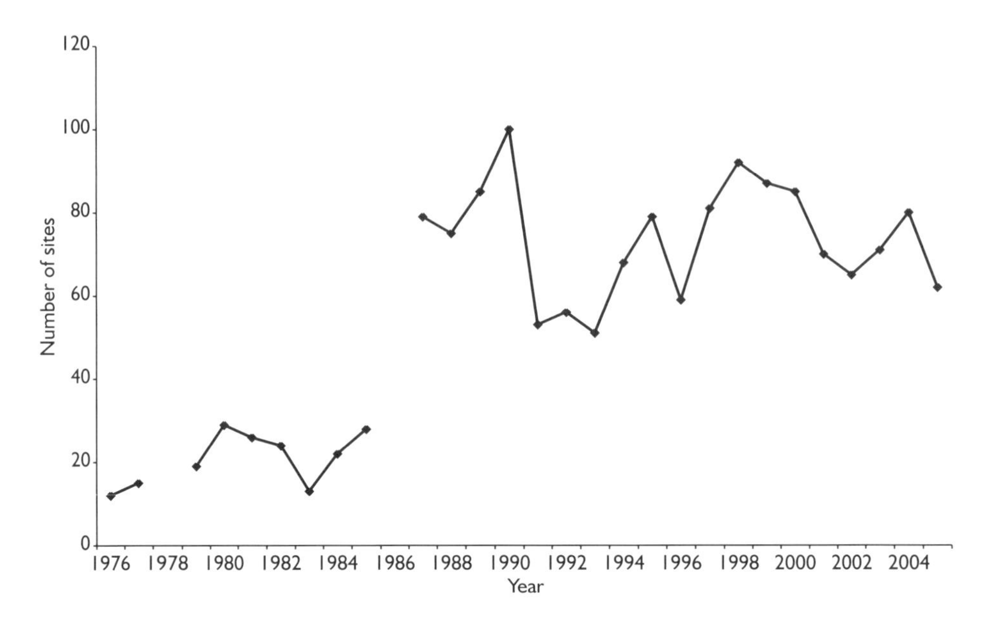

Figure 217: Number of sites with records of Hobbies 1976–2005.

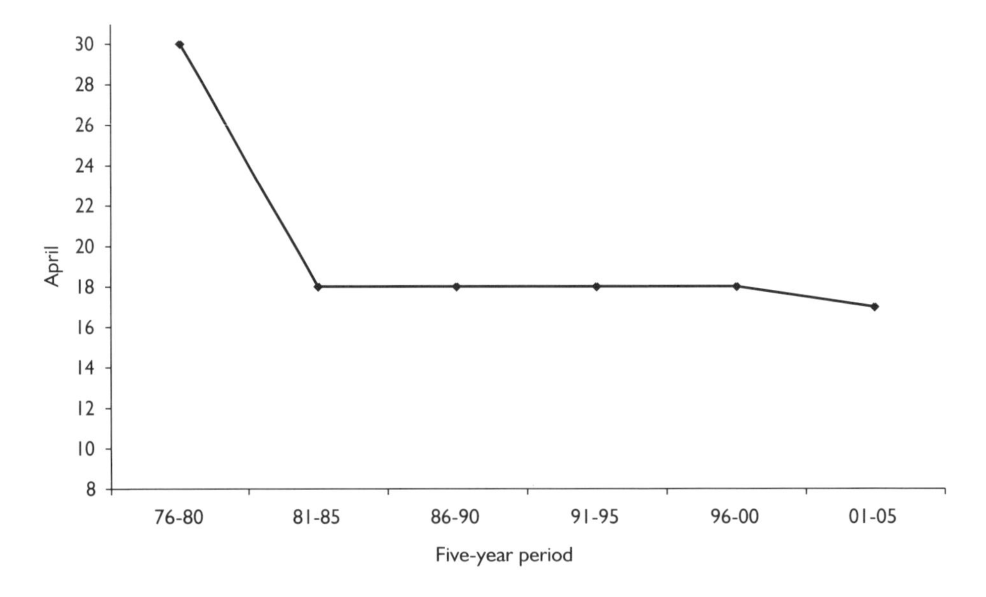

Figure 218: Average spring arrival dates of Hobby by five-year periods 1976–2005.

Seven have been seen later than October 15th, including that already mentioned at Eyebrook Reservoir on October 24th 1965; other late records, all of single birds, are as follows:

- Eyebrook Reservoir, October 30th 1996.
- Belgrave, Leicester, October 22nd 1984.
- near Stanford on Avon, October 20th 1991.
- Tinwell, October 19th 1997.
- Rutland Water, October 18th 1992.
- Leicester Forest East, October 16th 1983.

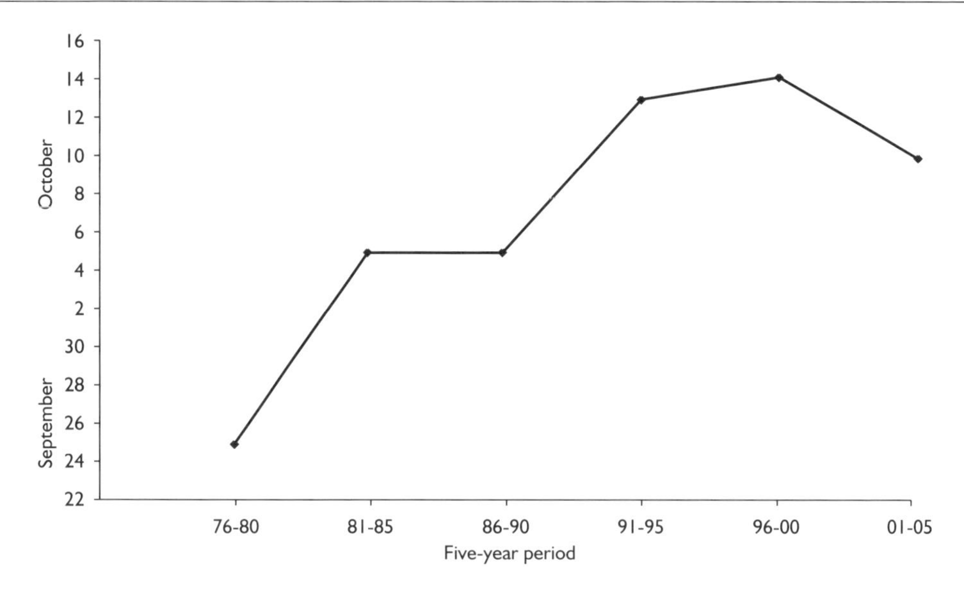

Figure 219: Average autumn departure dates of Hobby by five-year periods 1976–2005.

A recent phenomenon has been the occurrence of pre-breeding congregations, usually at food-rich wetland areas. Rutland Water has been the most favoured site for these small gatherings, with groups of seven on both May 18th 1997 and May 9th 1999 and six on June 5th and 6th 1998 being the highest counts. Elsewhere there have been five at Swithland Reservoir on both May 17th 1998 and May 12th 2001 and four at Quorn Borrow Pit on May 15th 1999, Lea Wood on May 12th 2001, Priory Water on May 15th 2005 and Eyebrook Reservoir on May 30th 2005. During the autumn small groups of up to five, usually consisting of family parties, are not uncommon and there have been two higher counts, both from Swithland Reservoir, of eight on September 9th 2001 and nine on August 30th 2004.

There are very few ringing recoveries involving Leicestershire and Rutland; the two most interesting concern a pullus ringed near Aylesbury (Buckinghamshire) on July 27th 1993 which was found injured near Melton Mowbray on April 30th 1996 and a pullus ringed at a breeding site in Leicestershire on August 7th 1998 which was found dead at Brackla, Bridgend (Wales) on May 9th 2000.

Hobbies breed over most of Europe, east through Asia, Japan and China and winter mainly in southern Africa and northern India. They are largely absent from Ireland and Scotland. In Britain they have spread markedly northwards since the 1970s; between 500 and 900 pairs were estimated during 1988–91 (Gibbons *et al.* 1993) but more recent estimates put the population at 2,200 pairs (Clements 2001).

RMF

Peregrine Falcon — *Falco peregrinus*

Scarce resident breeder, uncommon winter and passage visitor. Formerly a rare to scarce winter and passage visitor.

The Peregrine Falcon was a rare visitor to the counties in the 19th century: Browne described it as 'of rare occurrence' in Leicestershire, whilst Haines considered it a 'constant winter visitor, especially along the Welland valley' in Rutland. Its status during the first half of the 20th century was apparently similar, with the LROS archives stating that there had been 'a few records' during this period.

From 1941 to 1955, the Peregrine Falcon was a rare but regular visitor to the counties, with 37 individuals recorded during the period. The only blank years were 1943 and 1952; notable annual totals included seven in 1949 and five in

1951. The majority of records at this time occurred between November and May, although three were seen in July: single birds at Fleckney on July 4th 1947, Quorn on July 14th 1949 and St. Margaret's Church, Leicester on July 9th 1951.

From 1955 an alarming national reduction began due to the effects of organochlorine pesticides; by 1961, two-thirds of the pre-Second World War British population had disappeared. This was reflected locally, with records in only 11 of the 27 years from 1955 to 1981, involving just 16 individuals. There were long periods with no records, such as from October 1956 to February 1962, June 1968 to November 1973 and September 1977 to January 1981. All records from 1956 to 1981 are as follows:

- Ulverscoft, September 30th 1956.
- male, Stoughton Airfield, October 13th 1956.
- Queniborough, February 18th 1962.
- Loughborough, September 20th 1962.
- Wanlip, June 1st 1965.
- Leicester, November 10th 1965 and March 14th 1966.
- near Stanford on Soar, September 22nd 1966.
- Eyebrook Reservoir, August 15th 1967.
- Braunstone, Leicester, June 16th 1968.
- Cropston Reservoir and Swithland Reservoir, November 9th and 11th 1973; presumed same, Buddon Wood, February 10th 1974.
- East Goscote, September 9th 1974.
- Staunton Harold Reservoir, November 17th 1974.
- Wanlip Gravel Pits, December 4th 1975.
- Pickworth/Clipsham, January 18th 1976.
- Groby, March 12th 1977.
- Stanford Reservoir, September 24th 1977.

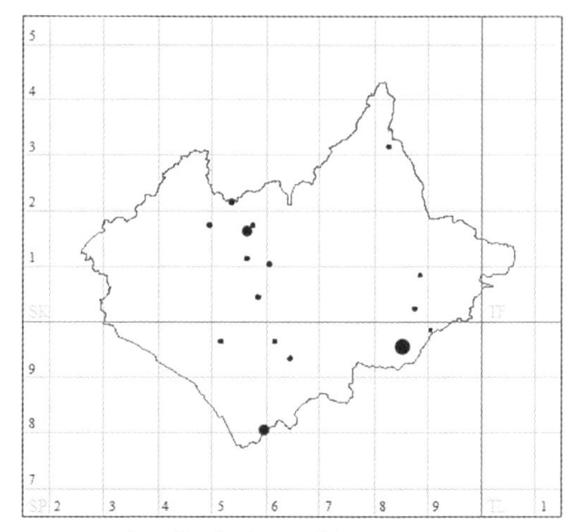

Dot = number of birds, 4 sizes of dot
1–2 (smallest), 3–4, 5–9, 10+ (largest)

Figure 220: Distribution of Peregrine Falcons 1941–55.

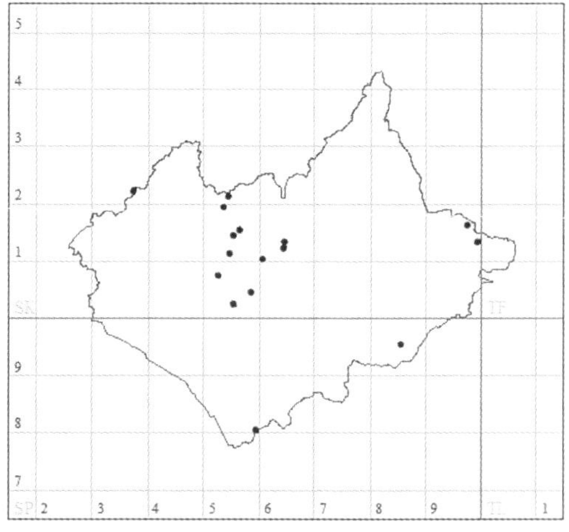

Dot = number of birds, 4 sizes of dot
1–2 (smallest), 3–4, 5–9, 10+ (largest)

Figure 221: Distribution of Peregrine Falcons 1956–80.

During the 1980s this majestic falcon recovered its pre-1955 status and once again became a regular, if scarce, visitor to the counties. Both Swithland Reservoir and Rutland Water became regular wintering sites during the decade and the first recorded multiple occurrence was two at Swithland Reservoir from February 2nd to 13th 1983; in 1990, at least two were at the same site in January and February and two were at Rutland Water from August 25th to October 21st. Away from these two sites this species was still rather rare, the only records from 1981 to 1990, all of single birds, being:

- Wanlip Gravel Pits, January 16th to February 19th 1981.
- Thurmaston, May 21st 1982.
- Peckleton, August 10th 1982; probably the same, Market Bosworth, August 21st 1982.
- juvenile female, Eyebrook Reservoir, August 18th 1984.
- Oadby, February 7th 1986; presumed same, Stoughton Airfield, February 15th 1986.
- juvenile found injured, Wymeswold, September 9th 1986.
- adult, Eyebrook Reservoir, September 16th 1988.
- juvenile male, Aylestone Meadows, December 17th 1988.

- Western Park, Leicester, June 12th 1989.
- juvenile female, Kirby Lakes, September 30th and October 7th 1990.
- juvenile female, Cropston Reservoir, October 13th 1990.
- Eyebrook Reservoir, October 21st 1990.
- female, Stanford Reservoir, October 28th 1990.
- juvenile found dead, Smeeton Westerby, November 18th 1990.

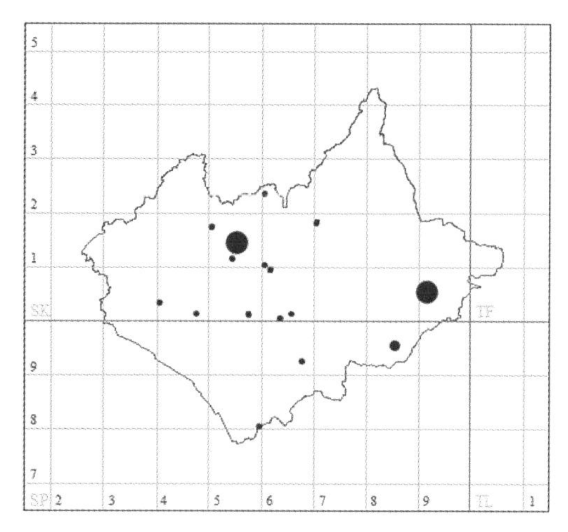

Figure 222: Distribution of Peregrine Falcons 1981–90.

The early 1990s continued in a similar vein to the previous few years, with regular wintering at Swithland Reservoir and Rutland Water and occasional records elsewhere. In 1993 an adult female remained at Swithland Reservoir until May 31st and the following year a pair bred at a quarry in Charnwood, successfully raising two young. Breeding has been confirmed every year since 1994 and by 2005 had taken place at a total of eight sites, all of which were quarries. Breeding has also been strongly suspected at another four quarry sites and in 2005 there were regular records from Leicester city centre, including a pair seen displaying, suggesting that nesting may take place there in future years.

With the establishment of a stable breeding population in the counties, reports have increased dramatically since the mid-1990s and in 2002 came from a record 64 sites.

A record of the 'North American' Peregrine Falcon *F.p. anatum*, allegedly shot at Newbold Verdon on October 31st 1891, was considered and rejected by the BOURC in 2003. This form was originally on the British List on the strength of this record, along with another in Lincolnshire in 1910, but as neither is now considered acceptable it has been removed from the British List (Harrop 2004).

Peregrine Falcons are cosmopolitan, breeding on all continents except Antarctica. At least 21 subspecies are recognised throughout the world. Northern and western European birds are sedentary, although there is some dispersal of juveniles, as evidenced by four ringing recoveries involving the counties:

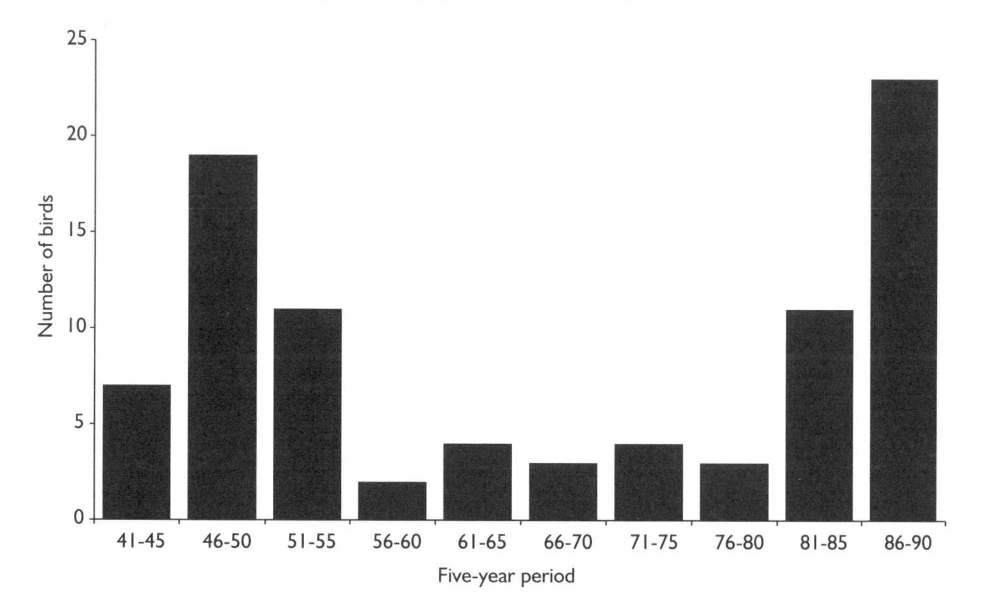

Figure 223: Number of Peregrine Falcons by five-year periods 1941–90.

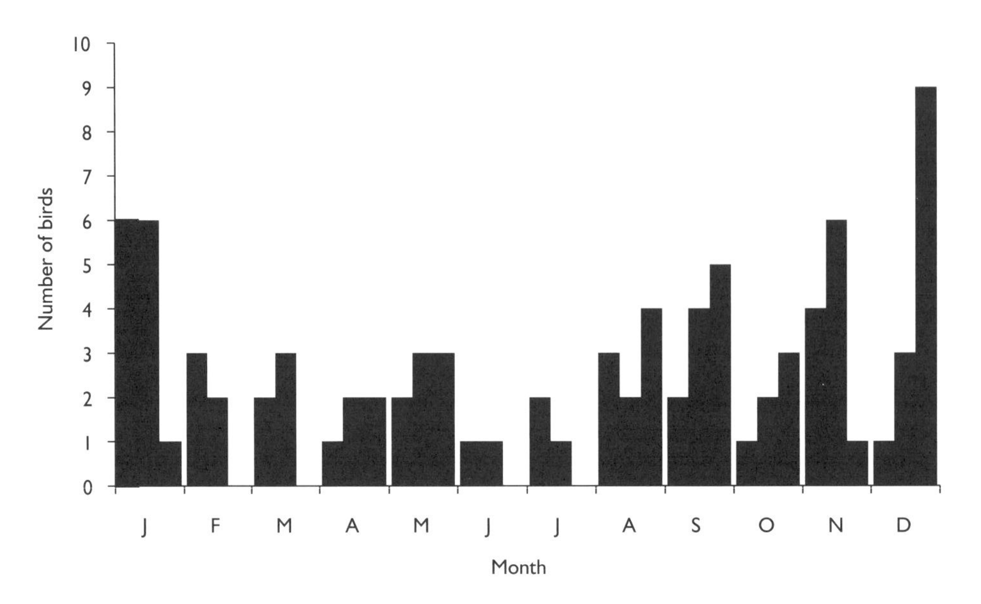

Figure 224: Monthly occurrence of Peregrine Falcons 1941–90.

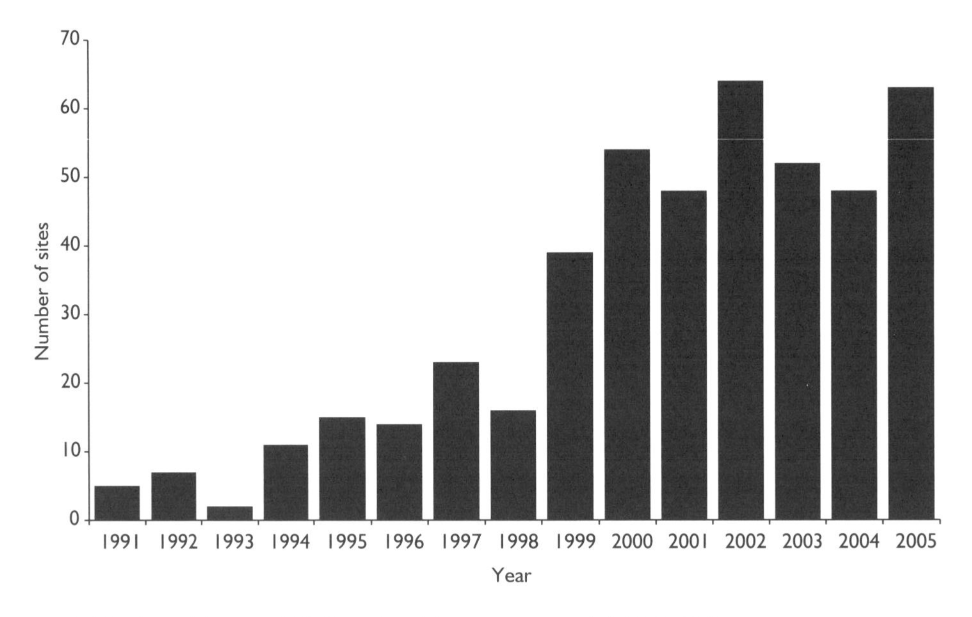

Figure 225: Number of sites at which Peregrine Falcons were recorded 1991–2005.

- a pullus ringed at a breeding site in Cumbria on June 8th 1990 was found long dead at Smeeton Westerby on November 18th 1990.
- a pullus ringed at a breeding site in West Yorkshire on May 27th 1994 was found injured at Castle Donington on October 24th 1995.
- a pullus ringed at a breeding site in Cheshire on May 19th 1998 was found injured at Shearsby on April 6th 1999.
- a pullus ringed at a breeding site in Rutland was found dead at Spalding (Lincolnshire) on September 28th 2002.

As mentioned above, this species suffered a marked decline due to the effects of persistent organochlorine pesticides from 1955, but the population has recovered since the 1980s and a national survey in 2002 found 1,402 breeding pairs in Britain, an increase of 10% on the 1991 figure and over 60% higher than the numbers recorded in the 1930s before the population crash (Baillie *et al.* 2006). Nevertheless, due to this species' potentially unfavourable conservation status, it has been added to the 'Amber List' of Birds of Conservation Concern (Gregory *et al.* 2002).

RMF

Water Rail *Rallus aquaticus*

Uncommon winter visitor, rare breeder.

Due to its skulking habits, the Water Rail is doubtless very under-recorded in the counties. In the 19th century Browne described it as 'resident but sparingly distributed' in Leicestershire, although he did not report on any breeding records. In Rutland this species' status was described similarly by Haines, who mentioned that breeding had occurred at Burley in 1902.

Today the Water Rail is a rare breeder and an uncommon winter visitor, although many breeding records must go undetected. Breeding has been confirmed in seven years since 1941:

1947 an adult with two small chicks was seen at Swithland Reservoir on July 15th.
1973 a pair bred at Exton, raising five young.
1975 a nest containing ten eggs was found at Wing.
1976 two pairs bred at Rutland Water and a pair was seen with one chick at Frisby Gravel Pits.
1992 a pair bred at Rutland Water.
2003 an adult with two chicks was seen at Birstall Gravel Pits on July 5th.
2004 a pair bred at Rutland Water, where they were seen with two chicks on August 1st.

Circumstantial evidence suggesting local breeding has also occurred in nine years:

1982 regular summer records at Aylestone Meadows.
1989 records from four sites during the summer: Rutland Water in June and August, Swithland Reservoir in July and August, Birstall Gravel Pits in August and Lockington Marshes, where breeding was strongly suspected and a juvenile was seen on September 3rd.
1990 a juvenile was at Rutland Water on August 12th.
1995 a pair probably bred at Wanlip South Gravel Pits, where juveniles were seen on August 9th and 11th. In addition, a female was giving the 'courtship song' at Priory Water from June 11th to 18th and juveniles were noted at Stanford Reservoir on July 14th, Thornton Reservoir on August 22nd and Rutland Water on August 27th.
1998 a juvenile was at Rutland Water on August 4th.
1999 a juvenile was at Groby Pool on August 26th and 28th.
2001 a juvenile was at Groby Pool on July 8th.
2004 at least one summered at Birstall Gravel Pits.
2005 a pair probably bred at Watermead Country Park North and a juvenile with a bill that was not fully grown was at Rutland Water on September 9th.

The number of Water Rails wintering in the counties is something of an unknown quantity. From 1941 to 1984 the number of sites at which Water Rails were recorded varied between just one in 1964 to 13 in 1949 and 1975, but since the mid-1980s the number of sites has increased significantly, although this may be down to increased observer coverage. Over 20 occupied sites have been visited annually in eight of the 11 years between 1995 and 2001, with 28 sites in 1999 and 27 sites in 2003 being the best years.

Water Rail numbers peak in November, December and January; the highest monthly totals are 41 birds in December 1999, 33 in November 2002 and 31 in November 2001. There are early April records in most years, although after then birds are scarcely recorded and the small number located between mid-April and mid-August probably refer to breeding birds.

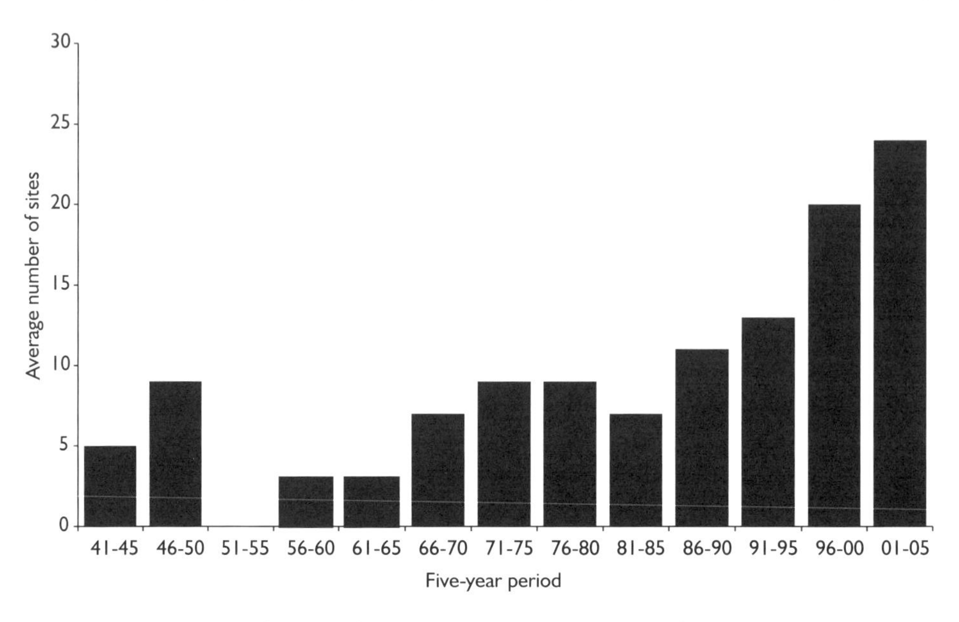

Figure 226: Average number of sites at which Water Rails were recorded by five-year periods 1941–2005.

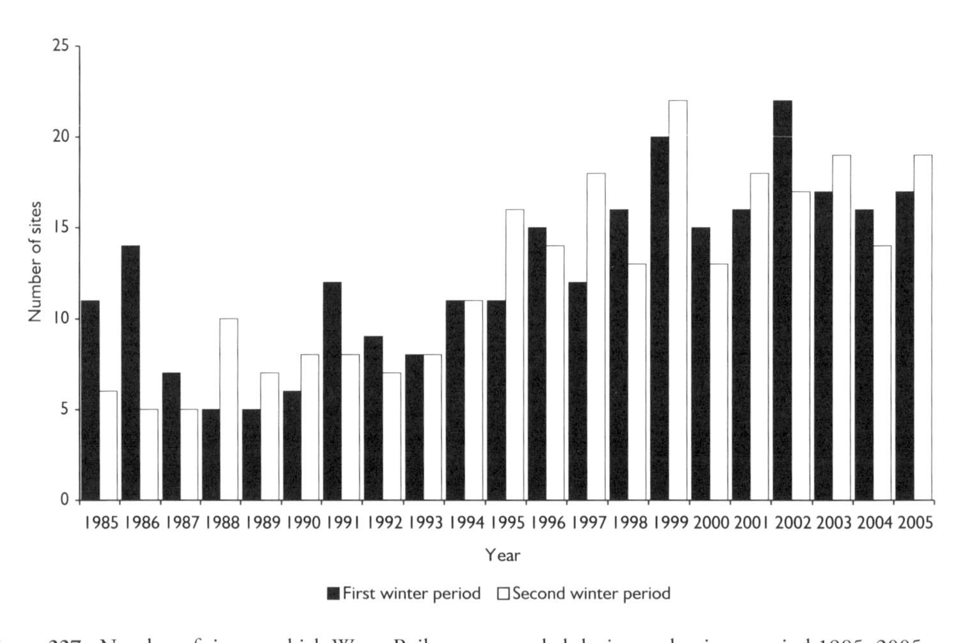

Figure 227: Number of sites at which Water Rails were recorded during each winter period 1985–2005.

Water Rails are rarely found in sizeable congregations, although areas of suitable habitat may contain several scattered birds. Apart from an exceptional 15 to 20 in a field by the River Soar at Birstall on December 14th 1953, the highest counts have come from Rutland Water in recent years as the various areas of reedbed mature:

- 12 on December 19th 1999.
- ten on December 6th 1998.

- ten on December 21st 2000.
- eight on November 17th 2001.
- eight on March 23rd 2003.
- eight on November 14th 2004.
- seven on February 10th 2002.

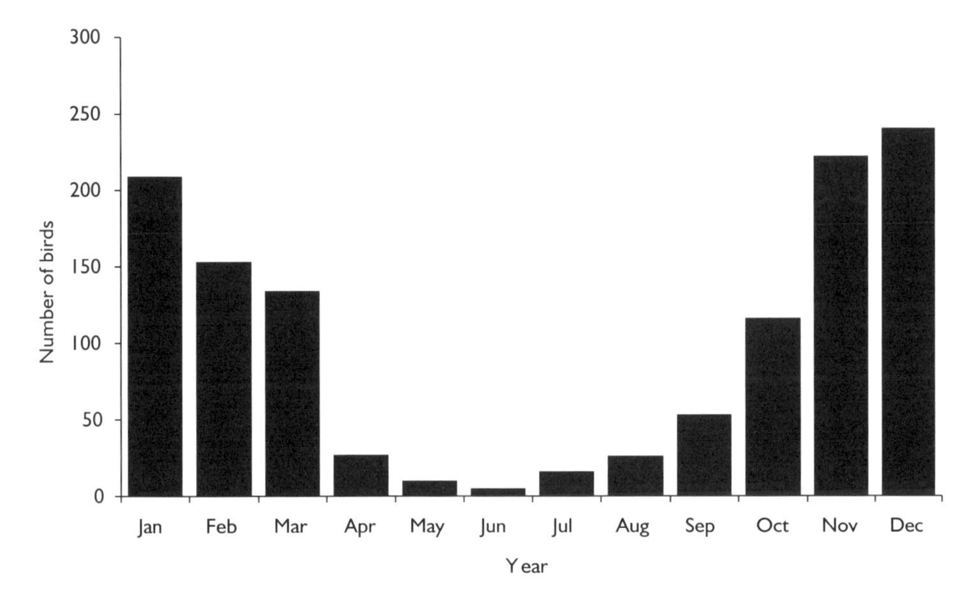

Figure 228: Monthly totals of Water Rails 1994–2005.

However, to show how difficult it is to determine Water Rail numbers accurately, the highest count at Rutland Water during 1995 was of five on both November 8th and December 9th but 24 were trapped and ringed in the Lagoon III reedbed during the year.

Counts of four or more are relatively scarce away from Rutland Water and have been recorded at just eight sites, where the maxima are:

- seven at Melton Country Park on March 4th 2001.
- six at Priory Water on December 5th and 31st 1999 and January 6th 2002.
- six in the Bistall Gravel Pits/Wanlip South Gravel Pits area in November 2003.
- five at Swithland Reservoir on November 24th 1985.
- five at Groby Pool on November 18th 1998.
- four at Kelham Bridge on December 12th 1990.
- four at Watermead Park on January 12th 1997.
- four at Groby Pool on November 15th 1997.
- four at Trent Valley Pit on November 17th 2002.

Water Rails breed in western Europe and north-west Africa through central Asia to Japan. Populations in western and southern Europe are generally sedentary, but birds from northern and eastern Europe are migratory. The British breeding population is estimated at between 450 and 900 pairs (Baker *et al.* 2006) and as there has been a moderate contraction of the breeding range over the last 25 years this species has been added to the 'Amber List' of Birds of Conservation Concern (Gregory *et al.* 2002).

RMF

Spotted Crake *Porzana porzana*

Rare vagrant from Europe, mostly in autumn: 12 modern records. Formerly a localised migrant which probably bred.

This species was much more frequent in the 19th and early 20th century than it is today. Browne described it as 'sparingly distributed; probably breeding' in Leicestershire and noted that specimens were obtained at Knighton in July 1883 and Quorn in the autumn of 1906, whilst two were found dead between Loughborough and Barrow upon Soar in early September 1889, having apparently been killed by flying into telegraph wires. The status of the Spotted Crake in Rutland during this period was much the same. Haines stated that it was 'not rare; found on the Gwash and Welland' and also noted several specimens: single birds picked up dead at an unknown site on January 16th 1883, killed at Preston in the autumn of 1893, killed by flying into telegraph wires near Oakham in September 1897 and shot near Burley in 1903.

Since the days of Browne and Haines, there have been 12 documented records, as follows:

1946	shot, Kilby Bridge, September 21st. The specimen is retained at the Leicester Museum.
1963	found dead, Cropston Reservoir, October 6th. The specimen is retained at the Leicester Museum.
1966	Hugglescote, September 24th.
1974	Market Harborough Sewage Farm, April 20th and 24th.
1984	Eyebrook Reservoir, April 28th.
1986	Stanford Reservoir, May 2nd.
1987	adult, Rutland Water, September 27th.
1995	juvenile, Wanlip South Gravel Pits, August 6th to 15th.
	juvenile, Stanford Reservoir, September 3rd to 9th.
1996	Rutland Water, August 9th.
2001	Thornton Reservoir, September 15th to 16th.
2002	juvenile, Eyebrook Reservoir, September 16th to October 5th.

The pattern of recent records shows the expected preponderance of autumn occurrences with the occasional spring record. Nine reports have been between August 6th and October 6th; of these, five have been found between September 15th and 27th. It is worth noting that the only year in which there has been more than one record (1995) saw a particularly large national influx of Spotted Crakes during the autumn (Fraser *et al.* 1997). Only four of the autumn birds have been aged but the majority of the remainder seem likely to have been juveniles. Due to this species' skulking habits it is not unreasonable to assume that many more pass through the counties' reedbeds undetected.

Two undated specimens are currently held at the Leicester Museum, from Stapleford Park and Sketchley, near Hinckley. It is not known whether these originate from the era when this species was more frequent in the counties, or are more recent records that have been inadequately documented.

In addition, after reviews carried out in 1994 and 2004 (Mackay 1995a, Fray 2005) the following records, which had previously been published, were no longer considered to be acceptable:

1961	Stanford Reservoir, February 5th.
1971	Stanford Reservoir, October 23rd.
	Wanlip, December 12th.
1977	Rutland Water, August 21st.
1982	Shacklewell Hollow, December 5th.
1987	Wistow, February 28th.

Spotted Crakes breed locally over most of Europe, east to south-west Siberia and north-east China. In Britain, it was much more widespread in the 18th and 19th century, but a marked decrease began in the latter century which continued until the mid-1900s. Numbers have since stabilised, but it remains a scarce breeder in Britain. A national census in 1999 revealed between 46 and 77 singing males at 40 localities (Gilbert 2002), the majority of which were in Scotland, although a persistent population has existed in Cambridgeshire for a number of years. Due to the small and localised nature of the British breeding population, this species has been added to the 'Amber List' of Birds of Conservation Concern (Gregory *et al.* 2002).

RMF

Little Crake *Porzana parva*

Very rare vagrant from Europe: one record.

The only record generally regarded as reliable is quoted by Browne, who states that one was shot near Leicester in January 1841 and was afterwards eaten. According to Haines, a Mr Elliot noted it as 'found on the Gwash and Welland' and mentions one undated specimen that had apparently been killed at 'Casterton'. This statement from Haines was ignored by Hickling, probably wisely, as although this species was encountered more frequently in Britain in the 19th century, it was by no means regular anywhere and Mr Elliot was presumably seeing either Water Rails or Spotted Crakes.

Little Crakes breed sparingly across Europe and western Asia, from Spain and France in the west to Kazakhstan in the east, although the breeding range is imperfectly known due to the species' secretive habits. They winter mainly in north-east Africa, south of the Sahara. There have been over 105 British records, although only 21 of these have been since 1970. This is perhaps one of the most tenuous species on the county list, given the rather scant evidence provided. Despite it now being a very rare bird in Britain, it could conceivably appear in Leicestershire and Rutland again, especially given the fact that four of the British records since 1970 have been in neighbouring Nottinghamshire, including a remarkable sequence of three individuals at Attenborough Gravel Pits between 1975 and 1983.

RMF

Baillon's Crake *Porzana pusilla*

Very rare vagrant from Europe: one record.

One was caught by a cat at Fleckney on May 19th 1970 but was rescued by J.C. Badcock and Clifford Holt; it was missing its tail, but otherwise appeared unharmed. After being photographed, it was released at Saddington Reservoir but was never seen again (*BB* 64:348).

Baillon's Crakes are locally common breeders from Spain patchily east through the Mediterranean basin to Ukraine and southern Russia and occasionally north to the Netherlands. The species also breeds across warm temperate Asia to Japan, as well as in Australasia, Madagascar and south-east Africa. European breeders winter mainly in the eastern half of sub-Saharan Africa. During the 19th century, this species was fairly regular in Britain and even bred in eastern England in 1858 and 1889; however, it is now a very rare vagrant, with only 16 British records since 1950. The Fleckney bird was just the third to be found in this country since 1950 and is the only modern record in the Midlands; there are three records from Nottinghamshire and one from Derbyshire, the most recent of these being in 1922. The majority of recent British records have been in spring, like the Leicestershire individual.

RMF

Corn Crake *Crex crex*

Formerly an uncommon to fairly common migrant breeder; now a very rare vagrant unrecorded since 1982.

The Corn Crake is undoubtedly the species in Leicestershire and Rutland which has suffered the most spectacular decline since the 19th century. At this time Browne described it as 'a summer migrant, generally distributed and breeding', whilst Haines stated that, in Rutland, it 'occurs all over the county'. Corn Crakes were so widespread during this period that little information was given by these two authors on the exact distribution of this species, although Browne refers to a nest containing nine eggs which was found in July 1883 in a field by Aylestone Mill and Haines mentions breeding at Exton, Seaton, Uppingham and Caldecott.

Towards the end of the 19th century, some authors started to note that numbers were decreasing (Holloway 1996). Haines was one of these; he confirmed that by the end of the 19th century this species was being found 'in decreasing numbers since the fields have been mown by machinery and its eggs and young birds thus destroyed'. In addition, a Mr W.J. Horn, writing to Browne in 1907, stated that Corn Crakes were less common in the Market Harborough district than formerly.

Unfortunately, there is little information available on the status of the Corn Crake in Leicestershire and Rutland during the first 40 years of the 20th century, although the LROS archives state that it began declining around 1915 but was still fairly common up to 1928. By the time LROS was formed in 1941, it is clear that this species had suffered a serious decline; the 1941 Annual Report sums up its status as 'local and uncommon, considerably decreased in recent years'. Numbers appeared to be maintained throughout a large part of the 1940s, but a major decline set in after 1947.

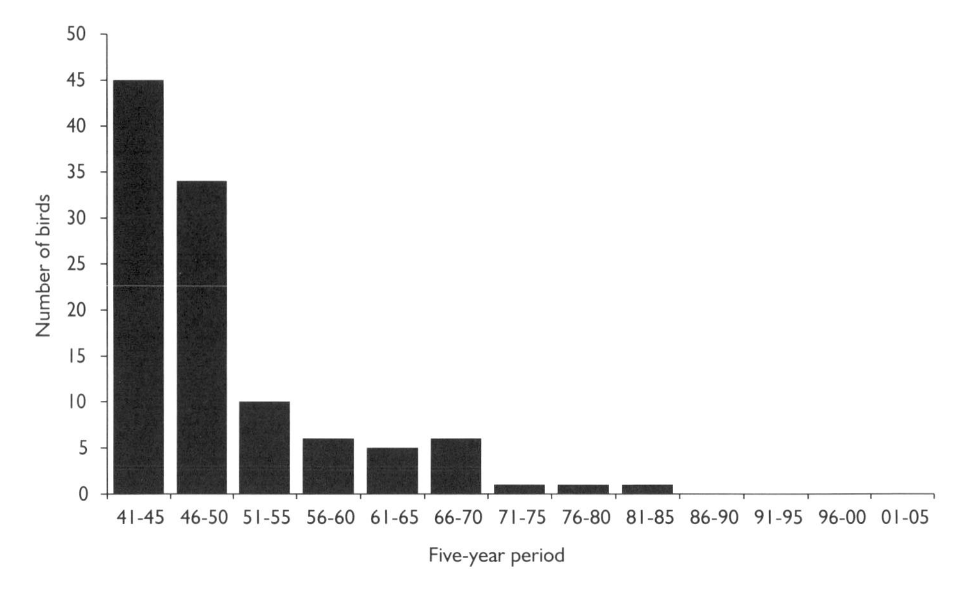

Figure 229: Numbers of Corn Crakes by five-year periods 1941–2005.

Even though reasonable numbers were still to be found in the 1940s, serious fluctuations were noted; there was only one record in 1941, but at least 16 birds were located in both 1944 and 1947, along with 14 in 1945. The stronghold for this species was the Soar valley to the north of Leicester, where records during this period included the following:

1944	three pairs at Mountsorrel Osiers, another three pairs between Barrow upon Soar and Mountsorrel and one pair at Sileby.
1945	up to 12 singing males between Barrow upon Soar and Birstall.
1946	single singing males at Barrow upon Soar, Sileby, Mountsorrel and Normanton on Soar, with two singing at Syston.
1947	eight singing males between Cossington and Barrow upon Soar, along with two at Quorn.

From a seemingly stable situation in 1947, the Soar valley population died out surprisingly quickly and the only subsequent records from this area were of single singing males at Mountsorrel Osiers on April 15th 1948, Normanton on Soar on April 14th 1950, Cossington on June 7th 1950 and Syston on June 9th 1954.

As the distribution map shows, the range of this species had clearly contracted by the 1940s. A large proportion of records away from the Soar valley came from nearby areas in north Leicestershire such as Anstey, Long Whatton, Garendon Park, Bardon Hill, Swithland Reservoir, Hoton, Woodhouse and Ibstock, whilst Corn Crakes hung on at Leicester City Farms until 1950, from where there were records in five years between 1941 and 1950, including three singing in June 1942. This species had all but abandoned other areas of the counties by the 1940s; three individuals at each of Stanford Reservoir, Narborough/Enderby and Oadby/Great Glen during the period hinted at possible lingering populations in these areas, but otherwise Corn Crakes were already extinct over the remainder of the counties.

The inexorable slide towards local extinction accelerated during the 1950s. There were only 16 individuals recorded between 1951 and 1960 and, of these, seven were passage birds found in September. The Soar valley

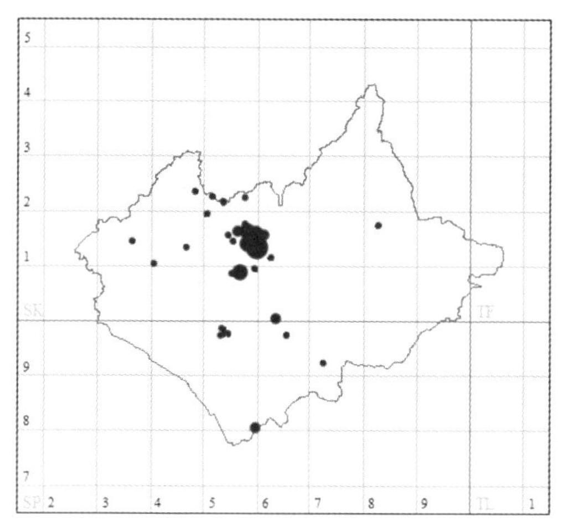

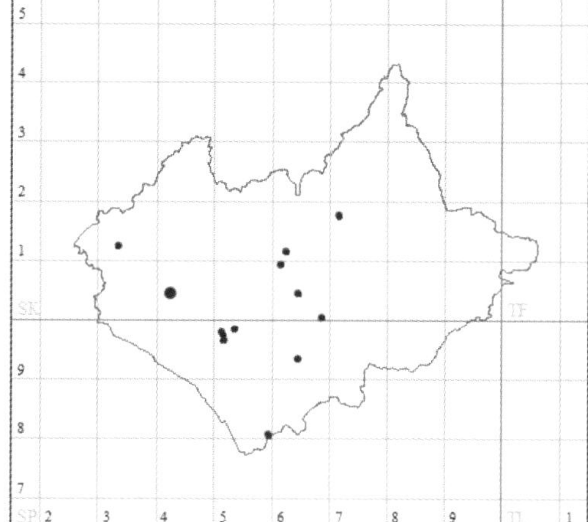

Dot = number of birds, 4 sizes of dot, 1–2 (smallest), 3–4, 5–9, 10+ (largest)

Figure 230: Distribution of Corn Crakes 1941–50.

Figure 231: Distribution of Corn Crakes 1951–60.

population had disappeared and records came from various widely scattered locations throughout Leicestershire, although interestingly there were again reports from Stanford Reservoir and the Enderby/Croft/Huncote area.

The period 1961 to 1970 saw a total of 11 records, nine of which involved singing males. However, no site recorded this species on more than one occasion during the decade and perhaps the most notable sighting was of one at Shacklewell Hollow in August 1970, the only confirmed record in Rutland since the time of Haines.

There have only been three records since the Shacklewell Hollow bird of August 1970: one near Weston by Welland in September 1974 and lone singing males at Kirby Muxloe on May 4th 1979 and between Breedon on the Hill and Osgathorpe for two weeks from June 19th 1982.

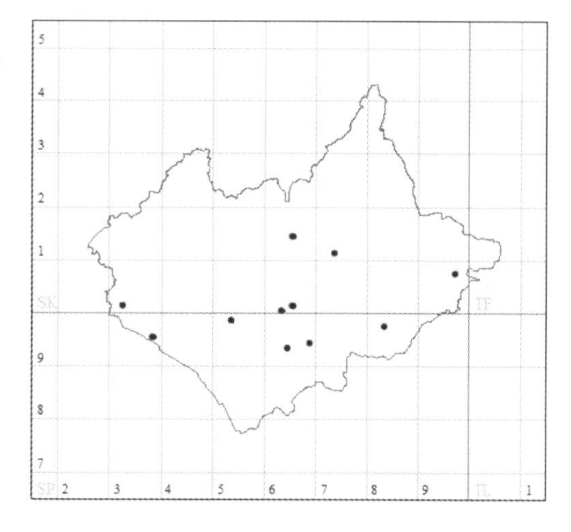

Figure 232: Distribution of Corn Crakes 1961–70.

When Corn Crakes occurred in the counties on a regular basis the majority of birds appeared to arrive in two waves, in mid-April and then from mid-May to mid-June. The earliest arrivals were singing males at Oadby from April 7th to 9th 1944 and April 7th to 12th 1945. Birds which were apparently on autumn passage were recorded from mid-August to mid-September, although the latest reports were single birds at Hoton on October 1st 1946 and Stanford Reservoir on October 4th 1947.

Corn Crakes breed from north-west Europe to central Asia and winter mainly in south and east Africa. There has been a severe decline over most of Europe and the species is now classified as Globally Threatened. In Britain, the decrease began in south-east England and eastern and central Scotland during the second half of the 19th century and became especially marked in southern England in the early 1900s (Parslow 1967). The decline is mainly attributed to changed methods of agriculture, particularly the earlier and more mechanised cutting of grass crops; loss of habitat due to the intensification of agriculture is also a contributory factor. In Britain, Corn Crakes are now mainly restricted to north and west Scotland, with most birds found on the Hebrides and Orkney, although a reintroduction programme has recently been instigated at the Nene Washes (Cambridgeshire), so it is possible that birds from this scheme may find their way to Leicestershire and Rutland

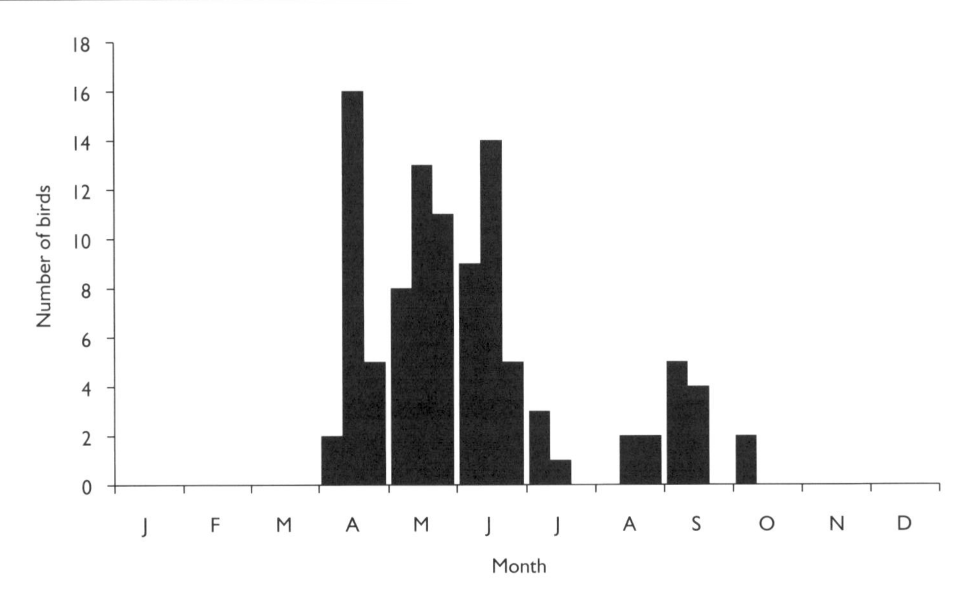

Figure 233: Monthly occurrence of Corn Crakes 1941–2005.

in future. Due to the rapid population decline and contraction of the breeding range, the Corn Crake has been added to the 'Red List' of Birds of Conservation Concern (Gregory *et al.* 2002).

RMF

Moorhen (Common Moorhen) *Gallinula chloropus*

Common resident breeder.

The familiar Moorhen has always been a common and widespread bird in the counties. During the 19th century it was reported by Browne to be 'resident and common, breeding quite close to Leicester', whilst Haines considered it to be 'extremely common' in Rutland.

Traditionally under-recorded, there is little data regarding this species' status and distribution during the first half of the 20th century; the first LROS Annual Report, in 1941, described it as 'resident and common', Pochin (1954) considered it a 'common resident' within the city boundary of Leicester and Otter (1965) reported it to be a common breeding species throughout east Leicestershire. Prior to the work of Warrilow in the mid-1970s, the only indication of breeding densities involved 23 nests around Quorn in 1943 and 42 pairs in the same area four years later.

During 1976–84 Warrilow recorded the Moorhen in 484 tetrads in the counties (76% of the total number of tetrads), with breeding confirmed in 343, making it almost three times more widespread than Coot. It showed a preference for slow-moving or still freshwater, with stands of emergent vegetation to provide nesting cover, and was found to breed on waters of almost any size. Suitable habitat was sparingly distributed in east Leicestershire and Rutland due to the undulating nature of the land, resulting in faster-flowing streams and fewer patches of standing water. Based on an average of four to eight pairs per occupied tetrad, Warrilow estimated a county-wide breeding population of between 1,900 and 3,800 pairs. Mitcham (1992) found it in 50% of Rutland tetrads and explained gaps in distribution by lack of suitable habitat following drainage of ponds and filling of ditches as well as predation by American Mink (especially in the upper Welland valley).

Moorhens suffer badly during severe winter weather. Mortality due to severe frosts in the winter of 1939–40 was reported to be very high whilst many were found dead during frosts in early 1947; after the latter winter, it was considered that the species had recovered its former status by 1949. During the severe winter of early 1963 there were several reports of birds frequenting gardens and feeding on household scraps and three paid regular visits to a house in Quorn, entering the porch to feed on food scraps. Moorhens suffered heavy losses during this period and 'quite a number were found dead and dying' (Gamble 1965). However, by 1964 the population was thought to have made a good recovery. The national population of Moorhens has shown a shallow long-term increase (Baillie *et al.* 2006); combined with the lack of recent severe winters, this would suggest that Warrilow's estimate is now likely to underestimate the total population.

The majority of Moorhens in Leicestershire and Rutland are likely to be sedentary, as evidenced by local ringing data showing that the furthest movement involved an adult ringed at Rutland Water on December 6th 1978 which was found dead at Theddingworth (32km to the south-west) on December 19th 1981. However, some immigration into the counties is apparent during the autumn and winter; WeBS counts reveal that the largest numbers are present during September, with totals gradually dropping throughout the winter and early spring. Over 500 birds have been recorded on WeBS counts on six occasions, five of them in September, although the highest aggregate count is 561 in October 2003.

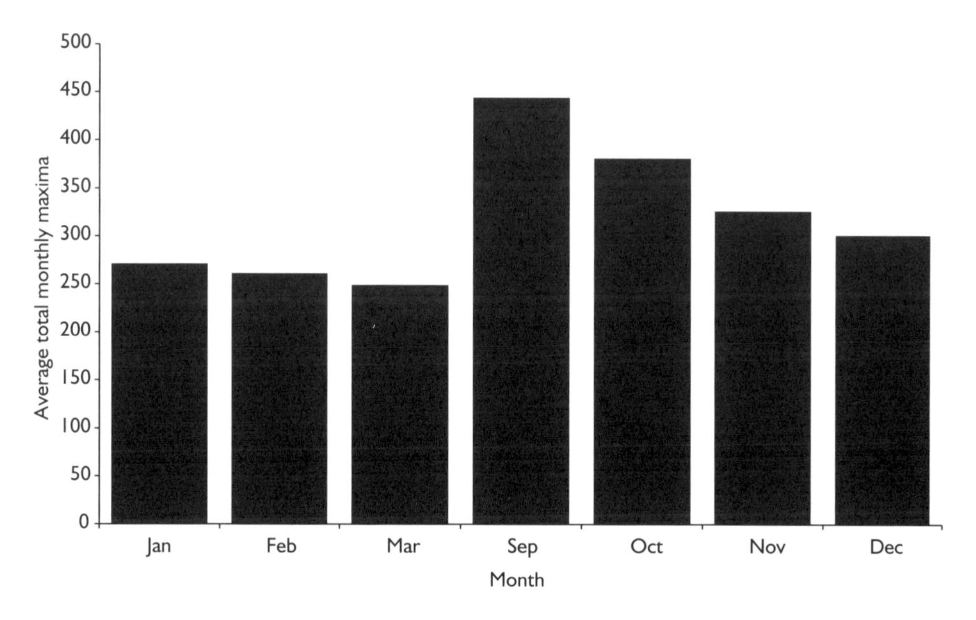

Figure 234: Average total monthly maxima of Moorhens at the main sites 1995–2005.

Large autumn and winter concentrations of this species have been noted since the 1940s, when they included 100 at Willesley Lake on December 18th 1949, 61 by the River Soar between Loughborough and Sileby on January 8th 1944 and 58 by the River Soar between Barrow upon Soar and Sileby in 1945. During the late 1980s and early 1990s regular counting along the River Soar between Aylestone and Belgrave, within the city boundary of Leicester, produced some exceptional totals, five of which exceeded 100:

- 148 on December 16th 1990.
- 133 on January 18th 1987.
- 130 on November 19th 1988.
- 129 on February 18th 1991.
- 120 on November 10th 1989.

Counts along other stretches of the River Soar within Leicestershire, particularly north of Leicester, have also revealed large numbers such as 174 between Zouch and Barrow upon Soar on January 13th 1990, 78 at Loughborough on December 17th 1988 and 69 between Normanton on Soar and Loughborough on November 12th 1988. The largest counts since the mid-1990s have come from Rutland Water, where totals have exceeded 200 on three occasions: 237 on October 22nd 1990, 229 on September 12th 1999 and 211 on October 7th 2001.

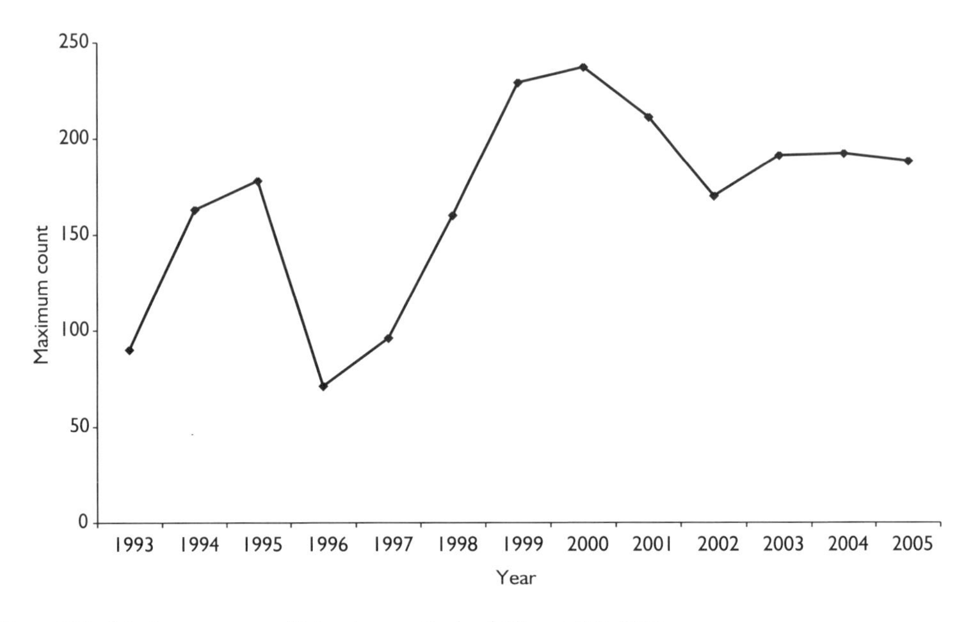

Figure 235: Maximum counts of Moorhens at Rutland Water 1993–2005.

Elsewhere, counts of 60 or more have been recorded at six sites, with maxima being:

- 132 at Priory Water on August 18th 2002.
- 127 at Wanlip Gravel Pits on January 17th 1982.
- 99 at Fort Henry Ponds on both October 5th 2002 and October 14th 2003.
- 75 at Frisby Gravel Pits on December 4th 2005.
- 73 at Swithland Reservoir on October 1st 1989.
- 60 at Saddington Reservoir on September 9th 1994.

An adult attacked and drowned a small chick at Rutland Water on May 29th 1995. This behaviour has been recorded before (Kramer 1989) but appears to be very rare.

There are two records of albinism: at Willoughby Waterleys in May 1953, four chicks out of a brood of six were described as albino and a juvenile at Rutland Water in 2003 had white wings.

Moorhens breed on all continents except Antarctica and Australasia. Most European birds are resident, although northern and eastern European and Siberian populations are partially or wholly migratory and winter mainly in western and southern Europe. The latest estimate of the British breeding population is 240,000 pairs (Baker *et al.* 2006).

RMF

Coot (Common Coot) ***Fulica atra***

Fairly common resident breeder, common winter visitor.

There is little information regarding the status of this species prior to the formation of LROS in 1941; during the 19th century, Browne considered it to be resident but unevenly distributed in Leicestershire, whilst Haines noted that in Rutland it bred regularly and in considerable numbers at Burley and Exton, but was not well distributed over the remainder of the county. The LROS archives describe the Coot as 'common' during the first 40 years of the 20th century.

The Coot is one of the least-studied breeding birds in the counties. The first LROS Annual Report in 1941 described its status as 'resident and common on all large waters' but until the work of Warrilow in the mid-1970s the only indication of breeding densities came from Frisby Gravel Pits, where 32 pairs bred in 1974 and

25 pairs nested the following year. During 1976–84 Warrilow recorded the Coot in 177 tetrads in the counties (28% of the total number of tetrads), with breeding confirmed in 138, making it the second most widespread species of wildfowl after the Moorhen. Over a third of breeding birds were located on ornamental pools, with another third on canals and rivers and the remainder at reservoirs and sand and gravel pits. They showed a preference for pools over 0.5 hectares that were sufficiently shallow to enable feeding by diving and upending and supported fringing emergent vegetation for nesting. Large parts of the east Leicestershire wolds and uplands were unoccupied, due to a lack of suitable habitat. Based on an average of four to six pairs per occupied tetrad, Warrilow estimated a county-wide breeding population of 700 to 1,000 pairs. Mitcham (1992) found 26 (22%) of Rutland tetrads occupied and estimated a breeding population of about 60 pairs.

There is a lack of data regarding wintering numbers prior to the 1970s. In 1941 a flock of 2,000 was at Eyebrook Reservoir on December 13th, a number that has never been exceeded at this site; the following year, 'for sanitary reasons strong efforts were made to reduce the large numbers breeding' at Eyebrook Reservoir. Prior to 1975 the only other counts to exceed 250 were 1,000 at Eyebrook Reservoir on January 5th 1969, 350 at both Cropston Reservoir on January 23rd 1955 and Swithland Reservoir in early October 1973, 321 at Wanlip Gravel Pits on January 17th 1971 and 251 at Groby Pool on November 16th 1974.

Following its construction in the mid-1970s, Rutland Water quickly became established as a site of national importance for Coot; the current threshold for qualification is 1,730 and by 2005 it was the third most important site in Britain (Collier *et al.* 2005). Four-figure counts have been recorded in every year since 1976, with over 3,000 recorded in all but three of those years and over 5,000 counted in six years, as follows:

- 7,453 on December 16th 1984.
- 6,184 on December 10th 1995.
- 5,660 on December 15th 1985.
- 5,631 on November 16th 1997.
- 5,502 on October 15th 1989.
- 5,401 on December 18th 1983.

Numbers have been comparatively low since 1998, with only two counts exceeding 4,000 during this time. The maximum aggregate counts over the whole of the counties have shown a similar decrease, the total of 4,997 in 2005 being the lowest since 1992. Whether this is the beginning of a long-term trend remains to be seen, although it may just be a local phenomenon as nationally both breeding numbers and wintering stock have been increasing steadily since at least the mid-1980s (Baillie *et al.* 2006).

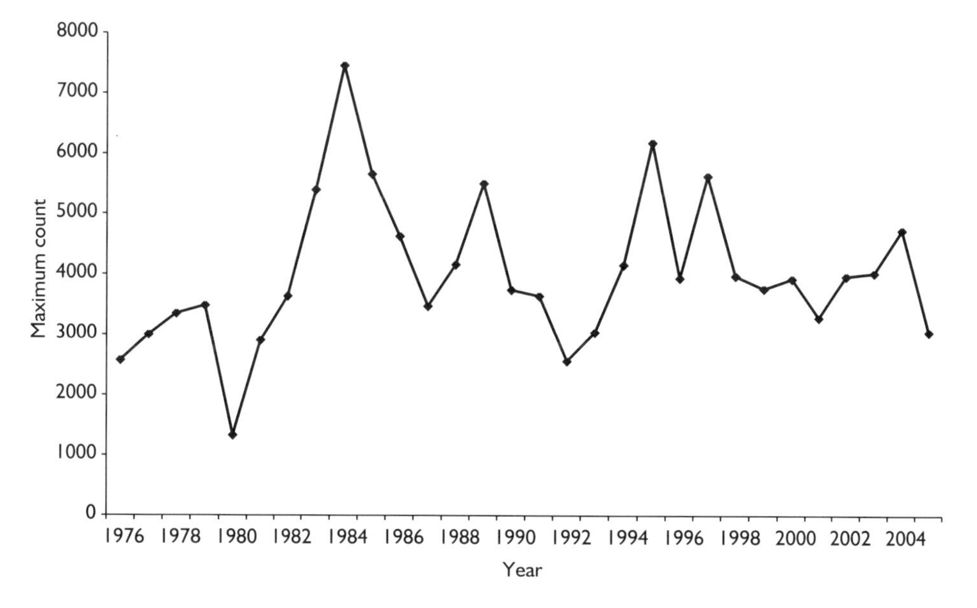

Figure 236: Maximum counts of Coots at Rutland Water 1976–2005.

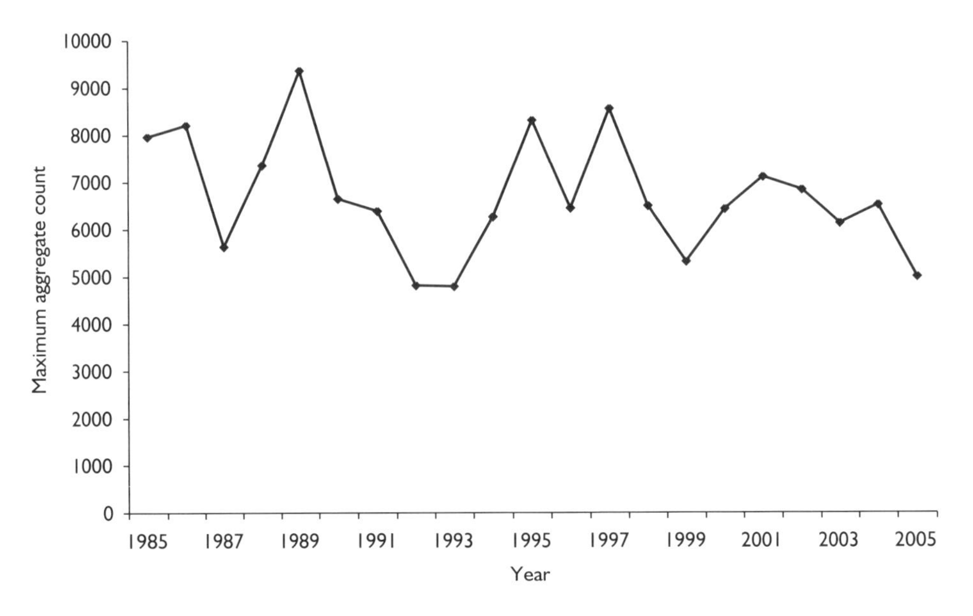

Figure 237: Maximum aggregate counts of Coots at the main sites 1985–2005.

Stanford Reservoir qualified as a site of national importance during the mid to late 1980s and although numbers here have fallen slightly in recent years it is still a site of great significance. A flock of 600 in late September 1975 was unprecedented for this water, but the following year 1,100 were recorded on September 12th. The next four-figure count was not until 1986, when there were 1,660 on December 14th, after which totals of 1,000 or more have been recorded in all but four years. The 1986 count of 1,660 has been exceeded in five years since, with maxima as follows:

- 2,115 on October 15th 1989.
- 1,950 on October 6th 2001.
- 1,865 on December 14th 1997.
- 1,800 on November 17th 1991.
- 1,750 on December 18th 1988.

Eyebrook Reservoir was the first site in the counties to record four-figure totals. As well as the flocks of 2,000 in 1941 and 1,000 in 1969 already mentioned, counts into four figures have been recorded in five years, with maxima as follows:

- 1,400 on October 7th 2001.
- 1,310 on October 22nd 2000.
- 1,284 on October 13th 1990.
- 1,099 on November 17th 1985.
- 1,055 on November 15th 1986.

Away from the three main sites, counts exceeding 300 have come from another six areas, where maxima have been:

- 830 at Wanlip Gravel Pits on January 14th 1979.
- 629 at Swithland Reservoir on October 12th 2003.
- 484 at Kirby Bellars Gravel Pits on November 11th 1987.
- 391 at Cropston Reservoir in October and November 1990.
- 359 at Trent Valley Pit on October 9th 2004.
- 354 at Groby Pool on September 13th 1992.

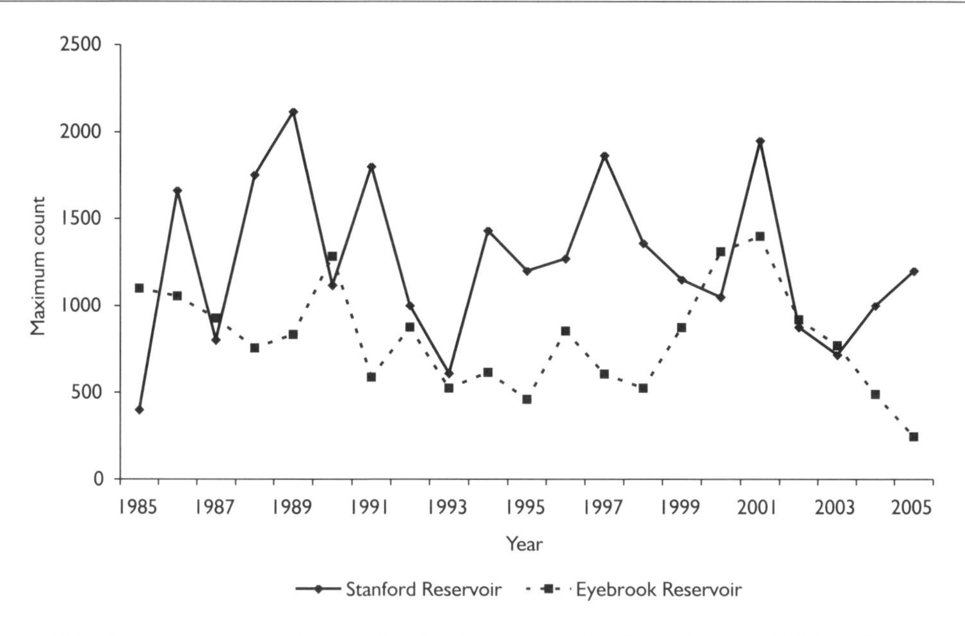

Figure 238: Maximum counts of Coots at Stanford Reservoir and Eyebrook Reservoir 1985–2005.

Significant numbers are found on the River Soar within the city boundary of Leicester, where the highest counts have been 250 on February 9th 1991, 247 on November 25th 1990 and 133 on January 18th 1987. See 'Wintering Birds' (pages 39–43) for details of highest counts at individual sites.

WeBS data show that large numbers are present during September but the peak counts are usually recorded in October and November. Numbers remain high during December but fall away rapidly from January onwards.

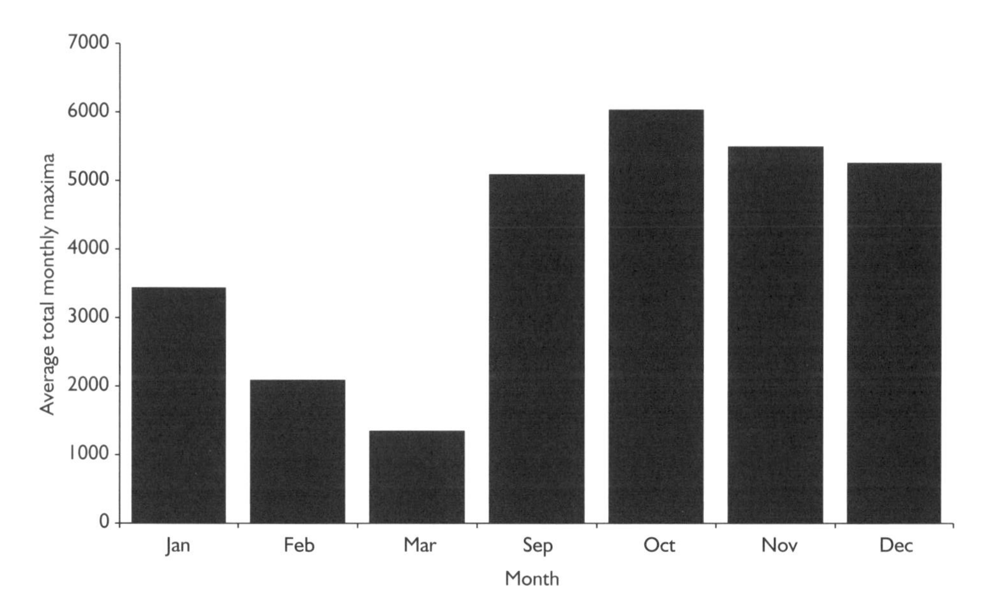

Figure 239: Average total monthly maxima of Coots at the main sites 1995–2005.

Like Moorhens, Coots suffer badly in severe winter weather. During the cold winter of early 1947 they were reported to have been almost wiped out at many sites; 24 were found dead at Cropston Reservoir on February 20th and a week later only one bird was present at the site but it was very weak and easily caught. A partial recovery in numbers was apparent from October 1947 although numbers in 1948 were still well below normal. Heavy losses were also reported in 1963, although far fewer than in 1947 and no reduction was reported during the breeding season. In times of cold weather Coots are often forced onto unfrozen patches of river in large numbers; examples in 1985 included 75 on the River Wreake near Frisby Gravel Pits on February 17th and 150 at the confluence of the Rivers Trent and Soar at Trent Lock the following day.

Albino or partially albino birds have been recorded on several occasions: at Wanlip Gravel Pits on December 17th 1972, Eyebrook Reservoir from August 19th to 30th 1992 and mid-May to August 28th 1993 and Rutland Water on August 31st 1996. One with a pale grey body and a dark grey head was at Priory Water on February 27th 1994.

Despite the fact that large numbers of Coots visit the counties during the autumn and winter, all local ringing recoveries are from England and only two had travelled further than 100km: an adult ringed in Essex on March 10th 1972 was found dead at Leicester on March 27th 1975 and one ringed at Slimbridge (Gloucestershire) on January 13th 1987 was found dead at Rutland Water on January 31st 1994.

Coots breed throughout much of Eurasia, north-west Africa and Australasia. Some northern and eastern populations in Europe are migratory and large numbers winter in western Europe. The latest estimates put the British breeding population at 21,700 to 27,600 pairs and the wintering figure at 173,000 birds (Baker *et al.* 2006).

RMF

Common Crane *Grus grus*

Very rare vagrant from Europe: four records.

Browne quotes Harley as saying that 'Mr Chaplin of Groby shot an example on the banks of the pool in the year 1822'. However, Browne did not appear to be impressed, stating that 'it must be remembered that many keepers and some few sportsmen are in the habit of calling the Heron a 'Crane' and as Harley did not state that he actually saw this specimen, the record must rest on its merits'. As such, this record was ignored by Hickling.

All four acceptable county records have occurred since 1996 and all have been of single birds. The first was seen soaring over the Egleton Reserve at Rutland Water by Ron Shergold on June 2nd 1996; it was in view from 08:45 to 08:52 and the lucky observer even saw it in the same airspace as a Spoonbill (Shergold 1997). The second record soon followed, when one was seen flying north over the same site by John Wright at 12:45 on May 8th 1997. The first 'grounded' bird was seen by several farm workers in a set-aside field adjacent to the Oakham Canal near Teigh from June 28th to July 2nd 2002; unfortunately, the observers did not realise the significance of the sighting until after the bird had gone. Luckily for those birders interested in adding this species to their county list, the fourth record occurred just six months later, when Cee Martin discovered a first-winter in maize stubble fields at Great Glen on January 1st 2003. This obliging bird, which was watched and photographed by many observers, remained faithful to the same couple of fields until January 6th, when the onset of frost and snow hastened its departure.

In addition, a crane species which flew over Rutland Water on January 2nd 1994 was almost certainly a Common Crane, as was one that flew over Oakthorpe on November 1st 2004, but the descriptions provided did not entirely rule out the Demoiselle Crane *Anthropoides virgo*.

Common Cranes breed from Scandinavia and the Baltic region east to eastern Siberia and also in Turkey and the Caucasus region. These populations winter in the south of the Iberian peninsula, locally in north-west and north-east Africa and in southern Asia. A small breeding population has been established in Norfolk since the 1980s; as the British breeding population is so small it is considered vulnerable and so this species was included on the 'Amber List' of Birds of Conservation Concern (Gregory *et al.* 2002). The Common Crane was removed from the list of species considered by the BBRC in 1987, after an upturn in numbers occurring in this country. Recently, there has been a trend towards the majority of sightings being during the spring and the two Rutland Water records conform to this pattern. Summer and winter records are less usual, but the Teigh bird was found after a record spring influx into Britain in 2002, involving some 161 individuals (Fraser & Rogers 2005).

RMF

Oystercatcher (Eurasian Oystercatcher) ***Haematopus ostralegus***

Uncommon passage migrant and scarce breeder.

Browne described the Oystercatcher as a 'rare and accidental straggler from the coast' and cited just two records: one at Loughborough in 1840 and one shot near the Leicester gasworks at Aylestone on September 26th 1887. It was apparently similarly rare in Rutland in the 19th century, with the only records known to Haines being a male shot at Burley Fishponds in January 1878, one obtained at the same site in 1886 and an undated bird killed at Thorpe by Water.

There were no certain records between the 1887 bird and one at Eyebrook Reservoir on March 30th 1943. Only ten more birds had occurred by 1950 but since then it has become decidedly commoner on passage and is now a regular breeding visitor, albeit in very small numbers. The following graph shows the approximate number of passage birds recorded in each five-year period.

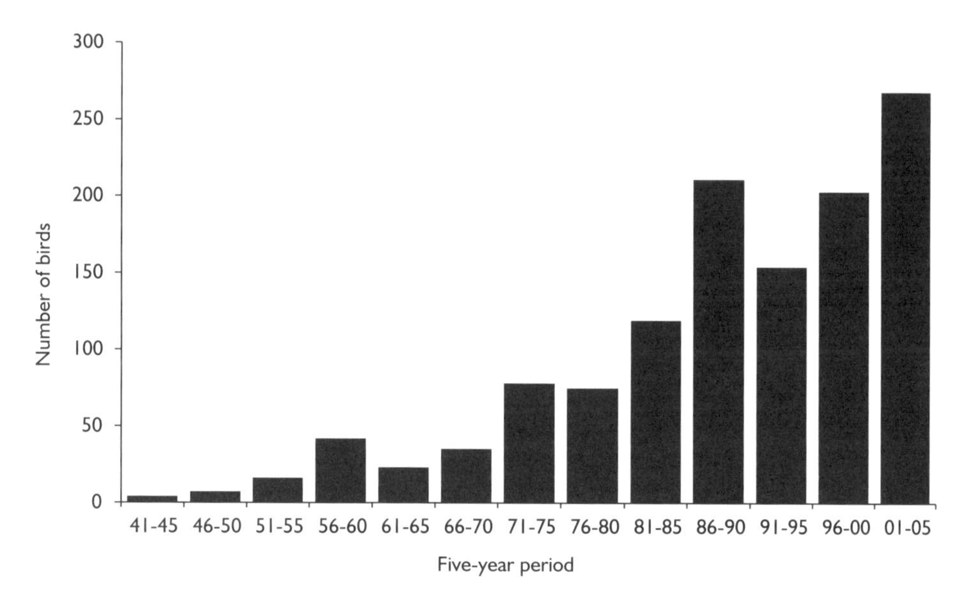

Figure 240: Number of Oystercatchers by five-year periods 1941–2005.

Significant numbers of Oystercatchers have occurred in all months, with peaks corresponding to the two passage seasons between March and May and in August. The largest autumn numbers have normally occurred in August but recently, with the exception of 1996, there has been an obvious change and very few birds have occurred after July. This has been strikingly apparent during the five years up to 2005, with just eight birds reported between August and December. This compares with the findings of Mason (1969), who noted that 42% of all Oystercatcher records at Eyebrook Reservoir during 1941–67 were in August, with only 26% during March and April. The pair of graphs that follow compare the monthly distribution in the periods up to 2000 and from then to 2005; the data used is based on arrival dates and excludes breeding birds.

The differences between the two periods are difficult to explain but may indicate that longer-distance migrants are not passing through the counties in autumn any more; the lack of records after July would not be unusual for birds breeding elsewhere in the Midlands for example, as they typically disperse soon after the young have fledged, usually by the end of July.

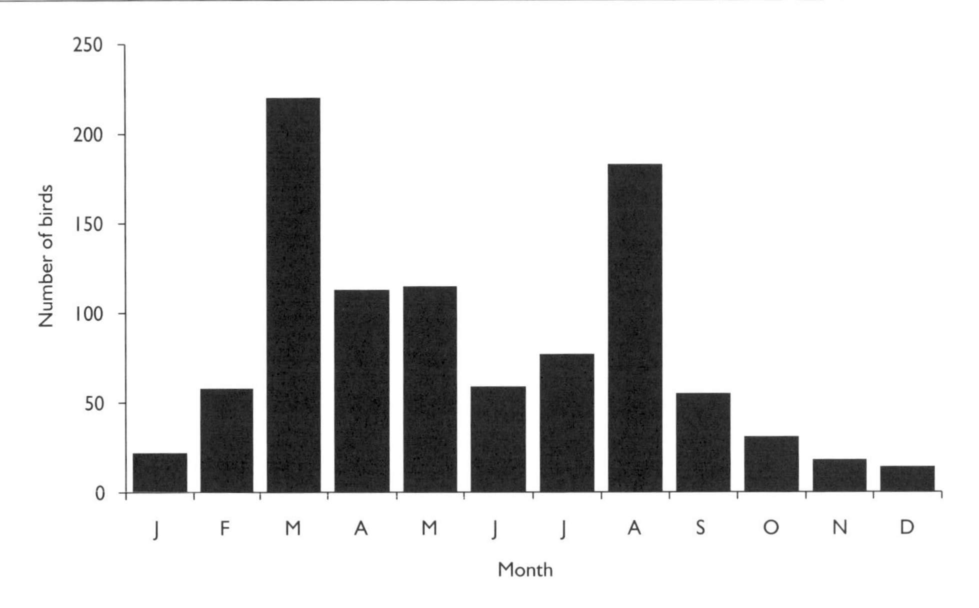

Figure 241: Monthly occurrence of Oystercatchers 1941–2000.

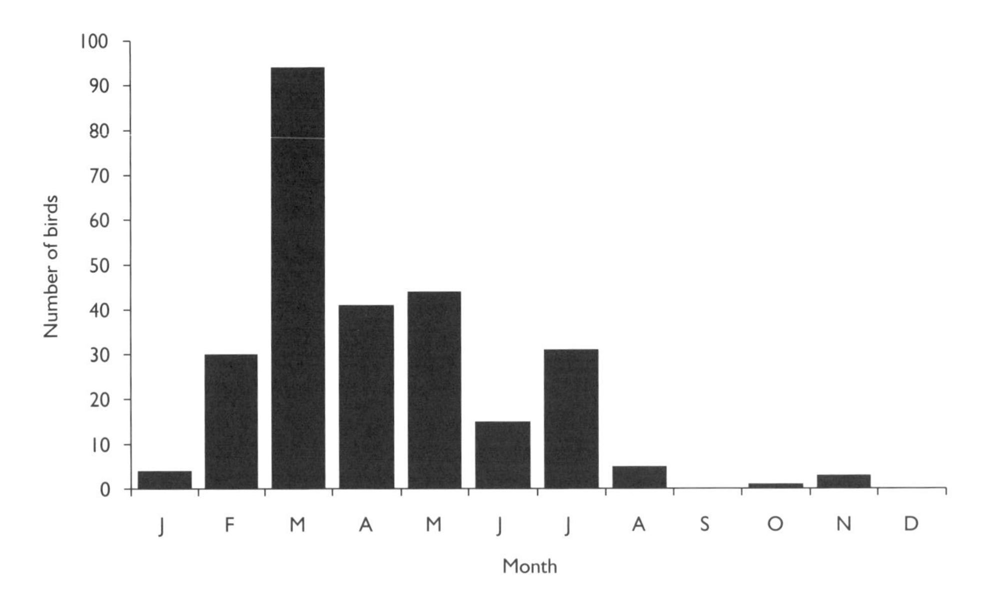

Figure 242: Monthly occurrence of Oystercatchers 2001–2005.

Most records of birds on passage have come from the two best-watched waters, Rutland Water and Eyebrook Reservoir, but this species can utilise a great variety of sites and two were even watched feeding on a cricket pitch at Peckleton in 1972. Birds in flight are usually very vociferous and there are several reports of small parties flying over and also of birds heard at night. Flocks of ten or more have been seen at Rutland Water on 12 occasions, including a previously unpublished flock of 91 in March 1981, but only three times elsewhere. The maximum counts for sites where three or more have been seen are as follows:

- 91 at Rutland Water on March 10th 1981.
- 30 flying over Eyebrook Reservoir on August 15th 1957.

- 11 at Kelham Bridge on August 21st 1996.
- ten at Trent Valley Pit on March 27th 2005.
- eight flying over Braunston-in-Rutland on September 1st 1974.
- seven at Watermead Park on July 6th 2001.
- six flying over Snibston on October 10th 1993.
- six at both Cossington South Gravel Pits on March 23rd 2004 and Cossington Meadows on March 30th 2004.
- four at Thornton Reservoir on February 2nd 1992.
- four at Fort Henry Ponds on June 2nd 2002.
- three at Cropston Reservoir on July 17th 1990.

Oystercatchers first bred in the counties in 1970, when a pair with three chicks was seen at Wanlip Gravel Pits. This area was occupied by presumably the same pair in both 1971 and 1972 but without any evidence of breeding.

Rutland Water has subsequently become established as the most regular breeding site. A pair was seen with one chick at Burley Fishponds in 1974, with another pair summering elsewhere on the site. After a gap of two years a pair made a failed attempt on the Egleton Reserve in 1977 and the following year their one chick died; they bred successfully in 1979 and since then single pairs bred, usually successfully, every year up to 2002, with a long-overdue increase to two pairs, both nesting on the Egleton lagoons, from 2003 to 2005. How many different pairs have been involved in the 32 years since 1974 is not known. Nests have been on artificial islands and also in nest-trays.

A nest was found at Trent Valley Pit in 1988 but the discovery was not followed up. A pair laid two clutches of eggs there in 1993 but unfortunately both were taken by predators. Different levels of breeding activity had been noted in the same area several times, from as early as 1985, but it seems likely that in most years the birds involved were actually nesting across the River Trent in Derbyshire. A pair did breed successfully at this site in 2000, fledging one young, and in 2001 a nest was flooded out; after a blank year in 2002 a nest and then food-carrying adults were noted in 2003 and a pair fledged one young in 2005. At nearby Lockington Gravel Pits, one pair bred successfully in 2004 and 2005, fledging one and two young respectively.

1997 saw a pair fledge three young at Watermead Park and further successful breeding followed there in each of the next four years. There was also a successful pair at nearby Wanlip North Gravel Pits in 2000. A pair fledged one young at Wanlip South Gravel Pits in 2002 and a pair with two juveniles at the same site in July

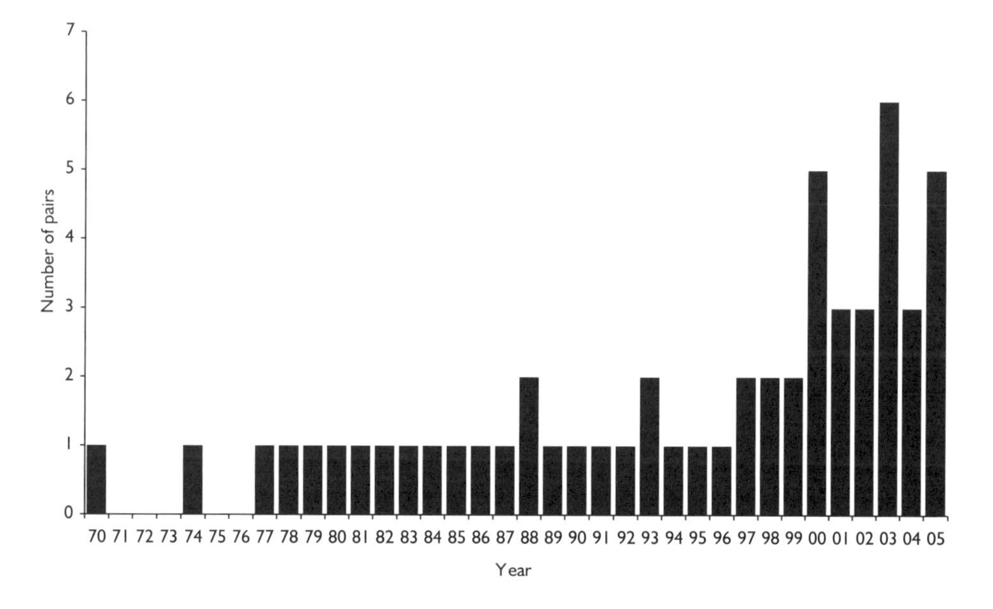

Figure 243: Number of breeding pairs of Oystercatchers 1970–2005.

2003 may possibly have bred undetected somewhere in the general area. In addition, there were pairs at Cossington Meadows in both 2001 and 2002 without any firm evidence of breeding.

A pair nested and raised one young at Quorn Lodge Borrow Pit in 2000, with the same or another pair nesting there each year to 2003 and again in 2005, being successful every year except 2003. One pair nested at Priory Water in 2003 but the nest was abandoned after May 11th.

Summarising, there has been successful breeding in the counties most years since 1970. Nesting has taken place at eight sites, three of which are very close together in the Soar valley north of Leicester, with successful breeding at all but one of them on at least one occasion. The most pairs attempting to breed in any one year has been six in 2003 and the highest number of successful pairs was five, in both 2000 and 2005.

The Oystercatcher has a discontinuous distribution across Europe and into central Asia. The western European population winters mainly around the coasts of the Irish and North Seas, but some move as far south as coastal West Africa. There has been a rapid increase in the British breeding population; in the early 1960s, there were an estimated 19,000 to 30,000 pairs nesting in the UK, increasing to 33,000 to 43,000 pairs by the mid-1980s and 113,000 pairs by the beginning of the 21st century (Gibbons *et al.* 1993, Baker *et al.* 2006). Oystercatchers began to colonise inland sites mainly between 1974 and 1986 as they spread along linear waterways (Baillie *et al.* 2006), coinciding with the slow colonisation of Leicestershire and Rutland. Despite this species proving to be something of a modern-day success story it has been added to the 'Amber List' of Birds of Conservation Concern, on the basis that over 20% of both the European breeding population and the East Atlantic Flyway non-breeding population uses the UK (Gregory *et al.* 2002).

SML

Black-winged Stilt *Himantopus himantopus*

Very rare vagrant from southern Europe: two records involving four individuals.

The first county record was of two at Eyebrook Reservoir on May 26th 1945. These birds were considered to be one of the two pairs which bred at Nottingham Sewage Farm (Nottinghamshire) the same year although, according to Staton (1945), all four stilts were present at the Nottingham breeding site on the date in question. The only other record was also of a pair, seen by Mark Andrews, near Orton-on-the-Hill on June 3rd 1987 (*BB* 87:52). Like the first sighting, this record related to birds which had taken up temporary residence in a neighbouring county; this pair was seen at Alvecote Pools (Warwickshire) from May 28th to June 4th.

Black-winged Stilts breed patchily in south-west and southern Europe and across south-west Asia to Pakistan and Kazakhstan. Most European birds winter in sub-Saharan Africa with relatively few in south-west Iberia and north-west Africa. They are rare but fairly regular vagrants to Britain, currently averaging around five records per year, with notable influxes of 40 in 1987 (corresponding with the second county record) and 25 in 1990. By the end of 2005 the British total stood at 364. Most records are of spring overshoots, particularly during May; both county records therefore match this established vagrancy pattern.

SML

Avocet (Pied Avocet) *Recurvirostra avosetta*

Rare to scarce passage visitor; recorded in all months except January and November, with the majority in April and May: 41 records involving 100 individuals. One breeding record.

Browne mentions a report of one flying over the confluence of the Rivers Soar and Trent near Lockington in June 1856 that was noted in the *Zoologist* at the time. However, this record was square-bracketed by Browne and has never been published subsequently, probably due to the fact that Avocets ceased breeding in England in the early 1840s and did not return until 1938; during the intervening period, its status in Britain was restricted to that of a rare visitor.

The first acceptable record for the counties was of one seen by B.N. Simmonds at Eyebrook Reservoir on December 16th 1955. Since then, there have been records in a further 20 years.

All records:

1955	Eyebrook Reservoir, December 16th.
1959	Eyebrook Reservoir, May 27th to 29th.
1960	eight, Hemington Gravel Pits, April 3rd.
	two, Eyebrook Reservoir, April 4th.
1968	Eyebrook Reservoir, May 10th to 12th.
1974	three, Eyebrook Reservoir, May 4th, with one until May 5th.
1976	21, Eyebrook Reservoir, May 23rd, with seven until May 25th.
	Eyebrook Reservoir, June 8th and 9th.
1980	two, Cropston Reservoir, August 1st.
1982	Rutland Water, May 8th.
1986	Eyebrook Reservoir, August 9th.
1987	Eyebrook Res, April 22nd.
	two, Rutland Water, April 29th.
1990	Eyebrook Res, April 6th and 7th.
1994	Bosworth Water Park, April 23rd.
1995	two, Swithland Reservoir, April 13th.
	Priory Water, October 14th.
1993	Melton Country Park, March 18th.
	Eyebrook Reservoir, March 23rd.
	two, Rutland Water, May 14th to June 14th.
	Swithland Reservoir, October 26th.
1997	Eyebrook Reservoir, February 17th.
	six, Rutland Water, May 16th to 18th.
1998	three, Birstall Gravel Pits, April 2nd; same three, Priory Water, April 2nd.
	seven, Rutland Water, April 22nd.
2001	two, Rutland Water, June 13th.
2002	Rutland Water, March 23rd.
	two, Rutland Water, March 24th (different from the above bird).
	three, Rutland Water, March 30th.
	two, Rutland Water, April 24th.
	Rutland Water, October 30th.
2003	Stanford Reservoir, April 15th.
	two, Rutland Water, April 16th.
	Rutland Water, April 20th to 24th.
	Trent Valley Pit, April 20th.
	two, Trent Valley Pit, April 21st (different from the above bird).
2004	five, Eyebrook Reservoir, April 16th.
	two, Rutland Water, July 31st.
	Rutland Water, September 20th.
2005	Rutland Water, May 12th.
	Swithland Reservoir, August 24th and 25th.

This species is becoming noticeably more frequent in the counties, with over half of the individuals recorded to date having occurred since 1995; the pre-1995 total is also heavily influenced by the remarkable flock of 21 at Eyebrook Reservoir in 1976 and, to a lesser extent, by the group of eight at Hemington Gravel Pit in 1960. Despite the increased frequency with which birds are appearing, these two flocks remain the largest seen in the counties.

Most have occurred on spring passage, with 88 individuals (88% of the total) being recorded between March 18th and June 13th. Figure 245 suggests that the peak time is the final ten days of May, but it was during this period that the flock of 21 at Eyebrook Reservoir was recorded; in reality, almost one third of all records (rather than individuals) have occurred between April 13th and 29th, making this the optimum period for Avocets in the counties.

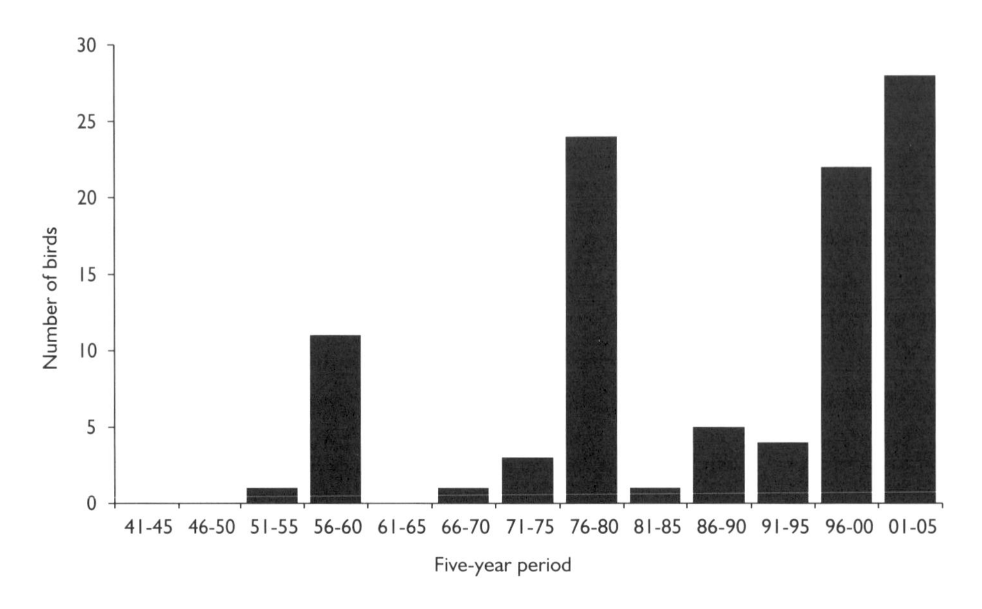

Figure 244: Number of Avocets by five-year periods 1941–2005.

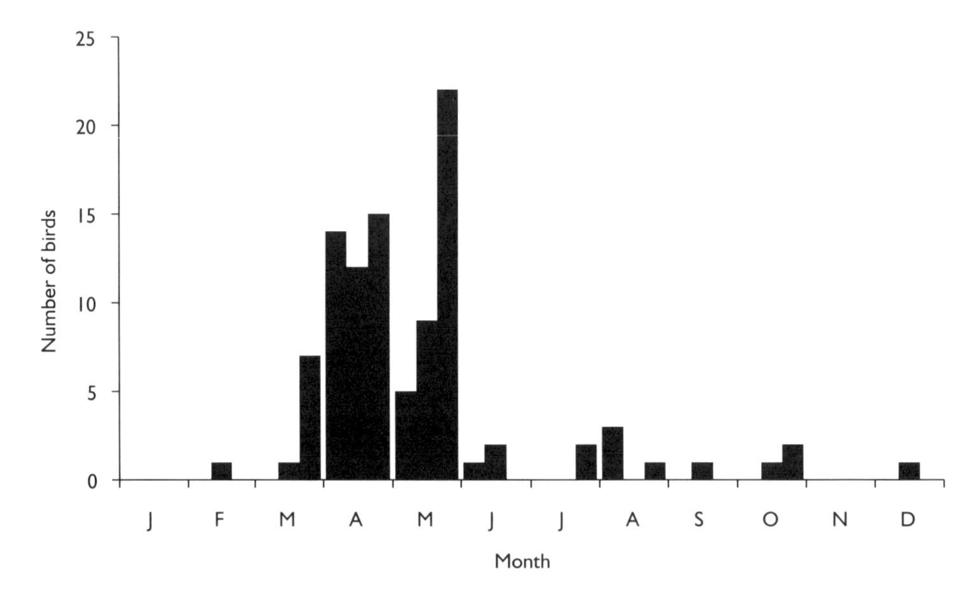

Figure 245: Monthly occurrence of Avocets 1941–2005.

76% of the total have been at either Eyebrook Reservoir (40 birds) or Rutland Water (36). It is a decidedly rare bird elsewhere in the counties, with the major reservoirs at Swithland, Cropston and Stanford having mustered only five records (seven individuals) between them; in fact, the Trent valley, with three records (involving 11 individuals) is the most favoured area after Eyebrook Reservoir and Rutland Water.

A pair attempted to breed on Lagoon I at Rutland Water in 1996. They arrived on May 14th and began brooding a clutch of eggs on a small island by the 20th; unfortunately all four eggs were broken by a neighbouring pair of Coots on the 26th. A second clutch laid on a nearby island disappeared overnight on June 2nd and

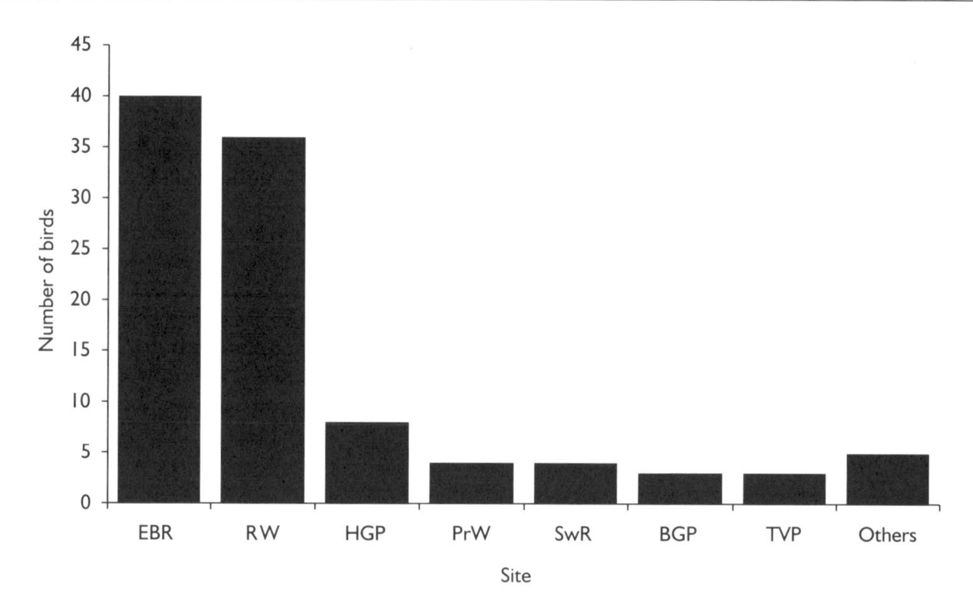

Figure 246: Sites where Avocets have been recorded 1941–2005.
Key to abbreviations: EBR = Eyebrook Reservoir; RW = Rutland Water; HGP = Hemington Gravel Pits; PrW = Priory Water; SwR = Swithland Reservoir; BGP = Birstall Gravel Pits; TVP = Trent Valley Pit

the birds were last seen on June 4th (Harrop 1997). 1996 was the year that Avocets first bred on the Ouse Washes in Cambridgeshire/Norfolk, with a pair also breeding at a London reservoir; until then nesting more than a few miles inland in Britain was unheard of. The six birds at Rutland Water in May the following year were observed displaying and copulating but they departed after just three days.

Avocets breed locally across temperate Europe and central Asia and also in east and south Africa. Northerly populations are migratory but those further south, including in Britain, are mainly more dispersive. In Britain, along with other parts of northern Europe, populations recovered from the middle of the 20th century following a marked decline in the 19th century and by 2005 the British breeding population had reached over 1,365 pairs (Holling *et al.* 2008). The Avocet has been added to the 'Amber List' of Birds of Conservation Concern as more than 50% of the British population breeds at ten or fewer sites (Gregory *et al.* 2002); most breeding birds are found in East Anglia and the south-east of England, but new colonies have recently become established in other areas, notably Lincolnshire, Yorkshire and Lancashire. Sporadic breeding attempts have taken place in a number of other counties and it is entirely possible that this species may attempt to nest in Leicestershire and Rutland again in the near future.

SML

Stone Curlew (Stone-curlew) ***Burhinus oedicnemus***

Very rare vagrant from the small British breeding population: four modern records. Formerly a rare localised breeder.

According to Browne, the Stone Curlew formerly occurred as a summer migrant. He quoted Harley who, writing in 1841, stated that 'it haunted the heath-lands at Saltby and prevailed also on the open park-lands of Croxton Kerrial and Waltham.' In addition, Browne mentioned a Mr Widdowson who 'noted it as having bred annually, many years ago, at Stonesby Heath.'

Haines considered that it bred in small numbers in Rutland in the mid to late 19th century but had ceased to do so by the end of the century. It was recorded from high grounds above Ketton between 1840 and 1845 and at Aunby Heath a few years later (although the latter site is actually in Lincolnshire). In addition, Haines quoted a Reverend Robert Hunt who, writing in 1886, said 'within the last three or four years I have known of a pair of Thick-kneed Plovers on Ryhall Heath. The nest with two eggs was destroyed by a cultivator in a fallow field while preparing for turnips. Within the last 15 or 20 years I have known of six or eight pairs of the birds passing the summer on the Heath. . .and I have shot several of the young ones . . . I am not aware of any of the birds being there now.' Haines also mentioned that breeding had apparently occurred at Barrowden Heath.

Since the times of Browne and Haines there have only been four records:

1969 one was seen by Kath Kirton as it flew in from over the dam and settled on the island at Eyebrook Reservoir during the evening of July 15th.

1987 one was watched by Michael Jeeves for 20 minutes during the morning of April 24th at Prior's Coppice. The bird was colour-ringed and although complete details were not obtained, it was possible to determine that it had been ringed as a chick in the Brecks (Norfolk/Suffolk) in 1982, 1986 or 1987.

1991 one was flushed from a stony field at Timberwood Hill by Jim Walker and Marie Cassidy on May 19th. It flew off north and was not seen again.

2003 one was flushed twice by Andy Smith from an area of newly-planted trees adjacent to Thornton Reservoir on May 4th.

Stone Curlews breed from western Europe and north-west Africa east to the Indian subcontinent and south-east Asia. Most populations are migratory, with large numbers of European birds wintering in north Africa. In Britain there are two main breeding areas, centred on the Brecklands of Norfolk/Suffolk and Salisbury Plain (Wiltshire); the current population estimate is just over 300 pairs (Holling *et al.* 2008). There has been a rapid contraction of the UK breeding range over the last 25 years, resulting in this species being added to the 'Red List' of Birds of Conservation Concern (Gregory *et al.* 2002).

SML

Cream-coloured Courser *Cursorius cursor*

Very rare vagrant from North Africa: one record.

One was shot at Timberwood Hill on October 15th 1827; the occurrence was well documented at the time and the specimen is still in the Leicester Museum collection. On the face of it this is one of the strangest records ever in the counties but there seems no reason to doubt it. It was only the fourth for Britain and the first to be so well documented.

Cream-coloured Coursers breed in the Canary and Cape Verde Islands, around the northern and southern fringes of the Sahara and east to Pakistan. Although there were 37 British records prior to 1958 there have been only seven since and this is a species that truly deserves the status of rare vagrant in Britain. All records have occurred in late September or October, corresponding with the dispersal of North African juveniles.

SML

Collared Pratincole *Glareola pratincola*

Very rare vagrant from southern Europe: two records.

Browne mentions one 'shot near Leicester' which appeared in the catalogue of specimens at the Leicester Museum. However, it would appear that Browne never actually located the specimen. Previous publications have dated this occurrence as June 19th 1849, but this refers to the date that Browne received the aforementioned catalogue; the actual date of the occurrence is unknown and this record is probably best regarded as unconfirmed.

This species' place on the county list is cemented by an adult on the Egleton Reserve at Rutland Water on July 3rd 1977. It was found by T. Pridmore and also seen by Chris Park and Tim Appleton; a couple of record photographs were obtained (*BB* 84:468).

The Collared Pratincole breeds in southern Europe (particularly Spain, Portugal and Greece), locally in North Africa and east to Kazakhstan, Iran and Pakistan; they winter in sub-Saharan Africa, where some also breed. It is the most frequent of the pratincoles to visit Britain, with 95 accepted records by the end of 2005; however, there have been only five other reports in the Midlands, three of which referred to a returning bird in Northamptonshire and Warwickshire in the mid-1990s. It generally occurs as a spring overshoot, with records showing a distinct peak in May, although June and July reports are not infrequent. The Rutland Water bird was part of a mini-influx of this species in 1977; six were recorded during the year.

SML

Black-winged Pratincole *Glareola nordmanni*

Very rare vagrant from eastern Europe or central Asia: two records.

One was found at Wanlip South Gravel Pits on August 10th 1975; the finders included Dave Gamble, Neil Lakin and Paul Powell and the record was documented by Colin Towe. It remained until August 13th, during which time it was seen by many observers and constituted the 15th British record (*BB* 69:340). Remarkably for such a rare species in Britain, another individual was found in 1986, when one, probably a juvenile, was at Eyebrook Reservoir on November 20th and 21st (*BB* 80:534). This was the 22nd British record but, unlike the previous bird, it was seen by just three fortunate observers: Ken Moulton, Mick Ketley and the finder, Graham Blackburn.

In Europe, Black-winged Pratincoles breed in the Black Sea areas of Romania and Ukraine, where they are rare and declining. To the east, they breed across the steppes of southern Russia to east Kazakhstan. They are long-distance migrants, wintering principally in southern Africa. In Britain, they are much rarer than Collared Pratincoles, with just 35 accepted records up to the end of 2005. The majority, including the Wanlip bird of 1975, have arrived during August; by contrast, the Eyebrook Reservoir individual of 1986 is the only November record in Britain. For Leicestershire to have produced two records is something of an achievement, as there have been only two other sightings in the Midlands: in Northamptonshire in August 1959 and September 1969.

SML

Little Ringed Plover (Little Plover) *Charadrius dubius*

Uncommon migrant breeder and passage visitor.

A bird described as an adult at Eyebrook Reservoir on October 24th 1948, seen by one observer and 'thought to be this species', is usually regarded as the first record for the counties but the published description is a little odd and the very late date also raises a doubt. The next, and rather more convincing, record was of one at the same site on April 30th 1950. Four juveniles were noted in July 1951, two single birds at Eyebrook Reservoir and two together at Loughborough Sewage Farm and an unaged bird was reported at Eyebrook Reservoir on August 8th 1954.

The first breeding in the counties occurred in 1955: two pairs each hatched two clutches of four eggs at Hemington Gravel Pits and at least seven young fledged. It was considered that only one male and two females were present, suggesting polygamy (Hickling 1955). A pair was present throughout the summer of 1955 at Eyebrook Reservoir but did not breed. Two pairs bred at Hemington Gravel Pits in 1956, with four pairs there the following year; nesting was regular there until at least 1973 but reported numbers were never more than three pairs again. The pits no longer exist.

Breeding away from the Hemington site was first reported in 1960 and then again in 1963, when a pair bred at Wanlip Gravel Pits. Subsequently birds have nested at many locations. Most breeding sites have been gravel pits, particularly in the Soar valley, but reservoir shorelines have also been used frequently, especially in drier summers such as 1976. This species has demonstrated an ability to utilise construction sites and flat areas covered in gravel awaiting development, even when there is very little water nearby. Nesting has also occurred on the floors of quarries several times, including at Groby, Whitwick, Enderby and Bardon. More unusual nest-sites have been in a crop field at Ratby, the Sykes Lane car park at Rutland Water and on the disused airfield at Bruntingthorpe, with up to three pairs on the crumbling runways.

The size of the breeding population has never been easy to assess as many sites that have been used are of restricted access and nesting pairs could easily go unreported. Many nests have probably failed due simply to the nature of the sites used. Based on the combined numbers of possible, probable and confirmed breeding pairs reported the total population did not exceed five pairs until 1972, when there were nine – three pairs at Hemington Gravel Pits and single pairs at six other sites. A combination of factors produced an increase to at least 15 pairs in 1976: the construction of the dam at Rutland Water provided suitable habitat for eight pairs and the summer drought resulted in pairs nesting beside the reservoirs at Swithland, Cropston, Saddington and Eyebrook. As many as 25 pairs may have nested in 1980, spread over 20 sites. The five years between 1992 and 1996 saw at least 20 pairs annually, with a peak of at least 28 in 1995. In recent years the highest number has been up to 28 pairs at 15 sites in 2004. Figure 247 includes the combined totals of possible, probable and confirmed breeding records.

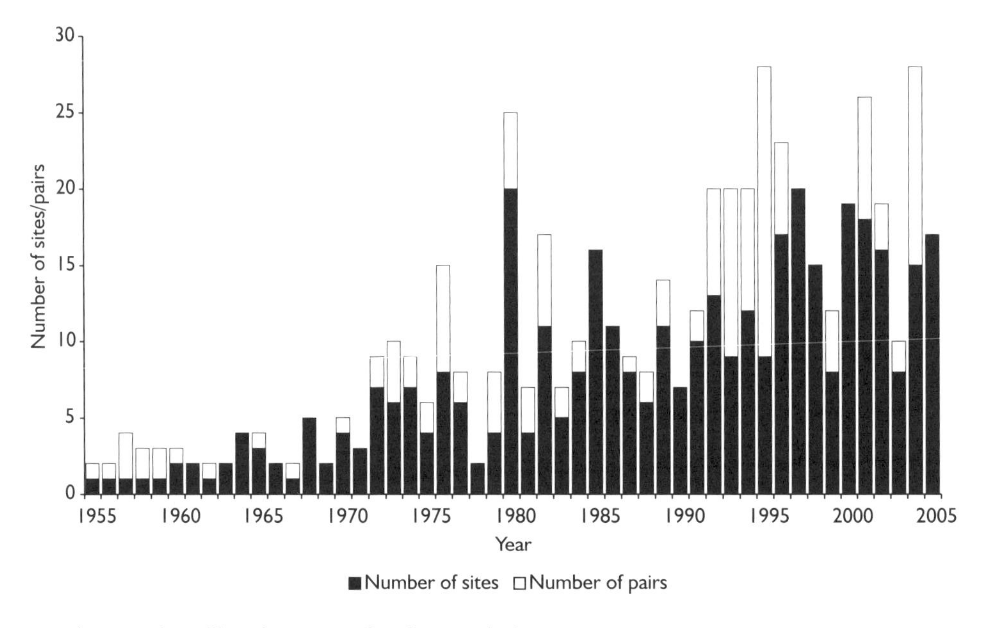

Figure 247: Number of breeding pairs of Little Ringed Plovers 1955–2005.

The earliest spring arrival was on March 5th 1985, when one was at Cossington Gravel Pits. There have been only four other records before March 12th, all of single birds:

- Rutland Water, March 8th 1985.
- Sence Valley Forest Park, March 9th 2001.
- Kirby Lakes, March 10th 1991.
- Castle Donington Power Station, March 11th 2001.

The average arrival date became significantly earlier from the mid-1970s to the mid-1990s, but since then has remained relatively constant.

The numbers recorded in March are always low and even later in the spring concentrations of more than six are unusual and probably relate to local breeding birds more than passage migrants. The highest spring counts have been as follows:

- 18 at Castle Donington on April 16th and 20th 2005.
- 14 at Trent Valley Pit on May 20th 1995.

- 13 at Castle Donington on April 9th 2004.
- ten at Eyebrook Reservoir on May 7th 1994.
- ten at Trent Valley Pit on April 12th 2003.
- ten at Rutland Water on May 11th 2003.
- nine at Trent Valley Pit on April 25th 1998 and April 10th 1999.
- nine at Cossington Meadows on April 9th 2005.
- eight at Trent Valley Pit on May 25th 1997 and June 11th 2005.
- eight at Castle Donington on April 4th 1999.
- eight at Albert Village Lake on April 19th 2002, April 17th 2003 and May 3rd 2004.
- eight at Cossington Meadows on April 3rd 2003 and May 30th 2004.
- eight at Castle Donington Power Station on May 6th 2004.

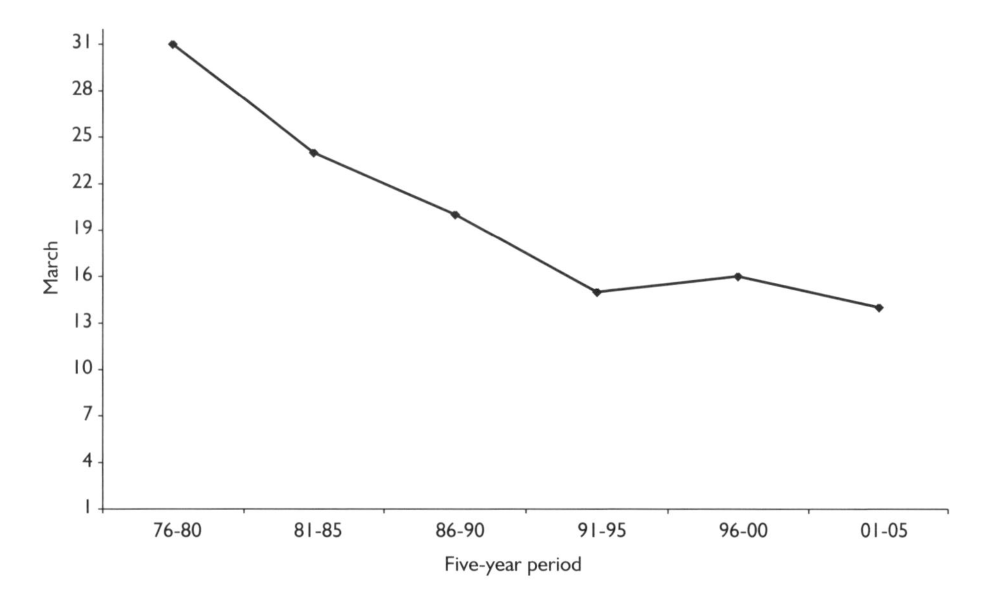

Figure 248: Average spring arrival dates of Little Ringed Plovers by five-year periods 1976–2005.

In most years small flocks have formed at suitable locations as early as late June. The extensive shoreline at Rutland Water can host several separate groups and all of the highest autumn counts have come from there:

- 34 on July 30th 1995.
- 30 on July 4th 1999.
- 28 on August 2nd 1999 and July 8th 2001.
- 27 on July 7th 1996.
- 25 on July 23rd 1980, July 16th 1984 and July 4th 2004.

The maximum autumn counts for other sites are as follows:

- 20 at Trent Valley Pit on June 18th 2003.
- 18 at Cropston Reservoir in July 1986 and on July 23rd 1990.
- 18 at Wanlip South Gravel Pits on June 29th 2002.
- 16 at Swithland Reservoir on July 15th 1995.
- 15 at Hemington Gravel Pits on July 9th 1961.
- 14 at Stanford Reservoir on July 12th 1992.
- 13 at Cossington Meadows on June 25th 2002.
- 12 at Watermead Gravel Pits on July 12th 1987.
- 11 at Enderby Pool in July and August 2004.

- ten at Eyebrook Reservoir on July 17th 1976.
- ten at Trent Farm Pool on July 14th 2002.
- ten at Wanlip Meadows on June 21st 2004.
- nine at Thornton Reservoir on August 1st 1974.
- nine at Sence Valley Forest Park on July 10th 1999.
- nine at Priory Water on June 30th 2002.
- nine at Lockington Gravel Pits on July 4th 2004.

As is evident from the preceding list, July is the main month for autumn concentrations and numbers fall away during August. In two years, 1988 and 1994, the final sightings of the year were in the last week of August but normally the latest date is during September; the general trend in more recent years is for earlier departures. The latest ever record is of a bird at Rutland Water on October 30th 1975; there have been October records in ten other years and only one since 1990. Just two others have occurred later than October 10th: single birds at Eyebrook Reservoir on October 11th 1978 and Watermead Gravel Pits on October 18th 1989.

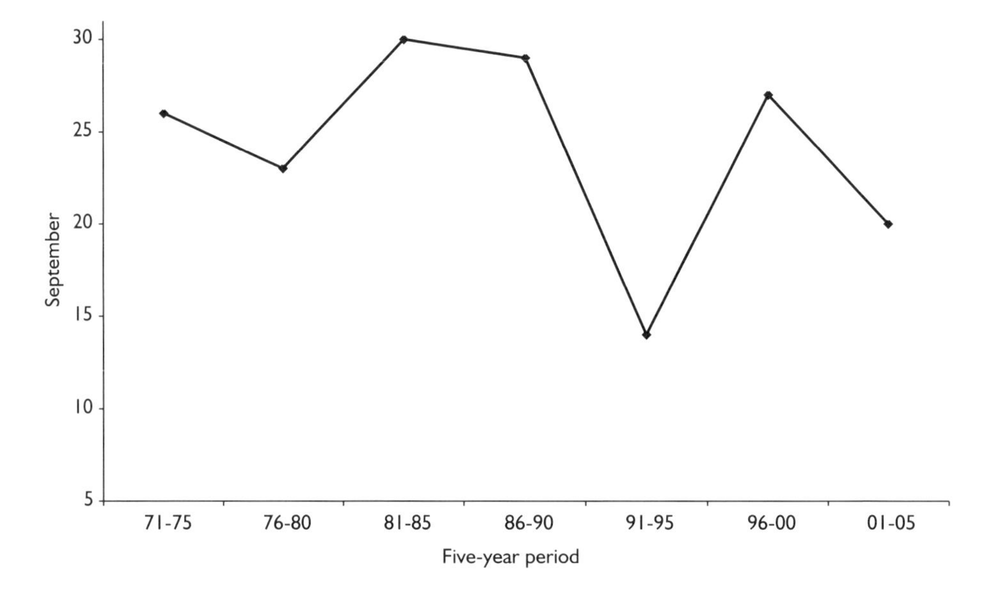

Figure 249: Average autumn departure dates of Little Ringed Plovers by five-year periods 1971–2005.

The Little Ringed Plover breeds throughout Europe, in north-west Africa, in a broad band from the Middle East across central and north-eastern Asia and also in the Indian subcontinent and south-east Asia. Northern European birds winter in north and west Africa. It first bred in Britain at Tring (Hertfordshire) in 1938 and has since colonised much of England and Wales. The British population is currently estimated at between 825 and 1,070 pairs (Baker *et al.* 2006). There have been six interesting recoveries of birds ringed locally. One ringed as a chick at Rutland Water in 1990 was found breeding at Long Eaton (Derbyshire), 48km to the west-north-west, in both 1992 and 1993. Three other birds ringed as chicks have been recovered during their first autumn migrations: found dead at Thrapston (Northamptonshire), 41km to the east-south-east, in August 1986; found dead near Seville (Spain), 1,799km to the south, in September 1963 and caught by ringers near Veurne (Belgium), 310km to the east-south-east, in August 2001. Another bird ringed as a chick in Leicestershire in 1973 was found dead 1,919km to the south-south-east in Tunisia in August 1974.

SML

Ringed Plover *Charadrius hiaticula*

Scarce migrant breeder, fairly common passage migrant and rare winter visitor.

Early references to the local status of this species are rather vague and possibly a little inaccurate, certainly as regards occurrences in winter. In the first LROS Annual Report, in 1941, it was described as a passage migrant and occasional winter visitor. Pochin (1954), summarising records within the Leicester city boundary, wrote 'towards the end of the 19th century was frequently reported in winter at the Abbey Meadows', although between them Browne and Haines knew of only nine 19th century records. Pochin also stated that, during 1935–52, it was 'a fairly frequent visitor in winter to the river and Sewage Farm'. The records detailed in the Annual Reports between 1941 and 1952 included just two that would now be considered as winter visitors.

It is now clear that spring arrivals can be as early as February and that autumn passage frequently extends into November, so only December and January really qualify as winter for this species. There have only been seven December records since 1941, all of single birds except two: a flock of ten flew south-west over Narborough Bog on December 30th 1981 and two were at Rutland Water on December 28th 1986. The 12 January records are all of single birds except for two at Leicester City Farms on January 17th 1942; ten of the 12 have been since 1984 and some of them may well relate to very early spring arrivals as a consequence of recent climate change.

Small numbers of potential breeding birds arrive at suitable sites, mainly gravel pits and reservoir margins, in February and March each year. The first breeding record for the counties was in 1965, when a pair raised two broods at Wanlip Gravel Pits (Gibbs 1967). One pair nested at the same site in each of the next two years but then there was a gap of eight years until single pairs nested at both Eyebrook Reservoir and Rutland Water in 1976. A pair lost two clutches of eggs at Rutland Water in 1978 and another pair may have been breeding there that year; breeding was also attempted there in 1979 and a pair with two young was seen in 1980, when a nest was found near Hemington. There were single cases of confirmed breeding in three of the next four years, all at gravel pits: Wanlip in 1981, Cossington in 1982 and Kirby Bellars in 1984. There was also a displaying pair at Eyebrook Reservoir in 1982 and two territorial pairs in 1984. Five nests were found at Wanlip North Gravel Pits in 1985, three of them being successful; displaying pairs were at Rutland Water and Thurmaston Gravel Pits that year. Just single nest-scrapes were found at the Wanlip site in 1986 and 1987. Successful breeding occurred at each of Cropston Reservoir, Eyebrook Reservoir and Frisby Gravel Pits in 1988, with a pair displaying at Bruntingthorpe Airfield. In 1989 pairs with young were found at Rutland Water and the gravel pits at Cossington and Sawley; there were also territorial pairs at three other sites. Only one pair was proved to breed in 1990, at Watermead Park; a pair nested at the same site in 1991, with another at Cropston Reservoir. Pairs with young were seen at both Dishley Pool and Thurmaston Gravel Pits in 1992, nest-scrapes were found at both Swithland Reservoir and Cropston Reservoir and pairs summered at three other sites. The number of confirmed breeding pairs reached five for the second time in 1993, with two pairs at Trent Valley Pit, one at Watermead Park, one at Eyebrook Reservoir, where the scrape was flooded by rising water levels, and one at Dishley Pool; a displaying pair was at Cropston Reservoir. Five pairs were confirmed again in 1994, with two at each of Dishley Pool and Watermead Park and one at Trent Valley Pit. A total of five pairs bred for the third year in succession in 1995, with two nests at Dishley Pool and pairs with young seen at each of Watermead Park, Cossington North Gravel Pits and Trent Valley Pit; displaying pairs were at three other sites and four other pairs summered, producing an all-time high of 12 pairs.

Unfortunately the numbers of pairs either confirmed or present have never matched those of 1995. Four pairs bred in 1996, at Dishley Pool, Watermead Park, Rutland Water and Ibstock Opencast (now Sence Valley Forest Park), with another pair displaying at the last site and two pairs displaying at Trent Valley Pit. The only definite breeding in both 1997 and 1998 involved one pair at Dishley Pool but birds were present at Watermead Park in both years and at both Sence Valley Forest Park and a development site at Hinckley in 1998. Single pairs with young were seen at Wanlip South Gravel Pits and Watermead Park in 1999, with a pair on a development site at Raw Dykes Road, Leicester. Pairs with young were found at both Cossington North and Wanlip South Gravel Pits in 2000 but the only confirmed breeding in 2001 was one pair with young at the former site. There was no confirmed breeding in 2002, for the first time since 1983, but there were displaying birds at both Cossington

North Gravel Pits and Eyebrook Reservoir. Since 2003, all confirmed breeding records have come from the Trent valley: a pair bred at a newly created gravel pit site at Lockington in 2003, when a pair was strongly suspected of breeding at Rutland Water; a pair bred at Castle Donington Power Station in 2004 and in 2005 a pair hatched chicks at Lockington Gravel Pits and another pair laid eggs (but may have lost them) at Castle Donington.

To summarise the breeding situation, there have been 61 confirmed nesting attempts at a total of 17 sites since 1965, with another 29 unconfirmed but possible. The greatest number of pairs proved breeding was five, in 1985 and from 1993 to 1995. Eight of the sites have been working or disused gravel pits, four reservoir margins, four areas of levelled and gravelled land awaiting development (at Dishley Pool, Hinckley and two areas of Castle Donington) and one country park developed from opencast mining. The most frequently used area has been the complex of gravel pits along the River Soar north of Leicester, with breeding confirmed at one or more sites in 20 years; gravel pits and development land in the Trent valley have been occupied in eight years and the development site at Dishley Pool was used annually between 1992 and 1998, by which time it had become too overgrown.

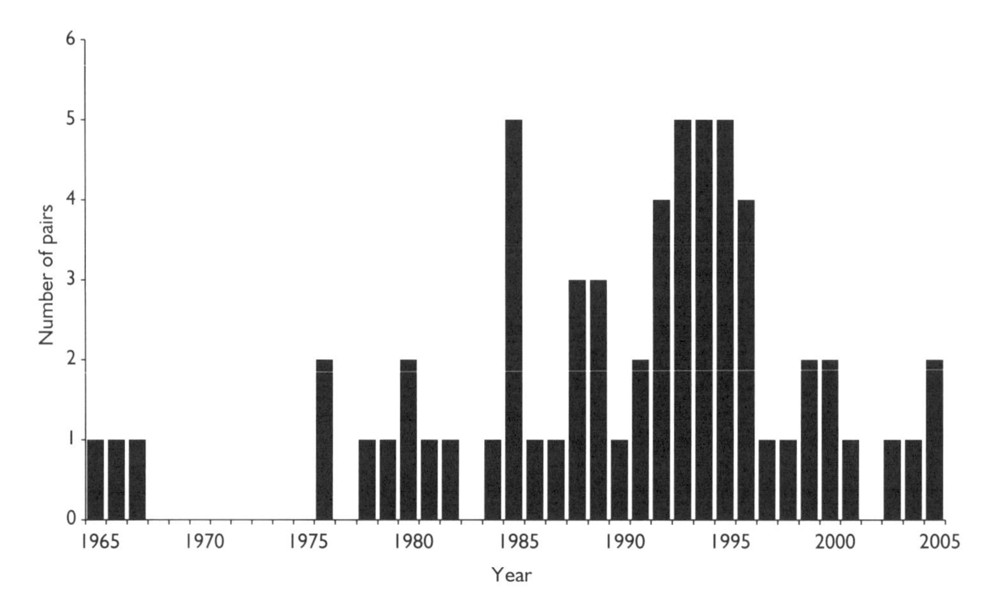

Figure 250: Number of breeding pairs of Ringed Plovers 1965–2005.

The main spring passage period extends from April to early June. It is normally easy to distinguish between migrants and the small number of local breeding birds. Rutland Water and Eyebrook Reservoir regularly attract small flocks, the largest counts being:

- 50 at Rutland Water on May 8th 1995.
- 46 at Rutland Water on June 3rd 1980.
- 30 at Eyebrook Reservoir on May 18th 1948.
- 26 at Rutland Water on April 26th 1997.
- 26 at Eyebrook Reservoir on June 9th 2003.
- 25 at Rutland Water on May 26th 1982.

There have only been two double-figure spring counts elsewhere, of 13 at Cropston Reservoir on the early date of March 17th 1992 and ten at Watermead Gravel Pits on May 1st 1985.

In 1991 it was realised that some of the passage birds in late spring, seven at Rutland Water on May 19th, belonged to the Arctic-breeding race *C.h. tundrae*. It is likely that this form had been overlooked in previous years and it still is to a lesser extent, as it has proved to be regular in May and June since observers' awareness was raised. Counts have included maxima at the main sites of 20 at Eyebrook Reservoir on June 2nd 1998, 14 at Rutland Water on June 8th 2003 and nine at Wanlip Meadows on May 27th 2001. The only April records are of one at Eyebrook Res on the 29th in 1995 and four at Priory Water on the 28th in 2002.

Autumn passage covers the period from late June through to October, with a recent and increasing tendency for birds to be still passing through in November; only eight of the years from 1982 to 2005 lacked November records but they had occurred in just four earlier years since 1941.

Autumn flocks are more widespread than in spring because of the increased availability of suitable resting and feeding areas around reservoirs as water levels drop. Nevertheless, all counts of 20 or more have come from the two main wader sites, with the highest all being in late August and September:

- 81 at Rutland Water on September 23rd 1985.
- 65 at Rutland Water on September 3rd 1998.
- 56 at Rutland Water on August 17th 1983.
- 50 at Eyebrook Reservoir on September 3rd 1974.
- 49 at Rutland Water on September 18th 2005.
- 46 at Eyebrook Reservoir on August 28th 1970.
- 46 at Rutland Water on September 11th 2003.
- 42 at Eyebrook Reservoir on August 31st 1976.
- 39 at Rutland Water on August 27th 1995.
- 38 at Rutland Water on August 22nd 1981 and September 8th 2001.

Maxima at other sites that have achieved double-figure counts are 16 at both Cropston Reservoir on September 30th 1973 and Stanford Reservoir on September 1st 1992, and 11 at both Loughborough Sewage Farm on August 30th 1958 and Swithland Reservoir on September 9th 1974.

Ringed Plovers have an almost circumpolar distribution, stretching from north-east Canada through Iceland and western Europe to northern Siberia as far as the Bering Straits. European birds winter along the coasts of western Europe and the Mediterranean and also in west Africa. In Britain, inland breeding numbers have doubled since the early 1970s (Gibbons *et al.* 1993), although this only makes up about 17% of the estimated total British breeding population of 8,400 pairs (Baker *et al.* 2006). As more than 20% of the East Atlantic Flyway non-breeding population uses Britain, this species has been added to the 'Amber List' of Birds of Conservation Concern (Gregory *et al.* 2002). The only ringing recovery involving the counties is of a bird ringed as a chick at Thornham (Norfolk) in June 1979 and seen at Rutland Water in October of the same year; it was identified by a colour-ring.

SML

Killdeer *Charadrius vociferus*

Very rare vagrant from North America: one record.

One was at Eyebrook Reservoir between September 28th and October 19th 1975, first found by Jim Walker. It was relocated at Swithland Reservoir on November 2nd, remaining there until the 19th. It constituted only the 18th British record. What was presumably the same bird then appeared at Thorne Moors (South Yorkshire) ten days later (*BB* 69:335).

Killdeers breed across most of North America, as well as in Central America, the West Indies and along the south-west coast of South America. The more northerly populations move south to winter in the coastal and southern United States. The majority of British records (which numbered 46 by the end of 2005) have occurred between November and March. The Leicestershire individual was the first to appear in September and only one subsequent British record has been in this month (in Hampshire in 1980), coincidentally also arriving on the 28th. Birds arriving in this country have been widely scattered, although there is a distinct westerly bias; records in the Midlands are few, the only others being single birds in Derbyshire in February and March 1964 and Nottinghamshire in April 1981.

SML

Kentish Plover *Charadrius alexandrinus*

Very rare vagrant from Europe: six records.

The first record for the counties involved one found by P. O. Summers and H. R. Colman at Eyebrook Reservoir on November 4th 1945; it was then seen regularly by a number of observers until November 14th. This is a very late date for this species to occur in Britain, but full details were sent to the editors of *BB* who commented that it was 'very thoroughly authenticated' and underwent 'the most thorough examination' (Jolley 1946a). There have been a further five records, four in spring and one in autumn. All but one have occurred at Eyebrook Reservoir.

All records:

1945 Eyebrook Reservoir, November 4th to 14th.

1949 a male was discovered by H.A.B. Clements at Loughborough Sewage Farm on April 2nd; it remained until the next day and was seen by several other observers. Another was identified by H. Southwell at Eyebrook Reservoir on September 4th.

1974 one, initially found by Kath Kirton, was at Eyebrook Reservoir from May 23rd to 27th.

1980 a female was watched at Eyebrook Reservoir by John Thatcher during the evening of May 15th.

1994 a female was seen briefly by Dean Roizer at Eyebrook Reservoir on May 20th.

There is no reason to doubt any of the records but no details now seem to exist for the two in 1949.

Kentish Plovers breed in temperate regions of Eurasia and North America, as well as in North Africa and along the western coast of South America. They are regular visitors to Britain, averaging approximately 30 records a year, the majority of which occur in southern coastal counties of England during the spring.

SML

Dotterel (Eurasian Dotterel) *Charadrius morinellus*

Very rare vagrant from Europe: at least eight records involving at least 36 individuals

Browne stated that this species 'formerly occurred in the county as a spring and autumn migrant', but the details he provides do not inspire confidence. He lists vague, undated records of five brought down by a shot at Charnwood Heath, one taken near Buddon Wood, a specimen apparently obtained at Coleorton and two shot at Illston on the Hill, as well as three seen near Tur Langton on the unlikely date of March 29th 1879. Subsequent authors have ignored all of Browne's reports and it is generally accepted that the only reliable record prior to the formation of LROS in 1941 is that detailed by Haines, of seven at Morcott on May 20th 1905; these birds were apparently then seen at Ridlington (five miles west of Morcott) on May 24th and 27th.

This is a very unpredictable species in Leicestershire and Rutland, with just seven modern records, as follows:

1944 two were 'called down' at Snarestone on May 4th.

1952 one was at Beacon Hill on May 12th.

1984 a 'trip' of 12 was at Cottesmore Airfield on April 26th and 27th. Subsequent counts were of nine on April 30th, ten on May 3rd, eight on May 12th and three on May 18th. It is unclear how many birds were involved, but it is thought that at least 13 were recorded during the period.

1985 six were at Cottesmore Airfield on May 4th and 5th, with six again on May 22nd. As in 1984, it is unclear how many birds were involved in these sightings.

1995 five, including two adults, flew over Priory Water on September 3rd. One, probably a juvenile, associated with Golden Plovers at Eyebrook Reservoir on November 19th and 20th.

1998 one in winter plumage was present with Golden Plovers at Eyebrook Reservoir on December 18th and 19th.

The spring records are as expected for this species, although the autumn records are much more unusual. The two birds at Eyebrook Reservoir in 1995 and 1998 were on rather late dates for a Dotterel to be in Britain, whilst the flock of five at Priory Water was perhaps even more of a surprise.

Dotterels breed discontinuously from Scotland through northern Scandinavia and north Eurasia. The British population, which is estimated at between 510 and 750 pairs (Baker *et al.* 2006), is restricted almost entirely to the Scottish Highlands. As at least 50% of the population breeds in ten or fewer defined areas, the Dotterel has been added to the 'Amber List' of Birds of Conservation Concern (Gregory *et al.* 2002). This species is a regular passage migrant elsewhere in Britain, with small flocks (known as 'trips') stopping off at favoured areas during April and May. A number of these traditional sites are close to Leicestershire and Rutland, in Northamptonshire, Nottinghamshire and Cambridgeshire and logic dictates that small 'trips' may well appear in the counties in spring in the future; the east, particularly Rutland and the Vale of Belvoir, would appear to be the most likely areas.

SML

American Golden Plover *Pluvialis dominica*

Very rare vagrant from North America: one record.

A juvenile was found amongst Golden Plovers on Lagoon I at Rutland Water on November 2nd 1996, remaining until the following afternoon. The original finder is unknown, but the bird was seen by many observers. What was presumably the same individual was later seen at Eyebrook Reservoir on December 4th and 8th (*BB* 90:469, Fray 1997).

In addition, a possible 'Lesser' Golden Plover was present in the Shepshed area from December 23rd 1984 to January 3rd 1985, but was unfortunately never conclusively identified (Smallshire 1985).

American Golden Plovers breed from Alaska across northern Canada to Baffin Island. They undertake a huge, often non-stop, migration to winter in South America. This species is one of the most regular American waders to reach these shores, with 275 accepted records by the end of 2005, when it was removed from the list of species assessed by the BBRC. Numbers have shown a marked increase since the mid-1970s, with notable influxes in 1995, 1996, 1998, 1999 (coinciding with the Rutland Water bird) and 2003. The peak months are September and October, with the majority of other reports in August and November. Most other counties in the Midlands have recorded this species in recent years and it is likely that careful searching of autumn Golden Plover flocks will provide further sightings in Leicestershire and Rutland.

SML

Golden Plover (European Golden Plover) *Pluvialis apricaria*

Common winter visitor and passage migrant.

This species was well known as a winter visitor in the 19th century but in much smaller numbers than now: Browne described it as 'not common' in Leicestershire, whilst Haines said it was regular in autumn and winter in Rutland. Concentrations of 500 or more are now commonplace but were not recorded until 1944, when a flock of 500 was near Uppingham on February 21st. The table below shows how the status has changed, especially since 1980; care has been taken to avoid duplication caused by flocks moving between adjacent areas and only one count from each winter period is used for each site.

Table 17: Golden Plover flock sizes 1941–2005

Period	Number of flocks of 500+	Number of flocks of 1000+	Maximum flock
1941–1950	1	0	500
1951–1960	1	0	500
1961–1970	2	0	600
1971–1980	7	3	1,500
1981–1990	46	17	2,500
1991–2000	53	38	5,000
2001–2005	30	25	4,000

The large winter flocks are generally found on farmland and wide reservoir margins between November and March, with smaller numbers normally present from August to October and in April. Certain areas traditionally attract large concentrations in most winters. The first one to be noted was that between Shepshed, Belton and Long Whatton; more recently the general Hoby, Thrussington, Ragdale and Six Hills area has been well frequented. Bruntingthorpe Airfield regularly attracted large flocks between 1984 and 1993 at least and other disused airfields at Wymeswold and Melton Mowbray have held up to 1,800 and 1,000 respectively. More recently, the Priory Water/Kirby Lakes area has been well utilised, as has Wanlip Meadows. The only reservoirs providing conditions which regularly attract large numbers, mainly for roosting, are Rutland Water and Eyebrook Reservoir but up to 2,000 have been counted at Stanford Reservoir. The largest flocks to have been recorded are as follows:

- 5,000 in the Priory Water/Kirby Lakes area from December 31st 1999 to January 9th 2000.
- 4,000 near Enderby Pool on December 24th 1998.
- 4,000 at Rutland Water on both January 28th 1999 and December 11th 2004.
- 3,650 at Thrussington on January 16th 1994.
- 3,500 at Eyebrook Reservoir on December 17th 1998.
- 2,800 at Rutland Water on November 30th 2003.
- 2,750 in the Priory Water/Kirby Lakes area on both December 8th 2002 and October 23rd 2005.
- 2,500 at Eyebrook Reservoir on December 4th 1990.
- 2,500 at Bruntingthorpe Airfield on February 16th 1992.
- 2,500 at Hoby on December 26th 1999.

The estimated total population each winter has generally been below 10,000 except in 1998–99, when it was probably 16,000+. LROS attempted surveys of the wintering birds between 1987 and 1989 (Mackay 1989a); the totals found, 5,587 in 1987–88 and 9,643 in 1988–89, were regarded as very approximate due to the extreme mobility and unpredictability of the flocks. 'Flock ranges' have been estimated as being as high as 20 square km (Fuller & Youngman 1979). The LROS survey also recorded the feeding habitats used by a sample of over 4,000 birds: 61.6% were found on grassland, 28.9% on winter cereals and 9.5% on ploughed fields.

Flocks of 500 or more have lingered into April in nine years, but only four times since 1990: 600 were at Trent Valley Pit on April 1st 1993, 646 at Packington on the same date in 2002 and 800 at Sence Valley Forest Park on April 8th 2005. A flock estimated at 1,000 birds that flew west over Saltby on April 25th 1998 provided the only ever four-figure count for the month. There have been nine May records, all of up to three except for 20 at Rutland Water on May 26th 1985 and 18 at Fort Henry Ponds on May 2nd 2004. Perhaps the latest spring bird was one at Eyebrook Reservoir on June 3rd 1998. Four other June records of single birds, from the 18th onwards, probably relate to early autumn passage, as with the 11 occasions when this species has been reported in July. August records are slightly more frequent but sightings are not normally regular until September and October. The earliest date for a flock exceeding 500 birds is October 11th, when 630 were near Hinckley in 1998. Four-figure flocks have been recorded eight times in October, all since 1992, with the largest being 2,750 in the Priory Water area on October 23rd 2005.

Birds still present in March and April have frequently shown the characteristics of the northern form *P.a. altifrons*. Nowadays little attention is paid to this but some careful observations of the birds using Lindley Airfield were made during 1948–50 (Howarth 1951). It was noted that, by the time the northern and southern forms became distinguishable by early April, the northern form outnumbered the southern form by three to one, reflecting the later arrival of northern birds on to their breeding grounds.

Golden Plovers breed in eastern Greenland and from Iceland east through north-western Europe to central northern Siberia. All populations winter to the south of their breeding range. In Britain, the estimated breeding population is 22,600 pairs, with up to 250,000 birds wintering in the country (Baker *et al.* 2006). The nearest breeding birds to Leicestershire and Rutland are on the heather moorlands of the Peak District in Derbyshire.

SML

Grey Plover *Pluvialis squatarola*

Scarce to uncommon passage and winter visitor; recorded in all months, with the majority in May, September and October.

Browne mentioned one found dead under telegraph wires at Aylestone on December 5th 1892 and Haines recorded that two were shot at Barrowden in 1895 but there were no further records until 1946, when two were at Sawley Gravel Pits on May 9th 1946 and another two were at Eyebrook Reservoir two days later. This species remained a rare visitor to the counties for the next 25 years; there were only six records, all of single birds, in the 1950s and a total of 12 blank years between 1946 and 1972. The highest annual total during this period was only four, in 1946, 1948 and 1964, and no more than two were ever recorded together, so the appearance of a flock of 12 at Eyebrook Reservoir on September 30th 1972 must have been a real surprise considering the previous status. Since 1972, the only blank year has been 1974; numbers seen in the counties have varied quite markedly from year to year since then, but show a peak from the mid-1980s to the mid-1990s. The best year was 1990, with some 72 birds in total, whilst 1982 produced 35 individuals and 30 were recorded in 1991. The ten years from 1996 to 2005 have averaged 12 birds per annum, although numbers during the early part of the 21st century have been lower, averaging fewer than ten birds per year. This pattern corresponds with national figures; numbers of passage and wintering Grey Plovers in Britain peaked in the mid-1990s, but by the 2003–04 winter had dropped to the same levels as in 1987–88 (Collier *et al.* 2005).

Most records are of one or two birds, although there have been six counts exceeding ten, as follows:

- 21 at Rutland Water, in fog, on November 6th 1982.
- 19 at Stanford Reservoir on September 23rd 1990.
- 18 at Rutland Water on September 26th 1990 (with 16 still present on October 15th).
- 12 at Eyebrook Reservoir on September 30th 1972.
- 12 at Eyebrook Reservoir on September 17th 1993.
- 11 at Rutland Water on September 15th 1995.

There have been another seven records of between six and ten, all at Rutland Water; these include both the spring maximum, of eight on May 4th 1990 and the winter maximum, also of eight, on February 27th 1982.

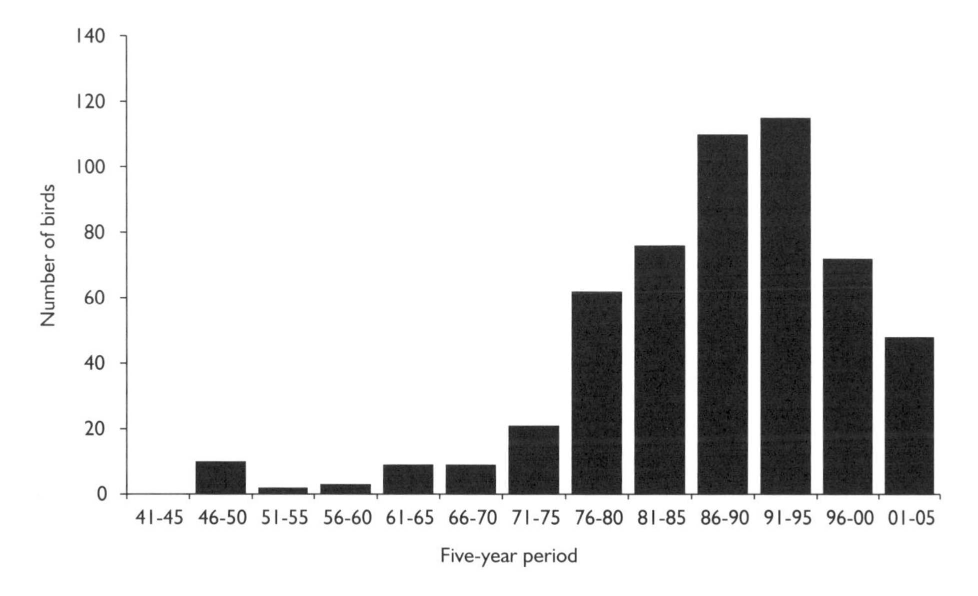

Figure 251: Numbers of Grey Plovers by five-year periods 1941–2005.

Away from Rutland Water, Eyebrook Reservoir and Stanford Reservoir, counts of more than two have only been recorded three times: four at both Priory Water on September 22nd 1990 and Cropston Reservoir on October 2nd 1990, and three over Groby Pool on September 21st 1994.

This species can appear at any time of year but with obvious peaks during May and from mid-September to mid-October. However, there has been a noticeable shift in occurrence patterns over the last 35 years. During 1941–67, 45% of all Grey Plover records at Eyebrook Reservoir were in May, with 13% in September and 10%

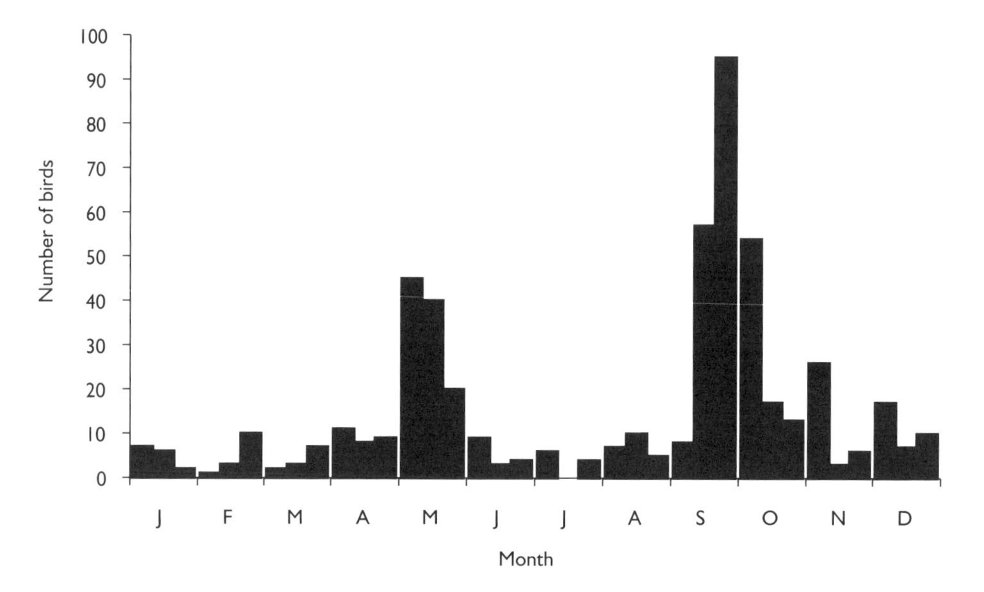

Figure 252: Monthly occurrence of Grey Plovers 1941–2005.

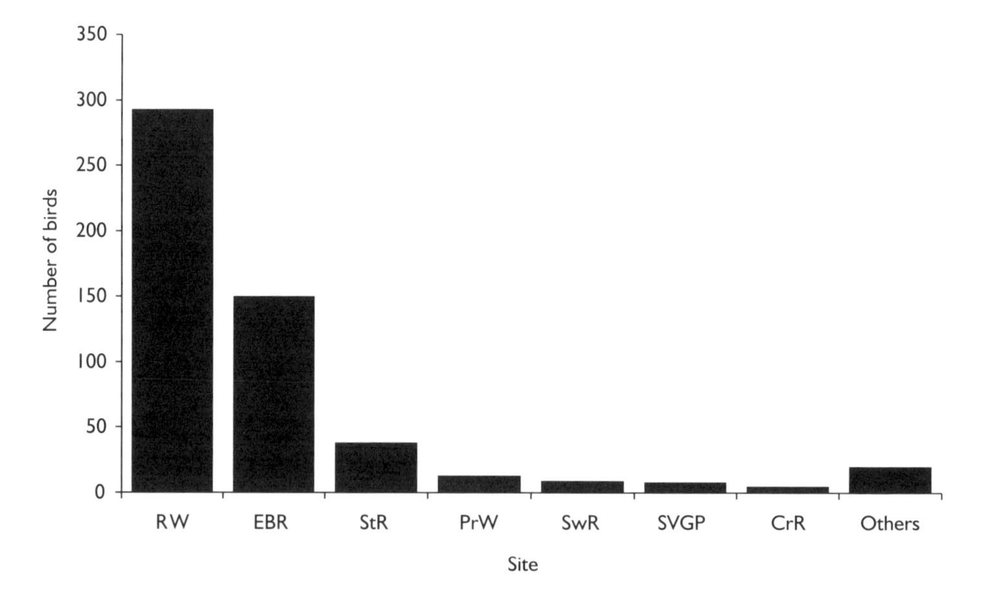

Figure 253: Sites where Grey Plovers have been recorded 1941–2005.
Key to abbreviations: RW = Rutland Water; EBR = Eyebrook Reservoir; StR = Stanford Reservoir; PrW = Priory Water; SwR = Swithland Reservoir; SVGP = Soar valley gravel pits; CrR = Cropston Reservoir

during October (Mason 1969), but in the counties overall between 1967 and 2005 May has accounted for only 18% of all records, with September producing 32% and October 16%. Birds now often remain for considerable periods during autumn and winter, especially at Rutland Water.

The obvious increase in numbers since the mid-1970s coincides with the construction of Rutland Water and this site now accounts for 55% of all records. A further 28% have been seen at Eyebrook Reservoir. The distinctive '*pee-u-eee*' call has indicated birds on nocturnal passage twice, over Quorn in early September 1956 and over Higham on the Hill on October 18th 1962.

Grey Plovers breed in the high Arctic, from northern Russia through Siberia and across northern Alaska and Canada. They winter around the coasts of Europe, Africa, southern Asia, Australasia and South America. The British wintering population is estimated at just over 50,000 birds (Baker *et al.* 2006), with The Wash being the most important single site in the country. As more than 50% of the British passage population is found at fewer than ten sites, and more than 20% of the East Atlantic Flyway wintering population uses this country, the Grey Plover has been added to the 'Amber List' of Birds of Conservation Concern (Gregory *et al.* 2002).

SML

Lapwing (Northern Lapwing) ***Vanellus vanellus***

Common to abundant passage and winter visitor, fairly common resident breeder.

This species has always been by far and away the commonest wader in the counties, both for breeding and wintering numbers. Browne described it as 'resident and generally distributed' in Leicestershire during the 19th century, whilst Haines considered it to be 'plentiful' in Rutland. Today, it is sufficiently widespread on unwatched farmland to make casual records of little value in assessing the status.

The size of the breeding population is largely unknown and any estimates have been little more than guess-work. In some years there have been as few as four breeding records submitted. Recent LROS Annual Reports have included accurate summaries of the available information, with 132 pairs mentioned as possibly breeding in 2002, but a majority of nesting birds will always have gone unrecorded. Anecdotal evidence and observers' general impressions suggest an overall decline during the lifetime of LROS. The frequently quoted reasons for the decline all involve changes in agricultural practices: the drainage of marshy areas and improvement of marginal wasteland, the loss of much permanent pasture to arable farming, the change to autumn-sown cereal crops and increased mechanisation leading to the destruction of nests; all apply to the local situation. It is hoped that the modern awareness of the species' ecological needs will lead to a reversal of the decline.

Warrilow made a tentative suggestion of a total breeding population in the region of 1,100 to 2,300 pairs during 1976–84, when Lapwings were found in 389 tetrads (65% of the total number of tetrads) and confirmed as breeding in 125 of them. The species' distribution throughout the counties was rather discontinuous, being absent from large tracts of east and north-east Leicestershire and north Rutland; these areas are the most intensively farmed parts of the counties, where the favoured habitat for Lapwings of a mixture of pasture and arable land has been lost and replaced by huge prairie-style fields. Looking at a longer period, Webster (1997) reported a decline of 80% in the number of nesting pairs in a sample of Charnwood tetrads between 1969 and 1994. Wilson *et al.* (2001) calculated a 59% decrease across the East Midlands between 1987 and 1998, whilst country-wide Chamberlain & Vickery (2002) noted a 44% decline during 1973–98 based on national CBC statistics. Unfortunately, local CBC data is of no use in monitoring the trends of this species, as Lapwings were absent from all farmland plots surveyed. However, based on the studies mentioned, there may have been 450–1,000 pairs nesting in the counties at the end of the 20th century.

The main breeding season extends from March to May. By late May small post-breeding flocks have sometimes started to form at wetlands; in 2003, for example, there were gatherings of 38 at Rutland Water and 17 at Eyebrook Reservoir on the 31st. These summer flocks increase in size and frequency during June, when the numbers recorded, especially towards the end of the month, suggest that continental birds may be involved. This idea is supported by occasional observations of small flocks flying west during the early summer, an early example of which was noted on June 4th 1968, when 50 flew west over Sharnford. The four largest June flocks are as follows:

- 811 at Eyebrook Reservoir on June 28th 2003.
- 600 at Rutland Water on June 8th 1984.

- 500 at Beeby on June 25th 1969.
- 500 at Eyebrook Reservoir on June 30th 1987.

Flocks generally continue to build up during July, with examples of 1,000+ recorded on six occasions. The largest flock in this month was one of 2,000 at Rutland Water on July 22nd 1984, following on from the unusually early 600 on June 8th. There is normally a further large influx during August and September, with the largest flocks as follows:

- 4,000 at Rutland Water on August 15th 1984.
- 4,000 at Rutland Water on August 22nd 1986.
- 4,000 at Eyebrook Reservoir on September 8th 1990.
- 4,000 at Eyebrook Reservoir on September 1st 1991.
- 3,000 at Bitteswell on September 20th 1986.
- 3,000 at Kirby Bellars on August 20th 1989.
- 3,000 at Rutland Water on September 1989.
- 2,450 at Eyebrook Reservoir on September 30th 1967.
- 2,000 at Cotes on September 8th 1945.
- 2,000 at Wanlip on August 12th 1975.
- 2,000 at Eyebrook Reservoir on August 6th 1989.

Apart from a flock of 5,000 at Lindley Airfield on October 10th 1948 numbers in October concentrations have never exceeded 3,000, the highest recent count being 2,967 at Rutland Water on October 8th 1995. This indicates that a significant proportion of the birds earlier in the autumn are purely on passage as opposed to arriving for the winter. Large numbers normally arrive from November onwards, partially depending on the hardness of the winter. Flocks of 10,000 or more have been recorded twice, one of them contributing to a total of 21,500 in just four flocks in February 1982. The largest counts for the period from November to February are:

- 10,400 at Rutland Water on November 6th 1994.
- 10,000 at Cranoe on February 13th 1982.
- 8,000 in the Shepshed/Belton area in January 1990.
- 7,000 at Eyebrook Reservoir in early December 1990.
- 6,000 at Ratby Meadows in early February 1981.
- 6,000 at Thrussington on February 12th 1984.
- 6,000 at Eyebrook Reservoir on November 16th 1994.
- 5,500 at Cossington on February 7th 1982.
- 5,500 at Rutland Water on November 8th 1984.

Additional winter flocks of 5,000 have been recorded six times, including twice in January 1948. The sizes of winter groups since 2001 have been consistently low, the largest counts in each of the four winters being just 2,000, 1,500, 820, 1,500 and 700. This period of lower numbers started in 1995, since when there have only been seven flocks higher than 2,500, the largest of which was 4,000 at Enderby in February 1999.

Lapwings are renowned for their cold weather movements and at the onset of severe conditions, especially heavy snowfall, they are forced to move to less inclement areas to the south and west. Some observations of these movements include 4,000 that passed over Aylestone on January 20th 1981 and 5,000 flying south over Enderby on January 20th 1984, with a further 1,300 moving south-east two days later. There was a total absence of birds during the extreme weather in February 1947 and a near-complete exodus from the counties was noted in the infamous cold spell early in 1963; many of those that remained during the latter winter were found in a very poor condition (Gamble 1965). Similar evacuations were noted in 1985, 1986 and 1987; a return movement of 2,500 flying north over Enderby on March 11th 1986 was noted as the conditions ameliorated.

Winter flocks usually disperse in March as birds move to their breeding areas. Early in the month there have been some counts comparable with those in the winter period, such as 4,000 at Ratby Meadows on March 5th 1977 and 3,000 at Stanford Reservoir on March 8th 1981. Large numbers are almost unheard of in April, a notable exception being 450 flying north-west over Glen Parva on April 9th 2001, presumably on spring passage.

Lapwings breed throughout much of Europe and across central Asia to China. They are largely migratory, although less so in the west and south of the breeding range. The British breeding population is estimated at approximately 154,000 pairs (Baker *et al.* 2006) and, due to the moderate decline in numbers over the last 25 years, this species has been added to the 'Amber List' of Birds of Conservation Concern (Gregory *et al.* 2002). Numbers wintering in Britain are much higher and are estimated at between 1,500,000 and 2,000,000 birds (Baker *et al.* 2006). Many Scandinavian birds winter in the UK, as shown by one found dead at Kegworth on December 26th 1953 that had been ringed as a chick in Norway on May 24th 1951. In addition, evidence that Scandinavian winter immigrants may remain in Britain to breed is provided by one found dead at Bottesford in June 1938 that had been ringed as a chick in Denmark in 1933. Another continental recovery involved one found dead at South Luffenham in November 1954 that had been ringed as a chick in the Netherlands in 1953. There are also two recoveries of birds which have moved to France: a chick ringed at Hemington in 1988 was shot at Ploemeur, 590km south-south-west, in December 1993 and an adult ringed near Leicester in November 1968 was shot 847km to the south in the Gironde region in February 1971. Three more recoveries involve long-distance movements within England: two ringed as chicks in West Yorkshire in 1955 were both found dead near Leicester in January 1956 and one ringed as a chick at Rutland Water on June 5th 1976 was found dead 296km north-north-west at Amble (Northumberland) on October 25th of the same year.

SML

Knot (Red Knot) ***Calidris canutus***

Scarce to uncommon passage migrant and rare winter visitor; recorded in all months, with the majority in May, August and September.

Strangely, Hickling overlooked all pre-1951 records when compiling the previous avifauna, stating that the first report for the counties was one at Eyebrook Reservoir on August 7th 1951. In fact, there had been three documented records prior to the formation of LROS in 1941: one shot at Bradgate Park in June 1912, two at Stanford Reservoir on December 17th 1936 and five at Swithland Reservoir on December 18th 1938. The 1941 LROS Annual Report described this species as a winter visitor, usually in severe weather, presumably in response to the reports in 1936 and 1938. Between 1941 and 1951 there were records in all but three years, but these records did not support the previous status description, with only three of the 18 birds being in winter and most of them actually occurring in autumn.

The Knot remained a rare visitor to the counties during the 1940s and 1950s, although groups of five were seen at Eyebrook Reservoir on both August 7th 1949 and August 24th 1952. Each successive decade up until 1990 saw an increase in numbers and the only blank years after 1950 were 1956, 1957, 1968 and 1982. Numbers peaked in the mid to late 1980s; slightly fewer birds on average have occurred since 1990, although the best year on record is 1998, with 25 individuals. Other good years have been 1984 and 1995 (20 individuals each) and 1985 and 1988 (19 individuals each). The peak in the late 1980s is in line with the national population index, which was at record levels around this time (Collier *et al.* 2005). The total number of individuals recorded in the counties to the end of 2005 is about 465, quite low for a wader that is so numerous as close as The Wash (Norfolk/Lincolnshire) but explained by this species normally having a migration strategy involving non-stop movements between established sites.

Most records are of one or two birds, although there have been eight counts exceeding five, as follows:

- ten at Rutland Water on May 21st 1980.
- ten at Rutland Water on September 17th 1984.
- nine at Swithland Reservoir on November 14th 1959.
- nine at Rutland Water on September 23rd 1985.
- nine at Eyebrook Reservoir on August 10th 1999.
- eight at Rutland Water on September 16th 1995.
- seven at Thornton Reservoir on May 3rd 1990.
- six at Rutland Water on September 11th 1988.

The Knot is mainly an autumn visitor to the counties, with August and September being the peak months, accounting for over 50% of all records. It is likely that the considerable numbers in October and November involve birds moving west from the autumn staging grounds around the continental Waddenzee (Wadden Sea).

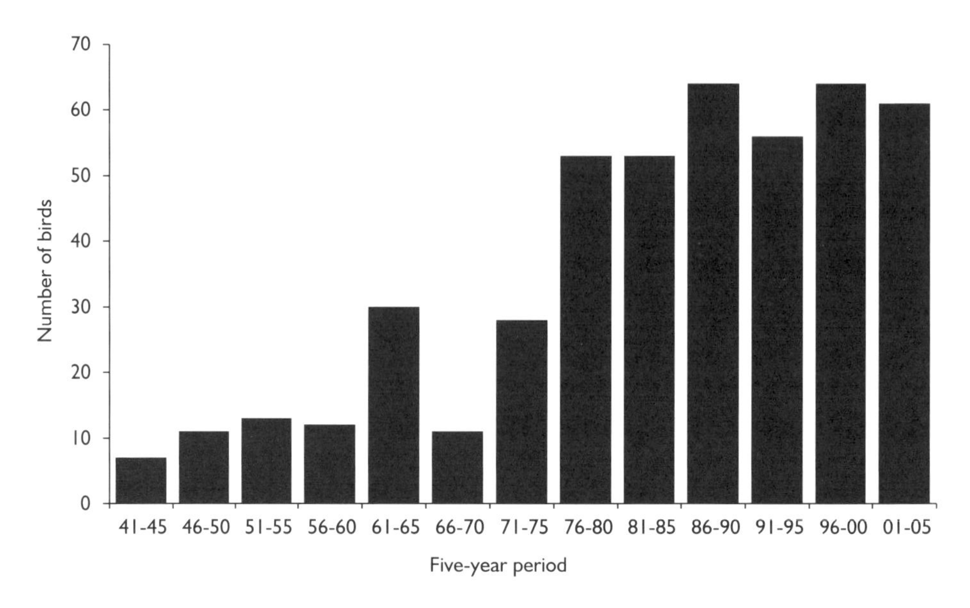

Figure 254: Numbers of Knots by five-year periods 1941–2005.

The smaller numbers in the winter months may include birds moving between the east and west coasts of Britain. There no longer seems to be a significant link to severe weather, though occasional records have coincided with cold spells, such as when five were at Eyebrook Reservoir on March 22nd 1962 and one was by the River Trent at Castle Donington on January 27th 1963. There has been a definite shift in occurrence patterns over the last 35 years. During 1941–67, Mason (1969) reported that 18% of all occurrences at Eyebrook Reservoir had been during March, with only 14% in September; the equivalent figures for all records throughout the counties for the period 1941 to 2005 are 4.5% in March and 27% in September.

There have been records in all months, although June and early July reports are very unusual. Spring passage generally ceases in late May and the only June records are of two at Eyebrook Reservoir on June 2nd 1998 and single birds at this site from June 11th to 13th 2001 and Rutland Water on June 12th 1987. There is then a clear gap of almost four weeks until the earliest autumn migrant, one at Eyebrook Reservoir on July 9th 1994. The only other records in this month prior to the 20th are single birds at Eyebrook Reservoir on July 13th 1964 and Rutland Water from July 14th to 20th 1985.

In recent years very few have occurred away from the top two sites of Rutland Water and Eyebrook Reservoir, which between them account for almost 86% of all records. Over the years, the reservoirs at Swithland, Cropston, Thornton and Stanford have mustered totals of 20, 13, ten and ten respectively, but apart from Loughborough Sewage Farm, which recorded single birds on both September 17th 1955 and April 12th 1958, the other seven sites that have been visited by this species all only have one record to their name, as follows:

- one at Leicester City Farms on February 7th and 8th 1942.
- one by the River Trent at Castle Donington on January 27th 1963.
- one at Hemington Gravel Pits on July 30th 1970.
- one picked up dying at Wigston on September 16th 1970.
- one at Trent Valley Pit on April 4th 1995.
- three at Priory Water on December 8th 1996.
- one at Enderby Pool on April 27th 1998.

Surprisingly, there has never been a record of Knot from the well-watched gravel pits in the Soar valley.

Knots breed discontinuously in the high Arctic of Siberia, Greenland and Canada. Birds of the *islandica* race, which breed in Greenland and north-east Canada, constitute the wintering population of Britain, which is currently estimated at approximately 283,600 birds (Baker *et al.* 2006). The two single most important sites for

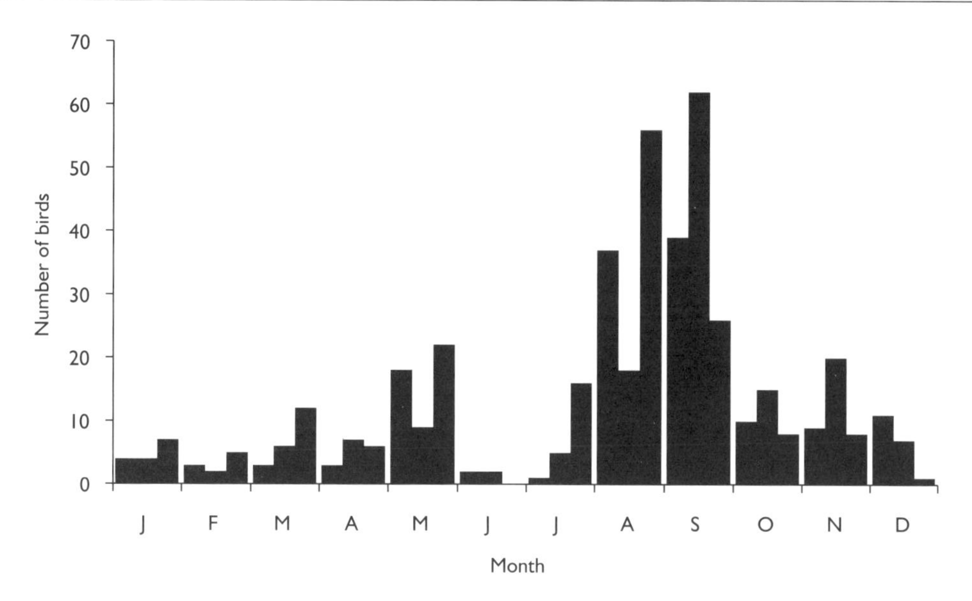

Figure 255: Monthly occurrence of Knots 1941–2005.

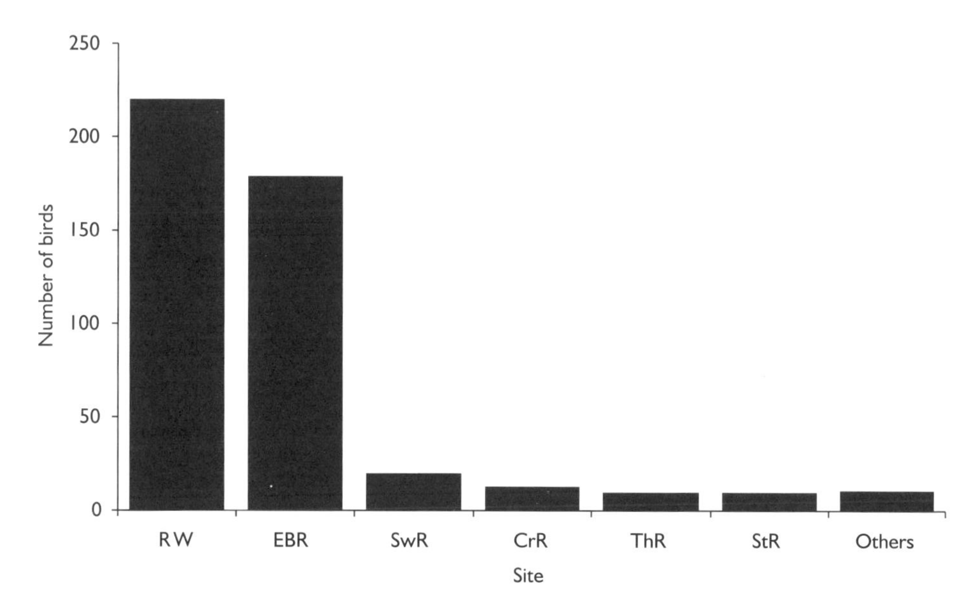

Figure 256: Sites where Knots have been recorded 1941–2005.
Key to abbreviations: RW = Rutland Water; EBR = Eyebrook Reservoir; SwR = Swithland Reservoir; CrR = Cropston Reservoir; ThR = Thornton Reservoir; StR = Stanford Reservoir

this species in Britain are Morecambe Bay (Lancashire) and The Wash (Norfolk/Lincolnshire), which between them hold in the region of 130,000 wintering birds (Collier *et al.* 2005). During passage periods, numbers in Britain are supplemented by birds of the nominate race, which breed in western Siberia and winter along the west coast of Africa. As more than 50% of the British wintering population is found at fewer than ten sites, and more than 20% of the East Atlantic Flyway wintering population uses this country, the Knot has been added to the 'Amber List' of Birds of Conservation Concern (Gregory *et al.* 2002).

SML

Sanderling *Calidris alba*

Scarce to uncommon passage migrant and rare winter visitor; recorded in all months, with the majority in May and August.

Browne makes reference to two rather vague reports of this species: an undated record of three or four shot 'near the reservoir in Charnwood Forest' and another shot some time around 1904 near Great Bowden. Haines mentions another undated record of one shot near Tixover some time in the 19th century. The LROS archives mention one seen at Leicester City Farms in January 1940.

The first confirmed modern record was on May 16th 1945, when two were at Cropston Reservoir. Since then approximately 475 have occurred in the counties. The most productive year has been 1995, when a total of 27 were recorded, 25 in the spring and two in autumn. Other good years have included 2003 (26), 1973 (22+), 1994 (22) and 2005 (20). Since 1945 there have been eight blank years, but none since 1969. This species has been reported much more regularly and in greater numbers in the last 30 years and this increase can only be partially explained by the creation of Rutland Water; even after discounting all birds there, the Sanderling is now almost three times commoner than it was between 1945 and 1970.

The largest counts have almost all been at either Rutland Water or Eyebrook Reservoir. Flocks of ten have occurred three times, at Eyebrook Reservoir on May 7th 1955 and at Rutland Water on both August 13th 1973 (during the creation period) and May 17th 1984. Counts of nine have also been recorded on three occasions, at Eyebrook Reservoir in May 1976 and at Rutland Water on both August 28th 1989 and August 24th 2003. Groups of seven have been seen at Eyebrook Reservoir twice, including on the rather early date of April 1st 1974. The highest count at other sites is eight, at Wanlip South Gravel Pits on May 15th 2001, with no other counts exceeding four.

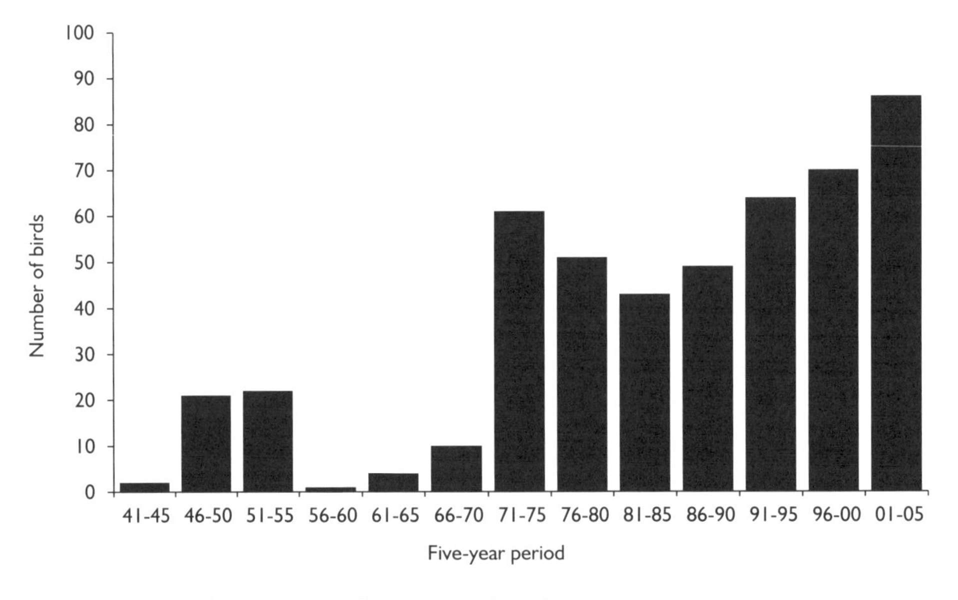

Figure 257: Numbers of Sanderlings by five-year periods 1941–2005.

Up to 2005, 281 had occurred in spring (April to June), 172 in autumn (July to November) and 15 in winter (December to March). 81% of spring birds have been in May, with the majority of the rest in late April and early June. Spring records prior to April 21st are scarce, the only ones being:

- seven at Eyebrook Reservoir on April 1st 1974.
- one at Rutland Water on April 12th 1988.
- one at Rutland Water on April 15th and 16th 1986.
- one at Eyebrook Reservoir on April 18th 2004.
- three at Eyebrook Reservoir on April 19th 1995.

Most June records are during the first few days of the month and the only ones after the 10th involve single birds at Rutland Water on June 16th 1991 and June 17th 2004, two at the same site on June 18th 2001 and two at Eyebrook Reservoir on June 19th 1949. This leaves a clear two-week gap before the first autumn record on July 4th (one at Stanford Reservoir in 1971). August is the main autumn passage month, with 51% of all records, followed by July and then September; only 12 have occurred in October and six in November.

Prior to 1996 there had only been three records, all in January, in the four months December to March but more recently there has been an obvious increase in winter and early spring appearances. There have now been records in all months from December to March, all of single birds unless stated:

- Rutland Water on December 7th and 8th 2003.
- Rutland Water on December 15th 2002.
- Rutland Water on December 21st 1997.
- three at Rutland Water from January 1st to 7th 1996.
- Rutland Water from January 3rd to 27th 2004.
- Rutland Water on January 3rd 1982.
- Eyebrook Reservoir on January 27th 1972.
- two at Swithland Reservoir on January 30th 1954.
- Priory Water on February 8th 2004.
- Rutland Water on February 25th 2004.
- Rutland Water on March 14th 1999.
- Rutland Water on March 14th 2003.

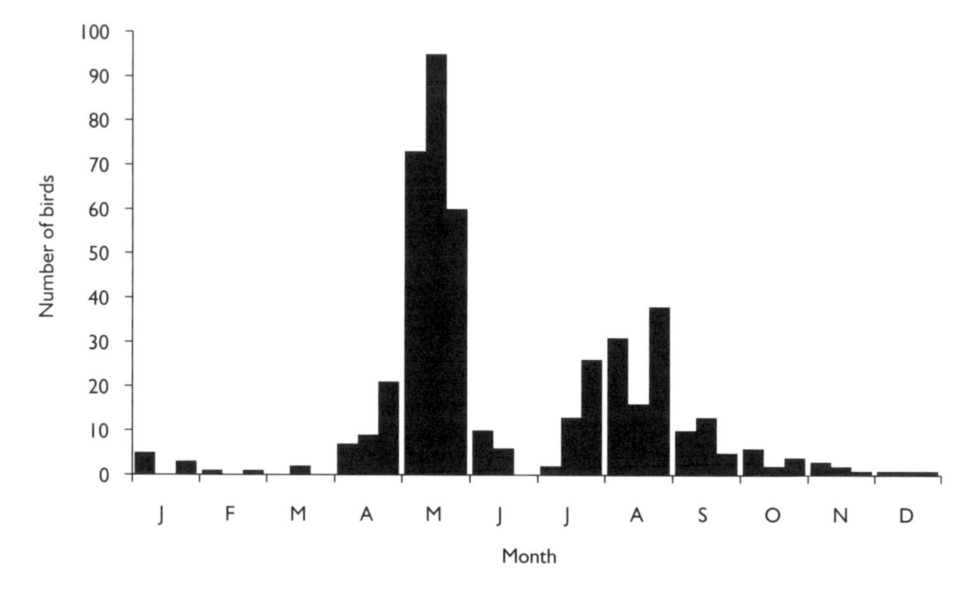

Figure 258: Monthly occurrence of Sanderlings 1941–2005.

Most records have occurred at the two waters with the most expansive areas of shoreline, with Rutland Water producing over 235 and Eyebrook Reservoir accounting for approximately 160. The remainder are shared between 13 sites, of which Swithland Reservoir has produced eight records involving 14 birds, Trent Valley Pit has a total of ten individuals and Stanford Reservoir has mustered nine.

Two records published in LROS Annual Reports are now considered unacceptable: one at Loughborough Sewage Farm on February 22nd 1948 and an exceptional 30 at Eyebrook Reservoir on May 18th 1948 (Fray 2005).

Sanderlings have a rather restricted breeding distribution that includes northern Canada, coastal Greenland and north-central Siberia. The winter range is around the coasts of Europe, Africa, the Americas, southern and

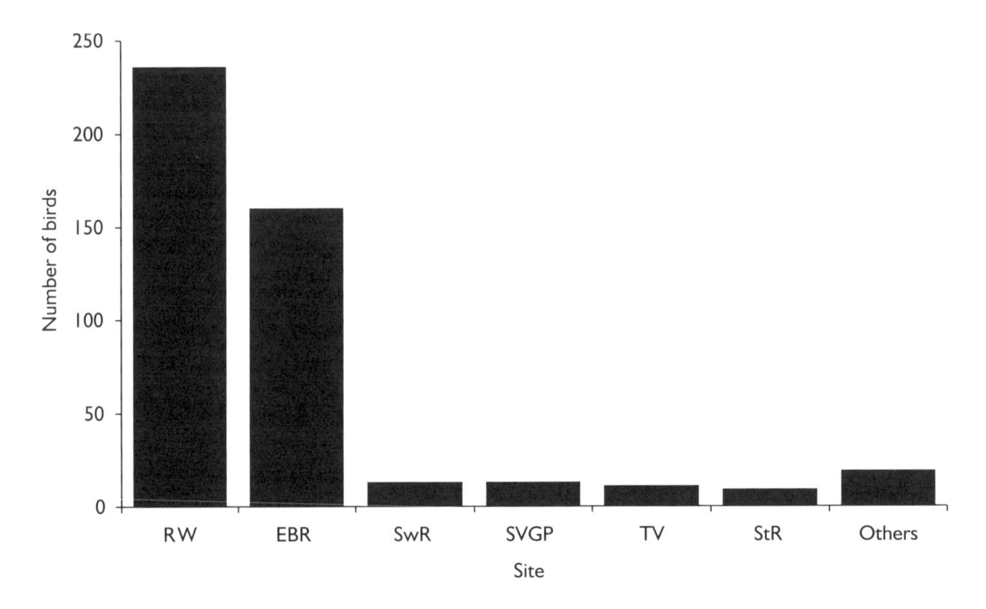

Figure 259: Sites where Sanderlings have been recorded 1941–2005.
Key to abbreviations: RW = Rutland Water; EBR = Eyebrook Reservoir; SwR = Swithland Reservoir; SVGP = Soar valley gravel pits; TV = Trent valley; StR = Stanford Reservoir

south-east Asia and Australasia. The British wintering population is currently estimated at just over 20,000 birds (Baker *et al.* 2006).

SML

Little Stint *Calidris minuta*

Rare spring and uncommon autumn passage migrant, and rare to scarce winter visitor; recorded in all months except June, with the majority from August to October.

The status of the Little Stint in the counties in the 19th century and early 20th century is a little uncertain. Browne details five records from Leicestershire: one shot at Abbey Meadows, Leicester in January 1867 (and recorded in the *Zoologist* at the time), three at Saddington Reservoir on September 22nd 1885, two of which were shot and presented to the Leicester Museum, single birds shot at Kibworth in March 1893 and Swithland Reservoir on September 22nd 1904 and an undated record of a bird shot at Saddington Reservoir. In Rutland, Haines knew of three occurrences: single birds, all shot, at Tixover on December 25th 1870, Seaton in about 1887 and Tinwell on November 6th 1880. The fact that there were no modern winter records until 1977–78 (see below) perhaps throws several of these old reports into doubt.

The first modern record was in 1945, when three were at Eyebrook Reservoir on September 16th. Since then the only years without any sightings have been 1965 and 1968. Annual totals are very variable, illustrated by at least 182 in 1996 being followed by just four the next year. 1996 was an exceptional year, with a major influx occurring during mid-September totalling at least 177 birds. The peak count at Rutland Water of 82 on September 21st was not only the largest number ever recorded at one site in the counties but also exceeded all other annual totals there. Away from Rutland Water records came from a further nine sites during this influx, with six of these recording their maximum ever counts, as follows:

- 15 at Swithland Reservoir on September 21st.
- nine at Stanford Reservoir from September 24th to 26th.
- eight at Priory Water on September 22nd.
- eight at Cropston Reservoir on September 29th.
- five at Ibstock Opencast (now Sence Valley Forest Park) on September 24th.
- three at Saddington Reservoir on September 20th.

During the 1996 influx the highest count at Eyebrook Reservoir was 45 on September 23rd, but this total did not exceed the numbers recorded in 1960 when a total of 74 occurred at this site during the year, with a peak count of 61 on September 19th. Comparable numbers to the 1996 total may have been achieved in 1960 had Rutland Water been in existence at the time. Other productive years have been 1998 (74 birds), 2001 (48), 1990 and 1993 (47 each) and 1975 (41).

Away from 1960 and 1996, counts exceeding 20 have been recorded on four occasions, all at Rutland Water: 52 on September 19th 1998, 34 on September 13th 1993, 23 on September 29th 2001 and 21 on September 17th 1995. Eyebrook Reservoir has achieved double-figure counts in four autumns excluding 1960 and 1996: 19 on September 6th 1998, 17 on September 6th 1975 and 15 on both October 6th 1964 and September 21st 2001. Only four other sites have recorded groups of four or more birds, as follows:

- up to six at Cropston Reservoir from September 13th to 30th 1973.
- six at Stanford Reservoir on September 16th 1990.
- five at Cropston Reservoir on August 31 st 1975.
- five at Stanford Reservoir on October 14th 1978.
- four at Loughborough Sewage Farm on September 28th and 29th 1957.
- four at Watermead Park on September 11th 1995.

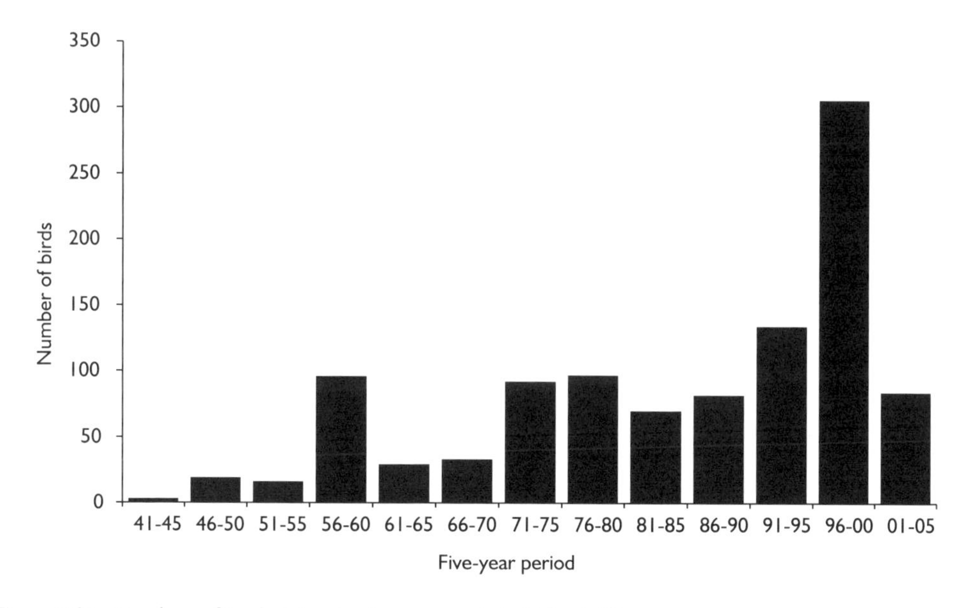

Figure 260: Numbers of Little Stints by five-year periods 1941–2005.

Birds on spring migration were not recorded in the counties until 1962, when one was at Eyebrook Reservoir from May 13th to 17th. The total at present is only 25; 15 of these have occurred since 1993, with 1999 producing a total of five birds at Rutland Water and Eyebrook Reservoir. Most spring records have been of single birds, although two have been seen together on four occasions and three were at Rutland Water on May 16th 1996. May records account for 19 of the total and almost half of these have been in the middle ten days of the month; one at Rutland Water on May 31st 1997 is the latest spring occurrence. Four have been seen in April: single birds at both Rutland Water on April 13th 1986 and Eyebrook Reservoir on April 28th 1976, and two at the latter site on April 30th 1999, although two at Eyebrook Reservoir on March 24th 1976 is the earliest spring report. All the spring records have been at either Rutland Water or Eyebrook Reservoir except for one at Swithland Reservoir from May 20th to 27th 1973, two at Watermead Gravel Pits on May 23rd 1987, with one until May 25th, and one at Wanlip South Gravel Pits on May 10th 2001. Broadly speaking, Little and Temminck's Stints are equally common in spring, unlike at other times of year when Temminck's Stint is much the scarcer.

Autumn passage occurs mainly in August and September but with an increasing trend for more to remain into October and even November or December. The peak has almost always been the second half of September in years when high numbers have been recorded, whereas October has seen the largest numbers in less outstanding years. Early returning birds have been seen in July in 13 years, all since 1969. The total for the month is 30 and ten of these were at Rutland Water on July 30th 1980; apart from four at the same site on July 29th 2000 all other records during the month have been of single birds. Only two have been recorded prior to the 20th, both at Rutland Water: on July 9th 1977 and July 17th 1991. Birds that pass through in July and all but the last few days of August are adults, with those later in the season being almost exclusively juveniles.

Very small numbers of birds have wintered in the counties spasmodically since the first one, at Cropston Reservoir in 1977–78. Leicestershire and Rutland are near the northern limit of the winter range of the species in Britain so regular wintering is surprising, especially inland; the majority of sites used in England are estuaries and coastal lagoons in the south, and the total number of wintering birds is normally fewer than 30. Rutland Water hosted individuals for each of the four winters from 1983–84 to 1986–87, with two birds in 1985–86. There was then a gap in the habit until another four–year period from 1998–99 to 2001–02, when birds were again regular at Rutland Water, often with flocks of Dunlins, with what were presumably the same birds also being seen less regularly at Eyebrook Reservoir, moving between the sites with the Dunlins; numbers in these four winters were five in 1998–89, at least one in 1999–2000, two in 2000-01 and at least one in 2001–02. After a gap of a year, one individual wintered in 2003–04 and 2004-05 and one looked set to winter at Rutland Water at the end of 2005. The wintering birds have remained until March in five of the 13 years concerned, not being recorded after January in the others.

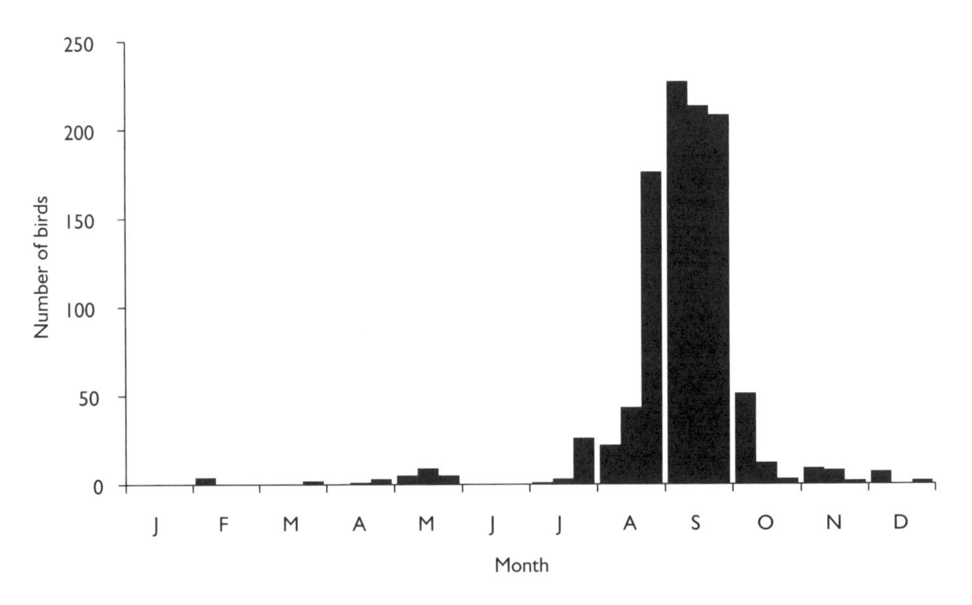

Figure 261: Monthly occurrence of Little Stints 1941–2005.

As with most waders in the counties, the vast majority of records have come from Rutland Water and Eyebrook Reservoir, which between them account for over 86% of all sightings. Elsewhere, only Stanford Reservoir, Cropston Reservoir, Swithland Reservoir, Priory Water and the Soar valley gravel pits have produced more than

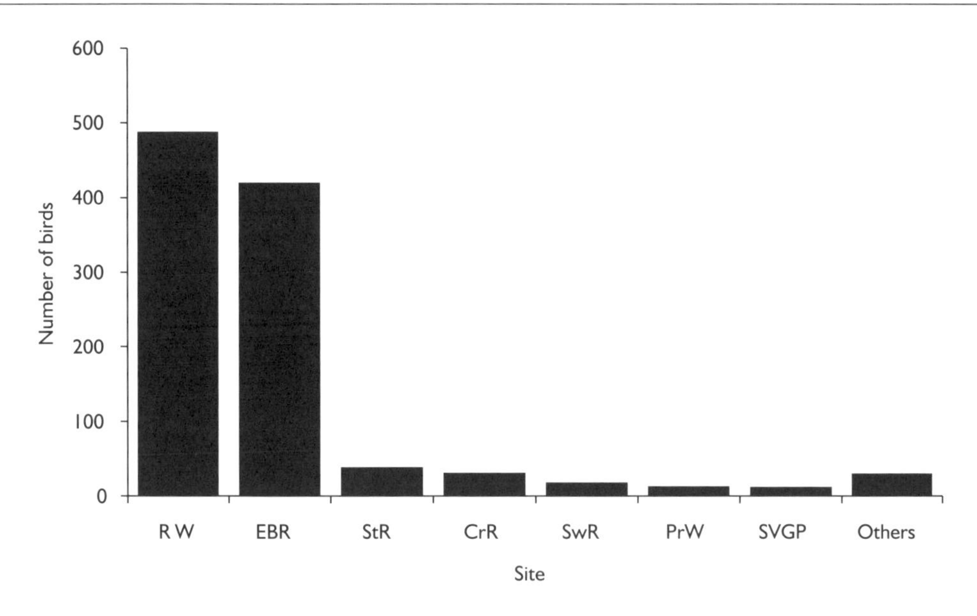

Figure 262: Sites where Little Stints have been recorded 1941–2005.
Key to abbreviations: RW = Rutland Water; EBR = Eyebrook Reservoir; StR = Stanford Reservoir; CrR = Cropston Reservoir; SwR = Swithland Reservoir; PrW = Priory Water; SVGP = Soar valley gravel pits

ten birds. Loughborough Sewage Farm mustered nine individuals during its existence, whilst Frisby Gravel Pits, Kelham Bridge, Cadeby Quarry, Saddington Reservoir, Trent Valley Pit and Ibstock Opencast/Sence Valley Forest Park all have two records to their name. Single birds have occurred at Quorn Sewage Farm and Quorn Borrow Pit.

Little Stints breed from coastal northern Scandinavia across the far-north of Russia and central Siberia, wintering mainly in sub-Saharan Africa, the Middle East and the Indian subcontinent. The numbers passing through Britain each autumn (it is always scarce in spring) are very variable, with the largest recorded national influxes being in 1960, 1996 and 1998: this matches the local situation perfectly. A total of 1,063 was recorded in Britain in September 1998 (Brown & Grice 2005). Even in the best years the numbers recorded in Britain are only a small proportion of the total East Atlantic Flyway population, in the order of 211,000 birds (Rose & Scott 1997). A juvenile that was caught and ringed at Rutland Water in August 1993 was controlled on its wintering grounds, salt-pans near Cervia (Italy) in January 1995; it was seen there again in November of the same year.

SML

Temminck's Stint *Calidris temminckii*

Rare passage migrant from north-east Europe; recorded in all months, with the majority in May: 29 records involving 40 individuals.

Browne noted that a record of one shot at Saddington Reservoir in 1860, which was mentioned in the *Midland Naturalist* in 1882, proved to be an error; on examination of the specimen the bird was confirmed to be a Little Stint. What was later published as the first county record, of one at Loughborough Sewage Farm on September 17th 1947, is now considered to be unreliable, so the first acceptable bird recorded in Leicestershire and Rutland was one seen by Peter Gamble and Dennis Felstead at Eyebrook Reservoir on May 16th and 17th 1948. The second followed almost immediately, when one was at Loughborough Sewage Farm on May 20th and 21st of the same year. In total, there have been records in 23 years involving 38 individuals.

All records:

1948	Eyebrook Reservoir, May 16th to 17th.
	Loughborough Sewage Farm, May 20th to 21st.
1949	Stanford Reservoir, September 7th to 11th.
1954	Eyebrook Reservoir, September 12th.
1955	adult, Sawley Gravel Pits, May 18th (incorrectly published in the LROS Annual Report as May 28th).
1966	Stanford Reservoir, May 30th to June 3rd.
1972	Cropston Reservoir, September 3rd.
1974	Market Harborough Sewage Farm, May 18th.
1980	two, Rutland Water, May 18th.
1982	Rutland Water, intermittently, October 16th to January 10th 1984.
1985	Rutland Water, May 11th to 13th.
	Rutland Water, August 3rd to 4th.
1987	adult, Rutland Water, September 5th.
1988	Rutland Water, May 24th to 25th.
1993	juvenile, Eyebrook Reservoir, September 16th to 22nd.
1994	two adults, Rutland Water, May 19th to 22nd.
1997	Rutland Water, May 16th.
	two, Rutland Water, May 25th and 26th.
1998	adult, Rutland Water, August 4th.
1999	two adults, Rutland Water, May 19th, with three adults on May 20th and four adults on May 21st and 22nd.
	juvenile, Kirby Lakes, August 15th.
2000	adult, Eyebrook Reservoir, May 5th to 6th.
	adult, Sence Valley Forest Park, May 7th to 9th.
2002	two adults, Eyebrook Reservoir, May 18th.
2003	two adults, Eyebrook Reservoir, May 12th to 15th.
2004	three adults, Wanlip Meadows, May 15th.
	adult, Rutland Water, July 10th to 13th.
	juvenile, Eyebrook Reservoir, September 3rd to 11th.
2005	two adults, Wanlip Meadows, May 16th to 18th.

Records have increased notably from 1997, with 22 individuals found since then, over half of all records. The two best years have been 1999 and 2004, with five birds in each. Rutland Water has accounted for 18 birds (45% of all records); between May 1980 and May 1999, 16 individuals were found at this site, with only one elsewhere during this period. However, since then there has only been one bird at Rutland Water and 13 elsewhere, six of which have been at Eyebrook Reservoir, taking this site's total to nine individuals. Records have come from a further eight sites, although only Stanford Reservoir and Wanlip Meadows have recorded this species on more than one occasion. Several of the counties' well-watched sites, such as Swithland, Thornton and Saddington Reservoirs and Trent Valley Pit have yet to record Temminck's Stint.

In total there have been 18 spring records, involving 29 birds and nine autumn records, all of single birds. Spring arrivals have all been between May 5th and May 30th, 20 birds having appeared between the 16th and 21st. Autumn arrivals have occurred between August 3rd and September 16th, with adults at the start of the period and mostly juveniles later. In addition, an adult was at Rutland Water from July 10th to 13th 2004; this was presumably a failed breeder or non-breeding individual.

As well as the normal spring and autumn records, there was a remarkable series of sightings at Rutland Water during 1982 to 1984; these extended from October 16th 1982 until January 10th 1984, with only three intervening months (December 1982, January 1983 and June 1983) being without any sightings. It seems very likely that only one bird was involved and it may well have been present throughout the period. Wintering records in England, even further south, are very rare; Lack (1986) only found one other such example during 1982–84.

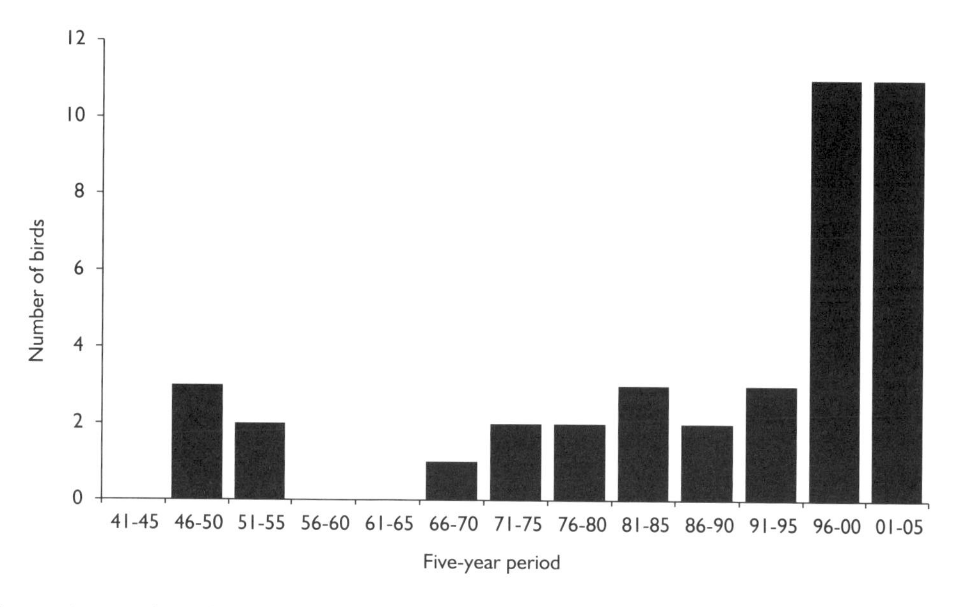

Figure 263: Numbers of Temminck's Stints by five-year periods 1941–2005.

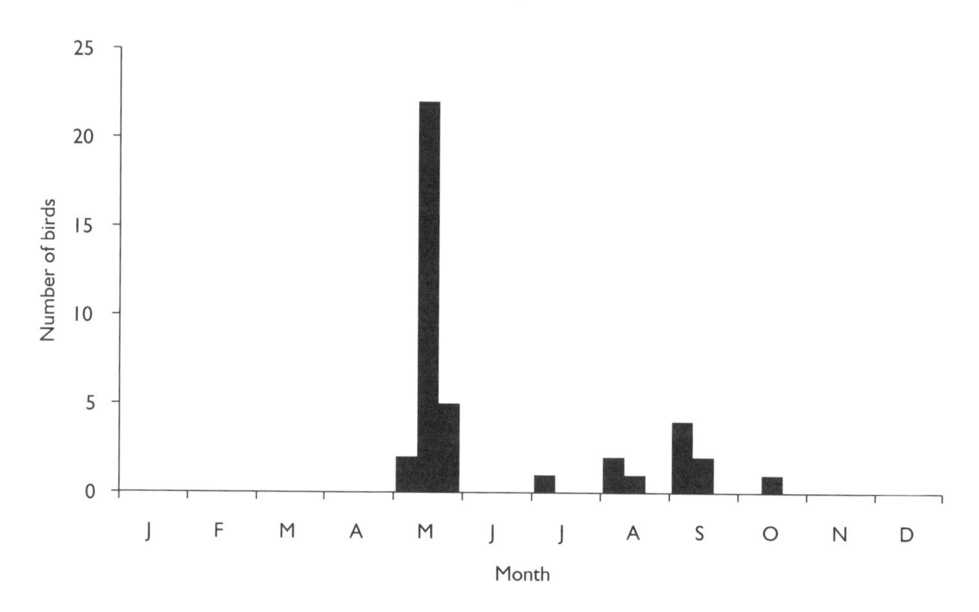

Figure 264: Monthly occurrence of Temminck's Stints 1941–2005.

Two together have been seen on six occasions, all within the peak of spring passage, with larger groups consisting of three at Wanlip Meadows in May 2004 and four at Rutland Water in May 1999. Four together at an inland site is most unusual.

In addition to the records mentioned above, one at Eyebrook Reservoir on September 21st 1948 was originally published but was found to be unacceptable on review in 2004 (Fray 2005).

Temminck's Stints breed along the northern fringe of Europe and Asia from southern Norway to easternmost Siberia and winter mainly across sub-Saharan Africa and in southern Asia. A tiny population of one or two pairs exists in Scotland, where breeding was first confirmed in 1934 and has probably occurred in at least 20 years since (Mudge & Dennis 1995). Due to the small size of the British breeding population, this species has been added to the 'Amber List' of Birds of Conservation Concern (Gregory *et al.* 2002). Temminck's Stints are more familiar in Britain as passage migrants, mainly during the spring but with smaller numbers during the autumn; there was an average of 61 records a year in Britain and Ireland between 1958 and 1985, with the majority in England (Dymond *et al.* 1989).

SML

White-rumped Sandpiper *Calidris fuscicollis*

Very rare vagrant from North America: three records.

All three records occurred at Rutland Water during a five-year period in the 1990s. The first was a summer-plumaged adult in Manton Bay from July 21st to 24th 1994, found by Alex Lees (Fray 1995, *BB* 88:514) and this was quickly followed by a moulting adult in the south arm from September 15th to 17th 1995, initially located by John Wright (*BB* 89:500). A winter-plumaged adult was found in the north arm on November 7th 1998, again by John Wright, later moving to Manton Bay and remaining until November 19th (*BB* 92:573–574).

White-rumped Sandpipers breed irregularly in north Alaska and more commonly in Arctic Canada and are long-distance migrants, overflying the western Atlantic to winter in southern South America from Paraguay to Tierra del Fuego. They are annual vagrants to Britain, usually during the autumn and average around ten records per year, although there were notable influxes of 27 in 1996 and 34 in 2000. By the end of 2005 the British total was 406 and the White-rumped Sandpiper was removed from the list of species assessed by the BBRC. This species is, however, particularly unusual inland, with the only other Midland counties to have recorded White-rumped Sandpiper being Staffordshire (three records), Worcestershire (one record) and Oxfordshire (one record). Given the scarcity of this species inland and the fact that all three county records involved adults at Rutland Water, it is quite possible that the same bird was involved each time.

SML

Baird's Sandpiper *Calidris bairdii*

Very rare vagrant from North America: two records.

Both records have been of juveniles at Eyebrook Reservoir. The first was found by Keith Allsopp and Ralph Lockwood on September 10th 1977, remaining until September 15th (*BB* 71:500), whilst the second, originally found by John Wright, was present from September 17th to 26th 1994 (Wright 1995, *BB* 88:511 & 514).

Baird's Sandpiper breeds in the high Arctic of northern Canada and Alaska, as well as in extreme north-east Siberia and in north-west Greenland. Like the White-rumped Sandpiper, it is a long-distant migrant, migrating through the North American interior to winter in South America south of the equator. It is an annual vagrant to Britain, generally during the autumn, but about half as frequent as the White-rumped Sandpiper; by the end of 2005, the British total was around 195 records. It is more of a freshwater species than White-rumped Sandpiper and this is reflected in the greater incidence of inland reports in this country: there have been two records each in Derbyshire, Staffordshire and Northamptonshire and single birds in Warwickshire and Nottinghamshire.

SML

Pectoral Sandpiper *Calidris melanotos*

Rare autumn vagrant from North America or Siberia; recorded in all months from July to October, with the majority in September: 30 records involving 32 individuals.

The first record for the counties was one seen by James Fisher and Julian Huxley at Eyebrook Reservoir on August 1st 1953. Since then, there have been records in a further 20 years and by the end of 2005 the county total stood at 30 records involving 32 birds.

All records:

1953	Eyebrook Reservoir, August 1st.
1955	Eyebrook Reservoir, September 18th to October 1st.
1971	Eyebrook Reservoir, October 2nd to 5th.
1973	Rutland Water, September 1st to 15th.
1974	Eyebrook Reservoir, August 18th.
1978	Eyebrook Reservoir, September 9th to 10th.
1980	Rutland Water, July 16th to 19th.
1981	Rutland Water, September 26th to October 3rd; probably same, Eyebrook Reservoir, October 10th to 16th.
1984	juvenile, Rutland Water, September 9th to 15th.
	Rutland Water, September 28th to October 13th.
1985	juvenile, Rutland Water, August 30th to September 9th.
1989	Eyebrook Reservoir, September 10th.
1991	Eyebrook Reservoir, September 15th.
1993	juvenile, Rutland Water, September 25th.
1995	juvenile, Rutland Water, August 31st to September 9th.
	juvenile, Rutland Water, September 4th to 9th.
	juvenile, Rutland Water, September 22nd and 24th.
1996	adult, Swithland Reservoir, September 15th.
1997	juvenile, Wanlip South Gravel Pits, September 27th.
2000	juvenile, Rutland Water, September 10th to 16th.
2002	juvenile, Rutland Water, September 7th to 20th.
	juvenile, Rutland Water, September 28th to October 12th.
2003	juvenile, Rutland Water, August 30th.
	juvenile, Rutland Water, September 11th and 12th.
	juvenile, Eyebrook Reservoir, September 17th to 22nd.
2004	juvenile, Trent Valley Pit, September 7th.
2005	adult, Rutland Water, August 6th to 8th.
	two juveniles, Eyebrook Reservoir, August 29th to September 9th, with one until September 11th.
	two juveniles, Rutland Water, September 2nd to 11th.
	juvenile, Sence Valley Forest Park, September 30th to October 8th.

This species has become noticeably more frequent in recent years, with all but eight of the records since 1984. Rutland Water is the dominant site, with 17 records (18 birds) to its name, whilst Eyebrook Reservoir has recorded ten individuals. Away from these two sites, this is a very rare bird in the counties; there have been single records from Swithland Reservoir, Wanlip South Gravel Pits, Trent Valley Pit and Sence Valley Forest Park, all since 1996, but several likely-looking sites (such as Stanford Reservoir and Cropston Reservoir) have yet to record this species.

Two years, 1995 and 2003, have produced three records and there were two in both 1984 and 2002. However, the record year is easily 2005 when six individuals were found, almost 20% of the total number of birds ever recorded. This was the only year in which two birds have been found together at the same site; indeed, from September 2nd to 9th 2005, there were four birds in the counties.

All records have been in autumn, with arrival dates ranging from July 16th (1980 at Rutland Water) to October 2nd (1971 at Eyebrook Reservoir); a bird at Eyebrook Reservoir in 1981 appeared on October 10th but was thought to have moved from Rutland Water, where it was first seen on September 26th. The main period for arrivals is between August 29th and September 28th, when 27 birds (84%) have appeared. Nine birds have been present on single dates only but six have remained for two weeks or more, with the longest stay being 16 days (September 28th to October 13th 1984 at Rutland Water). The average stay is seven days.

One at Rutland Water on June 20th and 21st 1984 was previously accepted but was rejected on review in 2004 (Fray 2005).

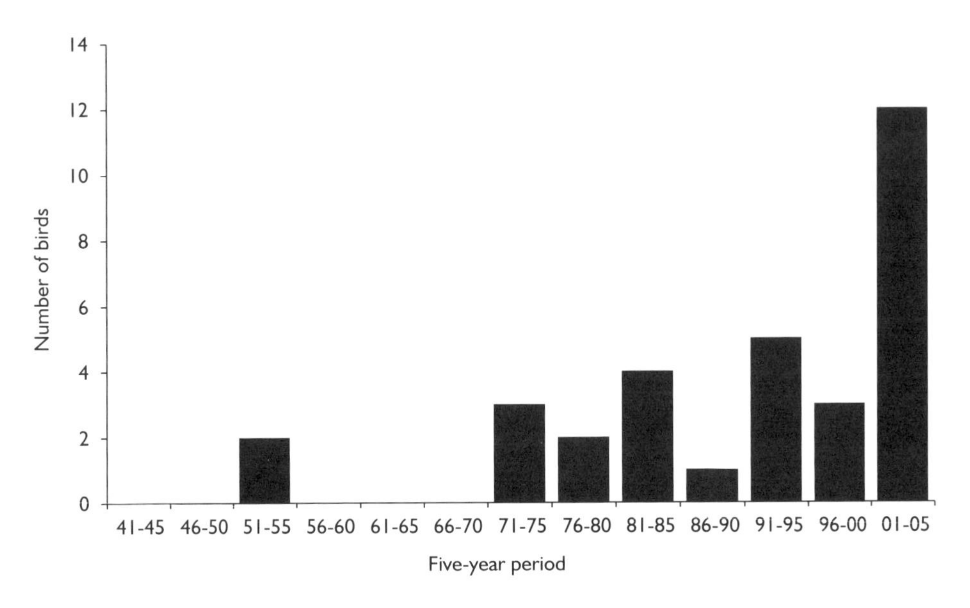

Figure 265: Numbers of Pectoral Sandpipers by five-year periods 1941–2005.

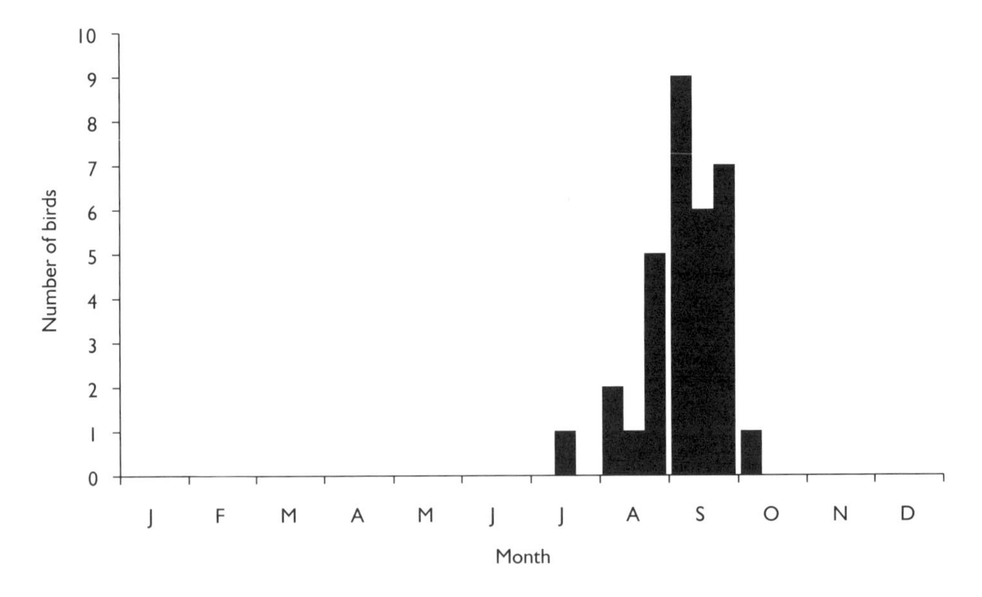

Figure 266: Monthly occurrence of Pectoral Sandpipers 1941–2005.

The Pectoral Sandpiper breeds in the coastal tundras of Siberia, from the Taymyr Peninsula east, and across northern Alaska and northern Canada as far as the western shores of Hudson Bay. It is a long-distant migrant, wintering in southern South America. This is by far the commonest 'American' wader in Britain and it is a regular visitor, mainly during the autumn.

SML

Curlew Sandpiper *Calidris ferruginea*

Rare spring and uncommon autumn passage migrant; recorded in all months except January to March and June, with the majority in August and September.

Browne vaguely mentioned a Curlew Sandpiper being shot on the banks of the River Soar by a Loughborough man and the LROS archives detail one shot at Saddington Reservoir some time before 1935, but there were no properly documented records of this species in the counties until two were at Eyebrook Reservoir on September 4th 1943, with another four there on the 18th. The lack of earlier records was probably due to very little suitable habitat existing, a problem solved by the wartime creation of Eyebrook Reservoir and even more so by the flooding of Rutland Water in the 1970s. The effect of these changes is obvious if the numbers that have occurred in each five-year period are compared.

There were no spring records until 1975 and the total up to 2005 is just 14, all but two involving single birds. Until 2000 all the spring birds had been in May but since then there have been two April records of single birds. Most of the birds seen in spring have been in breeding plumage but three, at Eyebrook Reservoir on May 18th 1975 and at Rutland Water on both May 14th 1992 and May 17th 1998, were not.

All spring records:

1975	Eyebrook Reservoir, May 4th.
	Eyebrook Reservoir, May 18th.
1980	Rutland Water, May 7th.
1981	two, Eyebrook Reservoir, May 16th.
1984	Eyebrook Reservoir, May 26th.
1986	Rutland Water, May 10th.
1989	Rutland Water, May 28th.
1990	Rutland Water, May 11th.
1992	Rutland Water, May 14th.
1993	Trent Valley Pit, May 10th.
1998	three, Rutland Water, May 17th.
2000	Rutland Water, April 29th.
2003	Rutland Water, April 27th.
2004	Rutland Water, May 25th.

The number of birds on autumn passage varies tremendously from year to year. Seven years have produced no birds at all, most recently in 1968, with another four each producing just one. The best year was 1978, when an estimated 123 occurred: oddly, numbers nationally were nothing unusual that year. Other above average years locally have included, in descending order, 1975, 1988, 1998 and 1985: all of these except 1975 were years of nationally high numbers (Brown & Grice 2005).

Since the early 1970s very small numbers of returning adults have been seen in July: the total to 2005 is 24 birds, with the earliest being one at Rutland Water on July 14th 1990 and the maximum count for the month being three at the same site on July 31st 1982. August usually sees rather more post-breeding adults and also the first juveniles passing through, but in some years there are no records until the peak month of September, when very variable numbers are recorded. These are almost exclusively juveniles though moulted adults may be overlooked. October has produced very few new arrivals recently, an average of just one per year since 1990 compared with two per year in the previous two decades. However, September flocks quite often stay into October so it is normal to see this species until mid-month There have been November records in eight years, all since 1979; only three of these involved newly arrived birds. There is one record of a bird in winter, at Trent Valley Pit on December 10th 1995: winter records anywhere in Britain are most unusual.

Only Rutland Water and Eyebrook Reservoir have ever held more than 15 birds. All counts of above 20 are listed:

- 47 at Rutland Water on September 14th 1988.
- 45 at Rutland Water on September 6th 1978.

- 40 at Rutland Water on September 13th 1985.
- 37 at Rutland Water on September 9th 1990.
- 36 at Eyebrook Reservoir on September 8th 1975.
- 28 at Rutland Water on September 6th 2005.
- 26 at Eyebrook Reservoir on August 30th 1972.
- 24 at Rutland Water on September 6th 1998.
- 22 at Eyebrook Reservoir on September 13th 1978.

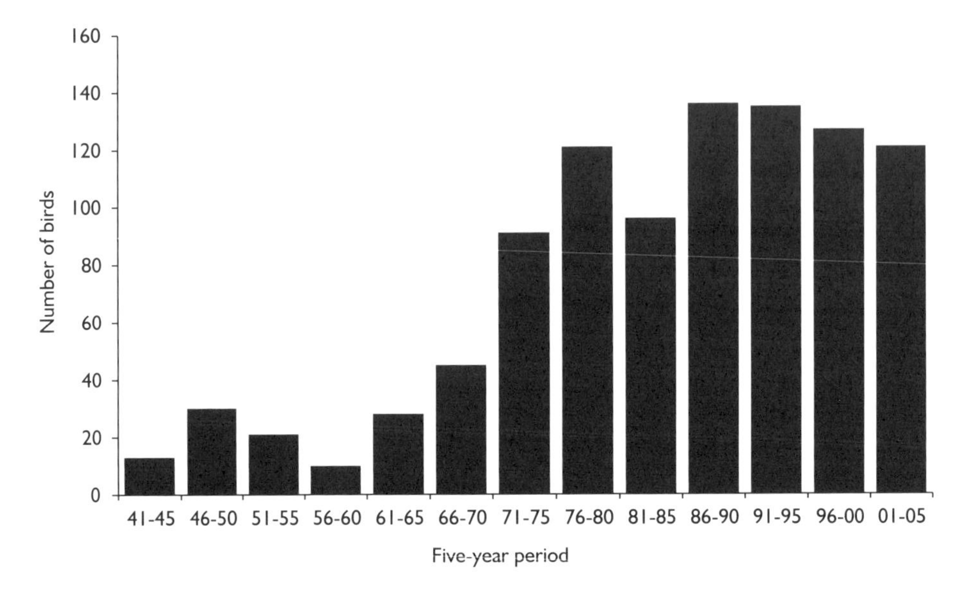

Figure 267: Numbers of Curlew Sandpipers by five-year periods 1941–2005.

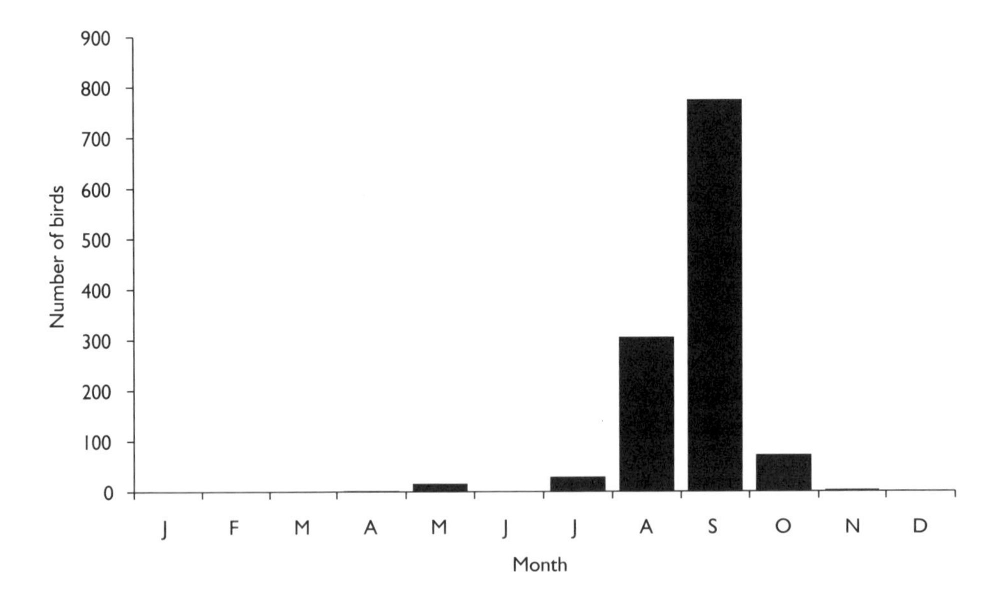

Figure 268: Monthly occurrence of Curlew Sandpipers 1941–2005.

Three other sites have produced records of more than two, the relevant maxima being:

- 14 at Cropston Reservoir on September 14th 1979
- 11 at Stanford Reservoir on October 1st 1978
- eight at Swithland Reservoir on September 3rd 1999

Cadeby Quarry and Saddington Reservoir have both produced records of two birds and single birds have been recorded at a further five sites: Frisby Gravel Pits, Loughborough Sewage Farm, Priory Water, Trent Valley Pit (three times) and Wanlip South Gravel Pits (twice).

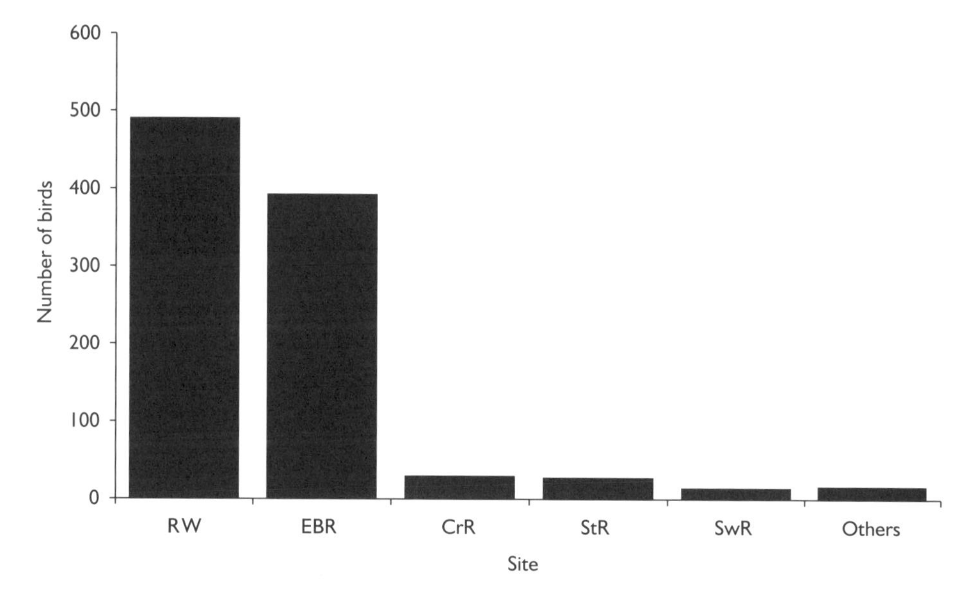

Figure 269: Sites where Curlew Sandpipers have been recorded 1941–2005.
Key to abbreviations: RW = Rutland Water; EBR = Eyebrook Reservoir; CrR = Cropston Reservoir; StR = Stanford Reservoir; SwR = Swithland Reservoir

Curlew Sandpipers breed in Arctic Siberia and winter in Africa and along the coasts of south and south-east Asia, Indonesia and Australia. Their occurrence in western Europe is highly variable each year, in a similar way to Little Stint, and is thought to be mainly dependent upon the prevailing weather conditions along the western fringe of the species' main migration routes through eastern Europe and the Middle East; breeding success is also possibly a contributory factor. An estimated 3,500 were in Britain and Ireland, mainly at coastal and estuarine locations, at the peak of the autumn 1969 influx (Brown & Grice 2005). Kirby *et al.* (1989) provided a detailed analysis of the 1988 influx but without suggesting the total number of birds involved.

SML

Purple Sandpiper *Calidris maritima*

Very rare vagrant from the Arctic, mainly in October and November: eight records involving nine individuals.

Browne, writing in VH, makes reference to five skins purchased by Leicester Museum in 1904 which were said to have been shot at Belgrave, Leicester. Recent investigations have revealed that the specimens are still at the Museum and are indeed of Purple Sandpipers in fresh juvenile plumage. The likelihood of five juvenile Purple Sandpipers appearing together inland in mid-August seems a little fanciful and Browne placed the occurrence in square-brackets, adding the comment 'the condition of the skins, however, with other hypotheses, suggests that at present the verdict should be not proven.'

The first county record occurred in 1956, when one was seen by Ronald and Mrs J. Hickling at Cropston Reservoir on February 11th (previously published as February 1st in error). Since then a further eight birds have been found, five of which have been since 1998. All records refer to single birds unless stated.

All records:

1956	Cropston Reservoir, February 11th.
1963	Eyebrook Reservoir, October 26th to 28th.
1979	Rutland Water, November 11th.
1980	Rutland Water, August 12th.
1998	Rutland Water, October 11th.
1999	Rutland Water, October 2nd.
2003	two, Rutland Water, October 5th.
	Rutland Water, November 4th.

Seven of the nine individuals have occurred between October 2nd and November 11th, coinciding with the main arrival period of wintering birds in north and west Scotland (Lack 1986).

A report of one at Eyebrook Reservoir on November 4th 1952 was originally published as the first record for the counties, but on review in 2004 was found to be inadequately documented (Fray 2005).

Purple Sandpipers breed mainly in the Arctic from north-east Canada to western Siberia, with some as far south as the Faroe Islands and southern Norway. They winter on coasts of western Europe as far south as Iberia and on the east coast of North America. Purple Sandpipers first bred in Scotland in 1978 (Gibbons *et al.* 1993) and up to three pairs have nested regularly ever since (Holling *et al.* 2007a). They are much commoner in winter in the UK, the estimated non-breeding population being around 17,500 birds (Baker *et al.* 2006). The Purple Sandpiper has been added to the 'Amber List' of Birds of Conservation Concern, due to the very small breeding population and the fact that more than 20% of the East Atlantic Flyway non-breeding population is found in the UK (Gregory *et al.* 2002).

SML

Dunlin *Calidris alpina*

Fairly common autumn passage migrant and winter visitor, uncommon spring passage migrant.

References to this species in the 19th century show that it was an autumn and winter visitor but was not seen in spring: Browne described it as an uncommon autumn and winter visitor in Leicestershire, whilst Haines mentioned it being frequent in winter at Tixover. Spring records had become regular by the time of the formation of LROS in 1941 and nowadays flocks of Dunlins occur in all months, but are least likely to be encountered in June.

The largest numbers are seen in winter, between November and February and almost exclusively at Rutland Water and Eyebrook Reservoir; in recent years it has become clear that birds move between these two sites in response to local conditions. Three-figure counts are now the norm in most winters but only occurred for the first time in 1972, when up to 130 were present at Eyebrook Reservoir in October and November. In the following list of the highest counts only one count from any particular winter is included:

- 531 at Rutland Water on November 3rd 1991.
- 425 at Rutland Water in January 1991.
- 382 at Rutland Water on January 14th 1990.
- 325 at Rutland Water on December 6th 1988.
- 286 at Eyebrook Reservoir on December 10th 1999.
- 254 at Rutland Water on December 11th 1985.
- 240 at Rutland Water on November 26th 2004.
- 237 at Eyebrook Reservoir on February 12th 1999.
- 234 at Eyebrook Reservoir on November 24th 2001.
- 224 at Rutland Water on December 19th 1984.
- 220 at Rutland Water on November 27th 1983.

- 200 at Eyebrook Reservoir on November 24th 1990, from January 30th to February 2nd 1998 and on November 27th 2000, February 2nd 2001 and December 5th 2002.
- 200 at Rutland Water in November 1998 and on December 4th 2005.

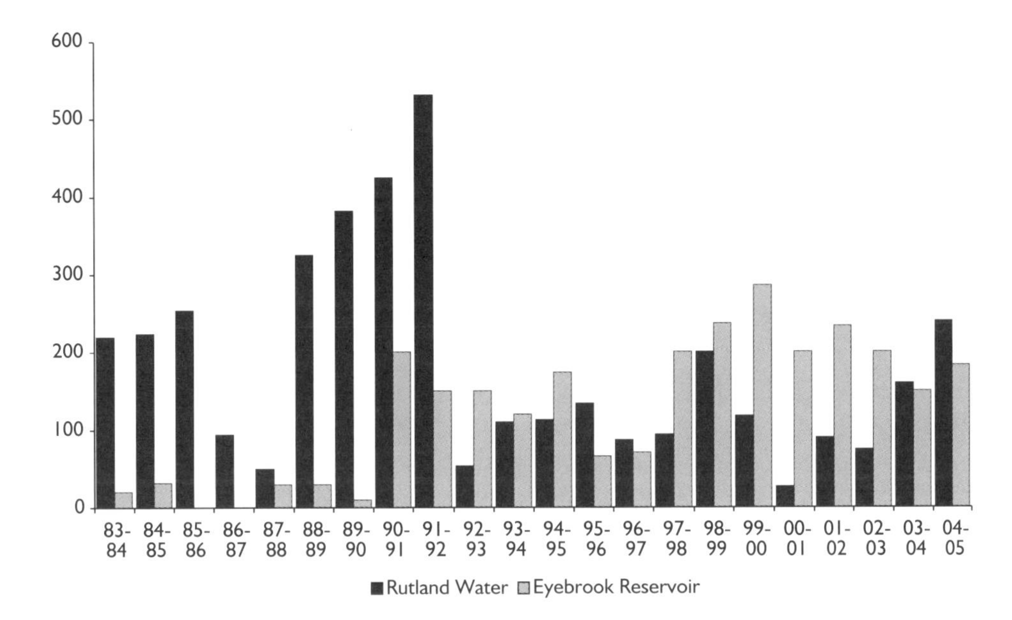

Figure 270: Wintering numbers of Dunlin at Rutland Water and Eyebrook Reservoir 1983–84 to 2004–05.

Records of more than single figures at other sites in winter are very unusual: up to 50 were at Swithland Reservoir when it was drained between December 1975 and February 1976 and 40 were at Birstall on February 10th 1990.

The winter flocks have usually dispersed by early March, being replaced by spring passage birds between then and the first few days of June; the main migration period is late April and early May. Flocks of more than 30 are unusual at this time of year and have only occurred nine times:

- 67 at Rutland Water on April 30th 2005.
- 64 at Rutland Water on April 26th 1997.
- 60 at Rutland Water on May 8th 1997.
- 52 at Rutland Water on May 12th 1990.
- 50 at Eyebrook Reservoir on both May 3rd 1946 and May 1st 1948.
- 40 at Eyebrook Reservoir on May 5th 1955.
- 33 at Rutland Water on May 24th 2003.
- 32 at Eyebrook Reservoir on May 3rd 1982.

Away from the two main sites no spring flock has ever exceeded 20, the largest counts being:

- 19 at Loughborough Sewage Farm on May 19th 1949.
- 16 at Trent Valley Pit on April 30th 2001.
- 14 at Trent Valley Pit on May 10th 1993.
- 12 at Wanlip South Gravel Pits on May 14th 2002.

In some years there has been only a gap of only a few days between the latest (presumed) spring birds and the onset of the return passage, which has been as early as June 14th. The main autumn passage period is normally between late July and November, but is obscured by the arrival of wintering birds by the start of October. 1990 was a very odd year in that an unprecedented autumn count of 326 was made on September 26th at Rutland Water as a result of a very early winter arrival. Flocks have tended to be both larger and more frequent in autumn than in spring, with counts of 50 or more recorded on at least 13 occasions, although it is difficult to separate autumn and winter flocks at the two main sites: the list of highest counts that follows excludes some from Rutland Water and Eyebrook Reservoir that are thought to relate to wintering birds:

- 90 at Rutland Water on September 15th 1994.
- 80 at Stanford Reservoir on October 12th 1975.
- 80 at Eyebrook Reservoir on September 30th 1994.
- 75 at Eyebrook Reservoir on September 28th 1974.
- 73 at Rutland Water on September 7th 1996.
- 72 at Rutland Water on September 30th 2001.
- 72 at Stanford Reservoir on October 6th 1990.
- 70 at Eyebrook Reservoir on September 25th 1967.
- 70 at Rutland Water on October 10th 1977.
- 62 at Rutland Water on August 27th 2005.
- 60 at Cropston Reservoir on October 7th 1973.
- 55 at Rutland Water in September 1993.
- 50 at Eyebrook Reservoir on August 6th 1946.

The autumn maxima at all other sites to have produced double-figure counts are:

- 32 at Sawley Gravel Pits on August 2nd 1948.
- 20 at Watermead Gravel Pits on July 21st 1987.
- 17 at Loughborough Sewage Farm on August 19th 1948.
- 17 at Priory Water on September 8th 1996.
- 12 at Kirby Lakes on September 12th 2004.
- 11 at Trent Valley Pit on both August 6th 1996 and August 24th 2003.

Few observers have ever attempted racial identification of the Dunlins occurring in the counties; the wintering birds are assumed to be of the nominate form but the races *arctica* and *schinzii* are likely to occur on passage. Individuals resembling *arctica* were reported from Eyebrook Reservoir twice in 1994, on May 7th and September 16th.

There are six ringing recoveries involving the counties, all likely to be of *alpina*. Three birds ringed at Rutland Water in October have been recovered: in south Wales the following January (1997), at Freiston (Lincolnshire) (ringed in 1988, recovered in July 1990) and at Terrington (Norfolk) (ringed in 1988, recovered in May 1992). A bird ringed at Oulu (Finland) in August 1970 was shot at Stapleford Park three months later, one ringed at Nidingen (Sweden) in September 1983 was found dead at Wanlip in April 1987 and one ringed at Seal Sands (Cleveland) on August 2nd 1997 was controlled at Rutland Water three weeks later.

Dunlins breed mainly in the Arctic and sub-Arctic regions of Eurasia and North America, as well as in Britain and Ireland and winter along the coasts of western Europe and the Mediterranean, in the Middle East, along the west African coast, in south-east Asia and in the eastern USA. The British breeding population is estimated at between 9,150 and 9,900 pairs, with over 555,000 birds wintering in the country (Baker *et al.* 2006). Over 20% of the East Atlantic Flyway non-breeding population uses Britain; there has been a moderate decline in this population over the last 25 years, resulting in the Dunlin being added to the 'Amber List' of Birds of Conservation Concern (Gregory *et al.* 2002).

SML

Ruff *Philomachus pugnax*

Uncommon to fairly common passage migrant, most frequent in autumn and scarce to uncommon winter visitor in most years.

Prior to 1941 the only documented records were detailed by Browne: a female shot at Saddington Reservoir on August 19th 1887 and an immature male shot at Leicester City Farms on December 14th 1899.

The occurrence and status of this species in the counties have been greatly affected by the creation of Rutland Water and Eyebrook Reservoir, as much as for any of the other regularly occurring waders. From 1941 to 1945

there were several reports from the newly flooded Eyebrook Reservoir, with a maximum count of ten on September 18th 1945, a year when up to 33 birds may have occurred during the autumn. The only spring record during the five years was of one at Leicester City Farms on March 19th 1944.

The pattern for the next 30 years was mainly of up to double-figure counts at Eyebrook Reservoir each autumn, with a maximum of 40 on September 3rd 1974, along with occasional spring records there and a few records elsewhere in most years. The only other site to attract birds regularly was Loughborough Sewage Farm, especially from 1946 to 1961; the maximum counts there were 19 on August 27th 1956 and 11 from August 8th to 18th 1948. There were also two January records in this period, of one at Loughborough Sewage Farm on January 18th 1956 and between 20 and 30 at Eyebrook Reservoir on January 22nd 1961 (Otter 1965); apart from these two records the extreme dates were February 4th and November 22nd.

Since 1975 Rutland Water has taken over as the principal site for Ruffs in the counties, with Eyebrook Reservoir continuing to attract similar numbers to those recorded earlier. The Ruff is scarce away from the two main sites and there has been an average of just 11 birds elsewhere in the counties during 1996–2005. The maximum counts for all sites to have held five or more birds are:

- 98 at Rutland Water on November 22nd 2002.
- 40 at Eyebrook Reservoir on September 3rd 1974.
- 19 at Loughborough Sewage Farm on August 27th 1956.
- 17 at Stanford Reservoir on September 1st 1992.
- 11 at Watermead Park on April 21st 1992.
- 11 flying over Thornton Reservoir on September 12th 1983.
- eight at Cropston Reservoir on August 13th 1986.
- seven at Birstall Gravel Pits on August 13th 1986.
- seven at Trent Valley Pit on August 28th 2000.
- six at Swithland Reservoir on September 7th 1974.
- six at Cadeby Quarry on August 18th 1996.
- six at Ibstock Opencast (now Sence Valley Forest Park) on September 1st 1997.
- five at Melton Country Park on September 24th 1991.
- five at Trent Farm Pool from April 11th to 19th 1999.
- five at Wanlip South Gravel Pits from March 27th to 30th 2002.

The exceptional flock of 98 at Rutland Water on November 22nd 2002 was present for just a few hours and had possibly been displaced from the Nene Washes (Cambridgeshire) by rapidly rising water levels. Otherwise counts at Rutland Water have exceeded 50 in six years, all since 1993 and always in autumn, the maximum being 73 on both September 11th 1994 and September 6th 1998.

Spring passage occurs mainly between March and early May and is very variable, there being no records at all in several years; even in the best years the numbers involved are normally much smaller than in autumn, as this species migrates on a more eastern route in spring, largely missing Britain. The largest spring counts include:

- 44 at Rutland Water on April 18th 1985.
- 34 at Rutland Water on March 23rd 2002.
- 32 at Rutland Water on May 2nd 1994.
- 14 at Eyebrook Reservoir on May 2nd 1994.
- 11 at Watermead Park on April 21st 1992.

Displaying males have been observed at Rutland Water on two occasions: one on May 22nd 1985 and seven, with two females, on May 1st 1999.

Autumn passage normally commences with a few breeding-plumaged males as early as the last few days of June and then builds up throughout July and August to reach a peak in late August or early September in most years. The highest autumn counts have already been covered in the treatment of site-maxima and it is noticeable that all bar one of the highest autumn counts at each site have been between August 13th and September

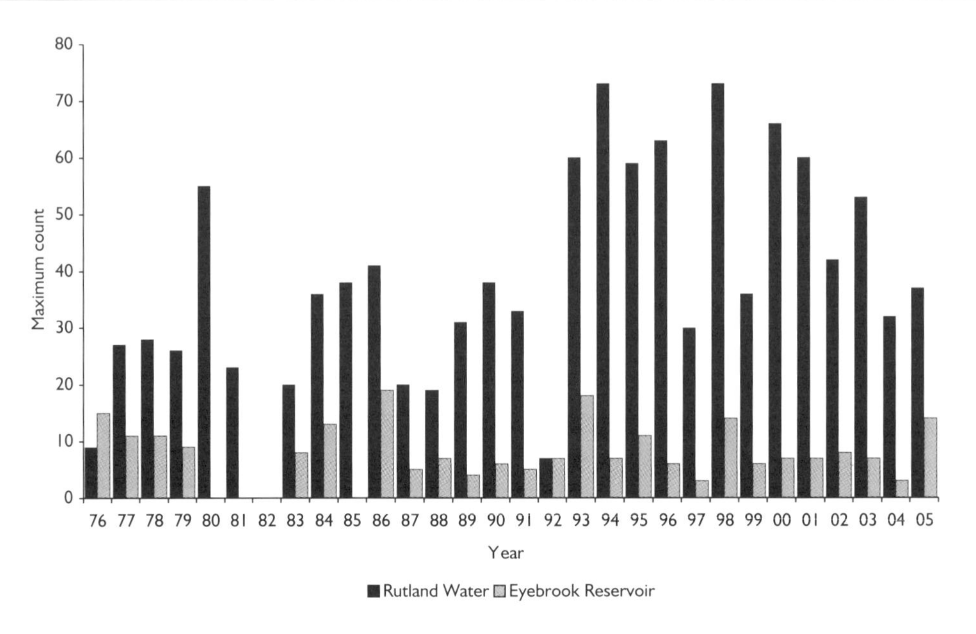

Figure 271: Maximum autumn counts of Ruff at Rutland Water and Eyebrook Reservoir 1976–2005.

12th; this corresponds with the findings of Mason (1969), who noted that the peak period for passage Ruffs at Eyebrook Reservoir during 1941–67 was from August 16th to September 15th.

There were just occasional winter records until 1977 but since then variable numbers have wintered at Rutland Water in every winter apart from two (1992–93 and 1993–94). The new habit began with three birds in the winter of 1977–78 and quickly became established. It has always been difficult to assess the numbers of

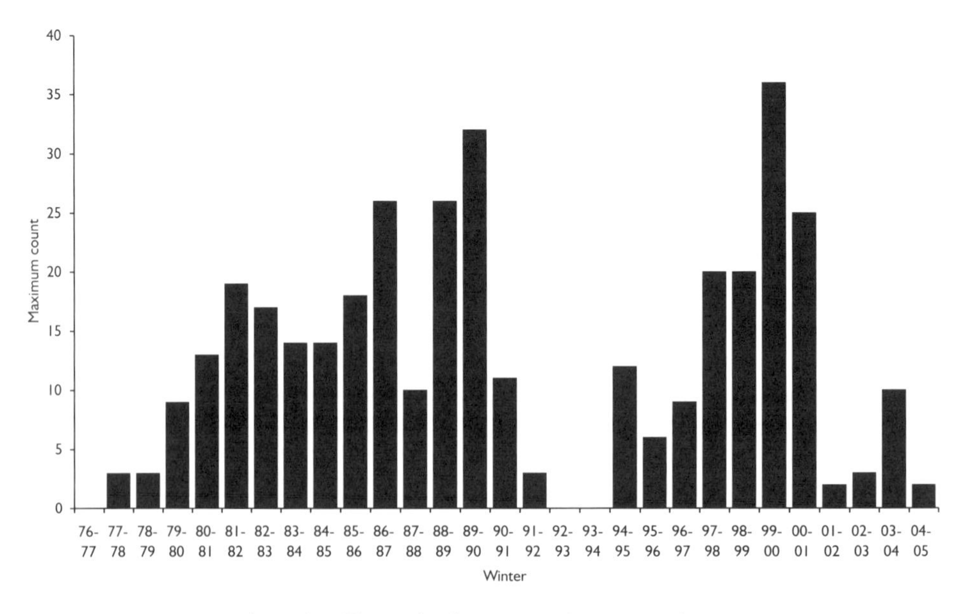

Figure 272: Wintering numbers of Ruff at Rutland Water 1976–77 to 2004–05.

wintering birds accurately as they disperse onto farmland to feed, as well as using the margins of the reservoir, returning to roost at dusk, usually on the Egleton Reserve; under-counting is quite likely and may well explain the rather large variation in day-to-day numbers. The highest winter counts have been 32 in 1989–90 and 36 in 1999–2000, but three of the last four winters have seen no more than three. Figure 272 is based upon the peak counts in December or January for each winter that birds have remained throughout both months.

Eyebrook Reservoir has also been used in winter recently, but never throughout the whole of the December and January period and it is possible that at least some of the birds there have been from Rutland Water. This was probably the case in the winter of 2000–01, when 29 were present up to December 14th and smaller numbers were seen until the end of the year, but then none in 2001 until January 14th. Similarly, in 1998–99 up to 26 were regular until mid-December but then there were not any until much smaller numbers from February 3rd.

A bird ringed as a pullus in the Netherlands in May 1971 was caught and released near Wigston in May 1974; this was one of only four or five recoveries of foreign-ringed birds at the time and is difficult to explain, as a three-year-old bird such as this would be expected to be on its breeding grounds in May.

Ruffs breed discontinuously through the Low Countries and southern Baltic and more widely from Scandinavia across Russia and northern Siberia, wintering mainly in sub-Saharan Africa but with some in western Europe, the Middle East and coastal areas of the Indian subcontinent. This species formerly bred across much of Britain but declined markedly during the 18th and 19th century and was not known to breed in the country between 1850 and 1940 (Gibbons *et al.* 1996). There has since been a partial recovery, but numbers are rather variable and the breeding population is so small that this species has been added to the 'Amber List' of Birds of Conservation Concern (Gregory *et al.* 2002).

SML

Jack Snipe — *Lymnocryptes minimus*

Uncommon winter visitor and passage migrant; recorded in all months except June and July.

Haines commented that small numbers of Jack Snipes were often found in the same areas as Common Snipes in Rutland and mentioned that as many as seven in a day had been shot at Burley Fishponds. Browne described the species as 'an autumn visitant to Leicestershire, sparingly distributed and departing early in the spring'.

The accurate status of this species is more difficult to assess than that of many species due to its secretive habit of remaining concealed in areas of wet vegetation. A great many will go completely undetected and those reported will be just a fraction of the true picture. Chance encounters such as flushing single birds from unlikely-looking spots such as a damp stubble field only serve to add to the uncertainty of quantitative statements. It really is impossible to say how many Jack Snipes occur locally, but there will be a lot more than are known about.

Large concentrations are unusual and are normally only found by determined searching of suitable habitat such as waterlogged floodplains and the vegetated margins of ponds and reservoirs. Finding four or five together is fairly common but records of larger groups are limited to the following:

- ten at Leicester City Farms on November 11th 1962.
- ten at Ratcliffe on the Wreake on December 7th 1975.
- ten at Rutland Water in November 1977.
- eight at Eyebrook Reservoir from December 5th to 31st 1954.
- eight at Eyebrook Reservoir on October 24th 1957.
- seven near Quorn from December 21st 1952 to January 11th 1953.
- six at Loughborough Sewage Farm on April 7th 1958.
- six at Frisby Gravel Pits on January 29th 1994.
- six at Frisby Gravel Pits on December 27th and 30th 1994.
- six near Shepshed in January and early February 2003.
- six at Watermead Park in January 2003.

The main period of occurrence is between October and March, with smaller but significant numbers of records in late September and early April. There have been some very early arrival dates, the most extreme being:

- Eyebrook Reservoir, August 5th 1962.
- Rutland Water, August 8th 1974.
- Loughborough Sewage Farm, September 1st 1948.
- Priory Water, September 2nd 1990.
- Kirby Lakes, September 3rd 1989.

All five of these records are exceptional as even in the north-east of Britain arrivals are not normally expected until mid-September. Departure from the breeding grounds does not normally start until late August and September, after both adults and young have moulted, so the two earliest dates are extraordinary and may possibly even refer to summering non-breeders.

In some years there is evidence of a spring passage. In 2005 for example a total of 13 were seen at eight sites during March whereas only 11 had been seen during the previous two months, with just four in February. The five latest spring records are:

- Eyebrook Reservoir, May 2nd 1962.
- unspecified site, April 26th 1975.
- unspecified site, April 25th 1953.
- Rutland Water, April 25th 1993.
- Rutland Water, April 24th.

The published records suggest that numbers vary considerably from year to year. Very few were recorded in the late 1960s and the early 1980s, with as few as just two in 1967 and five in 1982; numbers were generally higher in the 1970s and 1990s. The most productive year was 1994, with an estimated 50 birds, closely followed by 2003 with 48.

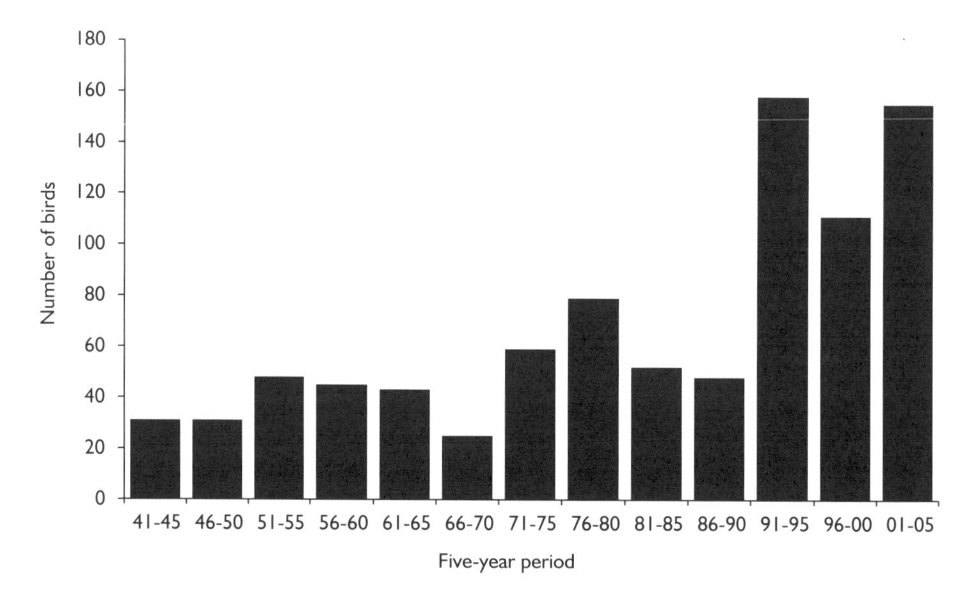

Figure 273: Number of Jack Snipes by five-year periods 1941–2005.

Jack Snipes breed throughout Scandinavia and east across the upper and mid latitudes of Russia. The winter range includes south and west Europe, Africa south to the southern fringe of the Sahara, and from Asia Minor to India and south-east Asia. Lack (1986) suggested that up to 100,000 winter in Britain and Ireland, with the majority in England; the figure is based upon an estimated 10,000 shot annually in the early 1980s (Brown & Grice 2005) and actual counts in Lack unsurprisingly indicated a much lower number. The Jack Snipe is included in Category 3 of the Species of European Conservation Concern but unlike most similarly graded species it is not on the 'Amber List' nationally as it only occurs as a non-breeding visitor in the UK (Gregory *et al.* 2002).

SML

Common Snipe *Gallinago gallinago*

Formerly a fairly common resident breeder, now a fairly common passage and winter visitor and rare breeder.

This species would have bred in many boggy areas 200 years ago but drainage for agriculture caused Browne to doubt whether it still bred even in 1889; Haines reported nesting in the Welland valley near Seaton in 1901.

When LROS began in 1941 the Common Snipe had apparently recovered somewhat as it was described as a widespread breeding species, but during the next ten years it became scarcer due to yet more areas being drained; breeding became restricted to areas such as riverbanks and the surrounds of reservoirs and sewage farms. Up to eight pairs nested at Leicester City Farms until about 1950. The status in 1960 was that 'small numbers breed'; by 1966 this had changed to 'breeds very sparingly', with Seaton mentioned as the only named locality. The fieldwork for the first BTO Breeding Birds Atlas, carried out between 1968 and 1972, produced evidence of at least probable breeding in 14 of the counties' 32 main 10-km squares. Webster (1997) records that from about this time suitable sites in Charnwood Forest became more important, especially the wetter areas of the Ulverscroft valley, where there were 12+ pairs in the early 1970s and still eight pairs in 1979, with another six pairs elsewhere in Charnwood that year. Away from Charnwood, four pairs bred at Thorpe Arnold in 1973 and single pairs at Potters Marston in 1971, Coleorton in 1972, Kilby Bridge in 1974 and both Rutland Water and Earl Shilton Sewage Farm in 1976; the 'drumming' display was reported at up to seven additional sites each year.

1980 saw an increase to 13 localities where 'drumming' was observed and breeding was proved at both Aylestone Meadows and Ullesthorpe. The Ulverscroft valley hosted breeding birds regularly, with several pairs still probably breeding in 1989, unfortunately the last year that the area was used. The only records of proved breeding elsewhere in the 1980s were at both Leire and Wanlip North Gravel Pits in 1986. During this period 'drumming' birds were located at up to eight sites annually, with a maximum of six at Rutland Water in 1984.

Warrilow found territorial pairs in 47 tetrads, spread over 20 10-km squares, between 1976 and 1984; breeding was proved in 12 tetrads and at least four of these were additional to the records previously known to LROS. Localities in river valleys accounted for 53% of the total, with 28% around lakes and reservoirs and the rest at gravel workings.

Since the demise of the Ulverscroft population the only evidence of continued breeding in the counties has been a few 'drumming' birds, at four sites in 1990, Seaton in 1992 and Knipton Reservoir in 2004 and the 'chipper' call heard at two sites in 1991, at Rutland Water in 1998 and Cossington Meadows in 2005. Most years recently have produced just occasional non-breeding single birds in midsummer, mainly at Rutland Water, and there were no breeding season records at all in 1994 and 1995.

The influx of autumn migrants commences in July and usually increases to give peak counts between October and February; occasionally, as in 1973, large numbers are seen in September and more rarely in August, such as when 105 were counted at Rutland Water on August 28th 1995. Most birds have departed by the second half of March and a count of 45 at Hemington Gravel Pits on April 19th 1970 is the largest any later. Counts of 100 or more have come from 18 sites but numbers of this species are frequently difficult to assess due to its feeding habits, so the following list of the highest counts are all estimates:

- 400 at Kelham Bridge in early January 1969.
- 330 at Wanlip Gravel Pits on November 16th 1980.
- 300 at Leicester City Farms on both January 13th 1945 and March 25th 1962.
- 300 at Rutland Water from January to March 1983.
- 250 at Cropston Reservoir on September 27th 1973.
- 250 at Eyebrook Reservoir on January 18th 1975.
- 250 at Rutland Water on October 31st 1984.
- 250 at Birstall on December 31st 1989.
- 225 at Stanford Reservoir in January and February 1973.

Numbers in recent years have been much lower and since 2000 the maximum has been just 150, at both Watermead Park on January 5th 2003 and Rutland Water on November 15th 2005.

Common Snipes breed over much of northern Eurasia. Northern populations winter mainly to the south of the breeding range. There are 35 recoveries of ringed individuals concerning Leicestershire and Rutland; 14 involve movement within the counties and include one caught at Ratcliffe on the Wreake in 1975 and found dead there ten years later. Seven are of foreign-ringed birds recovered here in autumn and winter, originating

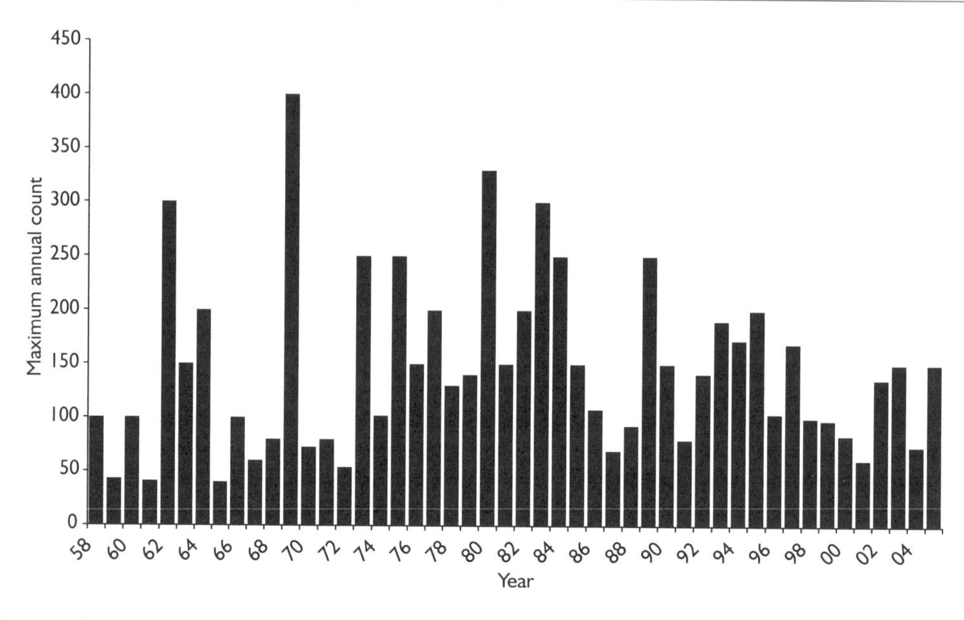

Figure 274: Maximum annual counts of Common Snipes 1958–2005.

from Norway, Sweden (two), Finland (two), Germany and the Czech Republic: all these were ringed in autumn and were probably on passage but they clearly show the directions, north-east and east, from which much of the winter population originates. Five of the birds ringed in the counties during autumn and winter have produced long-distance recoveries, three to the west or south-west (in Ireland, Cornwall and western France) in winter and two to the east-north-east (Denmark and Finland) in spring and autumn.

The nominate race breeds over most of Europe, including Britain, where the latest population estimate is 52,500 pairs (Baker *et al.* 2006). Numbers in this country have fallen rapidly since the 1970s as farmland has been drained and surveys in England and Wales have revealed a 62% decrease in breeding birds in wet meadows between 1982 and 2002 (Baillie *et al.* 2006). Due to this decline, the Common Snipe has been added to the 'Amber List' of Birds of Conservation Concern (Gregory *et al.* 2002). The north-western subspecies *G. g. faeroeensis* breeds in Iceland, the Faroe Islands, Shetland and Orkney and, although there is no firm evidence to suggest that it occurs in the counties, birds resembling this form have been recorded occasionally in autumn at both Rutland Water and Eyebrook Reservoir.

SML

Great Snipe *Gallinago media*

Rare vagrant from north-east Europe: 14 records, all in the 19th century.

There are no modern records of this species but Browne described it as having occurred on nine occasions in Leicestershire in the 19th century, when snipe-shooting was much more common; he cited three specimen records, one of which, a juvenile collected at Garthorpe on September 2nd 1885, has recently been rediscovered in the Leicester Museum collection (Harrop 2006a). Haines details five similar records.

All records:

1838	shot, Martinshaw Wood, winter (*Zoologist* 1886: 328).
1849	shot, Belton-in-Rutland, undated.
1861	shot and subsequently eaten, Tilton on the Hill, December.
1868	killed, Little Dalby, September 28th (*Zoologist* 1886: 329; *The Field* October 17th 1886).
1876	shot, Egleton, September.
1879	killed and subsequently eaten, Smeeton Westerby, undated (*Zoologist* 1886: 328).

1881	picked up dead, Billesdon Coplow, undated (*Zoologist* 1886: 328–329).
pre-1882	killed, near Lutterworth, undated.
1885	shot, Garthorpe, September 2nd (*Zoologist* 1886: 329, *The Field* September 12th 1885). The specimen remains at Leicester Museum.
	shot, Blaby, first week of September (*Zoologist* 1886: 329). The specimen was seen by Browne.
	shot, Oakham, October.
1887	seen, Ashwell, undated.
1895	shot, Wing, undated.

In addition, one was obtained at Noseley but no date is provided by Browne. Given the existence of a specimen there seems no reason to doubt that most, if not all, of these were correctly identified.

Great Snipes breed in Scandinavia (mainly Norway), Poland and the former Soviet Union east to western Siberia and winter over much of sub-Saharan Africa. There has been a marked decline since the 19th century, although some signs of a recovery have been noted in Scandinavia in recent years. Numbers in Britain (and indeed Leicestershire and Rutland) have reflected the European decline: prior to 1950 there were 492 British records, with only 148 subsequently to the end of 2005. There have been four modern records from Nottinghamshire (most recently in August to September 1989) and one in West Midlands in August 1995, so it is possible that the Great Snipe may occur again in Leicestershire and Rutland, though its preference for habitats away from water may make unfashionable sites the ones most likely to be chosen by a lone vagrant.

SML

Long-billed Dowitcher *Limnodromus scolopaceus*

Very rare vagrant from North America: one record. Also one record of an unidentified dowitcher.

An adult in summer plumage was found by Steve Lister on Lagoon I at Rutland Water on August 9th 2005. It remained throughout the day and was seen and photographed by a number of observers, but departed overnight (Lister 2007a, *BB* 100:42).

A dowitcher in summer plumage was found by Ken Moulton on the Egleton Reserve at Rutland Water on May 4th 1980 and was still present the following day. It was identified as a Long-billed Dowitcher but some features of the description, including a white vent, were not consistent with that species and the record was only accepted by the BBRC as an unidentified dowitcher species (*BB* 74:471). Despite the BBRC's caution, this bird was almost certainly a Long-billed Dowitcher; the only other candidate (Short-billed Dowitcher *Limnodromus griseus*) has occurred in Britain just once, with another one or two in Ireland and all of these have been since 1985. A total of 124 unidentified dowitchers has been recorded in Britain, although spring records (of both unidentified and specifically identified dowitchers) are rather unusual.

Long-billed Dowitchers breed in north-eastern Siberia and coastal northern and western Alaska and winter from southern USA to Guatemala. By the end of 2005 there had been 175 accepted records of this species in Britain, with the majority having occurred in September and October.

RMF/SML

Woodcock (Eurasian Woodcock) *Scolopax rusticola*

Uncommon resident breeder and fairly common winter visitor.

The Woodcock was apparently a rare breeding bird in Leicestershire and Rutland during the 19th century and was considered primarily a winter visitor. Browne described it as 'a winter migrant, sparingly distributed' and noted that it had bred at Martinshaw Wood, Donington Park, Coleorton, Owston Wood and Noseley. In Rutland, Haines reported that it 'generally returns in October', although breeding had been recorded at Barnsdale Wood around 1874. This accords with the known status of the Woodcock in Britain around this time: there were few British breeding records up to the 18th century, but by the end of the 19th century almost every county had a breeding population (Gibbons *et al.* 1993).

Today it is difficult to be sure of the true status of Woodcock in Leicestershire and Rutland due to this species being largely crepuscular. Between 1945 and 1979 there were only 23 cases of proved breeding, at a total of 16 sites and there have been none at all since then. The numbers of males indulging in their characteristic roding display at dusk suggest that the species is at least an uncommon breeder. The three main regions that contain the large areas of broadleaved or mixed woodland favoured by breeding birds are Charnwood Forest, the north-east of Leicestershire and the east and north of Rutland. Favoured sites include the plantations around Ulverscroft, Swithland Wood and Pickworth Great Wood, each of which has harboured four or more roding birds.

There have been three surveys to assess the size and distribution of the breeding population, two covering the whole of the counties and one concentrating on Charnwood Forest, which is the area with the largest numbers. The first was the fieldwork for the BTO Atlas from 1968 to 1972, which found proved or probable breeding in 17 10-km squares. Between 1976 and 1984, Warrilow recorded birds in a total of 75 tetrads, with breeding confirmed in 23, probably giving a more accurate idea of the distribution of Woodcocks than the somewhat casual records previously held by LROS. The main areas of population were Charnwood Forest, Belvoir, the larger woods of Rutland and the woods of east Leicestershire, with a few birds in the south-west of Leicestershire at sites such as Bosworth Park, Kirkby Mallory and Narborough Bog. Warrilow estimated the population to be 75–150 pairs. In 1994 Michael Webster coordinated a survey of roding males in Charnwood Forest and found 41; he suggested that each could have mated with three females, giving a Charnwood population possibly as high as 120 'pairs'.

Despite there having been no proved breeding in recent years, roding birds have continued to be widely reported; from 1990 to 2005 the display was observed at 41 sites (Figure 275). Few of these were known to still be in use at the end of the period, although there has been a lack of recent recording effort away from Charnwood Forest and the map possibly understates the present distribution as a result. The woodlands around Rutland Water no longer hold any breeding birds, but the nearby Burley Wood is still occupied. Even in the most productive of recent years, 1994, only 22 roding males were reported and in 2005 there were just seven, all in neighbouring areas of Ulverscroft in Charnwood. It is difficult to know whether this apparent decline is real, or a reflection on the recent lack of recording effort: however, nationally there has been a rapid decline in breeding numbers and a contraction of range in recent years, with potential causes being recreational disturbance, drying out of woodlands, overgrazing by deer and maturation of new plantations (Baillie *et al.* 2006).

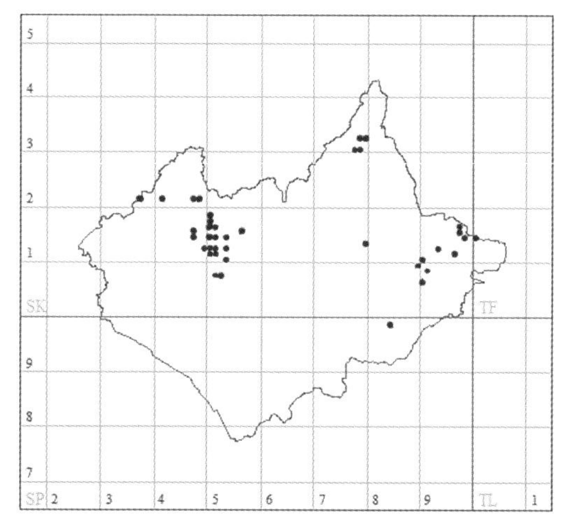

Figure 275: Distribution of roding Woodcocks 1990–2005.

This species is very inconspicuous between July and October, though in the past the confirmed breeding records mainly involved females flushed from their nests or found with young. It is not until late autumn brings an influx of birds from the continent, or perhaps northern Britain, that many get reported. During the winter this species is found much more widely than in the breeding season and even visits suburban gardens. Individuals have turned up in a variety of unexpected places, especially in late autumn, including one discovered in a Leicester poultry run on October 14th 1989 and one found inside a shop at Bridge Road, Leicester on November 9th 1990; these and the several others seen within Leicester city boundary would have been newly arrived migrants. Most records are of birds that have been flushed, either accidentally by birders or more deliberately by game drives; numbers are generally small but concentrations have been noted in bad weather or when driven out of coverts. Records have included:

- 30 shot at Gopsall Park during January and February 1957.
- 30 flushed by a shoot at Tilton Wood on November 29th 1982.
- 24 shot at the Belvoir Estate on January 6th 2005, with another eight shot there two days later.
- 20 on sale at Melton Mowbray market on January 8th 2002.
- 15 at Stoke Dry Wood on January 28th 1995.
- 15 flushed by a shoot at Barkestone Wood on December 27th 1999.
- 14 flushed by a shoot at Croxton Park on January 28th 2001.
- 12 wintering at Rutland Water in January 1997.
- ten flushed by shoots at Bosworth Park in November and December 1955.

Woodcocks breed from northern and central Europe and Scandinavia east through Russia to Japan. Fenno-Scandian birds move south or south-west in the autumn to winter in western Europe and even North Africa. Ringing recoveries involving Leicestershire and Rutland demonstrate this movement from the continent. In total, there have been seven recoveries of ringed birds within the counties, six of them as a result of shooting. Only one of the birds involved was ringed as a pullus, in Finland in June 1959; this was shot at Belvoir in January 1960. The others had all been ringed during October or November and so could have been on passage: two within Russia, one in the Netherlands, two on the north Norfolk coast and one in Cambridgeshire. One of the Russian-ringed birds travelled 2,093km west-south-west between being caught near Leningrad on October 15th 1994 and shot at Billesdon five weeks later. The two birds ringed in Norfolk, at Sheringham and Weybourne, illustrate the route that at least some winter visitors use to reach the counties.

The British population of Woodcocks is currently estimated at between 5,000 and 12,500 pairs (Baker *et al.* 2006) and, due to the rapid decline in numbers and contraction of the breeding range over the last 25 years, this species has been added to the 'Amber List' of Birds of Conservation Concern (Gregory *et al.* 2002).

SML

Black-tailed Godwit *Limosa limosa*

Formerly a scarce passage visitor, now a fairly common passage migrant and rare winter visitor; recorded in all months, with the majority from late March to early May and late June to late August.

Browne noted that one was shot at Cropston Reservoir in August 1887 and knew of two other undated 19th century records, single birds shot at Market Bosworth and Osbaston. In addition, the LROS archives refer to one shot at Saddington Reservoir in April 1897.

There were no 20th century records until 1945, when one was at Sawley Gravel Pits from March 28th to 31st. Since then, there have been just four blank years (1951, 1953, 1956 and 1960) but until 1976 the total number of birds recorded in any year only reached double-figures once, when there were at least eight at Eyebrook Reservoir and five at Loughborough Sewage Farm in 1947. Since 1976 there has been a marked increase in the occurrence of this species, firstly due to the creation of Rutland Water and then by a general upturn in numbers using the counties in autumn, as well as by some large flocks stopping off briefly on spring passage. This increase has become even more apparent in the 21st century, with annual totals of 180 in 2002, 160 in 2003, 142 in 2004 and a massive 430 in 2005. The only other years where the annual total has exceeded 100 were 1990 (166 birds) and 1995 (197 individuals). Figure 276 shows these continuing trends.

The main period for spring passage extends throughout April and towards the end of May, with significant numbers in late March. The largest spring counts have mainly been at Rutland Water, from where double-figure flocks have been recorded on nine occasions during this season, as follows:

- 150 on April 27th 1995.
- 127 on March 28th 1990.
- 55 on April 24th 1991.
- 29 on April 16th 2000.
- 25 on May 22nd 2001.
- 12 on April 24th 2005.
- 11 on April 18th 1990, May 10th 1997 and May 5th 2001.

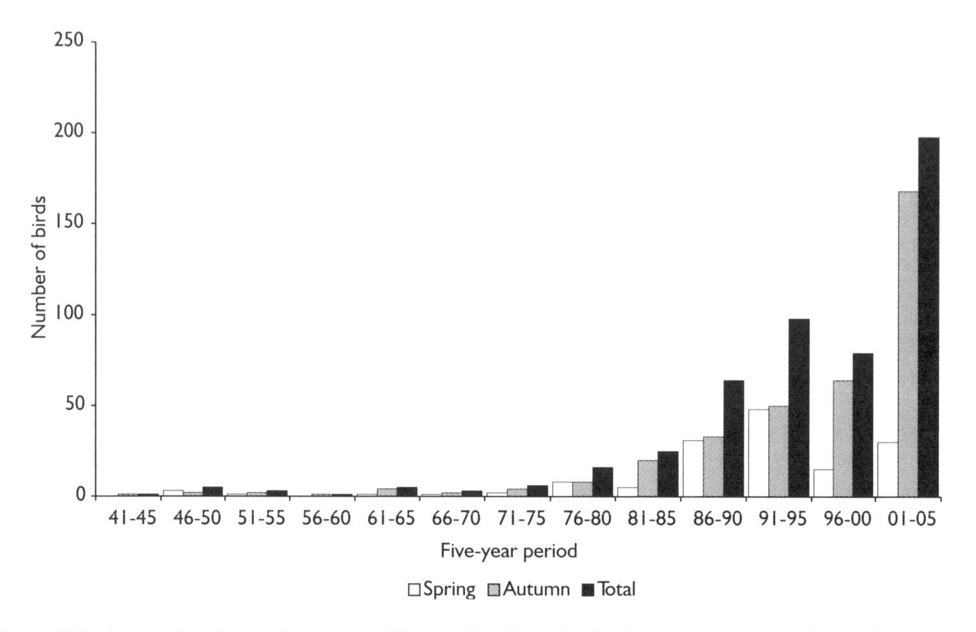

Figure 276: Seasonal and annual average of Black-tailed Godwits by five-year periods 1941–2005.

Double-figure spring counts have been recorded elsewhere on just two occasions: 37 at Eyebrook Reservoir on May 6th 2002 and 17 at Saddington Reservoir on May 1st 1976.

Spring passage tails off considerably after early May before autumn passage begins again in late June. A total of 26 birds have arrived during the first three weeks of June; whether these were late spring migrants or early autumn birds is open to conjecture:

- five at Cossington Meadows on June 7th 2004.
- two at Wanlip Meadows on June 8th 2004.
- three at Rutland Water on June 9th 1984.
- one at Rutland Water on June 11th 2002.
- one at Eyebrook Reservoir from June 12th to 14th 2003.
- two at Rutland Water from June 15th to 20th 2004.
- six at Trent Valley Pit on June 20th 1998.
- five at Rutland Water on June 20th 2005.

A bird in non-breeding plumage summered at Rutland Water in 2001, remaining from May 30th until being joined by the first autumn birds.

Autumn passage covers the period from late June through to October, with a recent trend for small numbers to stay into November and more rarely December. Double-figure counts have been recorded at Rutland Water in 17 autumns since 1984, including every year since 1994, with the largest being:

- 72 on June 27th 2005.
- 48 on August 13th and 22nd 2003.
- 46 on July 19th 2005.
- 43 on July 7th 1997.

Elsewhere, double-figure counts during the autumn have been recorded from six sites, as follows:

- 35 over Stanford Reservoir on August 21st 1993.
- 32 at Eyebrook Reservoir on July 6th 2005.
- 27 over Castle Donington on July 19th 2005.
- 17 at Eyebrook Reservoir on July 17th 2002.

- 14 at Trent Valley Pit on July 24th 1998.
- 12 at Eyebrook Reservoir on September 27th 1998.
- 12 over Oakthorpe on August 6th 1999.
- 11 at Eyebrook Reservoir on September 1st 1984.
- 11 at Swithland Reservoir on July 2nd 2000.
- ten at Eyebrook Reservoir on August 19th 2005.

Prior to 1976 the largest count in either season was of just eight, at Eyebrook Reservoir on August 31st 1961.

Autumn passage has become earlier over recent years. From 1941 to 1967, only 7% of all records at Eyebrook Reservoir occurred in July, with 41% in August (Mason 1969); the figures by the end of 2005, from all sites, were 16% in August and 35% in July.

Single birds wintered at Rutland Water in 1977–78 and 1983–84, as did two in 2002–03 and 2005–06, and late autumn birds have lingered into December in four other years, with four doing so in 1995. Midwinter arrivals are rare with four records in each of December and February and two in January, all of single birds unless stated:

- two at Rutland Water on December 5th 2003.
- Eyebrook Reservoir on December 15th 2003.
- Saddington Reservoir on December 18th 2005.
- Rutland Water from December 31st 1977 to January 24th 1978.
- Eyebrook Reservoir on January 24th 2003.
- Eyebrook Reservoir on January 30th 1998.
- Rutland Water from February 1st to 4th 1989.
- Rutland Water on February 10th 1981.
- Cropston Reservoir from February 24th to 27th 1992.
- Eyebrook Reservoir on February 25th 2004.

Rutland Water is by far the dominant site and 69% of all records have come from here. Eyebrook Reservoir accounts for a further 18%, with the Trent valley producing 4%. Away from these three areas, the Black-tailed Godwit is still a surprisingly scarce bird.

Black-tailed Godwits breed locally from Iceland to eastern Siberia. The nominate race *L. l. limosa* breeds in western Siberia and northern Europe and winters along the coasts of western Europe and the Mediterranean but

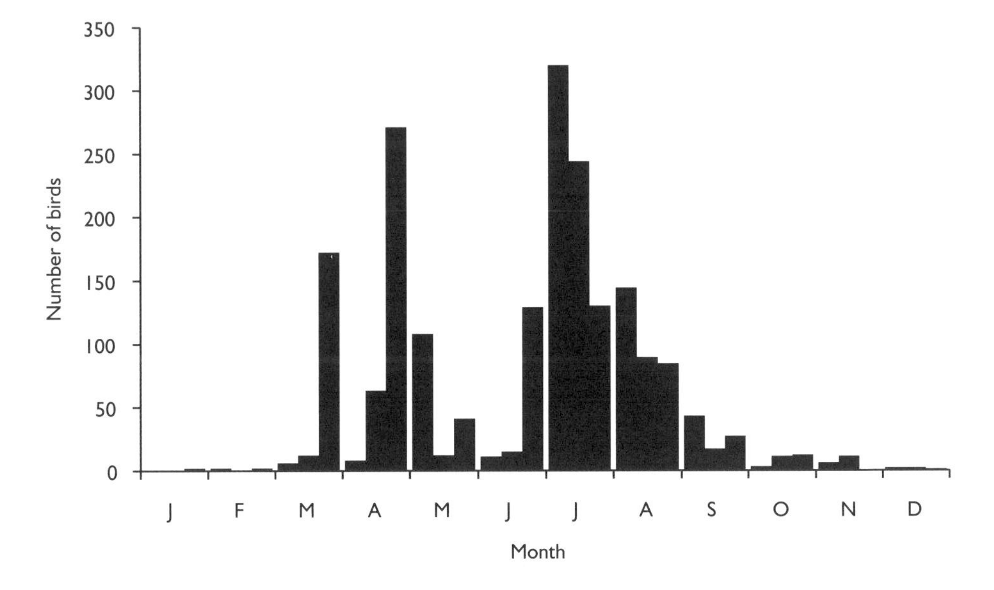

Figure 277: Monthly occurrence of Black-tailed Godwits 1941–2005.

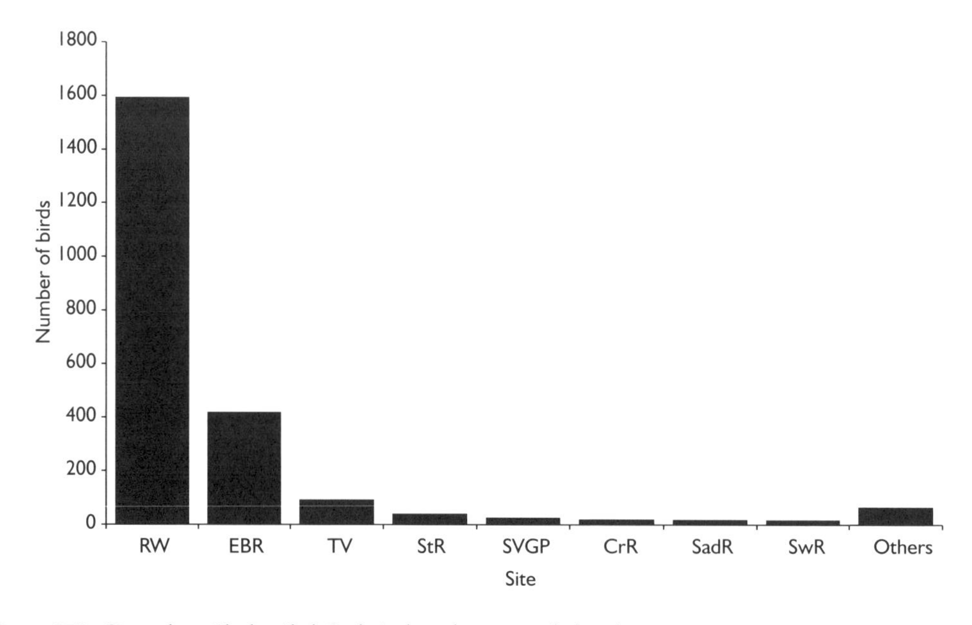

Figure 278: Sites where Black-tailed Godwits have been recorded 1941–2005.
Key to abbreviations: RW = Rutland Water; EBR = Eyebrook Reservoir; TV = Trent valley; StR = Stanford Reservoir; SVGP = Soar valley gravel pits; CrR = Cropston Reservoir; SadR = Saddington Reservoir; SwR = Swithland Reservoir

mainly in Africa. The race *L. l. islandica* breeds in Iceland, along with small numbers in the Faroe Islands and northern Scotland and winters largely coastally in Britain, Ireland and western France. The small British breeding population of the nominate race numbered between 58 and 70 pairs in 2005, the majority of which were at the Ouse Washes in Cambridgeshire (Holling *et al.* 2008). Due to the small number of birds breeding in Britain, and as the population has declined over both the short and long term, this species has been added to the 'Red List' of Birds of Conservation Concern (Gregory *et al.* 2002).

Few attempts have been made at naming the subspecies involved in Leicestershire and Rutland occurrences, but both *islandica* and the nominate form have been identified; records of the former include the flock of 29 at Rutland Water on April 16th 2000 and observations at the Ouse Washes would suggest that the other large spring flocks are likely to have been *islandica*. Several colour-ringed birds have been noted at Rutland Water in recent autumns and the five that have been traced have all been *islandica* birds caught on the Wash in Lincolnshire and Norfolk. One of these, a juvenile female ringed at Terrington (Norfolk) in October 2002, was reported at Cley (Norfolk) between April 4th and May 2nd before being at Rutland Water between October 24th and 29th 2003; it was back at Cley just three days later. Two others, both ringed at Holbeach St. Matthew (Lincolnshire), one in 1996 and one in 1998, provided quick recoveries by being observed at Rutland Water just eight days and five days later respectively.

SML

Bar-tailed Godwit *Limosa lapponica*

Scarce to uncommon passage migrant and rare to scarce winter visitor; recorded in all months, with the majority in April, May, August and September.

There were two 19th century reports of the Bar-tailed Godwit, but both were square-bracketed by Browne and Haines respectively: one caught in a snare at Leicester City Farms on February 19th 1892 was considered a 'doubtful record' by Browne, and two seen regularly by the Eye Brook. Two seen regularly by the Eye Brook early in the summer of 1894 were 'believed to be of this species' by Haines. The LROS archives make reference to single birds at Cropston Reservoir in February 1908 and January 1912 but, apart from these records, the Bar-tailed Godwit went unrecorded in the counties until three were at Eyebrook Reservoir on August 28th 1944. This species remained scarce until the 1970s: there were only 37 birds recorded between 1944 and 1969, with 11 blank years in this period. With the exception of two at Loughborough Sewage Farm on May 9th 1950 and one found dead at Quorn in the autumn of 1967, all of these records were at Eyebrook Reservoir.

Numbers increased dramatically during the 1970s and 1980s and the three best years occurred during this period: 1984 (64 birds), 1971 (55) and 1980 (52). Fewer birds were recorded during the 1990s and into the 21st century. The high numbers in the 1970s and 1980s and the subsequent drop, are difficult to explain; the wintering population nationally did not alter significantly during the period and, if anything, local conditions (essentially the existence of Rutland Water) would have been expected to favour a continuation of larger numbers occurring, in line with most other wader species. However, the occurrence of several large flocks in the 1970s and 1980s does somewhat distort the figures. Double-figure counts have been recorded on nine occasions, as follows:

- 51 over Stanford Reservoir on September 2nd 1971.
- 46 at Rutland Water on August 9th 1980.
- 35 west over Swithland Reservoir on November 3rd 1984.
- 26 at Rutland Water on September 1st 1990.
- 20 at Eyebrook Reservoir on April 20th 1976, with 18 two days later.
- 16 at Rutland Water on April 29th 1984, with 14 the following day.
- 16 at Rutland Water on August 27th 1988.
- 14 at Eyebrook Reservoir on April 20th 1974.
- 13 at Rutland Water on May 14th 1989.

In addition, flocks of six to nine have been recorded on a further seven occasions, all at Rutland Water or Eyebrook Reservoir with the exception of six at Wanlip Meadows on April 21st 2005.

The total numbers on spring and autumn passage are broadly similar. Spring migration is concentrated almost entirely in April and May, compared to autumn birds being spread over the five months July to November, but dominated by August and, particularly, September. Birds are now appearing more regularly on spring passage than previously: of all records at Eyebrook Reservoir between 1941 and 1967 only 11% were during the spring (Mason 1969), whereas the overall total for the counties during this season now stands at 40%.

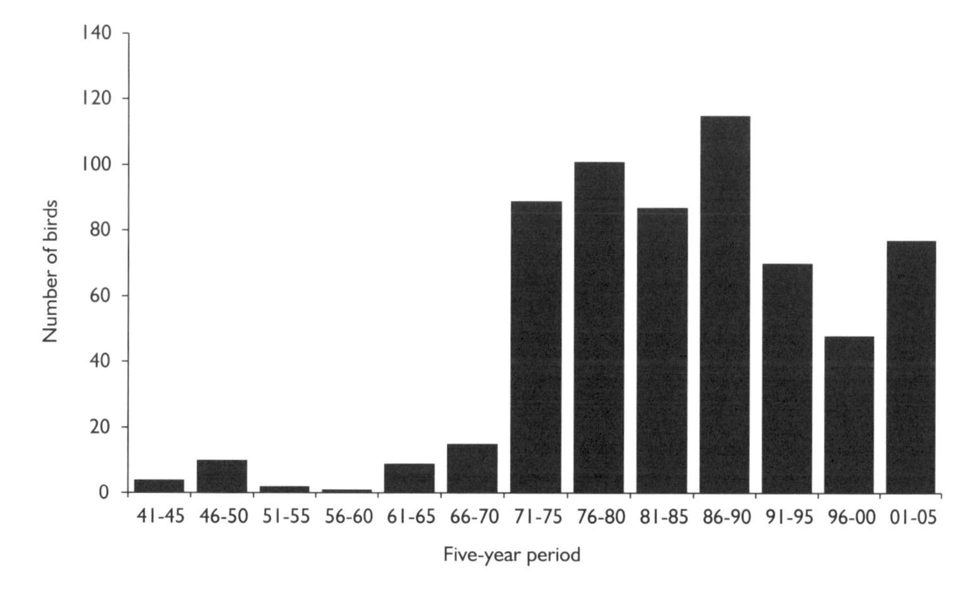

Figure 279: Numbers of Bar-tailed Godwits by five-year periods 1941–2005.

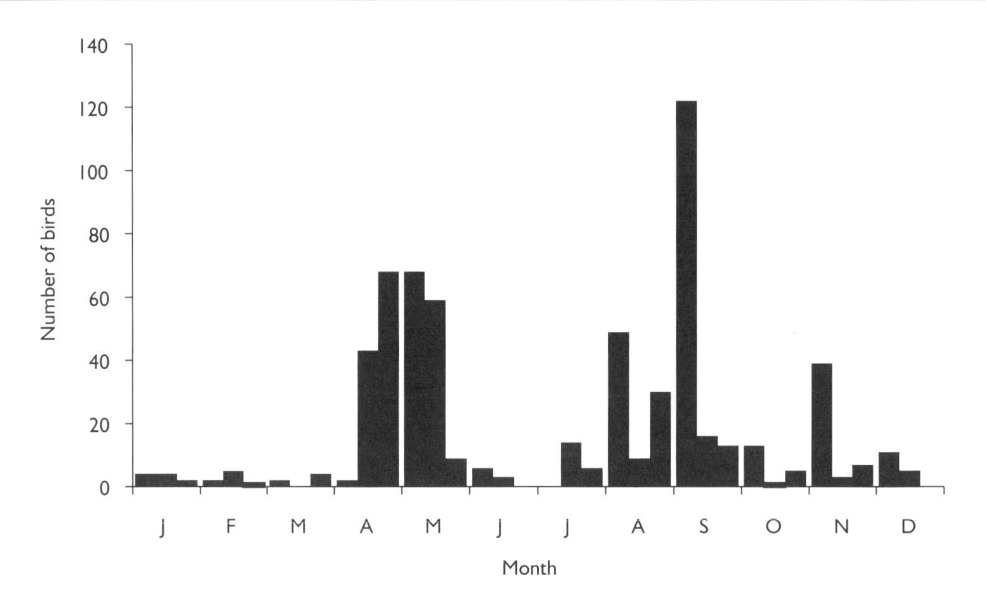

Figure 280: Monthly occurrence of Bar-tailed Godwits 1941–2005.

The total number of birds recorded is now about 625, 77% of which have occurred at either Eyebrook Reservoir or Rutland Water: these two sites clearly provide the conditions suitable to attract this species regularly and others do not. Of the 145 birds at other sites 86 occurred in two fly-over flocks, so 'grounded' Bar-tailed Godwits away from the premier sites average well below one a year. The totals for Stanford Reservoir and Swithland Reservoir are heavily influenced by these two large flocks; both sites have only five records each to their name, the same number as Trent Vally Pit. Cropston Reservoir, Thornton Reservoir and Wanlip Meadows are the only other sites to have recorded this species on more than one occasion.

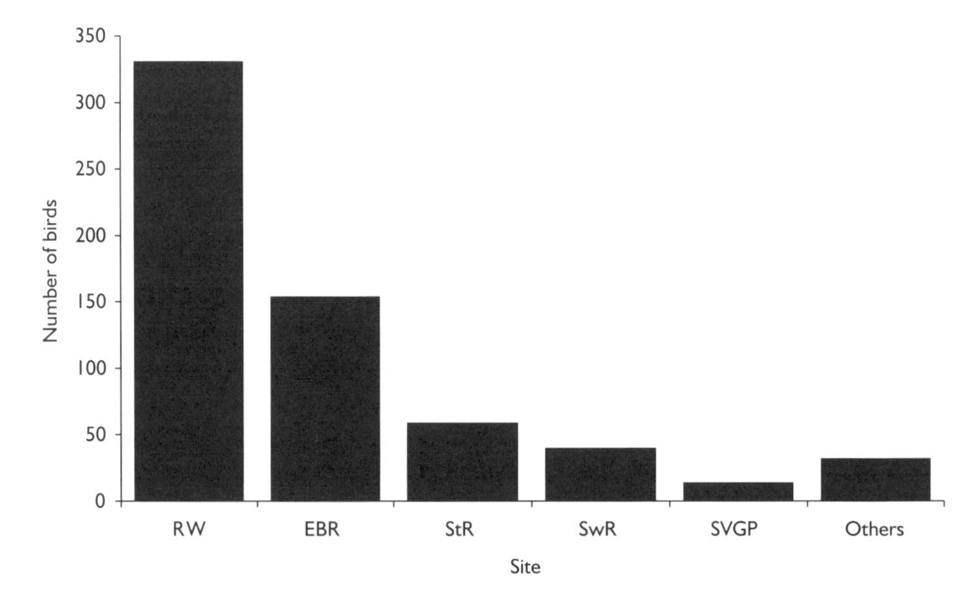

Figure 281: Sites where Bar-tailed Godwits have been recorded 1941–2005.
Key to abbreviations: RW = Rutland Water; EBR = Eyebrook Reservoir; StR = Stanford Reservoir; SwR = Swithland Reservoir; SVGP = Soar valley gravel pits

Bar-tailed Godwits breed in the Arctic from northern Scandinavia east across the far-north of Russia and Siberia and also in northern Alaska; they winter on the coasts of southern and western Europe, Africa, south-west Asia and Australasia. Britain has a wintering population in excess of 61,500 birds (Baker *et al.* 2006), with the Wash (Lincolnshire/Norfolk) being a particularly important area. As more than 20% of the East Atlantic Flyway non-breeding population is found in Britain, the Bar-tailed Godwit has been added to the 'Amber List' of Birds of Conservation Concern (Gregory *et al.* 2002).

SML

Whimbrel *Numenius phaeopus*

Uncommon or occasionally fairly common passage migrant; recorded in all months between March and October, with the majority in April, May, July and August.

It appears that this species was rare (or overlooked) in the 19th century. Browne quotes Harley as saying that it 'occurs occasionally in sparing numbers, as for instance in the meadows about Loughborough, at Bosworth and elsewhere in the county', but the only records specifically mentioned are one killed near Leicester on April 23rd 1856 and an undated bird shot in the Charnwood Forest district. In Rutland, Haines refers to an undated record from Seaton, a small flock by the River Welland in 1855, one shot at Burley on October 2nd 1890 and one at the latter site in April 1905.

Apart from two at Desford in May 1925 mentioned in the LROS archives, there were no records in the 20th century until 1946, when a total of eight birds was recorded at Eyebrook Reservoir. With the exceptions of 1947 and 1953 every subsequent year has produced at least one record and the overall average since 1946 is of about 25 birds annually. However, a noticeable increase is apparent from the 1980s onwards: the average number of birds annually between 1946 and 1980 was ten, but since 1981 this has risen to around 50. A peak in numbers in the 1980s was a result of several good years, with 1983 being the best of all, especially at Rutland Water where it was estimated that as many as 111 individual birds occurred during the year. A total of approximately 143 individuals was recorded throughout the counties in 1983, with other good years being 1993 (88), 1999 (79) and 2004 (70). In all of these years, numbers were boosted by large flocks, as follows:

1983	48 over Rutland Water on April 17th and 20 north over Stanford Reservoir on May 2nd.
1993	48 south-west over Rutland Water on August 20th.
1999	37 west over Fort Henry Ponds on August 5th.
2004	25 south-west over Wanlip South Gravel Pits on July 25th.

There have been a further eight flocks of 20 or more recorded in other years, as follows:

- 37 over Eyebrook Reservoir on July 27th 1987.
- 32 at Eyebrook Reservoir on May 7th 2001.
- 29 at Rutland Water on July 12th 1986.
- 27 at Eyebrook Reservoir on July 27th 1987.
- 25 at Rutland Water on both August 14th 1980 and July 23rd 1987.
- 23 over Quorn on August 18th 1962.
- 22 at Rutland Water on May 8th 1988.
- 20 at Carlton Curlieu on August 17th 1960.

Both spring and autumn passage seasons are concentrated mainly within two-month periods. The spring season is in fact even more precisely defined as there have only ever been three records before April 14th: single birds at Oakthorpe on March 24th 1961 and Eyebrook Reservoir on April 3rd 2003 and two at Rutland Water on April 2nd 2000, and just one May record has been later than the 26th. The latest spring occurrence was of one at Swithland Reservoir on June 5th 1983, although two reported at the same site on June 15th 1977 may have been very late spring stragglers or very early returning birds.

Average first arrival dates have remained fairly consistent since this species started to appear more regularly in the counties in the mid-1970s, although the more recent trend (since the mid-1990s) is for slightly earlier arrivals. In each of the six five-year periods from 1976 to 2005, the average arrival date has been between April 16th and 21st.

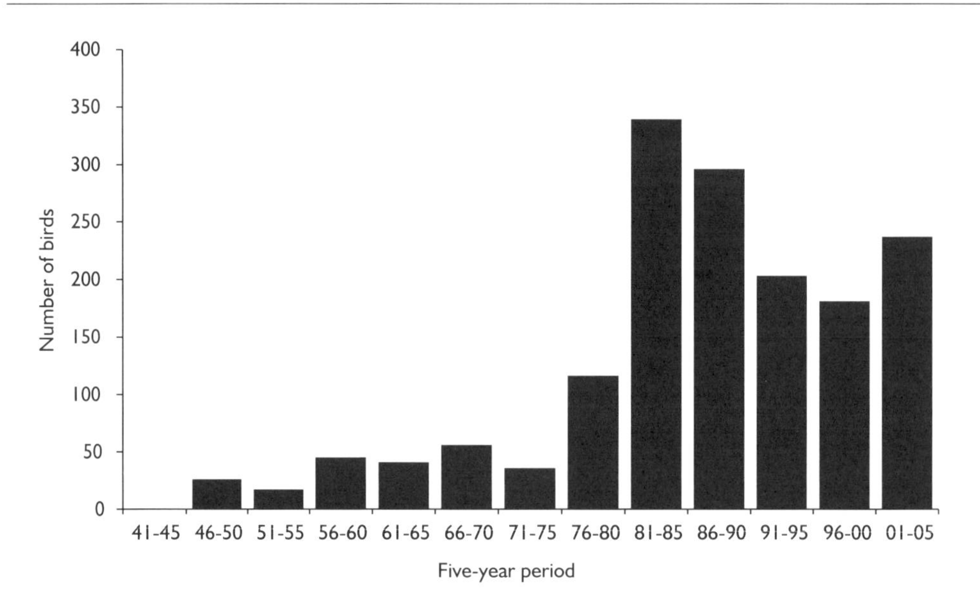

Figure 282: Numbers of Whimbrels by five-year periods 1941–2005.

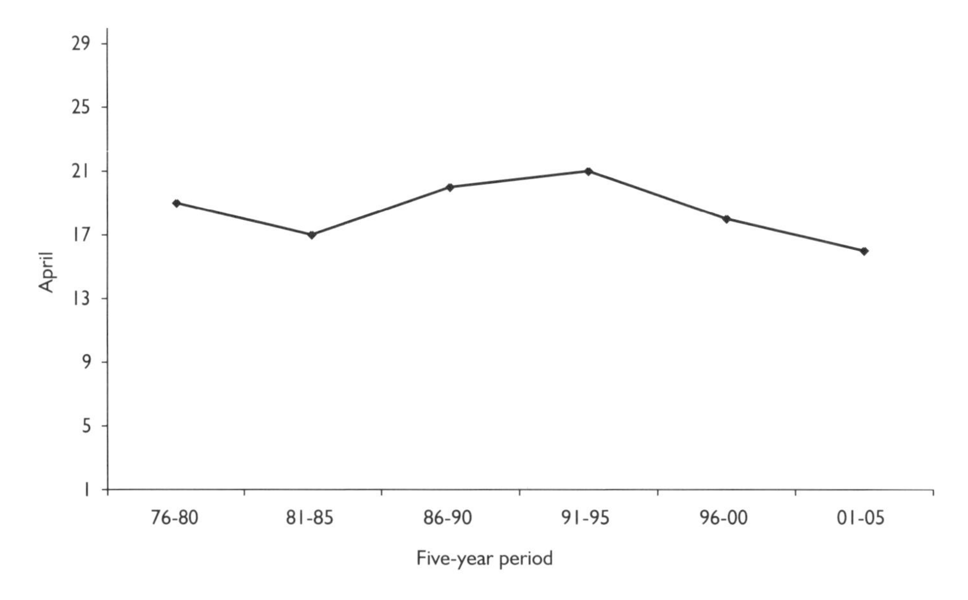

Figure 283: Average spring arrival dates of Whimbrels by five-year periods 1976–2005.

The earliest unambiguous autumn record is of two at Rutland Water on June 29th 1990. The bulk of the passage takes place between early July and the middle of August, declining rapidly into September. There have been only six records later than September 26th, with four October birds, as follows:

- two at Priory Water on October 25th 1988.
- one at Thornton Reservoir on October 17th 1971.
- one at Eyebrook Reservoir on October 3rd 1993.

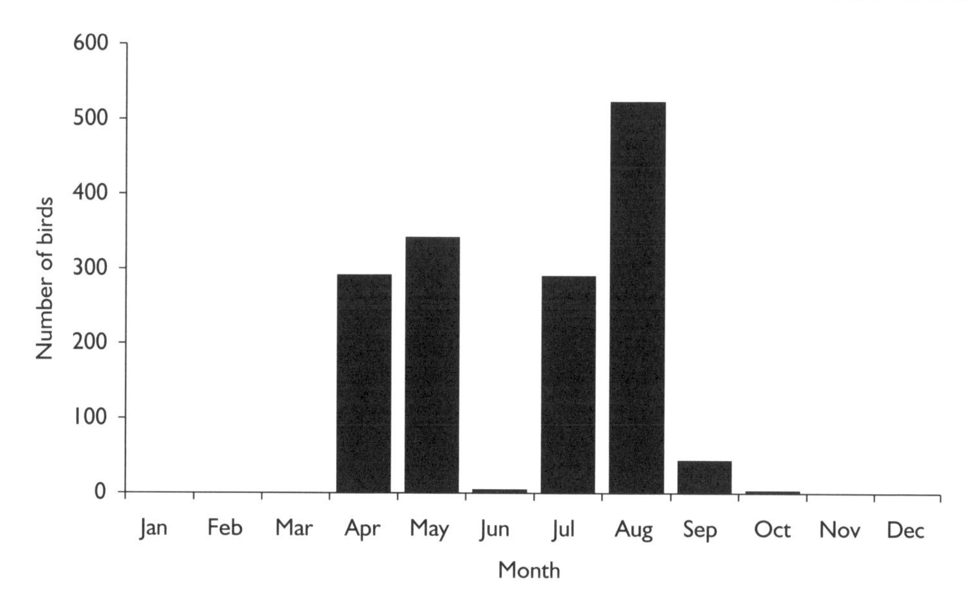

Figure 284: Monthly occurrence of Whimbrels 1941–2005.

Figure 284 showing the monthly occurrence of Whimbrels in the counties contrasts with the findings of Mason (1969), who noted that of all records at Eyebrook Reservoir between 1941 and 1967 only 14% were during the spring (mostly in April) and 76% occurred in August. By comparison, in the whole of Leicestershire and Rutland between 1941 and 2005, 42% of all birds occurred during the spring, with May being the peak month at this season; August, whilst still being the main month overall, accounts for just 35% of all records.

Whimbrels rarely stay very long and many records are of birds flying over without landing. The most notable exceptions to this are single birds at Loughborough Sewage Farm from May 11th to 15th 1957, Clipsham from May 20th to 26th 1977, Rutland Water from August 1st to 26th 2004 and Trent Valley Pit from April 23rd to 28th 2005. Nocturnal passage has been reported several times by observers who have heard the species' characteristic calls during the night.

The Whimbrel has a circumpolar breeding distribution; the nominate race nests from Iceland, northern Britain and Scandinavia to western Siberia, with other races breeding in southern Russia and in Alaska, north-west Canada and Greenland. Most nominate race birds winter around the coasts of sub-Saharan Africa. In Britain it is confined as a breeding species to Scotland, with around 95% in Shetland. The latest British population estimate is 530 pairs (Baker *et al.* 2006) and as more than 50% of the population breeds at fewer than ten sites, the Whimbrel has been added to the 'Amber List' of Birds of Conservation Concern (Gregory *et al.* 2002).

SML

Curlew (Eurasian Curlew) ***Numenius arquata***

Uncommon passage and scarce winter visitor, scarce migrant breeder.

During the 19th century the Curlew was considered by Browne as an 'accidental straggler' to Leicestershire, whilst Haines knew of at least eight occurrences in Rutland. It would appear that this species became more frequent during the early part of the 20th century: the LROS archives describe it as a regular winter visitor and spring migrant and by 1943 its status had been amended to 'regular passing migrant and occasional winter visitor' (Jolley 1944).

Curlews have yet to become anything more than tenuously established as a breeding species in the counties, despite a small population existing for over 50 years. Two pairs were suspected of nesting near Shenton in 1947 but the first definite breeding involved two pairs near Market Bosworth in 1949. Three pairs bred in the same general area of the south-west in 1952, when 'several' pairs were also reported in the north-east and one pair nested in a Charnwood Forest valley. The 1953 LROS Annual Report stated 'now well established as a breeding species in the western and south-western parts of the county' but in fact the number of pairs confirmed as breeding in the whole of the counties in any one year has only reached double figures once, ten pairs in 1983. Nesting birds have been found in cereal fields as well as the more expected grassland and some may go unrecorded. Birds reported as displaying or summering in the counties have frequently outnumbered those known to be breeding and it is quite possible that many of these were actually nesting, as breeding birds can easily be overlooked once the display stage is finished. Equally, birds clearly on passage at well-watched sites have sometimes been observed performing the full display.

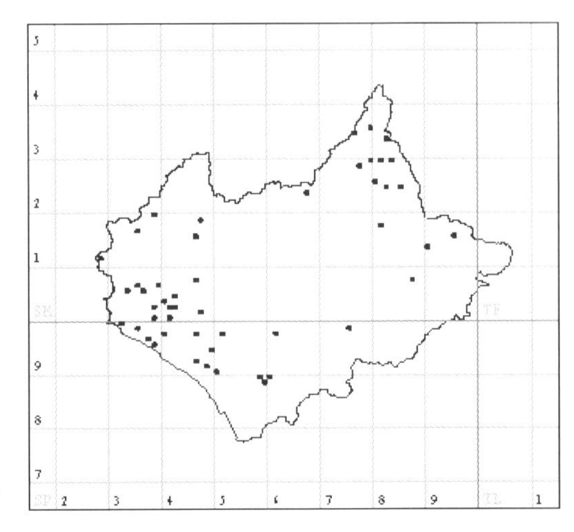

Figure 285: Distribution of breeding Curlews 1941–2005.

Confirmed breeding has been documented in 42 of the years between 1949 and 2005 and has occurred in 56 tetrads within 21 10–km squares, 14 in the west and south-west and seven in the east and north-east of the counties. Between 1976 and 1984 Warrilow confirmed breeding in 19 tetrads within nine 10-km squares. All sites where breeding has been confirmed at any time are shown in Figure 285.

Seven pairs nested at Bruntingthorpe Airfield in 1983, with possibly as many as six pairs there two years earlier, and up to four pairs bred in the Congerstone and Twycross area in 1967 and 1971. Otherwise all records are of either one or two pairs. Several areas in the south-west have had breeding birds in series of successive years whereas nesting in the north-east has been much more sporadic. There are only three confirmed breeding records for Rutland, at Egleton in 1978 and at both Cottesmore and Stretton in 2001.

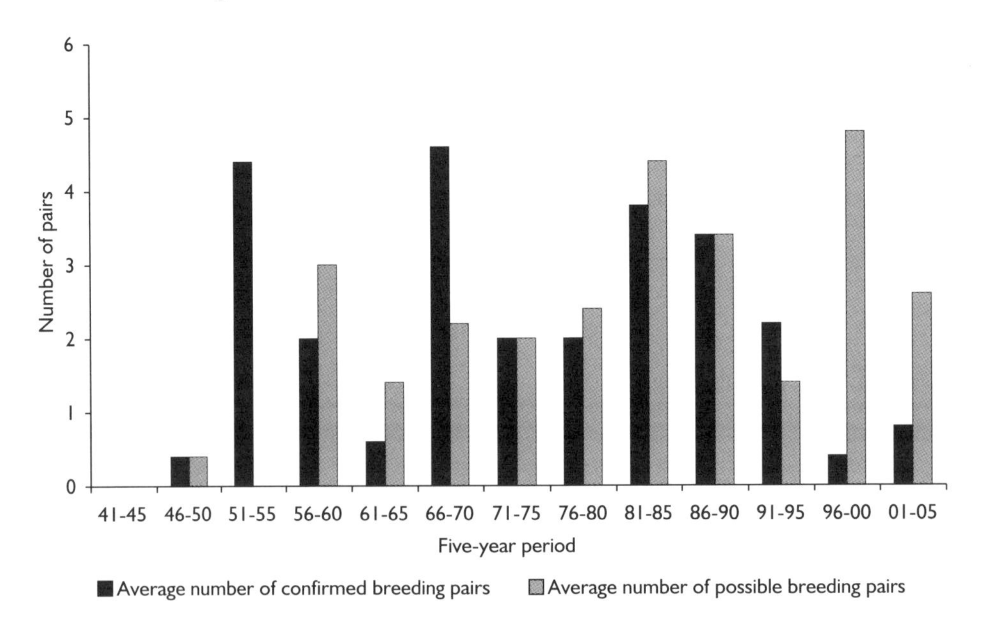

Figure 286: Average number of breeding pairs of Curlews by five-year periods 1941–2005.

Breeding has recently become much less common and has only been confirmed in five of the ten years leading up to 2005. The most recent instance in the species' stronghold of the south-west was at Aston Flamville as long ago as 1997.

This species is also a winter visitor and passage migrant, and it is often difficult to distinguish between the two categories. It is probably wise to restrict the meaning of winter to just November, December and January so as to exclude extreme migrant dates and the earliest arrivals of breeding birds. To date there have been records in 32 winters defined in this way; only 14 of the years between 1941 and 1979 produced winter birds but records have been annual ever since. Most winter records relate to small numbers of short-staying birds and true wintering was not noted until the 1985–86 winter, when a flock of 11 arrived at Rutland Water on December 7th and most of them stayed throughout January. Three roosted at Priory Water throughout December 1988 and January 1989, and six possibly wintered at Rutland Water in 1995–96. A flock that regularly gathered to roost at Rutland Water in the 1998–99 winter built up to 50 by December 12th, with at least 40 still present in January and subsequent counts of 29 in February and 17 on March 1st. Since 1999 wintering by small numbers of birds has been regular at Rutland Water, with maxima of 14 in 1999–2000 and 13 in 2001–02 but no more than seven in the five other winters. The birds normally dispersed during the day and returned to roost in the late afternoon. Wintering site-fidelity was shown by an individual with a distinctive damaged bill which was present in each of the three winters from 2001–02 to 2003–04.

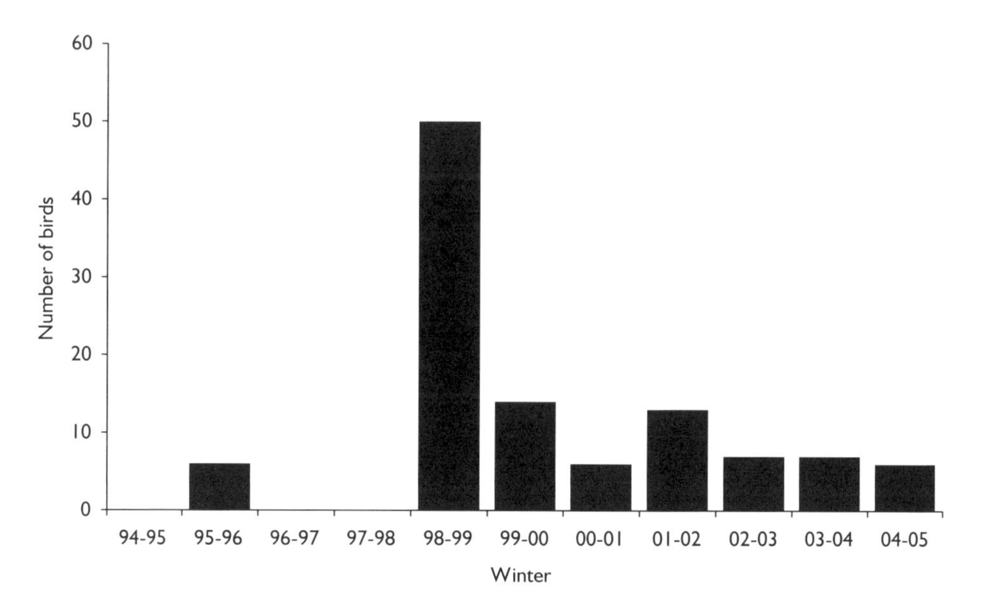

Figure 287: Wintering numbers of Curlews at Rutland Water 1994–95 to 2004–05.

As noted, most other winter records have involved only small numbers and counts of more than five have only been recorded nine times:

- 35 at Eyebrook Reservoir on December 29th 1995.
- 27 south over Swithland Reservoir on November 14th 1965.
- 25 west over Thornton Reservoir on January 4th 2002.
- 20 at Welham on January 11th 1958.
- 17 at Eyebrook Reservoir on January 3rd 1997.
- eight at Leicester City Farms in January and February 1942.
- eight at Croxton Kerrial on January 26th 1975.
- seven at Priory Water on December 15th 1991.
- six at Exton Park on December 22nd 1991.

Spring passage has been noted from late February until early May with the main period being March and April. Large flocks are unusual and all records of 10+ are listed:

- 22 near Ashby-de-la-Zouch on March 19th 1997.
- 16 at Countesthorpe on March 8th 1947.
- 13 at Leicester City Farms on February 22nd 1947.
- 12 at Halstead on March 26th 1949.
- 12 at Rutland Water on May 6th 1984.
- 11 near Cropston on April 25th 1993.

The bulk of autumn passage takes place in August and September but small numbers have been recorded as early as the start of June in recent years. One flew south over Quorn on June 1st 2002, eight were at Rutland Water on June 10th 2003 and there have been six records later in the month, all since 1977; most have been of just one or two birds but 12 were at Sence Valley Forest Park on June 16th 2001. October records are very unusual except for a few due to wintering birds arriving at Rutland Water in recent years. Flocks of 20+ have been recorded 19 times in autumn; those of 25+ are listed:

- 200 over Swithland Reservoir on August 8th 1979.
- 55 over Leicester City Farms on September 10th 1966.
- 50 at Loughborough on August 13th 1949.
- 50 at Eyebrook Reservoir on August 6th 1950.
- 50 over Narborough Bog on September 14th 1975.
- 48 at Rutland Water on August 11th 1984.
- 29 at Rutland Water on August 31st 1987.
- 27 at Rutland Water on September 9th 1978.
- 27 at Rutland Water on September 20th 1998.
- 25 at Rutland Water on August 23rd 1986.
- 25 at Rutland Water on October 2nd 1988.

There seems no obvious explanation for only one of the largest autumn flocks having been in the last 15 years and the one in question, in 1998, may actually have involved the start of the winter flock present at Rutland Water that year. Since 1989 the largest undoubted autumn passage flock has been of just 15, over Newton Harcourt on June 27th 1990.

Curlews breed across the Palearctic from France, Britain and Ireland to central Siberia, with nominate birds in the west and the race *orientalis* east of the Urals. Many winter in western Europe, with others mainly coastally around Africa, the Middle East and southern and south-east Asia. The Curlew is one of a few species which both breeds and winters in Britain at internationally significant levels and as was included on the 'Amber List' of Birds of Conservation Concern (Gregory *et al.* 2002). In 2008 it was added to the Red List of the International Union for Conservation of Nature and Natural Resources (IUCN) with the status of 'Near Threatened' due to recent declines in Europe and Central Asia. The British breeding population has been estimated at around 105,000 pairs (Baker *et al.* 2006). The UK 2005–06 WeBS maximum of 74,713 was considerably down on previous years and the lowest peak since 1987–88 (Musgrove *et al.* 2007).

SML

Common Sandpiper *Actitis hypoleucos*

Fairly common passage migrant and rare winter visitor; formerly also a very rare breeder.

During the 19th and early 20th century, Browne described the Common Sandpiper as a 'summer visitant, sparingly distributed'. It had apparently bred at Groby Pool and two nests were found at Bradgate Park in 1885, an egg from one of which is retained at Leicester Museum. Breeding was reported from Bradgate Park again in 1908, as well as by the Eye Brook near Skeffington in 1906. Haines said that this species was seen regularly on passage in Rutland during the 19th century and had bred near Caldecott in 1872 and at Burley Fishponds in 1899.

There are very few, if any, areas of water that have not attracted this species as it is able to use a much wider range of habitats than most other waders. Sites such as Thornton Reservoir have produced significant numbers of Common Sandpipers but hardly attract other waders at all.

It is unrealistic to attempt detailed analyses of numbers that have occurred as a large proportion will have gone undetected at sites that are not reported on regularly. Figure 288 simply shows the total numbers reported in each month during 1996–2005 in an effort to show the monthly distribution.

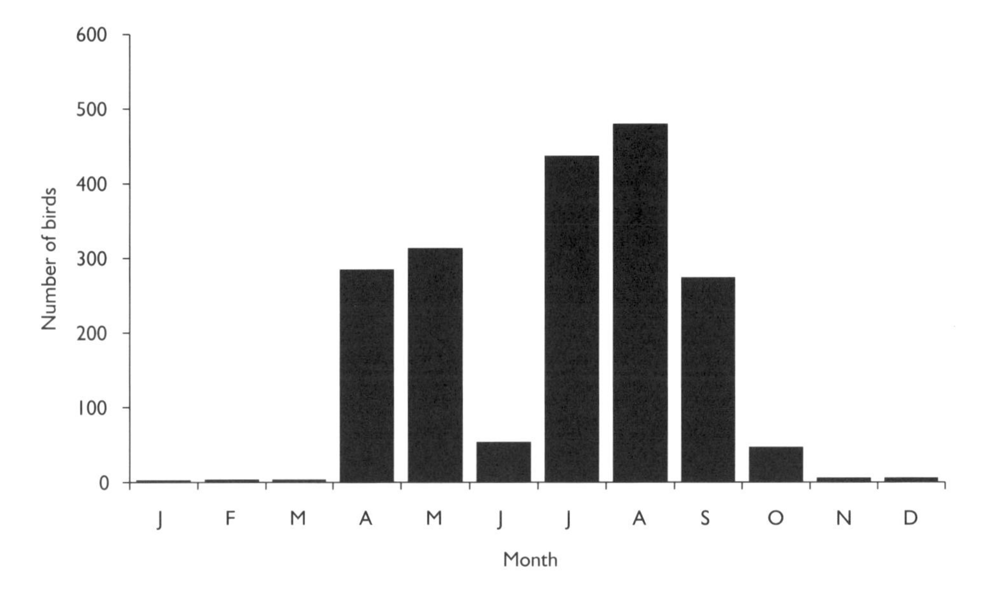

Figure 288: Total monthly numbers of Common Sandpipers 1996–2005.

Clearly, spring passage is mainly in April and May. Arrivals before then are unusual but the first spring dates have been in March seven times, the earliest being on March 6th 1975. Small numbers have been recorded moving through the counties as late as the first few days of June. The numbers involved are much smaller than in autumn, with more than four at one site being unusual in spring. The largest counts are as follows:

- 11 at Ratcliffe on the Wreake on May 15th 1982.
- nine at Eyebrook Reservoir on May 22nd 1961.
- nine at Rutland Water on May 8th 1987.
- nine at Thornton Reservoir on May 28th 1990 and April 21st 1993.
- eight at Eyebrook Reservoir on May 28th 1975.
- eight at Thornton Reservoir on May 3rd 1977 and May 10th 2001.
- eight at Saddington Reservoir on May 22nd 2001.

Another three sites, Stanford Reservoir, Thurmaston Gravel Pits and Birstall Gravel Pits have held six birds in spring, and two additional sites, Trent Valley Pit and Cropston Reservoir have held five.

As with several other species, it is difficult to be sure whether birds in mid-June are late spring individuals or early autumn ones. In this case it seems that from about the 10th it is returning autumn birds that are involved. The main passage period is July and August, with rather fewer in September and just a few stragglers in October and occasionally November. Some surprisingly large concentrations have been recorded at several sites but only Rutland Water and Eyebrook Reservoir have ever produced more than 20, the largest counts including the following:

- 62 at Rutland Water on August 12th 1980.
- 50 at Rutland Water on July 20th 2003.
- 42 at Eyebrook Reservoir on July 21st 1950.

- 37 at Rutland Water on August 1st 2004.
- 27 at Rutland Water on August 28th 1984.
- 26 at Rutland Water on July 31st 2002.
- 25 at Eyebrook Reservoir on August 6th 1946.
- 25 at Rutland Water on July 31st 2005.

The autumn maximum counts for other sites to have held seven or more are as follows:

- 20 at Trent Valley Pit on July 27th 1998.
- 15 at Stanford Reservoir in August 1944.
- 14 at Frisby Gravel Pits on August 10th 1975.
- 12 at Loughborough Sewage Farm on August 26th 1947 and Watermead Gravel Pits on July 27th 1988.
- 11 at Thornton Reservoir on August 5th 1974, Swithland Reservoir on June 30th 1987 and Cropston Reservoir on August 4th 1990.
- ten at Knipton Reservoir on July 18th 1993.
- seven at Saddington Reservoir on August 25th 1994.

There is evidence to suggest that Common Sandpipers pass through the counties earlier than previously in both spring and autumn. Mason (1969) found that, during 1958–67, almost four times as many birds occurred at Eyebrook Reservoir during May than April, whereas figures for 1996 to 2005 over the counties as a whole show similar numbers in each month. Likewise, July and August have produced similar numbers over the last ten years, whereas from 1958 to 1967 56% of autumn records at Eyebrook Reservoir were in August, with only 20% in July.

Single birds have wintered on 12 occasions and two birds once. The sites involved have been Stanford Reservoir (1958–59, 1959–60 and 1987–88), Eyebrook Reservoir (1960–61), Swithland Reservoir (1972–73 and 1973–74), Rutland Water (1987–88 (two birds) and 1988–89), Watermead Park (1994–95), Cropston Reservoir (1997–98), a jet-ski centre at Stoney Stanton (2000–01 and 2001–02)and Trent Valley Pit (2002–03). Most wintering birds have moved away by the end of March, before spring arrivals, but the Stoney Stanton individual(s) remained into April in both 2001 and 2002. Assuming that the same birds wintered in successive years at the four relevant sites, only ten individuals were involved. There have been another 14 records of birds in winter but none of these constituted true wintering. In total, there have been records during 24 winters, half of these since 1987.

In recent times there has been no proved breeding but birds have occasionally displayed at a reservoir and at several gravel pit sites, mostly since 1991 and nesting has twice been strongly suspected at Trent Valley Pit, by one pair in 1998 and two pairs in 1999.

Common Sandpipers breed from Britain and Ireland and through much of Europe to central Asia and across Russia and Siberia. Most western birds winter in sub-Saharan Africa, with small numbers in southern Britain and Europe. The latest British breeding estimate is 12,000 pairs (Baker *et al.* 2006), although the population has been declining since 1985 (Collier *et al.* 2005). There is one interesting ringing recovery involving Leicestershire and Rutland: a colour-ringed bird at Thornton Reservoir on April 22nd 2000 had been marked as a pullus in Scotland at Dewar Burn (Borders) in June 1999.

SML

Spotted Sandpiper *Actitis macularius*

Very rare vagrant from North America: one record.

An adult in summer plumage, originally found by Dave Summerfield, was at Eyebrook Reservoir on May 9th and 10th 1998 (Summerfield 1999, *BB* 92:578).

Spotted Sandpipers breed across much of North America and winter in the southern United States, more commonly south through Central America and across the northern two-thirds of South America, and in the West Indies. In Britain there had been 138 accepted records by the end of 2005, most involving either summer-plumaged adults in May and June or juveniles in September and October. It is perhaps surprising that Leicestershire and Rutland have only produced one bird to date, as there have been at least 11 other records in the Midlands; of these, there have been three in Derbyshire since 1999.

SML

Green Sandpiper *Tringa ochropus*

Fairly common passage migrant and scarce winter visitor.

This species has been well known in the counties since the 18th century but its status has changed markedly over the years. In the 19th century, Browne described it as a 'spring and autumn visitant, not common, sometimes remaining during winter' and the status given by Haines for Rutland during the same period was very similar.

The first LROS Annual Report, in 1941, stated that this species was a 'passage migrant and winter visitor in small numbers', also mentioning a count of 20 at Eyebrook Reservoir on August 15th, a number that has never been bettered at the site. Documented winter records were quite scarce in the 1940s and it was not until 1949 that birds actually wintered, at three sites that year: Quorn, Heather and Lindley, and then at Blackbrook Reservoir in 1956. The mid-1970s saw the start of more regular wintering and by about 1985 the numbers involved had reached low double-figures, a level that has just about been maintained since. Realistically it is difficult to be sure what constitutes a wintering individual as this species has long migration seasons in both spring and autumn; December and January are perhaps the only true winter months in this case. Sightings at this time have mainly been of one or two birds at a site, occasionally up to four and a record of ten at Cossington Meadows for much of January 2003 was most unusual.

The current distinctions between the seasons are illustrated by an analysis of the estimated numbers present each month during the years from 1995 to 2005, totalled and then averaged (Figure 289).

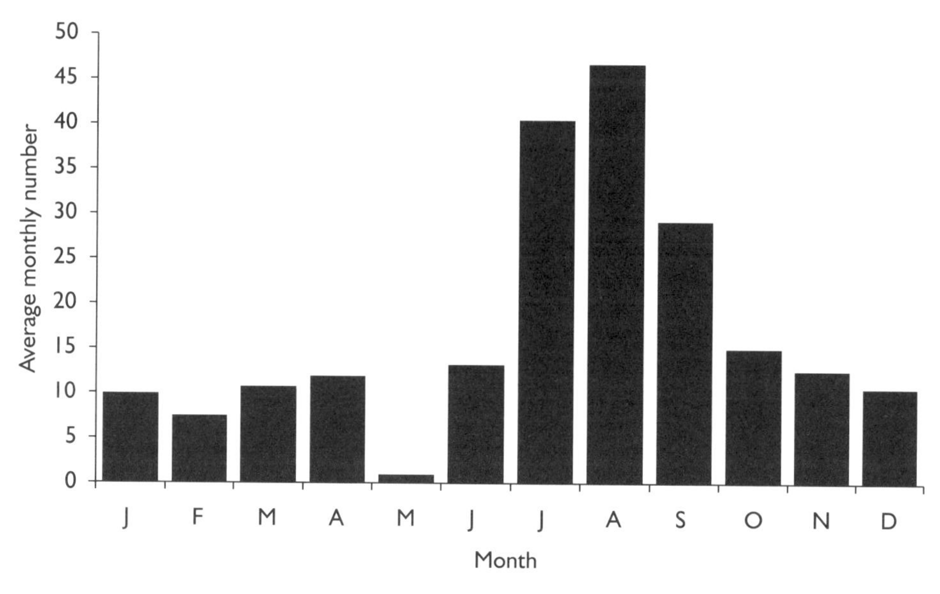

Figure 289: Average monthly numbers of Green Sandpipers 1995–2005.

It seems that numbers present fall away in February as wintering birds depart and then a small spring passage brings an increase in March, peaking in April. Very few birds occurred in May and in fact there were none at all in five of the 11 years. The autumn passage clearly starts in June and reaches a peak in August before slowly declining over the next three months.

The latest ever spring record was on May 27th, at Narborough in 2002, with a gap until the earliest returning bird, at Kelham Bridge on June 4th 2004. Records in early June were previously thought to relate to spring birds, but it is now clear that this species is returning earlier than it used to; June records in the counties were unknown until 1962 but then increased and became annual from 1980. The last four years have seen unprecedented June numbers: 17 in 2002, 24 in 2003, 28 in 2004 and 24 in 2005.

There have been some impressive counts at Rutland Water in recent years, including:

- 31 on July 20th 2003.
- 27 on July 21st 2002.
- 26 on both August 10th 2004 and July 17th and 19th 2005.
- 24 on August 21st 1996.
- 22 on July 29th 1995.
- 20 on August 15th 1999.

The maxima for the other sites that have recorded six or more are:

- 20 at Eyebrook Reservoir on August 15th 1941 and July 24th 1947.
- 17 at Leicester City Farms in August 1958.
- 15 at Cropston Reservoir in August 1967.
- 15 at Swithland Reservoir on August 30th 1990.
- 13 at Cossington Gravel Pits on July 14th 1979.
- 13 at Cossington North Gravel Pits on April 13th 2002.
- 12 at Saddington Reservoir on August 12th 1984.
- 12 at Trent Valley Pit on July 3rd 2004.
- ten at Heather on August 15th 1980.
- ten at Priory Water on July 31st 1994.
- ten at Kelham Bridge from August 10th to 12th 2004.
- eight at Watermead Gravel Pits on September 6th 1987.
- eight at Trent Farm Pool on August 21st 1999.
- seven at Stanford Reservoir on October 27th 1995.
- six at Wanlip South Gravel Pits on August 9th 1998.
- six at Lockington Gravel Pits on September 4th and 26th 2004.

It is noticeable that, with the exception of the one spring count, the maxima listed are spread over the four months from July to October, highlighting the complexity of the autumn passage of this species; there can be three or even four main arrivals during the season. Over the past few years the majority of highest counts have occurred in July and early August, approximately two weeks earlier than before on average; this links up with the recent surge in June records to demonstrate an earlier autumn passage for this sub-boreal zone breeder. Comparison with the findings of Mason (1969) also reveals that autumn passage is now earlier than previously: between 1958 and 1967, 79% of all autumn records at Eyebrook Reservoir were in August, with only 14% during July.

An individual described as an albino was at Eyebrook Reservoir during August 1952.

Green Sandpipers breed from Fennoscandia and the southern Baltic region eastwards to the Pacific coast and winter in Europe, Africa and southern Asia. One or two pairs usually breed in northern Scotland each year and, due to the small breeding population, this species has been added to the 'Amber List' of Birds of Conservation Concern (Gregory *et al.* 2002).

SML

Spotted Redshank *Tringa erythropus*

Scarce spring and uncommon autumn migrant, rare winter visitor.

Browne mentioned that one was shot at Thornton Reservoir in September 1880 but, apart from a reference in the LROS archives to one at Cropston Reservoir on October 16th 1940, there were no other records in the counties until at least two were seen at Eyebrook Reservoir in September 1945. Since then this species has occurred in all but three years. No more than eight were recorded in any one year until 1964, when a large autumn passage produced 96 bird-days at Eyebrook Reservoir including a maximum count of 13 on August 27th, along with six birds elsewhere (Hickling mistakenly mentioned a count of 30 at Eyebrook Reservoir, repeated by Mitcham: this was caused by 11 on August 30th being read as 30 on August 11th!). Subsequently

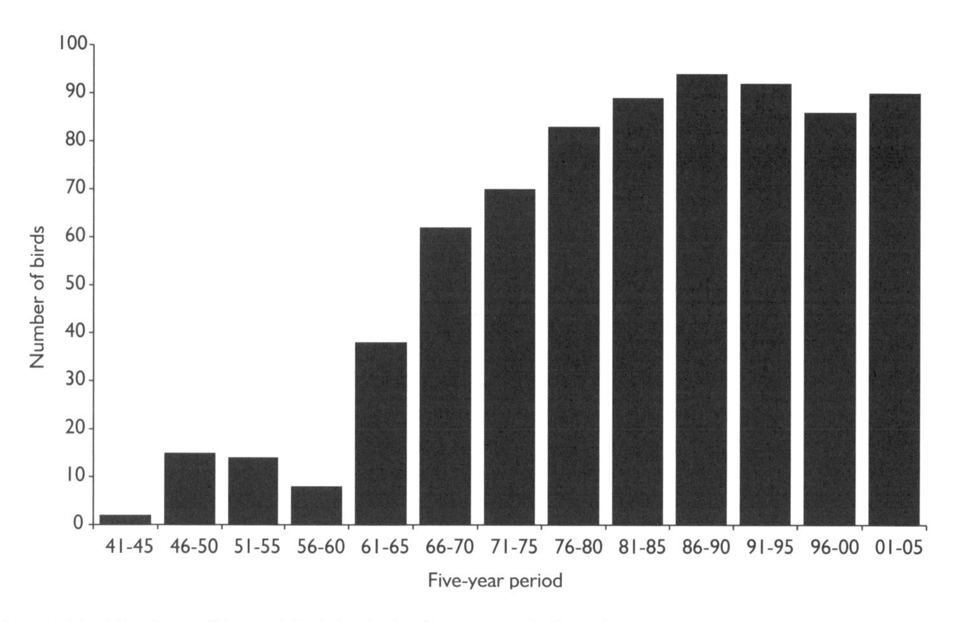

Figure 290: Numbers of Spotted Redshanks by five-year periods 1941–2005.

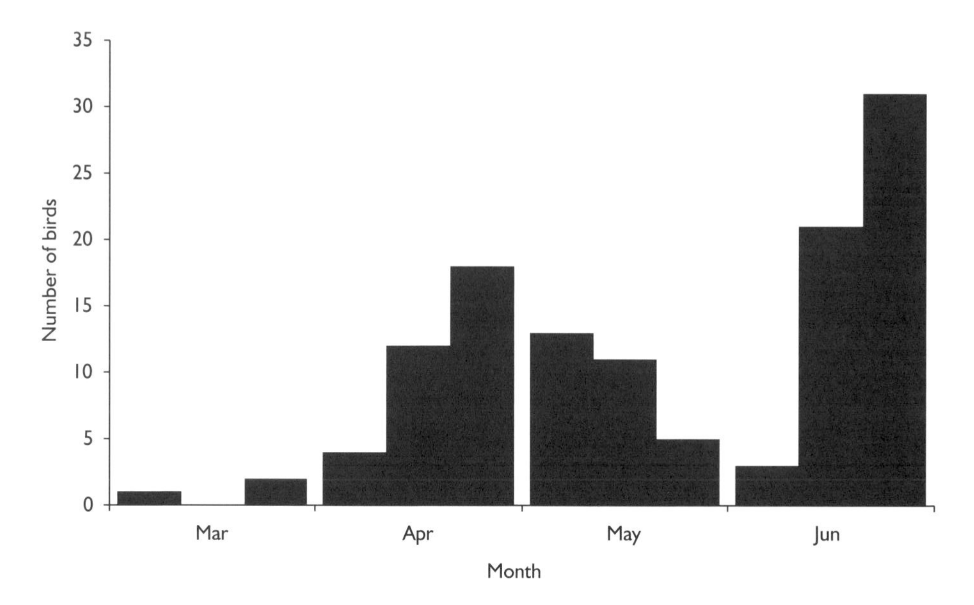

Figure 291: Monthly occurrence of Spotted Redshanks from March to June 1941–2005.

numbers have been very variable from year to year with, for example, 2005 producing just five and 2003 as many as 36.

Approximately 70 have occurred on spring passage between March and early June; the maximum in one year was eight in 1997. It is sometimes difficult to assign June birds to seasons but Figure 291 suggests that apart from the first few days of the month it has been 'autumn' birds that have been involved.

Autumn passage extends from the middle of June until October. It is not easy to assess the numbers of birds involved as individuals at the main sites often tend to keep apart from each other and can stay for long periods;

there may be overlapping influxes during a season, such as in 2003 when counts at Rutland Water built up from five to 12 in early September but then dropped to three before an October arrival saw another increase to 11.

All counts of more than two have occurred in autumn. The largest counts have been at either Rutland Water or Eyebrook Reservoir and the maximum elsewhere is seven, at Loughborough Sewage Farm on August 27th 1955. The top five counts are:

- 18 at Rutland Water on August 31st 1985.
- 14 at Eyebrook Reservoir on August 24th 1976.
- 13 at Eyebrook Reservoir on August 27th 1964 and October 11th 1969.
- 13 at Rutland Water on October 18th 1995.

There has been an increasing tendency for birds to occur in winter, either as new arrivals or lingering from the autumn. This first happened in 1961, when one was at Scraptoft on November 5th, but was spasmodic until 1998. Since then it has become regular, especially at Rutland Water, where birds remained into December in 1981, 1986 and 1987. In 2002–03 one was present irregularly at Rutland Water from mid-December until April, the first case of actual wintering, and the following winter one remained at this site from December 2003 to late March 2004. Midwinter movements are shown by isolated records at Stanford Reservoir on January 8th 1993, Cropston Reservoir on December 10th 1995 and Rutland Water on December 12th 2004.

There is one recovery of a ringed bird, unusual for two reasons. It is one of very few recoveries of a foreign-ringed Spotted Redshank in the country and the bird involved, a first-year ringed at Rieselfelder (Germany) on August 10th 1972, was found at Eyebrook Reservoir three weeks later on September 2nd with a five-inch Swan Mussel *Anodonta cygnea* attached to its leg, preventing it from flying. It was still present at Eyebrook Reservoir on October 1st, when it unsurprisingly appeared lame.

Spotted Redshanks breed discontinuously from Scandinavia through Russia and Siberia and winter mainly in sub-Saharan Africa and southern Asia, with smaller numbers in Europe. They are regular passage migrants and winter visitors to Britain but as more than 50% of this non-breeding British population occurs at fewer than ten sites, the Spotted Redshank has been added to the 'Amber List' of Birds of Conservation Concern (Gregory *et al.* 2002).

SML

Greenshank (Common Greenshank) ***Tringa nebularia***

Scarce to uncommon spring passage migrant and uncommon autumn passage migrant.

According to Browne, the Greenshank was a rare spring and autumn visitor to Leicestershire; he mentioned that it had been shot at Groby Pool, Swithland, Enderby and Shenton and had also been recorded at Saddington Reservoir and Melton Mowbray. Haines knew of only two definite records: single birds shot at Burley Fishponds in March of either 1879 or 1880 and at Exton in 1897. During the early part of the 20th century the LROS archives refer to single birds at Swithland Reservoir in 1910 and on September 15th 1929, and Cropston Reservoir on August 22nd 1940, although by the time of the formation of LROS in 1941 the status was that of a passage migrant in small numbers, mainly in autumn. Spring passage was very light, sometimes non-existent, until the early 1970s. As with many wader species, the creation of the most recent reservoirs at Eyebrook and especially Rutland Water has produced a great increase in the numbers occurring, both in spring and autumn.

Recently, spring passage has been averaging about 11 birds per year; the only year that stands out is 1990, which produced at least 38 birds, including two large counts on May 5th, of 18 at Rutland Water and 15 at Eyebrook Reservoir. There has only ever been one other double-figure count in spring, of ten at Rutland Water on April 28th 1976. The majority of the movement normally takes place during the second half of April and the first half of May but there have been five records of single birds in the first week of April and even three in March: single birds at Saddington Reservoir on March 17th 1973, Eyebrook Reservoir on March 25th 1997 and Watermead Park on March 26th and 28th 1993. Later birds have sometimes continued to pass through into early June and in some years it has been difficult to categorise June individuals as regards which way they are migrating; generally it seems that spring for this species extends to about June 15th and autumn can begin as early as June 19th, but a bird present at Rutland Water between June 8th and 18th in 2003 may well have already been on the way south. Average arrival dates have become earlier since the early 1980s.

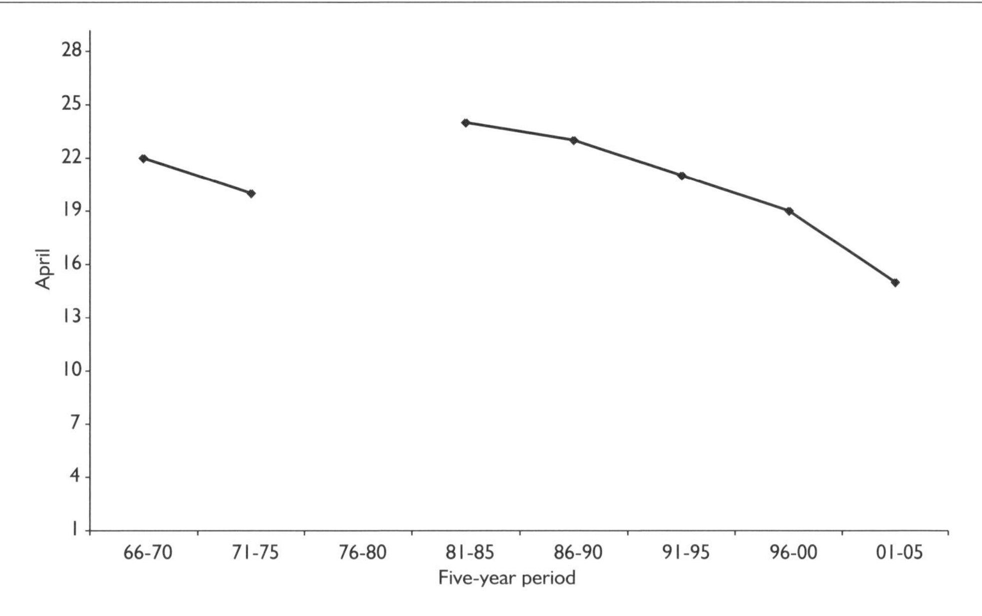

Figure 292: Average spring arrival dates of Greenshanks by five-year periods 1966–2005.

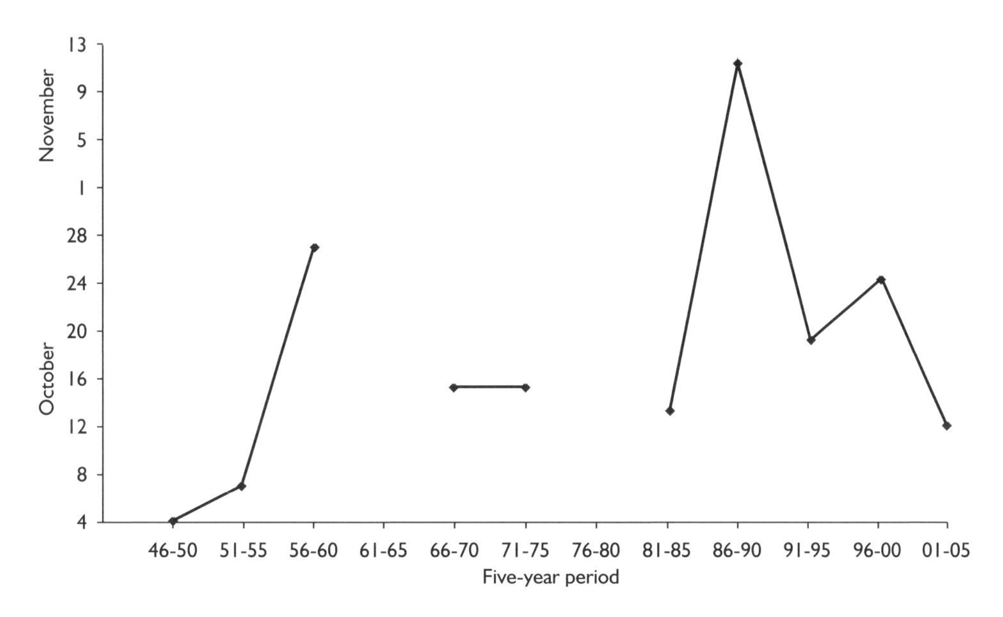

Figure 293: Average autumn departure dates of Greenshanks by five-year periods 1966–2005.

Autumn migration normally extends from late June through to October, with a recent tendency for odd birds to linger into November at one or other of the two main sites. However, there is no clear pattern regarding its average departure date (Figure 293).

The numbers involved in autumn are much higher than in spring and do not lend themselves to detailed analysis. The main months are August and September; nearly all of the larger counts were in August until recently but since about 1980 September has been producing some high ones. Not surprisingly, all counts exceeding 25 have come from the two main sites:

- 34 at Rutland Water on August 27th 1997.
- 33 at Rutland Water on August 12th 1980.
- 32 at Rutland Water on August 23rd 1987.
- 31 at Eyebrook Reservoir on August 26th 1976.
- 28 at Rutland Water on August 29th 1991.
- 27 at Eyebrook Reservoir on September 20th 1999.
- 26 at Rutland Water on August 12th 1984.
- 26 at Rutland Water on September 6th 1998.

The maximum counts at all other sites that have held more than five birds are:

- 15 at Stanford Reservoir on September 16th 1990.
- 13 at Swithland Reservoir on August 21st 1962.
- 12 at Leicester City Farms in August 1962.
- 11 at Wanlip Gravel Pits on August 13th 1975.
- 11 at Cropston Reservoir on September 7th 1987.
- nine at Saddington Reservoir on August 21st 1949.
- eight at Thornton Reservoir on August 12th 1974.
- eight at Cossington Gravel Pits on August 20th 1975.
- six at Trent Valley Pit on September 7th 1999.

In addition, eight flew over Cottesmore on August 31st 1995 and six over Markfield on August 20th 1987.

Winter records are very rare. A bird remained at Rutland Water until December 13th in 1986, one appeared at Eyebrook Reservoir on December 27th 1977 and one was at Trent Valley Pit on January 23rd 2004; there have never been any records in February.

Greenshanks breed from northern Britain through Scandinavia and northern Russia to central and eastern Siberia. Most winter in sub-tropical and tropical regions of Africa and Asia, although some move only as far as western Europe and the Mediterranean. In Britain, the Greenshank is restricted as a breeding species to Scotland, where the latest population estimate is 1,080 pairs (Baker *et al.* 2006).

SML

Lesser Yellowlegs *Tringa flavipes*

Very rare vagrant from North America: three records.

The first record for Leicestershire and Rutland was a juvenile seen briefly by John Wright at Watermead Park on September 14th 1986 (*BB* 86:484). The two subsequent records were of much more obliging birds, both being seen by large numbers of observers. In 1995 a juvenile, found by Simon Tilley, was at Stanford Reservoir from September 25th to 27th; it frequented the inflow of the reservoir and provided excellent views (*BB* 89:502). The third individual was also a juvenile and was found by Rod Baker on Lagoon I at Rutland Water on September 25th 2004; it remained until October 1st (*BB* 98:658).

In addition, a record of one at Stanford Reservoir from October 17th to 23rd 1964 was originally accepted by the BBRC as the first record for Leicestershire and Rutland (*BB* 58:360). However, on reviewing this record at a local level in 2004, certain discrepancies in the original descriptions were noticed and the BBRC was asked to reconsider its verdict; this resulted in the record being rejected (Fray 2005, *BB* 97:582).

Lesser Yellowlegs breed in eastern Alaska and across much of Canada. Some winter in the southern USA and Central America, but most travel further south to the West Indies and South America. They are annual vagrants to Britain in variable numbers, with a total of 269 accepted records by the end of 2005. The majority of reports concern juveniles found in the autumn, particularly during September; the Leicestershire and Rutland records therefore conform perfectly with this established vagrancy pattern. One of the peak years was 1995 with 12 British records, including the Stanford Reservoir bird; in contrast, the other county records in 1986 and 2004 arrived in rather poor years for this species in Britain, with just two and five records respectively.

SML

Wood Sandpiper *Tringa glareola*

Scarce or uncommon passage migrant; recorded in all months between April and November, with the majority in May, July and August.

There were only two certain 19th century records of the Wood Sandpiper: one at Groby Pool in 1840 and one killed at Exton in about 1897. In addition, Browne reported that it had been seen in the winter of 1852–53, but this was presumably a misidentification.

Prior to the formation of LROS in 1941, the only 20th century record was of one at Swithland Reservoir on May 10th 1923. It was not until 1945 that the Wood Sandpiper could be regarded as occurring regularly in the counties, though it may have been overlooked prior to then; there have only been four blank years since, the most recent being 1972. Numbers vary widely from year to year, especially in spring, but there is a long-term trend of the species becoming more frequent in the counties: the five best years have been 1977 (24 individuals), 1987 (22), 1997 (19), 2002 (18) and 1991 (17).

Wood Sandpipers are rarely seen in large concentrations in Britain and the largest counts locally have been:

- seven at Rutland Water on August 6th 1980 and July 31st 2000.
- six at Loughborough Sewage Farm in August 1954.
- six at Rutland Water on August 30th 1977.
- six at Rutland Water from July 21st to 23rd 1987.
- five at Eyebrook Reservoir on May 13th 1950.
- up to five at Loughborough Sewage Farm from August 10th to 12th 1951.
- five at Cropston Reservoir on August 10th and 11th 1952.
- five at Rutland Water on August 22nd 1997.

In addition, groups of four have been noted on a number of occasions at Rutland Water, as well as at Loughborough Sewage Farm, Eyebrook Reservoir, Stanford Reservoir, Wanlip Gravel Pits and Sence Valley Forest Park.

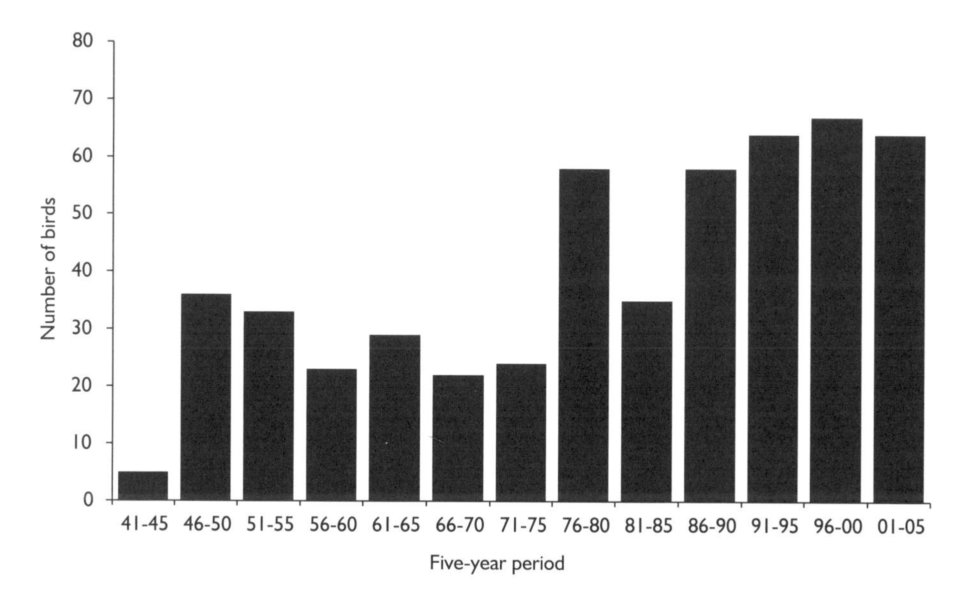

Figure 294: Numbers of Wood Sandpipers by five-year periods 1941–2005.

Spring passage is almost entirely confined to May and 92% of spring arrivals have been in this month. There have been two April records, both at Eyebrook Reservoir, of single birds on April 29th and 30th 1992 and from April 30th to May 2nd 1994. As with many species, it is difficult to assign some June records to seasons: 17

birds have arrived in this month, six on or before the 14th and 11 from the 22nd. It therefore seems likely that the latest spring record is of one at Rutland Water on June 14th 2003 and the earliest autumn arrival is one at Birstall Gravel Pits on June 22nd 1991. Autumn passage peaks in July and August and 79% of arrivals at this season have been in these two months. Six birds have arrived during October, as follows:

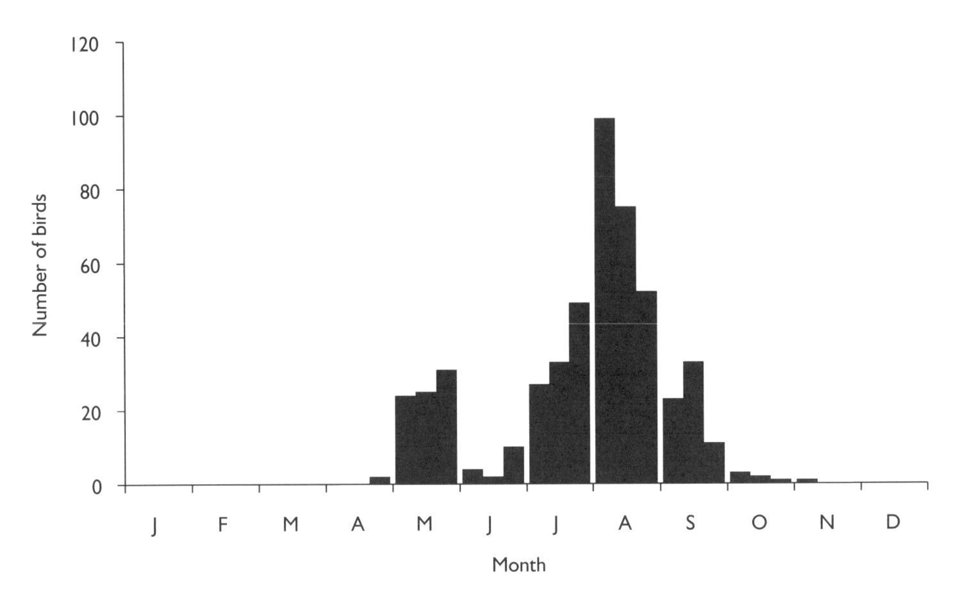

Figure 295: Monthly occurrence of Wood Sandpipers 1941–2005.

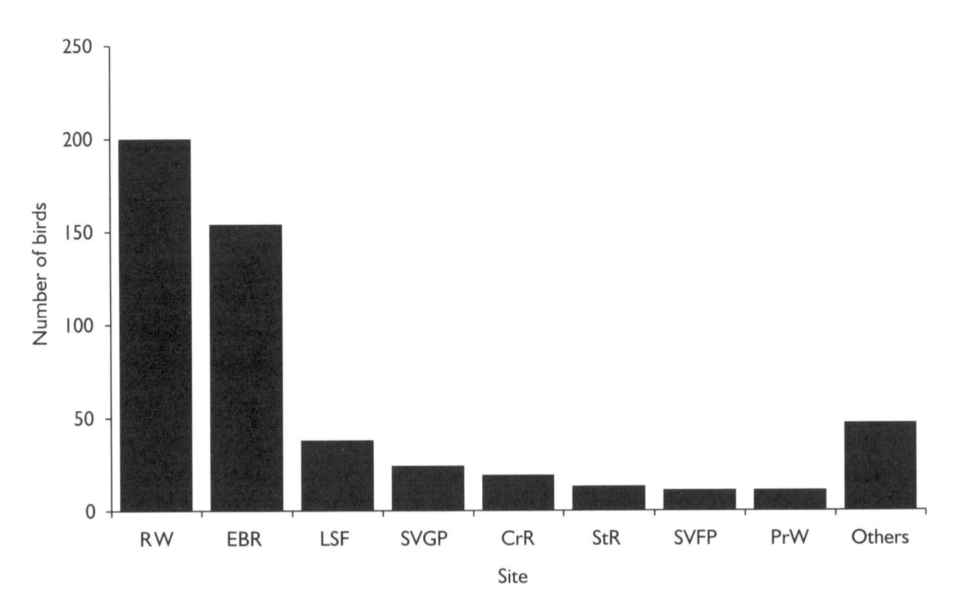

Figure 296: Sites where Wood Sandpipers have been recorded 1941–2005.
Key to abbreviations: RW = Rutland Water; EBR = Eyebrook Reservoir; LSF = Loughborough Sewage Farm; SVGP = Soar valley gravel pits; CrR = Cropston Reservoir; StR = Stanford Reservoir; SVFP = Sence Valley Forest Park; PrW = Priory Water

- Rutland Water from October 4th to 17th 1977.
- Eyebrook Reservoir on October 4th 1991.
- Stanford Reservoir on October 8th 1961.
- Cropston Reservoir from October 11th to 25th 1970.
- Stanford Reservoir from October 13th to 19th 1995.
- Swithland Reservoir on October 24th 1959.

The latest record, however, is of one at Stanford Reservoir on November 9th 1947, over two weeks later than any of the October records.

Strangely, spring records since 2000 have declined sharply, with just five birds by 2005 and none at all in 2002 and 2005; autumn records have continued at a similar level to previous years and in fact 2002 produced 18 birds, the best autumn ever. There is evidence that autumn passage is now occurring earlier than in the past: during 1941–67, 13% of records at Eyebrook Reservoir occurred in July, with 25% in September (Mason 1969); the equivalent figures for all sites in the counties now stand at 21% for July and 13% for September.

Wood Sandpipers have been recorded at 31 sites in the counties but nearly 70% of birds have been at either Rutland Water or Eyebrook Reservoir. In its heyday, Loughborough Sewage Farm was an important site for this species and produced 36 birds between 1948 and 1962. Elsewhere in the counties, the Wood Sandpiper is a scarce bird, evidenced by the fact that the well-watched Swithland Reservoir has only attracted nine birds since 1941.

The Wood Sandpiper breeds in tree-fringed mires of the boreal and tundra lands across northern Europe and winter mainly in tropical Africa, southern Asia and Australia. It is a common breeding species in northern Europe, with an estimated 500,000 pairs in Sweden, Finland and Norway, and has nested annually in Scotland since 1959 (Chisholm 2007); approximately 20 pairs bred in 2004 (Holling *et al.* 2007a). As the British breeding population is so small, the Wood Sandpiper has been added to the 'Amber List' of Birds of Conservation Concern (Gregory *et al.* 2002).

SML

Common Redshank *Tringa totanus*

Fairly common passage migrant, uncommon winter visitor and scarce migrant breeder.

The Common Redshank was not recorded in the counties until the late 19th century. In Rutland, Haines knew of no records before 1890, after which this species began to colonise the Welland valley. At Seaton, a nest with three eggs was found in 1893, following which ten pairs were present in 1901, three of which bred. Nesting again occurred at this site in 1902, 1903 and 1906, and also at Tixover in 1903, Exton in 1904 and Burley in 1905. Browne noted that this species was first recorded in Leicestershire around the turn of the century and quotes a Mr A. Dalby of Castle Donington who stated that Common Redshanks bred every year near the River Trent. In the early 1900s nesting was recorded on three occasions near Medbourne and one bird was seen at Market Harborough on May 18th 1906.

There is a dearth of published information during the early part of the 20th century until the formation of LROS in 1941, when its status was given as a passage migrant, widespread breeder in small numbers, but not common in winter. The following year's report changed the winter status to rare and mentioned that it occurred as a migrant chiefly in spring.

Up to 17 pairs were proved to breed annually from 1941 to 1950, with several additional pairs reported as possible or probable. The highest total was in 1946, when 11 pairs were confirmed and the total may have been as high as 30. Favoured areas used for nesting at the time were mainly damp meadows and included the Welland valley (12 pairs in 1950), the sewage farms at Leicester and Loughborough, the margins of Eyebrook Reservoir (six pairs in 1945) and the Quorn area (eight pairs in 1945 and six in 1946).

After 1950 breeding birds were much scarcer, with no more than two pairs confirmed in any year until 1974, when five pairs bred, all at different sites. Four pairs were confirmed in 1977. In 1984 the total of six included five at Hemington Gravel Pits and as many as ten additional pairs may have bred. Since then 1995 and 2004 have been the only years with more than three pairs definitely breeding: in 1995 there were four pairs at Watermead Park and single pairs at Trent Valley Pit and Bosworth Water Park, with another eight possible and probable elsewhere, whilst in 2004 two pairs bred at Cossington Meadows and single pairs at Trent Farm Pool and Rutland Water, with two other pairs possibly nesting elsewhere. Breeding was not proved in either 2002 or 2003 but there were up to ten possible pairs in the latter year. The sites used for nesting in recent years are mainly areas peripheral to gravel pits, both working and disused, and meadows are now rarely utilised. The area with the most confirmed breeding attempts since 1990 has been the Soar valley north of Leicester, especially the southern section of Watermead Country Park.

Birds are now regularly present in potential nesting areas as early as February, a month earlier than was the norm 60 years ago. It is frequently difficult to distinguish prospecting breeding birds from spring migrants, with the passage period extending until late April. Spring counts of 15+ have been as follows:

- 50 to 60 at Loughborough Sewage Farm on March 16th and 17th 1950.
- 26 at Rutland Water on April 8th and 13th 2004.
- 22 at Rutland Water on April 12th 2005.
- 21 at Eyebrook Reservoir on April 23rd 1991.
- 21 at Rutland Water on April 1st 2002.
- 20 at Eyebrook Reservoir on April 8th 1990.
- 20 at Wanlip South Gravel Pits on March 28th 2002.
- 19 at Wanlip South Gravel Pits on March 25th 2001.
- 18 at Cossington Meadows on March 18th 2005.
- 17 in the Welland valley on April 6th 1977.
- 17 at Trent Valley Pit on March 17th 2005.
- 16 at Watermead Park on March 19th 1995.
- 16 at Rutland Water on April 12th 2003.

The only additional site to have attracted more than ten during the spring is Trent Farm Pool, where there were 12 on March 25th 1999. It is interesting to note that all of the above peak counts have occurred between March 16th and April 23rd; this is at odds with the findings of Mason (1969), who noted that peak spring numbers of Common Redshanks at Eyebrook Reservoir between 1958 and 1967 occurred during May.

Autumn passage normally occurs beween late June and October, with the largest numbers usually from July to September. Only four sites have held more than ten birds at this time of year: Trent Valley Pit has a maximum count of 15 on June 8th 1993 and Swithland Reservoir 11 on July 19th 1972, but the highest counts are all from either Rutland Water or Eyebrook Reservoir:

- 92 at Rutland Water on August 9th 1980.
- 59 at Rutland Water on August 10th 2004.
- 42 at Rutland Water on October 23rd 2005.
- 32 at Rutland Water on August 10th 1996.
- 31 at Eyebrook Reservoir on August 9th 1980.
- 30 at Rutland Water on September 22nd 2000.
- 24 at Rutland Water on August 24th and October 19th and 21st, all in 2003.
- 19 at Eyebrook Reservoir on September 9th 1969.
- 17 at Eyebrook Reservoir on June 23rd 1957.
- 16 at Eyebrook Reservoir on September 2nd 1956 and in June 1961.

The status of the Common Redshank in winter has changed dramatically during the last 30 years. Winter records were rare until about 1974 and almost always involved single birds, the exception being nine that flew over Stanford Reservoir on November 20th 1947. After 1974 records became a little less unusual but it was still a surprise when a small flock wintered at Rutland Water in 1978–79: there were ten on December 17th and still eight on January 28th. Thee were no comparable records until up to five wintered at Hemington Gravel Pits in 1987–88; there were up to nine at Rutland Water in 1988–89, with a maximum of eight the following winter and then rather sporadic counts of up to 13 in 1990–91. Between seven and ten were seen regularly at Trent Valley Pit (broadly the same site as what was earlier referred to as Hemington Gravel Pits) in 1993–94, with maxima there of six in 1997–98 and ten in 1998–99. Birds have wintered annually at Eyebrook Reservoir since up to ten did so in 1998–99, with a maximum of 17 in 2000–01. Rutland Water has held regular winter flocks since 1999–2000; no more than six were seen for the first three years, but up to 15 remained in 2002–03, 14 in 2003–04, with 23 present on February 15th 2004, up to 18 in 2004–05 and 33 on December 13th 2005. As with other winter waders, there seems to be regular interchange of birds between the last two sites.

Away from the established wintering sites records of anything more than odd ones and twos are still unusual between November and January. Two notable exceptions were five at Priory Water on December 2nd 1989 and nine at Trent Farm Pool on December 31st 1999.

Common Redshanks breed in Iceland and Scandinavia and across central Eurasia, with a separate population in northern India and western China. The three Western Palearctic races winter along the coasts of western Europe, the Mediterranean and south to western Africa. The British breeding population has shown a decline since the 1940s (Gibbons *et al.* 1996) and the latest estimate is 38,600 pairs (Baker *et al.* 2006). Wintering numbers are much higher; indeed, over 20% of the East Atlantic Flyway non-breeding population uses Britain and for this reason, as well as the decline of the breeding population, the Common Redshank has been added to the 'Amber List' of Birds of Conservation Concern (Gregory *et al.* 2002). There are three relevant ringing recoveries, two of which involve international movements: a bird ringed as a pullus near Hemington in May 1989 was shot in France, 470km to the south, in August of the same year, one shot at Blackbrook Reservoir in January 1976 was found to have been ringed in the Netherlands in October 1975 and one found dead at Ridlington in January 1963 had been ringed at Holbeach (Lincolnshire) in September 1959.

SML

Turnstone (Ruddy Turnstone) ***Arenaria interpres***

Scarce to uncommon spring and autumn passage migrant, very rare winter visitor.

Browne details a couple of rather vague records in the 19th century: two shot at Abbey Meadows, Leicester in either 1880 or 1881 and another two shot at the same site in the spring of 1883. The first modern record was not until July 1940, when one was at Swithland Reservoir. No more were seen until 1946, when up to three were at Eyebrook Reservoir from May 3rd to 11th and one was at Sawley Gravel Pits from May 10th to 12th, but since then this species has occurred in all but three years, the most recent blank year being 1965.

2003 produced 54 birds, including 51 during the autumn and is the best year so far. Over 30 individuals have also been seen in four other years: 2005 (46), 2004 (39), 1988 (34) and 1995 (32). Prior to 1975, when the existence of Rutland Water began to alter the local status of this species drastically, 1948 and 1959 stood out as good years, with 14 and 19 birds respectively. Between 1940 and 1974 the number of birds recorded annually averaged 3.7, while since 1975 the comparable figure is 19.3.

Most records involve single birds or small parties of up to five, although there have been four records of six together, nine of seven and four of eight, all at either Eyebrook Reservoir or Rutland Water. Groups of nine have been noted on four occasions: at Rutland Water on April 30th 1984, August 30th 1991 and August 22nd 2002, and Eyebrook Reservoir on August 9th 2003. All counts of ten+ have been at Rutland Water:

- 18 on August 17th 2003, including a flock of 14 flying south-west.
- 15 on August 10th 2004.
- 12 from May 4th to 8th 1978.
- 11 on both May 4th 1990 and July 30th 2004.
- ten on both August 26th 1989 and August 29th 2003.

Away from Rutland Water and Eyebrook Reservoir, the only other sites that have attracted groups of more than two are Wanlip Gravel Pits, with three on July 26th 1985, and Priory Water, where three flew over on May 8th 1988.

Analysing the dates of arrival of all birds reveals that May dominates the spring passage and accounts for almost 85% of records during this season. Spring occurrences prior to April 20th are rare, the only ones being single birds at Eyebrook Reservoir on April 16th 1964 and Rutland Water on April 17th 1983, and up to five at the latter site from April 5th to 27th 1985. Ten individuals have arrived in the first ten days of June, but the only later records during this month have been single birds at Rutland Water on June 14th 1991 and June 16th 1991 and three at Eyebrook Reservoir on June 19th 1949; there have been no June records after this date, so it can be safely assumed that this marks the extent of spring passage of this species in the counties.

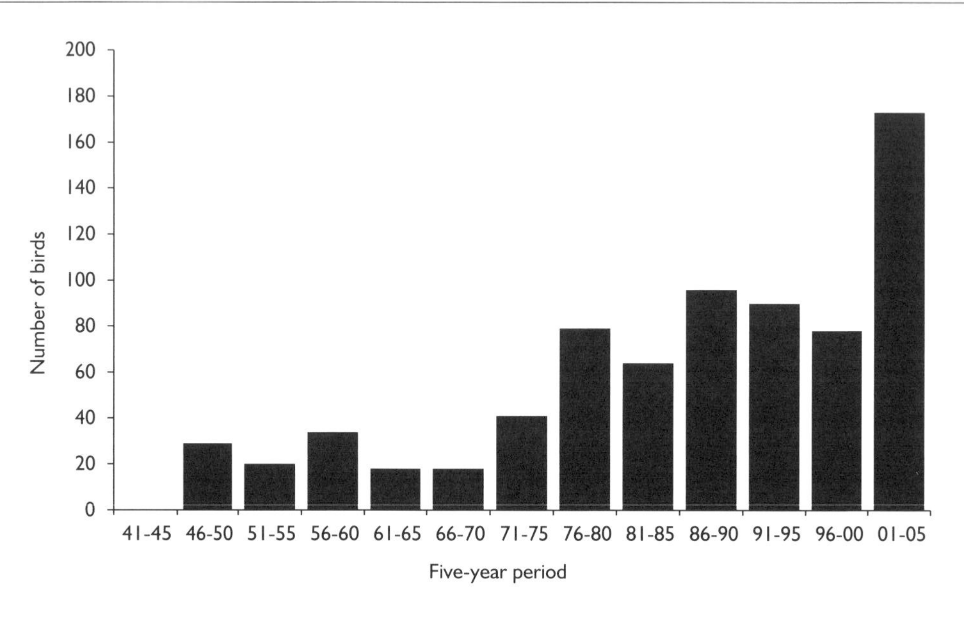

Figure 297: Numbers of Turnstones by five-year periods 1941–2005.

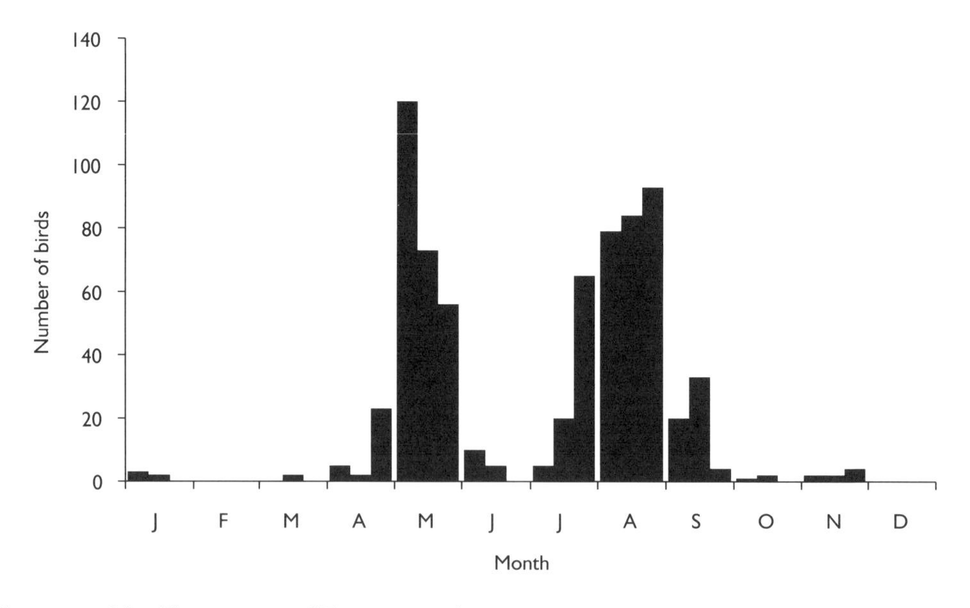

Figure 298: Monthly occurrence of Turnstones 1941–2005.

Autumn passage usually commences in mid-July; the only records prior to July 10th have been three at Eyebrook Reservoir on July 6th 1964 and up to two at the same site from July 7th to 20th 1974. Over 63% of autumn passage birds have occurred in August, with many fewer during September. October arrivals are very unusual, the only ones being single birds at Rutland Water on October 18th 1987 and Eyebrook Reservoir on both October 14th 1998 and October 3rd 2002; strangely, there have been more records during November (seven records involving eight individuals).

Winter occurrences are rare: there have been no records in either February or December, although five birds have appeared in January, as follows:

- one at Rutland Water on January 7th 1985.
- one at Priory Water on January 3rd 1996.
- two at Rutland Water on January 13th 1996.
- one at Eyebrook Reservoir from January 5th to 19th 2003.

Rutland Water and Eyebrook Reservoir account for 94% of all records. Only four other areas have recorded more than four birds: nine have been found in the Trent valley (six at Trent Valley Pit and three at Sawley Gravel Pits), eight have been recorded at both Stanford Reservoir and the Soar valley gravel pits and seven have been seen at Priory Water. The major reservoirs at Swithland and Cropston have mustered only seven birds between them, there have been three individuals at both Loughborough Sewage Farm and Frisby Gravel Pits and one at Enderby Pool. A number of well-watched sites have not recorded this species, including Fort Henry Ponds and the reservoirs at Thornton and Saddington.

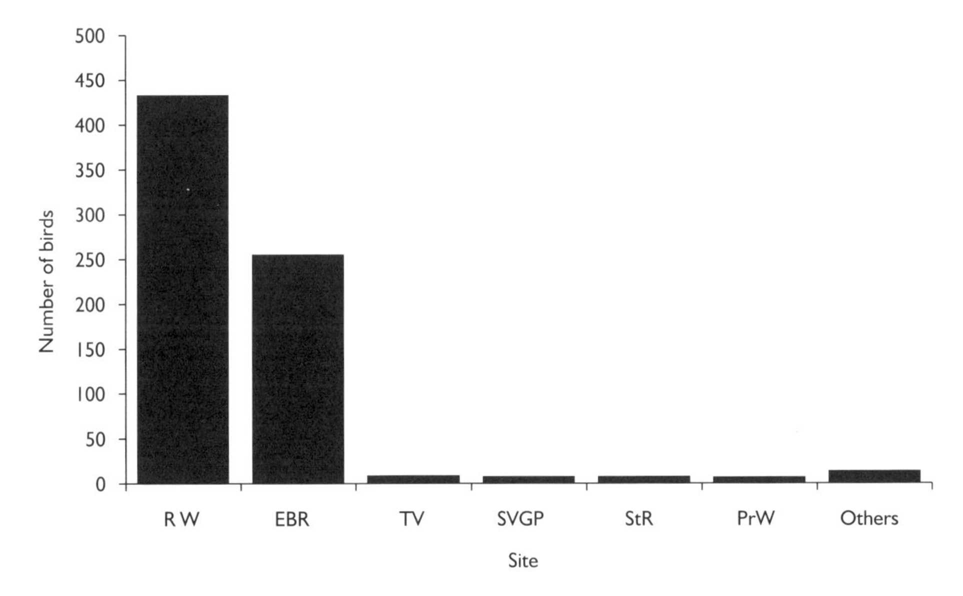

Figure 299: Sites where Turnstones have been recorded 1941–2005.
Key to abbreviations: RW = Rutland Water; EBR = Eyebrook Reservoir; TV = Trent valley; SVGP = Soar valley gravel pits; StR = Stanford Reservoir; PrW = Priory Water

Turnstones have a circumpolar distribution, breeding along the coasts of Scandinavia and along the Arctic coasts of Eurasia, North America and Greenland. They winter along the coasts of western Europe, Africa, southern Asia, Australasia and both North and South America. The British wintering population is currently estimated at just under 50,000 individuals (Baker *et al.* 2006) and as more than 20% of the East Atlantic Flyway non-breeding population winters in Britain this species has been added to the 'Amber List' of Birds of Conservation Concern (Gregory *et al.* 2002).

SML

Wilson's Phalarope *Phalaropus tricolor*

Very rare vagrant from North America: one record.

A juvenile moulting into first-winter plumage was at Stanford Reservoir from September 29th to October 3rd 1991; it spent most of its time on the Northamptonshire shore but crossed into Leicestershire on at least September 30th. The original finders were, rather appropriately, I.M. and J.M. Wilson (*BB* 85:528).

Browne reported that a specimen of this species exhibited at a meeting of the Zoological Society on May 18th 1886 was allegedly obtained at Sutton Ambion, near Market Bosworth. This would have been the first British record. Although Browne does not give his reasons, his comment 'to relieve the historian of any further anxiety I may say that, being behind the scenes in this matter, I can emphatically state that Wilson's Phalarope *was not obtained in the county, nor in Britain*' was enough to ensure that this record never gained any credibility. A brief discussion of this record also appeared in *BB* (Dixon 1955).

Wilson's Phalarope breeds in the temperate middle latitudes of North America and winters in southern South America. The first British record was in 1954 and it then occurred annually from 1961 to the mid-1990s, by which time it was averaging around five individuals a year. The British total stood at 214 by the end of 2005, but this species has recently become increasingly rare, with only seven accepted records during 1999–2005. The last good year was 1991, with 15 records, coinciding with the Stanford Reservoir bird. The vast majority of British records involve juveniles during the autumn, with approximately two-thirds of all birds appearing in September; the Leicestershire individual was therefore on a typical date.

SML

Red-necked Phalarope *Phalaropus lobatus*

Rare migrant from northern Europe; recorded in May, June, August, September and October, with the majority from late August to mid-October: 23 records involving 26 individuals.

Browne makes reference to 'a mounted specimen, said to have been shot at Birstall . . . purchased for the museum early in 1904 from a taxidermist'. This record has been repeated by subsequent authors as having occurred during the spring of 1904, but as the specimen was apparently purchased early that year it seems unlikely that the bird was shot during the spring of 1904. Unfortunately, the specimen can no longer be found at Leicester Museum, so it is unclear when this record really occurred.

It was not until 1951 that the next bird was found: one seen by a number of observers at Eyebrook Reservoir from October 7th to 14th. There have now been records in a total of 19 years, involving 26 individuals.

All records:

c1904	shot, Birstall, no date.
1951	Eyebrook Reservoir, October 7th to 14th.
1956	Loughborough Sewage Farm, September 8th.
1968	Stanford Reservoir, September 24th.
	Eyebrook Reservoir, October 13th.
1970	Stanford Reservoir, October 4th.
1975	juvenile, Rutland Water, August 26th to September 3rd (incorrectly published in the LROS Annual Report as being present from August 8th for 'a few days').
1976	Eyebrook Reservoir, August 28th.
	Frisby Gravel Pits, October 16th.
1983	two, Eyebrook Reservoir, September 3rd to 4th.
1984	Rutland Water, August 8th.
1987	female, Rutland Water, June 26th.
1990	adult, Rutland Water, May 18th.
1992	two juveniles, Swithland Reservoir, September 6th to 7th.
1995	juvenile, Swithland Reservoir, September 5th.
1996	juvenile, Rutland Water, September 8th.
1999	juvenile, Eyebrook Reservoir, August 22nd.
	juvenile, Rutland Water, October 17th to 25th.
	juvenile, Sence Valley Forest Park, October 19th.
2000	adult, Rutland Water, May 30th.
2001	female, Rutland Water, June 12th to 18th.

2003 two juveniles, Rutland Water, September 11th to 19th.
2004 male, Rutland Water, May 2nd to 6th.

This species has clearly been appearing more regularly recently, exactly half of all records having occurred since 1990. The construction of Rutland Water has undoubtedly played a part in this; of the 20 individuals reported since 1975, 11 have been from this site. Five records, involving six birds, have come from Eyebrook Reservoir; Swithland and Stanford Reservoirs have two records each (involving three birds at Swithland) and single occurrences have been at Loughborough Sewage Farm, Frisby Gravel Pits and Sence Valley Forest Park.

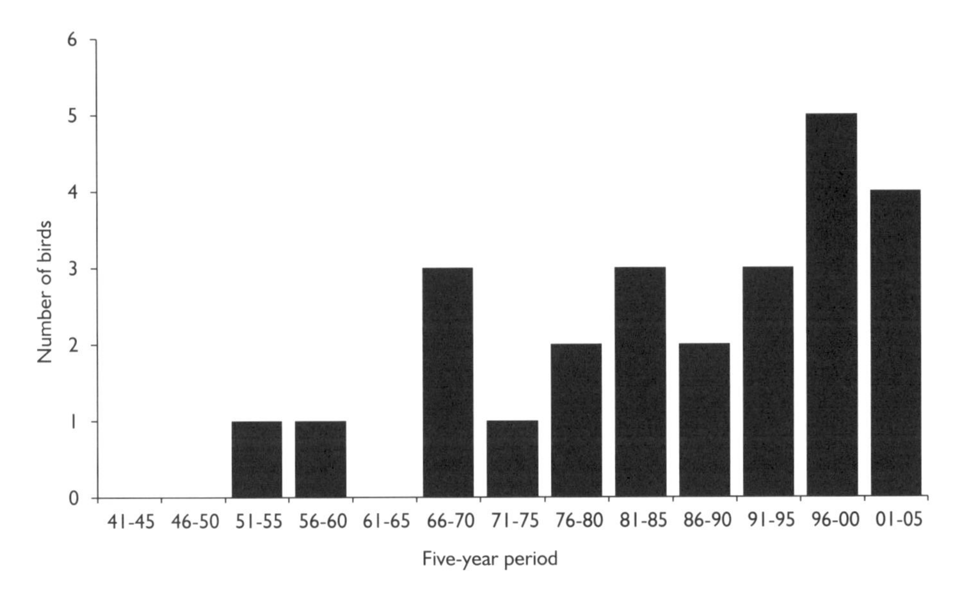

Figure 300: Numbers of Red-necked Phalaropes by five-year periods 1941–2005.

Red-necked Phalaropes are one of the latest migrants to reach Britain in spring, rarely doing so before late May (Gibbons *et al.* 1993); for example, the earliest-ever record in Shetland, the only regular British breeding area, was on May 10th 2005 (Pennington 2006). Therefore, the bird which arrived at Rutland Water on May 2nd 2004 was exceptional; other spring records fall between the more expected dates of May 18th and June 26th. Although spring birds are in the minority, it is interesting to note that three of the last four records have been during this season.

Arrival dates of the 20 autumn birds have ranged from August 8th to October 19th, of which 11 have appeared between August 26th and September 11th. Recent autumn birds have all been aged as juveniles and it is likely that the majority, if not all, autumn reports relate to birds of this age.

The average length of stay in autumn is three days and the longest nine days; 11 autumn records were on one day only. The juvenile at Swithland Reservoir on September 5th 1995 may have remained longer had it not been eaten by a Pike *Esox lucius*.

A number of the earlier records of this species are on rather late autumn dates, so in 2004 all October reports were reassessed; all remained acceptable with the exception of one at Eyebrook Reservoir on October 23rd 1970, which was originally published as this species but is now considered to be only acceptable as an unidentified phalarope species (Fray 2005). Another unidentified phalarope at Rutland Water on September 21st 1984 was probably this species (Appleton 1985).

The Red-necked Phalarope is one of the rarest breeding birds in Britain, with the majority in Shetland, where there were 30 breeding males in 2005 (Pennington 2006). Due to the small breeding population, and a historical decline over the last two centuries, this species has been added to the 'Red List' of Birds of Conservation

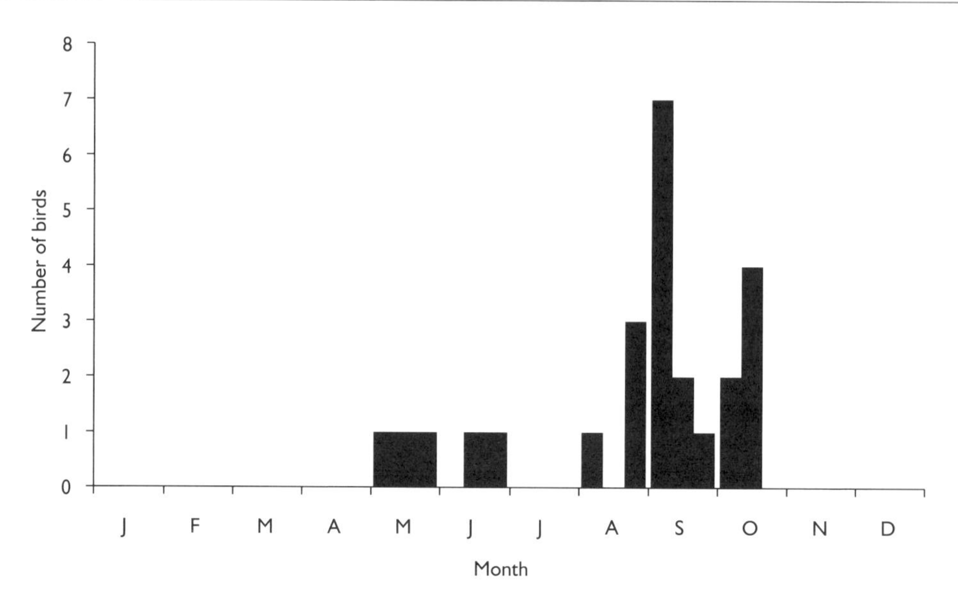

Figure 301: Monthly occurrence of Red-necked Phalaropes 1941–2005.

Concern (Gregory *et al.* 2002). It is also a scarce passage migrant in Britain, with a recent average of between 25 and 35 records per year (Fraser & Rogers 2005). The best year for migrants was 1999 (Fraser & Rogers 2001), coinciding with the peak year in Leicestershire and Rutland. Elsewhere, it is a relatively common breeding bird between 60° and 70° north, with 50,000 to 100,000 pairs in Iceland and 50,000 pairs in Sweden (Gibbons *et al.* 1993) as well as other populations in Finland, Norway, Siberia, Alaska, northern Canada and Greenland. It is pelagic during the winter, being found off the coasts of north-west South America and the Arabian Peninsula and in the seas around Indonesia and the Philippines.

SML

Grey Phalarope *Phalaropus fulicarius*

Rare, usually storm-driven, migrant from the Arctic; recorded from September to January, with the majority from mid-September to early November: 28 records involving 33 individuals since1941 and an unknown number previously.

According to Browne, Harley stated that 'during the autumn of 1841 and the following winter, many birds were captured throughout the county'. Browne details a further 14 or 15 occurrences during the 19th century, several of which are rather vague. Single birds were shot at Twycross in December 1853, on the Grand Union Canal at Foxton in both late 1854 and during the winter of 1860–61 and at Wellsborough some time between 1867 and 1872, whilst in October 1891 one was shot near Saddington Reservoir on the 16th, one was killed after striking telegraph wires at East Norton on the 17th and a further three were shot somewhere in Leicestershire, one of which was probably at Croft as a specimen from there was apparently sent to Leicester Museum at this time. Witherby *et al.* (1940) refer to good numbers occurring during the autumn of 1891 following strong south-westerly gales, coinciding with these latter records. Of the other 19th century occurrences mentioned by Browne, one killed after hitting telegraph wires near Leicester in 1868 seems likely to have been genuine, although one found dead in May 1864 on ploughed land near Fosse Road, Leicester was on a very odd date and on current knowledge cannot be considered reliable. Browne also refers to vague records of one at an unspecified site in autumn 1846 and two or three undated specimens obtained near Melton Mowbray. Given the number of birds reported by Browne it is surprising that Haines could find no records for Rutland.

During the early part of the 20th century Browne, writing in VH, mentions one shot near Leicester in October 1906. Since the formation of LROS in 1941 there have been 28 records, involving 33 individuals, as follows:

1951	Cropston Reservoir, September 15th.
	two, Eyebrook Reservoir, September 16th, with one until September 23rd.
1955	Eyebrook Reservoir, December 18th to January 15th 1956.
1971	Cropston Reservoir, November 30th.
1974	Eyebrook Reservoir, September 8th to 9th.
1975	adult, Saddington Reservoir, November 8th to 9th.
1977	Eyebrook Reservoir, November 12th.
1982	adult, Saddington Reservoir, November 7th, found dead on November 11th (skin retained at Leicester Museum).
1983	Rutland Water, January 22nd to February 3rd.
1987	three (at least two first-winters), Eyebrook Reservoir, October 16th, with two until October 17th.
	two first-winters, Swithland Reservoir, October 17th, with one until October 18th.
	first-winter, Rutland Water, October 18th, with two from October 19th to 22nd.
	Stanford Reservoir, October 20th.
	first-winter, Cadeby Quarry, October 24th to 26th.
1990	first-winter, Priory Water, October 28th.
1994	juvenile, Rutland Water, September 18th to 19th.
	juvenile, Eyebrook Reservoir, September 25th.
	first-winter, Eyebrook Reservoir, November 1st.
1997	juvenile, Rutland Water, September 21st.
1999	adult, Rutland Water, November 20th.
2001	adult, Rutland Water, October 13th to 17th.
	first-winter, Swithland Reservoir, October 18th to 20th.
2002	first-winter, Rutland Water, January 28th to February 2nd.
	first-winter, Rutland Water, October 20th to 24th.
2003	first-winter, Rutland Water, October 17th to 21st.
	first-winter, Stanford Reservoir, October 26th to November 5th.
2004	first-winter, Eyebrook Reservoir, October 11th.
2005	first-winter, Eyebrook Reservoir, October 26th.

The appearance of this species in the counties is often associated with strong autumn winds and the record total in 1987 occurred following the infamous 'hurricane' of October 15th, when large numbers of Grey Phalaropes were found inland, including up to 20 at Grafham Water (Cambridgeshire) (Hume & Christie 1989). The total of nine following this storm accounts for over one quarter of all individuals recorded since 1941 and also ensures that October is the main month of occurrence; it is interesting that prior to the 1987 storm there had been no modern records during October but, since then, eight of the 14 reports have been in this month, including the most recent five. With the exception of two at Eyebrook Reservoir in September 1951, all multiple occurrences of this species occurred during the aftermath of the 1987 storm.

Grey Phalaropes have appeared with increasing frequency in recent times and between 1997 and 2005 there have been only two blank years. Eyebrook Reservoir has provided nine records, involving 12 birds, whilst Rutland Water also has nine records (of ten birds) to its name. Of the other sites where this dainty wader has been reported, the normally rarity-starved Saddington Reservoir has produced two records, although the bird at Cadeby Quarry in 1987 was perhaps at the most unexpected locality.

In general, this species appears later in the autumn than the Red-necked Phalarope, 60% of all birds having arrived between October 11th and November 8th. The majority are short-stayers and 15 have been one-day birds; of the four that have remained for longer than five days, three have involved midwinter records. One of two at Swithland Reservoir on October 17th 1987 was eaten by a Pike, the same fate that befell a Red-necked Phalarope at this site in September 1995.

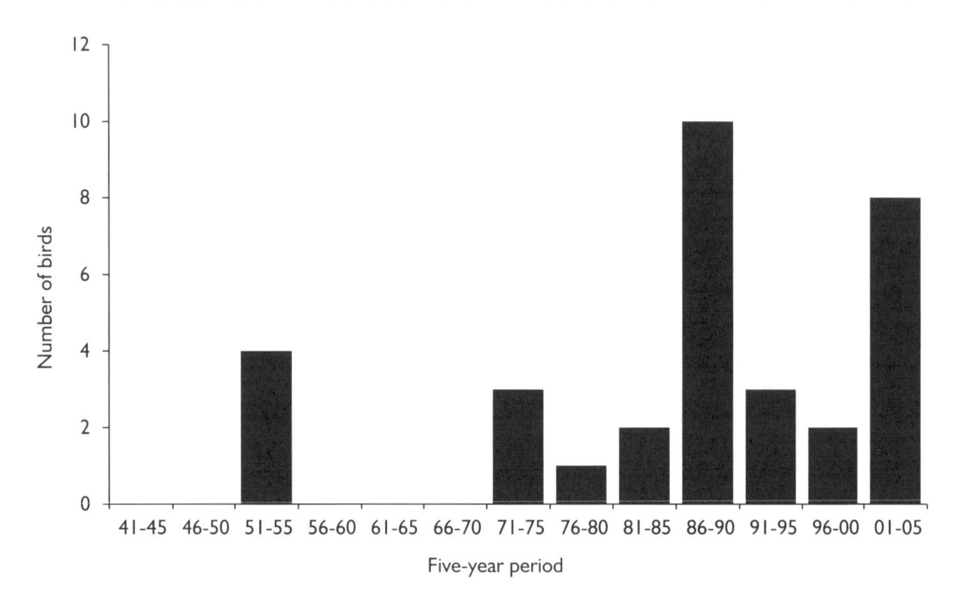

Figure 302: Numbers of Grey Phalaropes by five-year periods 1941–2005.

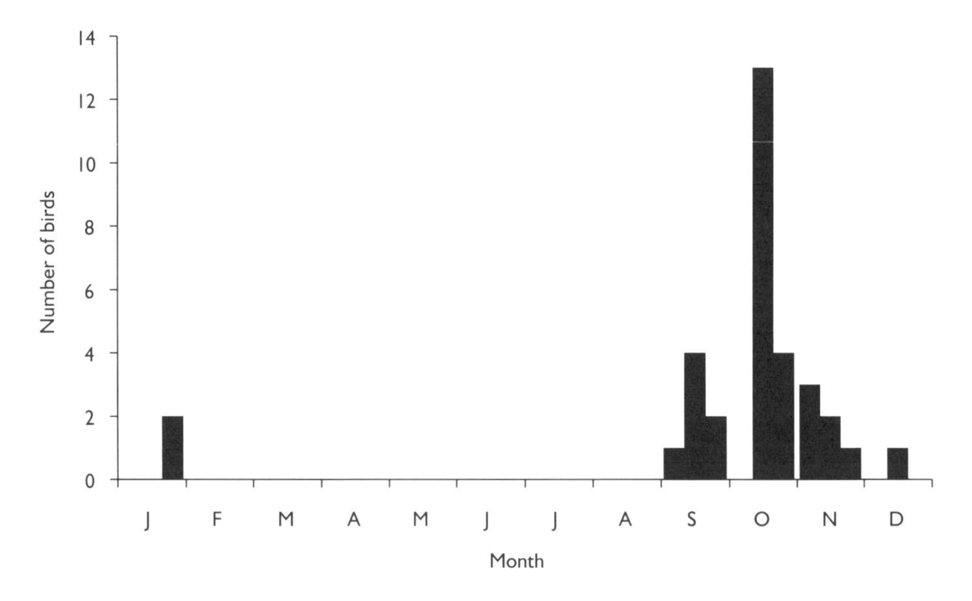

Figure 303: Monthly occurrence of Grey Phalaropes 1941–2005.

As it appears that the majority of birds occur from mid-October onwards, all September reports were reviewed in 2004; as a result, a previously published record of two at Stanford Reservoir in September 1950 is now considered unacceptable (Fray 2005).

Grey Phalaropes breed in Iceland and the high Arctic areas of Greenland, North America and Eurasia. They winter at sea, the nearest of the three major wintering areas to Britain being off the coast of west Africa. They are regular passage visitors to Britain, mainly in late autumn, although numbers inland vary considerably from year to year depending on the occurrence of stormy weather.

SML

Pomarine Skua *Stercorarius pomarinus*

Very rare vagrant from the Arctic: seven records.

Browne recorded five birds, the first four of which occurred in the 19th century:

1846	shot and wounded near Leicester in November and kept in captivity for a short period.
1878	an immature killed near Hinckley during the autumn, the specimen of which was presented to the Leicester Museum and remains there today.
1879	an immature shot near Somerby in November.
1889	one picked up at 'Bradgate Reservoir' (presumably Cropston Reservoir) in either October or November.

The fifth was in 1900, found exhausted in a pigsty at Wigston 'after a great storm' and kept in an aviary until 1906; 'it would come for food if called by its name 'Jacob', but was rather timid and afraid of dogs.'

There have only been two records since Browne's time, both of which occurred within the space of less than four years. In 1981 a dark-phase adult was seen flying over Rutland Water on May 9th by Jim Fowler, David Blakesley and C.J. Butler. In 1984 a pale-phase adult, originally found by J. Underwood and Mick Ketley, arrived at Eyebrook Reservoir on October 21st and remained until the 31st. The latter bird appeared following westerly gales and during its stay was watched eating a Black-headed Gull and later attempting to drown another unfortunate individual of this species.

The large number of unidentified skuas recorded in the counties may possibly include some of this species: see 'Unidentified skuas' below.

Pomarine Skuas breed on Arctic tundra from the White Sea in a circumpolar belt to western Greenland and are almost exclusively pelagic outside the breeding season, wintering principally in tropical waters off the west coast of Africa, in the Caribbean region, off central America and around Australasia. In Britain, they are scarce but regular passage visitors in variable numbers, mainly in May and from September to November, but they very rarely stray inland.

SML

Arctic Skua *Stercorarius parasiticus*

Rare vagrant, mainly in autumn: 14 records involving 19 individuals.

Haines recorded one as having been found moribund at Barrowden Heath in 1866, whilst Browne mentions a near-adult shot at Enderby in the autumn of 1880. There were no further records until 1969, when one was at Stanford Reservoir on June 11th. Since then birds have occurred in nine more years, as follows:

1978	dark-phase, Cropston Reservoir, May 23rd.
1980	dark-phase adult, Stanford Reservoir, August 9th.
1984	dark-phase adult, Rutland Water, October 20th.
1985	pale-phase adult, Swithland Reservoir, November 12th.
1991	dark-phase adult, Eyebrook Reservoir, May 8th.
1993	dark-phase juvenile, Swithland Reservoir, August 11th.
1998	dark-phase, Rutland Water, May 2nd.
	three dark-phase adults, Fort Henry Ponds, August 8th.
	pale-phase juvenile, Rutland Water, August 30th.
2002	pale-phase adult and three dark-phase juveniles, Rutland Water, September 22nd.
2005	intermediate-phase juvenile, Rutland Water, September 16th.

Its appearance is frequently associated with strong westerly winds. In contrast to the Great Skua, all occurrences have been on single dates only and the Arctic Skua remains a very difficult species to see in Leicestershire and Rutland.

This was until recently thought to be the commonest skua in the counties but, after a recent review, only the above-mentioned records remain acceptable (Fray 2005). The following, which were previously published as Arctic Skuas, are now considered acceptable only as unidentified skuas:

1952	Ashby-de-la-Zouch, October 6th.
1959	Bitteswell Airfield, November 3rd.
1976	Kirby Bellars Gravel Pits, September 12th.
1979	Eyebrook Reservoir, September 23rd.
1982	two, Thornton Reservoir, September 23rd.
1984	Rutland Water, June 9th.
1985	Rutland Water, June 12th.
1987	Rutland Water, April 19th.

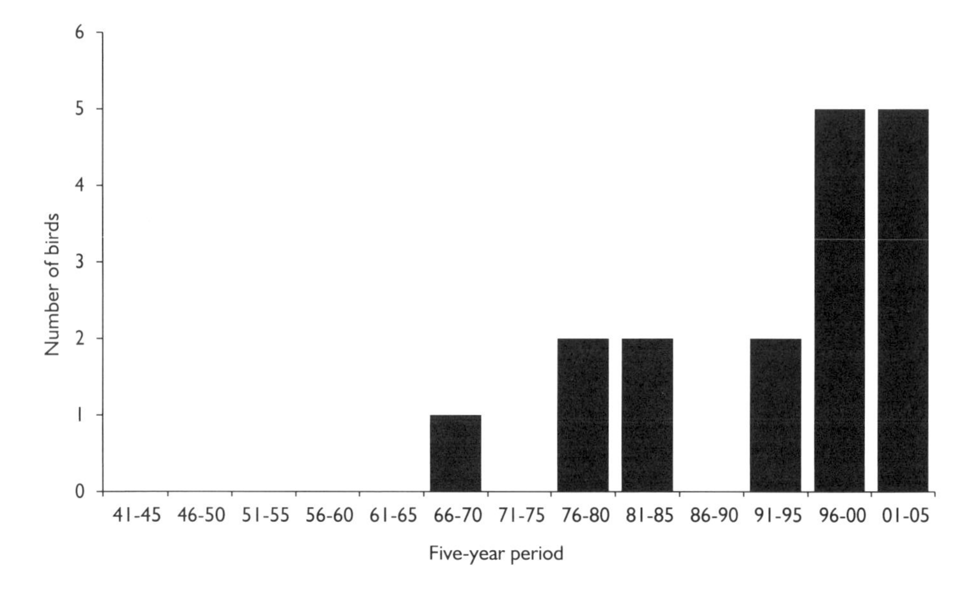

Figure 304: Numbers of Arctic Skuas by five-year periods 1941–2005.

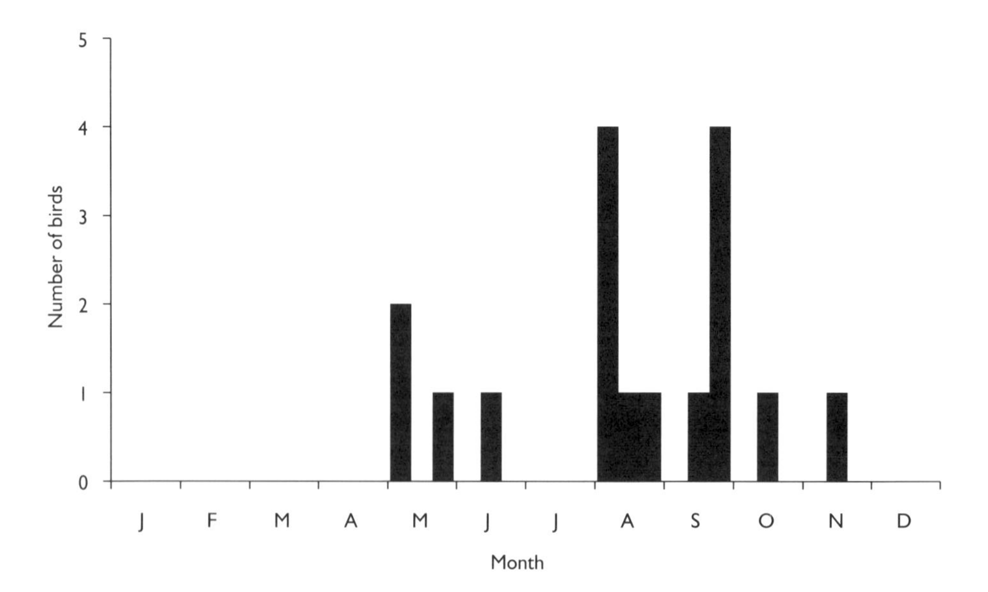

Figure 305: Monthly occurrence of Arctic Skuas 1941–2005.

The majority of the large number of other unidentified skuas recorded in the counties over the years, are thought likely to refer to this species: see 'Unidentified skuas' below. It is therefore probable that, despite there having been more accepted records of the Great Skua, the Arctic is the most regular of the skua species in the counties.

Arctic Skuas breed in a coastal band almost throughout the Arctic and sub-Arctic and winter principally off the coasts of western Africa, Arabia, Australasia and South America. In Britain, they are restricted as a breeding species to northern Scotland, with the majority nesting in Shetland and Orkney; the latest British population estimate is of just over 2,100 pairs (Mitchell *et al.* 2004). They are, however, regular passage migrants in British coastal waters.

SML

Long-tailed Skua *Stercorarius longicaudus*

Very rare vagrant from the Arctic: two records.

The first, long overlooked, record involved a bird that was inadvertently shot when flushed with a covey of Grey Partridges near Melton Mowbray on October 3rd 1926. Although the event was recorded in *BB* at the time (Mayes 1927), the record was never published at a local level until the specimen, which is a juvenile male, was discovered in the Leicester Museum during research for this book (Fray 2005).

The second record, which at the time was thought to be the first, was of a juvenile which flew west along the north arm of Rutland Water on September 21st 1997. Originally located by John Wright and Andrew Harrop, another three observers were fortunate to witness the occurrence (Harrop & Wright 1998).

The large number of unidentified skuas recorded in the counties may possibly include some of this species: see 'Unidentified skuas' below.

Long-tailed Skuas breed mainly in the Arctic, from southern Norway in a band along the northern edge of Eurasia, across northernmost Alaska and Canada and, more locally, around the coast of Greenland. They winter mainly in the Pacific and south Atlantic. They are scarce passage migrants to Britain in varying numbers, mainly in May and during August and September. Inland occurrences are rare but have been increasing in recent years, perhaps as a consequence of a greater awareness of the identification features of juveniles. Occasional records may be expected in Leicestershire and Rutland in the future, although given this species' peculiar habit of turning up inland at sites away from water, such as ploughed fields and golf courses, further occurrences may be at unexpected sites.

SML

Great Skua *Stercorarius skua*

Rare vagrant, mainly in autumn: 23 records involving 32 individuals.

Browne noted one shot near Wymeswold in December 1841 but only included this record in square brackets, indicating some element of doubt. In addition, the 1976 LROS Annual Report makes reference to one found moribund at Barrowden Heath in 1866, but this appears to be an error as both Browne and Haines detail this record as referring to Arctic Skua. Therefore the first confirmed record was, rather surprisingly, not until 1976, when one was seen by Tim Appleton at Rutland Water on September 21st. Since then, there have been records in a further 12 years, involving 31 individuals.

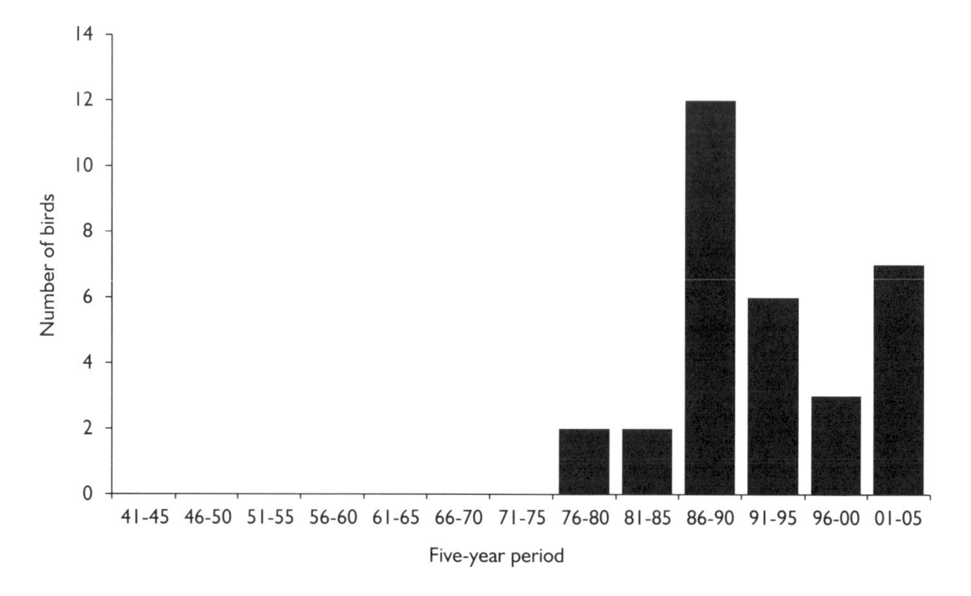

Figure 306: Numbers of Great Skuas by five-year periods 1941–2005.

All records:

1976	Rutland Water, September 21st.
1979	Cropston Reservoir, September 19th.
1983	Eyebrook Reservoir, September 18th.
1984	Rutland Water, September 23rd.
1986	Rutland Water, May 18th.
	Rutland Water, October 24th to 26th.
1987	Eyebrook Reservoir, August 13th.
	Stanford Reservoir, August 23rd.
	Eyebrook Reservoir, October 16th to 18th.
	four, Rutland Water, October 16th and 17th, with two until October 18th.
1989	Rutland Water, August 16th.
	Eyebrook Reservoir, September 10th.
	Braunstone, Leicester, September 16th.
1991	Swithland Reservoir, September 18th and 19th.
	Eyebrook Reservoir, October 5th.
1994	Rutland Water, May 21st to 25th.
	two, Rutland Water, September 25th.
1995	Eyebrook Reservoir, January 23rd.
1998	Sence Valley Forest Park, September 27th.
	Rutland Water, October 18th.
2000	Stanford Reservoir, October 22nd.

2001 six, Rutland Water, September 18th.
Eyebrook Reservoir, September 18th.

As with most other seabirds in the counties, the main site is Rutland Water, from where there are ten records involving 19 birds; elsewhere, only Eyebrook Reservoir (with seven records, all of single birds) and Stanford Reservoir (two records) have recorded this species on more than one occasion. By far the majority of records (29 birds) have occurred during the autumn, between August 13th and October 26th; the main period is the middle ten days of September, when 11 have been recorded. The smaller peak in mid-October is influenced by the infamous 'hurricane' of 1987, when five arrived on October 16th; these birds were part of a widespread influx of pelagic species inland (Hume & Christie 1989). The total of seven birds in 1987 has only been equalled once, in 2001, when seven birds occurred following northerly winds and heavy rain on September 18th. The group of six at Rutland Water that day is the largest group recorded; the only other multiple occurrence (apart from during the 1987 'hurricane') is of two at Rutland Water on September 25th 1994.

Most records are of birds seen on one day only but on three occasions birds have stayed for two or three days and once for longer: one at Rutland Water from May 21st to 25th 1994. The only other spring record came from the same site, on May 18th 1986. There is one winter sighting, of a bird at Eyebrook Reservoir on January 23rd 1995; this was a quite remarkable record, as few Great Skuas winter in British waters and the majority of these spend their time well offshore (Lack 1986).

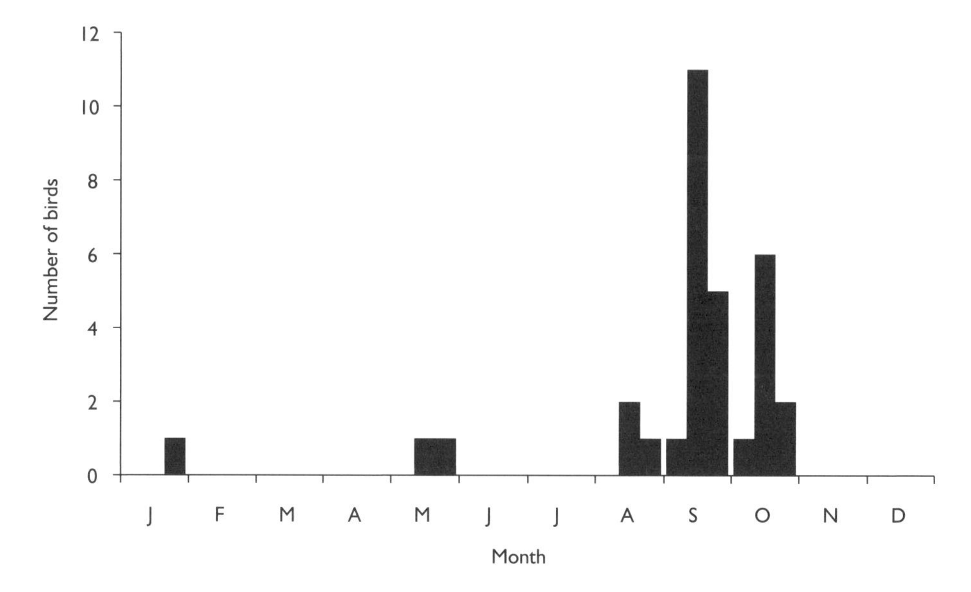

Figure 307: Monthly occurrence of Great Skuas 1941–2005.

Great Skuas are well known for their predatory behaviour and turning up lost at an inland reservoir does not seem to curb their aggressive instincts: the January individual was seen to kill and eat a Common Gull and others have been noted eating a Coot, chasing a Common Tern and unsuccessfully harrying ducks.

Though less likely than in the cases of the other three species, some of the records of unidentified skuas recorded in the counties may refer to this species: see 'Unidentified skuas' below.

Great Skuas are largely restricted as breeding birds to northern Scotland (especially Shetland), the Faroe Islands and Iceland, with recent colonisation of Norway and Spitzbergen. During the winter they are pelagic and disperse widely throughout the Atlantic at least as far south as Brazil and the Gulf of Guinea. Numbers in Britain increased steadily throughout the 20th century and the latest estimate is of over 9,600 pairs (Mitchell *et al.* 2004). As more than 50% of British breeding birds occur at fewer than ten sites and the United Kingdom hosts over 20% of the European breeding population, this species is considered vulnerable and as such has been added to the 'Amber List' of Birds of Conservation Concern (Gregory *et al.* 2002).

SML

Unidentified skuas *Stercorarius sp.*

The identification of vagrant skuas inland can be problematical and so a large number of reports have to remain inconclusive. Most appear in the counties during inclement weather, meaning good views are often difficult to obtain; in addition, many sightings are all too brief and an out-of-context skua on an inland reservoir can confound even the most experienced observer.

Unidentified skuas have been recorded in 21 years, involving 36 individuals. Of these, nine were originally accepted as Arctic Skuas, but following a major review in 2004 they were considered inadequately documented (Fray 2005). The majority of other records were also thought likely to have been Arctics, including three flying over Anstey on September 24th 1988, four at Swithland Reservoir on October 4th 1992 and seven at Eyebrook Reservoir on September 3rd 1994. Of the other skua species, one seen feeding on a Lesser Black-backed Gull corpse at Kirby Bellars Gravel Pits on September 12th 1976 was the most likely to have been a Pomarine Skua, whilst individuals thought to be Long-tailed Skuas were reported flying over Anstey (with three other skuas) on September 24th 1988 and at Eyebrook Reservoir on August 28th 1993.

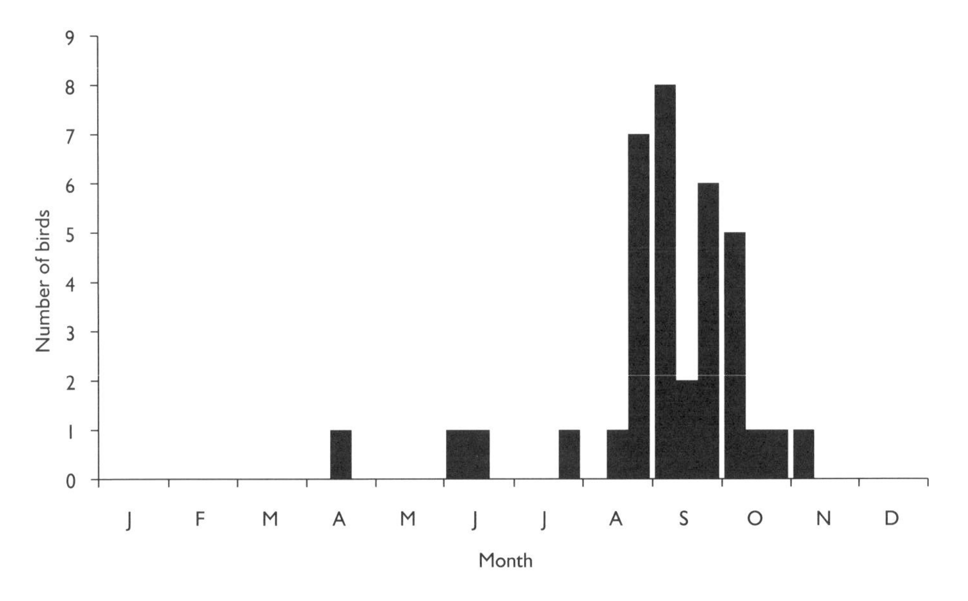

Figure 308: Monthly occurrence of unidentified skuas 1941–2005.

The pattern of occurrence is as expected, most records being between late August and early October, together with the occasional spring report. Although there are relatively few inland records of skuas, there is growing evidence of overland passage between the Wash and the Severn (Thomas 2007, McInerny & Griffin 2007): since Leicestershire and Rutland lie on this route occasional records are likely to continue and may even be predicted in suitable weather conditions.

RMF

Sabine's Gull *Xema sabini*

Very rare vagrant from the Arctic: four records.

Following rejection of an adult on the Grand Union Canal at Freemen's Meadow, Leicester, on November 17th 1953 (Mackay 1995a) there are just four accepted records of this exquisite gull, all at Rutland Water. The first was an adult seen for ten minutes in the south arm by P. Stancliffe, A.S. Parnell, L. Parnell and C.H. Mills on November 15th 1987. This bird was part of a remarkable influx following the infamous 'hurricane' of October 1987, when up to 100 Sabine's Gulls were seen inland. Most were found in south-east England, especially in the London area, although at least ten were at Grafham Water (Cambridgeshire) and five were noted in Northamptonshire. Rather strangely, the Rutland Water individual occurred a month after the storm, which devastated parts of southern Britain on October 15th and 16th; all other Sabine's Gulls found in neighbouring counties appeared during October 16th to 25th (Hume & Christie 1989). In 1995, a juvenile was found by Andy Forryan, again in the south arm, on September 17th. This bird arrived during a period of light winds combined with thunderstorms and heavy showers and remained from 13:25 to 14:40, allowing several other observers to see it before it flew off high to the west. The final two records both occurred in 1997: an adult seen by T. Layton for less than a minute after a torrential downpour on August 31st and a juvenile watched from 16:05 to 16:10 by Steve Lister on September 20th.

Sabine's Gulls have a circumpolar range in the high Arctic, breeding in Siberia, Alaska, Canada and Greenland. Siberian and Alaskan birds winter off the Pacific coast of South America, whilst those from Canada and Greenland winter in the southern Atlantic off south-west Africa. Out of the breeding season they are highly pelagic and are only usually seen off the coasts of Britain following strong winds. If the remarkable influx of 1987 is excluded, inland records are generally very rare.

AHJH

Kittiwake (Black-legged Kittiwake) ***Rissa tridactyla***

Scarce to uncommon passage or storm-driven visitor; recorded in all months except July, the majority from mid-March to late April.

In the 19th century, Browne described the Kittiwake as 'of accidental occurrence in spring and autumn' in Leicestershire and cited 16 records, whilst Haines knew of four similar occurrences in Rutland. There were eight documented 20th century records prior to the formation of LROS in 1941, including a long-staying individual at Stanford Reservoir from February 11th to 20th 1937.

The Kittiwake remained a rare and unpredictable visitor to the counties from the 1940s until the early 1970s, with sightings in only 15 of the 31 years between 1941 and 1971. There were 21 records during this period, all of single birds except for three at Eyebrook Reservoir on September 27th 1952 and two at Stanford Reservoir on May 5th 1964. Since 1971, however, there has only been one blank year (1980) and, although this is the most maritime of Britain's breeding gulls, it currently occurs in small numbers every year and has been recorded in all months except July. There was a tenfold increase in records during the 1980s and 1990s and the three best years on record all occurred during this period: 1992 (144+ individuals), 1988 (131+ birds) and 1981 (91 individuals). This mirrored a similar increase in numbers breeding in north-east England, notably in East Yorkshire between Bempton and Flamborough Head (Gibbons *et.al.* 1993), so it is tempting to speculate that many of our spring birds are heading for those colonies. However, records in Leicestershire and Rutland during the first five years of the 21st century have shown a distinct downturn and this may be connected to recent widespread breeding failures at many British breeding colonies.

Hume (1976) presented evidence for a spring passage of mainly adults through the English Midlands and in years when influxes occur precisely the same pattern is found in Leicestershire and Rutland. Birds on spring passage may occur in fine, calm weather and at these times, there are often records from several of the counties' reservoirs and gravel pits on the same day. The two largest spring movements occurred in 1988 and 1992:

1988 on March 12th, 89 (the largest flock ever recorded in the counties) were at Swithland Reservoir and two were at Eyebrook Reservoir; the following day there were still 40 at Swithland Reservoir, along with 31 at Rutland Warer and three at Eyebrook Reservoir.

1992 on March 14th, there were 65 at Swithland Reservoir and the next day there were 26 at Priory Water, 18 at Rutland Water, nine at Eyebrook Reservoir and five at Dishley Pool, as well as 11 still at Swithland Reservoir.

There have been another two exceptional counts, both at Rutland Water, of 85 on April 26th 1981 and 50 on February 27th 2000. The 1981 group was part of a widespread 'wreck' of inland seabirds following a severe north-easterly gale and blizzards; several other large inland flocks of Kittiwakes were recorded the same day, including up to 300 at Pitsford Reservoir (Northamptonshire) (Nightingale & Sharrock 1982).

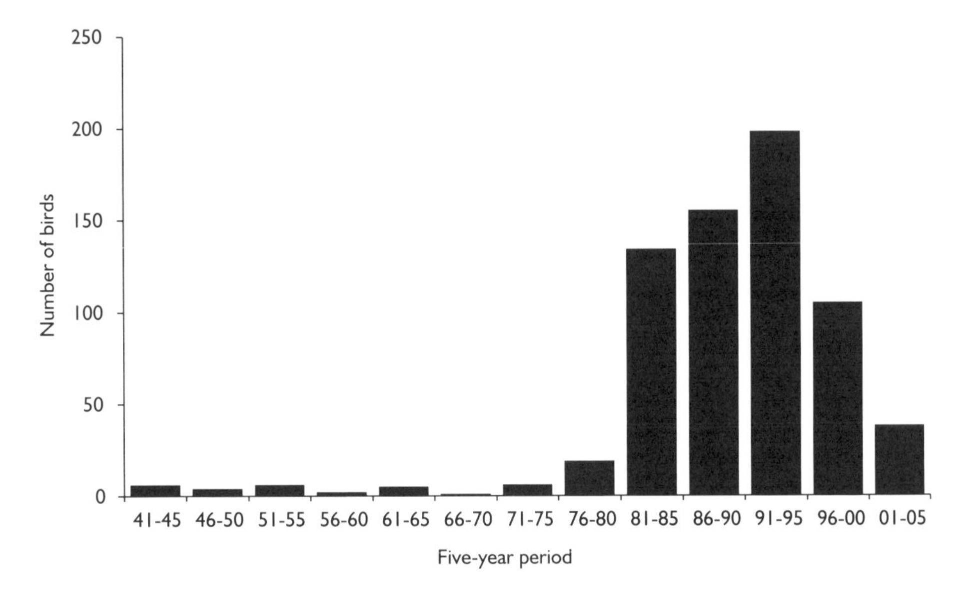

Figure 309: Numbers of Kittiwakes 1941–2005.

Almost 70% of all birds have been recorded in March or April and occurrences during the first half of May are not unusual. Late May records are rare and the only ones after the 22nd have all been at Rutland Water:

- an adult on May 27th 1994.
- four adults and an 'immature' on May 28th 1984.
- a first-summer from May 29th to June 1st 1993.
- one on May 31st 1992.

There have been three June records: three adults at Rutland Water on June 5th 1994, an adult which apparently fell down a chimney at Quorn on June 26th 1947 and a first-summer at Priory Water on June 29th 1997. Autumn occurrences prior to August 20th are unusual, with the only ones being:

- a juvenile at Eyebrook Reservoir from August 1st to 27th 1976.
- a juvenile at Watermead Park from August 5th to 17th 2000.
- one at Stanford Reservoir on August 12th 1945.
- six juveniles at Swithland Reservoir on August 15th 1999.
- a juvenile at Stanford Reservoir on August 17th 1953.
- a juvenile at Stanford Reservoir on August 18th 1945.

A small peak is detectable during November, but otherwise records in autumn and winter, which often follow gales, are unpredictable. Unlike the spring period, the majority of reports in autumn and winter involve single birds, although there have been six records of either two or three together, three adults and two first-winters at Rutland Water on January 29th 2000, six juveniles at Swithland Reservoir on August 15th 1999, seven adults at Groby Pool on February 22nd 1999 and six adults and two first-winters at Rutland Water on November 29th 1997.

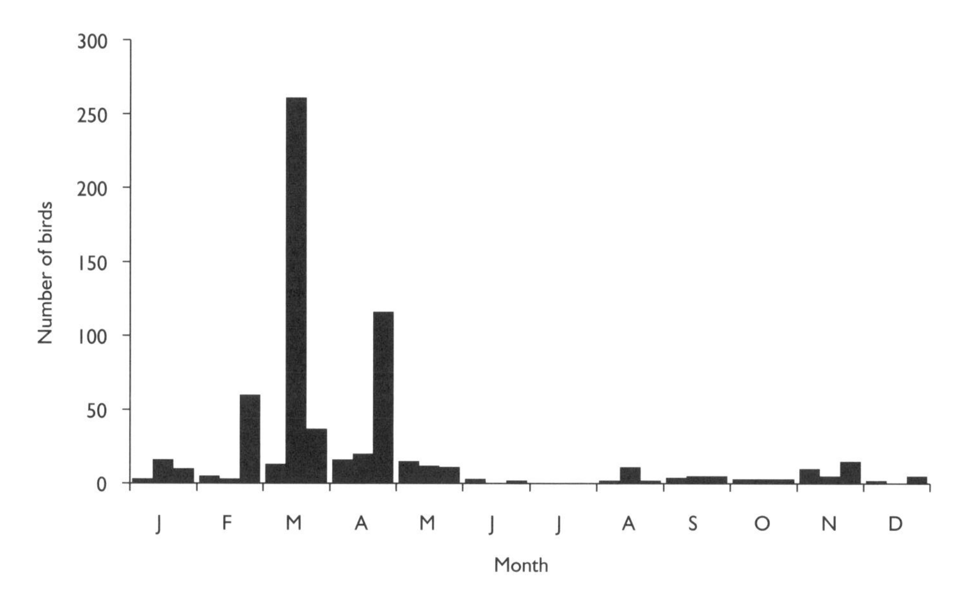

Figure 310: Monthly occurrence of Kittiwakes 1941–2005.

In most months, the vast majority of those aged are adults. In August and October, however, there have been more records of first-winters, which presumably reflects the early stages of post-fledging dispersal. The figure below excludes all birds that have not been specifically aged by observers.

Visits by Kittiwakes to Leicestershire and Rutland are typically brief, the vast majority being seen on one day only. A few have remained for up to five days, but all the longer-staying individuals have been juveniles: at Eyebrook Reservoir from August 1st to 27th 1976, Cropston Reservoir from August 20th to 28th 1982 and Watermead Park from August 5th to 17th 2000.

Kittiwakes have been recorded at most areas of water in the counties, although they are surprisingly rare visitors to some sites: Thornton Reservoir has only one record to its name (one on September 2nd 1973), the Soar valley gravel pits have recorded just four individuals (all at Watermead Park) and Cropston Reservoir has

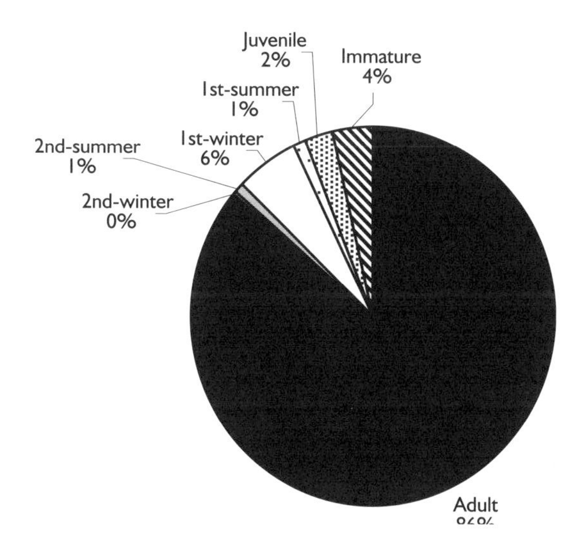

Figure 311: Age distribution of Kittiwakes 1941–2005.

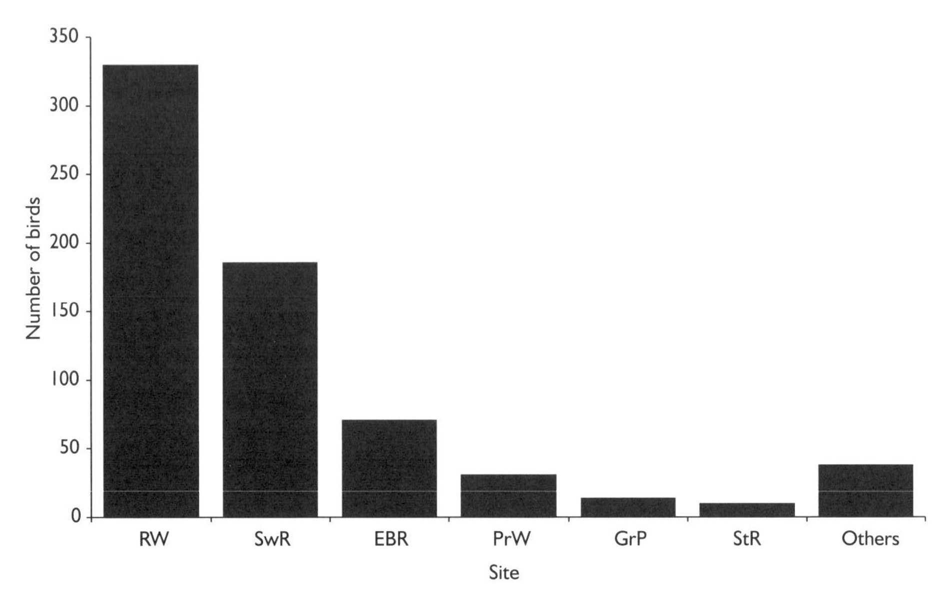

Figure 312: Sites where Kittiwakes have been recorded 1941–2005.
Key to abbreviations: RW = Rutland Water; SwR = Swithland Reservoir; EBR = Eyebrook Reservoir; PrW = Priory Water; GrP = Groby Pool; StR = Stanford Reservoir

mustered only six birds. The dominant sites are Rutland Water and Swithland Reservoir, which account for 48% and 27% of all individuals recorded respectively; these two sites, however, have both benefited from the appearance of several exceptional flocks. A few birds have been seen well away from water, including an adult at Ulverscroft Road, Leicester on February 4th 1942, a first-winter at Halstead on October 7th 2003 and single birds found dead at Potters Marston on February 13th 1946 and Broughton Astley on March 12th 1972.

Kittiwakes breed around the coasts of the north Atlantic and adjacent Arctic seas and disperse into the north Atlantic and North Sea after breeding. The latest estimate of the British population is over 366,000 pairs (Mitchell *et al.* 2004) and as over 50% of birds breed at fewer than ten main sites Kittiwake has been added to the 'Amber List' of Birds of Conservation Concern (Gregory *et al.* 2002). There must be a real possibility that this species will be added to the 'Red List' in the near future, as widespread breeding failures have been noted at many sites in the early part of the 21st century; for instance, by 2005 there had been an 82% decline in Shetland since 1981 (Pennington 2006). This rather gloomy picture ties in with the sudden drop in numbers recorded in Leicestershire and Rutland since 2000.

AHJH

Black-headed Gull *Chroicocephalus ridibundus*

Present all year, abundant in winter, uncommon breeder.

Although regarded as an accidental visitor in spring and autumn at the end of the 19th century by Browne, Haines described this species as the most plentiful gull in Rutland after the Herring Gull and considered it to be increasing. He recorded 'some' amongst over 400 gulls in Exton Park on 26 March 1898 and 20 near Barrowden on 28 February 1902. Since the early 1900s this species has indeed steadily increased. It is currently an abundant winter visitor and passage migrant and an uncommon but increasing breeder.

The first record of breeding involved a colony at Moira. Five pairs were present in 1943, increasing to 20 pairs in 1944 and 100 pairs in 1945. In 1946 100 pairs were again present but only 12 were successful following human interference and the colony was abandoned in mid-June; in 1947 only one pair was present. From 1947 to 1949 a small colony of four to five pairs bred at Loughborough Sewage Farm. In 1957 two pairs bred in

Leicester City Farms, where the difficult nature of the site made it necessary for the observer to climb the lower branches of a nearby oak in order to locate the nests (Jones 1959). Breeding was not proved again until 1990 when six young birds were observed at Trent Valley Pit on July 29th. The following year 20 pairs were present and breeding continued until 1993 when 24 pairs fledged 60 young. In 1994, however, the colony was flooded out and breeding did not occur again at this site. In 1999 one pair bred at Rutland Water, with three pairs there in 2001, at least 14 pairs in 2003, 19 pairs in 2004 and 28 nests (followed by at least 28 chicks) counted on the rafts and islands of the Egleton lagoons in 2005. There is every sign that this colony will continue to grow.

A dramatic increase in the number of wintering birds recorded took place between 1941 and 1950. If allowance is made for improvements in optical equipment and the increase in observers, the numbers of birds at reservoir roosts have probably doubled since then but are currently stable or declining. Nationally the dramatic increase continued until very recently, so our more stable population may reflect the lack of large rubbish tips locally. There have been several counts of more than 10,000 birds in the winter months, with notably high counts from Rutland Water of 30,000 on October 4th 1984, 25,000 on January 22nd 1983 and 21,000 on January 18th 2004. The latter two counts were recorded during the BTO winter gull roost surveys, which revealed a total of 67,500 birds roosting at seven sites on January 22nd and 23rd 1983, 44,810 at six sites on January 23rd and 24th 1993 and 54,360 at seven sites between January 16th and 18th 2004. 19,000 is the current threshold for sites of national importance in the UK, making the Rutland Water roost significant in this respect.

Table 18: Numbers of Black-headed Gulls during BTO winter gull roost surveys 1953–2004

	1953	1963	1973	1983	1993	2004
Eyebrook Reservoir	10,000	11,000	12,000	17,500	3,450	11,300
Swithland Reservoir	4,500	6,000	10,500	7,500	4,200	1,750
Cropston Reservoir	*	*	*	4,000	0	6,450
Thornton Reservoir	nc	nc	750	4,000	1,500	550
Stanford Reservoir	nc	nc	2,500	7,000	15,000	9,250
Rutland Water	nc	nc	nc	25,000	14,500	21,000
Others	1,600	3,500	0	2,500	6,160	4,060
Totals	16,100	20,500	25,750	67,500	44,810	54,360

*Counts for Swithland and Cropston Reservoirs were combined in 1953, 1963 and 1973. nc = site not counted

Birds have been noted on spring passage in mid-February and returning immature birds arrive from late July until mid-August. Over 1,000 are present in the main roosts from August onwards.

There have been several recoveries of birds ringed at expanding colonies around the Baltic Sea (see Table 19). The most notable of these involved a juvenile ringed in Bohemia (Czech Republic) in June 1949 which was found dead at Eyebrook Reservoir just nine weeks later. The furthest movement revealed by a ringing recovery involved a bird ringed at Lutterworth in November 1977 which was recovered 2,346km east-north-east near Leningrad (Russia) in August 1978.

Table 19: Recoveries of Black-headed Gulls

Country	**Number of birds from Leicestershire and Rutland**	**Number of birds recovered in Leicestershire and Rutland**	**Comments**
Baltic States	8	24	The vast majority of those recovered in Leicestershire and Rutland were ringed in June
Belgium	2	3	
Czech Republic	2	0	
Denmark	37	12	The large number of recoveries of birds ringed in Leicestershire and Rutland is difficult to interpret as they come from all months except January and December

Finland	13	9	
France	0	1	The single recovery from France (and Spain – see below) may reflect the fact that most birds ringed in Leicestershire and Rutland are wintering
Germany	11	2	
Netherlands	12	7	
Norway	4	4	
Poland	4	3	
Spain	0	1	See comments under France
Sweden	19	3	Almost all Leicestershire and Rutland ringed birds were recovered during the breeding season
Russia	2	0	Recovered near Pryazha (2,315 kilometres east-north-east) and near Leningrad (2,346 kilometres east-north-east)

Since 1987 up to three leucistic and partial albino birds have been recorded, normally in the winter roosts.

Black-headed Gulls breed throughout most of Europe and through central Asia. The species has increased markedly in western Europe since the middle of the 19th century. The British breeding population was estimated at 147,400 pairs in the period 1988 to 1991 (Gibbons *et al.* 1993), but since then there has been a significant decline in the breeding population which is currently estimated at just under 128,000 pairs (Baker *et al.* 2006); this has resulted in it being added to the 'Amber List' of Birds of Conservation Concern (Gregory *et al.* 2002). In this respect, the growing colony at Rutland Water is encouraging.

AHJH

Little Gull *Hydrocoloeus minutus*

Uncommon passage visitor, rare to scarce in winter.

Formerly rare, the Little Gull has become a scarce passage migrant, though numbers fluctuate. There were four records during the 19th century listed by Browne and Haines but only one of these was regarded as entirely sound. Haines stated that one 'appears to have been killed' at Burley Fishponds about 1882 and Browne referred to two other previous records before concluding that an immature specimen shot at Bradgate (now Cropston) Reservoir in the winter of 1889 (and preserved at Leicester Museum) was probably the only authentic local specimen.

There were no further records until 1945, when a juvenile was at Eyebrook Reservoir on August 29th and September 10th; this species remained scarce for the next 20 years, the only other records prior to 1960, all of single birds, being as follows:

- Stanford Reservoir, October 26th 1947.
- Loughborough Sewage Farm, April 22nd 1948.
- Eyebrook Reservoir, August 28th and 29th 1948.
- Sawley Gravel Pits, August 29th 1948.
- juvenile, Eyebrook Reservoir, September 1st 1958 (found dead on September 5th).
- first-winter, Swithland Reservoir, November 29th 1959.

Numbers increased steadily from the mid-1960s and the first double-figure annual total was recorded in 1971, when 11 birds were seen. Numbers increased again dramatically during the 1980s before levelling out, although the first few years of the 21st century saw yet another increase in numbers, with the highest-ever annual totals, of 70 in 2003 and 63 in 2005. Other notable annual totals have included 59 in 1987, at least 56 in 1990, 55 in 1995 and 50 in 1996. The increase in records described above was paralleled nationally and attributed by Hutchinson & Neath (1978) to an increase in the breeding population east of the Baltic.

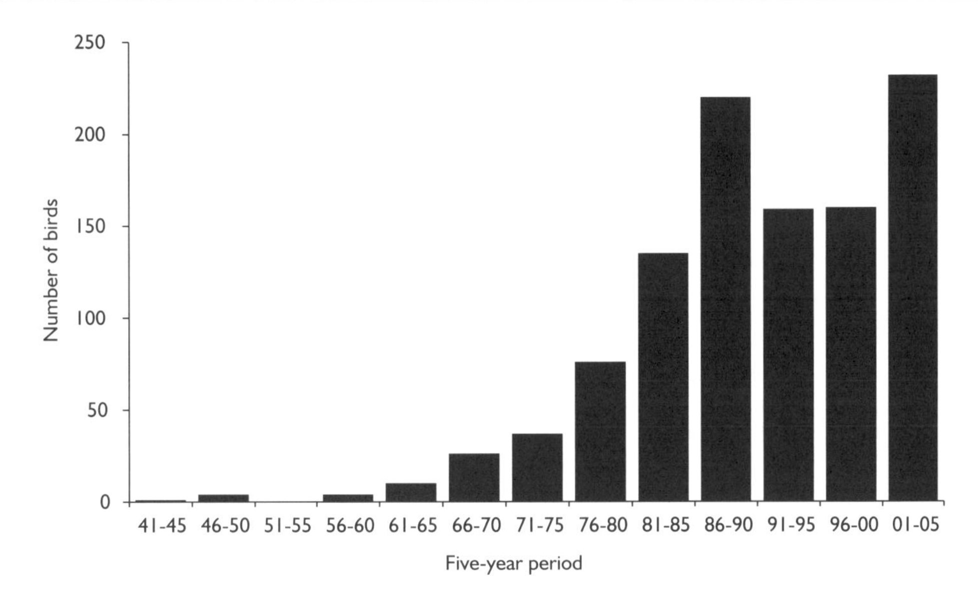

Figure 313: Numbers of Little Gulls by five-year periods 1941–2005.

The main spring passage occurs in late April and early May and the majority of the largest flocks recorded in the counties have been recorded during this period. The highest counts have come from Rutland Water, including an exceptional 55 on April 22nd 1987, with other double-figure flocks at this site during the spring being:

- 29 on April 28th 1979.
- 23 on May 4th 1990.
- 17 on April 15th 2003, with 11 different birds the following day.
- 15 on April 28th 1995.
- 14 on April 25th 2004.
- 12 on May 11th 1990
- 11 on May 1st 1984.
- ten on April 22nd and 24th 2005.

There have also been a further seven counts of six to nine at Rutland Water during the spring. Elsewhere there have been nine counts exceeding five during the spring, as follows:

- 13 at Swithland Reservoir on April 23rd 1988.
- 11 at Eyebrook Reservoir on May 4th 1989.
- ten at Stanford Reservoir on May 1st 1988.
- nine at Eyebrook Reservoir on April 4th 1974.
- eight at Stanford Reservoir on May 1st 1984.
- seven at Sence Valley Forest Park on May 10th 2001.
- six at Eyebrook Reservoir on May 1st 1984.
- six at Thornton Reservoir on April 28th 1992.
- six at Stanford Reservoir on April 13th 1995.

The first instance of a bird summering was a first-year that remained at Eyebrook Reservoir from April 23rd to August 28th 1976. Since 1982 there have been records of non-breeding birds, mostly first-summers, during June in 13 years; the majority have been at Rutland Water, although there were single birds at Swithland Reservoir on June 20th 1983, Eyebrook Reservoir on June 7th 1988 and Trent Valley Pit on June 11th 2005 and two at Eyebrook Reservoir on June 17th 1996.

Autumn passage commences and formerly peaked in August, though in some years there is a second influx during September or even October. In recent years autumn passage has become later and numbers recorded at this time of the year seem to be falling. There has certainly been a change in the pattern of records, with increasing numbers of birds (including a large proportion of adults) in spring. Autumn flocks tend to be smaller than those recorded during the spring and have only reached double-figures twice, with a further seven flocks exceeding five, as follows:

- 14 at Rutland Water on August 24th 1989.
- ten at Rutland Water on September 17th 1995.
- eight at Rutland Water on September 2nd 2005.
- seven at Eyebrook Reservoir on August 28th 1972.
- seven at Eyebrook Reservoir on September 19th 1996.
- six at Stanford Reservoir on August 28th 1972.
- six at Rutland Water on September 1st and 2nd 1990.
- six at Rutland Water on September 19th 1994.
- six at Rutland Water on September 28th 2003.

This species is relatively rare during the winter months and there have been only 14 birds that have arrived in the December to February period. Most of these are birds seen on one day only, with longer-staying single birds being:

- Eyebrook Reservoir, January 30th to March 19th 1966.
- first-winter, Rutland Water, January 6th to 13th 1985.
- Rutland Water, December 5th to 19th 1992.
- first-winter, Priory Water/Swithland Reservoir/Frisby Gravel Pits, December 4th 1994 to February 9th 1995.
- first-winter, Eyebrook Reservoir, January 27th to February 1st 1996.
- first-winter, Thornton Reservoir, February 2nd to 16th 2002.

Winter records are becoming rarer and the only ones since 1996 have been the first-winter at Thornton Reservoir in 2002 mentioned above and a first-winter at Groby Pool on December 7th 2002.

Rutland Water is by far the most important site in the counties for this species and has accounted for almost 60% of all records; in some years (for example 2004) it has provided over 80% of records. Eyebrook Reservoir

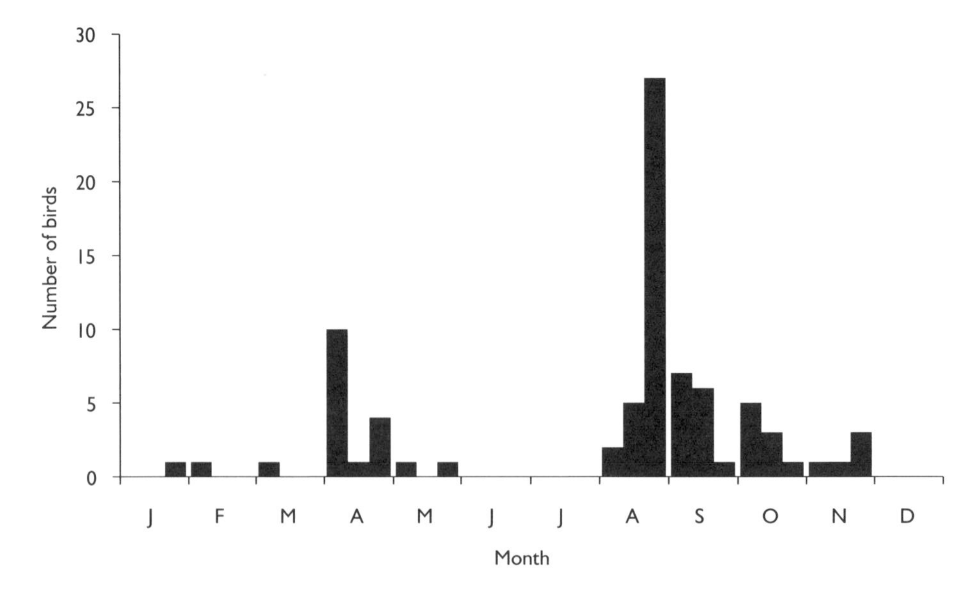

Figure 314: Monthly occurrence of Little Gulls 1941–75.

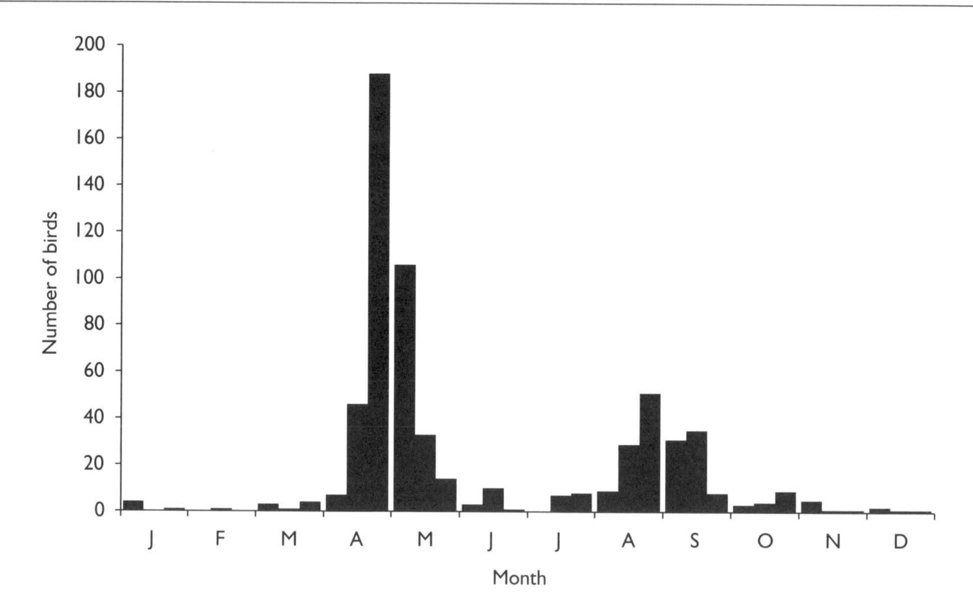

Figure 315: Monthly occurrence of Little Gulls 1976–97.

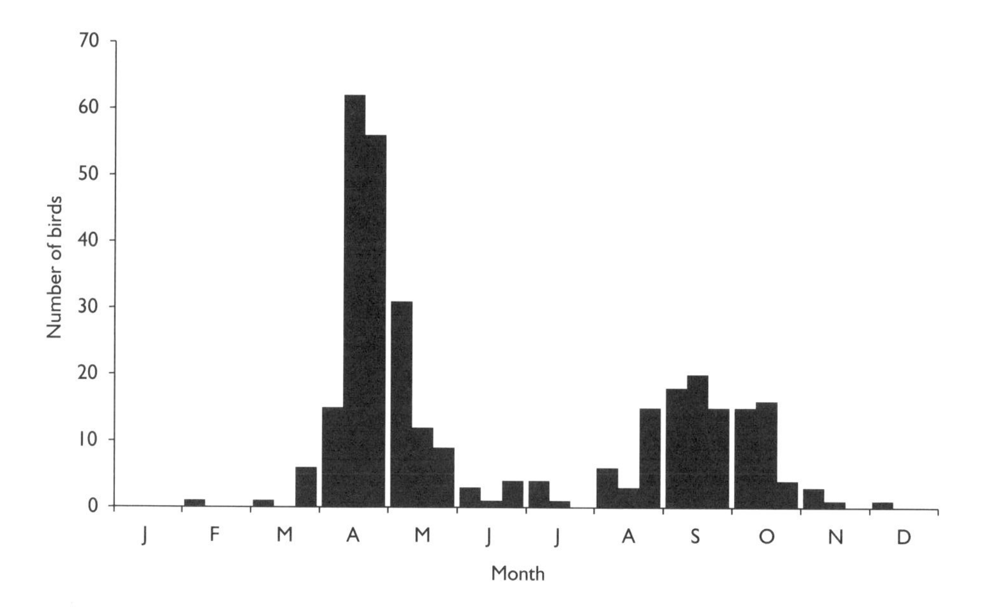

Figure 316: Monthly occurrence of Little Gulls 1998–2005.

is the next most regular site, followed by the counties' other large reservoirs at Stanford, Swithland, Cropston and Thornton. Away from these areas the Little Gull remains a scarce visitor and the only other sites that have recorded it more than once are the Soar valley gravel pits (nine records involving 13 individuals), Trent Valley Pit (five single birds), Priory Water (four records involving seven birds), Frisby Gravel Pits (three single birds) and Loughborough Sewage Farm (two single birds). Perhaps surprisingly, there have only been single records from Groby Pool (a first-winter on December 7th 2002), Saddington Reservoir (an adult on May 1st 1999), Blackbrook Reservoir (a first-winter on April 4th 1970), Sence Valley Forest Park (seven on May 10th 2001) and Quorn Borrow Pit (a first-summer on May 2nd 1994). Other sites where the Little Gull has been recorded

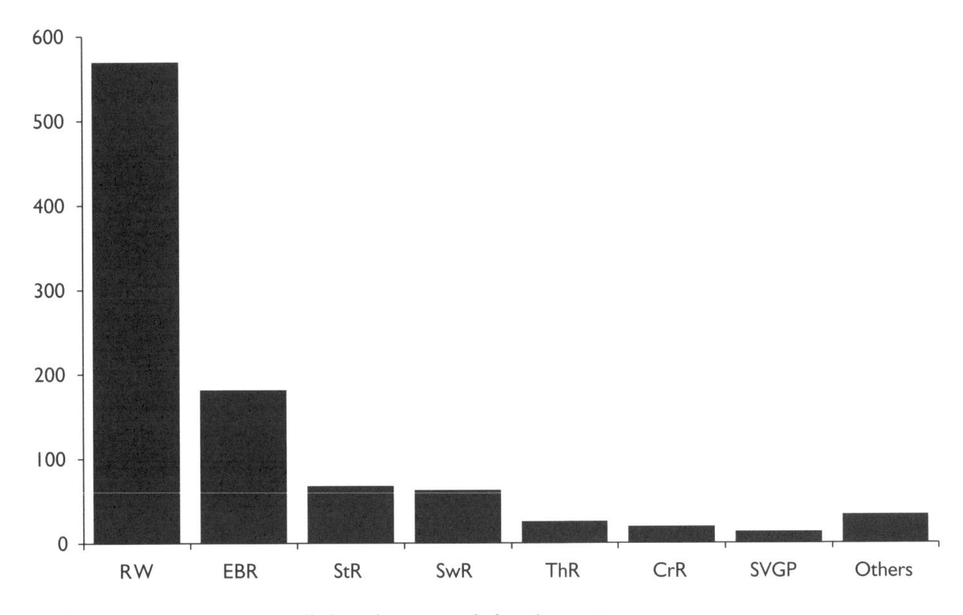

Figure 317: Sites where Little Gulls have been recorded 1941–2005.
Key to abbreviations: RW = Rutland Water; EBR = Eyebrook Reservoir; StR = Stanford Reservoir; SwR = Swithland Reservoir; ThR = Thornton Reservoir; CrR = Cropston Reservoir; SVGP = Soar valley gravel pits

are Sawley Gravel Pits (one on August 29th 1948), Willesley Lake (a first-summer from May 11th to 19th 1984) and Frolesworth Manor Lake (a juvenile on September 9th 2003), whilst two have been seen well away from water, at Walton on the Wolds on May 2nd 1982 and Scraptoft on November 30th 1993. Several likely-looking sites, such as Fort Henry Ponds, Knipton Reservoir and Belvoir Lakes, have never recorded a Little Gull.

Little Gulls breed from the Baltic into western Siberia, with another population in eastern Siberia. The exact wintering grounds of this species are unclear, although they are probably off the coasts of west Europe and in the Mediterranean. In Britain they are regular passage migrants; breeding attempts were made in 1975, 1978, 1987 and 2007, all of which failed (Spencer *et al.* 1989).

AHJH

Laughing Gull *Larus atricilla*

Very rare vagrant from North America: one record.

The only county record is of a first-summer found by Rob Fray at Trent Valley Pit on July 5th 1995. The bird was present in a pre-roost assembly of Black-headed and Lesser Black-backed Gulls from 20:40 to 21:20 before flying off north-east along the Trent valley (Fray 1996, *BB* 89:504).

Laughing Gulls are widespread coastal breeders found in North America south to the Caribbean. Those in the north of the range winter as far south as Mexico and Peru. By the end of 2005 there had been 152 British records, although over 50 of these occurred during a remarkable influx in 2005. British records show little pattern of occurrence, with birds appearing at all times of year at a wide scatter of localities; the Leicestershire bird was the 67th record for Britain. Inland occurrences are unusual, although not without precedent: there have been records from Derbyshire in 1980, West Midlands in 1985 and 1997, Worcestershire in 1996 and 2005 and Bedfordshire in 2001.

AHJH

Franklin's Gull *Larus pipixcan*

Very rare vagrant from North America: one record.

An adult was found in the roost at Stanford Reservoir during the evening of November 3rd 2002 and was located again on the following two evenings, when it was seen by many observers (Pullan 2004, *BB* 96:574). The same bird was then seen at Draycote Water (Warwickshire) on November 6th and may have been the same as that noted at Farmoor Reservoir (Oxfordshire) from August 17th to 28th 2002. The finder of the bird at Stanford Reservoir, Gary Pullan, was conscious of the identification pitfalls after finding a hybrid gull at Boddington Reservoir (Northamptonshire) in March 2001 which bore more than a passing resemblance to a Franklin's Gull (Pullan & Martin 2004).

Franklin's Gull breeds in the prairies of North America and winters mainly on the Pacific coasts of Central and South America. The first British record was in 1970, since when it has become a regular, if still rather rare, visitor to this country; the Stanford Reservoir bird was the 41st British record. This speces is even rarer inland than the Laughing Gull; the only similar records have been single birds in Buckinghamshire in June and July 1999 and South Yorkshire in December 1991.

AHJH

Mediterranean Gull *Larus melanocephalus*

Uncommon passage and winter visitor; recorded in all months, with the majority from October to March.

The first record for the counties was of a summer-plumaged adult seen by Tim Appleton and Chris Park at Rutland Water on April 1st 1980. The species remained rare for the next few years, with only four further records prior to 1987:

- first-winter, Rutland Water, November 28th to 29th 1981.
- adult, Cropston Reservoir, July 24th 1984.
- first-winter, Rutland Water, October 30th 1985.
- second-winter, Stanford Reservoir, April 17th 1986.

Since 1987, however, there has been a dramatic increase in records and this species has become a regular spring and autumn migrant, with fewer in winter. There was an average of 17 birds per year between 1991 and 1995, increasing to 29 during 1996–2000. The rate of increase has slowed slightly since then, with an average of 34 birds per year from 2001 to 2005. The best year was 2002, with some 41 individuals recorded, followed by 40 in 2005, 37 in 1997 and 36 in 2003. Movements between roosts often make it difficult to be sure of the exact numbers of individuals present, with five at Eyebrook Reservoir on February 7th 1999 the largest single count. There may also be a proportion of regularly returning individuals which further complicates interpretation.

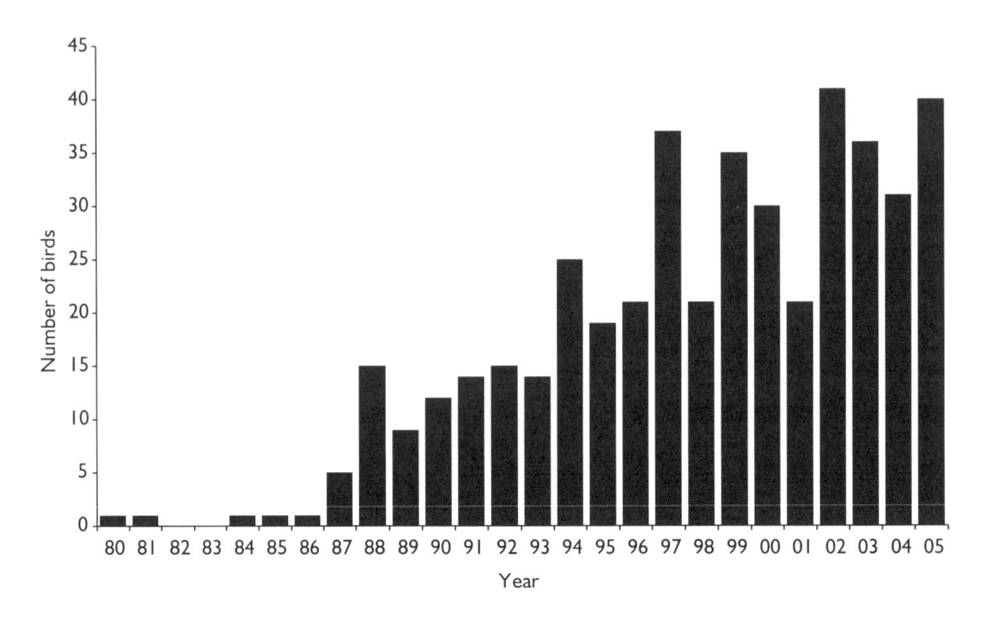

Figure 318: Numbers of Mediterranean Gulls 1980–2005.

The monthly pattern of records shows that the first autumn migrants usually begin to arrive during post-breeding dispersal in late July and August, although there have been two June records and five during the first ten days of July:

- first-summer, Wanlip South Gravel Pits, June 28th 2001.
- adult, Enderby Pool, June 30th 1994.
- adult, Rutland Water, July 1st 1987.
- adult, Rutland Water, July 6th 2005.
- adult, Rutland Water, July 7th 2002.
- first-summer, Wanlip Meadows, July 7th 2005.
- adult, Rutland Water, July 9th 2000.

From September onwards, numbers steadily increase to a distinct peak in late October and early November. Fewer remain during the winter, but there is an early spring passage, involving a large proportion of adults, in early to mid-March. A few of these birds linger into April but apparent new arrivals are rather scarce in this month. Just three individuals have been seen in May, presumably wandering non-breeders:

- second-summer, Rutland Water, May 11th 1997.
- second-summer, Rutland Water, May 16th 1998.
- first-summer, Eyebrook Reservoir, May 30th 1987.

Mackay (1995b) noted that, up to the end of 1994, first-year birds (almost all first-winters) had accounted for almost two-thirds of all records, with just under a quarter being adults. The following 11 years have shown a noticeable change in this pattern and now adults account for 41% of all records, 38% being first-year birds. The much higher proportion of adults now occurring suggests that at least some of our Mediterranean Gulls may be returning individuals. Another significant change over the last 11 years has been the number of juveniles occurring. The first record of a bird of this age came from Eyebrook Reservoir on August 9th 1989, although there were no others until two were seen in 1993. Since then, the number of juveniles has increased markedly; four were seen in 1998, 1999 and 2005, with five in 1994 and 2002 and as many as nine in 2000. Most occur during late July and August, with the earliest being one at Wanlip South Gravel Pits on July 11th and 12th 2003. Two colour-ringed juveniles at Eyebrook Reservoir in August 1994 originated from Hungary and the Netherlands, demonstrating how far some of our birds come and how quickly they travel after fledging. A further

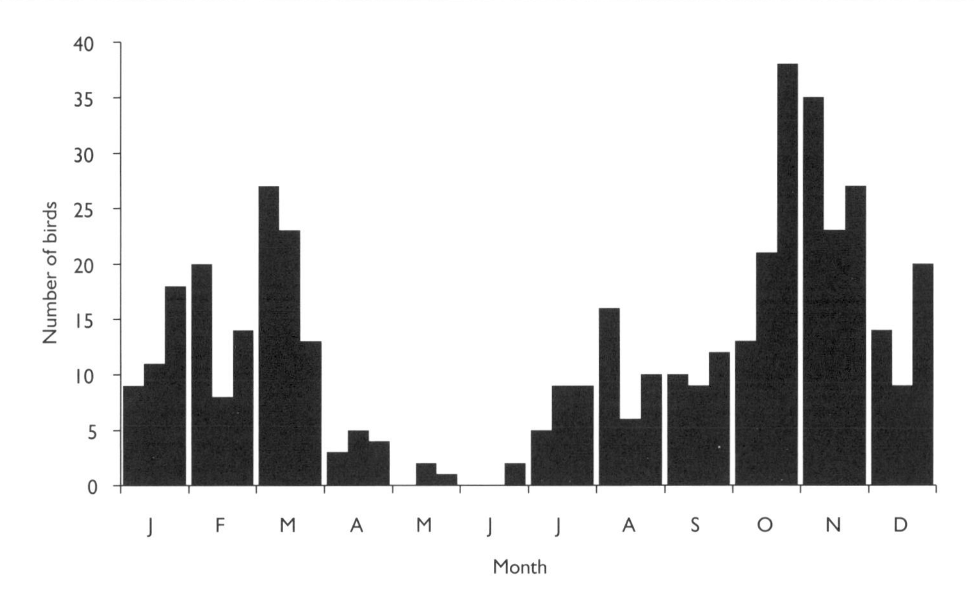

Figure 319: Monthly occurrence of Mediterranean Gulls 1980–2005.

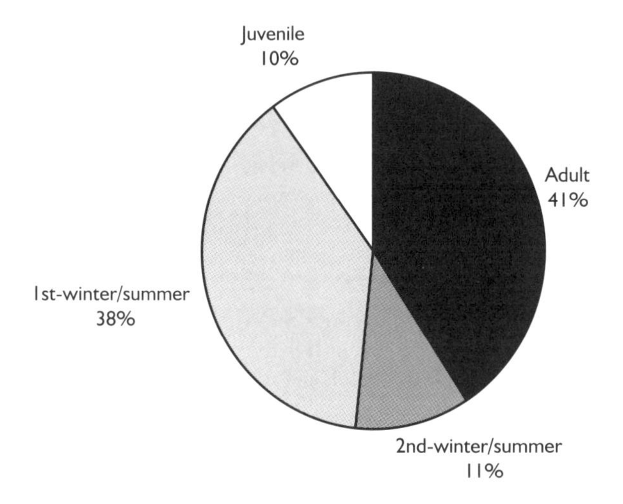

Figure 320: Ages of Mediterranean Gulls 1980–2005.

colour-ringed juvenile at Wanlip South Gravel Pits on August 13th and 15th 2001 had probably come from France or Belgium and a colour-ringed adult at Rutland Water on July 16th 2005 originated from Belgium.

Mackay (1995b) noted that the favoured site for Mediterranean Gulls in Leicestershire and Rutland up to the end of 1994 was Swithland Reservoir and speculated that this was mainly due to the roost at this water being more intensively watched than any other in the counties. This theory appears to have been borne out, as Eyebrook Reservoir and Rutland Water are now the dominant sites, coinciding with increased observer effort at these two roosts over the last decade. Swithland Reservoir still attracts birds regularly, but this species is not recorded with any great regularity at the other major reservoirs of Stanford, Cropston and Thornton, possibly due to a lack of intensive coverage of the roosts at these waters. Two sites which have recently produced a number of records of this species are Groby Pool and Wanlip South Gravel Pits, neither of which has a regular gull roost; however, both sites are regularly used for pre-roost gatherings by large numbers of gulls. Unlike most other species of gull, this species does not seem to be greatly attracted to rubbish tips; despite regular coverage during its existence in the 1980s and 1990s, the only record from Enderby Tip was of an adult on January 3rd 1994. An adult at Shawell Tip on January 24th 1995 was the only other bird seen in similar circumstances. Perhaps surprisingly, Mediterranean Gulls are rarely encountered away from the main areas of water in the counties, although notable records within the city of Leicester have included a first-winter on the River Soar at Swan's Nest Weir, Belgrave from February 10th to 14th 1992 and an adult at Victoria Park from February 10th to 12th 1995.

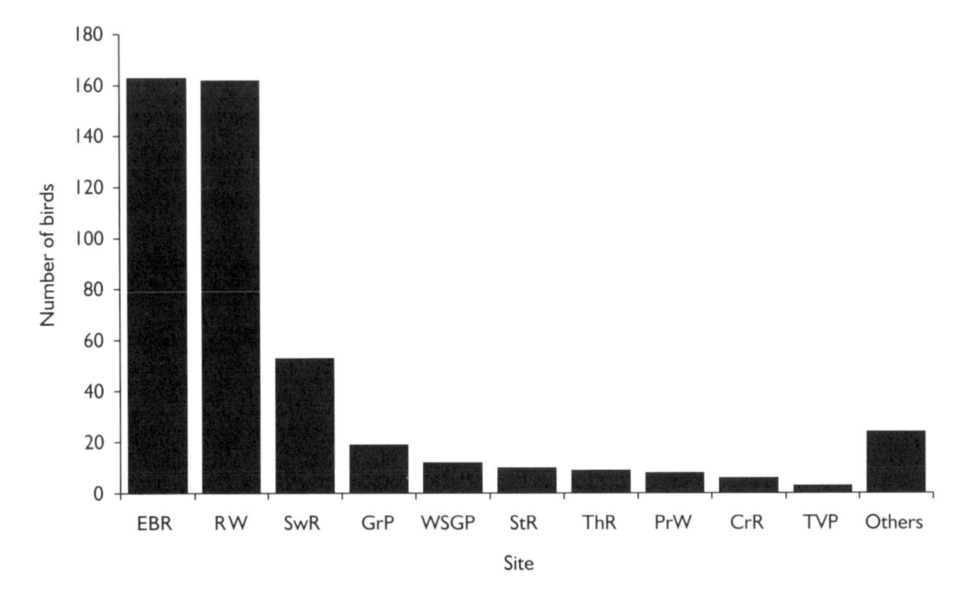

Figure 321: Sites where Mediterranean Gulls have been recorded 1980–2005.
Key to abbreviations: EBR = Eyebrook Reservoir; RW = Rutland Water; SwR = Swithland Reservoir; GrP = Groby Pool; WSGP = Wanlip South Gravel Pits; StR = Stanford Reservoir; ThR = Thornton Reservoir; PrW = Priory Water; CrR = Cropston Reservoir; TVP = Trent Valley Pit

Until recently Mediterranean Gulls bred mainly around the Black Sea, with the bulk of the population wintering in the Mediterranean. The dramatic increase in records in Leicestershire and Rutland during the last two decades follows a huge increase in the size of the Black Sea colonies at the core of the species' range, with subsequent expansion into Hungary and north-western Europe (Gibbons *et.al.* 1993). There is now a significant population in the Netherlands and a growing population in Britain. The first British breeding record occurred in Hampshire in 1968 and by 2005 the total number of pairs in England had risen to at least 243, mainly concentrated on the south and east coasts (Holling *et al.* 2008). Breeding has, however, been attempted in the neighbouring counties of Lincolnshire and Nottinghamshire, so it is not entirely impossible that this species may be added to the Leicestershire and Rutland breeding list in the future, although the relative paucity of Black-headed Gull colonies within the counties may be a major obstacle. As the British breeding population numbers fewer than 300 pairs, the Mediterranean Gull has been added to the 'Amber List' of Birds of Conservation Concern (Gregory *et al.* 2002).

AHJH

Common Gull (Mew Gull) — ***Larus canus***

Abundant winter visitor, scarce to uncommon in summer.

Common Gulls were much scarcer in the counties during the 19th century than they are today. Browne, who relied quite heavily on specimen evidence, described this species as 'of accidental occurrence, especially after stormy weather on the east coast' and seems to have considered it rarer than the Kittiwake. Haines, more plausibly, commented that individuals or small parties were seen throughout Rutland during the autumn and winter months. A record of three in the Welland valley near Medbourne on May 5th 1903 was considered exceptional.

The Common Gull is now predominantly a winter visitor and passage migrant, normally present in large numbers from mid-September until early May, with few non-breeding birds remaining during the summer. In winter it prefers to feed on well-drained grassland, so the oolitic uplands around Eyebrook Reservoir are ideal. Household refuse at rubbish tips also provides winter feeding.

Data relating to this species are surprisingly incomplete but, from counts made for ten-yearly BTO winter gull roost surveys, it seems that the large Eyebrook Reservoir roost reached a peak of 26,000 in 1963 and has since declined, though the very low 1993 figure should be interpreted with caution since on the date of the count many gulls roosted in fields out of sight. Away from Eyebrook Reservoir, large counts have also been made at Rutland Water, most notably of 20,000 in November 1984. 9,000 is the current threshold for sites of national importance in the UK, so both Eyebrook Reservoir and Rutland Water are important sites for winter roosts of this species. Regular counts from the main roosts would help to clarify the changing status of this species.

Table 20: Numbers of Common Gulls during BTO winter gull roost surveys 1953–2004

	1953	1963	1973	1983	1993	2004
Eyebrook Reservoir	15,000	26,000	18,000	17,500	990	16,100
Swithland Reservoir	80	0	450	500	300	385
Cropston Reservoir	*	*	*	100	0	660
Stanford Reservoir	nc	nc	350	400	324	8,110
Rutland Water	nc	nc	nc	12,000	8,000	12,080
Others	25	1	10	30	0	400
Totals	15,105	26,001	18,810	30,530	15,952	37,735

*Counts for Swithland Reservoir and Cropston Reservoir were combined in 1953, 1963 and 1973. nc signifies site not counted)

There are few counts of birds on passage but 1,500 were recorded at Saddington Reservoir on April 8th 1984. A total of 14,000 at Rutland Water on March 23rd 2002 (nearly all of which arrived from the west) may also have been passage birds.

There are relatively few recoveries of ringed birds. Those to date have involved birds from the Baltic States (two), Denmark (two), Norway (two) and Sweden (one).

Since 1985 there have been regular sightings of various leucistic and partially albino individuals present in the winter roosts, some of which have been misidentified as Iceland Gulls. Common Gulls feed mainly on earthworms but will also scavenge: an unusual record concerned one feeding on the corpse of a Brown Hare *Lepus europaeus* at Mowsley in December 1986.

Common Gulls breed throughout boreal and temperate zones of Eurasia and in Alaska and north-west Canada. They are largely migratory, wintering in western Europe, the Mediterranean, the Middle East, central Asia and western North America. The current British breeding population is estimated at just over 48,000 pairs (Baker *et al.* 2006), mainly in Scotland and northern England, but the breeding population (like that of Black-headed Gull) has undergone a significant decline so this species has been added to the 'Amber List' of Birds of Conservation Concern (Gregory *et al.* 2002). The falling roost counts at Eyebrook Reservoir appear to reflect this trend.

AHJH

Ring-billed Gull — *Larus delawarensis*

Very rare vagrant from North America: four records.

The first county record was of an adult found by Andy Mackay, Jeff Higgott and Steve Close in the large gull-roost at Swithland Reservoir on the evening of December 30th 1988. Unfortunately, the bird did not reappear the following evening, to the disappointment of the assembled crowd (Mackay 1989b). The same site produced the second county record, fewer than 11 months later, when Steve Close found a second-winter individual on November 28th 1989. Like its predecessor, this bird was also a brief visitor and was not seen again after the initial sighting. In 1991, a first-winter moulting to first-summer was found by Andrew Harrop in the north arm at Rutland Water on April 9th. Despite several unsubstantiated claims, it was only reliably seen again on April 25th and 30th. Finally, an adult was located by John Wright roosting with Common Gulls in the south arm at Rutland Water during the evening of April 5th 1998. What was almost certainly the same bird was then found by Andrew Harrop at Rutland Water two weeks later, on April 19th; it was watched from 12:00 to 12:10 on Lagoon I and then seen 40 minutes later in the south arm before flying off west.

The Ring-billed Gull breeds across central North America from south-east Canada through the Great Lakes region to the west coast and winters south to Central America and the Caribbean. In Britain, the first record occurred as recently as 1973, but by the end of 1987 it was appearing so frequently that it was removed from the list of species considered by the BBRC. Most records occur during November to April, with a distinct peak in late March and early April, presumably involving birds on spring passage; the two Rutland Water individuals provide good examples of this. Despite the much larger numbers appearing in this country and the increased number of observers watching inland gull-roosts, the Ring-billed Gull still remains genuinely uncommon in the Midlands. Further records, however, are to be expected in Leicestershire and Rutland, although this species is perhaps just as likely to be found loafing on a school playing field or coming to bread at a park lake as in a large gull-roost.

AHJH

Lesser Black-backed Gull *Larus fuscus*

Common passage and fairly common winter visitor, uncommon in summer.

During the 19th century this species was a rare straggler from the coast. The first record seems to have involved one at Groby Pool in 1850. Browne knew of four other specimen records, whilst Haines mentions records from four sites following the first at Ridlington about 1860.

In the 1940s this species was considered to be a fairly regular but not common passage migrant between April and October. By 1954 small numbers were recorded at all times of year and an exceptionally high count of 550 was made at Sawley Gravel Pits on October 28th 1956. Sustained observations at Swithland Reservoir in 1961 showed that the summer roost began to assemble during spring passage in May when about 100 were present; it had increased to 2,000 by the end of September and 1,000 were still present on November 7th. Counts of 4,000 were made at both Swithland Reservoir in September 1966 and Stanford Reservoir on November 17th 1976. An exceptional 6,000 were recorded at Rutland Water in autumn 1978 (Mitcham 1984). During the last two decades numbers have declined, with flocks seldom exceeding 2,000, although 5,000 were at Rutland Water on August 18th 2002.

Most winter flocks are of 50 or less, but counts at Stanford Reservoir have included 585 on January 23rd 1993, 650 on February 2nd 2002 and a remarkable 6,000 on January 22nd 1983 (Hickling 1984). The BTO winter gull roost surveys have usually produced only small numbers of this species; for instance, the counts during January 16th to 18th 2004 produced a total of just 359 birds at six sites, well below the threshold (500 birds) which would qualify one site as of national importance.

Table 21: Numbers of Lesser Black-backed Gulls during BTO winter gull roost surveys in Leicestershire and Rutland 1953 to 2004

	1953	1963	1973	1983	1993	2004
Eyebrook Reservoir	0	0	50	25	50	4
Swithland Reservoir	0	350	524	25	10	58
Cropston Reservoir	*	*	*	30	0	27
Stanford Reservoir	nc	nc	33	6,000	585	95
Rutland Water	nc	nc	nc	0	13	170

Others	0	50	9	0	4	5
Totals	0	400	616	6,080	662	359

*Counts for Swithland Reservoir and Cropston Reservoir were combined in 1953, 1963 and 1973. nc signifies site not counted)

The largest spring flock involved 1,000 birds at Rutland Water in April 1998. Breeding has not been recorded, but there have been two instances of breeding behaviour: two pairs were seen displaying at Rutland Water on June 2nd 1995 and a pair was present on the tern raft at Swithland Reservoir in April 1999. Inland breeding by this species is not unusual and urban nesting is increasing (Rock 2005), so the possibility should not be discounted.

The mix of populations visiting the counties was demonstrated by three colour-ringed birds observed at Rutland Water on June 6th 1998 which had been ringed in Suffolk (undated), in Avon on June 28th 1997 and in the Netherlands on July 8th 1996. Recoveries of locally ringed birds have included individuals which migrated to the Faroe Islands, Germany and the Netherlands (two), whilst two Norwegian birds have been recovered in the counties. Within Britain, all recoveries to date have involved birds which moved to the west coast between Cumbria and Gloucestershire. Of 13 colour-ringed birds observed at Rutland Water during autumn 2006 originated from Norway (four), Germany (one), Suffolk (three), Lancashire/Cumbria (three) and Gloucestershire and South Glamorgan (one each).

Birds considered to show characters of the very dark-mantled Baltic Gull *L. f. fuscus* were reported from Loughborough Sewage Farm on August 28th 1948 and Priory Water on October 25th 1992. The field identification of this form is highly problematical, however and it is considered by the BOU to be very rare in Britain. They are perhaps more likely to have been dark *L. f. intermedius* which was first recorded at Cropston Reservoir on July 13th 1986 and appears to be of regular occurrence amongst the more numerous British *graellsii*. Estimates of the relative abundance of *intermedius* have ranged from 90% in March to 8% in September, which perhaps reflects the difficulty of diagnosing subspecies in the field. Further recoveries of ringed birds will be needed to clarify the situation.

Lesser Black-backed Gulls breed in northern and western Europe from Iceland south to Portugal. The British race *L. f. graellsii* breeds in Iceland, Britain, Ireland, France and north-west Spain and winters mainly off Portugal, southern Spain and north-west Africa. *L. f. intermedius* breeds in the Netherlands, Denmark and southern Norway. *L. f. fuscus*, which is a vagrant to Britain, breeds from northern Norway and Sweden to the western Kola Peninsula and western White Sea but has declined since the 1960s. The latest British breeding population estimate is just over 110,000 pairs (Baker et al. 2006); this species has a localised distribution during the breeding season and is on the 'Amber List' of Birds of Conservation Concern (Gregory *et al.* 2002).

AHJH

Herring Gull *Larus argentatus*

Common winter visitor, scarce in summer.

The Herring Gull was first recorded in September 1869 when a specimen was caught alive at Rolleston and recorded by Potter, a taxidermist from Billesdon. Browne's treatment of the status of this species is sketchy but Haines described it as the gull species most often seen in Rutland during the 19th century. He commented that sometimes as many as 100 were present in the Welland valley from January until March, with other records in April and again in July and August.

British and Scandinavian birds (*argenteus* and *argentatus*) were formerly winter visitors in small numbers, mainly occurring between November and March. 50 at Eyebrook Reservoir on January 13th 1946 was considered quite exceptional. By 1948 birds were also noted on passage during March to May and July to September. Peak counts were noted at winter roosts during the late 1950s and 1960s (2,000 at Swithland Reservoir in January 1953 and January 1957 and 3,000 there in December 1966), but have since declined. The closure of rubbish tips near roost sites has in several cases had a significant impact on numbers. Counts of over 1,000 are currently unusual, though 1,700 were at Swithland Reservoir on January 9th 2003 and 1,500 were at Eyebrook

Reservoir during the BTO winter gull roost survey in January 2004 which recorded a total of 2,466 birds at six sites. The threshold for national importance is currently 4,500 birds.

Table 22: Numbers of Herring Gulls during BTO winter gull roost surveys 1953–2004

	1953	1963	1973	1983	1993	2004
Eyebrook Reservoir	250	500	500	1,000	380	1,500
Swithland Reservoir	2,000	1,000	750	250	103	435
Cropston Reservoir	*	*	*	700	0	53
Stanford Reservoir	nc	nc	8	1,000	38	273
Rutland Water	nc	nc	nc	600	150	200
Others	100	50	7	10	8	5
Totals	2,350	1,550	1,265	3,560	679	2,466

*Counts for Swithland Reservoir and Cropston Reservoir were combined in 1953, 1963 and 1973. nc signifies site not counted

Few remain during the summer months and there has never been any sign of breeding activity. Following the recognition of Yellow-legged and Caspian Gulls, further studies will be needed to define the true status of Herring Gull at this season.

There are relatively few ringing recoveries. Those to date have included two birds ringed in Leicestershire which were recovered in Norway (up to 2,150km to the north-north-east) and three birds ringed in Fife (Scotland) which were later recovered in Leicestershire. A large proportion of those present during the main winter period show characters of birds from Scandinavia or Russia (*argentatus*) and one such bird at Bradgate Tip on December 13th 1999 had yellow legs.

Adults described as leucistic were noted at Eyebrook Reservoir on October 22nd 2004 and Groby Pool on October 29th 2004.

Hybrids with the Glaucous Gull have been recorded: see 'Hybrids' on pages 676–684.

The nominate race of the Herring Gull, *L. a. argentatus*, breeds largely in Scandinavia as far south as Denmark. *L. a. argenteus* breeds in Britain, Ireland, the Faroe Islands, Iceland and from west France to the North Sea coast of Germany. The current British breeding population is just under 131,500 pairs (Baker *et al.* 2006) but, as there has been a moderate decline over the last 25 years, this species is on the 'Amber List' of Birds of Conservation Concern (Gregory *et al.* 2002).

AHJH

Yellow-legged Gull — *Larus michahellis*

Uncommon to fairly common late summer and autumn visitor, uncommon winter visitor, scarce in spring and early summer.

The first record of the Yellow-legged Gull in the counties involved an adult seen by Andy Mackay and Jeff Higgott at Swithland Reservoir on October 29th and November 8th 1987. By the end of 1990 there had been a further 18 individuals, the majority of which were located in the Swithland Reservoir roost, as follows:

1988 adult, Swithland Reservoir, August 4th to 16th; same, Mountsorrel Tip, August 10th.
adult, Swithland Reservoir, September 16th.
1989 adult, Swithland Reservoir, January 2nd.
adult, Swithland Reservoir, February 19th.
adult, Rutland Water, July 16th.
adult, Priory Water, August 20th.
adult, Swithland Reservoir, October 15th.
1990 adult, Swithland Reservoir, January 6th.
third-summer, Frisby Gravel Pits, July 29th.

two adults, Swithland Reservoir, August 10th, with one the following day.
adult and third-summer, Eyebrook Reservoir, August 26th.
adult and two first-winters, Priory Water, September 16th.
adult, Swithland Reservoir, December 27th.
adult, Eyebrook Reservoir, December 29th.

Numbers have increased significantly since 1990 and the Yellow-legged Gull is now recorded so frequently that some are not reported. Since 1998 over 100 birds have been reported each year apart from in 2000; the highest estimated annual totals have been 205 in 1998, 162 in 1999 and 143 in 2003.

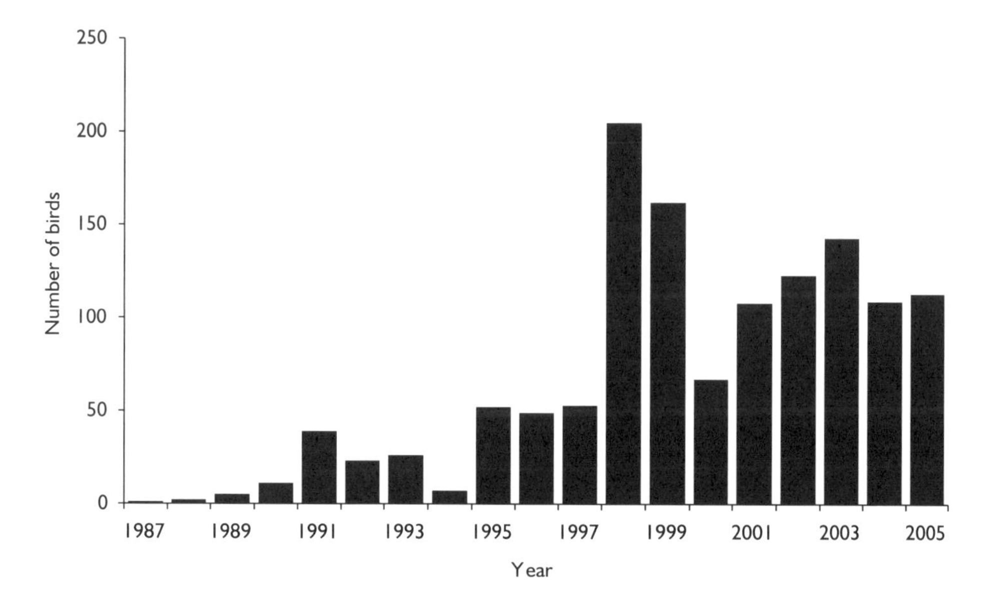

Figure 322: Approximate numbers of Yellow-legged Gulls 1987–2005.

Peak numbers occur in late summer and autumn, with fewer remaining during the winter. They are relatively rare in late winter and spring. In most years the main arrival takes place in September or October, notable examples being 46 in October 1999, 45 in September 2003 and 34 in both October 2001 and October 2002. Earlier influxes have taken place in several years, including 15 in August 1991 and 13 in August 1996, whilst a prolonged arrival in 1998 saw 27 new birds in July, 21 in August, 39 in September and 44 in October.

Double-figure counts have been recorded at three sites, with the majority occurring at Rutland Water; the highest counts at this site have been:

- 33 on September 21st 2003.
- 23 on September 7th 2003.
- 15 on August 21st 2005.
- 12 on September 25th 2005.
- 11 on July 25th 1999.
- 11 on August 14th 2001.
- 11 on October 30th 2005.

At Eyebrook Reservoir the largest counts have been 20 on October 22nd 1999, 17 on September 30th 1998 and 16 on October 16th 2001, whilst ten were at Groby Pool on October 11th 2004. The only other sites where more than four birds have been seen together are Swithland Reservoir; where there were seven on August 21st 1991, six on both October 24th 2000 and October 14th 2001 and five on September 27th 2003, and Castle Donington; where there were five at the disused power station site on September 17th 2000.

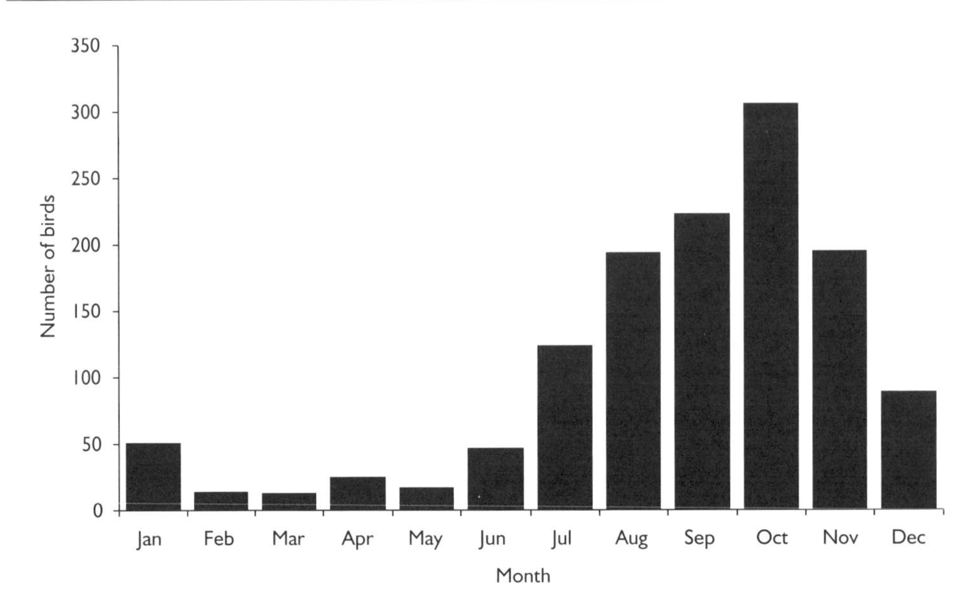

Figure 323: Monthly occurrence of Yellow-legged Gulls 1987–2005.

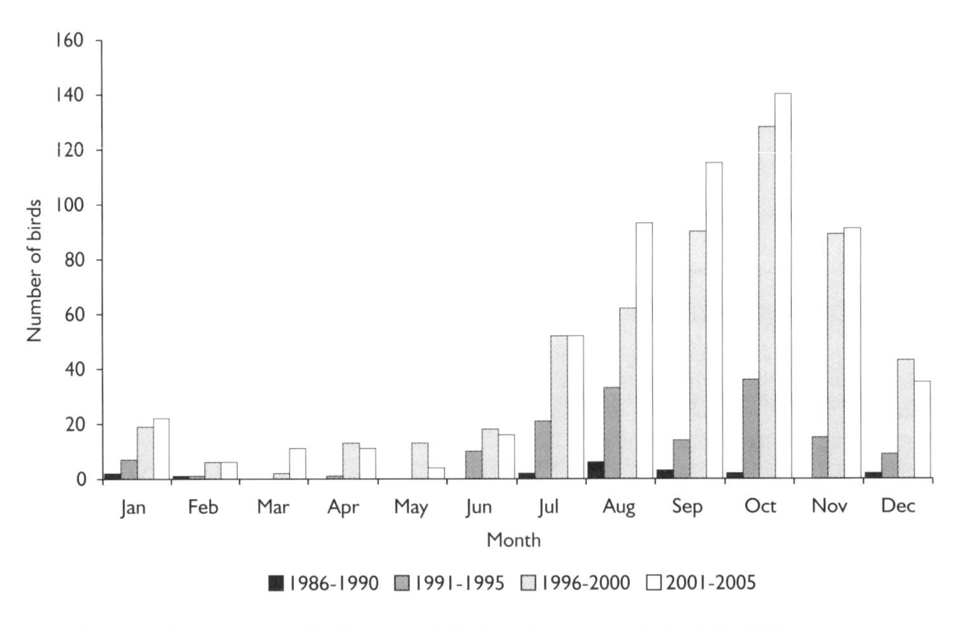

Figure 324: Monthly occurrence of Yellow-legged Gulls by five-year periods 1986–2005.

Although there is often a constant turnover of birds during the autumn, it has been possible to estimate the total number of individuals recorded during each month at some of the more well-watched sites. The best example of this is at Groby Pool, where at least 18 different birds were recorded during September 1998 and 21 were seen during both October 1998 and October 2002. Elsewhere, at least 23 were recorded at Eyebrook Reservoir during October 1999, with 20 there during October 2001 and at least seven were at Trent Valley Pit in July 1998.

Mackay (1995b) analysed records of this species between 1987 and 1994 and found that adults outnumbered other ages by about 2:1, which matches the age distribution of birds recorded in Essex and Kent. The only two subsequent years for which full data are available confirm these findings. Ringing programmes carried out on the continent have shown that birds in north-west Europe in late summer are predominantly adults engaged in northward post-breeding moult migration.

Table 23: Age composition of Yellow-legged Gulls in 1995 and 1997

	1st-year	2nd-year	3rd-year	4th-year	Adult
1995	3	4	8	5	32
1997	3	6	5	13	26

An adult at Groby Pool on September 3rd 1999 resembled the race *atlantis*, being rather small and round-headed, with a well-defined 'hood' of streaks, a mantle almost as dark as *graellsii* Lesser Black-backed Gull and a red gonys spot on both mandibles; however, at least one similar bird has been seen at Eyebrook Reservoir and was considered to be a heavily marked *michahellis*.

Formerly treated as a subspecies of the Herring Gull, this predominantly Mediterranean species has only recently (2005) been formally recognised by the BOU. Yellow-legged Gulls breed mainly around the Mediterranean and on the Atlantic islands. There has been a northward expansion of the breeding range in recent decades and although this species is mainly a non-breeding visitor to Britain a few now nest in southern England; up to four pairs were reported in 2005 (Holling *et al.* 2008), including mixed pairings with Lesser Black-backed Gulls in Bedfordshire and Cambridgeshire, so future breeding in Leicestershire and Rutland is not out of the question.

AHJH

Caspian Gull *Larus cachinnans*

Uncommon passage and winter visitor, recorded in all months except May and June with the majority from October to January: 201 indivduals.

Although not formally recognised as a separate species by BOU until 2007, the Caspian Gull was first convincingly recorded in Britain in August 1995. There were records from Leicestershire and Rutland the following year

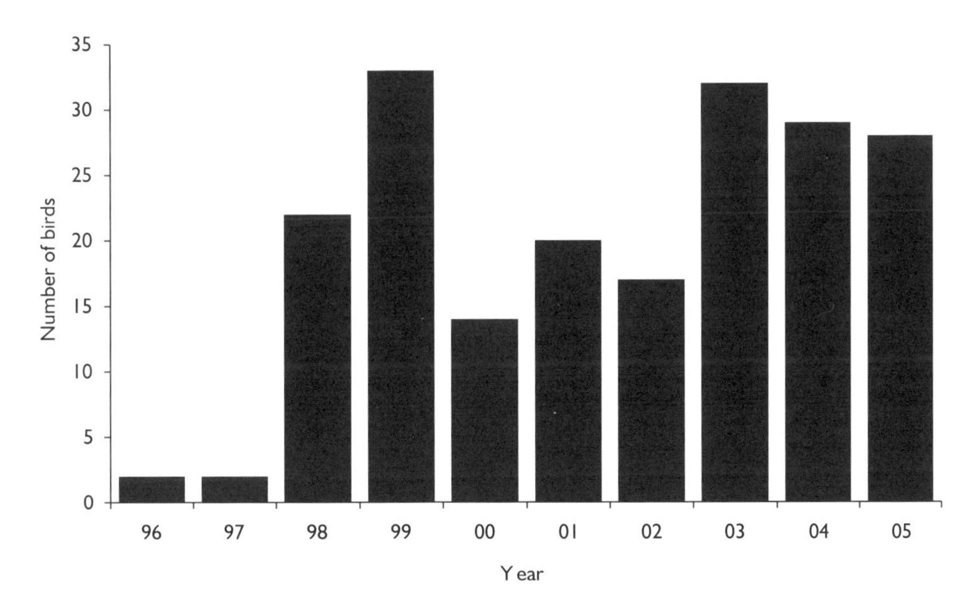

Figure 325: Numbers of Caspian Gulls 1996 –2005.

involving adults seen by Andrew Harrop at Rutland Water on October 20th and Eyebrook Reservoir on November 17th. There were a further two records in 1997, both of adults at Rutland Water, on November 1st and 22nd. Since then, as field characters have become better known, the Caspian Gull has been recorded regularly, though in smaller numbers than the Yellow-legged Gull. The best year so far was 1999, with at least 33 individuals recorded, followed closely by 32 in 2003. With the ongoing interest in gull identification, it is likely that these totals will be exceeded in the future.

The monthly pattern of records is strikingly different from that of the Yellow-legged Gull, showing a distinct peak in late autumn, particularly from late October to mid-November. Fewer remain during the winter and none have been recorded in late spring or early summer. The earliest autumn record was of a third-summer at Rutland Water on July 24th and 31st 2005, although there have been only four further records prior to September, all at Rutland Water: a third-summer on July 25th 1999, a first-summer from July 26th to mid-September 2005, an adult from August 8th to October 9th 1999 and a third-summer on August 14th 2005. During the late winter, very few have been seen after the end of February, with eight individuals in March and four in April:

- fourth-winter, Groby Pool, March 3rd 2002.
- adult, Eyebrook Reservoir, March 5th 2001.
- second-winter and third-winter, Groby Pool, March 6th 1999.
- adult, Eyebrook Reservoir, March 9th 2005.
- first-winter, Eyebrook Reservoir, March 20th 2003.
- first-winter, Eyebrook Reservoir, March 20th 2005.
- second-winter/summer, Rutland Water, March 24th 2005.
- first-summer, Rutland Water, April 2nd 2000.
- first-summer, Rutland Water, April 16th 2000.
- first-summer, Rutland Water, April 21st 2003.
- first-summer, Rutland Water, April 24th 2005.

Almost 63% of records have involved adult birds, perhaps suggesting that a number of individuals are now regularly returning to favoured sites in the counties. First-winters make up a substantial proportion of other records. It is noticeable that the four latest spring reports have invoved first-year birds.

As with most other scarce gulls in the counties, Eyebrook Reservoir is the favoured site for this species, and almost half of all records have been there. Some impressive build-ups have occurred here, including up to nine

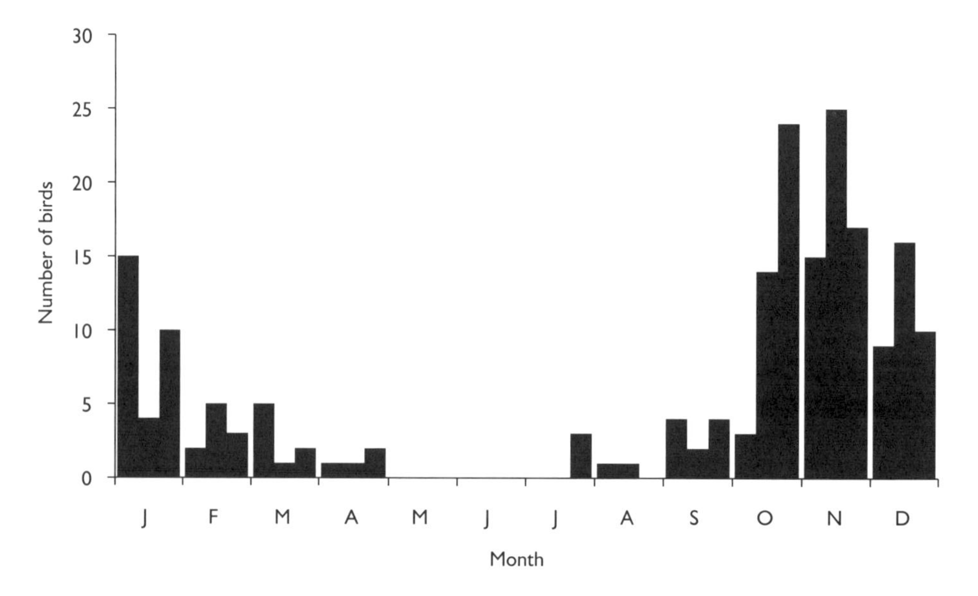

Figure 326: Monthly occurrence of Caspian Gulls 1996–2005.

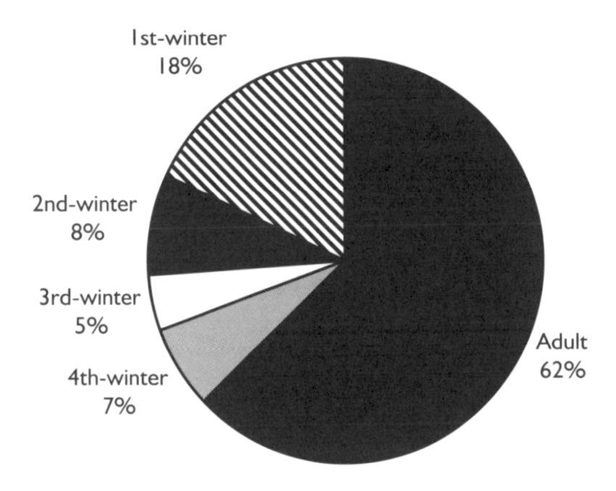

Figure 327: Age distribution of Caspian Gulls 1996–2005.

between November 14th and December 16th 1998 and a minimum of 11 between October 21st and December 7th 1999. Elsewhere, Groby Pool, with its excellent opportunities for viewing gulls at close quarters, has produced almost 50 individuals, whilst Rutland Water has accounted for most other records in the counties. Ten birds have been seen at Swithland Reservoir, most of which had been noted previously at Groby Pool. To date, only three other sites have recorded the Caspian Gull: Priory Water, an adult on September 19th 1999; Cropston Reservoir, an adult on December 6th 2002 and Huncote, an adult intermittently from December 13th 2002 to January 3rd 2003. The latter two records involved birds that had previously been seen at Groby Pool.

As its English name suggests, this species' main breeding range is centred around the Caspian Sea and northern Black Sea. It winters south of the breeding range, from the east Mediterranean to the Persian Gulf and western India and is being recorded with increasing frequency in western Europe outside the breeding season. There are

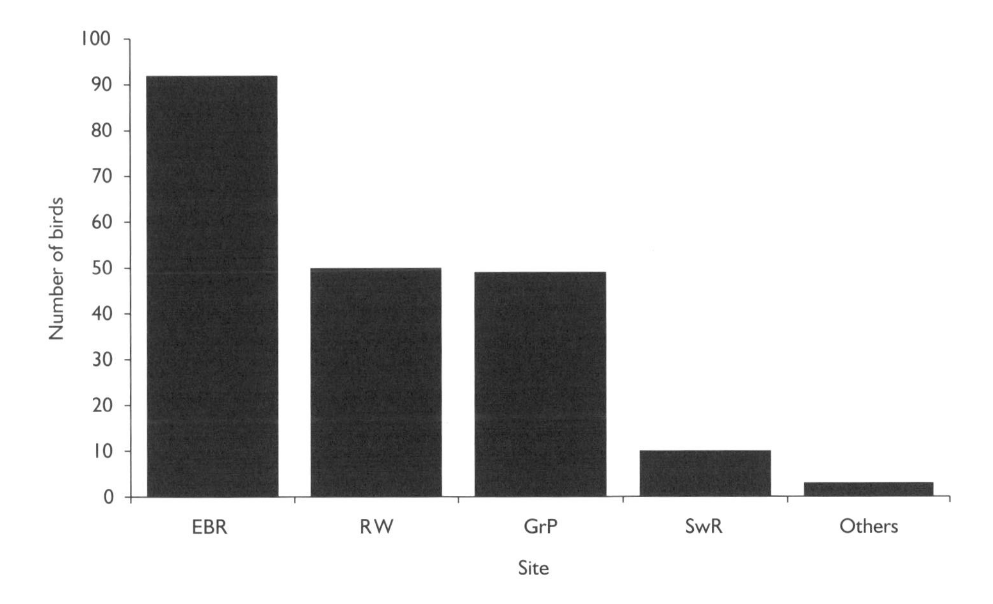

Figure 328: Sites where Caspian Gulls have been recorded 1996–2005.
Key to abbreviations: EBR = Eyebrook Reservoir; GrP = Groby Pool; RW = Rutland Water; SwR = Swithland Reservoir

indications that a recent westward expansion of the breeding range has taken place, although the clarification of field characters and resultant greater awareness amongst observers has no doubt contributed to the increased numbers being seen in western Europe.

AHJH

Iceland Gull *Larus glaucoides*

Scarce winter visitor, recorded in all months between November and May with the majority from December to March: 76 indivduals. Two distinct subspecies have occurred.

With the exception of one record of Kumlien's Gull (see below), all reports have referred to the nominate race.

Like the Glaucous Gull, this species did not appear in the region until roosts had become established at reservoirs. The first record related to an 'immature' seen by Ronald Hickling at Cropston Reservoir on February 23rd 1952 but the Iceland Gull remained a very rare winter visitor until the 1980s, with only four other records prior to 1981:

- adult, Cropston Reservoir, December 25th 1966 and January 1st and 29th 1967, with the same bird at Wanlip on January 3rd 1967.
- second-winter, Wanlip Gravel Pits, November 16th 1969.
- Swithland Reservoir, January 18th 1971.
- second-winter, Swithland Reservoir, March 20th to 24th 1979.

Since 1981, however, there have been only four blank years (1982, 1985, 1991 and 1993). With the exception of 1983, when there were two records, no year produced more than one bird until 1994, when a remarkable total of 11 birds occurred; at this time, there had been only 15 previous records. The dramatic increase in records during the 1990s is mainly the result of this and other notable influxes, including nine in both 1995 and 2002.

As the data show, Iceland Gulls usually arrive and depart later than Glaucous Gulls. Most are recorded in winter between December and February, with particular peaks in late December and mid-February. The earliest winter arrival was a first-winter at Eyebrook Reservoir on November 2nd and 4th 1994, but sightings in this month are quite rare, the only others being:

- adult, Eyebrook Reservoir, November 5th intermittently to December 18th 2003.
- adult, Cropston Reservoir, November 8th 1998.
- second-winter, Wanlip Gravel Pits, November 16th 1969.
- second-winter, Eyebrook Reservoir, November 16th intermittently to December 14th 2004.
- adult, Eyebrook Reservoir, November 24th 2004 intermittently into 2005.

A noticeable early spring movement is apparent in mid-March, but records after the 20th of this month are relatively infrequent. Four individuals have arrived after the end of March:

- adult, Rutland Water, April 2nd 1997.
- first-winter, Eyebrook Reservoir, April 3rd to 7th 1995.
- adult, Rutland Water, April 7th 2002.
- second-summer, Rutland Water, May 2nd 1999.

Most records involve single birds but two have been seen together on several occasions and four were present at Eyebrook Reservoir on January 7th 1995.

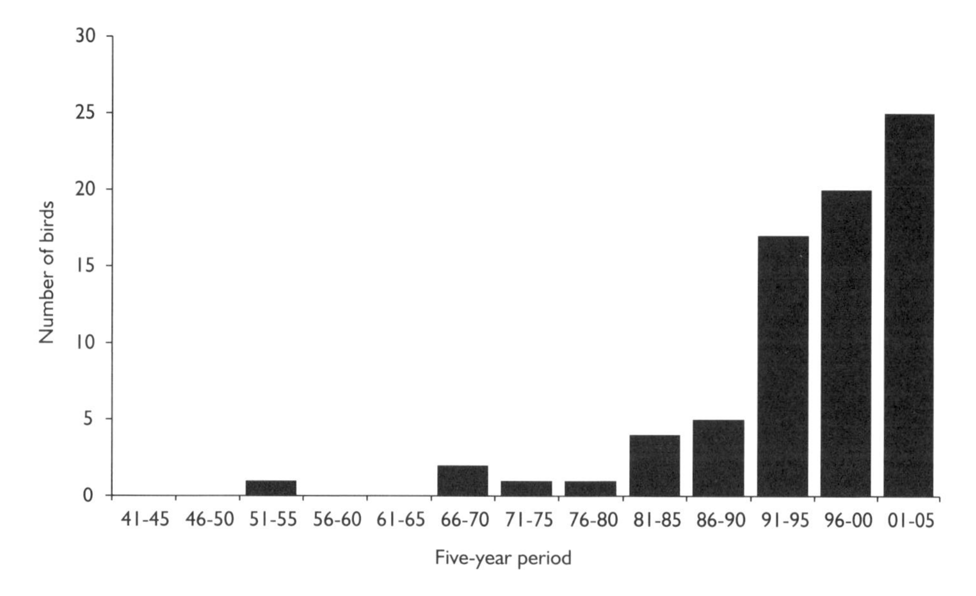

Figure 329: Numbers of Iceland Gulls 1941–2005.

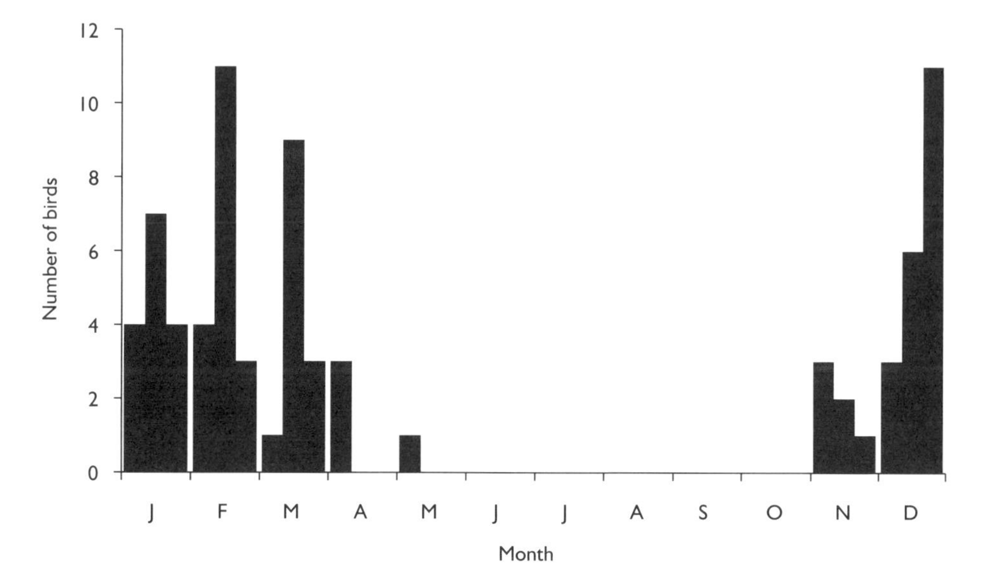

Figure 330: Monthly occurrence of Iceland Gulls 1941–2005.

Mackay (1995b) found that, by the end of 1994, almost half those aged had been first-winters, with about one quarter of records involving adults. Ten years later, the ratio of adults has increased noticeably and this age group now accounts for nearly 40% of all records. It may well be that some of our Iceland Gulls are now returning individuals.

The favoured site by far is Eyebrook Reservoir, which has accounted for almost 60% of all records. The dominance of this site is explained by the intensive coverage the roost receives and also the proximity of several large rubbish tips in nearby Corby (Northamptonshire). Swithland Reservoir follows in second place, although

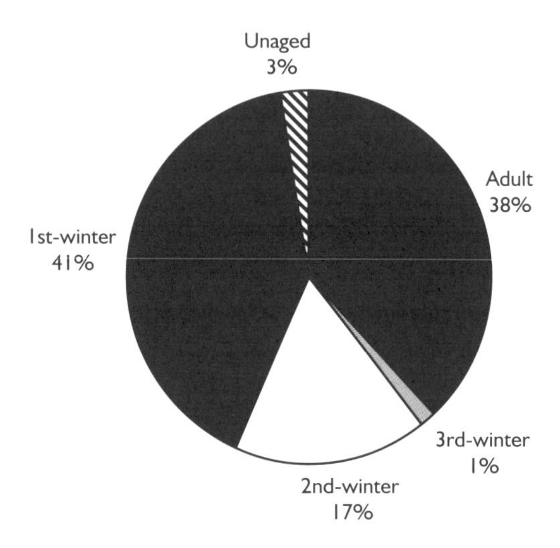

Figure 331: Age distribution of Iceland Gulls 1941–2005.

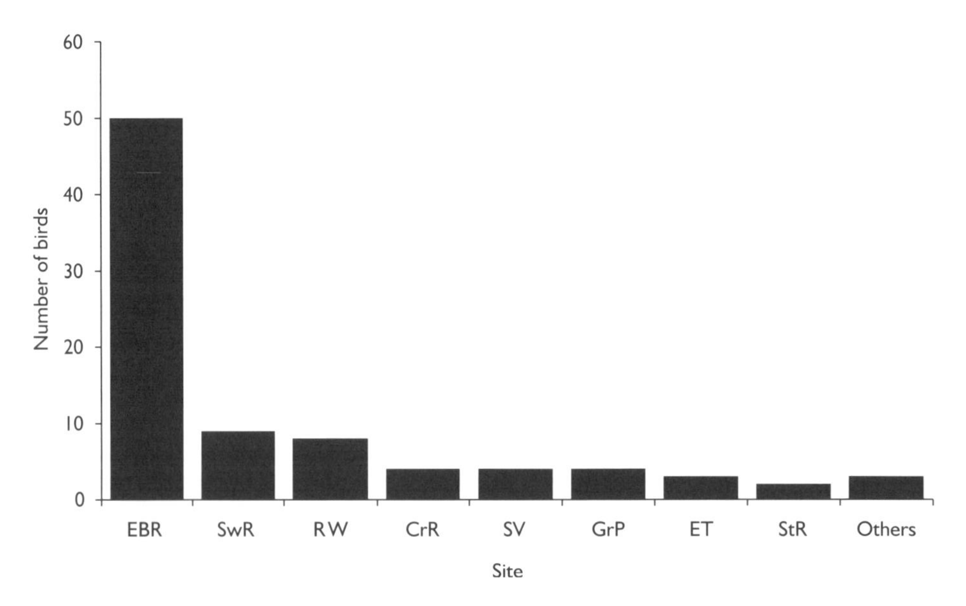

Figure 332: Sites where Iceland Gulls have been recorded 1941–2005.
Key to abbreviations: EBR = Eyebrook Reservoir; SwR = Swithland Reservoir; RW = Rutland Water; CrR = Cropston Reservoir; SV = Soar valley gravel pits; GrP = Groby Pool; ET = Enderby Tip; StR = Stanford Reservoir; CrR = Cropston Reservoir

following the closure of the nearby Mountsorrel Tip in the early 1990s, the number of large gulls roosting at this site has declined, with a consequent drop in records of the scarcer species such as the Iceland Gull. Records have come from a further ten sites, including the now-closed tips at Enderby and Shawell.

In addition, a report of one at Shawell Tip on November 24th 1995 was published in the LROS Annual Report but has since been found to be unacceptable (Fray 2005).

The nominate race of Iceland Gull breeds on the west and east coasts of Greenland and winters south of the breeding area in southern Greenland south to Britain. It is a scarce winter visitor to Britain in variable numbers, being more numerous in Scotland.

Kumlien's Gull *L.g.kumlieni*

An adult showing characters of this form was recorded in the roost at Eyebrook Reservoir by Andrew Harrop, John Wright and Mick Ketley on December 19th 1995 (*BB* 89:494 & 505).

Kumlien's Gulls, which breed on Baffin Island and winter in North America, are traditionally treated as a subspecies of Iceland Gull, but the taxonomy of the group remains controversial and a recent study (Weir *et al.* 2000) suggested that Kumlien's Gull is a hybrid between Iceland Gull and Thayer's Gull *Larus thayeri*.

AHJH

Glaucous Gull *Larus hyperboreus*

Scarce winter visitor, recorded in all months between October and April with the majority from December to February: 83 indivduals.

This species was first recorded in 1953, when one noted as an 'immature' was seen by Ronald Hickling at Barkby Lane Tip, Leicester on February 7th, with presumably the same bird at Blaby ten days later. With the exception of another 'immature' at Eyebrook Reservoir on March 12th 1955, the Glaucous Gull remained

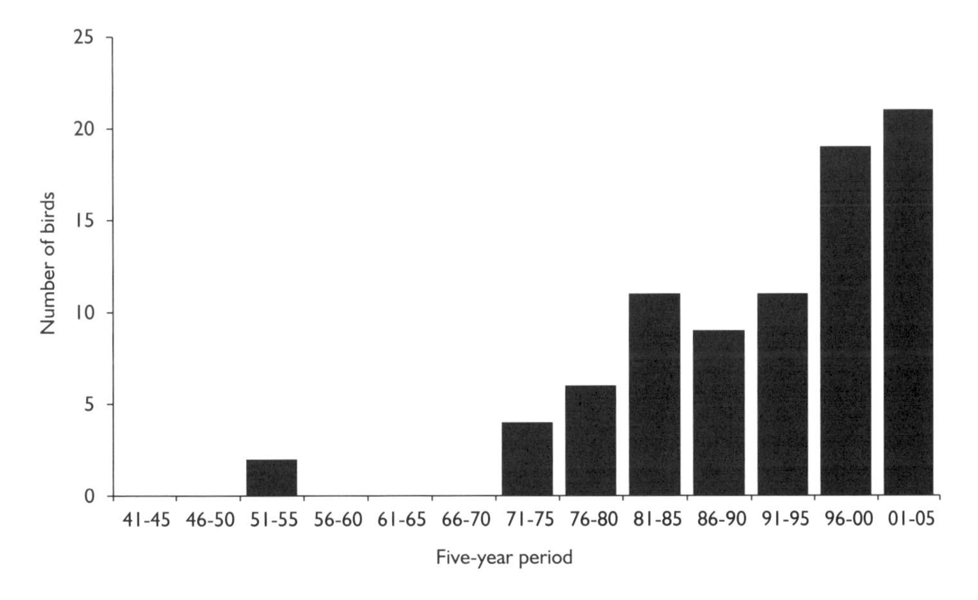

Figure 333: Numbers of Glaucous Gulls 1941–2005.

absent from the counties until 1971, although Hickling suggested that the identification of early records of Glaucous and Iceland Gulls may not have been entirely safe.

Unlike the Iceland Gull, the steady increase in records during the last three decades has not included any particularly large influxes and may be attributed to a growing interest in gulls and consequent observation of roosts. Since the third record for the counties, at Eyebrook Reservoir on November 14th 1971, there have been only six blank years, the last being 1993. There are usually fewer than four records a year, but five were recorded in 1986, 1999, 2002 and 2003 and six were seen in 1997 and 2001.

Glaucous Gulls tend to arrive and depart earlier than Iceland Gulls. The earliest winter arrival was an adult at Eyebrook Reservoir on October 14th 1972 and there have been a further four October arrivals:

- adult, Eyebrook Reservoir, October 15th to December 6th 1996.
- third-winter, Rutland Water, October 27th to December 18th 1991.
- adult, Eyebrook Reservoir October 30th 1995 to January 12th 1995.
- second-winter, Eyebook Reservoir, October 31st 1997 to January 10th 1998.

The majority of birds are recorded from late December to mid-February, whilst there is a developing pattern of a small passage occurring during mid-March. However, there have only been two records after March 20th:

- first-winter, Swithland Reservoir, March 21st and 22nd, with the same bird at Groby Pool on March 23rd.
- second-winter, Rutland Water, April 13th.

Most records refer to single birds but two have been seen together on six occasions and three have occurred together on three occasions:

- adult and two first-winters, Eyebrook Reservoir, January 12th 1996.
- adult, second-winter and first-winter, Eyebrook Reservoir, November 30th to December 2nd 1997.
- fourth-winter and two first-winters, Eyebrook Reservoir, December 31st 1999.

Mackay (1995b) found that, by the end of 1994, more than half those aged had been first-winters, with about one quarter of records involving adults. Ten years later, this ratio has changed very little and suggests that very few of our Glaucous Gulls are returning individuals. This contrasts with the increasing number of adult Iceland Gulls being recorded.

Mackay (1995b) noted that, by the end of 1994, the favoured site for Glaucous Gulls in the counties was Eyebrook Reservoir, followed closely by Swithland Reservoir. These waters are still the top two sites, but

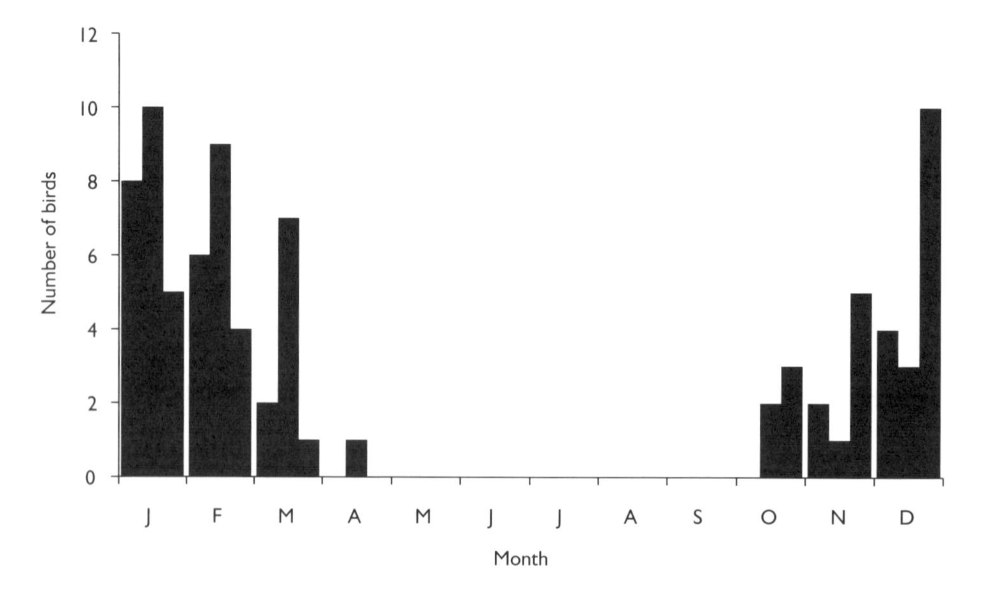

Figure 334: Monthly occurrence of Glaucous Gulls 1941–2005.

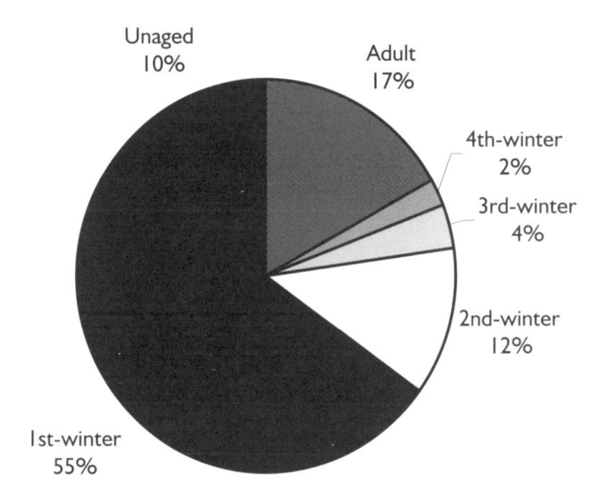

Figure 335: Age distribution of Glaucous Gulls 1941–2005.

Eyebrook Reservoir is now totally dominant. There are probably two reasons for this: firstly, the massively increased coverage of the roost at Eyebrook Reservoir and secondly the closure of Mountsorrel Tip, adjacent to Swithland Reservoir, in the early 1990s and consequent drop in roosting gull numbers at this site. Rutland Water has attracted relatively few Glaucous Gulls and many of the ones that have been recorded there have previously been seen at Eyebrook Reservoir. Elsewhere, only Groby Pool attracts this species with any regularity and six of its seven records have occurred since December 1997, corresponding with the opening of the nearby rubbish tip. Records have come from a further 12 scattered sites, including the now-closed tips at Enderby, Lount and Barkby Lane, Leicester.

A report of one at Shawell Tip on December 1st 1995 was published in the LROS Annual Report but has since been found to be unacceptable (Fray 2005).

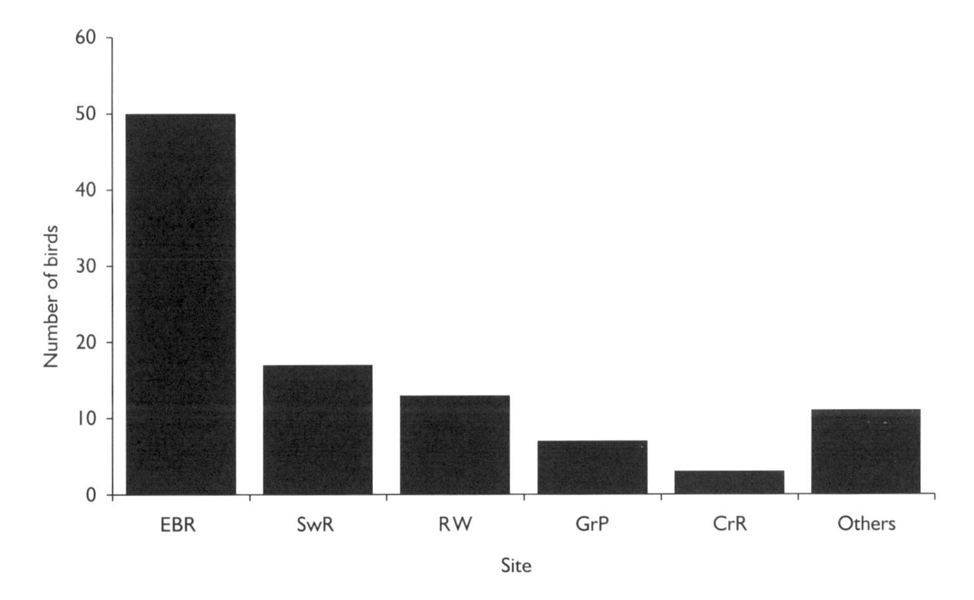

Figure 336: Sites where Glaucous Gulls have been recorded 1941–2005.
Key to abbreviations: EBR = Eyebrook Reservoir; SwR = Swithland Reservoir; RW = Rutland Water; GrP = Groby Pool; CrR = Cropston Reservoir

Hybrids with Herring Gulls have been recorded: see 'Hybrids' (pages 676–684).

Glaucous Gulls breed on the Arctic coasts of Canada and Russia, Greenland, Iceland and sub-Arctic islands. Eurasian birds are partly resident with some dispersal south, but North American birds move further, wintering mainly on coasts to the south of the breeding range. They are scarce winter visitors in variable numbers to Britain, being more numerous in Scotland and it is thought that most of those that visit Britain originate from Greenland (Dean 1984, Tucker 1985).

AHJH

Great Black-backed Gull *Larus marinus*

Fairly common winter visitor, scarce or uncommon at other times.

During the 19th century this species was very rare in the counties. Browne lists just two records and Haines a further three; details of all these occurrences are scant.

As its scientific name suggests, this species is more strictly maritime than other large gulls and consequently has always been relatively scarce in the counties. Nonetheless, its status is less clear than that of some other species because data are incomplete and there was confusion with the Lesser Black-backed Gull during the first half of the 20th century.

In 1941, it was considered to be an irregular migrant and winter visitor. The first double-figure flock related to 11 birds at Quorn on February 1st 1950. During the following decades numbers steadily increased, with 50 at Eyebrook Reservoir on October 25th 1965 and 71 at Swithland Reservoir in December 1973. In the same year, ten were present in the summer roost at Swithland Reservoir. By the late 1970s the species was considered to be a fairly common winter visitor and roosting flocks of 500 were recorded at Rutland Water in both January 1983 and early January 1984. Twenty years later a roost of 500 was counted at Eyebrook Reservoir during the BTO winter gull roost survey in January 2004, so the population may have reached a stable level. A total of 786 birds at six sites was counted during the same survey. Since 400 is the qualifying level for sites of national importance, the number in the Eyebrook Reservoir roost is significant.

Table 24: Numbers of Great Black-backed Gulls during BTO winter gull roost surveys 1953–2004

	1953	1963	1973	1983	1993	2004
Eyebrook Reservoir	0	0	5	100	30	500
Swithland Reservoir	0	1	16	25	13	67
Rutland Water	nc	nc	nc	500	170	50
Others	0	2	0	212	7	169
Totals	0	3	21	837	220	786

nc signifies site not counted

In 1998, 20 non-breeding sub-adult birds were present at Rutland Water on June 6th. Up to ten immature birds are normally present at this site during the summer: they are frequently seen hunting round the reservoir and several attacks on wildfowl have been recorded.

There have been two recoveries of ringed birds. A first-winter ringed at Enderby on February 7th 1981 was found dead in April the following year just 43 km east-north-east near Grantham (Lincolnshire); more interesting was a colour-ringed bird at Eyebrook Reservoir on January 5th 2003, which was seen again at Rutland Water on October 14th 2004 and originated in Norway.

Great Black-backed Gulls breed from eastern Canada and the United States to Svalbard and the Barents Sea, south to Britain and France. Southern populations are dispersive outside the breeding season and northern populations move south in winter. The British breeding population is currently estimated at just over 17,000 pairs (Baker *et al.* 2006).

AHJH

Bridled Tern *Onychoprion anaethetus*

Very rare vagrant from the tropics: one record.

An adult, first seen at 20:45 by Chris Lythall, Paul Powell and J. Pearson flying over Lagoon II at Rutland Water on June 8th 1984, was tentatively identified as a Sooty Tern *Onychoprion fuscata*. A large crowd had gathered the following morning and with the bird still present its true identity was revealed. It was last seen flying off east at 11:45 that morning (*BB* 78:559).

This was a truly remarkable record, being the eighth for Britain, only the fourth to be seen alive and the first inland. It was also the first to be seen by large numbers of observers. The British total now stands at 21, of which 11 occurred between 1988 and 1994; two of these also occurred inland, in Northamptonshire in 1993 and West Yorkshire the following year.

Bridled Terns occur throughout the tropics, the closest populations to Europe being in Mauritania, the Red Sea and the Persian Gulf; otherwise, they are widely distributed throughout the Caribbean, Indian Ocean, south-east Asia, Indonesia and Australia.

RED

Little Tern *Sternula albifrons*

Scarce passage visitor; recorded in all months between April and October, the majority in May and August.

Browne, writing in VH, details one which was seen at Knossington on October 2nd 1901 and shot the next day. Haines knew of three occurrences in Rutland: single birds shot at Burley Fishponds in approximately 1890 and Exton in 1896 and another seen at the latter site in 1901.

There is no local data on records during the early part of the 20th century, but over the 65 years since the formation of LROS the occurrence of this species has remained relatively consistent, with records in all but 12 years since 1941. Typically there are no more than five individuals recorded annually, although there have been 11 years with between six and ten birds seen, 11 were found in 1974, 1976, 1978 and 1992 and 13 were noted in 1983. The best decade was the 1970s, with an average of just under seven individuals recorded annually; conversely, the 1950s produced an average of just two birds per year and included a period when the only records between September 26th 1954 and August 12th 1960 were two single birds in 1957.

Two distinct passage periods are apparent and over 86% of all records have occurred between April 21st and June 10th or July 21st and September 10th; the spring passage period has produced approximately twice as many birds as the autumn one. Sightings prior to the last ten days of April are rare: the earliest was one at Trent Valley Pit on April 16th 2004 and there have been only three other records before April 20th:

- one at Stanford Reservoir on April 17th 2004.
- one at Eyebrook Reservoir on April 18th 1949.
- two at Swithland Reservoir on April 19th 1976.

Most spring records involve one or two birds, although three have been recorded on eight occasions, four have been seen together three times, five were at Eyebrook Reservoir on May 16th 1974 and up to six were at Rutland Water on April 26th 1992.

Autumn passage peaks in late August, although there have been several records during late June and early July, including three at Rutland Water on July 1st 2000. The data show that September occurrences are not unusual, although the only record during this month since 1983 was one at Thornton Reservoir on September 21st 1993. Reports later than this date are unusual, the only others during the last ten days of September being:

- three at Stanford Reservoir on September 21st 1953.
- one at Eyebrook Reservoir from September 21st to 26th 1954.
- four at Eyebrook Reservoir on September 23rd 1983, with two still present the next day.
- one at Stanford Reservoir on September 26th 1954.
- one at Eyebrook Reservoir on September 26th 1963.
- two at Swithland Reservoir on September 28th 1969.

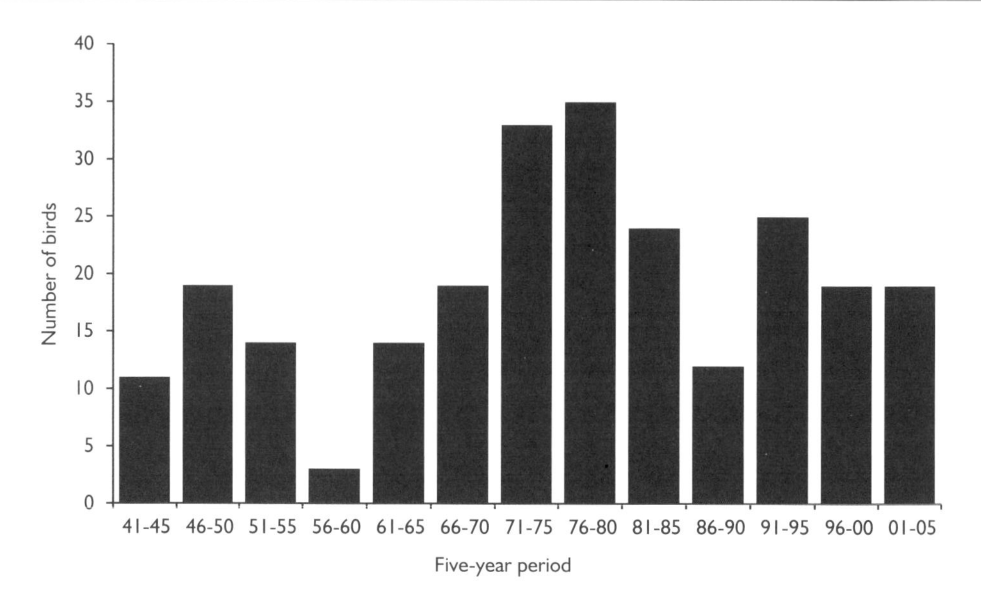

Figure 337: Numbers of Little Terns 1941–2005.

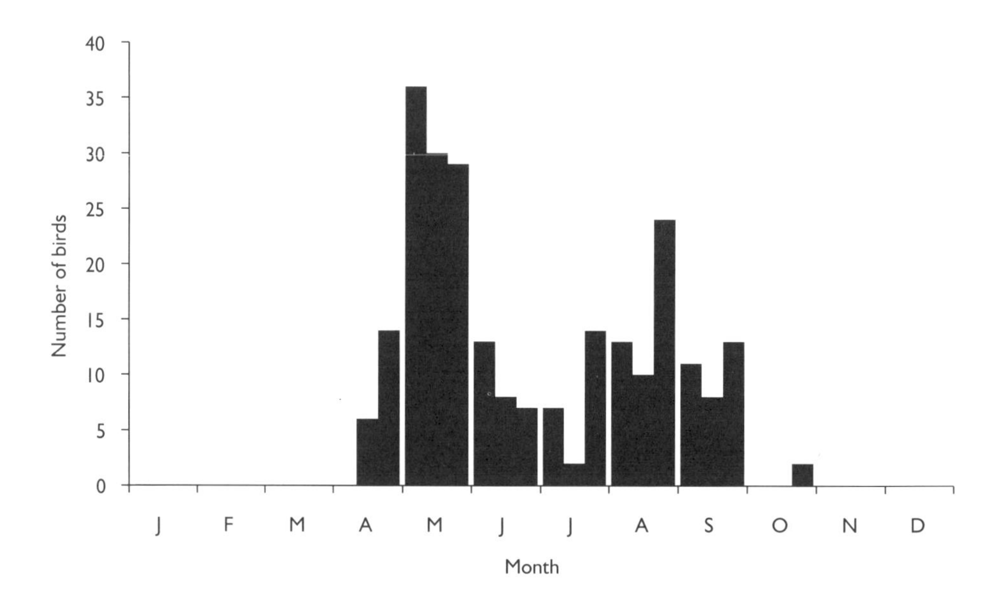

Figure 338: Monthly occurrence of Little Terns 1941–2005.

However, the latest autumn record by some margin was two at Eyebrook Reservoir on October 25th and 26th 1952 which, with the exception of the bird described by Browne in 1901, is the only record during this month.

As in spring, most autumn occurrences involve one or two birds, but three have been seen twice, there have been two records of four together, five were at both Eyebrook Reservoir on September 4th 1961 and Rutland Water on July 23rd 2000, six were at Eyebrook Reservoir on August 28th 1978 and seven were at Rutland Water on August 29th 1983.

A typical Little Tern record in the counties involves short-staying individuals; indeed, over 89% of all birds have been seen on one date only. There have only been four instances of birds remaining for four days or more:

- three at Stanford Reservoir from June 5th to 11th 1944.
- up to three at Eyebrook Reservoir from May 13th to 18th 1950.
- one at Eyebrook Reservoir from September 21st to 26th 1954.
- one at Rutland Water from June 11th to 14th 2005.

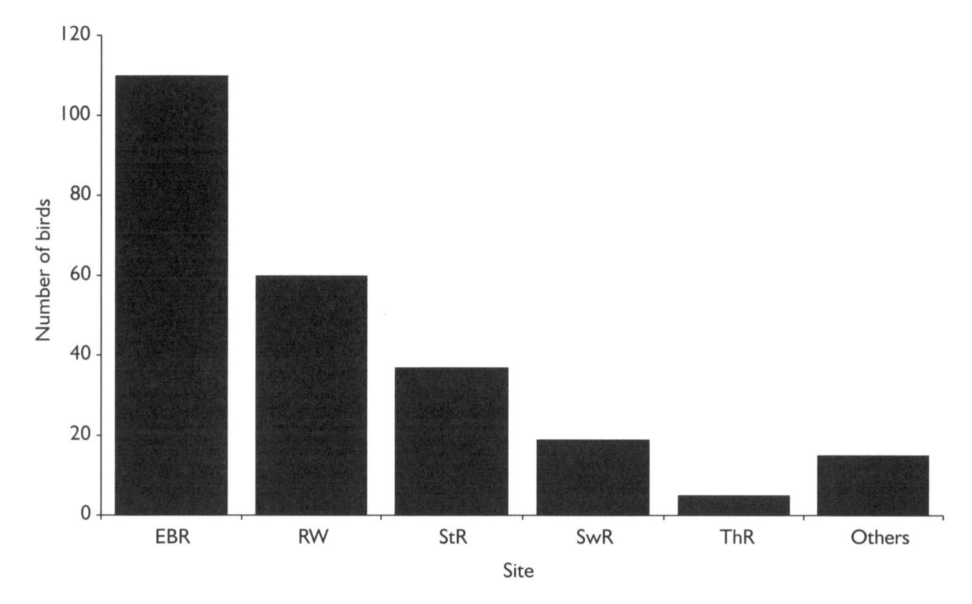

Figure 339: Sites where Little Terns have been recorded 1941–2005.
Key to abbreviations: EBR = Eyebrook Reservoir; RW = Rutland Water; StR = Stanford Reservoir; SwR = Swithland Reservoir; ThR = Thornton Reservoir

Little Terns have been seen at most areas of water in the counties, although not at Fort Henry Ponds, Belvoir Lakes and the underwatched reservoirs of Blackbrook and Knipton. They are surprisingly rare at both Cropston Reservoir, where the only records have been single birds on August 8th 1987 and July 8th 2004 and in the Soar valley, where one at Wanlip Gravel Pits on June 19th 1965 is the only occurrence. Eyebrook Reservoir is by far the most favoured site, with 44% of all records coming from here; Rutland Water, Stanford Reservoir and Swithland Reservoir are the only other sites to have recorded more than five individuals.

Following review in 2004, a record of one at Saddington Reservoir on the exceptional date of April 2nd 1973 was found to be inadequately documented and is no longer considered acceptable (Fray 2005).

Little Terns breed discontinuously from western Europe through eastern Europe and into central Asia, with other populations in eastern and southern Asia, Australia, west Africa and the western Indian Ocean. Western European birds winter around Africa. In Britain, the species breeds colonially on sandy or shingle beaches; the coast south from Lincolnshire to Hampshire holds over half the British breeding population. The latest population estimate is just under 2,000 pairs (Mitchell *et al.* 2004) and as there has been a moderate decline in numbers over the last 25 years, the Little Tern has been added to the 'Amber List' of Birds of Conservation Concern (Gregory *et al.* 2002).

RED

Caspian Tern *Hydroprogne caspia*

Very rare vagrant from Europe: seven records.

The first county record was of one seen by R.B. Ratcliffe at Stanford Reservoir on June 3rd 1968. It was present from 14:30 to 15:00 before flying off to the south-west (*BB* 62:473).

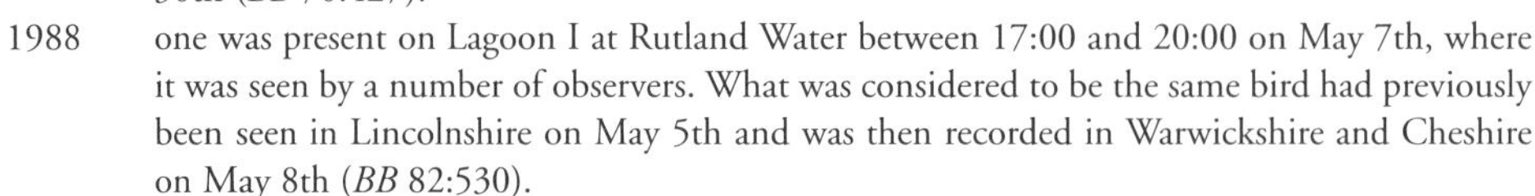

All records:

1968 Stanford Reservoir, June 3rd.

1972 one was seen at Eyebrook Reservoir during the evening of July 12th by S.S. and M.J. Garner (*BB* 66:344).

1976 Jean Ironside and Dave Willett recorded an adult at Eyebrook Reservoir on July 30th (*BB* 70:427).

1988 one was present on Lagoon I at Rutland Water between 17:00 and 20:00 on May 7th, where it was seen by a number of observers. What was considered to be the same bird had previously been seen in Lincolnshire on May 5th and was then recorded in Warwickshire and Cheshire on May 8th (*BB* 82:530).

1991 one found by H.R. and K.E. Carter was present at Eyebrook Reservoir from 13:00 to 16:10 on July 27th (*BB* 85:530).

1992 one seen by Andy Smith at Thornton Reservoir on June 20th was originally rejected by the BBRC (*BB* 86:539) but was later found to be acceptable (*BB* 87:532). What was probably the same bird was seen the following day at Belvide Reservoir (Staffordshire).

1998 one was seen briefly by Matthew Berriman and Tim Appleton on the Egleton Reserve at Rutland Water on August 1st (*BB* 94:479).

The Caspian Tern is a cosmopolitan breeder with a fragmented range covering much of Eurasia, Africa, Australasia and North America. The nearest breeding population to Britain is around the Baltic Sea and these birds winter mainly in west Africa, with some in the Mediterranean. It currently averages around five sightings a year in Britain and by the end of 2005 had mustered almost 280 records. The two best years are 1976 (12 records) and 1988 (18 records), neatly corresponding with two of the above individuals. A large proportion of British sightings have occurred between late June and early August and in this respect the Leicestershire and Rutland records conform to this established pattern. Mid to late July at Eyebrook Reservoir would seem to offer would-be finders the best chance of locating one of these giant terns in the future.

RED

Whiskered Tern *Chlidonias hybrida*

Very rare vagrant from southern Europe: one record.

A first-winter was seen by J.M. and K.A. Wilson at Stanford Reservoir on October 22nd 1991, spending most of its brief stay in the Leicestershire part of the reservoir (*BB* 87:534).

Whiskered Terns breed from Spain and France through southern Europe and discontinuously east to China. Other populations breed in east and southern Africa, northern India and Australia. Western Palearctic birds winter mainly in Africa. They are rare, but regular, visitors to Britain, with 146 records by the end of 2005; of these, the majority have occurred in May and June. The Leicestershire individual was on a very unusual date; there have been only four other October records in Britain and just one (in Bedfordshire and Buckinghamshire in 2001) on a later date than the Stanford Reservoir bird.

RMF

Black Tern *Chlidonias niger*

Uncommon to fairly common passage migrant; recorded in all months between April and December, with the majority in April, May, August and September.

Browne described the Black Tern as an 'occasional straggler' to Leicestershire in the 19th century and knew of records from Saddington Reservoir, Melton Mowbray, Nailstone, Swithland Reservoir, Lubenham and Abbey Meadows, Leicester. A flock of 40 was at Belgrave, Leicester on April 24th 1886, two of which were shot and presented to the Leicester Museum. In Rutland, Haines considered it to be the commonest of the terns, with

records from Burley Fishponds, Thorpe by Water and Gretton (which is actually in Northamptonshire); all were shot and 'that every specimen seen should have been destroyed is absolutely inexcusable and it is hateful to have to record it'. The LROS archives list three records for the early part of the 20th century, at Cropston Reservoir in August 1908, Sileby in October 1938 and Thurmaston in May 1919.

Today the Black Tern is a spring and autumn passage migrant in highly variable numbers. The first birds are usually seen during the last ten days of April, although the earliest report is of two at Eyebrook Reservoir on the exceptional date of April 1st 1949, almost two weeks earlier than any other record. Birds have arrived prior to April 20th in a further ten years, with records prior to April 17th being as follows (all relate to single birds unless stated):

- two, Eyebrook Reservoir, April 13th 1959.
- Cropston Reservoir, April 13th 1980.
- Swithland Reservoir, April 13th 1980.
- Rutland Water, April 13th 1980.
- two, Rutland Water, April 15th 2003.
- Watermead Gravel Pits, April 16th 1986.

The first spring arrival date fluctuates considerably; for instance, in 2001 and 2002 the first records were not until May 10th and May 17th respectively. Unlike the Common and Arctic Terns, the average spring arrival date of Black Terns has become gradually later since the mid-1980s. Note that, in the graph below, no data is available for the period 1951 to 1955.

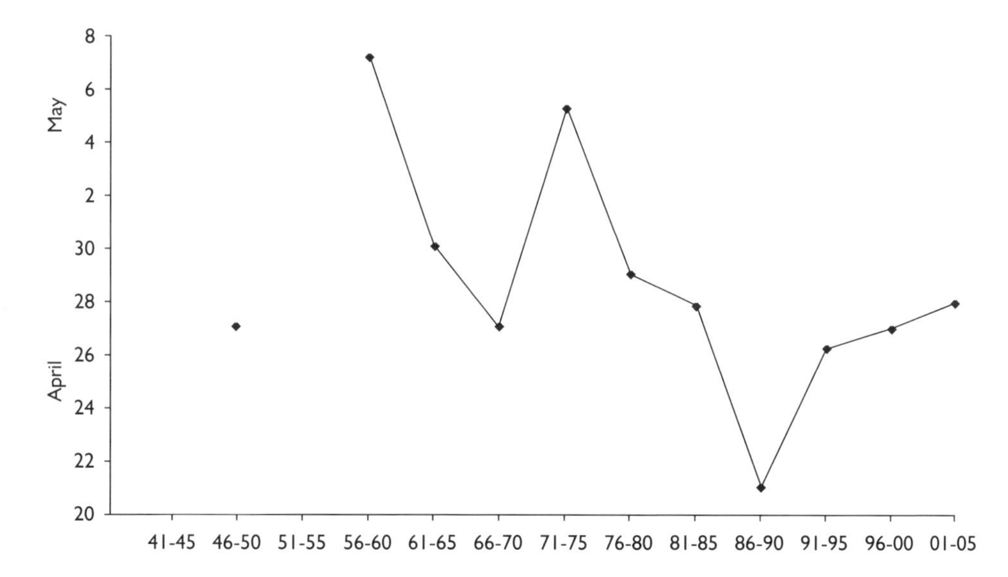

Figure 340: Average spring arrival dates of Black Terns by five-year periods 1946–2005.

Spring passage is normally most obvious during May, but is unpredictable and largely dependent upon weather conditions. In some years it can be disappointing involving just small numbers; for instance, only six birds were seen in the spring of 1972 and more recently there were only 12 in 1995, 15 in 2002 and 16 in 2003, whilst the springs of 1943, 1944, 1951, 1953 and 1955 were completely blank. Conversely some large flocks may be recorded, often concentrated into just a few days. The most spectacular of these passages occurred in 1997, when on May 3rd over 400 were recorded including 285 at Rutland Water: the largest spring flock ever to occur in the counties, and 110 at Eyebrook Reservoir. The following day only one could be found. Several flocks of up to 50 were counted in the first week of May 1990, with peak counts of 140 at Rutland Water on the 4th and 120 at Eyebrook Reservoir on the 2nd. These concentrated passage periods are not a recent phenomenon: what was described as 'a spectacular rush' occurred between May 16th and 19th 1948, when 90 at Eyebrook Reservoir on the 17th was the highest count, 200 were at Eyebrook Reservoir on May 23rd 1959 and in late May 1966 there were 67 at Stanford Reservoir on the 20th, 80 at Eyebrook Reservoir on the 30th and 32 at Saddington Reservoir on the 31st.

Away from the reservoirs previously mentioned, double-figure spring counts have occurred at seven sites, where maxima have been:

- 55 at Wanlip South Gravel Pits on May 7th 1988.
- 34 at Swithland Reservoir on May 10th 1959.
- 20 at Frisby Gravel Pits on May 18th 1992.
- 16 at Cropston Reservoir on May 18th 1948.
- 13 at Sawley Gravel Pits on May 9th 1946.
- 12 at Priory Water on May 24th 1991.
- 12 at Trent Valley Pit on May 12th 1993.

Odd birds occasionally linger into June, including a pair at Rutland Water on June 19th 1988 which were seen attempting to mate. Flocks in this month are very unusual but have reached double-figures on six occasions, only one of which has been since 1968:

- 45 at Eyebrook Reservoir on June 13th 1961.
- 29 at Eyebrook Reservoir on June 1st 1963, with 30 on the 3rd, 32 on the 4th and 15 on the 5th.
- 20 at Eyebrook Reservoir on June 11th 1946.
- 13 at Rutland Water on June 1st 1991.
- 12 at Stanford Reservoir on June 12th 1968, with 14 the following day.
- 11 at Eyebrook Reservoir on June 14th 1968.

Autumn passage is far more protracted and usually begins in mid to late July. Numbers in this month are usually small, although there were exceptional counts at Eyebrook Reservoir of 42 on July 4th 1963, 34 on July 31st 1971 and 14 on July 30th 1978, as well as 16 at Stanford Reservoir on July 29th 1969, 14 at Rutland Water on July 29th 2004 and 13 at this site on July 28th 1991. Autumn numbers, as in the spring, can be highly variable: 1952 was completely blank and there was only one individual seen in the autumn of 1955, but over 100 birds were recorded in the autumns of 1967, 1974, 1980, 1985, 1992 and 1994. By far the highest numbers were recorded in September 1992 (Table 25): on the 11th there were almost 1,300 birds in the counties, but most had departed by the 14th.

Table 25: Black Terns in mid-September 1992

	11th	**12th**	**13th**
Rutland Water	650	350	250
Eyebrook Reservoir	400	57	42
Thornton Reservoir	200	11	11
Watermead Park	20	0	0
Swithland Reservoir	4	0	0
Totals	1,274	418	303

An anticyclone which became dominant over northern Europe contributed to a largely southeasterly airflow at the time of the influx, which was the largest ever recorded in Britain. The birds were probably displaced from the Ijsselmeer (Netherlands), which is used in autumn by most of the birds which breed in the Western Palearctic. On 6 September 6th, 10,215 had passed Dungeness (Kent) and on September 11th, 710 passed Sheringham (Norfolk). The influx was most noticeable in east and southeast England and the Midlands; on the 11th there were 700 in Northamptonshire, 260 in Nottinghamshire, 220 in Derbyshire and 1,696 in the West Midlands.

The magnitude of this passage through the counties is put into perspective as the only other September count to exceed 50 was 80 at Eyebrook Reservoir on September 16th 1994. Another notable autumn movement occurred on August 30th 1985, when there were 70 at Rutland Water and 55 at Eyebrook Reservoir.

Other than those mentioned above, flocks at the two main sites of Rutland Water and Eyebrook Reservoir have exceeded 40 during the autumn on six occasions:

- 100 at Rutland Water on August 9th 1980.
- 70 to 80 at Eyebrook Reservoir on August 5th 1954.
- 53 at Eyebrook Reservoir on September 16th 1953.
- 50 at Eyebrook Reservoir on August 21st 1962.
- 49 at Eyebrook Reservoir on September 1st 1994.
- 42 at Eyebrook Reservoir on August 31st 1951.

Elsewhere, double-figure autumn counts are relatively unusual and, excluding those in September 1992, the only ones to have occurred have been:

- 55 at Stanford Reservoir on August 9th 1967.
- 43 at Stanford Reservoir on August 22nd 1977.
- 22 at Thornton Reservoir on August 31st 2005.
- 19 at Thornton Reservoir on September 19th 1987.
- 14 at Stanford Reservoir on August 5th 1971.
- 13 at Swithland Reservoir on August 31st 1990.
- Ten at Swithland Reservoir on September 21st 1991.

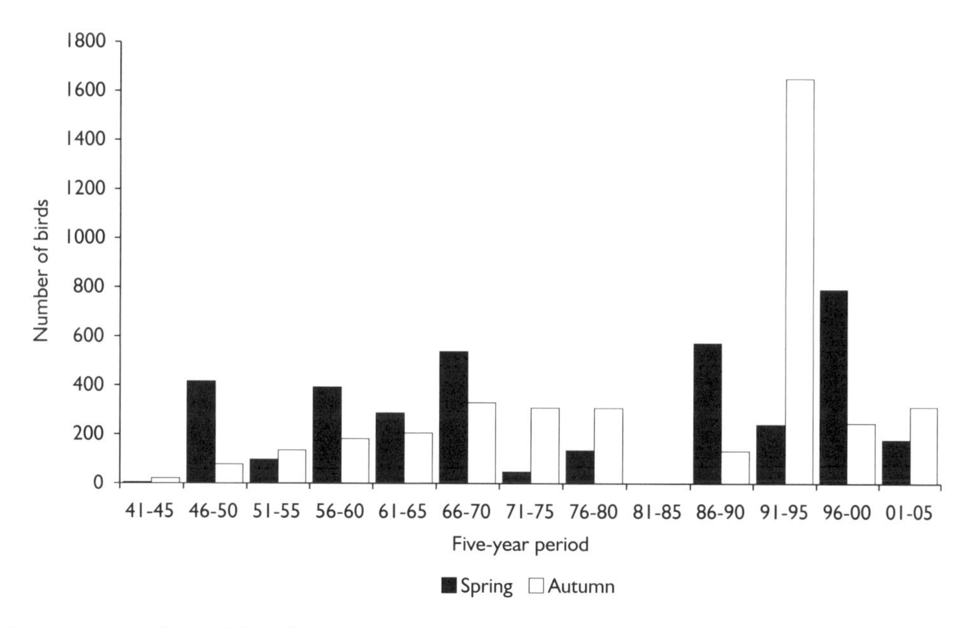

Figure 341: Numbers of Black Terns by five-year periods 1941–2005.

Birds have lingered into October in 35 of the 65 years between 1941 and 2005; numbers during this month are usually small, although ten were at Eyebrook Reservoir on October 1st 1967, 19 were at Rutland Water on October 4th 1982 and nine were at Eyebrook Reservoir on the late date of October 23rd 1967. As well as the latter flock, there have been records of single birds remaining later than October 20th in six years, including two which lingered into November and an exceptional December record, as follows:

- Swithland Reservoir, throughout October 1967 until November 6th.
- Eyebrook Reservoir, October 28th 1967.

- Rutland Water, October 25th 1984.
- Eyebrook Reservoir, December 2nd to 9th 1984.
- Saddington Reservoir, October 28th to November 4th 1991.
- Rutland Water, October 28th 2001.
- Rutland Water, October 14th to 26th 2004.

A previously published report of one at Eyebrook Reservoir on November 9th 1968 was reviewed in 2004 and found to be unacceptable (Fray 2005).

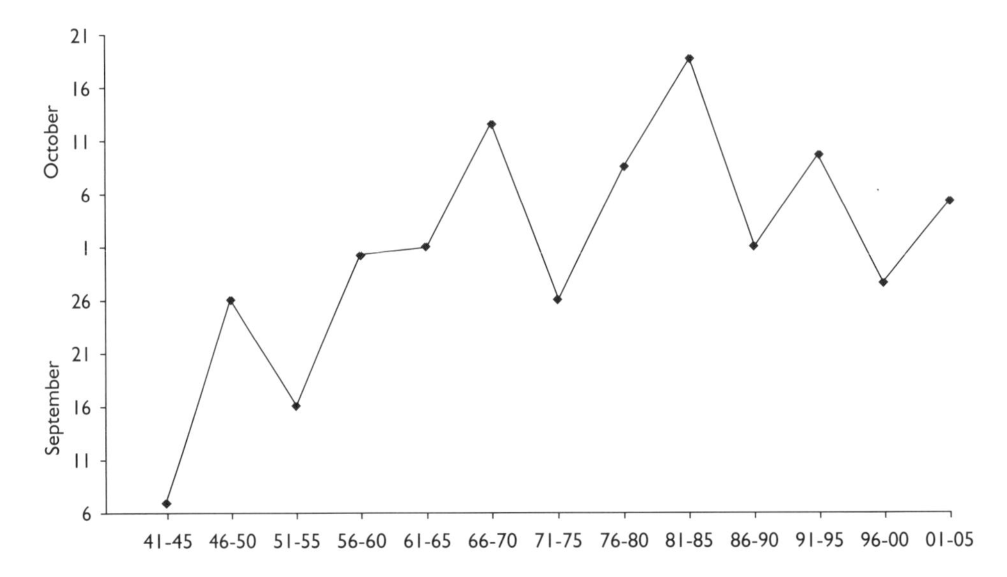

Figure 342: Average autumn departure dates of Black Terns by five-year periods 1941–2005.

Black Terns breed in most of Europe, from Spain to southern Sweden and east through Europe and west Asia to central Siberia, with another population in central North America. Eurasian birds spend the winter primarily along the coast of west Africa from Senegal southwards to Namibia and also in the Nile valley from southern Egypt to Sudan. They were regular breeders in some areas of eastern and south-east England until the 1850s. Recent breeding records have occurred in 1966, 1969, 1970, 1975 and 1978, the last occasion in Nottinghamshire.

RED

White-winged Black Tern (White-winged Tern) — *Chlidonias leucopterus*

Rare vagrant from Europe; recorded in May to September and November, with the majority in August and September: 16 records involving 18 individuals.

A recent review of historical and unpublished records found evidence of an adult at Packington on May 8th 1909; this record was also mentioned in the LROS archives. However, further investigation has revealed that the bird was present at the village of Packington in Warwickshire (Leigh 1910) and thus does not form part of the Leicestershire and Rutland record.

The first record for the counties was one at Eyebrook Reservoir from November 10th to 27th 1968 (*BB* 62:472, Uppingham School Field Club & Kirton 1969). It is likely that this bird was present from at least November 9th, as a Black Tern (which is no longer considered proven) was reported at the same site on this date. There have been a further 15 records, involving 17 individuals.

All records:

1968	Eyebrook Reservoir, November 10th to 27th.
1976	adult, Stanford Reservoir, May 24th (*BB* 70:426).
	juvenile, Rutland Water, September 2nd to 5th (*BB* 70:426).
	juvenile, Rutland Water and Eyebrook Reservoir, September 25th (*BB* 70:426).
1978	juvenile, Eyebrook Reservoir, August 1st to 2nd (*BB* 73:514).
	juvenile, Eyebrook Reservoir, August 29th to September 4th (BB 73:514).
	juvenile, Stanford Reservoir, September 12th (*BB* 73:514).
1979	adult, Eyebrook Reservoir, June 6th (*BB* 73:514).
1987	adult, Rutland Water, June 9th (*BB* 84:477).
1991	juvenile, Swithland Reservoir, September 21st (*BB* 85:531).
1992	juvenile, Rutland Water, September 11th to 13th (*BB* 86:493).
1994	adult, Watermead Park, July 12th (*BB* 88:522).
1999	juvenile, Rutland Water, September 5th to 9th (*BB* 93:538).
2004	first-summer, Rutland Water, July 8th to 11th (*BB* 98:622).
2005	juvenile, Rutland Water, August 28th to 31st (*BB* 100:53).
	three juveniles, Rutland Water, September 8th to 11th, with one until September 14th (*BB* 100:53).

One at Rutland Water on July 8th 2004 was initially reported both as a Black Tern and a Little Gull. Its true identity was determined as a first-summer individual of this species on July 11th, its final day at the site. It appears that this may be the first documented occurrence of a first-summer in Britain. The juvenile at Rutland Water from September 5th to 9th 1999 was also unusual in that it was in an advanced state of moult (Bradshaw & Wright 2002). The juvenile at Rutland Water from September 11th to 13th 1992 was part of a national influx involving up to 50 individuals and also coincided with an unprecedented national influx of Black Terns.

The breeding range of the White-winged Black Tern fringes eastern Europe, primarily Poland and Hungary, and extends eastwards into Kazakhstan and parts of central Russia. There have also been isolated breeding attempts in several European countries as far west as Belgium. This population spends the winter in suitable habitat across the whole of Africa south of the Sahara with the exception of most of the west coastal regions. A separate population breeds east of Lake Baikal and south into northern China, wintering primarily around the

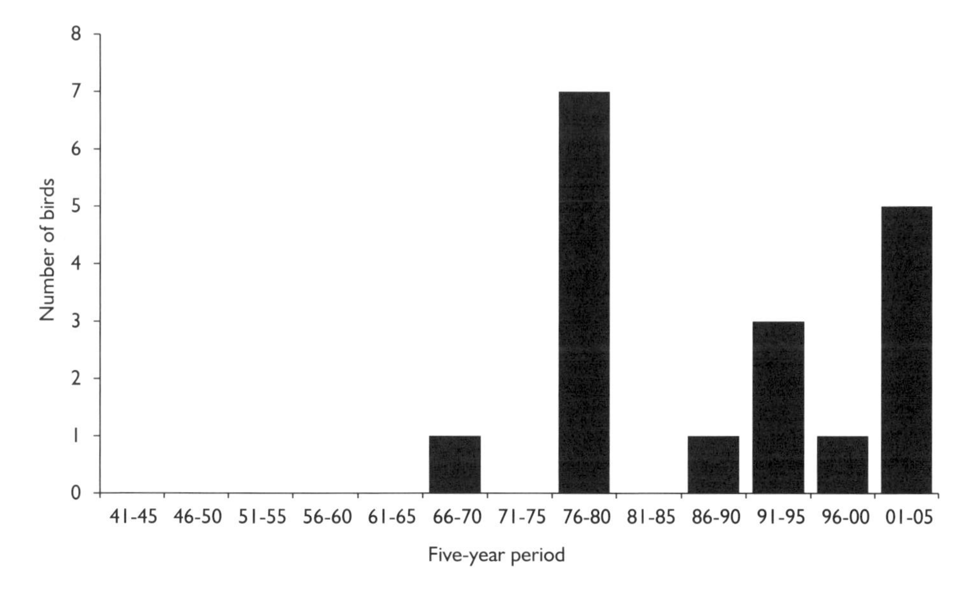

Figure 343: Numbers of White-winged Black Terns by five-year periods 1941–2005.

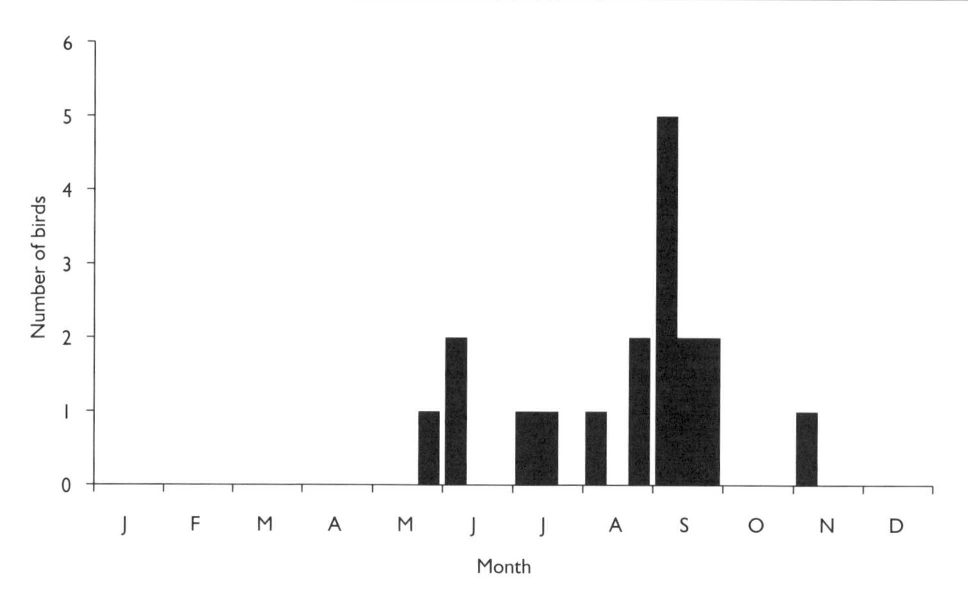

Figure 344: Monthly occurrence of White-winged Black Terns 1941–2005.

coastal regions of south-east China, throughout most of the East Indies, Sri Lanka and south into the northern coastal fringes of Australia. In an average year there are around 20 British records, but over 30 were recorded in 1970, 1976 (a good year locally) and 1977 and almost 50 in 1992. The White-winged Black Tern was removed from the list of species considered by the BBRC at the end of 2005, by which time the number of British records was 871.

RED

Sandwich Tern *Sterna sandvicensis*

Scarce passage visitor; recorded in all months between March and October, with the majority in August and September.

The first county record was not until 1945, when one was at Stanford Reservoir on April 14th. Since then, this species has been recorded in all but ten years up to 2005, with 2001 being the only blank year since 1974. Typically there are up to three occurrences annually, although there were four records in ten years and five in 2003. As Sandwich Terns often appear in the counties in small flocks, the total number of individuals recorded each year can vary greatly. Figure 345 suggests that this species has occurred more frequently since the mid-1980s and, whilst it is true that nine of the ten blank years since 1945 were between 1952 and 1974, numbers in recent times have been influenced by the occurrence of several large flocks.

Two distinct passage periods are apparent, from late April to mid-May and from late August to late September. Over three times as many individuals have been recorded in autumn as in spring, but there have been no more than three records in any spring or autumn period. Sightings prior to April 11th are rare; the earliest was of two at Swithland Reservoir on March 24th 2002, with the only other ones having been:

- one at Rutland Water on March 30th 1983.
- one at Priory Water on March 31st 1996.
- one at Eyebrook Reservoir on April 2nd 1999.
- one at Rutland Water on April 3rd and 4th 2004.
- two at Eyebrook Reservoir on April 6th 1966.

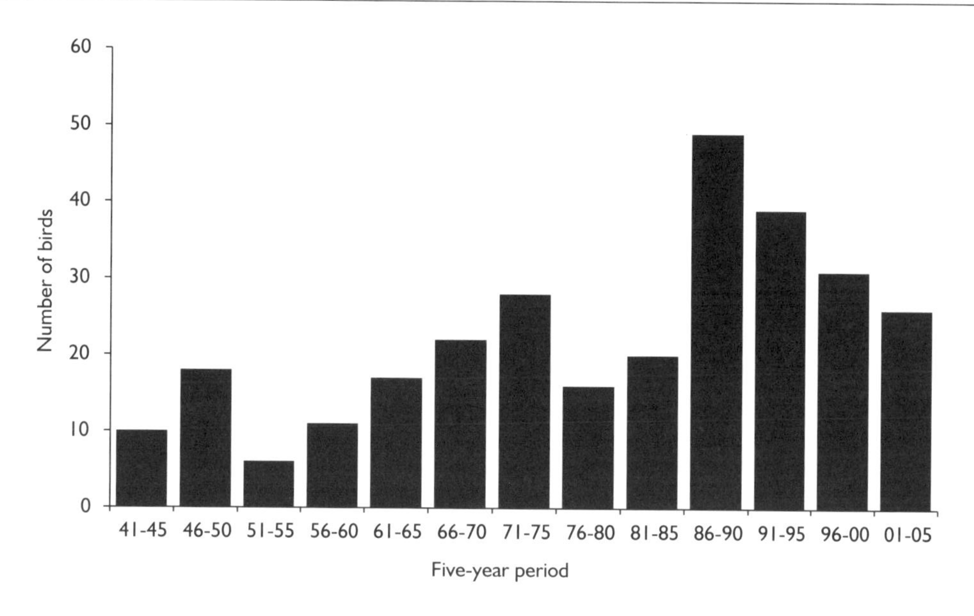

Figure 345: Numbers of Sandwich Terns 1941–2005.

Most spring records involve one or two birds, although three have been seen together on five occasions, four were at Rutland Water on both May 7th 1990 and April 23rd 2004 and nine were at Stanford Reservoir on May 20th 1945.

Autumn reports have been spread throughout the period from late June through to October, with notable peaks in late August and from mid to late September. The latest record was one at Stanford Reservoir on October 16th 1987; this bird occurred in the aftermath of the infamous 'hurricane' which brought small numbers of Sandwich Terns inland (including two in Northamptonshire and one in Cambridgeshire the same day), as well as unprecedented numbers of Sabine's Gulls and Grey Phalaropes (Hume & Christie 1989). The only other October records have been:

- two at Frisby Gravel Pits on October 13th 1990.
- one at Stanford Reservoir on October 13th 1957.
- one at Eyebrook Reservoir on October 7th 1973.

Autumn numbers are generally higher than those in spring. Three have been seen together on six occasions, there have been two groups of four and two of five and larger counts have been:

- six at both Cropston Reservoir on August 25th 1984 and Swithland Reservoir on September 20th 1995.
- seven at Stanford Reservoir on September 13th 1967.
- eight at both Stanford Reservoir on August 26th 1973 and Eyebrook Reservoir on September 20th 1996.
- nine at Rutland Water on September 27th 1998.
- 13 at Stanford Reservoir on September 20th 1964.
- 16 at Eyebrook Reservoir on September 17th 1995.
- 30 at Priory Water on September 25th 1988.

Despite there having been almost 300 Sandwich Terns recorded in Leicestershire and Rutland since 1945 this can be a difficult species to see in the counties, as the vast majority of records involve short-stayers; indeed, there have only been seven instances when birds have remained for more than one day:

- three at Barkby Gravel Pits on May 4th and 5th 1947.
- two at Eyebrook Reservoir on September 16th and 17th 1956.

- two at Eyebrook Reservoir from September 17th to 21st 1968.
- one at Eyebrook Reservoir on August 18th and 19th 1979.
- eight at Eyebrook Reservoir on September 20th 1996, three of which remained the next day.
- one at Rutland Water on May 4th and 5th 1997.
- one at Rutland Water on April 3rd and 4th 2004.

Sandwich Terns have been seen at most areas of water in the counties except for Trent Valley Pit, Fort Henry Ponds, Belvoir Lakes and the underwatched reservoirs of Blackbrook and Knipton. Eyebrook Reservoir has attracted over

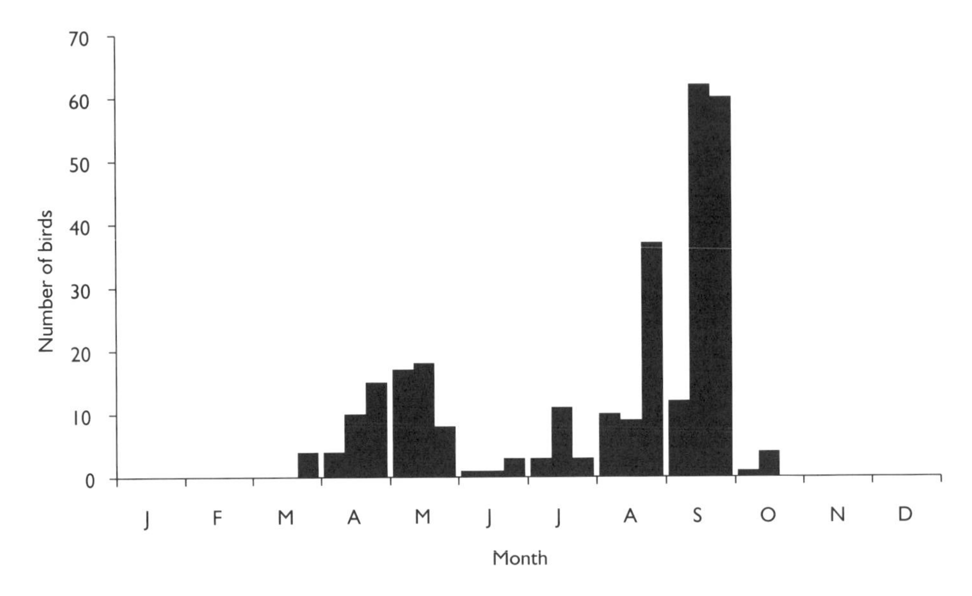

Figure 346: Monthly occurrence of Sandwich Terns 1941–2005.

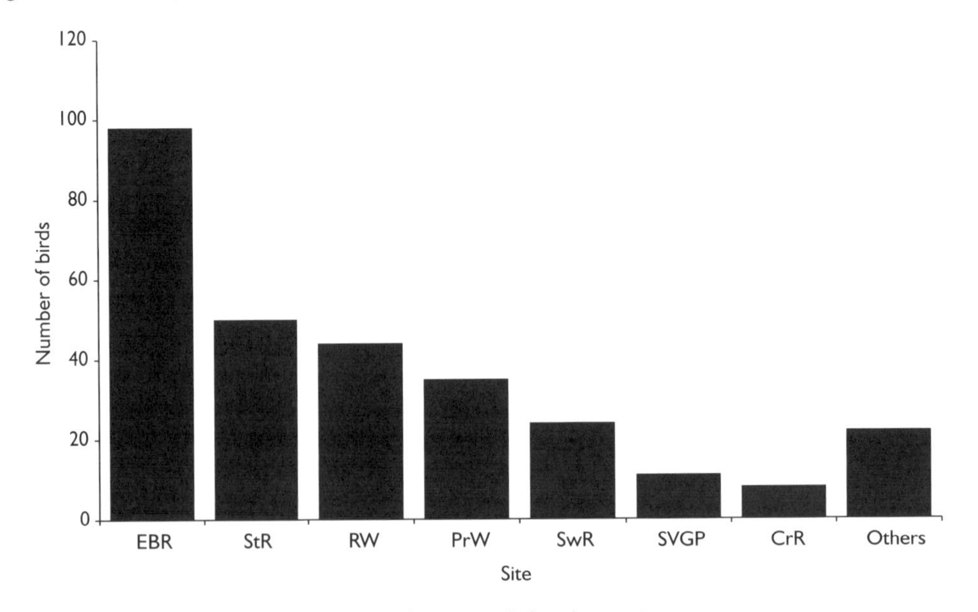

Figure 347: Sites where Sandwich Terns have been recorded 1941–2005.
Key to abbreviations: EBR = Eyebrook Reservoir; StR = Stanford Reservoir; RW = Rutland Water; PrW = Priory Water; SwR = Swithland Reservoir; SVGP = Soar valley gravel pits; CrR = Cropston Reservoir

one third of all birds recorded, with Stanford Reservoir surprisingly being more favoured than Rutland Water. The number of birds seen at Priory Water is heavily influenced by the large flock of 30 in 1988. There have been several records from slightly unexpected sites, including single birds at both Huncote Sand Pit on July 18th 1999 and Stoney Cove two days later and two at Stoney Stanton Jetski Centre on September 17th 2002.

Sandwich Terns breed discontinuously along coasts in Europe, eastern North America, Central America, the West Indies and eastern South America. European birds winter in southern Europe, the Middle East and off west Africa. In Britain, they are colonial breeders on sandy beaches and low-lying islands; the latest population estimate is approximately 10,500 pairs (Mitchell *et al.* 2004). As more than 50% of the British population nests at fewer than ten sites, the Sandwich Tern has been added to the 'Amber List' of Birds of Conservation Concern (Gregory *et al.* 2002).

RED

Common Tern *Sterna hirundo*

Uncommon to fairly common passage migrant, uncommon breeder.

In the 19th century, when the identification of terns tended to rest on specimens, this species was described as of accidental occurrence in spring and autumn in Leicestershire by Browne, though Harley had reported 'several' over the River Soar, Mr. Ingram informed him that it visited Belvoir Lake occasionally after easterly gales and four were reported at Swithland Reservoir on September 20th 1906. Browne listed five specimen records (of those dated, three were shot in October and one in November). Haines considered it a rare straggler to Rutland, citing three specimen records dated 1860, 1886 and 1904, though there must be some doubt about the last of these since it allegedly occurred in December.

It is rather difficult to determine the true status of this species during the early days of LROS as most records of Common and Arctic Tern were lumped under the heading of 'Commic' Tern. It was not until the late 1960s that species-specific records became more regular as observer awareness improved.

Common Terns are arriving distinctly earlier now than ever before. There were only two years up to the late 1980s with arrival dates in the first half of April (one at Eyebrook Reservoir on April 8th 1985 and two at Rutland Water on April 11th 1977), but since 1989 there have only been two years when the first record did not occur in the first half of April. There have been nine records prior to April 5th, all of single birds unless stated:

- two at Swithland Reservoir on March 27th 1989.
- Trent Valley Pit on March 28th and 30th 2005.
- Watermead Park on April 1st 2001.
- Swithland Reservoir on April 3rd 1999.
- Staunton Harold Reservoir on April 3rd 1999.
- Birstall Gravel Pits on April 3rd 2002.
- Rutland Water on April 3rd 2004.
- three at Cropston Reservoir on April 3rd 2005.
- Watermead Country Park North on April 3rd 2005.

Spring passage occurs typically from mid-April until late May and has almost always been described as light. Since breeding was first recorded in the counties and particularly since the establishment of Rutland Water as the major breeding site, it has become difficult to separate passage from breeding individuals. It would appear, however, that there has been an increase in birds recorded during the spring period, no doubt due to additional observer cover but also possibly as a result of the increase in breeding at inland sites throughout the country. The largest spring flocks away from known major breeding sites are:

- 70 at Stanford Reservoir on May 5th 1980.
- 63 at Eyebrook Reservoir on April 26th 1997.
- 60 at Eyebrook Reservoir on May 2nd 1990.
- 40 at Eyebrook Reservoir on April 18th 2003.
- 39 at Trent Valley Pit on May 13th 2001.

- 30 at Eyebrook Reservoir on May 7th 1994.
- 30 at Swithland Reservoir on May 12th 2002.

The trend towards inland nesting had become well established in central and eastern England by the late 1960s. The first breeding record in the counties occurred in 1967, when two young were raised at Wanlip Gravel Pits. A pair was recorded at the same site the following year, but there was no proof of breeding. With the increase in sand and gravel extraction within the counties, it was to be expected that there would be more breeding records. However, the next breeding attempts were not recorded until 1979: one pair at the newly established Rutland Water and two pairs in the Soar valley. Breeding has been recorded annually since then, but unfortunately data has rarely been complete, especially from the two main sites of Rutland Water and Watermead Country Park South and this should be taken into account when referring to Figure 349 counties. In most years at least one pair has bred in the Soar valley, but actual sites have moved as new gravel pits have been developed. The provision of nesting platforms at several sites has proved to be successful.

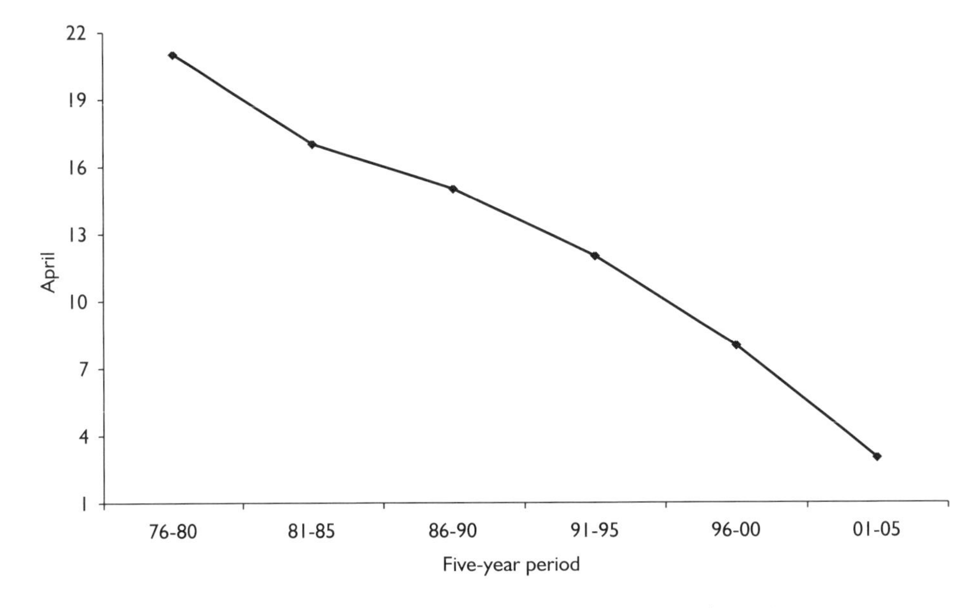

Figure 348: Average spring arrival dates of Common Terns by five-year periods 1976–2005.

In total, breeding has been recorded at 15 sites, as follows:

- Wanlip Gravel Pits complex (latterly Wanlip South Gravel Pits area): after the first breeding record for the counties in 1967, nesting was annual until 1987, with peaks of six pairs in 1986 and 1987. One pair in 1992 was the only other confirmed breeding record from this site.
- Rutland Water: bred annually since the first pair in 1979. No more than three pairs nested until 1989, when there were seven pairs. Since then much larger numbers have bred although complete data is lacking: a count of 47 pairs was recorded in 1991, 60 pairs nested in 2000 and at least 50 pairs nested in 2005. On May 22nd 1999, 180 individuals were reported around the Egleton Reserve but not all of these may have been breeding birds.
- Trent Valley Pit: five pairs bred in 1992, followed by two the next year. Single pairs attempted to breed in 1996, 1999, 2003, 2004 and 2005, although success was usually poor due to human disturbance. Breeding presumably occurred in this area in 1991 as at least two chicks were ringed at an unspecified site near Hemington in June, but no other details are known.
- Cavendish Bridge Gravel Pits: one pair in 1993.
- Watermead Country Park South: bred annually since the first two pairs in 1993. Data has not always been complete; the highest nest counts have been 21 in 1997, 17 in 1999 and 16 in 1998.
- Saltersford Flash: one pair in 1993.

- Stanford Reservoir: one pair in 1993 was followed by two in 1994, 13 in 1998 and ten in 1999. Nesting platforms were utilised at this site and data is probably incomplete.
- Swithland Reservoir: after the introduction of two nesting platforms successful breeding occurred almost annually from 1993, with peaks of four pairs in 1995 and 1998. However, in recent years both of the platforms have fallen into disrepair and are only used sparingly.
- Syston Gravel Pits: two pairs in 1995.
- Eyebrook Reservoir: bred annually since the first pair in 2001, with a maximum of six pairs in 2003.
- Priory Water: four pairs bred in 2002, 2004 and 2005, with six pairs in 2003.
- Birstall Gravel Pits: two pairs in 2002.
- Oakthorpe Flash: one pair in 2003.
- Glen Parva Gravel Pits: one pair in 2003.
- Cossington Meadows: one pair in 2005 used a nesting platform.

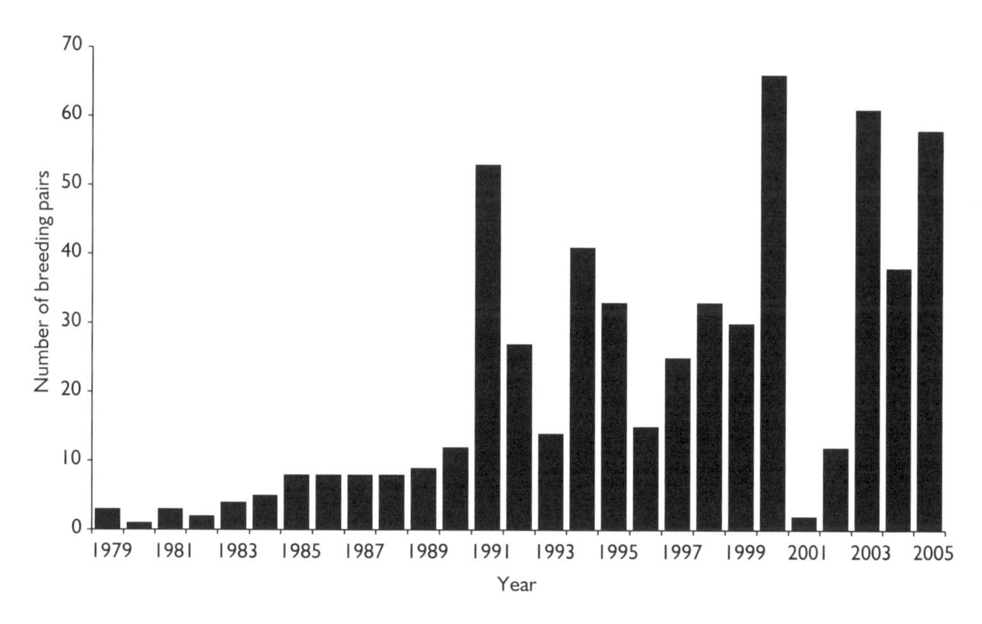

Figure 349: Number of breeding pairs of Common Terns 1979–2005.

Autumn passage has always been more protracted, commencing in July and continuing into October and has never been particularly remarkable. The largest counts have come from Rutland Water, but they no doubt consist primarily of local breeders. Away from this site the largest autumn numbers have been recorded at Trent Valley Pit, where an early autumn roost has became established in recent years: peak counts were 54 on August 3rd 2005, 49 on August 8th 2003, 45 on August 10th 2004 and 38 on August 6th 1998. Other autumn flocks considered to comprise passage birds rather than local breeders have included the following:

- 30 at Eyebrook Reservoir on August 11th 1996.
- 30 at Thornton Reservoir on September 25th 2005.
- 29 at Eyebrook Reservoir on August 30th 1985.
- 22 at Swithland Reservoir on August 19th 1990.

A few linger into October and there have been four November records: juveniles remained at Rutland Water until the 6th in 1994 and the 4th in 2002 and in the Cropston Reservoir/Swithland Reservoir area until the 3rd also in 2002. The latest record, however, was an adult at Wanlip South Gravel Pits which remained until November 14th 1998, when it was taken into care. It had been in the area for at least a fortnight, was obviously in a very poor condition and died a few days later.

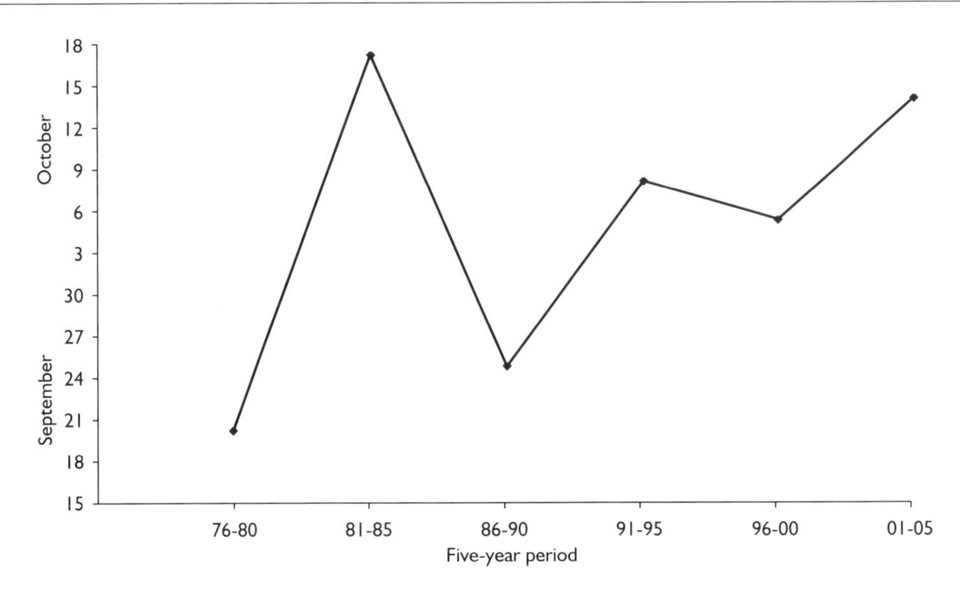

Figure 350: Average autumn departure dates of Common Terns by five-year periods 1976–2005.

Individuals reported as being in first-summer plumage have been recorded on six occasions since 1992, though such ageing requires care (White & Kehoe 2001): at Rutland Water on June 28th 1992, June 21st 1993, June 14th 1998, June 9th to 10th 2001 and May 13th to July 8th 2003 and at Kirby Lakes on July 4th 1993. A second-summer individual was reported at Rutland Water on July 20th 1996.

An interesting ringing recovery concerned one found dying, entangled in fishing line, at Priory Water on July 28th 1996: it had been ringed as a nestling at Kingsbury Water Park (Warwickshire) on July 9th 1981. Foreign ringing recoveries include:

- one ringed as a pullus at Wanlip Gravel Pits on August 6th 1967 was found dead in the Pyrenees-Atlantiques region (France) on December 13th 1967, a southerly movement of 1,034km.
- one ringed as a pullus near Hemington on June 19th 1991 was recovered at sea off Guinea-Bissau on December 15th 1991, a movement of 4,747km south-south-west.
- one ringed as a pullus near Hemington on June 19th 1991 was found 5,194km to the south at Lome (Togo) on August 10th 1992.
- one ringed as a pullus at Watermead Country Park South on July 3rd 2001 was recovered 5,230km to the south at Accra (Ghana) on April 6th 2002.

The Common Tern breeds at numerous coastal sites and at several inland locations around the British Isles and Ireland. The most recent estimate of the British breeding population puts it at 10,134 pairs (Baker *et al.* 2006). A similar pattern is reflected across northern Europe, with more extensive breeding in southern Sweden and Finland. The breeding range extends from eastern Europe throughout the mid-latitudes of the former USSR to the Kamchatka peninsula. A second population breeds primarily throughout most of southern Canada and coastal sites of eastern U.S.A. Non-breeding and passage birds are usually coastal, wintering around the coasts of Africa, the Arabian peninsula, parts of India, the East Indies and the west coast of Australia. European birds winter mainly in West Africa.

RED

Arctic Tern *Sterna paradisaea*

Uncommon to fairly common spring and scarce autumn passage migrant.

Recorded overland passage through the counties by this species dates back to the 19th century. Browne described it as of accidental occurrence in spring and autumn, though Harley had noted that in the spring of 1842, following north-westerly gales, Arctic Terns were especially abundant from May 7th to 10th and might be seen 'in small groups, varying in number from one bird up to ten, fifteen and even twenty individuals' on the streams and pools and along the Rivers Soar and Trent. In Rutland, before the development of the reservoirs, Haines knew of up to four records dated 1842, 1883 and 'two in the Burley House collection, which may have been obtained there.'

During the early years of LROS there was very little information on this species as most Common and Arctic Tern records were lumped under the heading of 'Commic' Tern. The most significant records in those early days were five in spring 1948 and a strange record of one, in full breeding plumage, at Stanford Reservoir on November 2nd and 3rd 1957, the latest-ever record for the counties. It was not until the late 1960s that species-specific records became more regular as observer awareness improved. As the above status indicates, there are normally far more records during the spring than in the autumn. Spring passage has regularly been concentrated around the end of April and early May, with just a few records occurring outside this period. Some exceptional numbers have been recorded, often in poor weather conditions (see also 'Commic' Tern), but in other years numbers have been poor. It is probable that many of the 'Commic' Tern records involving large numbers refer to this species.

The earliest record involved one at Swithland Reservoir on April 7th 1991, although arrivals prior to April 15th are rare and have only been recorded on eight other occasions. All were single birds unless stated:

- two at Rutland Water on April 8th 2003.
- Rutland Water on April 9th 2000.
- Thornton Reservoir on April 9th 2000.
- Eyebrook Reservoir on April 11th 1974.
- seven at Rutland Water on April 11th 1981.
- Rutland Water on April 13th 1990.
- Eyebrook Reservoir on April 13th 2002.
- Eyebrook Reservoir on April 13th 2003.

The average arrival date has become noticeably earlier since the 1980s: it was April 21st during 1981–85 but by 2001–05 it had become April 14th. Average arrival dates prior to the 1980s cannot be calculated due to the lack of data.

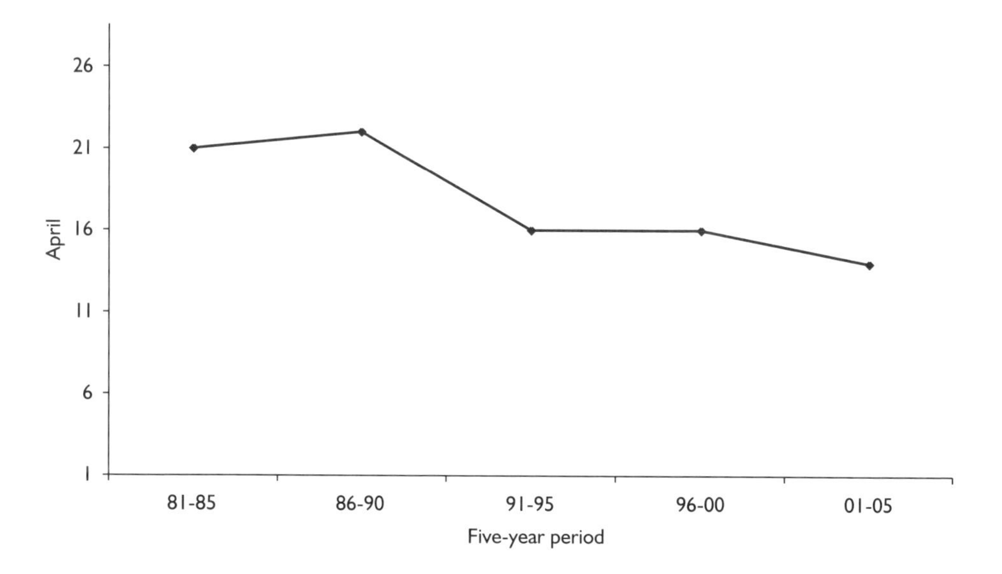

Figure 351: Average spring arrival dates of Arctic Terns by five-year periods 1941–2005.

There have been very few spring records after mid-May and only seven in June, all single birds unless stated:

- Rutland Water on June 1st 1993.
- seven at Rutland Water on June 2nd 1991.

- Eyebrook Reservoir on June 2nd 1996.
- Swithland Reservoir on June 3rd 1984.
- Rutland Water on June 5th 1994.
- five at Swithland Reservoir on June 7th 1975.
- Watermead Park on June 20th 1993.

The bird at Rutland Water on June 1st 1993 was in first-summer plumage, as was one at the same site on May 27th and 28th 2000. An adult apparently summered at Rutland Water in 2001, being recorded on three dates during June and July.

Numbers during the spring can be highly variable. The best years have included 2005 (440 birds), 1983 (404 birds), 1991 (321) and 1985 (257), although these totals pale into insignificance with the spring of 1998 when a huge influx in early May produced aggregate totals of 1,021 birds on the 1st and 1,093 the following day. Totals at individual sites during this period included 800 at Rutland Water on the 1st, with 670 there the following day and 260 at Eyebrook Reservoir and 105 at Swithland Reservoir on the 2nd.

Apart from in 1998, three-figure flocks have been recorded on seven occasions:

- 210 at Rutland Water on May 9th 1983.
- 180 at Rutland Water on April 28th 1985.
- 170 at Rutland Water on May 2nd 1983.
- 140 at Rutland Water on April 26th 2005.
- 110 at Eyebrook Reservoir on May 6th 1991.
- 110 at Swithland Reservoir on May 4th 2005.
- 100 at Rutland Water on April 30th 1988.

Away from the three main sites of Rutland Water, Eyebrook Reservoir and Swithland Reservoir, counts exceeding 25 have been recorded at a six sites, where maxima are:

- 71 at Thornton Reservoir on May 5th 1991.
- 35 at Wanlip North Gravel Pits on May 2nd 1998.
- 32 at Trent Valley Pit on May 12th 2005.
- 30 at Priory Water on April 26th 1995.
- 28 at Cropston Reservoir on April 23rd 1990.
- 27 at Watermead Park on May 5th 2001.

Autumn passage extends over a much longer time period than spring but the numbers involved are small. Most records involve juveniles during late August and September although there have been a few July records, including seven at Rutland Water on July 29th 1991 and four at Swithland Reservoir on July 31st 2000. The best years for autumn birds have been 2005 (17 individuals), 1989 (16), 1991 (15) and 1992 (14). Flocks during the autumn are rare and the only significant count has been ten at Rutland Water on August 28th 1989.

There have been records during October in seven years, all of juveniles, as follows:

- Swithland Reservoir from October 19th to 26th 1983.
- Wanlip South Gravel Pits on October 22nd 2004.
- Watermead Park on October 12th and 14th 2001, with presumably the same bird at nearby Wanlip South Gravel Pits on October 17th.
- Rutland Water on October 10th 2002.
- Rutland Water on October 8th 1988.
- Eyebrook Reservoir from September 28th to October 6th 1991.
- Swithland Reservoir from October 1st to 4th 1982.

The latest record, however, remains that at Stanford Reservoir on November 2nd and 3rd 1957 mentioned previously.

The Arctic Tern breeds at a number of coastal and island sites in the British Isles, primarily in Scotland. The most recent estimate of the British breeding population is 52,621 pairs (Baker *et al.* 2006). Because it has a localised distribution both as a breeding bird and on passage, and there have been recent significant declines in populations in the Northern Isles, this species has been added to the 'Amber List' of Birds of Conservation

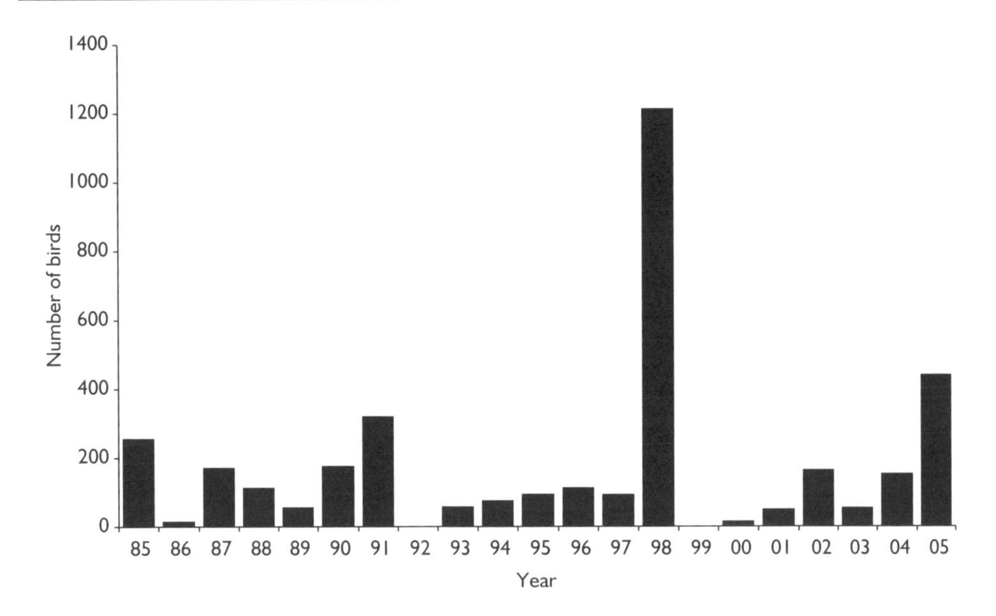

Figure 352: Numbers of Arctic Terns in spring 1985–2005.
Note that no data is available for 1992 and 1999.

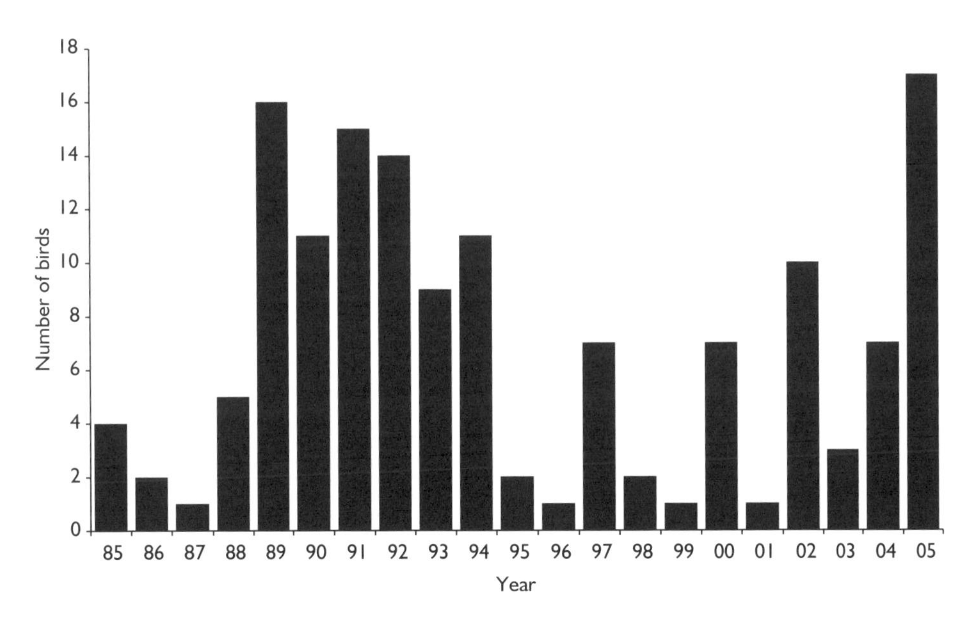

Figure 353: Numbers of Arctic Terns in autumn 1985–2005.

Concern (Gregory *et al.* 2002). In Europe breeding occurs in suitable habitat around the coasts of Ireland, the Netherlands, Denmark and Germany. It also breeds around the coasts of Scandanavia and at inland sites, particularly in the north of the region. The main European breeding population is in Iceland, where there are up to 100,000 pairs. Breeding also occurs around the entire coastal fringe of the Arctic Ocean, including Franz Josef Land and Spitsbergen, through to Alaska and the northern territories of Canada eastwards as far as

Newfoundland. Coastal breeding also occurs in Greenland. It is considered to be declining in the more southern part of its range. Arctic Terns perform the most extensive migration of any bird species, moving around the coasts of Europe, Africa, western North America and both western and eastern South America, spending the winter in the Southern Ocean as far south as the Antarctic pack ice.

RED

'Commic' Tern *Sterna hirundo/paradisaea*

During the period from the establishment of LROS in 1941 through to the early 1970s, most records of Common and Arctic Terns appeared in Annual Reports under the heading of 'Commic' Tern, as many observers lacked the experience to separate the two species in the field confidently. This practice continued well into the 1980s, but had largely disappeared by the early 1990s with the improvement in field guides and optical equipment. This summary is included to complete as full a picture as possible of the two species concerned.

In those early years, counts of up to 30 were the norm in spring, with smaller numbers in the autumn. The only exceptional count during this period was of 50 at Eyebrook Reservoir on September 26th 1965. It would appear that most birds were considered to be Common Terns, as comments appeared in the Annual Reports against specific records where it was considered that the individuals involved were Arctic Terns. The first such individual was reported in 1947, with a few in 1949, but there were very few others until 1974 when the two species were first reported under separate headings.

Three-figure spring counts were recorded during periods of bad weather: 106 at Eyebrook Reservoir on April 23rd 1981, with 100 the following day and 100 at both Cropston Reservoir and Thornton Reservoir on May 2nd 1983. In 1991, 100 were at Rutland Water on May 6th and 300 at Eyebrook Reservoir the next day; the majority of these were probably Arctic Terns since this is the peak passage period for that species and large flocks have proved to be regular in early May.

Late autumn records have included the following:

- one at both Wanlip Gravel Pits and Swithland Reservoir on November 2nd 1963.
- one at Swithland Reservoir on November 2nd 1967.
- two at Eyebrook Reservoir on November 4th 1967.
- a juvenile, considered as probably an Arctic Tern, at Rutland Water on November 5th 1989.

RED

Roseate Tern *Sterna dougallii*

Very rare vagrant from Europe: three records.

The first county record was of one found dead by E. Lambert at Hinckley on May 7th 1954; the skin was deposited at Leicester Museum where it remains today. The first live bird was found in 1974, when one was watched by Richard Richardson, Tim Cleeves and J. G. Martin at Eyebrook Reservoir from 18:30 to 19:00 on April 27th. It was identified in flight, amongst a flock of Common and Arctic Terns, primarily by its 'enormously long tail streamers'. Despite the large increase in active observers over the following 30 years and the associated advances in expertise and optical equipment, it was not until 2004 that the third individual was found; this record involved an adult found by Andy Forryan in the north arm at Rutland Water during the morning of August 15th. It was present intermittently for the remainder of the day, but was only seen by a small number of other fortunate observers.

A report of one at Staunton Harold Reservoir on September 1st 1968 was published as the second record for the counties, but following review in 1995 was found to be inadequately documented and subsequently rejected (Mackay 1995a).

Roseate Terns breed in small colonies in north-west Europe (mainly Britain and Ireland), as well as in the Azores, the Indian Ocean, south-east Asia, Australasia, the West Indies and north-east United States. European birds winter off the coast of west Africa. The British population has crashed by around 80% since 1969 (Gibbons *et al.* 1993) and due to this decline the species has been added to the 'Red List' of Birds of Conservation Concern (Gregory *et al.* 2002). The latest estimate of the British population was of 104 pairs in 2005, the majority of which were in Northumberland (Holling *et al.* 2008).

RED

Guillemot (Common Guillemot) ***Uria aalge***

Very rare storm-driven vagrant from Europe: nine records.

There were six records during the 19th century, along with another in 1900, although the reliability of these reports is unclear. Browne described three records: an undated bird shot on the River Soar at Cossington, the specimen of which he saw and confirmed its identification, one 'said to have been killed at Husband's Bosworth' in 1883 and one reported to have been shot at Belgrave, Leicester on the odd date of July 21st 1893. In Rutland, Haines reported that single birds were shot in the Welland valley in 1873 and at Seaton in 1879, with another shot near Lyddington on an unspecified date. He also mentioned one reported in flight near Lyddington in 1900.

More recently, two birds were found in 1996 to establish this species' place firmly on the county list. Following strong winds, one was found exhausted in a field close to the Northamptonshire border near Welford on February 20th and taken into care; it was subsequently released off the north Wales coast in March (along with a Puffin that had been found exhausted in the county at the same time). A second individual was picked up at Melton Mowbray on December 20th, again after strong winds. A rather ill-advised release attempt was made at Rutland Water the following morning, but the bird was clearly unwell and was recaptured before being taken to the RSPCA at Hunstanton (Norfolk).

Guillemots breed widely along the north Atlantic and north Pacific coasts and winter at sea. Apart from a few hundred birds in France and Iberia, Britain is the southern limit of the species' range in the north-east Atlantic, with a population estimated at over 1,320,000 pairs (Mitchell *et al.* 2004). As more than 20% of the European population breeds in Britain, the Guillemot has been added to the 'Amber List' of Birds of Conservation Concern (Gregory *et al.* 2002). Despite its abundance on the coast, this species rarely strays inland, even during the most severe of storms.

RMF

Razorbill ***Alca torda***

Very rare storm-driven vagrant from Europe: one or two records.

Haines mentions one killed in 1879 at Seaton during a flood, but for unknown reasons this record has been ignored by subsequent authors, possibly as a Guillemot was also reportedly shot at Seaton during the same year. This species' was therefore firmly added to the county list in 1970 with the presence of an individual at Staunton Harold Reservoir from October 18th to November 13th. Although most of this site is in Derbyshire, the bird was occasionally seen in the southern inlet in Leicestershire.

Razorbills breed along the coasts of Scandinavia, the Faroe Islands and Iceland, as well as on the west coast of Greenland and north-east Canada. Smaller numbers are found in France and Germany. In Britain, they are found mainly on northern and western coasts, with the bulk of the breeding population in Scotland. The latest British estimate is just under 165,000 pairs (Mitchell *et al.* 2004) and, as more than 20% of the European population breeds in the United Kingdom, the Razorbill has been added to the 'Amber List' of Birds of Conservation Concern (Gregory *et al.* 2002). This is a truly marine bird which rarely enters even sea lochs or estuaries and as such it is very rarely encountered inland; further appearances in Leicestershire and Rutland may be a long time in coming.

RMF

Little Auk *Alle alle*

Rare storm-driven vagrant from the Arctic, usually in October and November: 18 records since 1941 and approximately 21 previously.

Browne convincingly describes three records from the 19th century: two caught alive in a turnip field at Nanpantan on November 6th 1837, both later dying; one found alive (but later succumbing) at Smeeton Westerby on November 18th 1893, the specimen of which was presented to Leicester Museum and one shot at Belgrave, Leicester on October 20th 1894. In addition, one was apparently found dead at an unspecified site during the autumn of 1840 and 'several were picked up at various times in the Melton Mowbray area' prior to 1885. More unbelievable was one reportedly found alive in a garden at Barkby on June 4th 1903. Browne saw the specimen and confirmed that it was a Little Auk and was happy to include the record in VH; however, the chances of a bird which breeds in the high Arctic being found in Leicestershire in June seem remote and it must be assumed that some sort of fraud was involved in this record.

Haines refers to eight records from Rutland in the 19th century, involving nine individuals. Of these, two should be treated with caution at best: one at Casterton on April 5th 1881 and one 'near Stamford' on October 18th 1894. The former record, like that at Barkby in June 1903, is on an unlikely date, whilst there must be some degree of doubt as to whether the bird near Stamford was actually in Rutland given Haines' frequent disregard for county boundaries. The other six records described by Haines seem more likely to be genuine:

c1840	picked up at Casterton, no date.
1853	found alive in a pigsty at Exton, no date.
	found alive in a ditch at Luffenham, December 20th.
c1858	found dead at Barrowden, no date.
1884	Pickworth, no date.
1885	two, Essendine, no date.

There are no published records of Little Auk between the time of Browne and Haines and the formation of LROS in 1941, but specimens at Leicester Museum include single birds found at Kilby Bridge in February 1902 and Kibworth Beauchamp in January 1930. In addition, the LROS archives mention single birds at Cossington in December 1917 and Swithland Reservoir on December 15th 1933. Since 1941, there have been 18 records, all of single birds, as follows:

1942	an immature male was found feeding with domestic poultry at Rolleston on November 18th; it eventually died and the specimen was sent to Leicester Museum.
1957	a live bird was watched at Swithland Reservoir for much of the day on November 10th. Two days later, dead birds were found at Beacon Hill and Grace Dieu, both of which are now at Leicester Museum.
1967	found dead at Tolethorpe on November 2nd; the specimen is at Leicester Museum.
1974	found dead at Pickworth Drift on November 5th; the specimen is at Leicester Museum.
1975	one was found on a small pond at Ashby Magna on November 11th, but died later. The specimen was sent to the Leicester Museum.
1983	one was found dead at Stretton on February 13th, whilst in November dead birds were found at Clipsham on the 5th and Great Glen on the 7th; the latter two specimens are at Leicester Museum.
1987	one was found in a bedraggled state at Shepshed on November 4th; it was released the following day at Tetney (Lincolnshire) and flew off strongly.
1988	an apparently healthy individual was in the north arm at Rutland Water on November 20th.
1995	three apparently healthy birds were seen: in the south arm at Rutland Water on October 29th, at Eyebrook Reservoir on November 3rd and by the dam at Rutland Water the following day. The latter bird was eventually killed and eaten by a Great Black-backed Gull.
1996	one flew past Normanton Church at Rutland Water on November 13th and a healthy-looking individual was at Eyebrook Reservoir the following day.

1997 one was in the south arm at Rutland Water on October 25th, but was picked up dead the next day.

Of these 18 records, 17 have occurred between October 25th and November 20th, with the first week of November producing seven birds. Most have occurred following strong northerly winds; the three live birds in 1995 were found at a time when huge numbers were present in the North Sea, although the two the following year were more surprising as few were present close inshore in that area at the time. The February record in 1983 occurred following strong north-easterly winds, when up to 1,200 were found dead on the east coast of Britain and almost 100 were found inland (Lack 1986).

Little Auks breed in the high Arctic, with most in Greenland and on Svalbard. They are colonial birds, with as many as 30 million pairs worldwide, making this species possibly the most numerous seabird in the world (Lack 1986). They are widespread in the northern part of the North Sea in winter, although are usually highly pelagic, being rarely seen from land. Strong onshore winds occasionally result in large numbers being seen from the British east coast and birds sometimes appear inland in conditions such as these, usually either dead or in an exhausted state. With this in mind, the series of six live, apparently healthy, birds between 1995 and 1997 was particularly notable.

RMF

Puffin (Atlantic Puffin) ***Fratercula arctica***

Very rare vagrant from Europe: six records.

There have been six records of this popular seabird, a remarkable number for a species which rarely strays inland. The first involved an individual found dead at Peatling Magna in December 1921, the skin of which was deposited at Leicester Museum. There have been five records since, all of which have an element of the extraordinary about them.

All records:

1921 found dead, Peatling Magna, December.

1951 one was picked up at Shelthorpe on May 23rd by D. Bishop and released at Swithland Reservoir the next day. A skin at Leicester Museum is labelled as having been found dead at Swithland on June 2nd 1951 and presumably relates to this bird.

1971 an immature was seen on one of the water-filled slate quarries in Swithland Wood by Jean Ironside on October 3rd, a most bizarre location for any species of bird, let alone a Puffin!

1984 one was seen by G. Boden as it flew over Whetstone Pastures at 19:15 on April 23rd, another remarkable record given the clear, calm weather conditions at the time.

1995 an adult was found by a rather surprised Allen Pocock at Eyebrook Reservoir on June 25th, again during a day of clear and calm weather; it remained until June 27th and was seen and photographed by large numbers of observers. Unfortunately, it was found dead on the latter date and examination revealed that it was at least 25% under the average weight for an adult.

1996 an exhausted individual was found in a builders' yard at Croft on February 20th after a period of strong winds. It was taken into care before eventual release off the north Wales coast in early March (along with a Guillemot that had been found exhausted in the county at the same time).

Puffins are colonial nesters in burrows on steep sloping sea cliffs, primarily in northern and western Britain, Scandinavia and Iceland. They winter at sea, usually well away from land, in the north Atlantic as far south as the Canary Islands. The current British population estimate is around 580,000 pairs (Mitchell *et al.* 2004). As more than 50% of the British population nests at fewer than ten sites, this species has been added to the 'Amber List' of Birds of Conservation Concern (Gregory *et al.* 2002).

RED

Pallas's Sandgrouse *Syrrhaptes paradoxus*

Very rare vagrant from central Asia: at least five records involving a minimum of 45 birds.

Several birds were reported in Leicestershire and Rutland during an irruption of this species into western Europe in 1888 but details are rather confused and it is unclear how many individuals were involved and when they were seen.

Browne details the following from Leicestershire:

- a small flock between Saddington and Mowsley on May 23rd; this sighting was recorded in *The Field* on June 9th 1888 and has been repeated by subsequent authors, although Browne's words in VH that 'Dr Macaulay thought he saw a covey of these birds between Saddington and Mowsley' do not inspire total confidence and it is debatable whether this record is truly acceptable.
- 12 between Buddon Wood and Swithland from June 3rd to 6th, one of which was shot and wounded on the latter date. Again, this occurrence was recorded in *The Field* on June 9th 1888.

In Rutland, Haines recorded the following:

- several seen, one of which was shot, at Cottesmore on May 30th. This was recorded in *The Field* on June 9th 1888.
- 12 at Southorpe Mill Farm, near Stamford, from May 31st to June 1st; however, the village of Southorpe is in Cambridgeshire and, combined with the fact that Haines quite often did not take too much notice of county boundaries, it is likely that these birds were not seen in Rutland.
- four at Burley on December 29th, repeated by Hickling. However, the event was apparently recorded in *The Field* on June 9th 1888, meaning that the record could not possibly refer to December and seems more likely to have been late May or early June, in line with the majority of other reports.
- 15 at Seaton. Haines did not date this record, although Hickling stated that it was in December. As with the Burley record above, the event was recorded in *The Field* on June 9th 1888 and it is likely that the actual occurrence was during late May or early June.
- one shot at Glaston some time in 1888; this record was not mentioned by Hickling but *The Field* of April 13th 1889 reported that 12 were seen at Glaston in April 1889.

It is unfortunate that details of this irruption have become muddled over time, but it is probably safe to say that records involving five flocks, totalling at least 45 birds, can be considered acceptable.

Pallas's Sandgrouse breed in central Asia, where they are largely resident, although they periodically irrupt in to western Europe. There is no obvious reason for these invasions, but theories put forward include food shortages, poor weather and increased sunspot activity. The 1888 irruption was the largest ever and this enigmatic species even bred in Britain that year (in Yorkshire and Morayshire). There have been no large-scale movements since 1909; subsequently there have only been six records of Pallas's Sandgrouse in Britain, the last in Shetland in 1990.

RMF

Feral Pigeon *Columba livia*

Feral. Fairly common resident breeder.

This species is considerably under-recorded in the counties and always has been. Neither Browne nor Haines make mention of it and even Hickling ignored its existence as recently as 1978. Although no specific information is available, it is likely that this species has been resident in the major towns, as well as Leicester itself, since well before the foundation of LROS.

Feral Pigeon was not surveyed by Warrilow during 1976–84 and the first published information comes from Mitcham (1984), who reported flocks of 100+ feeding on arable fields around Oakham, Tinwell and Great Casterton and considered that the likely source of these birds was Stamford (Lincolnshire). This species has only appeared in the LROS Annual Reports since 1992.

As they occupy a niche in the environment which is very similar to our own (heavily populated suburban areas), Feral Pigeons are considered a pest because of the mess they make on public buildings and private housing alike. Regular articles appear in the press regarding the damage they are causing to property and the health hazards which may arise. They continue to thrive as a direct result of their ability to take advantage of discarded food to be found in urban areas and direct feeding by the public, despite the efforts of local authorities to eliminate them from town centres. They also benefit from their prolonged breeding season: young being fed in a nest at Melton Mowbray on December 12th 1998 was either a very early or very late breeding record!

The majority of records since 1992 have referred to large flocks. In November 1993, 800 were at Scraptoft on the 25th and 600 at Trent Valley Pit on the 21st. A flock of 500 was at Braunstone, Leicester on January 23rd 1994 and the same number was present in the Sanvey Gate area of Leicester throughout 1995 and 1996.

Interesting behaviour was recorded at Priory Water on July 2nd 2000 when five spent several minutes circling and frequently dropping down onto the water, where they floated for a few seconds sometimes with wings outspread.

Feral Pigeons have a cosmopolitan breeding distribution due to their domestication by man and are descended from wild Rock Doves. No formal attempt has been made to estimate the British population, although Sharrock (1976) guessed at upwards of 100,000 pairs.

RED

Stock Dove (Stock Pigeon) ***Columba oenas***

Common resident breeder.

The Stock Dove is a relatively poorly-studied bird in Leicestershire and Rutland and is often overlooked when feeding with large flocks of Wood Pigeons. Browne considered its status in Leicestershire in the 19th century as 'resident, but not so common as Wood Pigeon', whilst during the same period Haines commented that it had 'apparently never become very common' in Rutland, but was considered to be 'fairly abundant' at Exton, Normanton and possibly Ketton.

The first indication of the status of the Stock Dove in the 20th century was provided by the inaugural LROS Annual Report, in 1941, which considered it to be resident and widespread. A full status summary appeared in the Annual Report the following year, as follows: 'generally speaking, widespread in small numbers as a breeding species. Very common in some parks and quarries where suitable holes exist in the trees and rocks. Bradgate Park is their stronghold and on an adjoining estate of 50 acres, seven nests were found in 1941. As against this, they are not at all common throughout the eastern and southern parts of the county, although they appear to be fairly common in the south-west corner, but here again there is parkland containing old oak trees. Observers at Oadby, Quorn and Coalville report very few, but at Croft they are more numerous and there was one quarry with at least 12 breeding pairs, whilst at Snarestone they are more common as a breeding species than the Wood Pigeon.'

Subsequent LROS Annual Reports mention this species as increasing in the mid-1940s, but then decreasing through to the mid to late 1960s. The severe winter of 1962–63 also contributed to the decline and breeding numbers were reported as considerably reduced the following summer. The general decline of the Stock Dove was mirrored nationally: it is thought that the British population decreased tenfold between 1950 and 1961, most markedly in the most intensively agricultural areas, probably due to the increasing application of pesticides and organochlorine seed-dressings at this time which had an adverse effect on nesting and fledging success (O'Connor & Mead 1984). During this period, however, numbers increased in suburban habitats and Pochin (1954) noted that Stock Doves had begun nesting within the Leicester city boundary at Stoneygate in the early 1950s. More recently, Fray *et al.* (1990) found this species to be present in all four green areas surveyed within the city boundary in 1989.

Between 1973 and 1998, there was a 96% increase in Stock Dove numbers on national CBC plots (Chamberlain & Vickery 2002). Local CBC results are difficult to interpret, as at all sites surveyed this species was never very common; however, the general trend at Stoughton and King's Hill Lodge, Uppingham was definitely upwards.

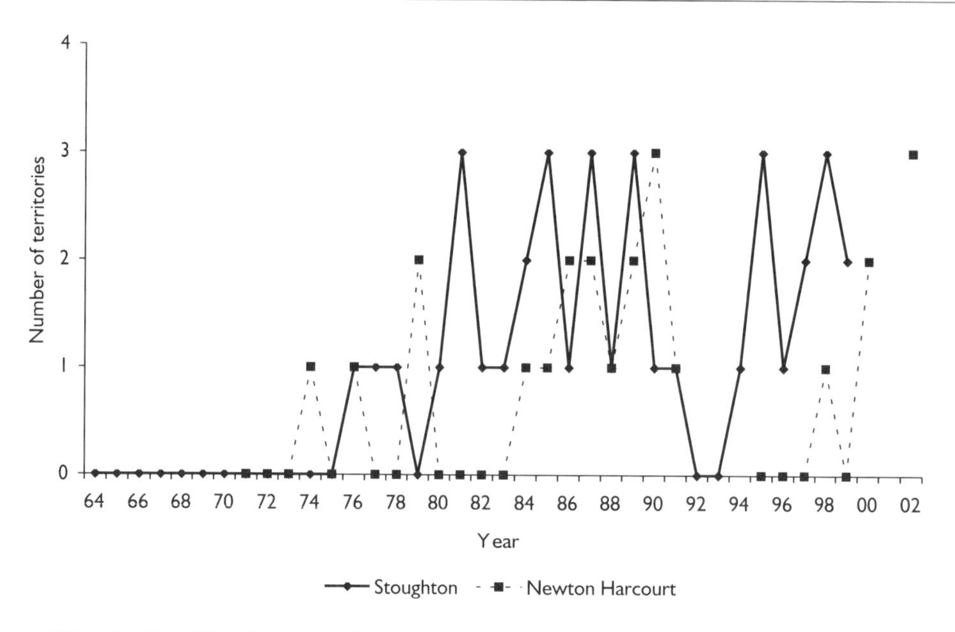

Figure 354: Number of breeding pairs of Stock Doves on two Leicestershire CBC plots 1964–2002.

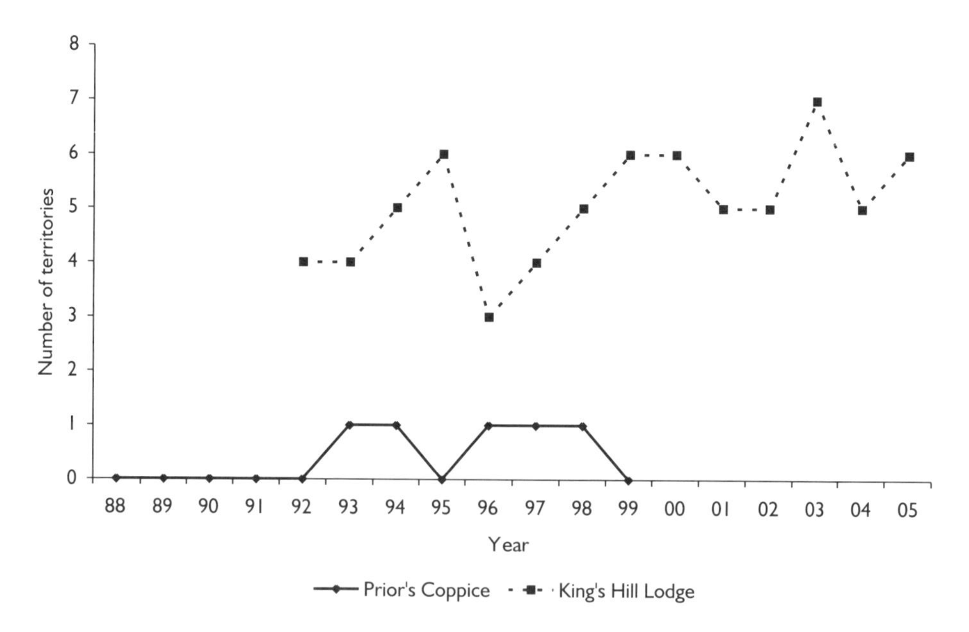

Figure 355: Number of breeding pairs of Stock Doves on two Rutland CBC plots 1988–2005.

The most meaningful attempt at calculating the county-wide population of this species was by Warrilow, who during 1976–84 recorded Stock Doves in 423 tetrads in the counties (66% of the total number of tetrads), with breeding confirmed in 87. It was least common in the extreme west and parts of north-east Leicestershire and tended to favour habitat near parkland or mature woodland with abundant nesting holes, where the surrounding farmland was easily accessible. An estimate of four to six pairs per occupied tetrad gave a proposed county population of 1,700 to 2,500 pairs. In addition to the work of Warrilow, interesting breeding records have included a loose colony of 25 pairs around Huncote Sand Pit in 1975, 20 pairs at Enderby Quarry in 1980 and a pair at Glenfield in 1949 which laid four clutches in a nest built in a small barrel wedged in the fork of a tree and fledged at least three young.

There have been a number of three-figure counts, almost all of which have occurred since the 1970s. Eight flocks have numbered 200 or more, as follows:

- 500 at Rutland Water on February 23rd 1977.
- 400 at Branston on March 5th 2000.
- 300 at Eyebrook Reservoir on February 18th 1996.
- 300 at Wymondham Rough on March 2nd 1997.
- 245 at Cropston Reservoir on March 5th 1989.
- 220 at Priory Water on November 20th 1994.
- 200 at Lockington Marshes on January 19th 2003.
- 'several hundred' at Shenton on March 5th 1987.

There is conflicting evidence as to whether British Stock Doves are migratory. O'Connor & Mead (1984) stated that British Stock Doves were sedentary, but there is an overseas recovery of local origin: one ringed at Eyebrook Reservoir on July 26th 2000, a date that presumably indicated that this was a local breeding bird, was found dead at Campagne d'Armagnac, Midi-Pyrénées district (France) on November 11th the same year, a southerly movement of 966km. In addition, small numbers were noted migrating over Deans Lane, Woodhouse between November 5th and 17th 2005, with a maximum of 29 on the 5th (Lister 2007b).

Stock Doves breed over most of Europe, as well as North Africa and parts of the Middle East. Southern and western birds are largely resident, but those in northern and eastern areas are migratory. The latest British population estimate is 309,000 pairs (Baker *et al.* 2006) and as over 20% of the European population breeds in Britain, Stock Dove has been added to the 'Amber List' of Birds of Conservation Concern (Gregory *et al.* 2002).

RED

Wood Pigeon (Common Wood Pigeon) ***Columba palumbus***

Abundant resident breeder and winter visitor.

This species seems to have increased since the 19th century, when Haines stated that though it had increased since 1860 in Rutland it was 'not especially numerous except perhaps in the Normanton district.' Browne considered it resident and generally distributed in Leicestershire, though he gave few details. It seems likely that the population increased following expansion into newly available arable and suburban habitats during the latter part of the 19th century.

The Wood Pigeon has become a highly successful species, occupying virtually every habitat within the counties, nesting primarily in woodland and old tall hedges but also wherever there are trees and bushes close to open ground. The extent of its spread into suburban habitats is indicated by the fact that it was the eighth most-frequently recorded species during the Leicestershire Garden Bird Survey from January 1996 to June 2005 and was recorded in 69% of gardens.

During 1976–84, Warrilow recorded the Wood Pigeon in 612 of the counties' tetrads (96% of the total number of tetrads), with successful breeding in 345. Based on a figure of 40 pairs per occupied tetrad, a county-wide population of 25,000 pairs was estimated. In Rutland, Mitcham (1992) found all 117 tetrads occupied and described it as ubiquitous, whilst Webster (1997) recorded confirmed or probable breeding in 86% of 1-km squares in Charnwood.

Local CBC data shows that the breeding population of this species is, in the main, increasing. At Stoughton, territories were not calculated until 1984, when there were an estimated nine pairs at the site. Numbers increased quickly, to 20 pairs in 1987, with later peaks of 21 pairs in both 1993 and 1996; however, during the last three years of this census numbers fell. At Newton Harcourt, breeding pairs were estimated at between two and five pairs anuually between 1989 and 2000, increasing to six pairs in 2002, whilst at King's Hill Lodge, Uppingham, estimated territories increased from a starting point of 32 pairs in 1992 to a peak of 48 in both 1996 and 2004.

Numbers are augmented during the winter months by continental birds. It has remained abundant throughout the life of LROS, much to the disquiet of many farmers and gardeners whose crops suffer as a result of its

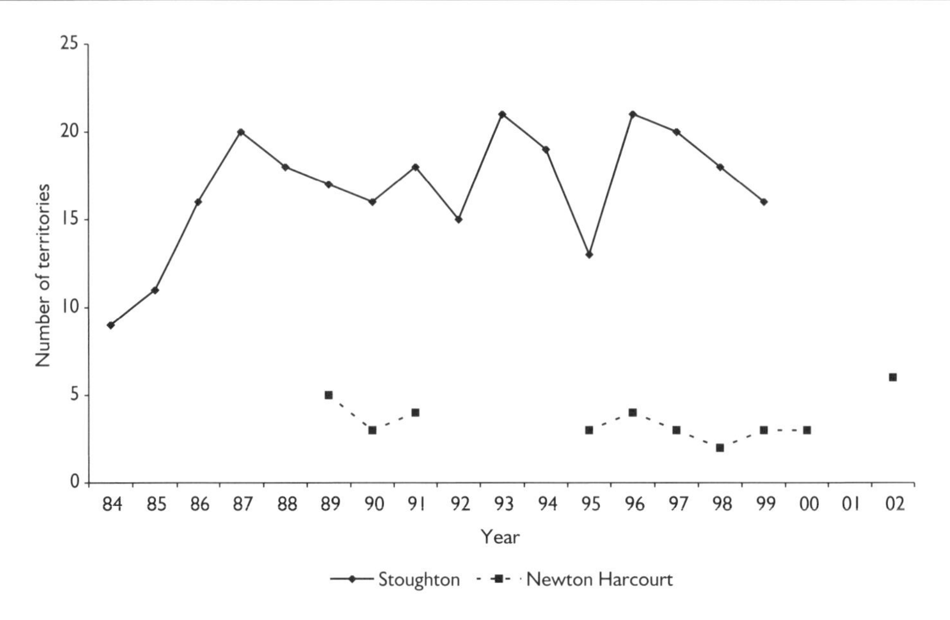

Figure 356: Number of breeding pairs of Wood Pigeons on two Leicestershire CBC plots 1984–2002.

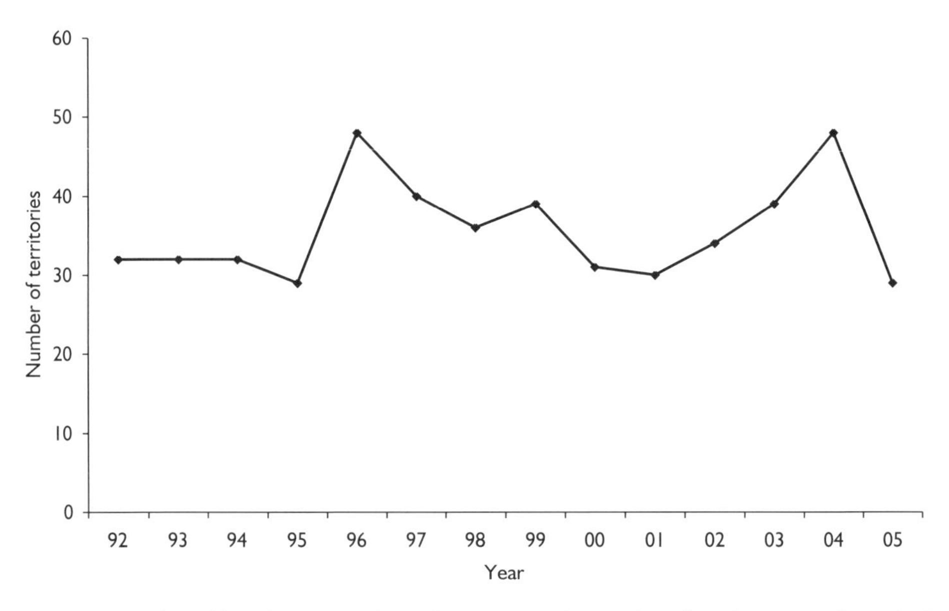

Figure 357: Number of breeding pairs of Wood Pigeons on the King's Hill Lodge, Uppingham CBC plot 1992–2005.

feeding activities. It is especially partial to shoots of growing cereals, peas and brassica crops (particularly kale), as well as stubble field seed. Over the years the majority of records have referred to large flocks of up to 4,000 individuals. The highest counts reported are:

- 8,000 at Ambion Wood during January 1961.
- 7,350 at Deans Lane, Woodhouse on November 13th 2005.
- 5,000 at Glen Parva on January 3rd 1981.
- 5,000 in the Market Bosworth area on December 31st 1993.

During the first three months of 2004, an aggregate count of 17,340 was recorded from 13 sites and between October 23rd and November 17th 2005 an aggregate total of 14,915 was counted migrating south-west at Deans Lane, Woodhouse (though this passage was not repeated the following year).

Several records have referred to eggs or young in the nest during October, emphasising the protracted breeding season of this species, which appears to be capable of year-round breeding. Examples of this are: a juvenile estimated to be about two months old at Narborough on April 16th 1986; two almost fully-fledged young at a factory nest-site in Leicester on November 22nd 1986 and a pair with a fledged juvenile at Braunstone, Leicester on January 14th 2003.

The severe winter weather of 1946–47 and 1962–63 provided some interesting observations. In February and March 1947, huge flocks stripped bare acres of kale and were approachable to within 15 yards before taking flight; within ten minutes of the termination of a shoot they were back again feeding ravenously. Some were reported ravaging cabbages and standing on the tops of brussel sprouts tearing off the leaves. The prolonged winter of 1963 saw numbers drastically reduced through starvation; large numbers were also shot as they lost their wariness, feeding close to human habitation on anything that was available. At a plantation at Quorn many were seen going to roost with large nodules of ice attached to their legs.

The only significant ringing recovery involves a bird ringed in Cambridgeshire on January 9th 1968 which was found dead in Leicestershire (100km to the north-west) on February 1st 1969.

Wood Pigeons of the nominate race *C. p. palumbus* are found extensively in Europe and North Africa, east to western Siberia, eastern Turkey and Iraq. British populations are largely resident but those in northern and eastern Europe and western Siberia are migratory. The British population has recently been estimated at between 2,450,000 and 3,040,000 pairs (Baker *et al.* 2006).

RED

Collared Dove (Eurasian Collared Dove) ***Streptopelia decaocto***

Common resident breeder.

The Collared Dove has undergone a remarkable and dramatic range expansion in Europe from its homeland in central Asia since the 1930s. In 1955 a pair bred successfully at Overstrand (Norfolk) but the first British record was probably one at Manton, near Brigg (Lincolnshire) from late July until September 1952. The expansion continued apace resulting in the first Leicestershire record in 1961, when one was disturbed at a newly threshed corn stack at Ratby on May 12th. Three years elapsed before the second record, one at Stoke Dry on June 8th 1964, the first record for Rutland. It is probable, however, that the species was not being fully recorded, as it appears that a sizeable population had become established by 1965, with reports from seven sites and the first breeding records at Fenny Drayton and Stoneygate Road, Leicester. Over the next three years numbers increased rapidly. In 1967 a large colony had built up at Dishley and was said to be 'causing trouble around corn stores' and a roost of 300 was in the village churchyard on March 14th 1968. By 1969 it was considered a 'common resident', its somewhat monotonous 'coo-coooo-coo' song being heard throughout the counties and colonies developing in the city of Leicester. In 1972 its status was upgraded to 'resident breeder, fairly common and widespread', a status achieved from 'unknown' in just eight years.

The population continued to increase, attaining its current status in 1985, however this increase was at a slower pace, possibly reflecting the changes in farming practices at that time, which resulted in less loose grain around farm buildings and fewer stubble fields for winter feeding.

The best estimate of the counties' population was provided by Warrilow, who recorded this species in 474 tetrads in the counties (74% of the total number of tetrads) during 1976–84, with breeding confirmed in 106. It was absent only from parts of east Leicestershire and, based on an estimate of four to six pairs per occupied tetrad, a county-wide population of 1,900 to 2,800 pairs was proposed. There is a feeling that, in the early part of the 21st century, numbers of this species may have levelled out or possibly declined, but firm evidence is not available. However, CBC results from Stoughton do show that the highest breeding numbers were recorded in the mid-1970s and from 1979 onwards there was usually just one pair. Whether this situation is representative of the counties as a whole is debatable, as the habitat at this site suffered greatly during the 1980s from agricultural intensification.

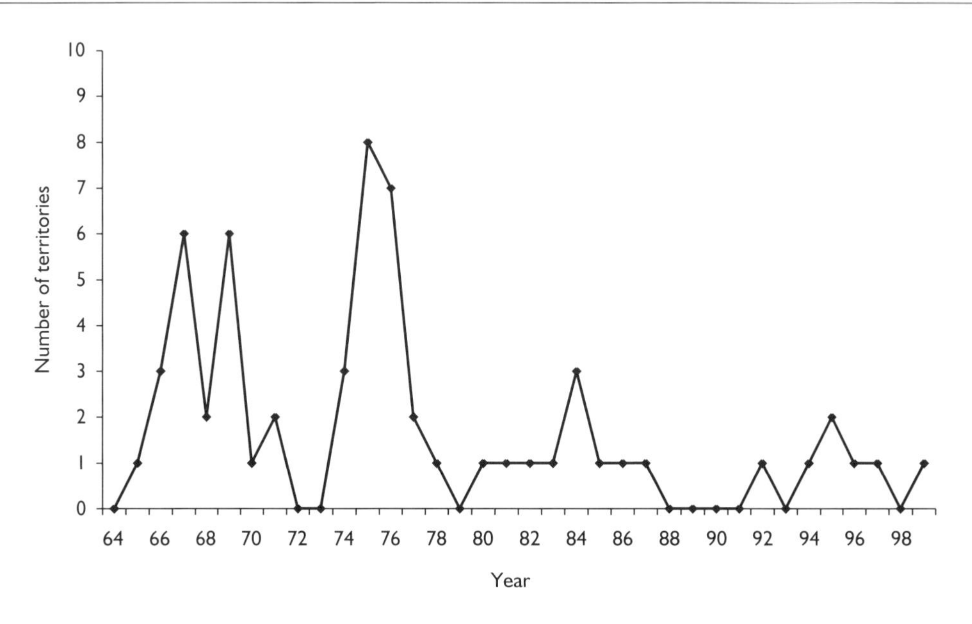

Figure 358: Number of breeding pairs of Collared Doves on the Stoughton CBC plot 1964–99.

Collared Doves favour suburban habitats and two recent studies have shown how numerous and widespread this species can be in such areas. Fray *et al.* (1990) found the Collared Dove to be the ninth-commonest bird at four green sites within the city of Leicester in 1989; a particularly large concentration was noted at Abbey Park, where an estimated 17 territories made it the third most numerous species at this site. Meanwhile, the Leicestershire Garden Bird Survey found Collared Dove to be the fourth most-frequent species during the period January 1996 to June 2005, visiting over 82% of all gardens.

Since 1977 there have been 19 three-figure flocks reported but, perhaps surprisingly, the 1968 Dishley group is still the largest ever count. Flocks have exceeded 150 on a further six occasions, as follows:

- 220 at Enderby on October 8th 1989, with 180 there on October 29th of the same year.
- 220 at Lockington Grounds on September 28th 2003.
- 200 at Kirby Bellars on December 28th 1990.
- 175 at Enderby on September 7th 1996.
- 160 at Huncote on October 24th 1991.
- 160 at Lubbesthorpe on August 31st 1993.

In common with other members of the *Columbidae* there are a number of records of out-of-season breeding activity, including nest-building in December 2001 and early January of both 1997 and 2003 and two fledged young from a nest in Ketton on November 24th 1986. Examples of amusing breeding behaviour include a nest on the top of a telegraph pole in a Leicester street and one gathering copper wire to use in building a nest in a copper beech tree!

Collared Doves now breed over much of Europe following their spectacular range expansion in the 20th century. They are widespread in Britain, the latest population estimate being 284,000 pairs (Baker *et al.* 2006). Ringing recoveries involving Leicestershire demonstrate their wide-ranging dispersal. Of two that were ringed in March 1974 at Earl Shilton, one was killed at Tadcaster (North Yorkshire) on August 14th the following year and the second was shot in a grain store at Leamington Spa (Warwickshire) in April 1976. In addition, three that had been ringed at Dishley all moved over 100km to the north-west: one ringed on October 14th 1980 was found dead at Latchford (Cheshire) on June 28th 1982, one ringed on October 19th 1980 was recovered at Neston (Cheshire) on May 1st 1982 and one ringed on October 5th 1981 was shot at Bretherton (Lancashire) on July 3rd 1982.

RED

Turtle Dove (European Turtle Dove) ***Streptopelia turtur***

Uncommon migrant breeder, recently declined.

Although this species has never been common in the counties, it is clear that numbers have declined. In the 19th century Browne described it as a sparingly distributed summer visitor in Leicestershire and recorded breeding at Aylestone, Tilton on the Hill and Arnesby. Haines stated that it was very uncommon in Rutland until about 1840 and the first nest was not recorded until 1859. Thereafter it became more plentiful, arriving about the end of April. A measure of the numbers involved is provided by counts of up to 30 in a field near Uppingham in about 1885 and about 50 in a ploughed field at Market Harborough, where it was otherwise considered uncommon, on an unspecified date.

In contrast with the Collared Dove, the Turtle Dove has suffered a substantial decline, particularly in recent years. In the early 1940s it was described as 'fairly common and well distributed' throughout the counties and was considered to be increasing, with flocks of up to 30 quite common in oat fields. Since the formation of LROS it would appear that the peak year was 1945, as a marked decrease was apparent in 1949. It was still considered as 'fairly common to common' up to the mid-1980s; however, it is difficult to obtain a true picture of the status during this period as few details are available. There was some indication of an easterly bias, borne out by the fact that all counts of 20+ during this period came from the eastern half of the region and included 70 at Keythorpe on June 1st 1968, 60 at Whitwell in May 1975 and 42 at Owston Wood on June 12th 1977.

Warrilow recorded Turtle Doves in 384 tetrads in the counties during 1976–84 (60% of the total number of tetrads), with breeding confirmed in 75. It was absent from urban areas and other areas east of Melton Mowbray, between Market Harborough and Lutterworth and west of Ibstock. Based on an average of three to five pairs per occupied tetrad a county-wide population of 1,100 to 1,900 pairs was proposed, but in light of the recent population crash this figure is now much too high. In Rutland, Mitcham (1992) found 41% of tetrads occupied and described the distribution as 'sparse'. By the time of the 1992–94 survey of Charnwood, Webster (1997) found just 10% of 1-km squares occupied and breeding was proved only twice.

During 1986–1994, the Turtle Dove was considered to be 'uncommon to fairly common', with records from between 23 and 33 sites each year and a high total of 44 sites in 1992. Although reports during the period appear to have increased much of this was in response to fieldwork requests rather than a real increase in numbers. Breeding was proved from 1990 to 1994 at between one and three sites and song was recorded at 17 sites in 1994. Since 1995 this species' status has been regarded as 'uncommon' with an obvious recent decline,

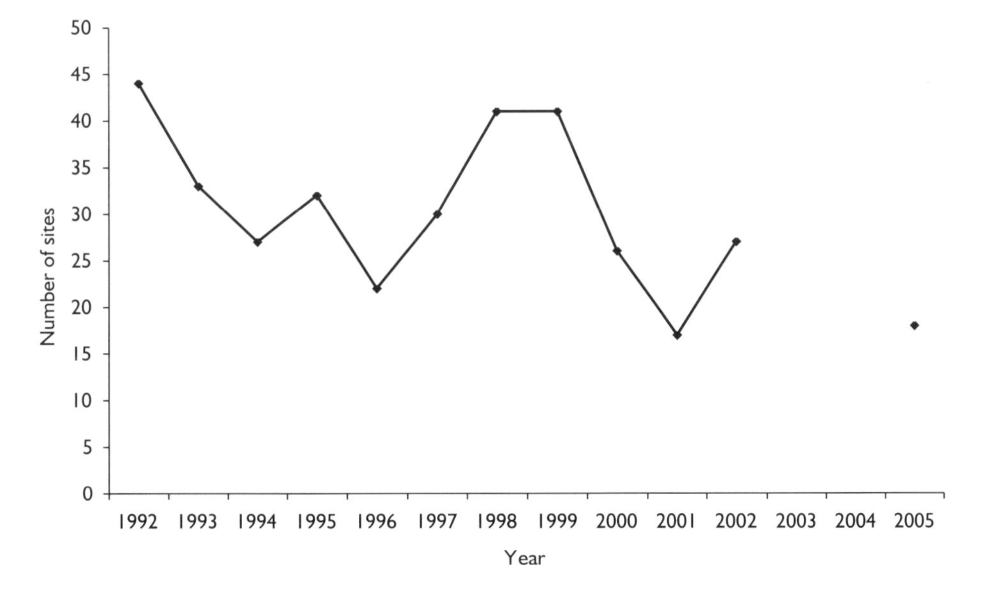

Figure 359: Number of sites with records of Turtle Doves in Leicestershire and Rutland 1992–2005.

particularly in Rutland which had been the stronghold. In most years records came from at least 30 sites, with 41 in both 1998 and 1999 but only 17 in 2001 and 18 in 2005. Breeding has only been proved in three years since 1995 and at just one site on each occasion. Nationally the Turtle Dove population declined on farmland by 79% between 1973 and 1998 (Chamberlain & Vickery 2002), although the reasons are not fully understood. Many are still slaughtered annually during passage through the Mediterranean, particularly in spring. Changes in farming practices have also had a marked effect due to the loss of important feeding and nesting habitat. The change from a hay crop to silage, with the consequent loss of weed seeds is probably another important factor. Some measure of the recent decline is demonstrated by CBC data from Stoughton, where there has been a steady decline since the mid-1980s and breeding was last recorded in 1989 when two pairs were present.

Figures 361 and 362 show the extent of this species' decline between 1995 and 2005, particularly in west and north-east Leicestershire.

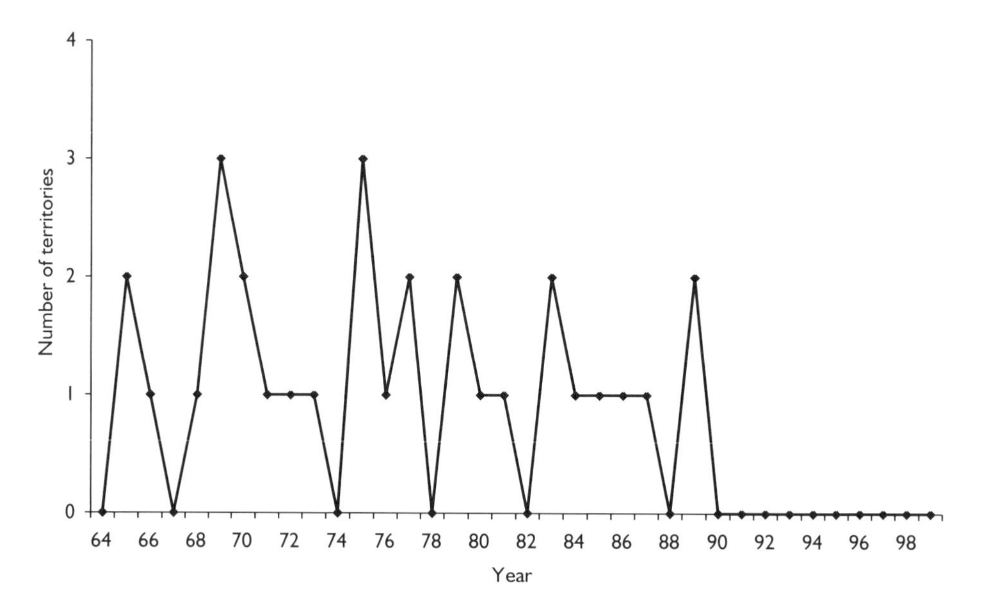

Figure 360: Number of breeding pairs of Turtle Doves on the Stoughton CBC plot 1964–99.

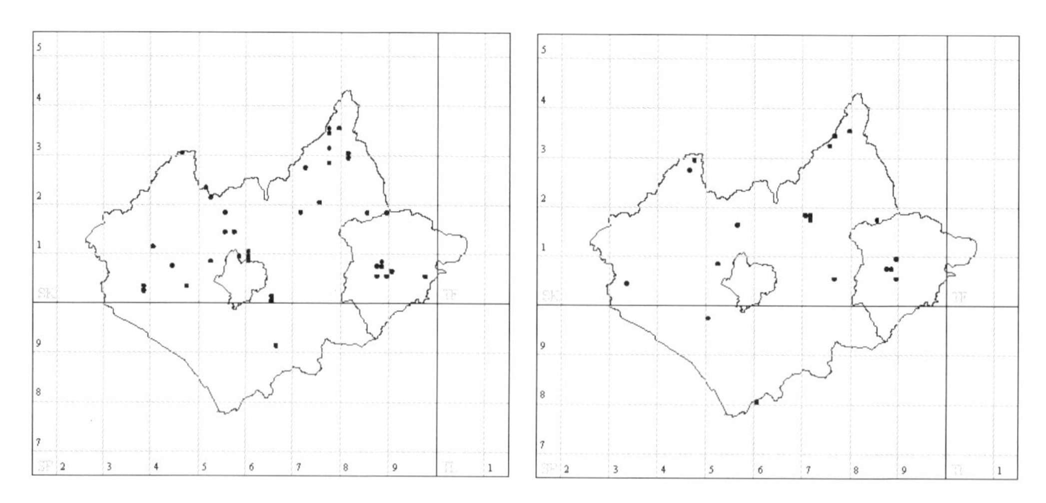

Figure 361: Distribution of Turtle Doves 1995.

Figure 362: Distribution of Turtle Doves 2005.

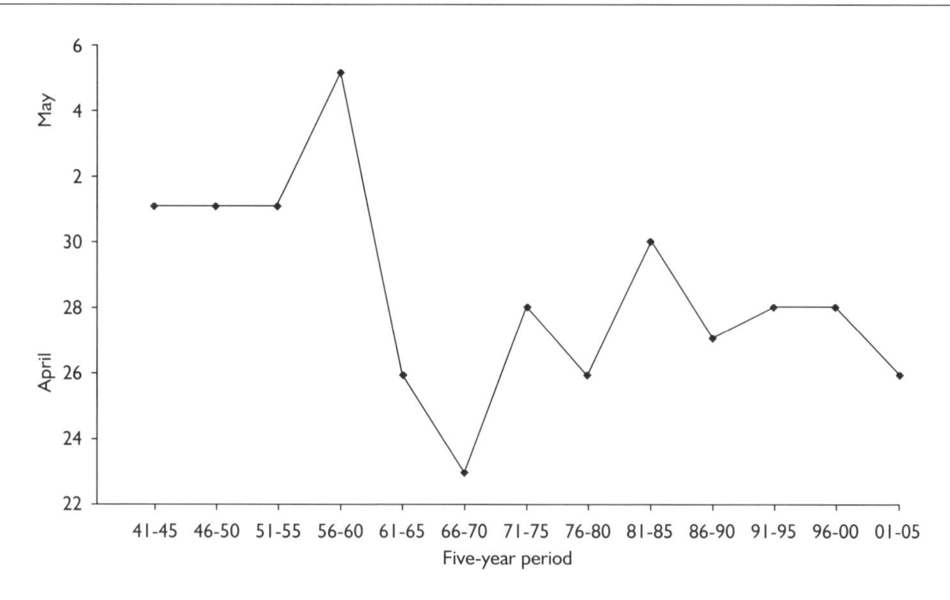

Figure 363: Average spring arrival dates of Turtle Doves by five-year periods 1941–2005.

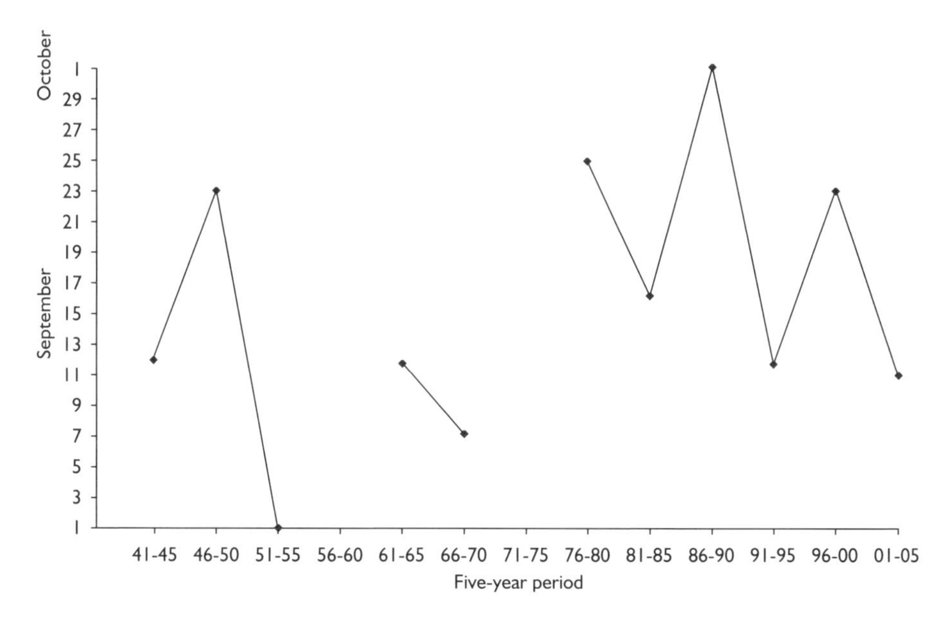

Figure 364: Average autumn departure dates of Turtle Doves by five-year periods 1941–2005.

The first birds usually arrive during the period from late April through to the beginning of May. There have been four arrivals on April 19th: at Blakeshay Wood in 1945, Tugby in 1964, an unspecified site in 1969 and Whetstone in 1980, but the earliest ever was one at Ketton on April 15th 1966 (Mitcham 1984). The average spring arrival date has remained remarkably consistent since the 1960s.

Most birds have departed by early September but there have been October records in ten years; of these, five have occurred during the first three days of the month, with later records, all of single birds, being:

- Rutland Water, October 18th 1986.
- Wardley, October 6th 1950.

- Eyebrook Reservoir, October 4th 1975.
- Oadby, October 4th 1980.
- Brooksby, October 4th 1996.

In common with several other migrant species which are in decline, such as the Yellow Wagtail and the House Martin, the average departure date of Turtle Doves is becoming earlier and is probably a reflection on the reduced numbers now present; in the four years from 2002 to 2005, the latest record was on or before September 4th in three of these years.

Turtle Doves of the nominate race *turtur* breed in Europe east through Turkey to the Caspian, in western Siberia and south to Kazakhstan, in deciduous woodland, primarily in agricultural areas but also in open country with shrubbery and copses. They are migratory and winter in the northern Afrotropics as far south as Ghana and Cameroon. The British breeding population during 1988–91 was estimated at 75,000 territories and was already in sharp decline (Gibbons *et al.* 1993). More recent estimates put it at 44,000 territories (Baker *et al.* 2006): this rapid decline has resulted in the Turtle Dove being placed on the 'Red List' of Birds of Conservation Concern (Gregory *et al.* 2002).

RED

Ring-necked Parakeet (Rose-ringed Parakeet) ***Psittacula krameri***

Rare to scarce visitor; all records probably refer to escaped birds.

The first published record of Ring-necked Parakeet in Leicestershire and Rutland was of two at Birstall on February 7th 1982. Since then there have been records in 15 of the 23 years up to 2005.

All records:

1982	two, Birstall, February 7th.
1984	Bushby, May 20th.
	Glenfield, June 15th for several days.
1985	Rutland Water, December 15th.
1987	female, Oadby, February 24th and March 13th.
	Sandringham Road, Wigston, October 13th.
1988	Rutland Water, February 17th.
	Scraptoft, September 8th to October 13th.
	female, Barrowden, October 2nd to 3rd.
1990	Rutland Water, February 11th.
	two, Quorn, February 18th.
	Leicester Forest East, May 27th.
	two males, Bradgate Park, July 28th.
	Humberstone Park, Leicester, September 16th.
1992	Wing, January 4th.
1995	Shenton, for two weeks in late December.
1997	near Shepshed, April 5th.
	Birstall, December 13th to January 31st 1998.
1998	between Welford and Foxton, July 4th.
	two, Newbold Verdon, July 24th.
	seven, Market Bosworth, November 8th.
1999	Swithland Reservoir, May 9th.
	Uppingham, July 28th.
	female, Ashby-de-la-Zouch, December 6th.
	Swithland Reservoir, December 25th; presumed same, Rothley, December 29th to January 1st 2000.
2000	Syston, July 25th.
	Humberstone Park, Leicester, August 2nd and 6th; presumed same, Hamilton Park, Leicester, August 25th.

	two, Hinckley, for a week in early September.
2001	three, Desford, January 26th.
	Abney Street, Leicester, May 23rd.
	Melton Mowbray, August 24th.
	Loughborough University, September 13th.
2002	Knighton, Leicester, February 11th.
	Quorn Borrow Pit, October 13th.
	Tugby, December 15th and 17th.
2003	East Park Road, Leicester, March 31st; presumed same, Abney Street, Leicester, April 22nd.
	Quorn, August 9th.
	Trent Valley Pit, October 24th.
2004	Syston Grange, August 21st.

There is no particular pattern to this species' occurrence in the counties and it is considered that all records refer to local escapes rather than wandering birds from the established feral population in south-east England. Due to its status and its similarity to other parakeet species it is possibly under-recorded.

Ring-necked Parakeets are found naturally in central and west Africa and the Indian subcontinent and a combination of escapes and introductions has seen this species become established in Britain; it was admitted to Category C of the British List in 1984. Regular breeding in south-east England began in 1971 and by 1986 the British population had reached 1,000 birds (Morgan 1993). Its numbers have continued to increase: 5,886 individuals were recorded at four roost sites in southern England in the winter of 2001–02 (Butler 2002) and the latest population estimate is of 4,300 pairs (Baker *et al.* 2006).

RED

Cuckoo (Common Cuckoo) ***Cuculus canorus***

Fairly common migrant breeder.

Probably the most well known of all our summer migrants, the Cuckoo's arrival is eagerly awaited by birdwatchers and the general public alike. Unfortunately it is no longer heard as much as it used to be.

In the 19th century Haines described it as abundant everywhere in Rutland and noted that the average date of arrival between 1736 and 1800 was April 21st but that from 1899 to 1905 it had been earlier (April 13th, very similar to today). He knew of just three March reports, the earliest being March 15th 1776. A measure of its abundance is that on one occasion 12 birds were seen together near Uppingham on May 12th 1899. In addition to the species mentioned below, the following were listed as foster parents: Robin, Song Thrush, Sedge Warbler, Common Whitethroat, Spotted Flycatcher and Linnet. Browne recorded it as close to Leicester as Aylestone and Knighton.

In the early days of LROS the Cuckoo was considered common and widespread. In 1945 it was reported as 'exceptionally numerous' and in 1947 'reports suggest an increase over recent years'. However, in 1949 numbers were recorded as 'below normal' and a year later a 'poor season' was reported. Little information is available for the decade of the 1950s, when a national decline in numbers began; reports thereafter considered it to be generally decreasing, although it was still reported as fairly common throughout the 1970s. A survey carried out by the RNHS during the establishment of Rutland Water, when the reservoir was being filled, found that numbers decreased steadily from 17 in the first summer to none in the fifth. Mitcham (1984) estimated the number of territories in Rutland as between 30 and 40; this may have been too low, however, as in 1992 he recorded the Cuckoo in 69 (59%) of Rutland tetrads and noted that up to 15 were at Rutland Water in 1988. This compares with a much lower density of occupation in Charnwood, where Webster (1997) found only 29% of 1-km squares occupied. During 1976–84, Warrilow recorded this species in 465 tetrads within the counties (73% of the total number of tetrads), with breeding confirmed in 47. It was absent from the conurbation of Leicester, which was to be expected, although the lack of records from parts of east Leicestershire and southern Rutland was less easy to explain. Warrilow estimated a county-wide population of between 900 and 1,800 birds.

The recent impression gained is that the general decrease has continued, which would correspond with the national picture, although there is limited statistical evidence to support this view. At the Stoughton CBC plot numbers were fairly steady during the late 1960s and early 1970s, then rose from the late 1970s to the early 1990s before returning to former levels. Some evidence that there may have been a very recent decline may be found in LROS Annual Reports, which noted 88 birds at 62 sites during spring in 2002 but between 59 and 64 birds during the following three springs. An interesting theory on the continued recent decline of the Cuckoo is that if potential foster species are nesting earlier, their clutches might be hatching before Cuckoos can lay amongst them. Combined with declines in many foster species, Cuckoos might be finding it increasingly difficult to locate suitable foster nests.

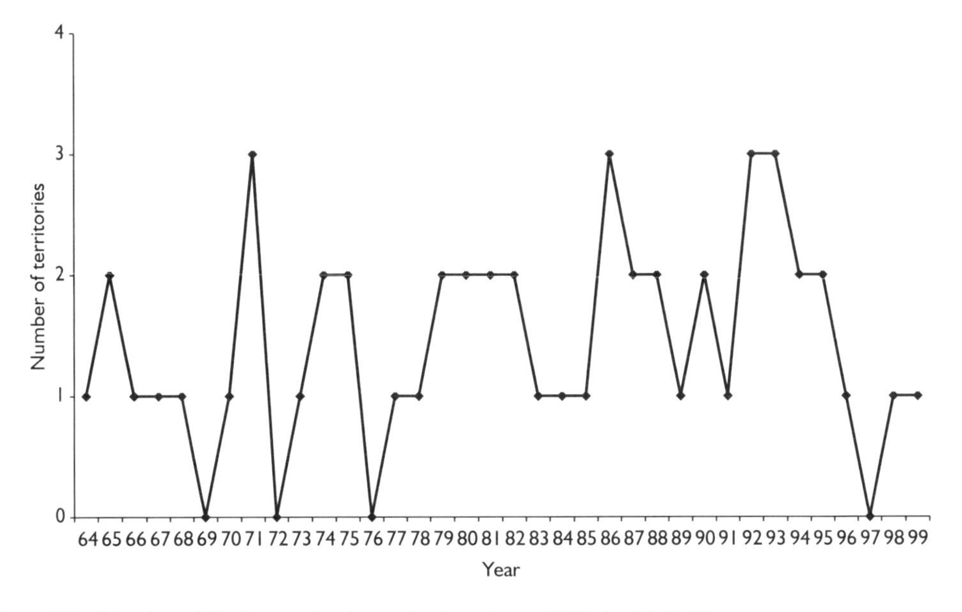

Figure 365: Number of Cuckoo territories on the Stoughton CBC plot 1964–99.

As well as the three March birds mentioned by Haines, there have been reports in March in four years, involving six individuals, all of which occurred in the first part of the 20th century:

- unspecified site on March 24th 1945.
- Western Park, Leicester on March 26th 1944.
- unspecified site on March 26th 1945.
- Uppingham on March 27th 1946.
- Queniborough on March 27th 1950.
- Birstall on March 31st 1946.

The majority of the earliest arrival dates since 1950 have occurred during the period April 10th to 26th, with an earlier arrival in just seven years. The Cuckoo is one of the few migrant species that apparently arrived earlier 60 years ago than it does today and it is perhaps wise to treat these March records with a degree of caution, particularly as there are regularly claims in the local media of earlier arrivals, even in mid-winter! Since 1950 there have been eight arrivals prior to April 10th, as follows:

- Priory Water on April 2nd 1993.
- Stockerston on April 4th 1981.
- Thurcaston on April 5th 1980.
- unspecified site on April 6th 1971.
- Saddington Reservoir on April 6th 2002.
- Kirby Muxloe on April 8th 1985.
- Belton on April 9th 1993.
- Rutland Water on April 9th 1995.

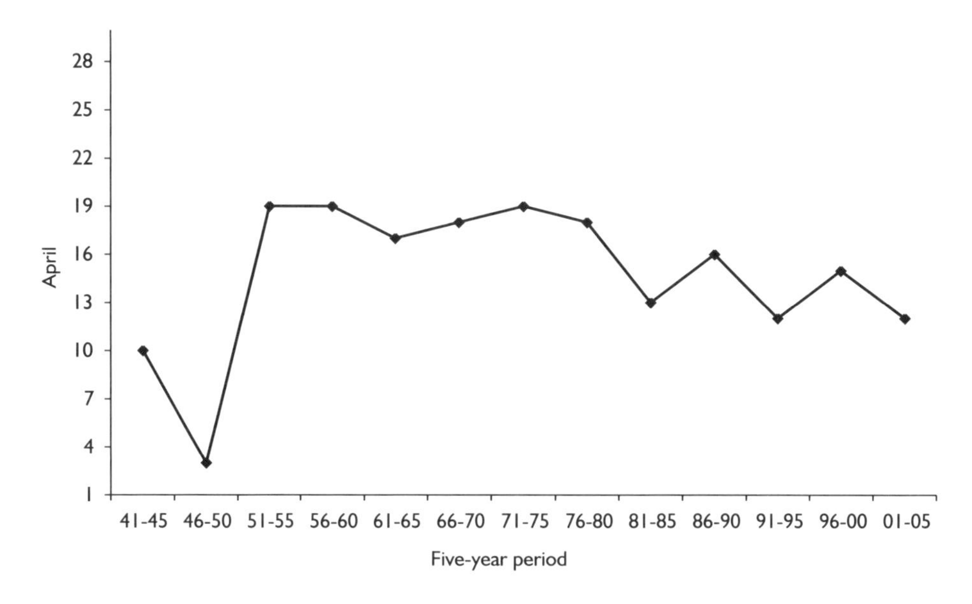

Figure 366: Average spring arrival dates of Cuckoos by five-year periods 1941–2005.

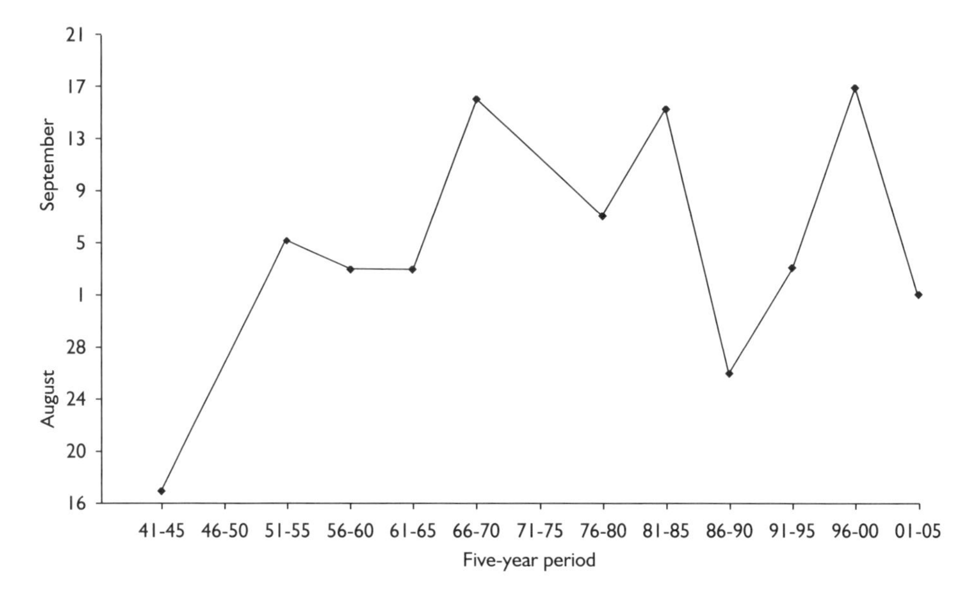

Figure 367: Average autumn departure dates of Cuckoos by five-year periods 1941–2005.

The breeding biology of the Cuckoo results in the majority of adults departing for their wintering grounds by the end of June, although one was still singing at Eyebrook Reservoir on July 11th 1980. The majority of records from July onwards refer to juveniles, most of which have departed by mid-September. There have been nine records later than September 20th, as follows:

- Burton Overy on September 21st 1980.
- Cossington on September 22nd 1980.
- Enderby on September 24th 1965.
- Frisby Gravel Pits on September 24th 1980.

- Eyebrook Reservoir from September 19th to 25th 1996.
- unspecified site on September 30th 1978.
- Seaton on October 10th 1998.
- Swithland Reservoir on October 12th 1992.
- Scraptoft Lane, Leicester on October 21st 1984.

Ten species have been recorded as foster parents: Meadow Pipit, Tree Pipit, Pied Wagtail, Common Redstart, Blackbird, Reed Warbler, Willow Warbler, Greenfinch, Yellowhammer and Dunnock, the last being the most regularly duped. Egg-laying in one Dunnock nest was recorded as taking 30 seconds, the Cuckoo flying off with the fosterer's egg impaled on its bill before it was eventually swallowed.

An interesting record came from a Desford garden in 1948, when one stunned itself flying into a window. When picked up, it laid an egg on the knee of its rescuer before flying off. Also in 1948, one was seen to go to roost in low bushes in a derelict garden, from where it was heard to be singing continuously but quietly so that it could only be heard at a distance of a few yards. Its call gradually dropped in pitch until it was finally silent, presumably asleep, as it was by then completely dark.

Two 'hepatic' females have been recorded: at Priory Water on May 12th 1994, with presumably the same individual at Frisby GP on May 15th, and at the Lyndon Reserve, Rutland Water, on April 22nd 2001 and again on May 13th.

A juvenile ringed at Theddlethorpe Dunes (Lincolnshire) on August 18th 1985 was found dead at Long Clawson on May 28th 1989.

The Cuckoo is a summer visitor throughout the whole of Europe with the exception of the extreme north of Norway, Iceland and a few Mediterranean islands. Its breeding range extends eastwards throughout central Asia and China (except the north-west) to the Kamchatka peninsula, with the exception of the coastal areas bordering the Arctic Ocean and parts of Kazakhstan. The European population winters in Africa south of the equator. The British breeding population began to decline in the 1950s; it was estimated at 13,000 to 26,000 pairs during 1988–91 (Gibbons *et al.* 1993) but more recent estimates put it at 9,600–19,300 pairs (Baker *et al.* 2006). The recent and continuing significant decline in the breeding population has resulted in this species being added to the 'Amber List' of Birds of Conservation Concern (Gregory *et al.* 2002).

RED

Barn Owl *Tyto alba*

Uncommon resident breeder.

A favourite of many, the status of the Barn Owl in the counties has fluctuated somewhat over the years. Browne described it as resident and generally distributed, whilst Haines made the comment that it 'does not seem to have ever been very uncommon'. Blaker (1934) considered it to have been in a steady decline since at least the First World War and his population estimate for the counties was 245 pairs.

At the time that LROS was formed in 1941, it was described as 'widely but thinly distributed, not as common as formerly'. By 1946 it was thought to be increasing, with records from almost 30 sites and breeding records from eight. However, as a result of the extremely severe winter of 1946–47 there was a very serious decline, with many picked up dead around stack yards. Individuals were also seen hunting in gardens in built-up areas and one even took a dead House Sparrow from the hand! By 1950 it was considered to have made a remarkable recovery since the aforementioned severe winter but subsequently very little information is available until 1960, by which time it was considered to be uncommon, widespread but seriously declining, with records from just 11 sites. Between 1960 and the mid-1970s records came from an average of 15 to 20 sites per year, but breeding was only recorded in five years, with a maximum of three pairs in any one year. There was no mention of a reduction in numbers after the severe winter of 1962–63, but it was only recorded from ten sites in that year.

Warrilow, following his fieldwork during 1976–84, considered the Barn Owl to be on the verge of extinction as a breeding species in Leicestershire and Rutland. The survey had been intensive and included discussions with many farmers and landowners; however, he could only find nine cases of confirmed breeding during this period, three of which were known to have failed and a further eight pairs which possibly bred. Most of the survey work provided isolated reports, but there were small clusters of records from the Belvoir area, around Hinckley and to the north-east of Uppingham. As a result of national survey work undertaken between 1982 and 1985, Shawyer (1994) estimated the population in the counties to be 25 pairs, somewhat contradicting Warrilow's findings. Shawyer also found that a small proportion of birds had been contaminated with organochlorines, but the subsequent ban of such pesticides had not led to a revival in numbers as it had with the Sparrowhawk.

It would appear that the population reached its lowest ebb during the 1980s: LROS's own reports during that period indicate a species in serious decline, with breeding records of one or two pairs in just five years. In 1984 there were just eight records, none of them between April and September. As well as the use of pesticides and direct persecution by man, a number of additional reasons contributed to a national population reduction during this time, including the loss of rough grassland for hunting, the loss of breeding sites through the demolition of old farm buildings and the removal of old trees with nesting cavities, and the increase in road traffic. Many LROS Annual Reports include records of roadside fatalities, particularly in the winter months. Extreme weather conditions, especially prolonged snow cover and heavy rainfall during the breeding season, are also contributory factors.

A slight improvement was apparent by the early 1990s, with records from up to 20 sites annually, but although breeding was suspected in a number of years it was only proven in 1990. It was thought that part of the reason for the increase in records may have been a result of birds being deliberately released into the wild or escaping from captivity, as this species has become very popular as a captive breeding bird in recent years. Evidence to support this view included two close to Leicester city centre in 1990, at Welford Road on February 1st and King Richard's Road on August 13th, the former of which was found dead. Another dead bird was picked up at Braunstone, Leicester on May 2nd 1992 and one, wearing jesses, was rescued after becoming tangled in a tree at Oadby on November 14th of the same year.

Since 1996, when three pairs bred, there has been a considerable improvement, with records from an average of almost 30 sites annually, primarily in the north and east of the counties. At least ten pairs bred in 1999 and nine in 2002, five of which used nest boxes. An LROS survey in 2004 found at least 32 pairs bred successfully: 19 pairs were in Rutland, with eight in north-east Leicestershire and only five elsewhere (one in the north-west, one in the west and three in central Leicestershire). At least 19 pairs utilised nest boxes, thus emphasising the importance of these artificial nest sites. Much of this data was provided by the Rutland Barn Owl Project, an organisation which provides landowners with nest boxes and monitors the results.

Table 26: Barn Owl records 1996–2005

Year	**1996**	**1997**	**1998**	**1999**	**2000**	**2001**	**2002**	**2003**	**2004**	**2005**
Sites	23	30	30	30	33	34	28	23	44	53
Nests	3	3	2	10	6	4	9	1+	32	19+

Figures 368–371 show the distribution of all records received of Barn Owls in Leicestershire and Rutland in 1975, 1985, 1995 and 2005; the drastic reduction in the 1980s, followed by a significant recovery into the 21st century, is readily apparent.

Barn Owls are almost cosmopolitan, although they are absent from much of northern Europe. They are largely resident, but there is some dispersal of young birds, as evidenced by the following ringing recoveries involving Leicestershire and Rutland:

- a pullus ringed at Langholm (Dumfries and Galloway) on September 29th 1984 was found dead near Bisbrooke on January 19th 1986.
- a pullus male ringed at Wilsford (Wiltshire) on June 25th 1995 was controlled at Rutland Water on January 3rd 1996.
- a pullus ringed at Newbridge (Oxfordshire) on July 1st 1996 was found dead at Ashby-de-la-Zouch on February 23rd 1997.

- a pullus ringed at Rutland Water on June 23rd 1998 was found dead at Spalding (Lincolnshire) on November 20th 1998.
- a pullus male ringed at Rutland Water in 2000 was found breeding in a nest box near Sutton Bridge (Lincolnshire) in May 2004.

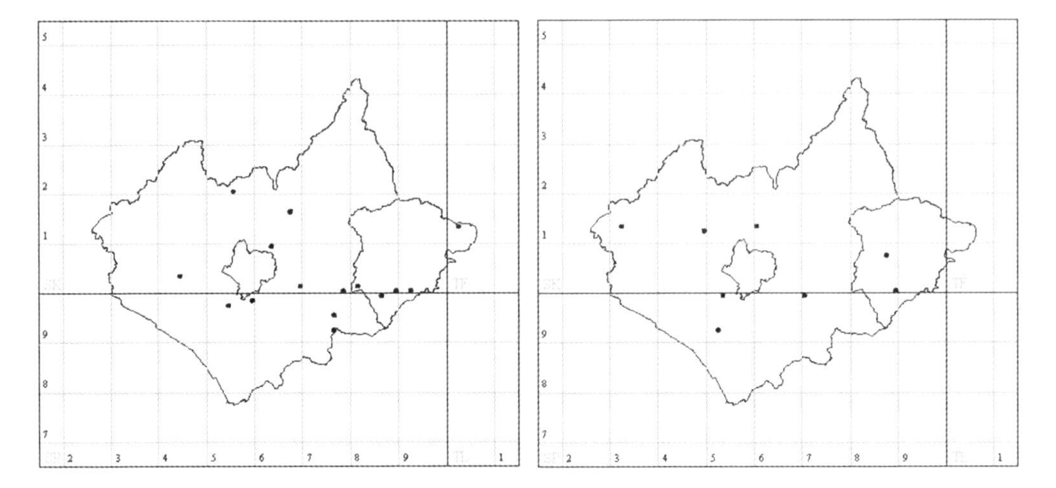

Figure 368: Distribution of Barn Owls 1975.

Figure 369: Distribution of Barn Owls 1985.

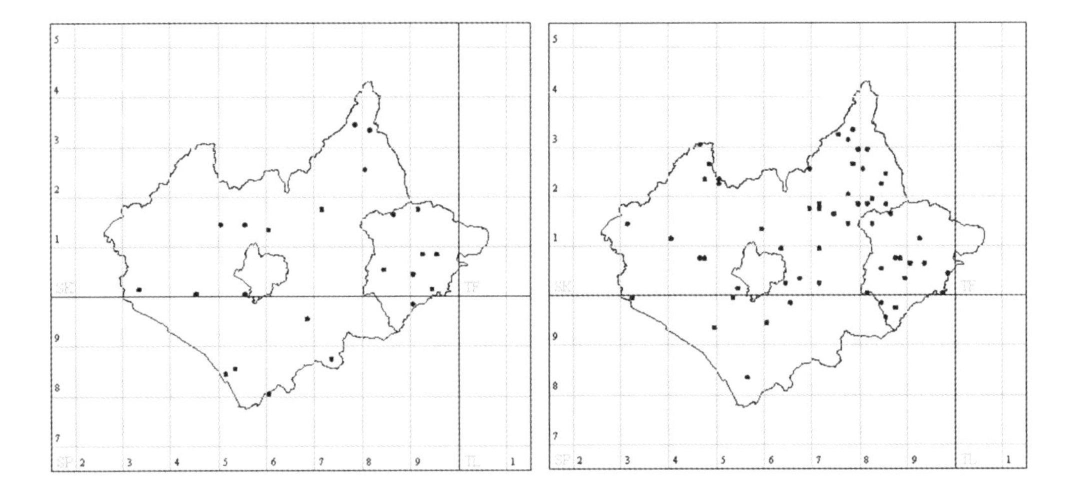

Figure 370: Distribution of Barn Owls 1995.

Figure 371: Distribution of Barn Owls 2005.

Birds found in Britain are of the nominate race *alba* but 'dark-breasted' birds of the subspecies *guttata* are occasional vagrants from central Europe and have apparently bred in Britain recently. One at Rutland Water from January 8th to March 10th 2004 was originally considered to be of the subspecies *guttata* as it had a brownish upper breast, but subsequently proved to be an unusual variant of the nominate race. The most recent estimate of the British breeding population is 4,000 pairs (Baker *et al.* 2006). As a result of the contraction of its breeding range, this species has been added to the 'Amber List' of Birds of Conservation Concern (Gregory *et al.* 2002).

RED

Little Owl *Athene noctua*

Introduced. Fairly common resident breeder.

The Little Owl was introduced into Britain in the late 19th century, chiefly in Kent and at Oundle (Northamptonshire), where it became firmly established by 1888 to 1890. It was from the Oundle population that this species spread rapidly into Rutland: according to Haines it was first obtained at Normanton in 1891, reached Glaston four years later, Seaton in 1897 and Exton in 1899. Thereafter it spread throughout Rutland before reaching Leicestershire at the beginning of the 20th century. Browne states that the first record for Leicestershire came from Glooston Wood in 1900, with the first breeding record in 1906. Hickling stated that it had become widely distributed in the counties by the 1920s, probably reaching a peak as a breeding species around 1940.

In 1946 it was considered to be on the increase but the severe winter weather in early 1947 took its toll, with numbers probably reduced by 66%. The 1948 LROS Annual Report spoke of a 'great decrease' and the 1949 and 1950 Annual Reports indicated that numbers were still below the 1946 levels. During the severe winter weather of 1947 there were reports of individuals approachable to within six feet, too weak to fly. Also during this period, a Blackbird was taken as prey and even a Moorhen was attacked.

Very little information is available for the 1950s, but by 1960 it was reported as 'widely distributed and common but probably less common than formerly'. Throughout the 1960s it was considered as widespread but becoming uncommon, numbers again reduced as a result of the severe winter of 1962–63, although there had been something of a recovery by 1968.

During 1976–84 Warrilow recorded the Little Owl in 254 tetrads in the counties (40% of the total number of tetrads), with breeding confirmed in 72. He found that it was mainly concentrated in farmland and parkland areas from the southern edge of Charnwood to Hinckley, from Bruntingthorpe through Houghton on the Hill to Barkby, between Wing and Clipsham in Rutland and around Belvoir. It was absent from large parts of west and north-east Leicestershire and avoided large woodlands and built-up areas. Local CBC data suggest that only one pair is likely to be present per occupied tetrad and on this basis Warrilow proposed a county-wide breeding population of between 250 and 300 pairs. Later surveys have found that 24% of Rutland tetrads were occupied (Mitcham 1992), although it was thought that there had been a recent decline in the population there, whilst in Charnwood Webster (1997) found that just 10% of 1-km squares were occupied during 1992–94, reflecting the fact that the larger areas of woodland which characterise this area are not suitable for Little Owls.

In the last 20 years it would appear that numbers have remained reasonably static, confirming its current status of fairly common resident breeder. The table below provides details of the averages for the last ten and 20 years for which this data has been available. The apparent increase in the number of sites over the last ten years is likely to be due to better observer reporting, whilst the low confirmed breeding totals are a reflection on the fact that this species favours habitats such as farmland and parkland that are not commonly visited by birdwatchers. Considering the relatively sedentary nature of this species it is likely that breeding occurred at the majority of sites where this species was recorded.

Figure 372 shows the distribution of all records received of this species during 2005.

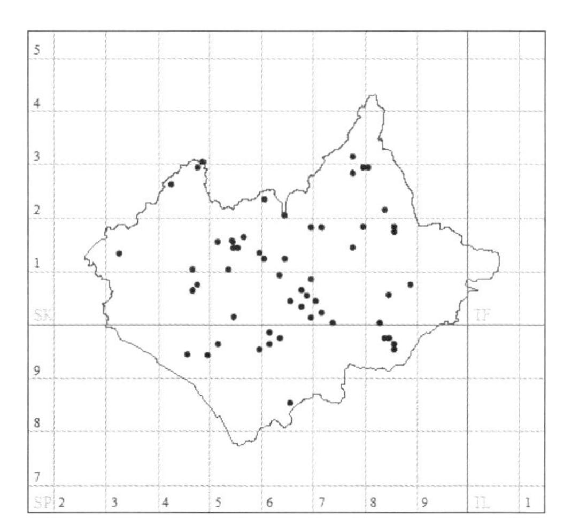

Figure 372: Distribution of Little Owls 2005.

Table 27: Little Owl records 1986–2005

	Average number of sites from which records received	Average number of sites at which breeding confirmed
1986–2005	50.3	4.2
1996–2005	60.2	4.0

As with other owl species, several records over the years have referred to roadside corpses. It is easy to see how this happens: on August 1st 1985 two juveniles were found sitting in the middle of a road at Shenton, on May 9th 1993 one was 'jumping about in the middle of the road' at Barrow upon Soar and, during the summer of 1997, adults were recorded feeding in the road on rabbit kills at both Tilton on the Hill and Ashwell.

One ringed as a pullus at Ratby on June 11th 1960 was found dead near Grantham (Lincolnshire) on May 3rd 1964. A bird described as melanistic was at Lubbesthorpe in August 2004.

Little Owls are found extensively in Europe (apart from the far north), northern Africa and the Arabian peninsula and in central Asia. The latest British population estimate is of 5,800 to 11,600 pairs (Baker *et al.* 2006). Recent data suggests a possible moderate long-term decline in Britain; however, trends are poorly known because the species has large territories and is difficult to detect except by dedicated surveys (Baillie *et al.* 2006).

RED

Tawny Owl *Strix aluco*

Fairly common resident breeder.

In the late 19th century Browne's assessment was that it was 'not very common' in Leicestershire and Haines considered it generally though sparingly distributed in Rutland. Since the 1940s, it has been considered as a common or fairly common resident breeder, widespread throughout the counties. A population decrease occurred after the severe winter of 1947, but the LROS Annual Report for that year stated that it seemed to have been 'less adversely affected than other owls by the severe weather'. A pronounced increase was noted in 1948 and 1949; however, 11 carcasses on a gamekeeper's gibbet at Wardley Wood in March 1948 provide evidence of its persecution in those early days. Fortunately the only other report of this nature was in 1963.

During the period from 1950 until the late 1970s, very little information is available as most Annual Reports provided just a general statement confirming its status as a 'common and widespread resident breeder'. No specific mention was made of a population decrease after the severe winter weather in 1962–63.

As a highly nocturnal owl, it is somewhat difficult to determine the true status of this species. Its favoured habitats are woodland, normally broad-leaved, but also parkland, churchyards and well established gardens with mature trees. During 1976–84 Warrilow recorded the Tawny Owl in 305 tetrads in the counties (48% of the total number of tetrads), with breeding confirmed in 90. He noted a high density in the wooded areas of Charnwood and it was also found regularly in mature gardens in suburban Leicester. It was absent from large areas of west and north-east Leicestershire. Warrilow estimated a breeding population of 300 to 600 pairs. Webster (1997) found confirmed or probable breeding in 48% of 1-km squares, where calling was found to be more regular during the late autumn than in winter. In Rutland Mitcham (1992) found that 35% of tetrads were occupied, mainly in the woodland belt which extends across the centre of the county.

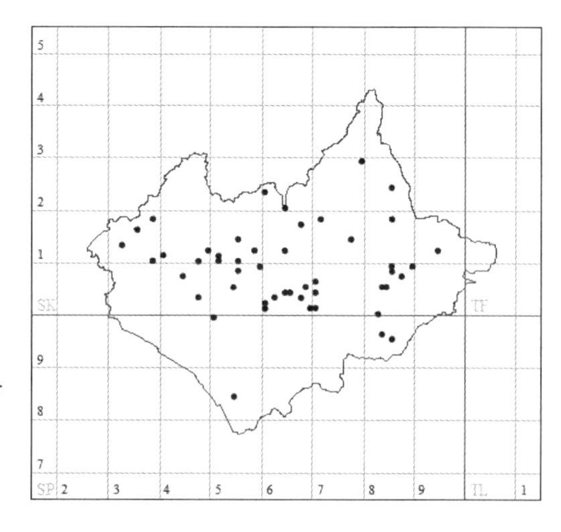

Figure 373: Distribution of Tawny Owls 2005.

Since the mid 1980s most Annual Reports have detailed the number of known breeding records and the number of sites from which records have been received. Table 28 provides details of the averages for the last ten and 20 years for which this data has been available and indicates that the population is relatively stable. Due to this species' nocturnal habits the actual number of breeding pairs is much higher than the table suggests and considering the relatively sedentary nature of this species it is likely that breeding occurred at the majority of sites where this species was recorded.

Table 28: Tawny Owl records 1986–2005

	Average number of sites from which records received	Average number of sites at which breeding confirmed
1986–2005	46.5	6.2
1996–2005	53.3	6.8

In the early days of LROS many reports came from within the city boundary of Leicester and from built-up areas. A similar pattern has continued since that time, with birds heard more often than seen. The Tawny Owl was the 23rd most-frequently recorded species during the Leicestershire Garden Bird Survey from January 1996 to June 2005, being reported from 6% of gardens.

Unfortunately many records have referred to birds found dead on or near roads, presumably as a result of hunting on roadside verges. Poignant evidence of this was recorded in January 1992, when one was found dead on a road with a mouse in its talons. Apart from the mouse, the only other prey items recorded have been Redwing, juvenile Carrion Crow, Stock Dove, Song Thrush and 'sparrows'; during the period of severe winter weather in 1962–63, the latter two prey items were taken during daylight hours. Other records of interest include two juveniles trapped in a chimney at Birstall for five days in 1986 before being released and taken into care and two adults which were eventually forced from a hedgerow by four or five Magpies which had been using it as a regular roost site. The latter observation was made by torchlight at 21:00 on the evening of January 17th 1982. One found in a Melton Mowbray workshop on December 20th 2003 had a lucky escape as it was only discovered a few minutes before the building was to be closed for the two-week Christmas period. In 1993, the last of three young fledged from a nest at Narborough on March 26th, where the first egg had been laid during the first week of January.

The only ringing record of note is of a pullus ringed at Kidderminster (Worcestershire) on April 21st 1991 which was found at Rutland Water on about August 2nd 1994.

The Tawny Owl has two main populations, one found in the Western Palearctic and the other in central and eastern Asia. All populations are mainly resident. The British breeding population is currently estimated at 19,400 pairs (Baker *et al.* 2006).

RED

Long-eared Owl *Asio otus*

Rare resident breeder, scarce winter visitor.

The Long-eared Owl is rarely seen due to its nocturnal habits and its preference for coniferous woodland during the breeding season. Its current breeding status is uncertain. During the 19th century both Browne and Haines considered it resident but local and scarce; localities where it was recorded included Quorn, Gopsall Wood, Laughton Hills, Ketton and Empingham. The LROS archives mention records from Bradgate Park in 1911, Barkby Holt in February 1927 and Nether Broughton in March 1932.

In the 30 years from the establishment of LROS in 1941 through to 1970, the Long-eared Owl failed to be recorded in a total of 19 years, with complete absences between July 1951 and the summer of 1959 and between 1965 and 1970 and only one between November 1943 and April 1949 (at Leicester City Farms in March 1946). Breeding was reported in just five years during this period:

1941 one pair bred at Snarestone.
1949 two pairs bred at Belvoir.
1951 six pairs bred at Belvoir.
1959 one pair bred in north Leicestershire, raising three young.
1965 one pair bred at the same north Leicestershire site as in 1959, raising three young.

Although there was no definite proof, it seems likely that breeding continued in Belvoir during the 1950s, as several fresh carcasses were seen on a gibbet at Belvoir Woods on May 6th 1956. Apart from the breeding records, those years when records occurred usually involved single birds, although two were at Swithland Reservoir in November 1943 and two were at Exton in April 1950.

From 1970 to the present day there has been an increase in records, although this may be accounted for by the increase in observers. There has been at least one record in every year except three (1978, 1988 and 2003), with multiple records in several years and a number of roost sites reported. Breeding has been confirmed in nine years since 1970:

1972 a pair bred at Normanton Thorns, Bottesford.
1973 a pair bred at Croxton Kerrial.
1974 a pair again bred at Croxton Kerrial. A pair also bred at Hambleton but the chicks were found shot.
1995 a pair bred north of Dishley Pool, raising three young.
1996 a pair again bred north of Dishley Pool and two pairs bred in Rutland, raising broods of three and two young.
1997 a pair again bred north of Dishley Pool, raising one young. Display was seen at one of the 1996 Rutland sites but there was no confirmation of breeding.
1998 a pair bred for the fourth successive year north of Dishley Pool, raising at least one young.
2001 a recently fledged juvenile was seen at Cottesmore Airfield on August 1st.
2005 single pairs bred at Wymeswold and Pasture Wood.

Breeding no doubt occurs more frequently than records suggest and the following reports during the breeding season, all but one of single birds, suggest as much:

- Croxton Kerrial, June 1975.
- Owston Wood, May 18th 1977.
- Rutland Water, July 10th 1983.
- found dead, Rutland Water, May 9th 1984.
- Stanford Reservoir, June 2nd 1991.
- found dead, Uppingham, May 15th 1992.
- Stanford Reservoir, June 28th 1997.
- two, King Lud's Entrenchments, May 3rd to 15th 1999.
- Benscliffe Wood, June 15th 2000.
- Melton Country Park, July 2nd 2000.
- Stathern, June 26th 2004.

Long-eared Owls are known for their communal winter roosts, which are often long-established and occupied for many years. Leicestershire and Rutland contain very few traditional roost sites, although there are some notable exceptions. Probably the longest-standing regular site for this species is King Lud's Entrenchments, where there were single birds in April 1975, March 1976 and March 1977 and unconfirmed rumours of larger numbers around this time. There was then an absence of records for over 20 years, although this was likely to have been due to lack of coverage by birdwatchers as when several observers visited this vastly underwatched site in the late 1990s, specifically to search for Long-eared Owls, they found up to five in late December 1998 which were still present in January 1999. Over the next few winters the highest counts were five on February 20th 2000, four or five on January 7th 2001 and eight on November 16th 2002.

Between 1985–86 and 2000–01, Wanlip North Gravel Pits harboured birds during nine winters, the highest counts being six in January and February 1993, February 1998 and January and February 2000, five from December 1990 to January 1991 and four from January to March 1994. There have been no reports from this site since January 2001, although this sizeable area is mostly private and as such is largely underwatched.

There have been records from Rutland Water in ten winters since 1975–76; the majority have involved single birds on one or two dates only, but higher counts have included up to nine in two roosts from January to May 1976 as the reservoir began to fill, up to six in January 1997 and three in February 1981, early 1984 and from January to March 1991.

The two largest winter counts, however, have been at sites apparently used in only a single year. In 1992 a well-watched roost on islands at Birstall Gravel Pits from January 10th to April 4th contained a maximum of nine on January 22nd and February 2nd, whilst in early 1997 three roosts in the Wymondham/Edmondthorpe area contained a remarkable total of 24 birds. The only other record involving more than two birds came from Stoughton Airfield, where up to four roosted from January to mid-March 1995. Examination of pellets at Lubbesthorpe, where one had roosted from February 15th to March 23rd 1986, contained the remains of Wood Mouse, Field Vole, Common Shrew and the feather quills of small passerines.

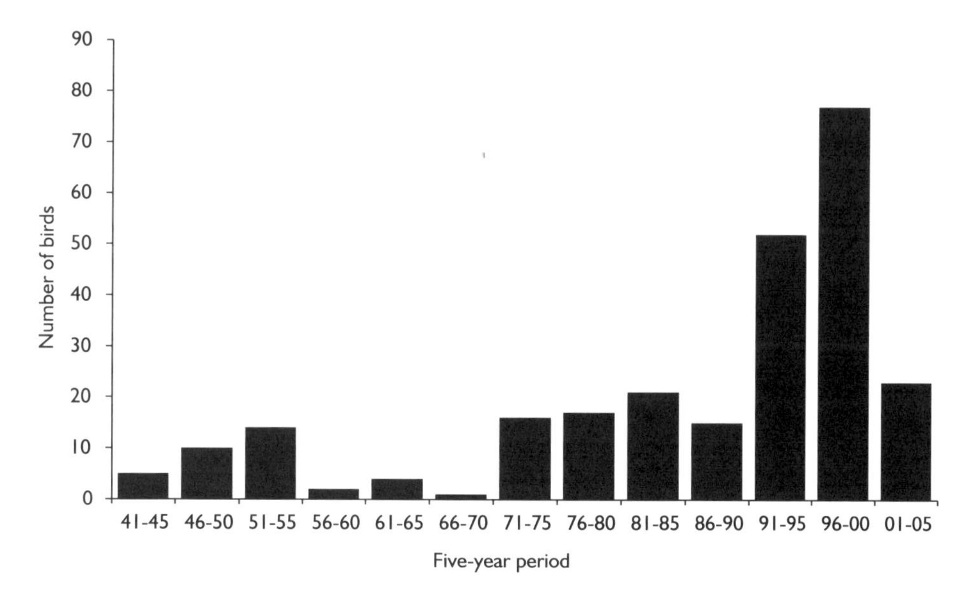

Figure 374: Numbers of Long-eared Owls 1941–2005.

As well as human persecution, Long-eared Owls have also suffered from poisoning, as demonstrated by one found dead at Great Casterton on March 25th 1975; analysis of tissue proved that it been poisoned by dieldrin. A dead bird at Wymondham in late May 1989 was also thought to have been poisoned. Another hazard for this species is traffic and a number have been found dead by roads. An apparent road casualty picked up at Wymondham on November 11th 1991 was taken into care after a successful wing amputation.

The following ringing recoveries have been reported and include two examples of movement from/to the continent:

- an adult at Frisby Gravel Pits on October 23rd 1975 was killed at Ely (Cambridgeshire) on December 24th 1975.

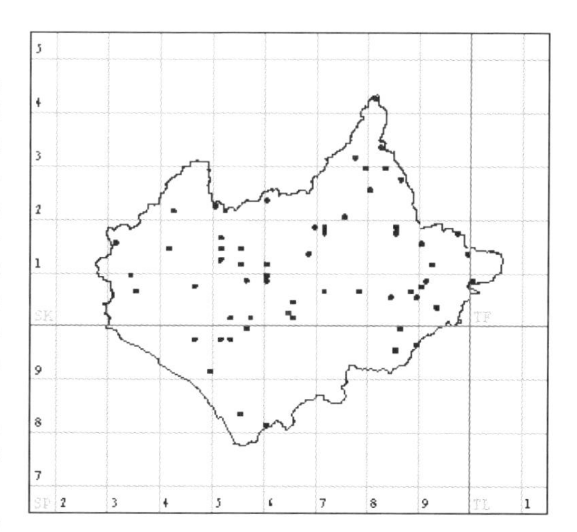

Figure 375: Distribution of Long-eared Owls 1941–2005.

- an adult ringed at Stanford Reservoir on February 28th 1982 was recovered a month later at Bermuda village, Nuneaton (Warwickshire).
- a pullus ringed at Great Longstone (Derbyshire) on June 7th 1990 was found dead at Uppingham on May 15th 1992.
- a pullus ringed at Haslington (Cheshire) on May 29th 1992 was found dead near Hathern on August 28th 1992.
- a pullus ringed at Valthermond (Netherlands) on April 29th 1996 was found dead near North Luffenham on April 12th 1997.
- an adult ringed at Wanlip North Gravel Pits on January 2nd 2000 was found dead at Ruotsinpyhtaa (Finland) in May 2001.

The nominate race of the Long-eared Owl breeds over most of Eurasia, but is absent from northernmost areas and from southern Asia. Other races breed in North America and parts of Africa. Most are resident, although northern populations are mainly migratory. The British breeding population is currently estimated at 1,100 to 3,600 pairs (Gibbons *et al.* 1993, Baker *et al.* 2006).

RED

Short-eared Owl *Asio flammeus*

Uncommon winter and passage visitor.

During the 19th century Browne considered the Short-eared Owl to be a winter migrant to Leicestershire, generally distributed but not common, and noted that it had been recorded at Melton Mowbray, Smeeton Westerby and Leicester amongst others. In Rutland it was described as an autumn migrant by Haines that was 'not at all plentiful'. The LROS archives, describing the first 40 years of the 20th century, refer to this species as a winter visitor in small numbers, with records between Thurnby and Stoughton on March 9th 1940, Eyebrook Reservoir on November 24th 1940 and Leicester City Farms on December 21st 1940.

Today the Short-eared Owl is an uncommon winter and passage visitor to the counties. Numbers fluctuate considerably from year to year, largely dependent on habitat availability and food supply; larger numbers are recorded during years when there is an abundance of voles. Once in their wintering quarters Short-eared Owls often stay in that area through to the following spring. A number of traditional wintering sites have been utilised, but these have changed over the years as habitats have become less suitable. Eyebrook Reservoir was a regular site in the 1940s and 1950s but there have been few records from there in recent years; however, nearby Great Easton became a regular wintering site in the first few years of the 21st century. Leicester City Farms was also an important site in the 1940s, as was Stanford Reservoir in the late 1960s and 1970s. More recently Rutland Water and the Soar valley gravel pits have provided suitable habitat, along with some of the regenerated coalfields of north-west Leicestershire, such as Sence Valley Forest Park.

Since the formation of LROS in 1941 there have only been two years (1951 and 1961) when this species was not recorded. In most winters there are only a few records, but several large influxes have occurred, as follows:

1945–46 14 were at Leicester City Farms on December 9th 1945, with 24 there on January 6th 1946, representing the largest ever concentration at one site in the counties. At least ten more birds were at a further four sites during the period.

1949–50 Up to ten were at Eyebrook Reservoir from October 2nd 1949 to May 19th 1950, with five birds at a total of four other sites.

1978–79 Approximately 31 birds were recorded at a total of 14 sites, with a maximum of eight in the Wanlip Gravel Pits area on February 18th 1979. This influx was mirrored nationwide, with an estimated 1,549 birds recorded in England during the period (Davenport 1982).

1982–83 The most widespread influx, with records from 19 sites involving up to 39 birds and maximum counts of six at Rutland Water from late November 1982 to January 16th 1983, six at Sawley Gravel Pits during December 1982 and four at both Welham on January 2nd 1983 and Bruntingthorpe Airfield on March 6th 1983.

2002–03 30 arrived during November and December 2002, with a further seven appearing in early 2003. Almost all birds were at just four sites, with maximum counts of nine at both Rutland Water in late November 2002 and Luffenham Airfield on November 24th 2002, seven at Cossington Meadows from December 12th to 18th 2002 and six in the Trent Valley Pit area during the early part of 2003.

2004–05 A total of 41 birds was recorded, making this the largest ever influx. The highest counts were eight at Luffenham Airfield on October 29th 2004, at least eight in the Trent Valley Pit/Lockington Gravel Pits area throughout the period and seven at Garthorpe on January 13th 2005.

Other notable concentrations have included 13 roosting in a young conifer plantation at Buckminster from January to March 1977, eight at Eyebrook Reservoir on January 9th 1947 and six at Stapleford Park during the 1970–71 winter.

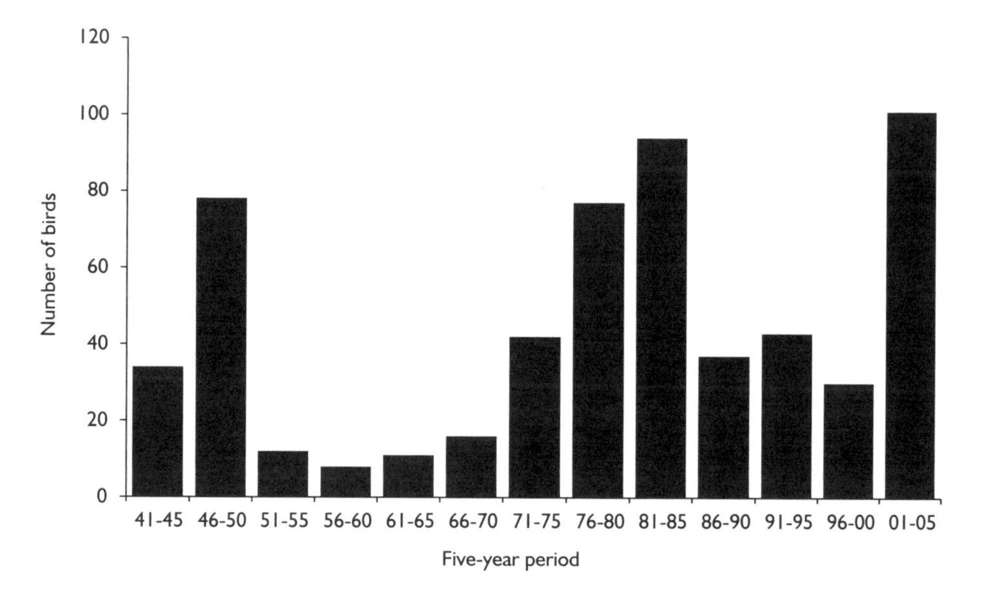

Figure 376: Estimated numbers of Short-eared Owls by five-year periods 1941–2005.

Wintering birds regularly remain into April and have lingered into May on four occasions: at Eyebrook Reservoir in both 1947 and 1950, Stanford Reservoir in 1971 and Sence Valley Forest Park in 1999. Passage birds have been reported in May in seven years, involving nine birds; most have been during the first half of the month, with later records of single birds at Garthorpe on May 17th 1997, Belmesthorpe on May 18th 1975, Bruntingthorpe Airfield on May 24th 1983, Stanford Reservoir on May 29th 1983 and Eyebrook Reservoir on May 29th 1991. There have three been June records: at Stanford Reservoir on June 3rd 1977, Seaton on June 17th 1997 and Bruntingthorpe Airfield on June 25th 1968, whilst single birds were at Rutland Water on July 21st 1982 and Eyebrook Reservoir from July 31st to August 1st 1949. Partial display-flight was seen at the latter site in November 1949 and displaying birds were also noted at Sence Valley Forest Park in May 1999, but there has never been any suggestion that breeding has occurred in the counties.

The first returning birds are usually seen in October, although there have been September records in 18 years since 1941 and seven in August, all of single birds unless stated:

- Rutland Water, August 9th 2004.
- Leicester City Farms, August 16th 1957 for three weeks, with two on August 23rd.
- Rutland Water, August 16th 1989.
- Rutland Water, August 17th 1985.
- Little Dalby, August 19th 1995.
- Eyebrook Reservoir, August 22nd 1974.
- Bruntingthorpe Airfield, August 22nd 1988.

Analysis of 28 pellets at Leicester City Farms in 1945 found fur and bones from 54 Field Voles but there were no other mammal remains. One hunting at Thurmaston on November 28th 1982 was seen to catch six voles in a 90–minute period.

Short-eared Owls of the nominate race breed over large parts of Eurasia and North America, but are absent from southern Asia and southern Europe. Other races are found in South America and the Pacific. Most populations are migratory or nomadic and some European birds winter south of the Sahara. The latest British population estimate is 1,000 to 3,500 pairs (Baker *et al.* 2006) and due to this species' unfavourable conservation status it has been added to the 'Amber List' of Birds of Conservation Concern (Gregory *et al.* 2002).

RED

Nightjar (European Nightjar) *Caprimulgus europaeus*

Formerly a scarce to uncommon migrant breeder, now a rare migrant breeder.

During the 19th century Browne knew of several records of Nightjars from the Charnwood Forest area, as well as from Belvoir Woods. Haines considered that this species was a local summer migrant in Rutland which had increased during the late 19th century and bred most commonly at Burley and Ketton. According to the LROS archives it was very local during the first 40 years of the 20th century but used to occur regularly at Bardon Hill, Bradgate Park and The Brand, Woodhouse Eaves. Its preference for a heathland habitat suggests that it was probably never widespread but, according to the first LROS Annual Report in 1941, it bred in small numbers in several parts of Charnwood Forest until 1937. It definitely bred in 1940 at Lea Wood and Markfield. Since the formation of LROS in 1941, the Nightjar's population has fluctuated in accordance with the felling and replanting of various woods which has resulted in the creation of areas of suitable breeding habitat, albeit temporarily.

In the early 1940s, one or two pairs were breeding annually in Charnwood Forest. The population reached its peak in this area in the mid to late 1940s as a result of the felling of several woods. In 1946 there were records in Charnwood of singing males from seven sites involving at least 12 birds, whilst the following year there were 18 birds at five sites, including up to 12 pairs at Bardon Hill. In 1948 there were as many as 14 pairs at Bardon Hill, with single pairs at four other sites. Regularly occupied areas during this period included Copt Oak, Bradgate Park (maximum of two pairs in 1946), Martinshaw Wood, Benscliffe Wood (maximum of two pairs in 1946), Buddon Wood (maximum of four pairs in 1949) and Blakeshay Wood (peak of three pairs in 1947). Away from Charnwood there were churring males during the 1940s at Ambion Wood in 1943, Swinford in 1946 and Belvoir, Kilby and Coalville in 1948. Occasional out-of-range birds were recorded, including exhausted birds picked up at Barkby on July 25th 1942, Shackerstone on September 18th 1942 and Quorn on October 3rd 1945; in addition, two were seen within the city boundary of Leicester, at Rowley Fields on September 26th 1943 and Duke's Drive, Clarendon Park in 1947.

During most years of the 1950s breeding occurred regularly at Bardon Hill, but in declining numbers: after six pairs in 1953 only one pair was found in 1958, by which time the new conifer plantation at this site was maturing fast. Churring continued to be heard at other Charnwood Forest sites throughout the 1950s, although only at Benscliffe and Blakeshay Woods were birds found in more than one year. Elsewhere, several were heard singing at Owston Wood in 1955 and one was heard at Lindley in August 1957. Numbers were obviously in serious decline by the end of the 1950s and this decline continued into 1960s. Few birds were reported, mainly in the Charnwood Forest area, with Benscliffe Wood providing the only confirmed breeding records. Nightjars were last thought to have bred in Charnwood in 1964, though there have been probable breeding records again recently.

Between the mid-1960s and 1975 attention switched to Rutland, where the large scale planting of conifers provided ideal breeding habitat. Warrilow reported successful breeding at Stretton Wood between 1964 and 1974 and both he and Mitcham (1984) recorded successful breeding at Clipsham Park Wood between 1967 and 1974. Breeding also occurred at Morkery Wood in Lincolnshire, just over the Rutland border, in at least two years during this period and three were heard at Ayston on May 16th 1965. It appears, however, that these areas were abandoned around 1975, when the habitat became unsuitable as the conifers matured. During the same period, Charnwood Forest appears to have been completely deserted as there were no records in this area until 1975, when one was in song at Ulverscroft on June 16th.

Since 1975 there have been 16 years with no records at all of Nightjars. Churring birds, all single birds unless stated, have been heard in only nine years:

1978	undisclosed location in Charnwood Forest during June and July.
1979	undisclosed location in Charnwood Forest from mid-June to July 7th.
1982	Benscliffe Wood from May 29th to June 16th.
1988	Swithland Wood on May 31st.
1992	Plungar during the summer.
1993	Plungar during the summer, with a dead bird found on the road there in August.
1999	Blakeshay Wood from June 14th to July 9th.
2004	Blakeshay Wood, a male from May 31st and a female from June 6th. Breeding probably occurred as one bird was still present on September 3rd. An additional male was heard at nearby Benscliffe Wood on June 14th and 15th.
2005	Blakeshay Wood from May 24th to June 10th.

The recent return of the Nightjar to Charnwood Forest was predicted by Mackay (1999). He commented on the large areas of conifers being felled at that time in Charnwood which would provide suitable breeding habitat in the near future. This prediction was based on data from Gibbons *et al.* (1993) which found that by 1992 over 50% of the British population of Nightjars was to be found in recently felled conifer plantations.

Most other records since 1975 have been of presumed migrants, almost half of which have been found dead, as follows:

1977	dead, Ryhall, August 27th.
1981	Stanford Reservoir, July 26th.
	dead, Goadby Marwood, undated.
1983	male, Ravenstone, May 20th to 22nd.
	Rutland Water, June 1st.
	dead, Knipton, August 6th.
1986	dead, undisclosed site in the north-east of the counties, August 23rd.
1997	Ashby-de-la-Zouch, July 19th.
2001	Wardley Wood, June 1st.

Of these, perhaps the most notable record was that at Rutland Water in 1983; the bird was found roosting in a tree in the car park of the Egleton Reserve following an overnight thunderstorm and allowed many observers excellent views during the day.

Detail on arrival and departure dates of Nightjars is very limited. Singing birds are usually first located between mid-May and mid-June, although the earliest on record is one at Rothley on April 29th 1944. During the autumn the latest record is of a bird picked up at Quorn on October 3rd 1945.

Four previously published records were rejected following a review in 1994 (Mackay 1995a): at Rutland Water from July 28th to August 3rd 1988, Narborough on July 17th 1989, Fleckney on October 15th 1989 and Buddon Wood on April 30th 1990.

Nightjars breed over much of Europe, the Middle East and central Asia. The nominate race is found in central and southern Europe as far north as Scandinavia. It winters throughout sub-Saharan Africa. The British

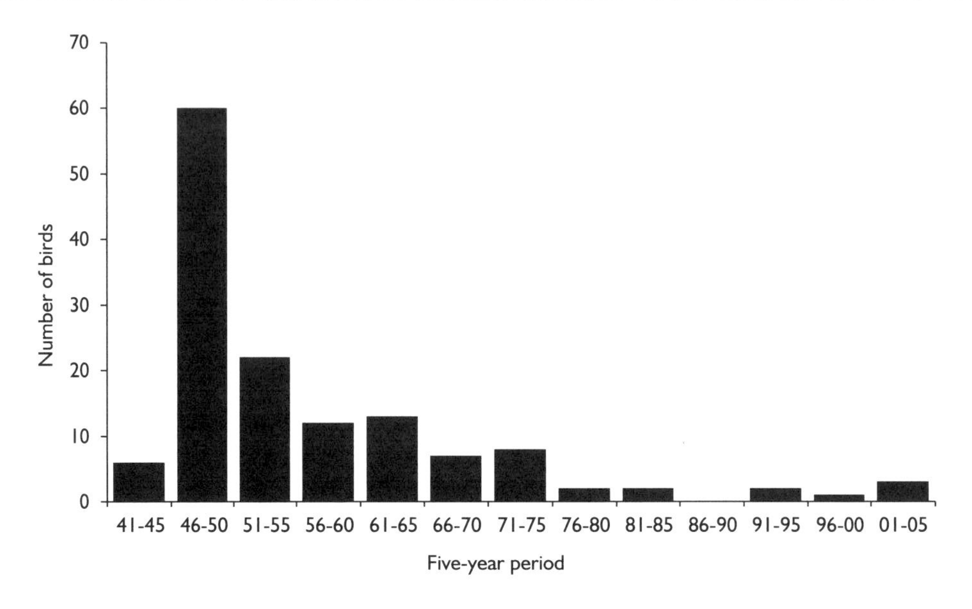

Figure 377: Estimated numbers of churring male Nightjars by five-year periods 1941–2005.

breeding population was estimated at 3,400 churring males in 1992 (Morris *et al.* 1994) but had increased to 4,600 churring males by 2004 (Baillie *et al.* 2006). Despite this, the Nightjar has been added to the 'Red List' of Birds of Conservation Concern on the basis of a rapid contraction of the breeding range during the last 25 years of the 20th century (Gregory *et al.* 2002).

RED

Alpine Swift *Apus melba*

Very rare vagrant from southern Europe: two records.

There have been two acceptable records of this spectacular swift, beginning with one seen over the northern end of Swithland Reservoir by H. Wills on April 13th 1942. The second concerned one seen by Tim Appleton and M.J. Pearce over Lagoon III at Rutland Water on August 8th and 10th 1978; this record was originally rejected by the BBRC (*BB* 72:546), but was reconsidered and accepted based on new evidence some 15 years after the original sighting (*BB* 87:539).

Browne refers to a report of this species in the Fosse Road area of Leicester on September 23rd 1839 which had apparently 'been quoted in nearly every work since 1839 as having occurred in Leicestershire'. However, Browne considered that 'insufficient evidence' had been provided and, as such, this record has never gained widespread credence.

A record of two Alpine Swifts at Beacon Hill on May 24th 1950 was originally accepted and published in the LROS Annual Reports, but on review in 1995 was considered inadequately documented (Mackay 1995a).

Alpine Swifts breed throughout southern Europe, North Africa and the Middle East, with other races occurring in Arabia, eastern and southern Africa and the Indian subcontinent. Palearctic breeders probably winter in the northern African tropics, although distinguishing them from local populations is not possible. They are rare visitors to Britain, predominantly as spring overshoots, although they have been recorded in every month except January and December. The majority are found in southern and eastern coastal counties, but inland records such as those in Leicestershire and Rutland occur occasionally. By the end of 2005, the British total was around 575 and at this time it was removed from the list of species assessed by the BBRC.

RED

Common Swift *Apus apus*

Common migrant breeder.

There is little information on the status of the Common Swift in Leicestershire and Rutland during the 19th century, although it would appear that it has always been a common summer visitor. In Leicestershire, Browne considered that it was one of the last summer migrants to arrive and the first to leave, whilst Haines commented that in his day it generally arrived during the first week of May in Rutland, but seemed to have arrived earlier in the 18th century when arrival dates of April 16th in 1749 and April 17th in 1739, 1740 and 1747 were recorded.

Nowadays a few individuals usually arrive before the end of April, but it is in early May when there is normally a sudden simultaneous large arrival at a number of sites. In the 62 years for which data is available, the first record has occurred in April for 50 of those years. The average spring arrival date has gradually become earlier since the mid-1970s and during the last ten years has been April 21st. The first bird has been seen on April 19th in five years (1959, 1962, 1987, 1997 and 2003) but arrivals earlier than this are rare and have only been recorded on four occasions:

- Leicester, April 10th 1952.
- Thornton Reservoir, April 16th 1996.
- Eyebrook Reservoir, April 18th 1968.
- Thornton Reservoir, April 18th 2005.

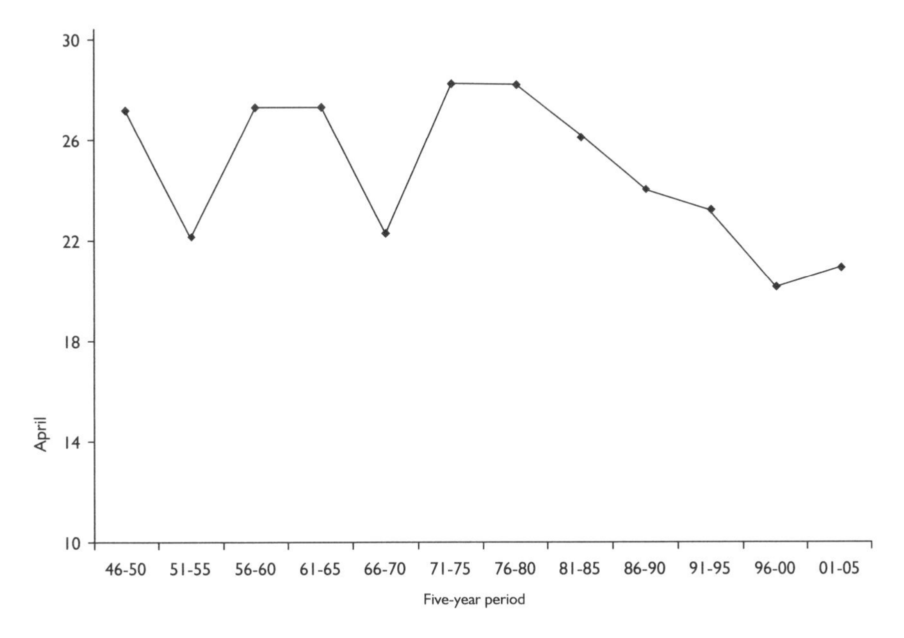

Figure 378: Average spring arrival dates of Common Swifts by five-year periods 1946–2005.

Common Swifts are more closely associated with inner urban areas than suburban or rural districts, as nest sites are more readily available in older factories and terraced houses than in modern buildings. They breed in those towns and villages where suitable sites are still available. Estimating the breeding population within the counties is difficult as many of the large flocks and village street 'screaming' parties contain a number of non-breeding birds; however, the big population in the centre of Leicester has certainly decreased as Victorian properties have been cleared for redevelopment.

During 1976–84 Warrilow recorded the Common Swift in 150 tetrads in the counties (23% of the total number of tetrads), with breeding confirmed in 78. The distribution map for this species closely matches a map of urban areas in the counties, with large unoccupied gaps in east and north-east Leicestershire. Based on an average of five to ten pairs per occupied tetrad Warrilow produced a county-wide breeding population of 750 to 1,500 pairs, whilst accepting that estimating the numbers per occupied tetrad was somewhat arbitrary. Mitcham (1992) recorded breeding in a very similar 22% of tetrads in Rutland.

Comments in more recent LROS Annual Reports have indicated a possible reduction in breeding numbers, though there are often contrasting views. In 1987, cold wet weather in June was thought to be responsible for a poor breeding season. In 1991, a 'remarkably good' breeding season was recorded at Huncote, whereas in Thurnby another observer reported that no Common Swifts had nested in the village for the first time in 27 years. In 2002, the Huncote site was judged to have had an 'above average' breeding season and the same was reported at this site in 2003, although numbers were thought to be down by 30%. There has been very little breeding data from any other site in the last few years. A further indication of the possible decline in the breeding population is apparent from flock sizes: between 1997 and 2002 there were no four-figure flocks recorded, probably reflecting the recent run of wet summers. However, a flock of 1,200 was at Rutland Water on June 18th 2003 and 1,400 were at the same site on May 4th 2004. Evidence of late breeding occurred in 1997, when young were still being fed in a nest at East Park Road, Leicester on September 7th.

One of the features of Common Swifts is large feeding flocks during the late spring and early summer; these flocks include birds which travel considerable distances from other areas when feeding conditions are favourable. The largest flocks have all been recorded at Rutland Water:

- 15,000 to 20,000 on June 21st 1996.
- 5,000 on July 2nd 1991.
- 4,000 on June 10th 1986
- 3,000 on May 26th 1996 and June 14th 1997.

Elsewhere there have been eight flocks of 2,000 or more, as follows:

- 3,000 at Swithland Reservoir on May 17th and 24th 1987 and July 12th 1989.
- 2,500 at Glen Parva on August 18th 1984.
- 2,000 at Eyebrook Reservoir on May 12th 1963, May 17th 1987 and May 22nd 1997.
- 2,000 at Swithland Reservoir on May 18th 1975.
- 2,000 at Glen Parva on June 20th 1982.

It was thought that birds in the huge flock at Rutland Water in June 1996 were probably taking advantage of good feeding conditions between high pressure to the west and low pressure to the east.

As with spring arrivals, autumn departures are often just as sudden and large flocks are regularly recorded migrating in late July and early August. Most birds have normally departed by mid-August but in almost every year some have lingered into September, occasionally in considerable numbers. In 1980, there were 27 at Lubbesthorpe on the 15th and a small party was seen almost daily over the Saffron Lane area of Leicester up to the 26th; in 1999, 200 were over Aylestone Meadows on the 6th. The late departure in 1980 may have been caused by wet weather during the summer, which possibly delayed or prevented breeding. October records have occurred in 13 years, mostly single birds, but six were at Eyebrook Reservoir on October 24th 1966. October sightings are usually during the first few days of the month, with later records, all of single birds, being:

- Eyebrook Reservoir, October 30th 1966 (with six there on October 24th as mentioned above).
- Uppingham, October 29th 1946.
- Hugglescote, October 20th 1963
- between Cottesmore and Market Overton, October 18th 1983.
- Rutland Water, October 17th 1976.
- Belgrave, Leicester, October 16th 1954.
- Swithland Reservoir, October 16th 1976.

There have been four November records: single birds at Glen Hills, Leicester on November 12th 1984, Eastwell on November 11th 1982, Uppingham on November 5th 1977 and Leicester on November 3rd 1971. See also 'Unidentified swifts' on page 436.

A partial albino, showing a white belly, was at Priory Water on June 19th and 26th 1988 and a leucistic bird was at Rutland Water on June 20th 2001.

Many hundreds have been ringed in the counties and several of the returns show considerable site-fidelity and longevity, for example:

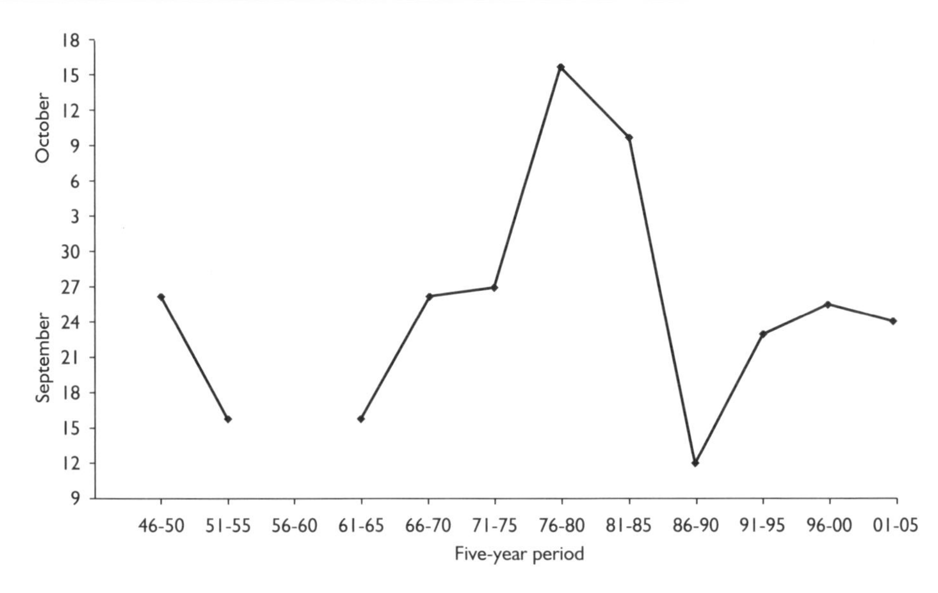

Figure 379: Average autumn departure dates of Common Swifts by five-year periods 1946–2005.

- an adult ringed at Leicester on June 22nd 1962 was controlled at Frisby on the Wreake on July 22nd 1973.
- an adult ringed at Frisby on the Wreake on July 22nd 1973 was found dead at Old Dalby on August 9th 1977.
- an adult ringed at Frisby on the Wreake on July 22nd 1973 was controlled at Queniborough on June 25th 1978.
- an adult ringed at Swithland Reservoir on May 16th 1975 was controlled at Queniborough on July 6th 1978.
- a first-year at Swithland Reservoir on June 19th 1977 was found dead at Leicester on May 23rd 1987.
- an adult ringed at Queniborough on July 6th 1978 was found dead near Wanlip Gravel Pits on May 28th 1979.
- an adult ringed at Queniborough on July 6th 1978 was found dying at Leicester on August 1st 1980.
- an adult ringed at Queniborough on July 6th 1978 was found dead at Syston on June 24th 1982.

Other recoveries of interest are as follows:

- an adult ringed at Leicester on July 23rd 1961 was 'struck down with a sapling whilst in low flight' at Bakwa-Nzeba, Bulape (Democratic Republic of the Congo) on February 3rd 1965.
- an adult ringed at Hertford (Hertfordshire) on July 10th 1974 was found dead at Leicester on May 17th 1977.
- an adult ringed at Swithland Reservoir on June 19th 1977 was controlled at Sinderland Green (Cheshire) on June 30th 1978.
- one ringed at Queniborough on June 18th 1978 was retrapped at Adwick le Street (South Yorkshire) on June 16th 1985.
- an adult ringed near Castle Donington on May 23rd 1987 was found dead at Darlington (County Durham) on June 19th 1989.
- an adult ringed at Pensthorpe (Norfolk) on June 11th 1995 was found at Billesdon on May 19th 1996.

Common Swifts breed over much of Europe, as well as north Africa, the Middle East and Asia north of the Himalayas. All populations winter in sub-Saharan Africa. Breeding numbers are notoriously difficult to estimate, but the British population was put at 80,000 pairs during 1988–91 (Gibbons *et al.* 1993).

RED

Unidentified swifts *Apus sp.*

There have been three records of birds seen on either very early or very late dates:

- an individual over the Wanlip/Syston area on November 1st 1999 was suspected by the observer to be a Pallid Swift *Apus pallidus*, but unfortunately the views obtained failed to determine the true identification. A record influx of Pallid Swifts, involving up to 12 individuals, occurred in Britain during late October and early November of that year.
- one over Leicester city centre on February 23rd 2000 was thought to be a Common Swift. Was it an exceptionally early migrant, arriving some two months before the normal arrival date? The possibility of it having over-wintered in Britain or Europe seems highly unlikely.
- a very late bird at Ab Kettleby from November 5th to 9th 2005 was never seen well enough to be conclusively identified.

RED

Kingfisher (Common Kingfisher) *Alcedo atthis*

Uncommon resident breeder.

The Kingfisher is normally associated with slow moving streams and rivers and standing freshwater such as reservoirs and gravel pits. Its status has undergone a number of changes over the years, largely depending on the severity of the winter weather and the loss of its favoured habitats (for example through the straightening of water courses and the removal of steep banks which provide nest sites). During the 19th century, Haines noted that it was resident and found sparingly on all the Rutland rivers and streams, though it was 'not much in evidence' between November and February. Browne also considered it resident but sparingly distributed in Leicestershire.

When LROS was established in 1941, the Kingfisher was considered to be a common resident breeder, with increases in numbers until the severe winter weather of January 1945 when none were seen between mid-January and April and only one pair was known to have bred during the following summer. After a moderate recovery in 1946, it was virtually wiped out by the extremely severe winter of 1946–47. Between March and September of 1947 there were records from just four sites. From 1948 onwards there were year-on-year increases up to and including 1951, after which there was no information in annual reports until 1960–62 when it was reported as 'uncommon but widely spread'.

The harsh winter weather of January/February 1963 took a very heavy toll and there were only four records during the whole of the year! Recovery was slow: in 1964 there were just nine records, with a similar number in 1965. Throughout the remainder of the 1960s it remained uncommon but with a gradual increase in numbers and breeding success and by 1970–71 it was recorded at 70 sites and the population was considered to be at a 'maximum' (although it was still considered an 'uncommon resident'). In 1974 its status was changed to 'fairly common' but reverted to 'uncommon' in 1977, although records during this period did not appear to match the status change; there were reports from 60 sites in both 1973 and 1976, 30 sites in both 1974 and 1975 and again in 1979 and 1980. Hickling recorded it as breeding in 20 of the counties' 29 tetrads, with an estimated breeding population of between 50 and 100 pairs. Warrilow's figure for the breeding population during 1976–84, based on an average of one or two pairs per occupied tetrad, was 150 to 300 pairs, found mainly along the river valleys and sections of the Grand Union Canal. Mitcham (1992) found that 26% of Rutland tetrads were occupied, with a continuous distribution along the Welland valley and the Eye Brook.

Perhaps because it was not as severe as 1947 and 1963, the bad winter weather of 1978–79 did not appear to have a particularly noticeable effect on numbers, but a serious downturn was experienced after the winter of 1981–82, with records from fewer than 30 sites compared to at least 40 in 1981. Since then up to the present day, there has not been a prolonged spell of freezing conditions. Its status during this period has remained as an 'uncommon resident', with records per year ranging from 32 sites in 1986 to a maximum of 75 in 1993, with an overall average of 55.9 for 1995–2004.

Although obviously breeding throughout the history of LROS, the first actual breeding records were not reported until 1966 (three pairs). Since then confirmed breeding has been recorded almost annually, normally by one to six pairs, but there were ten in 1987, nine in 1990 and up to 18 pairs in 2003. The average number of breeding records for the period 1995 to 2004 was 5.8, though this is certainly a considerable underestimate. In 1987, a survey by canoe of eight kilometres of the River Soar found four breeding pairs. An interesting development was recorded in 1998, when a pair bred in the artificial Sand Martin nest-bank near Wanlip South Gravel Pits, raising up to three broods.

In more recent years there has been an increase in records from private gardens as a result of the attraction of well-stocked garden ponds. At Saddington during several weeks in 1981, one regularly visited a garden and used a bird table as a convenient perch adjacent to the goldfish pond. In September of the same year, one was seen in the same garden pecking at its reflection in the lounge window.

Interesting records include: one flying across the junction of London Road and Stoneygate Road, about a mile from the centre of Leicester in 1976; one in the middle of Great Fenny Wood in March 1981; one being chased by a Black-headed Gull in the Great Central Street area of Leicester in 1991; one released unharmed after being found in an Oakham house in 1991 and finally, the ultimate fishing opportunist, a juvenile was recorded at Barrow-upon-Soar in 1992 landing on a fishing rod and calmly eating a small fish.

Ringing recoveries reflect the relatively short-distance movements made by British birds, including the following:

- a first-year ringed at Ratcliffe on the Wreake on August 22nd 1975 was found dead at the same site on February 9th 1976.
- a first-year ringed at Stanford Reservoir on August 7th 1976 was killed at Rugby (Warwickshire) on August 16th 1976.
- a first-year ringed at Stanford Reservoir on August 28th 1976 was killed at Crick (Northamptonshire) on September 25th 1976.
- a first-year ringed at Rutland Water on December 6th 1975 was found dead near Hemel Hempstead (Hertfordshire) on July 21st 1976.
- a first-year ringed at Elmesthorpe on September 20th 1977 was found dead in West Yorkshire on August 28th 1978 after having been trapped at Wombwell (South Yorkshire) on July 11th 1978.
- an adult female ringed at Scalford on December 26th 1996 was found decapitated in the middle of the cricket pitch at Melton Country Park on May 16th 1997.
- a first-year female ringed at Rutland Water on August 7th 2000 was found dead at Newcastle-under-Lyme (Staffordshire) on October 14th 2000.

Kingfishers breed over most of Europe as far north as southern Scandinavia, as well as in north-west Africa, southern Asia and Australasia. Most European birds are resident, but north-eastern populations are migratory. The British breeding population is currently estimated at 4,300–7,100 pairs (Baker *et al.* 2006) but on account of its unfavourable conservation status this species is on the 'Amber List' of Birds of Conservation Concern (Gregory *et al.* 2002).

RED

European Bee-eater *Merops apiaster*

Very rare vagrant from southern Europe: three records.

There have been three records of this beautiful Mediterranean vagrant, beginning with one seen by Ron Hickling at Loughborough Sewage Farm on September 13th 1958 (*BB* 53:167). One was watched for 15 minutes by Dave Willett at Victoria Park, Leicester on September 6th 1967 (*BB* 61:347, Willett 1968) and finally one was observed circling and calling above Oxey Crossroads, Loddington by Frank Pickering on May 22nd 1992 before it drifted away to the south-west.

Haines quoted an extract from Lilford (1895), who reported that a pair nested in the bank of a pond at Kilthorpe, near Ketton, in the summer of 1868. One adult was apparently shot and preserved by A.C. Elliot of Stamford, but the brood was successfully fledged. This record was repeated by Hickling but completely omitted by Mitcham (1984). As there appears to be an element of doubt about some of the records from A.C. Elliot's collection, this record remains at best unconfirmed (Macfarlane 2002).

There has also been one record of an unidentified bee-eater which almost certainly was of this species: see below.

European Bee-eaters breed around the Mediterranean and into the Middle East and south-west Asia and winter primarily in sub-Saharan Africa. They are annual visitors to Britain in varying numbers, occasionally appearing in small flocks, with the majority occurring in spring during late May and early June. They are much scarcer in autumn, making the first two Leicestershire records somewhat unusual. Breeding has occurred in Britain on at least four occasions: in Scotland in 1920, Sussex in 1955, Durham in 2002 and Herefordshire in 2005.

RED

Unidentified bee-eater *Merops sp.*

One was heard calling by Steve Lister over Cossington North Gravel Pits at 17:20 on June 25th 2002. This was almost certainly a European Bee-eater, but unfortunately the bird was not seen, thus preventing its true identity from being determined. It is not thought likely, however, to have been any other bee-eater species.

RED

Roller (European Roller) *Coracias garrulus*

Very rare vagrant from southern Europe: one record.

A male was found in a moribund state in a broiler house, which it had probably entered through a ventilator, at Castle Farm, Kirby Muxloe on June 21st 1968. It was in a very emaciated condition, with an empty crop and weighed only 96.5 grammes, instead of the usual 140 grammes. It died the same day. There was no indication that the bird had escaped from captivity and there was no information that the species was being kept locally. The skin was sent to Leicester Museum, where it remains today. This record was accepted at local level in 1968, but was only submitted to and accepted by the BBRC in 2000 (*BB* 93:544).

Rollers breed from Iberia and Morocco eastwards through the Mediterranean, Asia Minor and the Middle East, north into eastern Europe and east to the Russian steppes; they winter principally in east Africa. This is a declining species which has become extinct as a breeding bird in Sweden and Germany and this is reflected in its occurrences in Britain; there have been around 230 records, but 135 of these were before 1958. Most, including the Kirby Muxloe bird, occur in late spring and summer.

RED

Hoopoe *Upupa epops*

Rare vagrant, mainly in spring: 15 records since 1941 and 13 previously.

Browne details seven records, four of which are rather vague: undated birds at Bradgate Park and near Lutterworth, one at an unknown site in 1867 and one shot 'prior to 1905' at Lockington. The other three were all shot: at Nailstone in 1828, Stapleton on September 15th 1851 and Peatling on May 11th 1883. Haines knew of five records from Rutland in the 19th century: single birds shot at Tickencote in 1838, Burley in 1880, Cottesmore on May 29th 1888 and Ketton on August 30th 1888 and one seen at Braunston-in-Rutland in 1889.

The LROS archives refer to one at Enderby in 1940, following which there have been a further 15 records, all of single birds, as follows:

1947 Syston, September 23rd.
1948 Stathern, April 26th.

1952	Great Bowden, April 15th.
1956	Keyham, April 13th.
1965	Sileby, May 23rd.
	Laughton, May 25th.
1973	Eyebrook Reservoir, May 17th.
	Stoughton, May 26th.
1975	Clipsham Quarry, September 7th.
1977	Thornton, March 21st to 23rd.
1978	Beacon Hill, May 31st.
1987	Bruntingthorpe Airfield, April 26th.
1989	Barrowden, May 30th.
1991	Swithland Reservoir, August 4th.
2004	Kirby Bellars, May 9th.

Most records have occurred in the spring, with mid-April and late May being the favoured times: four were between April 13th and 26th and six were between May 17th and 31st. The earliest individual, at Thornton in 1977, is the only bird to have been seen on more than one day, although the one at Bruntingthorpe Airfield in 1987 may have been present two days earlier.

A record of one at Brooksby on July 13th 1945 was originally published in the LROS Annual Report but on review in 1994 was found to be unacceptable (Mackay 1995a).

Hoopoes breed in farmland, open country, vineyards and orchards over much of southern and eastern Europe, Asia and Africa. Northern races are migratory and most winter in sub-Saharan Africa and southern Asia. They are scarce visitors to Britain; the majority occur as spring 'overshoots' with smaller numbers during the autumn, in line with the records from Leicestershire and Rutland.

RED

Wryneck (Eurasian Wryneck) ***Jynx torquilla***

Formerly a scarce migrant breeder, now a rare to scarce passage migrant; recorded in April, May, August, September and October, with the majority in August and September: 48 individuals since 1941.

During the 19th century, Browne described the Wryneck as a 'summer migrant, sparingly distributed, less common than formerly'. It was known to have been common around Foxton in the 1840s and nested at Kibworth in 1881 and 1882, Horninghold in 1890 and Market Harborough in 1903, this being the last breeding record for the counties. In Rutland, it was considered to be 'sparingly distributed' by Haines, with nests found at Seaton in about 1860, Oakham in about 1883, Bisbrooke in 1886, 1896 and 1897, Braunston-in-Rutland in 1889 and Allexton in 1899.

There are no documented records of the Wryneck in Leicestershire and Rutland between the breeding report from Market Harborough in 1903 and one found dead at Kilby Bridge on August 25th 1954. The only other record prior to 1969 was one in a Nanpantan garden on September 19th and 20th 1961; however, since 1969 there has been at least one record in all but seven years up to 2005. All records have been of single birds and in the vast majority of years there was just one report, although two were found in 1988, 1989 and 1997, three in 1974, 1976, 1984, 2002 and 2003 and four in 1981. Almost half of the 45 records were of individuals found in gardens and at least six refer to birds found dead or dying.

There have been six spring records, as follows:

1984	Misterton, May 2nd to 4th (possibly for two or three weeks prior to these dates).
1986	Nanpantan, May 6th.
1988	Oakham, April 15th.

1996	Queniborough, April 28th.
1997	Bushby, May 6th.
2003	Cropston, April 20th.

Autumn arrivals have occurred over a protracted period. The earliest was at Eyebrook Reservoir on August 23rd 1977 but the majority have arrived in September. Two have been initially found in October, at Shenton on the 2nd in 1981 and Oakthorpe on the 4th in 1992; however, the latter individual may have been present since the 1st and it remained until the 5th, making it the latest record for the counties.

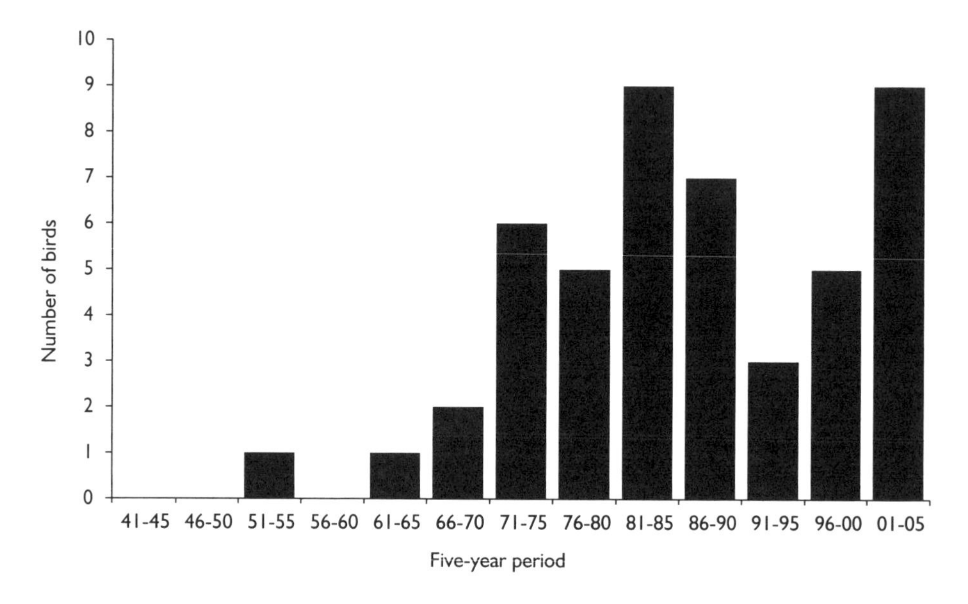

Figure 380: Numbers of Wrynecks 1941–2005.

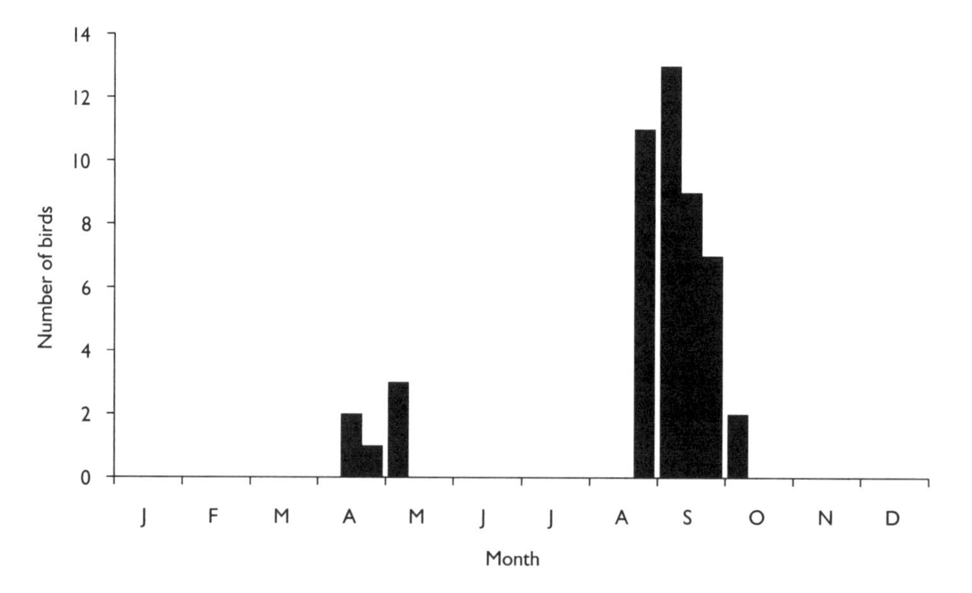

Figure 381: Monthly occurrence of Wrynecks 1941–2005.

A total of 32 records refer to birds seen on just one day, with another 13 staying from two to four days. The longest-stayers are one that remained in gardens at Melton Mowbray for six days from September 2nd to 7th 2002 and one at Stanford Reservoir for 12 days from September 20th to October 1st 1969; the latter bird was obviously exhausted when first found as it was seen clinging to the overflow channel wall.

Wrynecks have appeared at 37 widely scattered sites in Leicestershire and Rutland, although there is a curious shortage of records from the eastern half of the counties. Nine areas have recorded this species on two occasions, including a small stretch of disused railway line at Shenton which played host to birds in both 1981 and 1984. There have been three records from Bushby, two of which (in 1979 and 1981) were in the same garden!

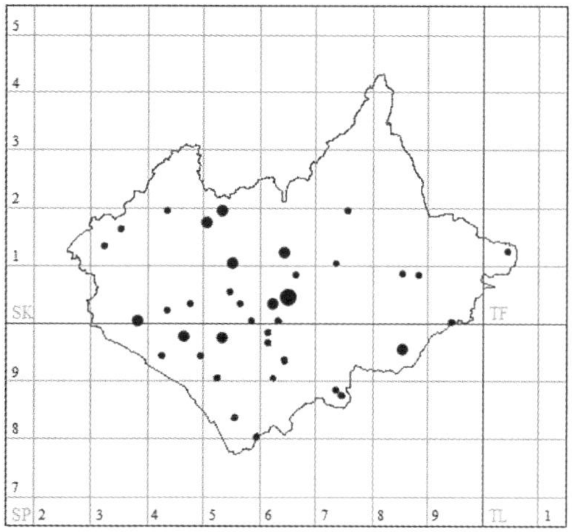

Dot = number of birds, 3 sizes of dot
1 (smallest), 2, 3 (largest)

Figure 382: Distribution of Wrynecks 1941–2005.

A record of one at Quorn on July 21st 1963 was published in the LROS Annual Report but was considered unacceptable on review in 2004 (Fray 2005).

The Wryneck breeds over most of Europe into Siberia and eastern Asia and winters mainly in sub-Saharan Africa. It was once widely distributed as a breeding bird in Britain, but suffered a massive decline from the 1800s and was more or less extinct as a breeding species in the country by the 1970s. Sporadic breeding attempts still take place, often in the Scottish Highlands, but this species is now regarded as a scarce passage migrant, mainly in the autumn. The rapid decline has resulted in Wryneck being added to the 'Red List' of Birds of Conservation Concern (Gregory *et al.* 2002).

RED

Green Woodpecker *Picus viridis*

Fairly common resident breeder.

In the 19th century, the Green Woodpecker was described as 'resident and generally distributed' in Leicestershire by Browne and 'resident and wonderfully common' in Rutland by Haines, who considered it had increased since 1840.

With the exception of one or two years following severe winters (such as 1940–41, 1946–47 and 1962–63), the Green Woodpecker has been considered as a common and widespread resident throughout the history of LROS. In 1943 it was reported as fast recovering from the severe winters of the recent years and had returned to The Brand, Woodhouse Eaves after a three-year absence in line with the 'general increase of these birds in the rest of the county since the hard winters of 1940–41 and 1941–42' (Brady 1944); by 1944 it was considered to be back to its pre-1940 status county-wide. These gains were eliminated by a very marked and serious decline after the severe winter weather in early 1947, when it was 'completely wiped out' over huge areas of the counties where previously it was common; however, numbers appeared to be back to normal in most areas by 1949. Very little data is available for the 1950s and early 1960s, but the population was again severely affected by the severe winter of 1962–63, when 'although only one dead bird was reported the species suffered badly and its characteristic laughing call was seldom heard during the 1963 breeding season' (Gamble 1965). It was reported from only 11 sites in 1964 and it was not until 1967 that numbers were considered to be getting back to normal. Since the late 1960s through to the present day, the status of Green Woodpecker has remained as a fairly common resident breeder, with a probable temporary decline in numbers after the harsh winter in 1981–82.

Apart from a census around Quorn in 1945, when 24 pairs were found, there is very little information regarding the size of the counties' population until the work of Warrilow between 1976 and 1984. He recorded this species in 234 tetrads (37% of the total number of tetrads in the counties), with breeding confirmed in 45, making it the most widespread of the three resident woodpeckers in Leicestershire and Rutland. It also had the most uniform distribution of the three, typically preferring parkland, woodland edges and agricultural land with large trees and old hedgerows, and being the woodpecker least closely associated with densely wooded areas. It was absent from areas of north Rutland, north-east Leicestershire and the extreme west of Leicestershire, as well as the city of Leicester, but was (and still is) particularly widespread in Charnwood Forest. Warrilow estimated an average of one or two pairs per occupied tetrad, giving a county-wide breeding population of between 240 and 480 pairs, an estimate which supports its current status in the counties. Birds continue to remain faithful to specific sites such as Bradgate Park, where up to nine are regularly reported. This site has considerable feeding areas of unimproved grassland with numerous ant hills.

Since 1979 almost all LROS Annual Reports have detailed the number of pairs proved to have bred and the number of sites at which the species has been recorded. The increase in both averages is probably due to improved observer reporting, although national statistics indicate that the Green Woodpecker has increased during this period. Unfortunately, local CBC data does not reveal any trends as this species has always been thinly spread at such sites; there has, however, been an increase in records in recent years from suburban gardens. In 1984 the population was reported as 'at best holding its own' with just one breeding record reported, although the picture has improved since then. The number of sites at which the species has been recorded has increased steadily over the last 25 years, peaking at 105 in 2005. The highest number of breeding records was 15 in both 1998 and 2000. This figure is almost certainly on the low side, as many observers have commented on the elusive nature of the species during the breeding season.

Table 29: Green Woodpecker records 1980–2005

	Average number of sites from which records received	**Average number of sites at which breeding confirmed**
1980–89	43	4
1990–99	67	7
2000–05	89	10

An interesting record came from Wing on September 26th 1986, where one trapped in a tennis court net was released at some cost to the rescuer and the netting.

Green Woodpeckers breed throughout much of Europe. In Britain they are widespread throughout England, Wales and southern Scotland, but absent from northern Scotland and Ireland. Numbers in Britain have risen steadily since 1966, except for a period of stability or shallow decline centred around 1980 that was probably the result of a series of harsh winters. Recent CBC and BBS results suggest that the increase is continuing across much of the British range, probably as a result of milder winters (Baillie *et al.* 2006). Despite this, the species has been added to the 'Amber List' of Birds of Conservation Concern, due to it having an unfavourable conservation status in Europe (Gregory *et al.* 2002). The British population is currently estimated at 24,200 pairs (Baker *et al.* 2006).

RED

Great Spotted Woodpecker *Dendrocopos major*

Fairly common resident breeder.

During the 19th century the Great Spotted Woodpecker was considered resident but not common by both Browne and Haines. Strongholds included Charnwood Forest and several parkland areas including Burley and Exton. It is currently widespread throughout the counties, particularly favouring the larger woods, but also regularly seen in parkland and gardens, especially in the winter months. In the last 30 years or so it has become a regular visitor to garden bird tables and feeding stations.

In the early 1940s its numbers were considered to be increasing and by 1946 its population was thought to exceed that of the Green Woodpecker. It did not seem to be adversely affected by the severe winter of early 1947 and by 1950 was reported as the most common woodpecker in the counties. Again, very little data is available from the 1950s and 1960s, when it was considered as widespread and fairly common. It did not seem to be affected to the same degree as the Green Woodpecker during the severe winter of early 1963. There is very little information regarding numbers and breeding activity until the late 1970s, although nationally its population showed a marked increase from the 1970s onwards; Dutch Elm Disease, which greatly increased the amount of standing dead timber and its associated insects, has been linked to this increase (Baillie *et al.* 2006).

During 1976–84 Warrilow recorded the Great Spotted Woodpecker in 226 tetrads in the counties (35% of the total number of tetrads), with breeding confirmed in 73. Its distribution showed a close association with the more heavily wooded areas of the counties, with most records coming from Charnwood Forest, the Vale of Belvoir and the woodlands of east Leicestershire and Rutland. The Charnwood population was estimated by Webster (1997) at 100 to 150 pairs, with breeding confirmed or probable in 42% of 1–km squares in the region. Mitcham (1992) found that 32% of Rutland tetrads were occupied, mainly in the central woodland belt, with notable concentrations in Burley Wood and Pickworth Great Wood.

Warrilow reported on a survey of 39 deciduous and mixed woodlands in east Leicestershire in 1987 and 1990, which determined a total of 12.5 territories, equating to a mean breeding density of 320 pairs per tetrad. By adopting a figure of 2.6% woodland cover for the counties, an average of four to eight pairs per occupied tetrad gave an estimated county-wide population of between 900 and 1,800 pairs.

The majority of LROS Annual Reports since 1979 have detailed the number of breeding records and the number of sites at which the species has been recorded. The increase in both averages is considered to be chiefly as a result of observer reporting, although national data indicates that Great Spotted Woodpeckers began a further increase in the early 1990s, probably due to the increasing provision of winter food in gardens and perhaps through benefiting from the maturation of new forests (Baillie *et al.* 2006). CBC data from Stoughton supports this, although numbers at this site are small: Great Spotted Woodpeckers were absent from 1964 to 1982 and present, but not considered to be breeding from 1983 to 1988, but one or two pairs bred in most years from 1989 onwards. Conversely, data from Prior's Coppice shows that four pairs held territory in 1993 but this had fallen to just one pair by 1999.

Table 30: Great Spotted Woodpecker records 1980–2005

	Average number of sites from which records received	**Average number of sites at which breeding confirmed**
1980–89	47	6
1990–99	63	10
2000–05	91	11

The Great Spotted Woodpecker's known habit of nest box predation was first recorded in the counties in 1955, when four nest boxes at Higham Grange were attacked and a total of 34 Blue and Great Tit young were taken.

Great Spotted Woodpeckers breed over most of Europe, through Siberia and eastern Asia. There are also localised populations in north-west Africa and the Middle East. Although some birds may erupt from breeding areas in response to shortages in their food supply, this species is mainly sedentary, as evidenced by the following four ringing recoveries involving the counties:

- a juvenile female ringed at Castle Donington on November 18th 1984 was controlled at Attenborough Nature Reserve (Nottinghamshire) on April 6th 1985.
- a juvenile ringed at Hoby on August 12th 1990 was found dead at Rearsby on June 13th 1993
- a first-winter female ringed at Attenborough Nature Reserve (Nottinghamshire) on January 19th 1991 was controlled at Loughborough on May 26th 1996.
- an adult male ringed at Ketton Quarry on November 18th 1998 was controlled at the same site on August 16th 2000.

This species is a common resident breeder throughout England, Wales and all but the extreme north of Scotland, but is absent from Ireland. The British breeding population during the period 1988–91 was estimated at 25,000 to 30,000 pairs (Gibbons *et al.* 1993) and this figure has risen to 37,000 to 44,400 pairs in the light of more recent data (Baker *et al.* 2006).

RED

Lesser Spotted Woodpecker *Dendrocopos minor*

Uncommon resident breeder.

During the 19th century it appears that the Lesser Spotted Woodpecker was more numerous than today, since Haines described it as resident and fairly common in Rutland and Browne thought it 'probably' rarer than Great Spotted Woodpecker in Leicestershire – he would be in no doubt today. The LROS archives described it as 'not uncommon but inclined to be local' during the early part of the 20th century.

In the 1940s it appeared to be expanding its range, spreading into new localities, with between 20 and 30 breeding pairs reported. A report in 1946 estimated that 20 pairs were present in the breeding season within a six mile radius of Quorn. It appeared to be unaffected by the severe winter of early 1947, as there were breeding records from at least 30 sites during the summer of 1947. As with many species there is little data available for the 1950s, but by the 1960s it was considered uncommon with reports from up to 12 sites per annum and little evidence of breeding success.

During 1976–84 Warrilow recorded the Lesser Spotted Woodpecker in 147 tetrads in the counties (23% of the total number of tetrads), with breeding confirmed in 35. The highest densities were found in Charnwood Forest and central and south-west Leicestershire; elsewhere it was thinly distributed, with minor concentrations in central Rutland and around Market Harborough. It was almost entirely absent from southern Rutland and large parts of east and north-east Leicestershire. A breeding population of between 150 and 300 pairs was estimated at this time. This survey work was completed during a high population period when Dutch Elm Disease was rampant, resulting in an increase in nest sites and food availability from the diseased trees.

In 1980 this species was reported from 35 sites and was also appearing more frequently than the other woodpeckers in built-up areas, certainly not a comment which would apply today. In 1981 it was reported from 50 sites, the highest number of sites in any year before or since. However, since the early 1980s the Lesser Spotted Woodpecker has declined significantly and very rapidly on a national level and has also contracted in range (Gibbons *et al.* 1993). Competition with, and predation by, Great Spotted Woodpeckers and reductions in small-diameter dead wood suitable for foraging, are the most likely causes of decline, while the species' large home ranges suggest that landscape-scale changes in woodland (loss of mature broadleaved woodland, losses of non-woodland trees such as elms and woodland fragmentation) may also be important (Baillie *et al.* 2006). Surveys carried out since Warrilow's work suggest that this species has declined locally. In Rutland, Mitcham (1992) found just 9% of tetrads occupied during 1988–90 and commented that the population had declined since the early 1980s; a similarly low figure of confirmed or probable breeding in 5% of the 1–km squares in Charnwood during 1992 to 1994 was reported by Webster (1997).

As can be seen from Table 31, since the 1980s there has been a steady decline both in proven breeding records and in sites at which the species has been recorded. Breeding has only been proved in three years since 2000 (two pairs in 2000, one in 2004 and two in 2005).

Table 31: Lesser Spotted Woodpecker records 1980–2005

	Average number of sites from which records received	Average number of sites at which breeding confirmed
1980–89	35.3	2.3
1990–99	29.5	2.0
2000–05	22.4	0.8

An interesting record came from Glenfield in 1990, when one was seen drumming on a television aerial.

The Lesser Spotted Woodpecker is found extensively across Europe and northern Asia and in a small area of north-west Africa. Over 20 races have been described for the Western Palearctic alone, but variation is mostly clinal. In Britain it is an uncommon resident breeder throughout most of southern England, the Midlands and Wales, but with a patchy distribution in northern and eastern England. It is absent from Scotland and Ireland. The British subspecies *comminutus* is endemic. The breeding population in Britain during 1988–91 was estimated at 3,000 to 6,000 pairs (Gibbons *et al.*1993) but the species was already in decline and more recent estimates are significantly lower (1,400 to 2,900 pairs in Baker *et al.* 2006). This rapid decline has led to the Lesser Spotted Woodpecker being added to the 'Red List' of Birds of Conservation Concern (Gregory *et al.* 2002).

RED

Wood Lark *Lullula arborea*

Formerly a scarce to uncommon breeder, now a rare passage migrant; recorded in all months except January, June and August, with the majority in April, September and October: 34 individuals since 1941.

The Wood Lark was formerly a scarce breeder in Leicestershire. Browne quotes Harley as saying that it 'appears to be a permanent resident. . .around Newtown Linford, Groby and neighbouring districts. . .but even in such places it is not abundant'. It had apparently virtually disappeared by the 1820s and definitely by the 1840s. The situation in Rutland in the 18th and 19th century is slightly confused. Haines reported that singing birds were at Lyndon in January 1762 and February 1768 and nests were supposedly taken at Wing, Bisbrooke Gorse and Preston Gorse between 1855 and 1860, although he considered that the description of the nests referred to a species of pipit. Haines also reported that nests had been found at Barnsdale in about 1876, near Stoke Dry Wood in 1890 and near Ketton in 1901, one was apparently shot at Uppingham around 1870 and single birds were seen at Exton in 1888 and on October 3rd 1891, but he seemed dubious about a number of these records.

Since 1950 there have been records in 13 years involving 34 individuals, of which 11 records (18 individuals) have been since 1998.

All modern records:

1950	one singing, near Benscliffe Wood, April 19th.
	three, Barrow upon Soar, October 29th.
1951	one feeding on the Rutland bank of Eyebrook Reservoir, May 14th.
1953	two, Bradgate Park, July 15th, with one on July 18th and 24th.
1962	one singing, Bradgate House Old Wood, near Newtown Linford, October 14th.
1974	one, Kibworth, April 20th.
1975	one feeding with Goldfinches at Eyebrook Reservoir, October 5th.
1987	four landed briefly before flying off north at Glen Parva, October 4th.
	two north-east over Stanford Reservoir, December 13th.
1998	six in stubble fields at Gumley, September 26th.
1999	one, Bardon Hill, April 11th.
	one, Tickencote, October 3rd.
2001	two south over Deans Lane, Woodhouse, October 4th.
2003	one south-west over Deans Lane, Woodhouse, March 6th.
	one over Holwell, April 6th.
	one south with Sky Larks at Lockington Marshes, November 15th.
2004	one over Wanlip South Gravel Pits, February 8th.
	one south over Deans Lane, Woodhouse, October 7th
2005	one north-east over Rutland Water, March 8th.
	two south-west over Deans Lane, Woodhouse, October 9th.

The recent upsurge in records is probably attributable to increased observer coverage of migration watchpoints, particularly in Charnwood Forest: Deans Lane, Woodhouse has provided four records, totalling six individuals, since 2001. Wood Larks have increased nationally in recent years, most notably in the neighbouring county of Nottinghamshire, and this may also be a factor.

The majority of modern records have involved either spring or autumn migrants. Spring records have all been of single birds and have occurred between March 6th and May 14th, although the individual at Wanlip South Gravel Pits on February 8th 2004 may well have been an early passage bird. Autumn records have occurred between September 26th and November 15th, although the majority (six records involving 11 individuals) have

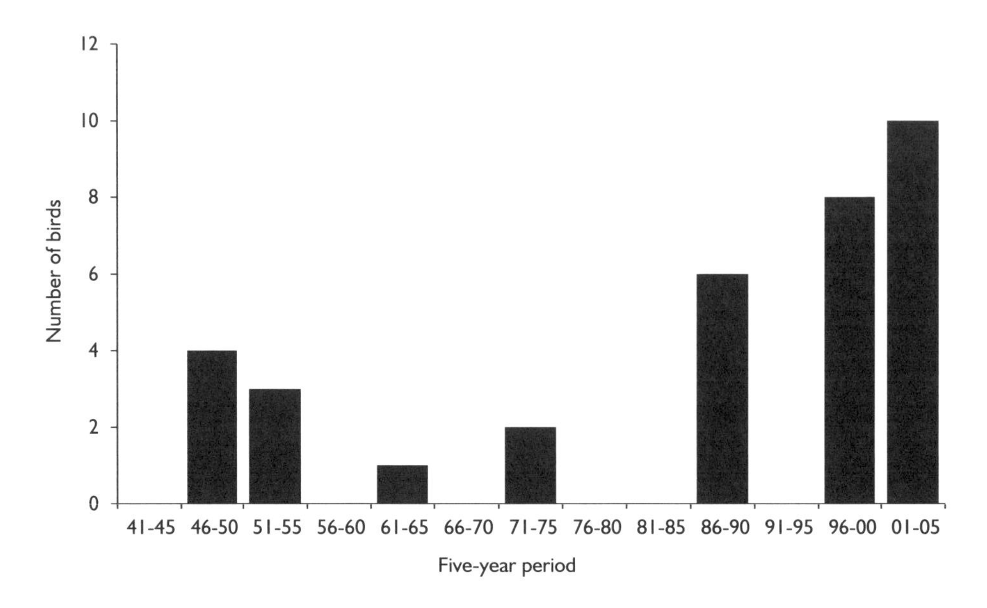

Figure 383: Numbers of Wood Larks 1941–2005.

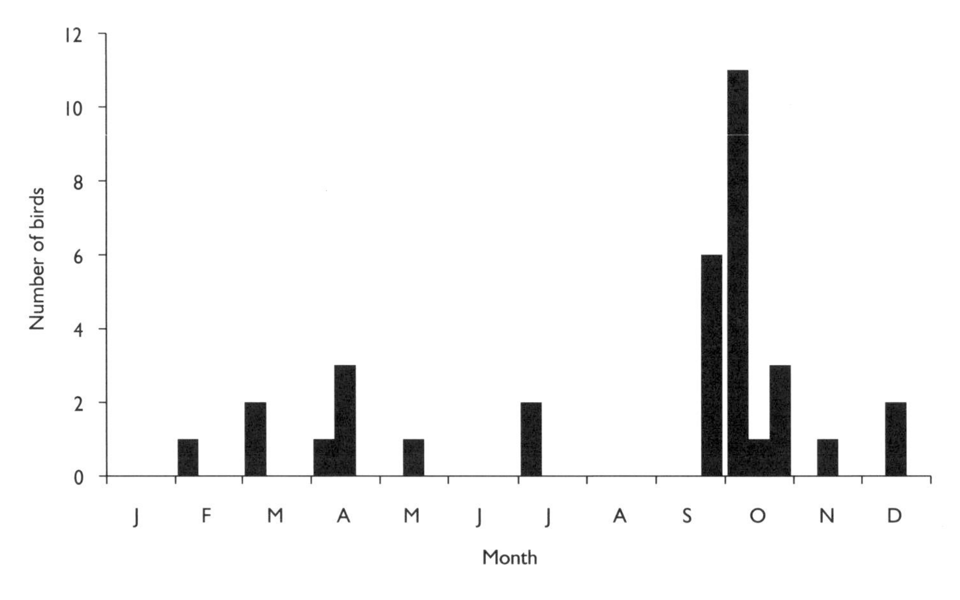

Figure 384: Monthly occurrence of Wood Larks 1941–2005.

been concentrated between October 3rd and 9th. The exceptions are two at Bradgate Park in July 1953 and two at Stanford Reservoir in December 1987.

Despite the upsurge in records since 1998, the Wood Lark remains a very difficult bird to encounter in the counties; the only bird in recent times that has been seen by observers other than the finder was the Bardon Hill individual in 1999, which remained for several hours.

The nominate race of the Wood Lark breeds throughout much of Europe, with other subspecies in north-west Africa and south-west Asia. In Britain, Wood Larks declined significantly throughout the 19th and much of the 20th centuries (Gibbons *et al.* 1996) and there was a 62% reduction in occupied 10-km squares nationally between the 1968–72 and 1988–91 breeding atlases (Baillie *et al.* 2006). This rapid contraction of the breeding range resulted in this species being added to the 'Red List' of Birds of Conservation Concern (Gregory *et al.* 2002). However, the population increased from 250 pairs in 1986 to 600 pairs in 1993, helped by mild winters and increased habitat availability due to storm damage in plantations, forest restocking and heathland management (Baillie *et al.* 2006). A national survey in 1997 estimated a total population of between 1,426 and 1,552 pairs, accompanied by a range expansion into new areas (Wotton & Gillings 2000). Most are to be found in southern England (particularly the New Forest) and East Anglia, although there is now a healthy population in Nottinghamshire, where there were 125 breeding pairs in 2004 (Holling *et al.* 2007a). Given the recent increase in records in Leicestershire and Rutland, perhaps a pair will find suitable habitat in Charnwood Forest in the not too distant future and settle down to breed.

RED

Sky Lark *Alauda arvensis*

Common resident breeder, autumn migrant and winter visitor.

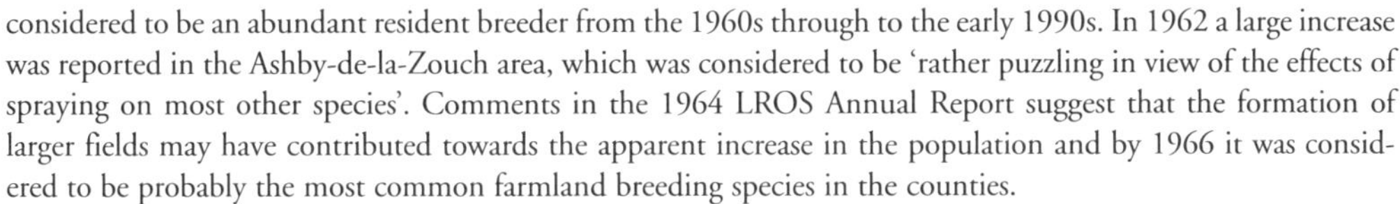

During the 19th century the Sky Lark was described as abundant in Rutland by Haines, and Browne noted that it flocked in 'many hundreds' in winter, though in severe seasons it appeared to leave the Midlands, 'probably withdrawing farther south.' A white specimen was shot at Aylestone in about 1875. In the early part of the 20th century, the LROS archives describe this species as 'common'.

In the early 1940s it was considered to be a common resident whose numbers had been decreasing but were then thought to be fairly constant. After the severe winter of early 1947 there was a very pronounced decrease in the population, but numbers were thought to be on the increase again by the end of the decade. Little information is available from the 1950s but it was considered to be an abundant resident breeder from the 1960s through to the early 1990s. In 1962 a large increase was reported in the Ashby-de-la-Zouch area, which was considered to be 'rather puzzling in view of the effects of spraying on most other species'. Comments in the 1964 LROS Annual Report suggest that the formation of larger fields may have contributed towards the apparent increase in the population and by 1966 it was considered to be probably the most common farmland breeding species in the counties.

During 1976–84 Warrilow recorded the Sky Lark in 618 tetrads in the counties (97% of the total number of tetrads), making it the seventh most-widespread species in the counties; it was recorded in more tetrads than such species as the Wood Pigeon, Wren, Robin, Carrion Crow and House Sparrow. Breeding was confirmed in 203 tetrads. It was found to be most common on farmland, but also occurred in a variety of other habitats such as heathlands in Charnwood, disturbed grounds at sand and gravel pits, playing fields, airfields and reservoir margins. Analysis of CBC data from Newton Harcourt during 1971–1982 gave an average territory density of 378 pairs per tetrad, considerably higher than the mean territory density of the East Midlands of 92 pairs per tetrad (O'Connor & Shrubb 1986). The mean territory density at Stoughton during 1964 to 1979 was 84 pairs per tetrad, much closer to the regional average. Based on this, Warrilow proposed an average of 80 to 100 pairs per occupied tetrad, giving a county-wide breeding population of between 50,000 and 62,000 pairs.

Since the time of Warrilow's work, the Sky Lark has suffered a dramatic decline both nationally and locally. Chamberlain & Vickery (2002) noted that this species had declined nationally by 53% on farmland during 1973–98, with the greatest rate of decline occurring in the early 1980s. The most likely cause of the decline is considered to be the increase in the winter sowing of cereals, which restricts opportunities for late-season nesting attempts because of vegetation height and may reduce overwinter survival by reducing the area of stubbles. Local CBC results demonstrate this dramatic decline, particularly at Stoughton. During 1964–81 the average number of territories per year at this site was 18.3, with peaks of 28 in 1974 and 27 in 1977; in 1982 only one territory was located and the average over the next 18 years was just four. By 1999 the Sky Lark had been lost as a breeding species at this site. It is known that Sky Larks usually avoid oilseed rape for nesting (Chamberlain & Vickery 2002) and the large areas of this crop at Stoughton from the mid-1980s onwards must have been a contributing factor in the decline. A similarly dramatic decline was noted at Newton Harcourt in the early 1980s, where there were 21 territories in 1981 and only ten the following year. At the counties' other farmland CBC site, at King's Hill Lodge, Uppingham, numbers have remained fairly stable since the commencement of survey work in 1992. Given the overall CBC data, it is likely that Warrilow's estimate is out of date and the county breeding population may now be less than half of the 50,000 to 62,000 pairs proposed. This said, the Sky Lark is still widespread, as shown by Mitcham (1992), who found that 95% of squares in Rutland were occupied and considered that it may have been overlooked in the others.

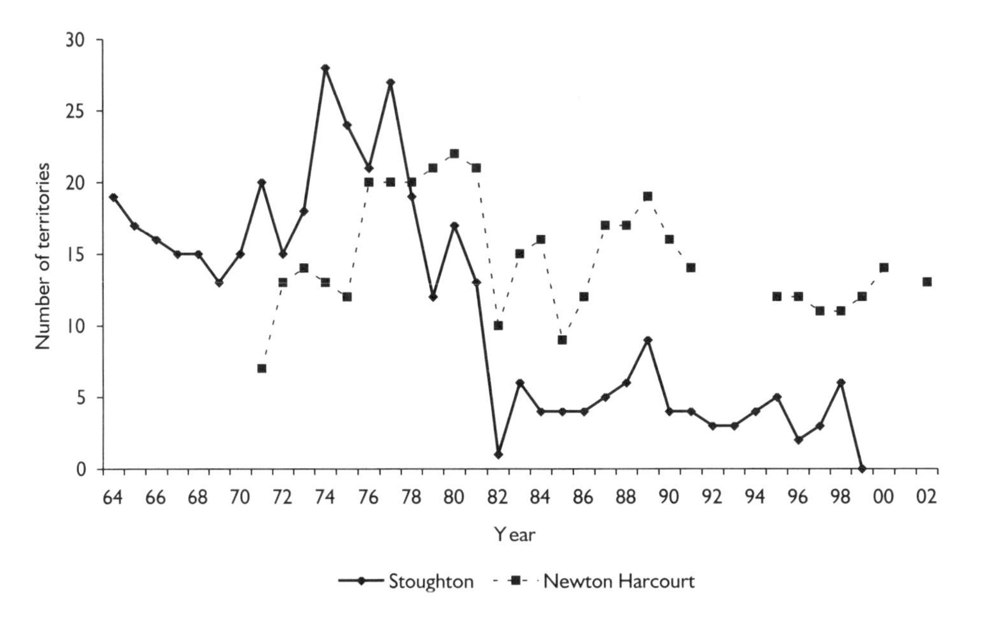

Figure 385: Number of breeding pairs of Sky Larks on two Leicestershire CBC plots 1964–2002.

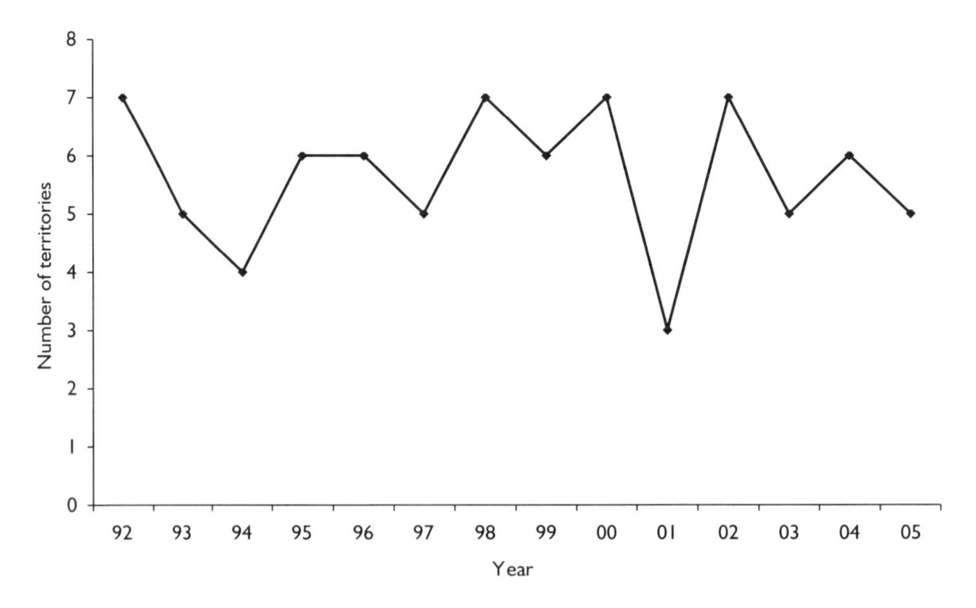

Figure 386: Number of breeding pairs of Sky Larks at the CBC plot at King's Hill Lodge, Uppingham 1992–2005.

Winter flock sizes have been one of the factors used to assess the population, although these flocks will almost certainly have included continental migrants. Throughout the last 50 years three-figure flocks have been a regular occurrence; most were of 300 or fewer, but 1,500 were at Normanton Park on December 4th 1976, 1,000 were near Langham in January 1978 and well over 1,000 were at Rutland Water during the winter of 1977. The 1990s saw a contrast of good and bad years. In a hard weather influx in early February 1991 an aggregate total of 2,000 was recorded at 12 sites, including 550 at Tolethorpe on the 10th and 400 at Eyebrook Reservoir on the 11th. These numbers contrast sharply with those recorded in 1990, when the largest flocks in the two winter periods were just 39 and 110 respectively. In 1993 the highest counts were 50 at just two sites and there was no significant autumn passage. However, in subsequent years counts of 100+ were recorded at up to nine sites, with January 1997 providing counts of 454 at Melton CP and 500 at Kirby Bellars on the 3rd and 420 at Tickencote on the 7th. Since 2000 there have been very few three-figure flocks: the only ones to exceed 200 were 600 at Lockington Marshes on January 2nd 2002 and 340 at Stoughton Lodge Farm on November 15th 2005.

Autumn passage movements, primarily during October, have been a noticeable feature in many years. Exceptional numbers occurred in 1948, when 1,000 were feeding on Lindley Airfield on October 10th and a 'constant stream of passage birds' was recorded. In the same year, at Bruntingthorpe Airfield on November 14th, it was considered 'impossible to estimate the huge number present'. Several other significant movements have been recorded, but apparently none matching those of 1948:

- 'heavy passage' at Eyebrook Reservoir on October 19th 1958.
- 200 south-west at Saddington in 15 minutes on October 22nd 1967.
- 'flocks totalling several hundred' westwards at Eyebrook Reservoir on October 16th 1985.
- 'continuous overhead southerly movements' throughout October 1991.
- 400 flying south at Kilby Bridge in a two-hour period on November 3rd 1992.
- 203 over Tinwell in a two-hour period soon after dawn on October 17th 1997.
- 241 over Priory Water on October 8th 2000.

Unusual records include individuals and flocks frequenting gardens during the severe winter weather of early 1963, one feeding in a Braunstone, Leicester garden on December 28th 1981, one singing on the wing at Saddington at 03:15 on May 22nd 1966 and two seen at Great Central Street, Leicester throughout June 1977, possibly utilising the disused Great Central Railway Station as a breeding site.

One in song at Bradgate Park on May 13th 1996 showed an abnormal amount of white in the wings, the white trailing edge extending across the whole of the secondaries and parts of the inner primaries. What was presumably this individual was seen at the same site on May 24th 1997.

Sky Larks breed throughout Europe, in north-west Africa, Asia Minor and across parts of Asia to Japan and eastern Siberia. European birds move south and west in the winter augmenting the resident populations. They are resident throughout the British Isles with the exception of the highland regions and the extreme north of Scotland, where they are summer visitors. The latest British population estimate is 1,700,000 pairs (Baker *et al.* 2006). The rapid marked decline mentioned above has led to its current position on the 'Red List' of Birds of Conservation Concern (Gregory *et al.* 2002).

RED

Shore Lark (Horned Lark) ***Eremophila alpestris***

Very rare vagrant from Europe: two records involving three individuals.

The first county record involved one seen by Mick Ketley for just a few minutes on the 'island' at Eyebrook Reservoir during the afternoon of November 14th 2001, before it flew up and was lost amongst a flock of gulls (Ketley 2002). The second record soon followed: two were watched at close range by B. Spence on the dam at Rutland Water from 14:00 to 14:30 on November 6th 2002, but could not be relocated later in the day.

Shore Larks breed in northern Eurasia from southern Norway, through Fennoscandia to the eastern Siberian Sea, with other populations in the mountains of north-west Africa, south-east Europe, Asia Minor and central Asia, as well as North America south to Mexico. Scandinavian birds winter around the southern Baltic and

North Seas. They are passage migrants and winter visitors to Britain, where they are found primarily on the east coasts of England and Scotland. Inland records are rare, although most Midlands counties have several records to their name; a number of the recent occurrences in neighbouring counties have been in traditionally under-watched habitat such as farmland and waste ground so, whilst further records in Leicestershire and Rutland are likely, they may be at unfashionable sites.

RED

Sand Martin *Riparia riparia*

Fairly common migrant breeder.

During the 19th century, Browne described the Sand Martin as 'commonly distributed' and mentioned a breeding colony at Aylestone. In Rutland, Haines reported regular nest-sites at Glaston, Pilton, Edith Weston and Collyweston (although the latter village is in Northamptonshire), as well as one-off breeding attempts at Morcott, Uppingham and Ketton.

Throughout the history of LROS, the Sand Martin has always been considered a fairly common migrant breeder, but there were national population crashes after the winters of 1968–69 and 1983–84 which were reflected at a local level. This species has certainly not recovered to the levels recorded before the crashes, but numbers in the counties appeared to be increasing again by the late 1980s.

The breeding distribution of Sand Martins is strongly affected by the availability of breeding sites, which are often closely associated with the activities of man. Sand pits and, to a lesser extent, gravel pits and quarries are regularly utilised, but in some years suitable habitat is not available at particular sites or is partly or totally destroyed during the breeding season by man's activities or by natural events, such as cliff collapses. Its vulnerability to human disturbance has also prevented the expansion of breeding colonies at these sites. Once a sand pit becomes exhausted the colony normally disappears as the site is usually destroyed by infilling or flooding, but it may re-establish itself again at a new working within the area.

This has happened at Rothley Sand Pit, where there was a large colony in the 1940s at which considerable fieldwork took place (Jolley & Storer 1945). In 1944 there were 530 holes, with an estimated breeding population of 190 pairs, but by 1948 the population was down to between 120 and 150 pairs. The reduction was attributed to heavy mortality during a very cold spell in late April and early May 1947 when 56 birds were found dead, including 21 in one hole! Sand continued to be extracted at this site until around 1950 when the colony disappeared, only to become re-established again in 1955 when a new pit was opened. Over 500 pairs were recorded in 1970 and the colony was still in existence in 1993, with 20 to 30 nest-holes occupied.

Similar situations have occurred at other sand pits. At Dunton Bassett there was a maximum of 720 nest-holes in 1968, but only 70 in 1993, about half of which were occupied. At Huncote, small numbers were first recorded in 1942, 55 pairs were reported to be breeding in 1976, but there were 140 nest-holes in both 2001 and 2004 and 141 in 2005.

Since 1991, the Trent Valley Pit area has contained a breeding colony, with a peak of 292 nest-holes in 2000. Gravel Pits normally only provide limited opportunities for colonies to develop, although spoil heaps at such sites and at quarries have been utilised, as well as excavated heaps of both sand and gravel. River bank nesting, mainly on the Trent where it forms part of the Leicestershire county boundary, but also in Rutland at South Luffenham, Ketton and Tinwell, is somewhat limited but is recorded occasionally, along with nesting in drainage holes in canal and river retaining walls.

A number of artificial nest-banks have been constructed in recent years. The first such site was built at Wanlip South Gravel Pits in 1993 and, although no nesting took place that year, Sand Martins bred for the first time in 1994 and have used the nest-bank every year since; peak counts have been 42 occupied nest-holes in 2002, with 32 breeding pairs in 2004, 26 of which were double-brooded. Another four artificial nest-banks have been constructed following the success of the Wanlip site. At Dishley Pool, a nest-bank was built in 1998 and had a peak count of 28 occupied holes in 2004 and was followed by one at Rutland Water which was first used in 2001 and had 30 pairs in both 2004 and 2005. A nest-bank at Sence Valley Forest Park was first occupied in 2004, with eight pairs breeding in 2005 and nearby the first pair bred at Kelham Bridge in 2005. These statistics emphasise the importance of these artificial sites.

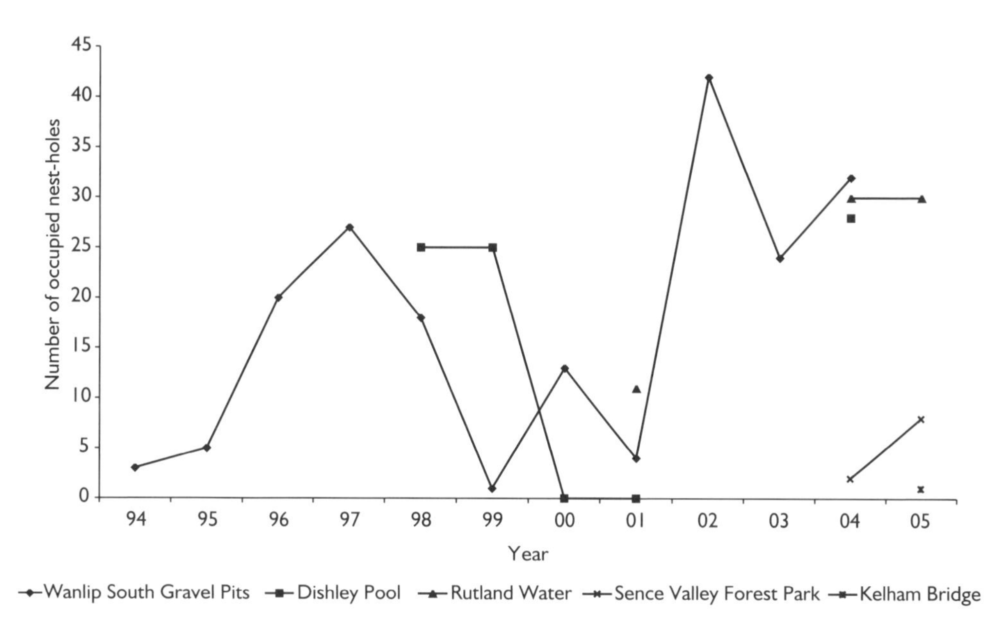

Figure 387: Number of breeding pairs of Sand Martins at artificial nest-banks 1994–2005.

Hickling estimated the breeding population to be less than 1,000 pairs and almost entirely confined to sand pits. During the survey work carried out by Warrilow between 1976 and 1984, confirmed breeding was recorded in 22 tetrads, at the following site types: sand and gravel pits (12), river banks (four) and opencast pits and quarries (one each); however, only a small number of these were occupied in each year in which the survey took place. Although about 400 occupied nest-holes were found in 1979, only about 30 were occupied in 1984. His data indicated that the breeding population was less than 100 pairs in most years during the survey period. The situation appears to have improved in recent years. In 2000, using the peak counts at five sites, there was

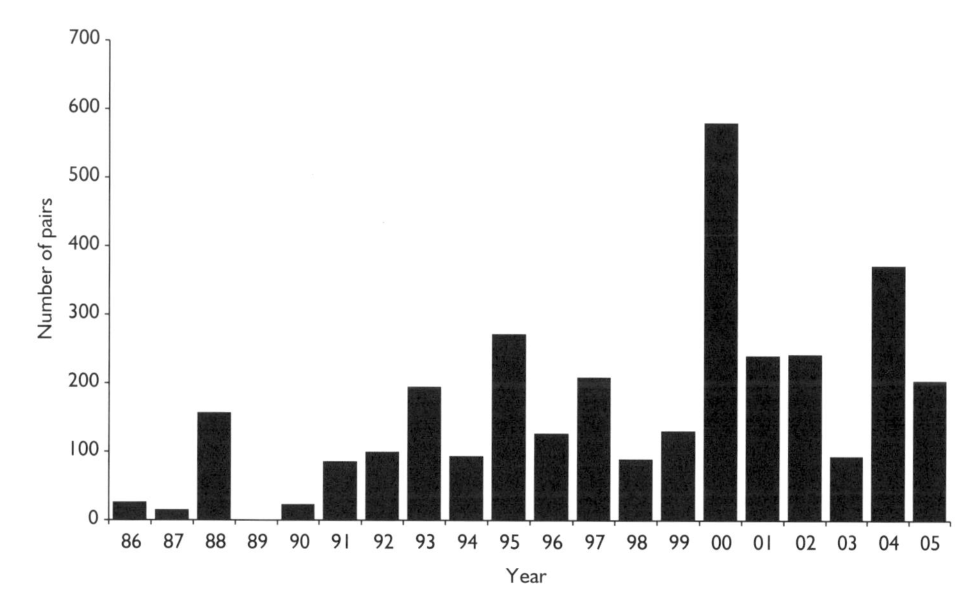

Figure 388: Estimated number of breeding pairs of Sand Martins 1986–2005.

an aggregate total of 580 nest holes and in 2004 perhaps as many as 370 pairs were probably breeding at a total of ten sites.

The Sand Martin is always one of the earliest summer migrants to arrive in the counties, the first normally occuring well before the end of March. The earliest record is of one at Rutland Water on March 5th 1992 and birds have appeared prior to March 10th in another six years, as follows:

- one at Swithland Reservoir on March 6th 1983.
- one at Rutland Water on March 8th 1989.
- one at Dishley Pool on March 8th 2001.
- single birds at both Rutland Water and Cropston Reservoir on March 8th 2003.
- one at Rutland Water on March 9th 1995.
- three at Cropston Reservoir and two at Eyebrook Reservoir on March 9th 2002.

Where data is available (almost every year since 1943), the first has been recorded in March in all but seven years and in every year since 1976. Since 1989, the first has been recorded no later than March 17th and since the mid-1970s the average arrival date of this species has been getting consistently earlier. The latest arrival date was April 10th 1963; this may be due to the harsh weather in the early part of 1963, when severe frosts were recorded well into March.

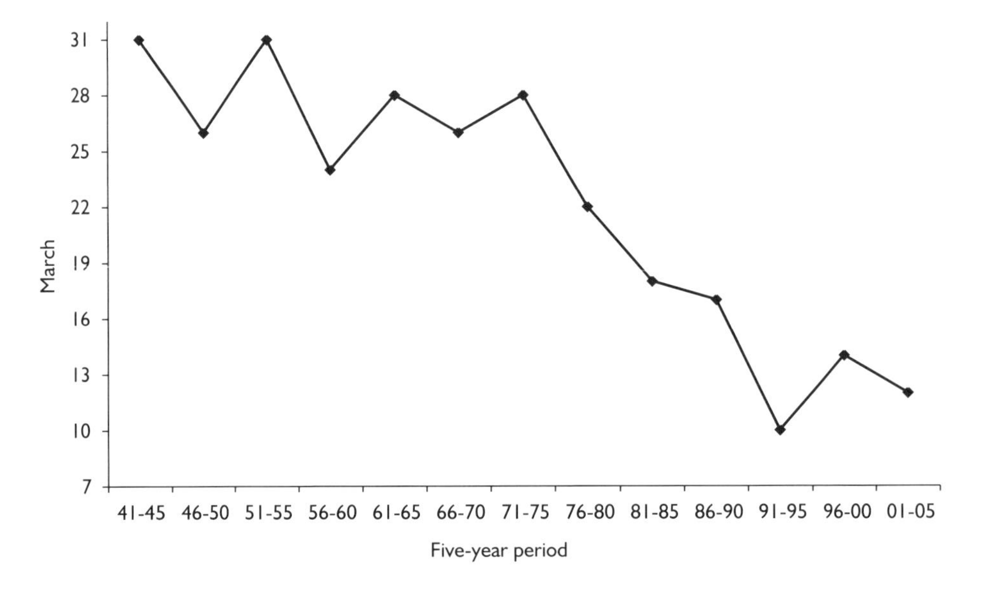

Figure 389: Average spring arrival dates of Sand Martins by five-year periods 1941–2005.

The largest spring flocks have occurred in April or May, but in five years three-figure flocks have been recorded before the end of March:

- 500 at Kirby Bellars Gravel Pits on March 28th 1989, a year when 'spring passage was the best for many years'.
- 220 at Rutland Water on March 26th 1995.
- 180 at Rutland Water on March 24th 2002.
- 150 at Swithland Reservoir on March 28th 1981.
- 100 at Swithland Reservoir on March 27th 2005.

Three-figure spring flocks have been recorded in most years and there have been seven counts of 1,000 or more, as follows:

- 3,000 at Rutland Water on April 22nd 2000.
- 'several thousand' at Stanford Reservoir on April 14th 1950.

- 1,500 at Swithland Reservoir on April 13th 1966.
- 1,200 at Rutland Water on April 16th 1994.
- 1,000 at Stanford Reservoir on May 5th 1946.
- 1,000 at Blackbrook Reservoir on May 1st 1947.
- 1,000 at Rutland Water on April 21st 2001.

The majority of three-figure counts reported during the autumn have occurred since 1990. Flocks of 250 have occurred on three occasions (in 1983, 1995 and 2002), but the largest counts are:

- 1,800 at Trent Valley Pit on July 16th 2005.
- a roost at Trent Valley Pit in 1995 which peaked at 1,000 on August 9th.
- 450 at Rutland Water on August 6th 2003.
- 400 at Rothley Sand Pit on September 15th 1943.
- 300 at Trent Valley Pit on July 7th 2004.

As well as being early to arrive, the Sand Martin is also quite early to leave, with few lingering after the end of September. However, the last record has occurred during October in all but three of the last 17 years and there is a record of young still being fed in a nest at Shawell on October 4th 1981. Birds have been recorded later than October 15th in nine years, including three in which the last record was in November, as follows:

- one at Rutland Water on November 9th 1986.
- one near Birstall Gravel Pits on November 6th 1982.
- one at Frisby Gravel Pits on November 2nd 1976.
- one at Rutland Water on October 30th 1984.
- two at Braunstone, Leicester on October 20th 1957.
- one at Croft on October 19th 1953.
- seven at Barrowden on October 19th 1992.
- three at Wanlip Gravel Pits on October 18th 1981.
- three at Swithland Reservoir on October 16th 1983.

There is a wealth of data concerning Sand Martins ringed or recovered in Leicestershire and Rutland. A total of 16 birds ringed in the counties have been recovered elsewhere in Europe, in France (seven), Spain (four), Belgium (two) and the Channel Islands, the Netherlands and Germany (one each). Two juveniles have been

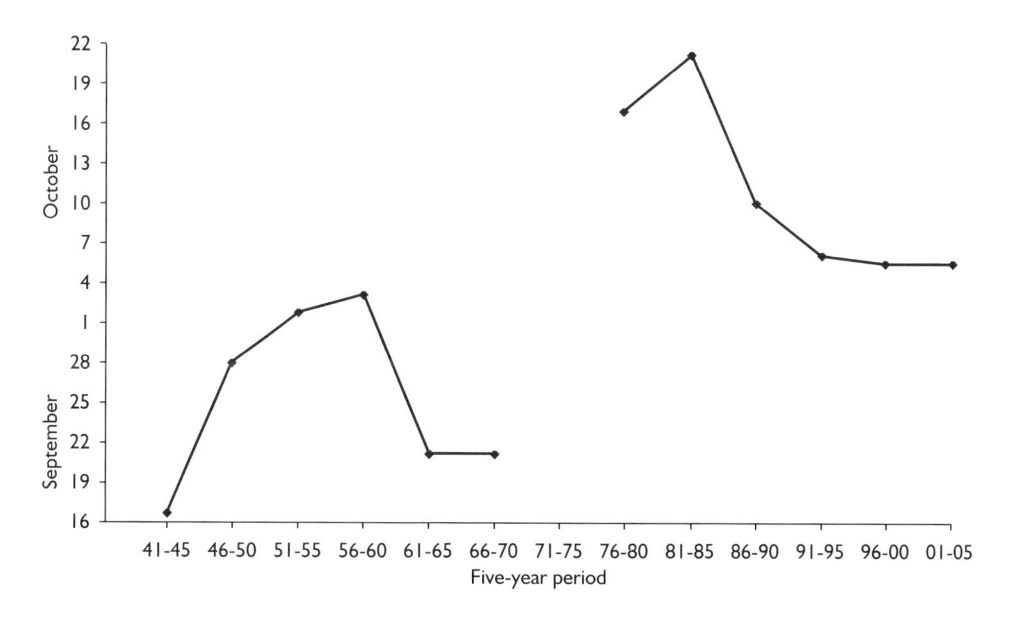

Figure 390: Average autumn departure dates of Sand Martins by five-year periods 1941–2005.

found near Saint-Louis (Senegal): one ringed at Hemington on June 16th 1992 was controlled on November 28th of the same year and one ringed at Rutland Water on September 2nd 1995 was controlled on November 24th 1995. By contrast, only one foreign-ringed bird has been found in the counties: a juvenile ringed at Las Minas (Spain) on August 22nd 2001 was controlled at Ratcliffe on Soar on May 28th 2002 and later at Wanlip on June 21st 2002. Within Britain, birds ringed in Leicestershire and Rutland have been found in North Yorkshire, Kent, West Sussex, East Sussex, Norfolk, Suffolk and Hampshire amongst others.

Examples of site-fidelity include a juvenile ringed at Rothley Sand Pit in 1945 which was retrapped at the same site as a breeding adult on August 3rd 1946, eight ringed at this site in 1946 which were all retrapped the following year and nine ringed at Huncote Sand Pit in 1952 which were all retrapped there in 1953. By contrast, evidence that birds move between colonies in the breeding season is provided by an adult female ringed at Attenborough (Nottinghamshire) on July 3rd 1979 which was retrapped at Cossington Gravel Pits 18 days later on July 21st, when it was found to have a brood patch. Two examples of juvenile dispersal show that birds sometimes move north before migrating south: a juvenile ringed at Dorchester (Oxfordshire) on July 13th 1976 was controlled at Stanford Reservoir on August 7th of the same year and a juvenile ringed near Hemington on July 18th 1996 was controlled at Catterick (North Yorkshire) on July 21st 1996.

Sand Martins breed over much of Eurasia and in North America. European populations winter in the Sahel region of North Africa and in East Africa south to Mozambique. They are summer visitors to most of the British Isles, but are absent from the Outer Hebrides, Orkney and Shetland. There were serious population crashes after the winters of 1968–69 and 1983–84 attributed to severe Sahel droughts, which reduced large areas in that region to desert (Cowley 1979, Jones 1987). In 1984, the national population was considered to be only one tenth of that before the crash (Mead 1984). The British population is currently estimated at between 77,500 and 250,000 pairs (Baker *et al.* 2006) and as this species has an unfavourable conservation status outside Europe it has been added to the 'Amber List' of Birds of Conservation Concern (Gregory *et al.* 2002).

RED

Crag Martin (Eurasian Crag Martin) ***Ptyonoprogne rupestris***

Very rare vagrant from southern Europe: one record.

One was found by Steve Lister at Swithland Reservoir at 09:30 on April 17th 1999, where it remained intermittently until 17:40. During its short stay, it was seen by an estimated 1,500 observers, constituting Leicestershire and Rutland's biggest ever twitch (*BB* 93:544, Lister 1999, Lister 2000). What was presumably the same bird was then seen in West Yorkshire the following day.

Crag Martins breed widely in southern Europe and further east and have been gradually expanding in the Alps and other northern parts of their range since about 1960. Northern birds are migratory, with some wintering as far south as Senegal and Ethiopia. In Britain, they are extreme rarities; the Swithland Reservoir bird was only the fifth to be recorded and the first to be seen by any number of people. Since one in Orkney in May 1999 the only other accepted British record to date involved a bird in Surrey in October 2006.

RED

Swallow (Barn Swallow) ***Hirundo rustica***

Common migrant breeder.

Browne described the Swallow as commonly distributed in Leicestershire during the 19th century and knew of four November records, the latest concerning two at Melbourne Road, Leicester on November 15th 1891. In Rutland, Haines considered this species to be greatly decreased in numbers by the end of the 19th century; the latest record known to him was of one at an unspecified site on November 18th 1904.

Together with the Cuckoo, the Swallow is probably the species which most people associate with summer and as such its arrival from its African wintering quarters is eagerly awaited. The main arrival is from mid-April onwards, but in most years a few arrive in early April and in March. Table 32 shows the number of years in which the first arrival has occurred during March:

Table 32: March arrival dates of Swallows by five-day periods 1941–2005

Period	Pre-10th	10th to 14th	15th to 19th	20th to 24th	25th to 31st
Number of years	1	2	3	8	19

Average spring arrival dates are becoming earlier and there have been March records in every year since 1993. There have been six records prior to March 20th, all of single birds unless stated, as follows:

- two, Shepshed, March 8th 1993.
- Fleckney, March 10th 2001.
- Rutland Water, March 12th 1994.
- Enderby, March 15th 1949.
- Swithland Reservoir, March 15th 1989.
- Barrow upon Soar, March 19th 2000.

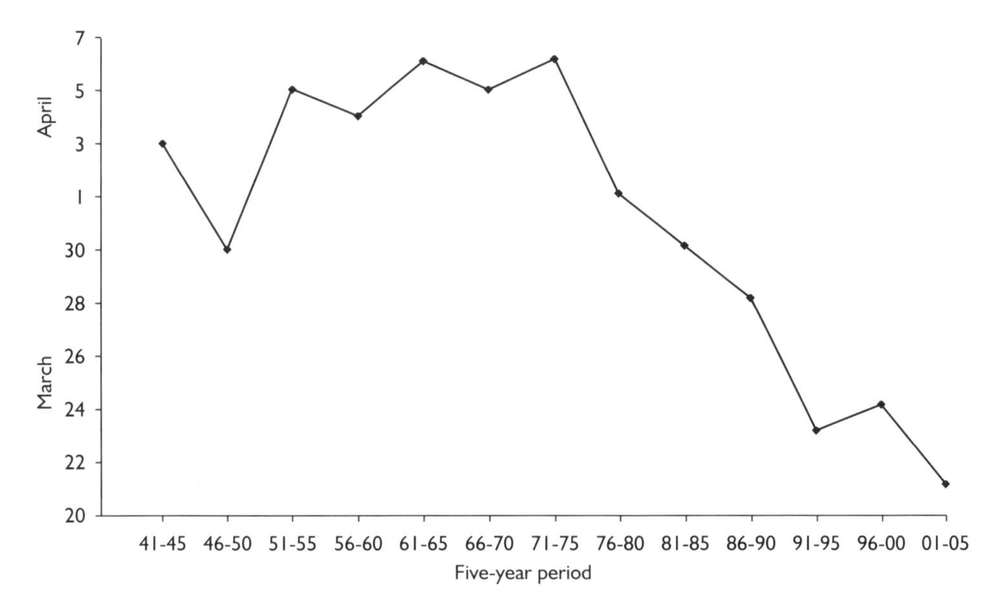

Figure 391: Average spring arrival dates of Swallows by five-year periods 1941–2005.

The Swallow was considered abundant and widespread until 1969 when its status was changed to 'common', presumably as a result of a perceived reduction in breeding pairs. It has retained this status to the present day. Hickling considered this species to be an abundant summer visitor, breeding in all areas of the counties, with an estimated population of between 13,000 and 15,000 pairs. This estimate was based largely on studies in south-west Leicestershire which found 102 pairs at 41 farms (hatching 683 young) in 1961 and 151 pairs at 61 properties the following year, giving an approximate breeding density of 18 pairs per tetrad. During 1976–84, Warrilow recorded the Swallow in 585 tetrads in the counties (91% of the total number of tetrads), with breeding confirmed in 286, making this species the most widespread summer visitor in the counties. National CBC data at the time gave average population densities on farmland of 12.8 pairs per tetrad and based on these figures Warrilow proposed a county-wide breeding population of between 7,500 and 10,500 pairs. This is likely to be a more accurate figure than Hickling's; indeed, the current population is considered to be towards the lower end of the range estimated by Warrilow.

A number of interesting nest records have been recorded. In 1944, a nest in a Swithland school collapsed, but the nest pieces were stuck together with adhesive. The whole nest was then repositioned on the wall and the young fledged successfully. In 1945, three pairs nested on an iron girder inside a railway tunnel. Whenever a train passed through they sat tight during the incubation period, but took flight once the young had hatched.

In 1946, two pairs nested on a ledge in a ventilator in the roof of the pumping room at Swithland Water Works. The temperature in the room never dropped below 38°C and was possibly as high as 49°C in the roof space. In 1980, a nest was found 18 inches below ground in an open-topped manhole at Enderby, but was deserted when the cover was refitted. In 1983, a pair nested underground in an old air-raid shelter at Saltby Heath.

Very little data is available regarding spring and autumn flock sizes until the 1980s, since when maximum flock sizes have been recorded annually. Although there have been considerable differences from one year to the next, it is difficult to use these figures to determine population trends as many of the counts relate to migration or bad weather movements.

Spring passage in 1999, 2000 and 2002 appeared to be rather poor, with no three-figure counts reported, but in 2004 there were three-figure counts from six sites, the highest of which was 750 at Cropston Reservoir on April 29th. The highest spring flock sizes since 1985 are 5,000 at Rutland Water on May 8th 1997 and 1,000 at both Rutland Water on an unspecified date in mid-May 1985 and Eyebrook Reservoir on May 10th 1998. There has been a maximum of between 300 and 750 in a further eight years.

During the autumn the highest counts since 1979 have been as follows:

- 5,000 per hour in a three-hour migration watch at Hinckley on September 25th 1999.
- 2,000 at Rutland Water on October 2nd and 3rd 1981.
- 2,000 at Cadeby Quarry on August 14th and 20th 1991.
- 1,000 at Kilby Bridge on September 1st 1997.

In addition, 'thousands' were at Rutland Water on August 30th and 31st 1989. There has been a maximum count of between 300 and 500 in a further ten years.

Most birds have departed by late September, but with the exception of the 2,000 at Rutland Water on October 2nd and 3rd 1981, numbers during October are generally small. Table 33 shows the number of years in which the final departure date has occurred during November:

Table 33: November final departure dates of Swallows by five-day periods 1941–2005

Period	1st to 5th	6th to 10th	11th to 15th	16th to 20th	21st to 25th	26th to 30th
Number of years	11	5	5	4	2	1

Unlike a number of other summer migrants, the average departure date of the Swallow has not become later in recent years. There have been seven November records after the 16th, all of single birds unless stated:

- Eyebrook Reservoir, November 26th 1968.
- unknown site, November 25th 1976.
- Quorn, November 24th 1963, with two there at November 17th 1963.
- Fenny Drayton, November 23rd 1963.
- Whetstone Pastures Farm, November 18th 1983.
- Newbold Verdon, November 18th 2000.

The latest ever record, however, was of one flying south-west over Rutland Water on the exceptional date of December 8th 1979.

Unusual plumaged individuals have been reported on a number of occasions. Three pure white birds fledged from a nest at Fleckney in 1964 and other pure white individuals were seen at Eyebrook Reservoir on August 26th 1964 and Shearsby in July 1989. One at Western Park, Leicester on July 15th 1946 had a very pale, fawn-grey head, nape and back with very pale, fawn-cream wings and tail; a similar-plumaged bird was also reported at Enderby on September 3rd of the same year.

Ringing activity has resulted in several overseas recoveries, as follows:

- an adult ringed at East Norton on August 5th 1934 was found dead at Bethlehem, Free State (South Africa) around mid-February 1936.
- a pullus ringed at Twycross on July 12th 1959 was controlled at Shabunda (Democratic Republic of the Congo) on March 5th 1960.

- a pullus ringed at Higham on the Hill on August 15th 1963 was found dead near Bothaville, Free State (South Africa) on February 17th 1964.
- a first-year ringed at Leicester on August 22nd 1969 was found dead at Free State (South Africa) on February 1st 1972.
- a pullus ringed at Earl Shilton on June 16th 1972 was controlled at Firgrove, Cape Province (South Africa) on February 15th 1973.
- a pullus ringed at Belton on August 1st 1988 was found dead in Algeria on May 2nd 1989.

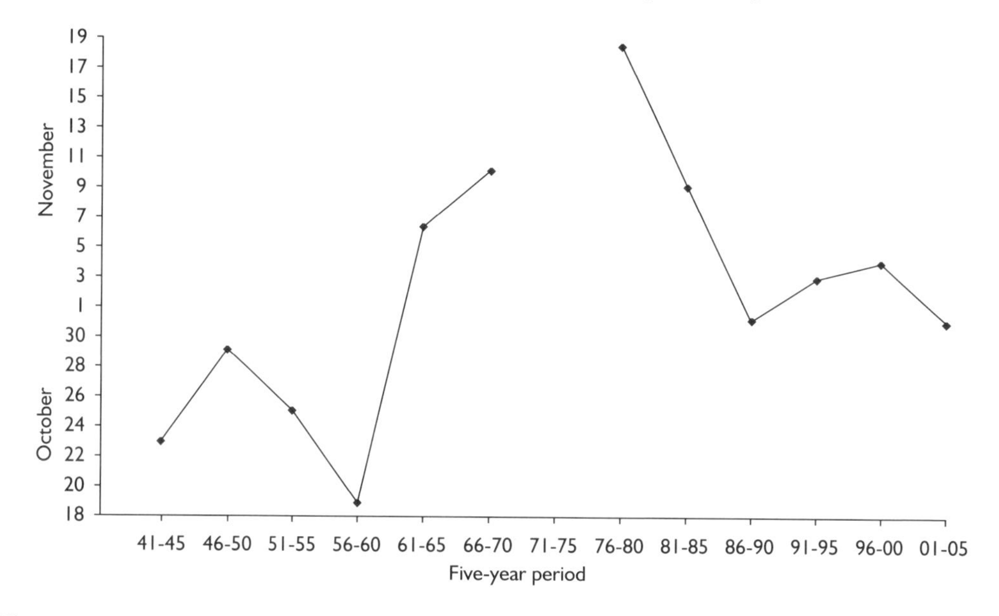

Figure 392: Average autumn departure dates of Swallows by five-year periods 1941–2005.

Of the more local ringing recoveries, two demonstrate how site-faithful Swallows can be: five birds ringed at Cotes in 1950 were all controlled there on April 24th 1951 and two birds ringed at East Goscote during the summer of 1975 were both retrapped there during the summer of 1977.

Swallows breed over most of Eurasia, north Africa and North America. European populations winter in sub-Saharan Africa. The latest British population estimate is 678,000 pairs (Baker *et al.* 2006) and as there has been a widespread decline across the European continent this species has been added to the 'Amber List' of Birds of Conservation Concern (Gregory *et al.*2002).

RED

House Martin *Delichon urbicum*

Common migrant breeder, declining.

In the 19th century Browne described the House Martin as a commonly distributed breeding summer migrant in Leicestershire. He noted that because it was double- and sometimes even triple-brooded it occasionally remained late: his latest record was dated November 23rd 1851 and a nest with young had been recorded as late as the early days of November. Haines broadly agreed, though he considered that in parts of Rutland there had been a decline in numbers.

The majority of House Martins arrive in the counties from mid to late April onwards, but in most years there are a few early April records. There have been 13 years since 1941 when the first bird has appeared in March; a reflection on the earlier recent average arrival date is that eight of these years have been since 1994. Virtually all

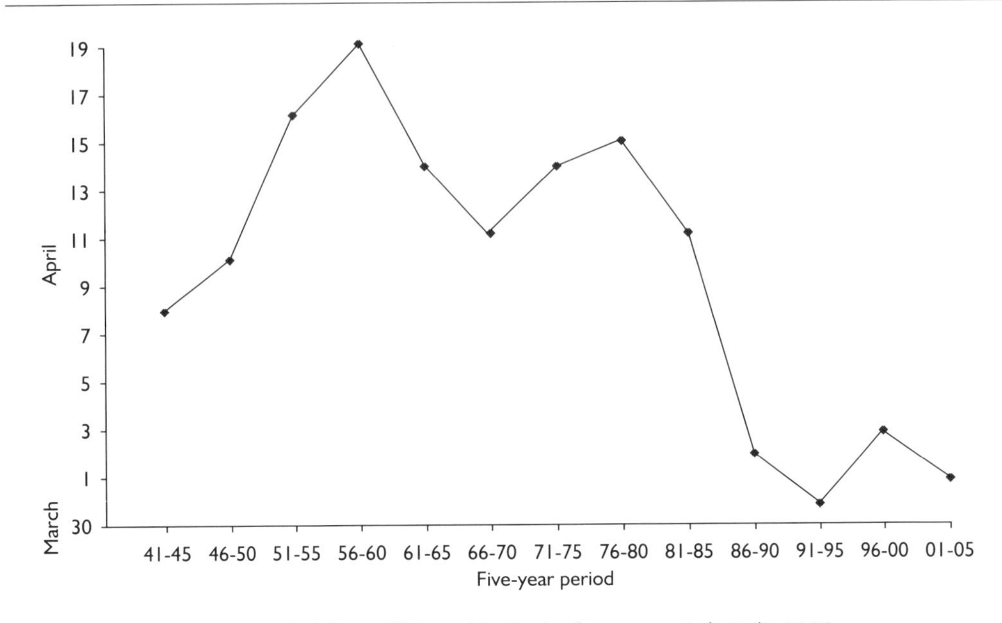

Figure 393: Average spring arrival dates of House Martins by five-year periods 1941–2005.

March records have been from the 26th onwards, the exceptions being two at Watermead Gravel Pits on March 13th 1989, with three there the following day, and one at Quorn on March 15th 1995.

During the lifetime of LROS, the House Martin has been considered as a common but unevenly distributed migrant breeder. However, it is not as common as it used to be. As early as the 1940s the population was generally thought to be decreasing and in 1948 it was suggested that the decrease was partly due to the spread of the House Sparrow, which harried the martins around their nest sites. Another possible cause of the decline was attributed to the 'colour-washing' of stucco walls favoured as breeding sites, as the birds rarely appeared to return to these sites. Little archive evidence is available throughout the 1950s, but a comment in the 1961 Annual Report was of a 'continued decline in breeding numbers in west Leicestershire, a decline which has been going on for some five years'. This trend of decline has continued to the present day with a general decrease in numbers and breeding colonies reported. Hickling commented on the loss of breeding habitat, especially in the city of Leicester, where terraced houses, a former popular nesting site, have been demolished. Although they will nest on more modern housing, it appears that fewer pairs were doing so and in some cases were being actively discouraged by the home owners. Mitcham (1984) commented that the availability of mud for nest-building may also be a limiting factor.

During 1976–84 Warrilow recorded the House Martin in 401 tetrads in the counties (63% of the total number of tetrads), with breeding confirmed in 293. The fewest records came from the higher ground in east Leicestershire and on the nearby wolds. Warrilow considered that the breeding population fluctuated between 3,000 and 7,500 pairs. Mitcham (1992) found that 75% of Rutland tetrads were occupied.

Very little recent data is available with regard to the breeding population, but there have been a number of anecdotal comments to the effect that breeding numbers were low at specific sites. In 1995, an observer of traditional and well-monitored sites at Huncote commented that there had been a 'drastic drop in numbers unprecedented in 40 years – two sites, which had previously held 13 pairs, were completely abandoned'. Requests for more breeding evidence resulted in reports from 16 sites in 2000, including 16 nests at St. Mary's Hospital, Melton Mowbray and 13 at an Aston Flamville farm, but it is not known if these sites were in decline.

Since the early 1980s, maximum spring and autumn flock sizes have been recorded annually. During this period a maximum spring flock size of between 300 and 500 has been recorded in nine years. Counts of 1,000 were recorded at Rutland Water on May 11th 1984, May 21st and 22nd 1985 and June 8th 1989; a flock of 500 was at Eyebrook Reservoir on the latter date during a period of wet weather. The largest spring flocks occurred in 1987, when 2,000 were at Swithland Reservoir on May 24th and in 1994, when an estimated 2,000–3,000 were at Eyebrook Reservoir on May 19th.

As expected, autumn counts are generally higher than those in spring. A maximum of between 300 and 800 has been recorded in eight years since 1980 and a maximum of up to 2,000 has occurred in a further eight years, including counts of 1,000 on the rather late dates of October 2nd and 3rd 1981 and October 6th 1990, both at Rutland Water. The highest autumn counts have all occurred in September:

- up to 5,000 at Rutland Water from September 8th to 17th 1989.
- between 4,000 and 5,000 at Groby Pool on September 12th 1983.
- 4,000 at Rutland Water on September 4th and 5th 1984.

High counts are often associated with periods of bad weather; one such count involved a flock of at least 1,300 feeding very low at Rutland Water in a south-westerly gale on September 14th 2004. The lack of exceptional numbers in both spring and autumn during the last ten years or so is probably a further indication of a national population decrease.

Most House Martins have left the counties by late September, but there are always October records and a few stragglers have occurred in November. Table 34 details the number of years in which the final departure date has occurred during that month by five-day periods:

Table 34: November departure dates of House Martins by five-day periods 1941–2005

Period	1st to 5th	6th to 10th	11th to 15th	16th to 20th	21st to 25th	26th to 30th
Number of years	8	5	1	2	2	2

As can be seen, records after November 10th are rare and the only ones, all of single birds, have been:

- Sheepy Magna, November 29th 1953.
- Tugby, November 26th 1968.
- Quorn, November 24th 1953.
- Quorn, November 21st 1982.
- Rutland Water, November 21st 1986.
- Aldgate, November 19th 1977 (Mitcham 1984).
- Eyebrook Reservoir, November 18th 1984.
- Whitwell, November 15th 1967.

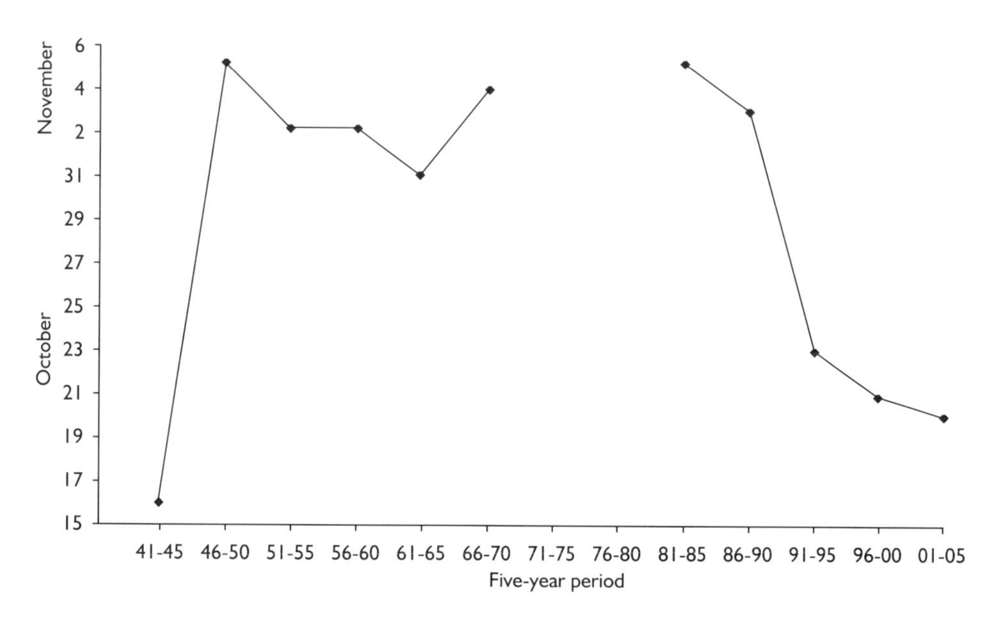

Figure 394: Average autumn departure dates of House Martins by five-year periods 1941–2005.

In contrast with the number of recent March arrivals, the last year in which there was a November record was 1991, whereas in the 1980s there were November records in six years. Similarly, there have been a number of occasions where young were still being fed in the nest well into October (such as at Woodhouse Eaves on October 24th 1987 and Enderby on October 18th 1980) but there has only been one such record since 1990, at Brooksby on October 13th 1997.

Unusually plumaged birds have been recorded on a number of occasions: one at Rutland Water on October 3rd 1981 had white primaries in one wing, a completely white bird was at Rutland Water on September 24th 1990 and a partially albino individual at Swithland Reservoir on May 26th 1993 had a white crown and a thin black line through the eyes onto the ear coverts. There have also been a number of records of unusual behaviour. A colony at Ulverscroft Priory in 1962 held 30 to 40 pairs which were nesting in multiple clusters, one on top of the other, in the apex of a ruined arch and a flock of 26 became trapped in a ward at Carlton Hayes Hospital, Narborough, on September 21st 1982, having entered the building during a heavy rain storm. In attempting to escape several hit the windows, but having once done this they seemed to learn from the experience and did not make repeated attempts; all were eventually released unharmed.

There are a number of ringing recoveries including the following from overseas:

- an adult ringed at St. Sulpice de Favières (France) on May 5th 1977 was controlled at Ratcliffe on the Wreake on May 22nd 1977. This bird was retrapped at Queniborough on both May 14th and June 25th 1978. Out of 37 caught in this area in 1977, this individual was one of 13 retrapped in 1978.
- a first-year ringed at Burley on September 11th 1983 was controlled at Grouville Marsh, Jersey (Channel Islands) on May 6th 1985.
- an adult female ringed at Rutland Water on July 21st 2001 was found dead at Varazze (Italy) on April 18th 2002.

Amongst the most interesting of the British ringing recoveries are the following:

- a first-year ringed at Beachy Head (East Sussex) on September 15th 1977 was found dead at Croxton Kerrial on May 20th 1980.
- a first-year female ringed at Quorn on October 13th 1983 was controlled at Soberton (Hampshire) on September 5th 1986.
- a first-year ringed at St. Alban's Head (Dorset) on September 26th 1987 was found dead at Sheepy Magna on July 21st 1992.

Confirming the site-faithfulness of some House Martins is a record of an adult ringed at Stoke Dry on August 24th 1958 which was killed by a cat at the same site on July 3rd 1960.

The House Martin is a summer visitor, breeding throughout virtually the whole of the British Isles and Europe, with the exception of the extreme north of Scotland, the Outer Hebrides, Iceland and the extreme north of Scandinavia. Its breeding range extends eastwards through the central latitudes of Asia to Japan and parts of China. It also breeds in northern Morocco, Algeria and Tunisia. Birds from Europe and western Asia spend the winter throughout most of Africa south of the Sahara. Populations from the remainder of Asia move south for the winter into northern India and eastwards into Thailand and the Philippines. The most recent British breeding estimate is 253,000 to 505,000 pairs (Baker *et al.* 2006), but a moderate decline in the breeding population during the past 25 years has led to this species being added to the 'Amber List' of Birds of Conservation Concern (Gregory *et al.* 2002).

RED

Red-rumped Swallow — *Cecropis daurica*

Very rare vagrant from southern Europe or Asia: two records.

The first county record was one found by Andy Mackay at Swithland Reservoir on April 30th 2003; it remained until early afternoon the next day (*BB* 97:591, Mackay 2005). This county first had been long-expected, but it was something of a surprise that the second record for Leicestershire and Rutland should be less than a year later, again at Swithland Reservoir, where one found by Steve Lister was present from March 22nd to 29th 2004 (*BB* 98:666).

Red-rumped Swallows are widespread and locally common in north-west Africa, Iberia, the Balkans and Greece, but are uncommon in the central Mediterranean. To the east, they breed discontinuously in west and south Turkey and the Middle East. European birds are believed to winter alongside African birds in tropical Africa. In Britain, Red-rumped Swallows occur typically as spring overshoots in April and May, with a smaller peak in October and November. The 2003 individual arrived during a large influx of this species into Britain, although the bird in March the following year was rather early; there have only been nine British records earlier than March 22nd. By the end of 2005 there had been 511 British records of the Red-rumped Swallow and it ceased to be considered by the BBRC after the end of 2005. Further records in Leicestershire and Rutland are to be expected.

RMF

Richard's Pipit *Anthus richardi*

Very rare vagrant from Siberia: one record.

The only county record involves one seen by Steve Close at the inflow of Cropston Reservoir from 14:35 to 15:35 on October 16th 1990. The bird was watched feeding with a loose flock of Linnets and Meadow Pipits before flying off to the south-east (Close 1991).

Richard's Pipit breeds across southern Siberia and eastern China, wintering from Pakistan east through India to southern China and south-east Asia. It is a scarce but regular migrant to Britain, mainly occurring from mid-September to November; most are found in the Northern Isles and along the east and south coasts. Inland records, whilst by no means common, are not all that unusual and it is perhaps surprising that there has only been one record to date, especially as neighbouring counties such as Derbyshire, Northamptonshire and Nottinghamshire have each recorded several. Enterprising observers who search farmland, grassland and hilltops in autumn may be rewarded with further records.

RMF

Tree Pipit *Anthus trivialis*

Uncommon summer visitor, formerly much more common.

This species was formerly much commoner than it is today. In the 19th century, Haines described it as a common migrant in Rutland, arriving in early April, whilst Browne stated that it was a generally distributed breeding summer visitor in Leicestershire. Railway embankments were considered to be favourite nesting sites.

Even as recently as 60 years ago the Tree Pipit was a common and widespread summer visitor, inhabiting farmland with trees and hedges as well as more wooded areas. Nowadays this species is almost entirely confined to Charnwood Forest and in vastly reduced numbers. Breeding is now limited to two distinct habitats: transient clearings in forestry plantations, and open uncultivated areas with scattered trees such as those found at Beacon Hill, Bradgate Park and Charnwood Lodge. Recent years have produced no more than 20 singing males and a handful of confirmed breeding records annually.

It is difficult to believe how different things used to be. As recently as 1963 there were 19 pairs at Owston Wood, 12 pairs at Launde Park Wood and eight pairs at Wardley Wood, all sites that are long-abandoned now. A decline was already obvious at that time, as 12 singing birds at Leicester City Farms in the early 1950s had dwindled to none. Bradshaw (1969b) summarised the decline as follows: 'The Tree Pipit at the present day is only locally common in Leicestershire. It is to be found mainly on the Charnwood Forest and locally in the north-west, the Melton Ridge from Six Hills to the Vale of Belvoir, high ground in the Burrough-Tilton area, railway cuttings and woodland in east Leicestershire. As a hedgerow and meadowland bird it has declined drastically in recent years and is now rare in south and south-west Leicestershire and parts of east Leicestershire.'

During 1976–84 Warrilow recorded the Tree Pipit in 56 tetrads in the counties (9% of the total number of tetrads) spread over 15 10-km squares. It was concentrated in three main areas: Charnwood Forest, where Bradgate Park, Charnwood Lodge, Ulverscroft, Nowell Wood, Pasture Wood, Martinshaw Wood and Lawn Wood all held small loose colonies; east Leicestershire, where Sauvey Castle, Launde Wood and Owston Wood were favoured sites; and Rutland, with Burley Wood, Barnsdale Wood, Exton Park, Clipsham Park and Clipsham Quarry being the most important sites. Warrilow estimated a county-wide population of 100 to 150 pairs. Mitcham (1992) found eight occupied tetrads in Rutland (7% of all tetrads), corresponding with the number of pairs in each year, but noted that the birds disappeared as young conifer plantations matured.

By the early 1990s the Tree Pipit's range had effectively contracted to just Charnwood Forest: since 1990 the only singing birds away from this area have been at Exton Park in 1991 and 1993, Tunneley Wood in 1992 and 1993, Clipsham Park Wood in 1992, Snibston in 1993, Rutland Water in 1993, 1998 and 2001, Moira in 1994, Stretton Wood in 1999 and Bagworth Heath in 2004. In Charnwood, Webster (1997) estimated 50 to 100 pairs in the area during 1992–94, suggesting a population decline of 60% to 80% over the preceding ten years. Bradgate Park alone was thought to hold 14 pairs in 1994, compared with perhaps three in 2004 and none in 2005. Since 1994 the maximum number of singing males recorded throughout the counties was 24 in 1998, all but one of which was in Charnwood.

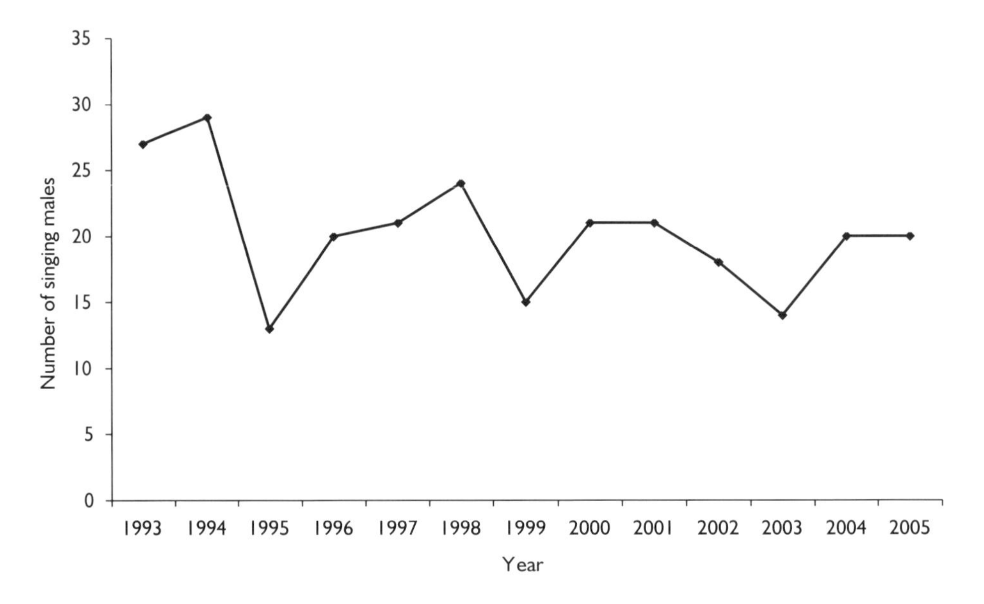

Figure 395: Numbers of singing Tree Pipits 1993–2005.

The main reason for the species' decline must be the clearance of farmland hedges and trees, coupled with the general intensification of agriculture over much of the counties. Another factor may be that Tree Pipit spring arrival dates are now averaging five days later than they were 50 years ago: April 13th from 1996 to 2005 compared with April 8th between 1942 and 1968 (Mason 1970). Most other summer visitors are now arriving significantly earlier than before and the only species with a similar pattern to the Tree Pipit is the Whinchat, long since lost as a breeding species locally. The earliest spring arrivals were single birds at Priory Water on March 22nd 1992 and Rutland Water on March 22nd 1993. There have been a further ten records prior to April 5th, all of single birds unless stated:

- Lindridge Wood, March 24th 1945.
- unspecified site, March 27th 1972.
- Beacon Hill, March 31st 1993.
- Blackbrook Reservoir, April 1st 1990.
- Snibston Discovery Park, April 1st 2001.
- Halstead, April 2nd 1950.
- Eyebrook Reservoir, April 3rd 1942.
- Eyebrook Reservoir, April 3rd 1966.
- Croft, April 4th 1982.
- two, Beacon Hill, April 4th 2005.

Local breeding birds seem to leave in July but their departure is not well recorded. Tree Pipits are largely inconspicuous on migration; small autumn flocks used to be recorded at Croft Hill when the species was a lot commoner but nowadays there are only a few records of single birds each year, mainly detected by call as they pass overhead. Most autumn migrants are noted in August and early September, although there have been five October records, all of single birds, as follows:

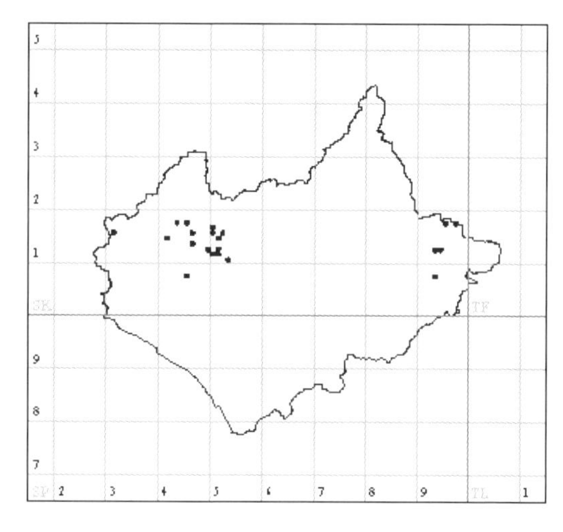

Figure 396: Distribution of singing Tree Pipits 1990–2005.

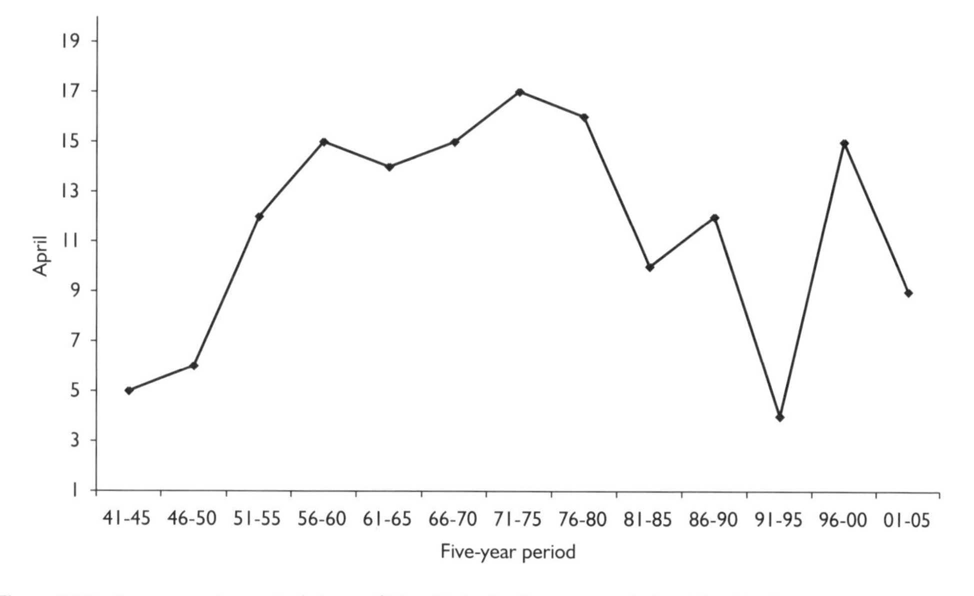

Figure 397: Average spring arrival dates of Tree Pipits by five-year periods 1941–2005.

- Snibston Discovery Park, October 13th 1994.
- found dead, Greetham, October 8th 1968.
- Blaby, October 3rd 1948.
- Bardon Hill, October 1st 2000.
- Trent Valley Pit, October 1st 2000.

Tree Pipits breed over most of Europe, as well as in Asia Minor and in a broad band across Russia to eastern Siberia. European populations winter in sub-Saharan Africa. The British population was estimated at around

120,000 pairs during 1988–91 (Gibbons *et al.* 1993) but more recent estimates put it at 74,400 pairs (Baker *et al.* 2006). As a result of this decline the Tree Pipit has been added to the 'Amber List' of Birds of Conservation Concern (Gregory *et al.* 2002).

SML

Meadow Pipit *Anthus pratensis*

Common passage migrant, fairly common winter visitor, uncommon breeder.

This species was apparently poorly recorded in the 19th century: Browne mentioned that it nested near Leicester and Haines listed Seaton, Barrowden and Luffenham Heath as breeding sites in Rutland, but otherwise there is little information as to its status. Today, the true breeding status of the Meadow Pipit is difficult to appraise without focussed survey work as it continues to be under-recorded.

The fieldwork for the first BTO breeding atlas, carried out between 1968 and 1972, suggested that 14 of the counties' main 29 10-km squares held breeding Meadow Pipits. Between 1976 and 1984 Warrilow found evidence of at least probable breeding in 18 of the 29: only seven squares (SK31, SK62, SK81, SK82, SK83, SP78 and SP79) did not feature in either one or other of the two sets of results.

It is unclear whether there has been any long-term change in the size of the breeding population. Back in 1942 Meadow Pipits were 'common on Charnwood Forest heaths, very local elsewhere' and much the same could be said today. Warrilow estimated the population as between 110 and 325 pairs, well above the likely numbers now. A comparison of the distributions plotted for Charnwood Forest by Warrilow and by Webster (1996) shows that the number of tetrads with proved or probable breeding reduced from 17 in 1976–84 to just 11 in 1992–94. The more casual records since 1994 suggest that this decline has continued in Charnwood and that the main distribution has moved north-west to the coalfield grasslands during the past ten years.

This species breeds in a variety of habitats locally. Probably the main one is rough grassland, such as found at Bradgate Park and around much of Rutland Water; further large areas have recently been established on the post-industrial areas of the north-west, including at Sence Valley Forest Park and around Albert Village Lake. Another important habitat is the small fragments of heathland that survive at places such as Charnwood Lodge and Beacon Hill in Charnwood Forest. Meadow Pipits have also bred alongside watercourses, on field margins and on disused airfields; between 1958 and 1978 varying numbers bred on an area of playing fields and abandoned allotments at Aylestone.

Recent LROS Annual Reports have listed all proved breeding records as well as summaries of additional sites where breeding was thought possible: 2003, for example, had proved breeding at just three sites and song or distraction behaviour at 15 more. The most productive sites in recent years (since 1990) have included Sence Valley Forest Park (up to ten pairs in 1997 and 1999), Bardon Hill (ten pairs in 1994), Charnwood Lodge (20 singing in 1993) and Bradgate Park (eight singing in 1996).

Meadow Pipits are more widespread in winter, when they utilise a wider range of habitats. Farmland habitats such as waterlogged meadows, stubble fields and sheep pastures are all used extensively. Flock sizes are normally small but concentrations of up to 100 are not unusual. Larger counts have been recorded on 11 occasions but only once in the last ten years, despite increased observer activity. The largest five winter flocks are:

- 205 at Priory Water on February 14th 1993.
- 200 at Sence Valley Forest Park on January 18th 2000.
- 180 at Far Coton on January 6th 1986.
- 150 at Stoughton Airfield on December 4th 1993.
- 150 at Rutland Water on December 10th 1995.

Spring passage is principally during March and the first half of April. Published observations of actual visible migration at this time of year are very few: 'hundreds' flew north-east over the Uppingham area on March 27th and 28th 1963 and 110 passed north over Ryhall on March 27th 1999. There are, however, 20 other records of spring counts of 100 or more and it is possible that some of these may have included birds flying over as well as grounded birds. All spring counts of 150 or more are listed below:

- 274 at Kirby Lakes on March 24th 1996.
- 250 at Huncote Sand Pit on April 5th 2003.
- 200 at Stanford Reservoir on April 4th 1976.
- 150 at Priory Water on March 24th 1990.
- 150 at Kirby Lakes on March 24th 1991.
- 150 at Queniborough on March 31st 1997.
- 150 at Eyebrook Reservoir on April 15th 2003.

Autumn passage extends from early September (or rarely late August) until early November. Meadow Pipits often dominate visible migration watches, especially in September and observers at vantage points such as Trent Valley Pit, Croft Hill, Beacon Hill and especially Deans Lane, Woodhouse have recently been producing some interesting counts, including:

- 1,125 south over Deans Lane on September 21st 2003.
- 359 south over Deans Lane on September 17th 2003.
- 288 south over Deans Lane on October 9th 2005.
- 285 south over Beacon Hill on October 6th 2001.
- 227 south over Deans Lane on September 16th 2004.
- 207 south over Deans Lane on September 26th 2005.
- 187 south-east over Trent Valley Pit on August 31st 2004.
- 186 south over Deans Lane on September 28th 2005.
- 170 over Croft Hill on September 30th 1999.

There are 24 other three-figure autumn counts: observers (and report editors) may not always have differentiated between visible passage and grounded birds. Six counts have exceeded 150:

- 400 at Narborough on September 26th 1988.
- 400 at Sileby on September 30th 1993.
- 300 at Narborough on September 25th 1995.
- 200 at Whatborough Hill on October 17th 1989.
- 170 at Frolesworth Manor Lake on September 18th 2003.
- 160 at Sence Valley Forest Park on October 23rd 1999.

Meadow Pipits breed over much of northern Europe as far south as Italy. Most populations are migratory, wintering in south and west Europe, north Africa and the northern parts of the Middle East. The British population is currently estimated at approximately 1,600,000 pairs (Baker *et al.* 2006) but has shown a downward trend since the mid-1970s; the main cause is thought to be losses of marginal land in parts of their breeding range (Baillie *et al.* 2006). Due to the moderate decline in the British breeding population in the last 25 years, this species has been added to the 'Amber List' of Birds of Conservation Concern (Gregory *et al.* 2002). In view of the large number of migrants that clearly pass through Leicestershire and Rutland, it is rather surprising that there have not been any significant ringing recoveries involving Meadow Pipits in the counties.

SML

Red-throated Pipit *Anthus cervinus*

Very rare vagrant from northern Europe or Siberia: one record.

One in summer plumage was found by Roger Davis adjacent to Mallard Hide on the Egleton Reserve at Rutland Water on May 9th 1981. It was seen by a number of other observers during the day and was reportedly present until May 11th, although the BBRC accepted it for May 9th only (*BB* 75:515). During its stay, it was seen to chase Common Swifts repeatedly (Fowler *et al.* 1984).

Haines refers to a record of one seen near Ayston on February 20th 1905 which 'had most distinctly a reddish chin and throat with whitish belly.' However, Haines included this report in square-brackets and subsequent authors have ignored it, probably wisely given the unlikely date.

This species has one of the most northerly breeding ranges of any passerine and summers in a narrow belt across the tundra almost entirely within the Arctic Circle from northern Scandinavia east to Alaska. It winters largely in the tropics of Africa and in south-east Asia, as well as in small numbers in parts of the Mediterranean and the Middle East. It is an annual vagrant to Britain, with most records from the east and south-west coasts; inland occurrences are very unusual and the only other records from Midlands counties have been two in Derbyshire and one in Warwickshire. The peak months are May, September and October, so the Rutland Water bird fits in with established vagrancy patterns. By the end of 2005 there had been over 435 British records and Red-throated Pipit ceased to be considered by the BBRC as a result.

RMF

Water Pipit *Anthus spinoletta*

Scarce passage and winter visitor: recorded in all months between October and April, with the majority in October, November and April; 61 individuals.

The Water Pipit was only recognised as a species distinct from Rock Pipit in 1986 and it is possible that some earlier records were lost or overlooked amongst those of the commoner species. There had been just five individuals documented before the 'split', the first being one at Stanford Reservoir from March 27th to April 10th 1971. A further 56 have occurred since 1986, with annual records since 1990, giving a total of 61 by the end of 2005. The best year to date was 2003, with eight individuals, followed by seven in 1995 and six in 1997.

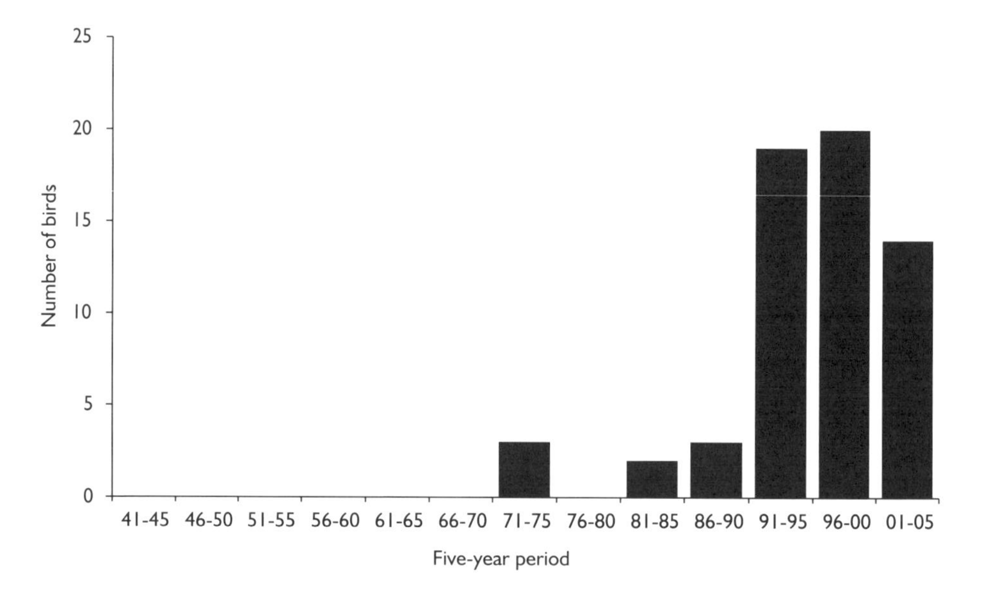

Figure 398: Numbers of Water Pipits 1941–2005.

The records fall neatly into three categories: spring migrants (20 birds), autumn migrants (25) and winter visitors (16). Birds on spring passage have appeared on dates between March 15th (at Eyebrook Reservoir in 1990) and April 22nd (at Trent Valley Pit in 2003) but the majority, 15 of the 20, have been found during the first ten days of April. All spring records have been of single birds except on two occasions: four were at Trent Valley Pit on April 8th 1995, with one still present the next day and three were at Melton Sewage Farm on April 6th and 7th 1991, with two remaining to the 11th and one to the 16th. The resultant stay of this last bird, 11 days, has only been exceeded once in spring, by the 14 days of the one at Stanford Reservoir in 1971. Most records in spring, including all those since 1996, have been of one-day birds; the only ones to remain more than a day at this season, other than those already mentioned, were single birds at Frisby Gravel Pits from April 10th to 12th 1974, Eyebrook Reservoir from April 5th to 9th 1990 and Thornton Reservoir on April 8th and 9th 1990.

The 25 birds on autumn passage have arrived fairly evenly between October 5th (at Kirby Lakes in 2003) and November 18th (at Priory Water in 2001). The largest group was three at Rutland Water on November 1st 2003, although a total of four was recorded at this site during the period October 25th to November 4th that year. Two together have occurred at Priory Water on both October 11th 1992 and November 9th 1997 and Eyebrook Reservoir on October 8th 1994. All of the 15 single birds have been one-day records, with two being purely fly-overs. The longest autumn stay is ten days, by one at Rutland Water from October 26th to November 4th 2003, although a bird may have been in the Kirby Lakes area for 29 days between November 2nd and 30th in 1997 but was only actually recorded on four dates during this period.

With the exception of one at Cossington Meadows on January 1st 2005, all winter records were between 1992 and 1999. Arrival dates range from December 12th to January 31st. Three sites have proved suitable for long-stayers: Trent Valley Pit has had single wintering birds from December 12th 1992 to March 12th 1993 and from January 16th to March 28th 1999; the boggy grassland of the tertiary treatment works at Rutland Water attracted two birds from January 4th to February 15th 1997, two again from December 14th 1997 to February 28th 1998 and three on December 6th 1998, two of which remained until March 6th 1999; Priory Water held one bird from January 31st to March 20th 1999. The other six winter records have all involved single birds for periods ranging from one day (four times) to seven days.

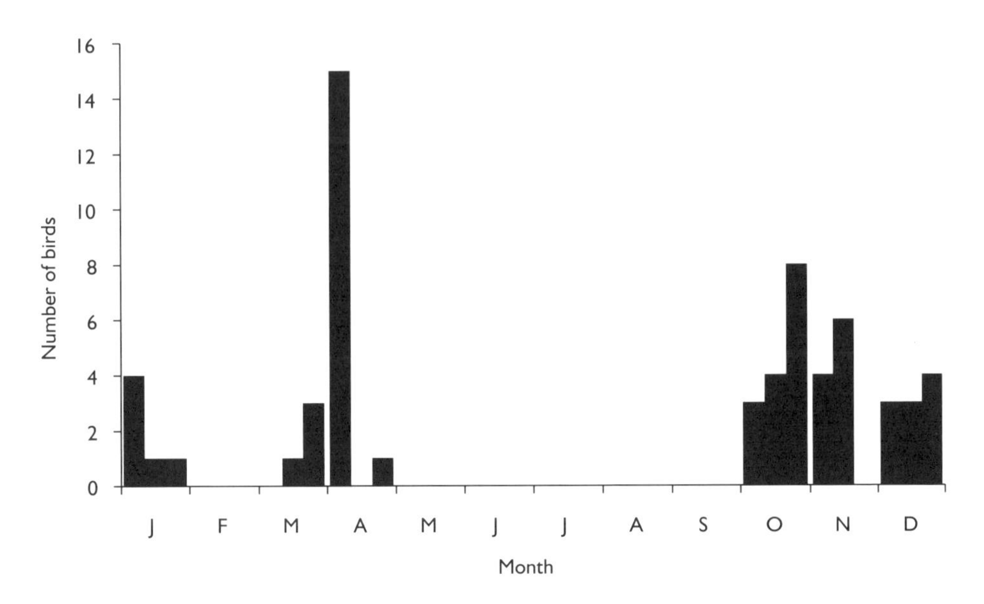

Figure 399: Monthly occurrence of Water Pipits 1941–2005.

In winter and on passage this species normally frequents marshy areas such as flood plains, waterlogged fields and the shallow edges of gravel pits and reservoirs. Five areas have proved to be the most attractive to Water Pipits:

- Wreake valley: 14 records involving 18 birds, split between Priory Water/Kirby Lakes (ten records involving 12 birds), Frisby Gravel Pits (two records of single birds) and Melton Sewage Farm (two records involving four birds).
- Rutland Water: 11 records involving 18 birds.
- Trent Valley Pit: six records involving nine birds.
- Soar valley: six records, all of single birds, with four in the Cossington area, one at Thurmaston Gravel Pits and one at Wanlip South Gravel Pits.
- Eyebrook Reservoir: five records involving six birds.

The only other sites to have recorded this species are Stanford Reservoir, Thornton Reservoir, Leicester Forest East and Sence Valley Forest Park; none of these sites have more than one record to their name. It is quite possible that this species is overlooked, especially in autumn and winter, and it could be considerably commoner than the records suggest. Over 60% of the birds between 1990 and 2005 were found by just four observers who clearly knew what to look for.

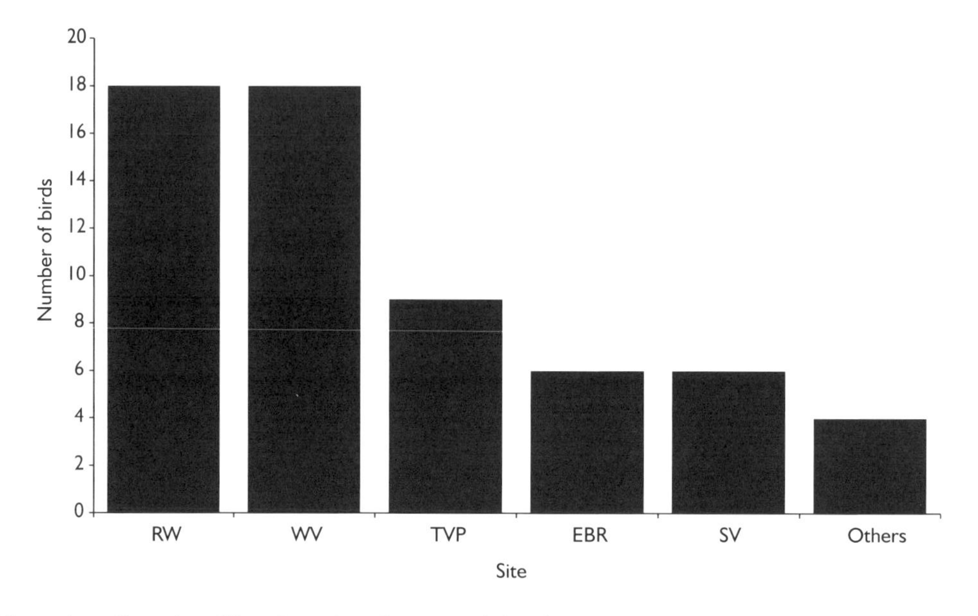

Figure 400: Sites where Water Pipits have been recorded 1941–2005.
Key: RW = Rutland Water; WV = Wreake valley; TVP = Trent Valley Pit; EBR = Eyebrook Reservoir; SV = Soar valley

There are two previously published records which after review in 2004 are now regarded as unacceptable: one (of two recorded) at Eyebrook Reservoir on April 5th 1981 and one at Church Langton on November 9th 1986 (Fray 2005).

Water Pipits breed in the mountains of southern and central Europe and in both western and central Asia. Many of them winter in lowland areas close to the breeding sites, but others move further in directions ranging between north-north-west and east-south-east, to Belgium, France, Portugal and the Mediterranean coasts from Spain to Italy. Small numbers winter in Britain, mainly in freshwater habitats in the south-east of England.

SML

Rock Pipit — *Anthus petrosus*

Rare spring and scarce autumn passage visitor, very rare in winter; recorded in all months between September and April, the majority in March, October and November: 201 individuals.

The first Rock Pipit to be observed in the counties was one at Loughborough Sewage Farm on October 4th 1957. Another 15 were recorded by the end of the 1960s, followed by an upturn in numbers during the 1970s when 37 were found, including six in 1973 and 11 in 1977. The 1980s produced just ten birds in six years, but since 1990 this species has become much more regular and the total now stands at 201 individuals. This total includes 15 of the 18 birds recorded simply as Rock/Water Pipit before the 1986 split of the two species; the other three are possibly more likely to have been Water Pipits.

Ten or more birds a year have occurred seven times since 1994, the best years being 2003 (15 individuals), 1994 (13) and 2002 (12). Most records are of single birds but there were four at Eyebrook Reservoir on October 29th 1961 and Rutland Water on September 26th 1993, October 9th 1999 and October 24th 2003. Counts of three have come from Rutland Water eight times, Eyebrook Reservoir on October 5th and 6th 2004, Cropston Reservoir on October 14th 2003 and October 11th 1990, Stanford Reservoir on October 9th 1977 and from October 8th to 24th 1972, Thurmaston Gravel Pits from October 13th to 22nd 1975 and Saddington Reservoir on October 4th 1973. There are 16 additional records of two birds, all at Rutland Water except for Swithland Reservoir on October 15th 1989, Eyebrook Reservoir on both October 25th 1980 and October 17th 1963 and Stanford Reservoir on October 23rd 1977 and April 2nd 1971.

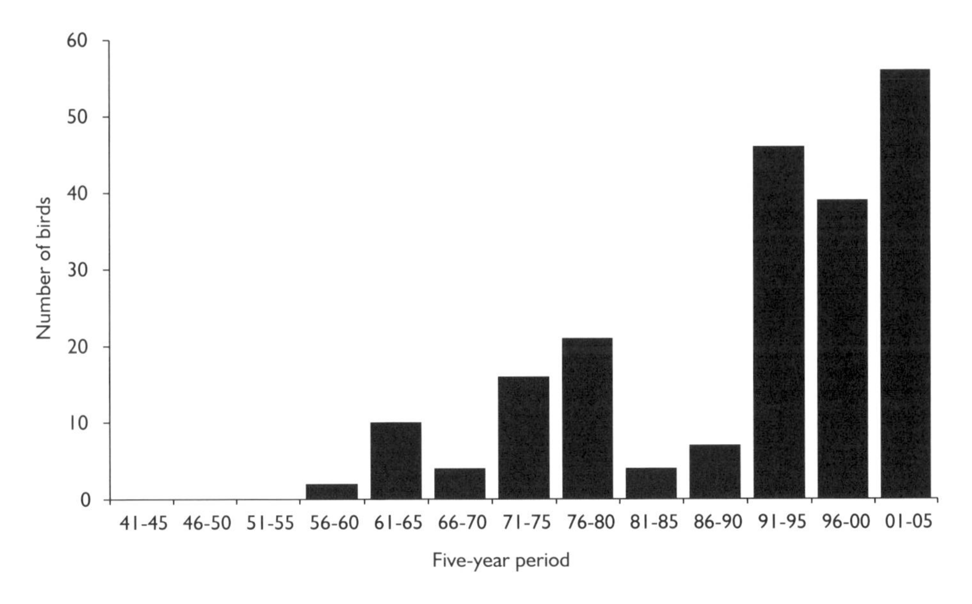

Figure 401: Numbers of Rock Pipits 1941–2005.

The LROS Annual Reports used to describe the Rock Pipit as a scarce winter visitor but really it has always been primarily a passage migrant, commonest in autumn.

Spring passage, when a total of 37 birds has been recorded, is essentially in March (73%) with one record in February (Rutland Water on the 26th in 1994) and eight records of nine birds in April, the latest being at Rutland Water on April 20th 1996.

The vast majority of autumn migrants have occurred in October (73%) and early November. A total of 15 birds have arrived in September, the earliest being two at Rutland Water on September 24th 2000. Reports after mid-November are rare and the latest autumn record is probably one at Eyebrook Reservoir on November 28th 1998. Most (81%) autumn birds have been seen on single dates only but a few have lingered; this is particularly the case for records of more than two birds, such as up to three at Stanford Reservoir from October 8th to 24th 1972 and Thurmaston Gravel Pits from October 13th to 22nd 1975 and up to four at Rutland Water from October 3rd to 30th 1999.

Birds have been seen in winter only very rarely. Records of one at Eyebrook Reservoir on November 30th and December 20th 1969 could have related to a wintering bird and one was at the same site on December 5th 1981. Two birds were regularly seen at the tertiary treatment works at Rutland Water and the nearby Oakham Sewage Farm between December 6th 1997 and February 8th 1998. The habitat used by these two seemed far more typical of Water Pipit, two of which were also present.

The change in status of Rock Pipit in Leicestershire and Rutland is clearly due to increased observer awareness and the creation of Rutland Water; this site has produced 112 individuals (55% of the total). Eyebrook

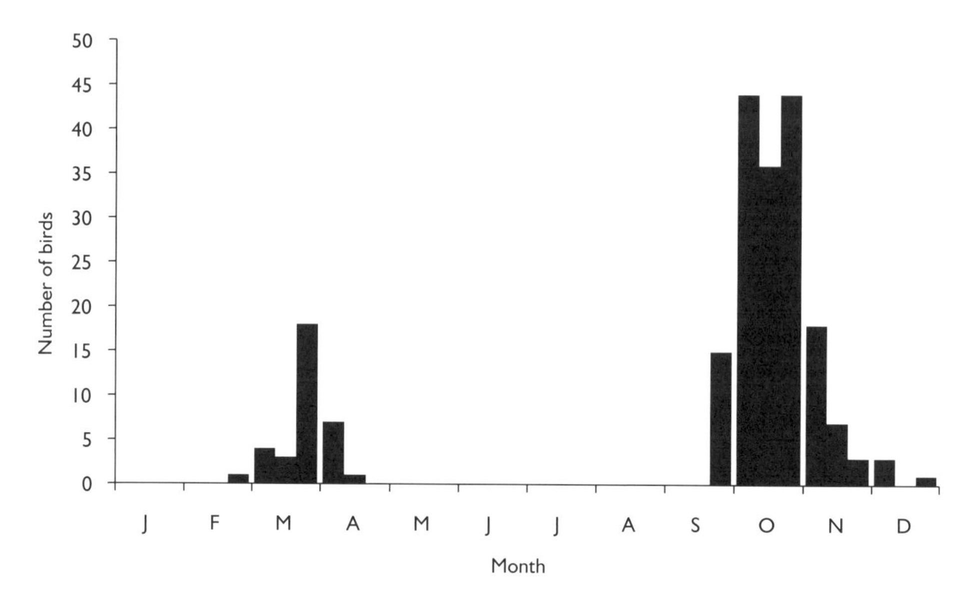

Figure 402: Monthly occurrence of Rock Pipits 1941–2005.

Reservoir has accounted for 36 birds (18%). The only other sites where more than ten birds have been recorded are the three reservoirs at Swithland (14), Stanford (12) and Cropston (11). Rock Pipits are obviously drawn to large areas of water when on passage as all but 10 of the 201 have occurred at reservoirs. The only records away from such sites, which all refer to single birds, are:

- Loughborough Sewage Farm on October 4th 1957.
- Frisby Gravel Pits from April 10th to 12th 1974, on April 6th 1975, March 3rd 1976 and October 27th to November 1st 1976.
- Priory Water on October 2nd 1994.
- Trent Valley Pit on November 1st 1997.
- Packington Sewage Farm on October 6th 1998.
- Knipton on October 13th 2001.
- Grove Park, Enderby on March 26th 2005.

Following review in 2004, a number of previously published records were found to be unacceptable: single birds at Saddington Reservoir on September 3rd and 17th 1971, Eyebrook Reservoir on April 4th 1975 and Sysonby Sewage Farm on December 24th 1975 and January 1st 1976 (Fray 2005).

The nominate race of the Rock Pipit breeds in Britain, Ireland and north-west France. In Britain it is widespread around the entire coastline with the exception of parts of southern and eastern England; the British population is currently estimated at 34,000 pairs (Baker *et al.* 2006). The race *A. p. littoralis* breeds along the coastline and on islands of Denmark, western Norway and the Baltic countries, dispersing south and west for the winter. Since 1991 seven individuals showing the characteristics of *littoralis* have been identified on spring passage, as follows:

- Rutland Water from March 23rd to 27th 1991.
- Eyebrook Reservoir on April 4th 1993.
- Rutland Water on March 20th 1994.
- Rutland Water on March 23rd 1996.
- Rutland Water on April 7th 1996.
- Eyebrook Reservoir on March 27th 1998.
- Cropston Reservoir on March 28th 2004.

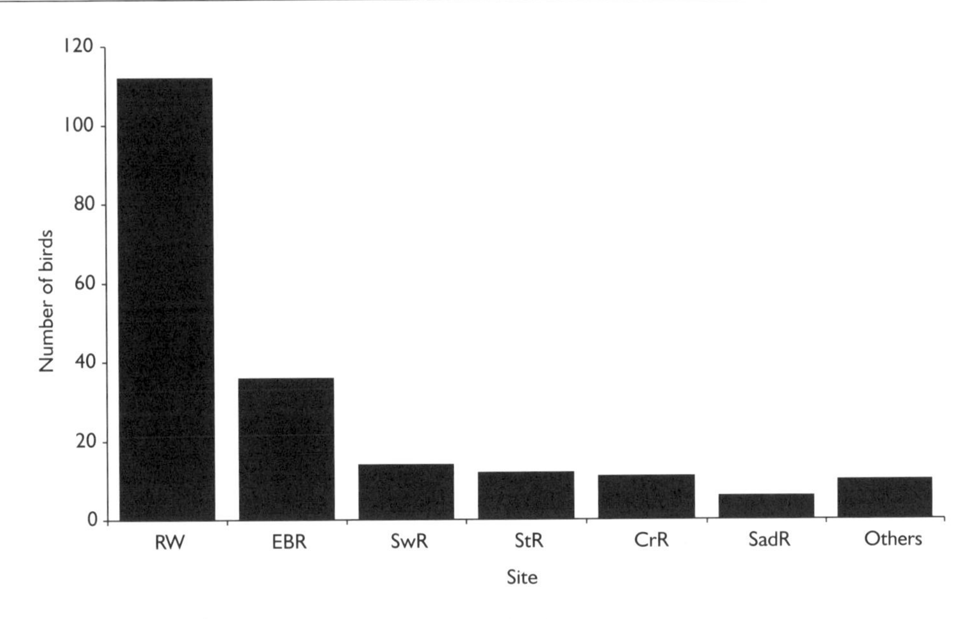

Figure 403: Sites where Rock Pipits have been recorded 1941–2005.
Key: RW = Rutland Water; EBR = Eyebrook Reservoir; SwR = Swithland Reservoir; StR = Stanford Reservoir; CrR = Cropston Reservoir; SadR = Saddington Reservoir

All have been in the period March 20th to April 7th; earlier in the spring and at all other times that Rock Pipits occur in Leicestershire and Rutland it is impractical to attempt racial identification in the field as *littoralis* is effectively indistinguishable from the nominate form except in breeding plumage, and even then many individuals are poorly marked compared to the most conspicuous birds. It is quite likely that most, or even all, records actually involve the race *littoralis*, especially as *littoralis* is migratory and the nominate British-breeding *petrosus* is largely sedentary and coastal at all times of year.

SML

Yellow Wagtail *Motacilla flava*

Uncommon to fairly common migrant breeder and fairly common passage migrant; recent and ongoing decline. Three distinct subspecies have occurred.

The British race, Yellow Wagtail *M. f. flavissima*, is currently an uncommon migrant breeder and fairly common passage migrant. The nominate race, Blue-headed Wagtail *M. f. flava*, is a rare spring visitor and Grey-headed Wagtail *M. f. thunbergi* is a very rare spring vagrant. Five records of Sykes's Wagtail *M. f. beema* have been published previously in LROS Annual Reports but are now considered unacceptable: see 'Unconfirmed and other unacceptable records' (page 685–688).

Yellow Wagtail *M. f. flavissima*

During the 19th century, Browne described the Yellow Wagtail as generally distributed and noted that it was common in the meadows of the River Soar around Leicester. In Rutland, Haines considered this species to be 'fairly well distributed' but not common. During the early part of the 20th century, it was described as breeding 'in all suitable localities' according to the LROS archives.

At the time of the formation of LROS in 1941, the Yellow Wagtail was considered to be a fairly common, but local, summer migrant. The best population indication is provided by Warrilow, who recorded this species in 410 tetrads (64% of all tetrads in the counties) during 1976–84, with breeding confirmed in 153. It bred widely on low-lying meadows, upland pasture and cereal fields all over the counties except in north Rutland and east Leicestershire, where it was very uncommon. Not surprisingly it was absent from the main towns and the city of Leicester. Increases since the late 1950s were found, particularly in the area between Tilton on the Hill, Kibworth and Market Harborough. Using breeding density data from the CBC plots at Stoughton and Newton Harcourt, Warrilow estimated that an average of three or four pairs per occupied tetrad would give a county-wide population of between 1,200 and 1,600 pairs.

Local CBC data show that numbers of Yellow Wagtails were at their highest around the time of Warrilow's work. At Stoughton, there were five pairs in 1979 and four pairs in both 1975 and 1983, totals that have not been attained since. A marked increase was noted at Newton Harcourt from the late 1970s, peaking at 12 pairs in 1983: a combination of lower hedges and more widespread growing of oilseed rape was considered to be the most likely explanation (Scott 1983). From the mid to late 1980s, however, numbers fell dramatically at both sites, especially at Stoughton, where it was only considered to have bred once between 1992 and 1999. This decline mirrors national statistics, the suggested causes of which include farmland drainage, the conversion of pasture to arable land, the loss of insects associated with cattle and the change from spring to winter cereal crops, all resulting in the loss of feeding and breeding habitats (Baillie *et al.* 2006). From this it is clear that Warrilow's population estimate is no longer accurate, although to what extent this species has declined locally is not clear.

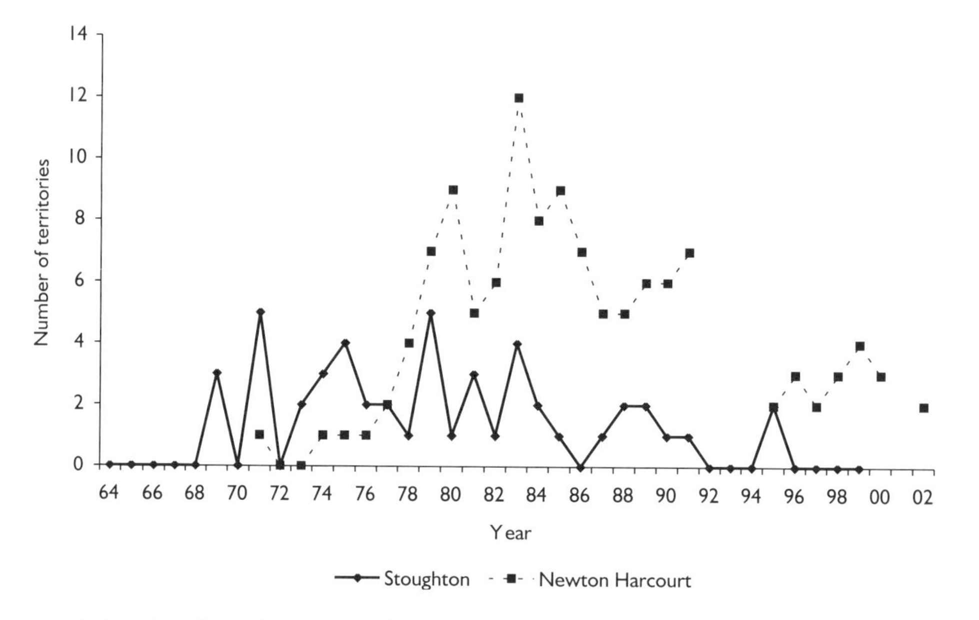

Figure 404: Number of breeding pairs of Yellow Wagtails on two Leicestershire CBC plots 1964–2002.

This decline has also been apparent locally in recent years with regards to migrant flocks. Since 1981 there has been a mixture of good and bad years, with the largest spring flock only reaching or exceeding 100 on six occasions:

- 250 at Rutland Water on April 15th 1985.
- 200 at Eyebrook Reservoir on May 2nd 1989.
- 180 at Rutland Water on April 16th 1984.
- 150 at Wanlip North Gravel Pits on April 28th 1995.
- 100 at Rutland Water on May 5th 1996.
- 100 at Trent Valley Pit on April 27th 1997.

In 1986 there were no large spring flocks and one observer reported that for the first time in 15 years there were no April sightings in the Soar valley between Glen Parva and Narborough. The decline has accelerated in more recent years and since 1998 the largest spring flock was just 42, at Rutland Water on April 22nd 2001. There were only two double-figure spring counts in 2005, the highest being a mere 13, at Trent Valley Pit on April 19th.

As expected, autumn flocks have always tended to be higher. Several LROS Annual Reports contained comments indicating 'large passage' without quoting any actual numbers, but a staggering 1,000 were estimated to be at Eyebrook Reservoir on August 8th 1960. In the drought year of 1976, unusually large roosting flocks were found in vegetation around almost empty reservoirs, including 300 at Saddington Reservoir in early September and a similar number were at Rutland Water in August 1977. Since 1981, the maximum autumn flock size has reached three figures on just eight occasions:

- 150 at Eyebrook Reservoir on July 30th 1992.
- 132 at Eyebrook Reservoir on September 8th 2001.
- 120 at Rutland Water on August 14th 1988.
- 120 at Stanford Reservoir on July 17th 1989.
- 120 at Eyebrook Reservoir on August 27th 1994.
- 100 at Birstall Gravel Pits on September 10th 1982.
- 100 at Eyebrook Reservoir on September 7th 1985.
- 100 at Rutland Water on September 8th and 19th 1999.

Since 2001, the largest autumn flock has been 52 at Rutland Water on September 6th 2005. It would appear that the days when large flocks were to be found feeding amongst cattle at Eyebrook Reservoir are long gone.

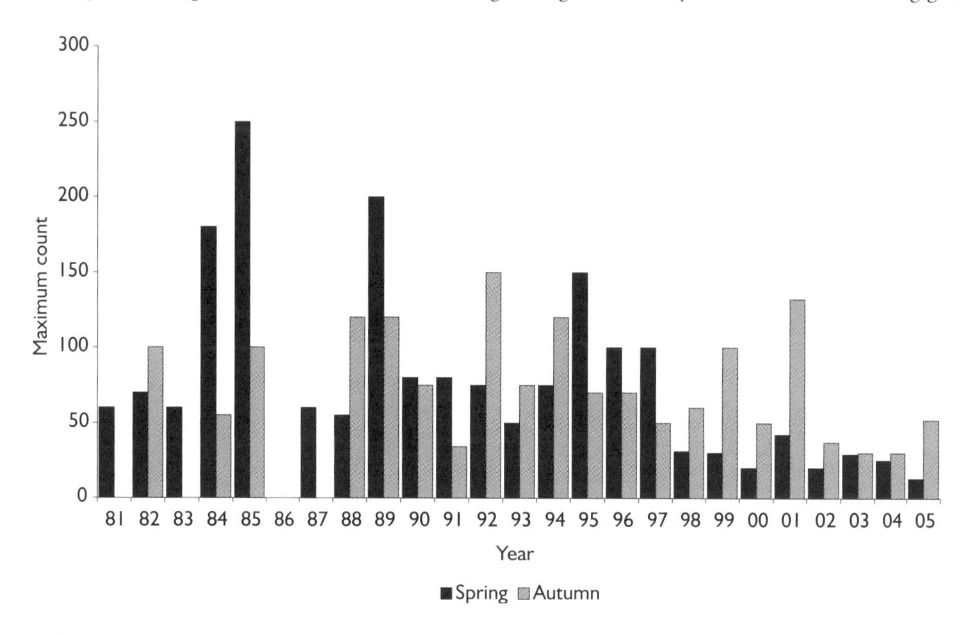

Figure 405: Maximum spring and autumn counts of Yellow Wagtails 1981–2005.

Most birds arrive from early April onwards, but there have been records in March in 22 years. The earliest arrival was one at Rutland Water on March 16th 2002; another 13 birds have arrived prior to March 26th, as follows:

- one at Eyebrook Reservoir and two at Scraptoft on March 18th 1990.
- one at Thornton Reservoir on March 21st 1945.
- one at Stoughton Airfield on March 22nd 1992.
- one at Cotes on March 25th 1945.
- one at Moira on March 25th 1947.
- one at an unspecified site on March 25th 1972.
- single birds at both Trent Valley Pit and Rutland Water on March 25th 2000.
- two at Great Dalby on March 25th 2002.

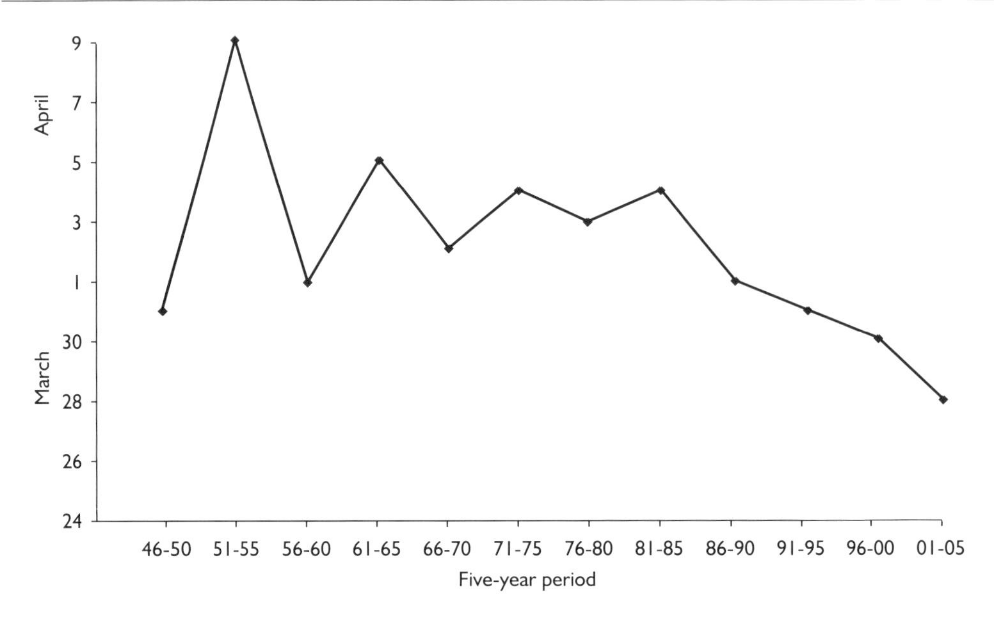

Figure 406: Average spring arrival dates of Yellow Wagtails by five-year periods 1946–2005.

The average arrival date is clearly becoming earlier; there have been March records in 12 years since 1989 compared to just ten in the previous 45 years and since 1997 only 1999 and 2005 have not produced a March record.

The majority of birds have usually departed by late September, the final record usually occurring in the last few days of September or the first week of October. There have been eight records later than October 20th, including six in November, as follows:

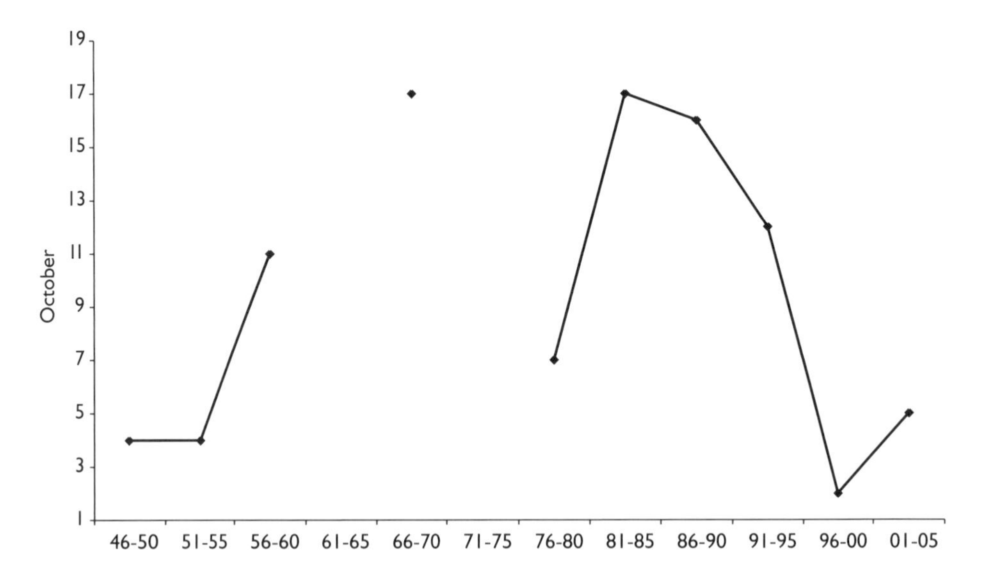

Figure 407: Average autumn departure dates of Yellow Wagtails by five-year periods 1946–2005.

- one at Eyebrook Reservoir on November 25th 1969.
- one at Rutland Water on November 15th 1986.
- one near Narborough on November 4th 1982.
- one at Leicester Forest East on November 3rd 1986.
- one at Oadby on November 2nd 1958.
- one at Rutland Water on November 2nd 1991.
- one at Stanford Reservoir on October 28th 1951.
- one at Saddington Reservoir on October 25th 1995.

It is interesting that the average departure date for Yellow Wagtail has become earlier in more recent years, in contrast to most migrant birds in the counties and is perhaps a reflection on the reduced numbers now present.

Rather surprisingly for a long-distance migrant, there have been no foreign ringing recoveries involving Leicestershire and Rutland. Four birds ringed at Radipole Lake (Dorset) in August 1975 and 1976 were recovered in the counties in subsequent years and a juvenile male ringed at Frisby on the Wreake on August 15th 1976 was controlled at Radipole Lake nine days later.

Yellow Wagtails breed in suitable habitat throughout most of lowland England, but are absent from most of Scotland, west Wales, south-west England and from Ireland. There are also populations on the adjacent North Sea coasts of south-west Norway, the Netherlands and northern France. They winter in Africa away from desert areas. As Britain holds almost the entire population of the race *flavissima*, population changes in the United Kingdom are of special significance. According to CBC and BBS results, the Yellow Wagtail has been in decline since the 1980s (Baillie *et al.* 2006) and this has resulted in it being added to the 'Amber List' of Birds of Conservation Concern (Gregory *et al.* 2002). Further losses since 1999 suggest that addition to the 'Red List' may be appropriate (Baillie *et al.* 2006). The current British population estimate is between 11,500 and 26,500 pairs (Baker *et al.* 2006).

Blue-headed Wagtail — *M.f. flava*

A comprehensive review of all records of Blue-headed Wagtail was undertaken in 2004, as on current knowledge it is considered that females are not safely assignable to one particular race and many may be variants or hybrids. This review resulted in 21 previously published records, involving 30 individuals, being considered unacceptable (Fray 2005).

The following records of the Blue-headed Wagtail remain acceptable although descriptions do not seem to exist (or have been lost) for a number of them.

All records:

1944	male, Croft, June 29th to July 19th.
1946	male, Swithland, May 19th.
1947	male, Loughborough Sewage Farm, April 26th to August 11th.
1948	male, Leicester City Farms, May 4th.
	male, Bradgate Park, August 22nd.
	male, Loughborough Sewage Farm, August 26th.
1952	male, Eyebrook Reservoir, April 12th.
1953	male, Sawley Gravel Pits, April 25th.
1973	Swithland Reservoir, April 21st to 23rd.
1975	Eyebrook Reservoir, May 3rd, 29th and 31st and July 2nd.
1977	Eyebrook Reservoir, April 20th.
1981	Eyebrook Reservoir, April 11th.
1982	Saddington Reservoir, May 24th.
1983	up to three, Rutland Water, April 16th to 24th.
	male, Eyebrook Reservoir, April 19th.
1984	up to three, Rutland Water, April 16th to May 2nd.
	Bradgate Park, April 25th and 26th.

1985	male, Rutland Water, April 13th.
	male, Rutland Water, May 5th.
1986	Rutland Water, April 27th.
1987	Eyebrook Reservoir, April 21st.
	Rutland Water, May 8th.
1988	male, Aylestone Meadows, May 7th.
1989	male, Quorn, April 26th.
	male, Wanlip Gravel Pits, April 30th.
	male, Stanford Reservoir, May 28th.
1991	male, Stanford Reservoir, June 2nd.
1992	male, Trent Valley Pit, May 3rd.
1996	male, Eyebrook Reservoir, April 16th.
	male, Oakthorpe, April 26th to 30th.
	male, Watermead Park, May 11th.
	male, Thornton Reservoir, May 20th.
1997	male, Trent Valley Pit, April 20th and 24th.
	two males, Eyebrook Reservoir, April 22nd.
1998	male, Eyebrook Reservoir, April 11th to 13th.
2000	male, Rearsby, June 4th.
2001	male, Sence Valley Forest Park, April 22nd to 30th.

In addition, according to the LROS archives, one was recorded at Rearsby in August 1896, although further details are lacking.

Since 1941, there have been records of Blue-headed Wagtail in 25 years, involving 42 individuals. The vast majority (78%) have occurred between April 11th and May 11th and there have only been three later than June 4th (one in 1944 and two in 1948).

The male at Croft in 1944 was paired with a bird considered to be a female Blue-headed Wagtail; a nest containing four eggs was found, three of which hatched but the young disappeared the following day (Pochin 1945). Similarly, the long-staying male at Loughborough Sewage Farm in 1947 was paired with an apparent female Blue-headed Wagtail; they were seen occasionally feeding four well-grown young in July.

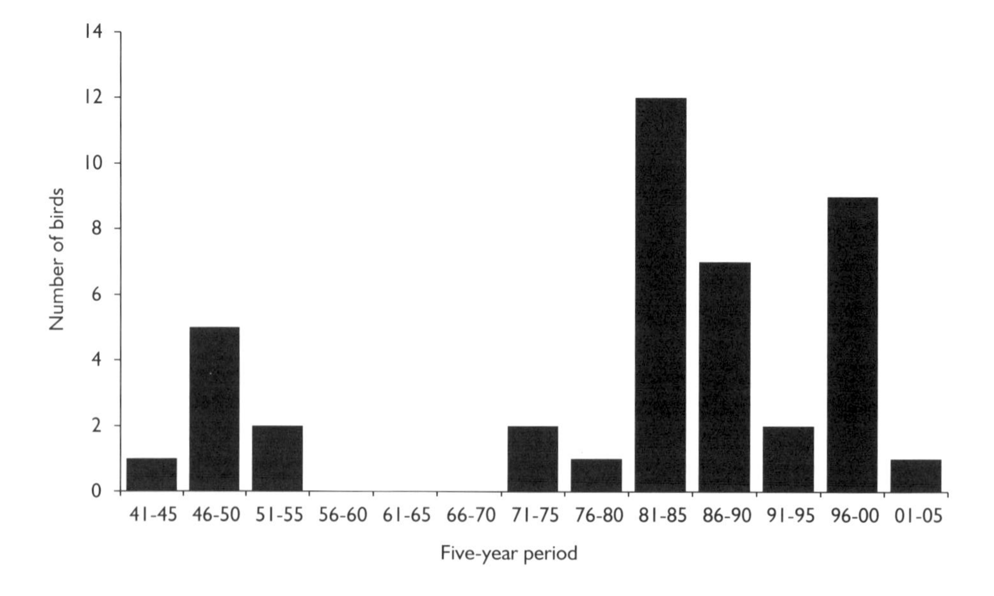

Figure 408: Numbers of Blue-headed Wagtails 1941–2005.

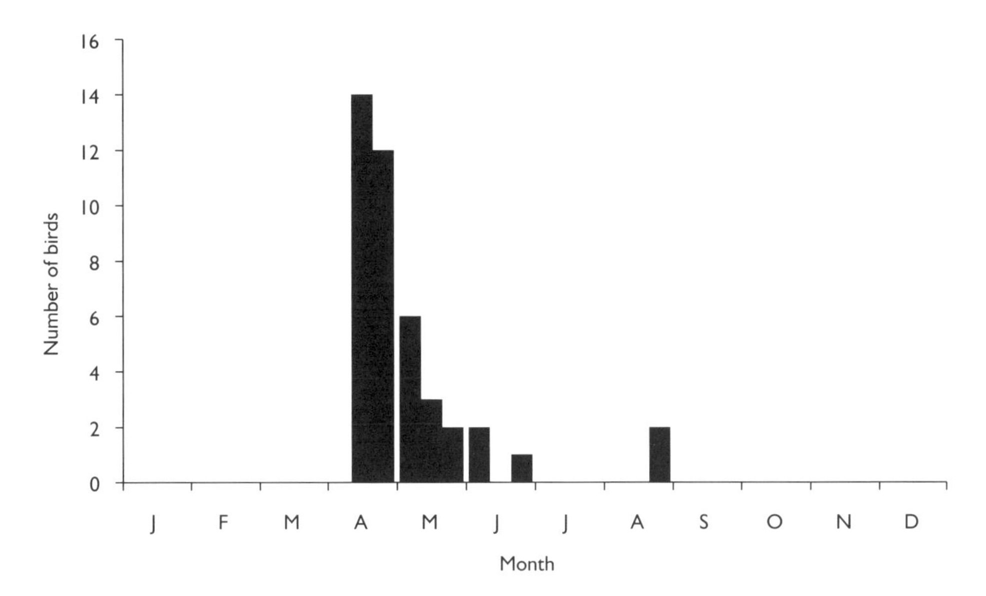

Figure 409: Monthly occurrence of Blue-headed Wagtails 1941–2005.

Blue-headed Wagtails breed over most of continental Europe, north to southern Scandinavia and east to the Urals, and winter in Africa.

Grey-headed Wagtail *M.f. thunbergi*

A male showing the characteristics of this race was on the dam at Rutland Water on May 12th 2001; it was joined by a second male the following day, one of which remained until the 15th. Both birds were seen by many observers and well photographed.

Browne makes reference to a note, written by a Mr Macaulay in the *Midland Naturalist* of 1881, which stated 'I observed the Grey-headed Wagtail near Kibworth on May 2nd 1880'. Browne then goes on to say 'as this species has never yet occurred in Britain, Mr Macaulay concurs with me now in thinking that he must have been mistaken.' In addition, a record of a male at Eyebrook Reservoir on April 12th 1983 is no longer considered acceptable (Fray 2005).

Grey-headed Wagtails breed in Scandinavia, northern Russia and western Siberia and interbreed with Blue-headed Wagtails in overlap zones. They winter in Africa. This subspecies is a rare visitor to Britain, usually on the east coast or the Northern Isles, and inland records such as that at Rutland Water are unusual.

RED

Citrine Wagtail *Motacilla citreola*

Very rare vagrant from eastern Europe or Siberia: one record.

A first-summer male was found along the western shoreline of Eyebrook Reservoir by Ian Merrill during the afternoon of May 18th 1991. It remained until dusk, being seen and photographed by many other observers during this time and appeared to go to roost, but could not be found the following day (*BB* 85:536, Merrill 1992).

The Citrine Wagtail has a large distribution over much of northern and central Asia, extending into north-east and central areas of European Russia; it winters mainly in the Indian subcontinent and south-east Asia. In recent years the species has spread to the west and south-west, leading to breeding attempts in a number of north

European countries including Sweden, Finland and Germany. In Britain it is a scarce but increasing vagrant, averaging around four or five records a year; there had been fewer than 60 British records at the time of the Leicestershire bird but by the end of 2005 the British total was 178. The vast majority occur in Shetland and the Eyebrook Reservoir individual was the first to be found inland; there have only been two subsequent records in the Midlands, in Northamptonshire in November 1996 and Warwickshire in May 1997. Spring reports are very much in the minority and the Leicestershire record was only the fourth such occurrence.

RMF

Grey Wagtail *Motacilla cinerea*

Uncommon resident breeder and winter visitor.

Browne considered the Grey Wagtail to be primarily a winter visitor in small numbers to Leicestershire in the 19th century, being frequently recorded close to the city of Leicester. It was known to have bred near Skeffington in 1893. Haines described it as a winter visitor to Rutland during the same period, usually arriving in September and departing by the end of April. The status of this species remained similar during the first part of the 20th century, although breeding was recorded at Belvoir in 1914 or 1915 and at an unknown site in 1918.

At the time LROS was founded in 1941, the Grey Wagtail was still considered to be a scarce winter visitor. A comment in an early Annual Report indicated that most seen in September and early October were passage birds, whereas those recorded from mid-October onwards tended to remain in the area throughout the winter. A few were recorded on bomb sites at Leicester in 1946 and some were known to roost with Pied Wagtails at the Campbell Street Post Office in the city during the winter months of the late 1950s. A small breeding population presumably existed during the 1940s, as juveniles were reported during the summer months in some years. During the 1950s breeding was proved by at least one pair in almost every year, two pairs bred in Charnwood Forest in 1952 rearing broods of three and five young (Felstead 1953) and at least six pairs bred in 1961. However, between 1963 and 1969 almost all records occurred during the winter months, a juvenile at

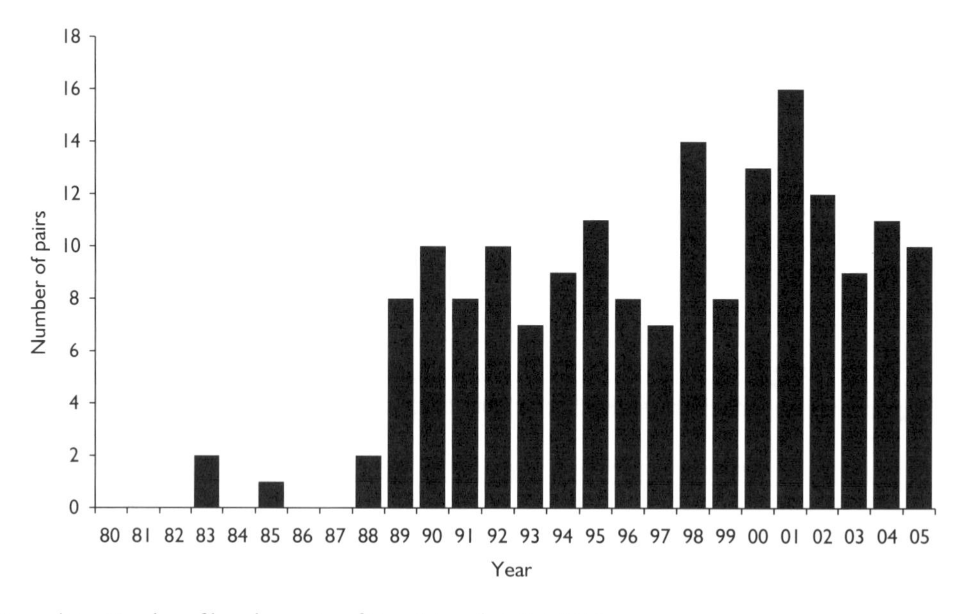

Figure 410: Number of breeding pairs of Grey Wagtails 1980–2005.

Swithland Reservoir on June 30th 1966 being the only possible evidence of breeding. This downturn may have occurred as a result of the severe winter weather in 1963, which may have badly affected the small resident population.

By 1970 it was recognised that there was a resident breeding population, but only one or two pairs were proved to have bred in around ten years during the period up to 1988. During 1976–84 Warrilow recorded the Grey Wagtail in 50 tetrads in the counties (8% of the total number of tetrads), with breeding confirmed in 18. Since 1989 there has been a considerable increase in breeding records. At least seven pairs were confirmed to have bred in each year up to 2005, between ten and 13 pairs bred in five years, 14 pairs bred in 1998 and 16 in 2001. In most years during this period, suspected breeding was also recorded. Many of the early breeding records came from the Charnwood Forest area, where Webster (1997) estimated a population of ten to 15 pairs. Mitcham (1984) considered that suitable habitat for this species in Rutland was somewhat limited, although breeding had been proved at one site during 1968–72. A pair certainly bred at Tinwell in 1990 and again in 1992, when breeding was proved at a further three sites in Rutland: Fort Henry Ponds, Duddington and Oakham. It is probable that there were earlier Rutland breeding records.

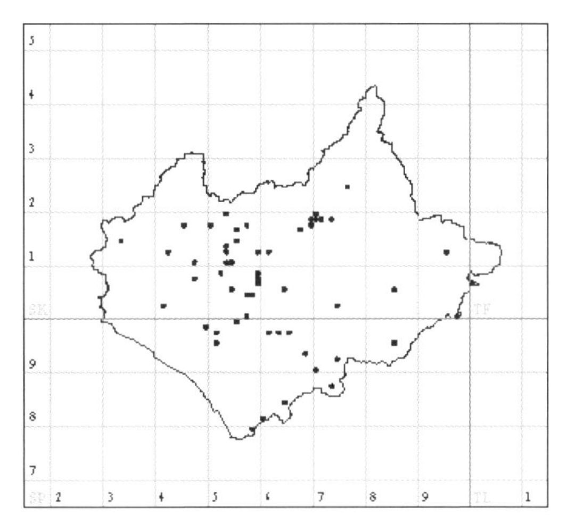

Figure 411: Distribution of Grey Wagtail breeding records 1976–2005.

Around the time of the upsurge in breeding records, the number of sites from which this species was recorded also increased, from as few as 21 in 1983 to over 50 in every year since 1988 and a maximum of 82 in 2001. Part of this increase is probably down to observer reporting and record analysis as opposed to a population explosion, but the increase in quarries and gravel pits has also been a contributory factor. It is now regularly recorded from the city of Leicester (11 records in both 1988 and 1997), where it takes advantage of weirs and canal locks. Another measure of this increase is that Grey Wagtail was the 33rd most-frequently recorded species

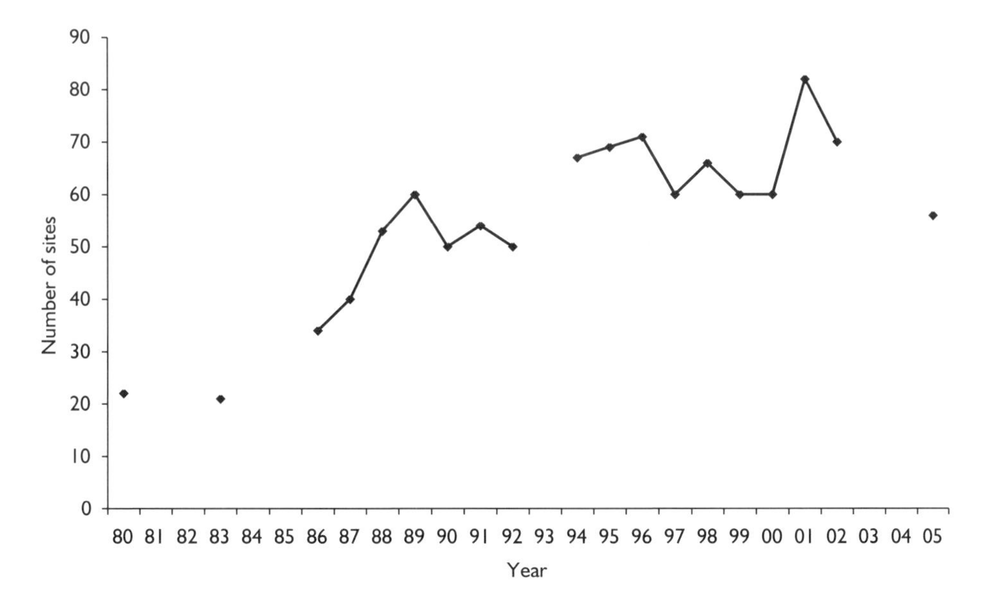

Figure 412: Number of sites with records of Grey Wagtails 1980–2005.

during the Leicestershire Garden Bird Survey between January 1996 and June 2005, being recorded in over 1% of all gardens. It is certainly a more common resident than it was 50 years ago.

Counts of up to five individuals are regular in the winter months at favoured sites, but the highest numbers have usually involved family parties, the maximum being ten, mainly juveniles, at Swithland Reservoir on both August 8th and 19th 2004. Two counts of nine, at Priory Water/Kirby Lakes on November 17th 1996 and Trent Valley Pit on September 29th 2005, probably consisted of passage birds rather than family groups.

An interesting record concerned an adult male and a first-winter male which were involved in a prolonged fight on a petrol station forecourt at Great Central Street, Leicester on March 3rd 2003. At the end of the fight the younger bird was left in a traumatised state and was taken into care, but was successfully released later the same day.

There are just two ringing recoveries: an adult male ringed at Paul do Boquilobo, Ribatejo (Portugal) on December 22nd 1984 was found dead near Swithland Wood on July 1st 1985 and a nestling ringed at Eyebrook Reservoir on July 15th 1999 was found dead at nearby Great Easton on August 5th the same year.

Grey Wagtails breed in most of Europe east to the Caucasus and Iran, as well as in north Africa and in Asia east of the Urals. More northerly populations are migratory. The latest British population estimate is 34,400 to 41,300 pairs (Baker *et al.* 2006) but a moderate population decline has led to this species being added to the 'Amber List' of Birds of Conservation Concern (Gregory *et al.* 2002). The increase in the Leicestershire and Rutland population is therefore a welcome exception to this trend.

RED

Pied/White Wagtail — *Motacilla alba*

The familiar British race, Pied Wagtail *M. a. yarrellii*, is a common resident breeder, passage migrant and winter visitor. The nominate race, White Wagtail *M. a. alba*, is an uncommon passage visitor during the spring and a rare autumn migrant, although the identification of this race was not fully understood in the early days of LROS and even now causes some difficulties, particularly during the autumn.

Pied Wagtail — *M. a. yarrellii*

Common resident breeder, passage migrant and winter visitor.

In the 19th century, Haines described this species as common in the summer but stated that during severe weather only a small remnant remained, with return passage in February. Browne, however, considered it a common resident and noted a roost of 300 in 1906. He also included a record of one with black cheeks and forehead which was recorded on April 10th 1902.

There is no information available on the status of the Pied Wagtail during the first 40 years of the 20th century other than a brief comment in the LROS archives stating that it was 'common'. Throughout the history of LROS, from 1941 onwards, this species has been recognised as a common resident breeder but during the early 1940s, although being well distributed, it was considered as scarce except at sewage farms and reservoirs. A decrease in numbers was apparent after the severe winters of both 1946–47 and 1962–63, but these were the only recorded downturns in the population. From the mid-1960s onwards it has been considered as a common and widespread breeder.

During 1976–84 Warrilow recorded the Pied Wagtail in 388 tetrads in the counties (61% of the total number of tetrads), with breeding confirmed in 158. Somewhat surprisingly it was not the most widespread wagtail in the counties, nor was it as numerous as the Yellow Wagtail. This is almost certainly not the case today, given the decline of the latter species. Warrilow found wide areas of unsuitable habitat to the west of Ashby-de-la-Zouch, in parts of east Leicestershire and to the south of Bruntingthorpe. Although the survey work coincided with two bad winters (1978–79 and 1981–82) he felt that the low population in these areas was more likely to be due to farmland management, such as the trend towards arable farming and to crop monoculture. The national CBC farmland density in 1982 gave a figure of 6.4 pairs per tetrad, which Warrilow considered to be at the upper limit for any tetrad in the counties. He estimated the total breeding population at that time to be within the range of 1,200 to 2,000 pairs. Mitcham (1992) found this species in 49% of Rutland tetrads and considered that gaps in distribution were possibly the result of a shortage of surface water because many farm ponds have been filled in, combined with relatively few buildings suitable as breeding sites in farmland tetrads. In Charnwood, Webster (1997) found confirmed or probable breeding in 35% of 1–km squares (compared with just 5% for the Yellow Wagtail). Local CBC data gives little indication as to whether this species is increasing or decreasing in the counties, as numbers at the farmland sites at Stoughton and Newton Harcourt have always been small and breeding has rarely been suspected or confirmed; however, at King's Hill Lodge, Uppingham, two territories were recorded every year from 1992 to 2005, suggesting a stable population.

The ability of the Pied Wagtail to survive in urban and suburban environments is shown by its 22nd position in the Leicestershire Garden Bird Survey during the period January 1996 to June 2005, with records from 7% of gardens. A survey of four green spaces within the city boundary of Leicester in 1989 located territories in three areas (Abbey Park, Aylestone Meadows and Western Park) (Fray *et al.* 1990).

The highest counts have occurred at roost sites and pre-roost gatherings. In some cases such sites have been used over a number of winters, in others just for a brief period. One of the earliest roost sites located was on the roof of the Campbell Street Post Office building in Leicester. First noticed in December 1949, when 200 were present, it was probably in use throughout the 1950s although it was not specifically reported again until 1958, when 500 were roosting in February. It was still in use in 1960, but by 1962 it was considered to have been abandoned. Probably the most well-known roost site was around the area of the old Lewis's store in Humberstone Gate, Leicester, which peaked at a remarkable 1,500 on February 6th 1986. Table 35 details the highest recorded counts at this site:

Table 35: Peak counts of roosting Pied Wagtails at Humberstone Gate, Leicester, 1974–89

Year	**1974**	**1975**	**1976**	**1978**	**1980**	**1981**	**1983**	**1984**	**1985**	**1986**	**1987**	**1988**	**1989**
First winter period	288 Feb		300 Feb		300 March	450 Jan	220 Jan	550 Feb	400 Jan	1,500 Feb	600 Jan	939 Feb	
Second winter period		750 Nov	150 Nov	80 Dec		200 Nov				488 Dec			960 Nov

In more recent years roosts of up to 300 have been regular but three have exceeded 500, as follows: 700 to 800 at Baxter Gate, Loughborough in January 1991 and 650 in November 1991; 500 in the Vaughan Way/St. Peter's Lane area of Leicester in November 1992 and 500 at the Castle Cement Works, Ketton in February 1995. An exceptional pre-roost gathering of 341 was at Wigston on April 5th 2003.

Passage movements are often noticeable during the spring and autumn and the population is supplemented by continental migrants in winter. There have been regular counts of up to 200 away from roost-sites since 1990, with the largest flocks being 400 at Grove Park, Enderby on October 16th 2005, 300 at Melton Mowbray on both January 26th and February 9th 2001, 220 at Rutland Water on September 14th 2002 and 200 at Earl Shilton on January 19th 2003. Unfortunately there are very few specific counts from earlier years for comparison purposes. Mitcham (1984) recorded 'several hundred' feeding around Rutland Water in August 1975 and comments in earlier LROS Annual Reports such as 'heavy spring passage at Croft' in 1947 and 'striking spring passage through Eyebrook Reservoir' in 1960 give some indication that it has always been common on passage. An interesting comment in the 1949 Annual Report stated that autumn passage numbers over Croft were considerably less than those of the Yellow Wagtail; the reverse is more likely to be the case at a migration watch-point today.

Two interesting records occurred during matches at the old Leicester City football stadium at Filbert Street. In 1972, four fed on the pitch during the whole game apparently undisturbed by the players, the floodlights or the 27,000 crowd. It was reported that 'they used the open spaces between players skilfully'. On December 7th 1996, three were seen flying around the ground, apparently totally disorientated in thick fog for the full duration of the floodlit match, even though night had fallen by the time that the game ended. Other records of interest include a partial albino male at Priory Water on April 9th 1996 which had a broad white collar, heavy white mottling on the crown and appeared to be whiter in the wing, and a female in an Oadby garden during January 1987 which tried to defend two bird tables against all other species in a most aggressive manner.

There have been a number of ringing recoveries, a selection of which follows. As would be expected, most ringing recoveries confirm short-distance movements and relatively short longevity; the Spanish recovery comes from one of the main continental wintering areas of this subspecies:

- a first-year male ringed at Quorn on August 19th 1960 was controlled at Romford (Essex) on November 5th 1960.
- a first-year ringed at Armthorpe, Doncaster (South Yorkshire) on July 27th 1962 was found dead at Earl Shilton on December 4th 1962.
- a first-year female ringed at Frisby on the Wreake on October 19th 1974 was found dead at Annfield Plain (County Durham) on June 23rd 1976.
- an adult ringed in Berkshire on December 1st 1974 was found dead at Leicester around August 12th 1976.
- an adult male ringed at Burley Fish Ponds on April 27th 1978 was found dead at Rosas (Spain) on April 27th 1979.
- an adult male ringed at Lyne (Surrey) on March 17th 1979 was found dead at Syston on June 5th 1980.
- a first-year ringed at Elmesthorpe on August 6th 1979 was controlled at Rotherham (South Yorkshire) on May 30th 1980.

Pied Wagtails are confined to Britain and Ireland and breed sporadically on adjacent continental coasts. They are resident breeders in these areas with the exception of parts of the Pennines, northern Scotland and the northern Scottish Isles, where they are summer migrant breeders. The latest British population estimate is 255,000 to 330,000 pairs (Baker *et al.* 2006).

White Wagtail *M.a. alba*

Uncommon spring and rare autumn passage migrant, very rare in winter.

According to Haines, the first occurrence of this race in Rutland was in 1885, when one was at Exton Park in the spring. There were two or three records in subsequent years, including one in the Welland valley on March 21st 1902. It was not recorded by Browne in Leicestershire during the 19th century.

The status of the White Wagtail is a little confused during the first half of the 20th century, probably as a result of a lack of understanding of its identification features. The LROS archives describe it as a spring migrant prior to 1940 but give no details on its abundance, whilst the first LROS Annual Report, in 1941, considered it to be a passage migrant in spring, although its exact status was unknown. Pochin (1954) stated that it was 'fairly frequently reported as a passage migrant in spring and autumn' within the city boundary of Leicester. Published records do not match these statements: from 1941 to 1950 there were reports of 48 individuals, of which nearly two-thirds were during the autumn and included a 'small flock' at Croft Hill on September 21st 1944, seven at Loughborough Sewage Farm on August 26th 1947 and six at Eyebrook Reservoir from August 5th to 8th 1950. Extreme dates were August 5th (1950 at Eyebrook Reservoir as previously mentioned) and October 15th (three at Cropston Reservoir in 1949). Even today, identification in the autumn is at best problematical and it is probably wise to treat these autumn records with a degree of caution, especially as we now know that this race is rare as an autumn passage migrant.

Published information on this race locally has not always been very informative, but there have certainly been records in every year since 1975. It is usually difficult to determine the numbers involved, but since 1990 a spring total of 20+ has been recorded in at least 12 years, with by far the highest being a minimum of 56 in 2001. The apparent increase since the 1990s is probably due to greater observer interest. Small groups of up to four are regularly recorded, with occasional reports of five or six and higher counts as follows:

- 20 at Beacon Hill on April 24th 1965.
- 12 at Eyebrook Reservoir on April 11th 1993.
- ten at Eyebrook Reservoir on April 10th 1994.
- nine at Rutland Water on April 26th 1997.
- eight at Eyebrook Reservoir on April 19th 1962.

- eight at Rutland Water on April 19th 1992.
- eight at Trent Valley Pit on April 16th 2001.
- seven at Eyebrook Reservoir on May 1st 1989.
- seven at Rutland Water on April 23rd 1995.
- seven at Castle Donington on April 13th 2001.
- seven at Rutland Water on April 19th 2005.

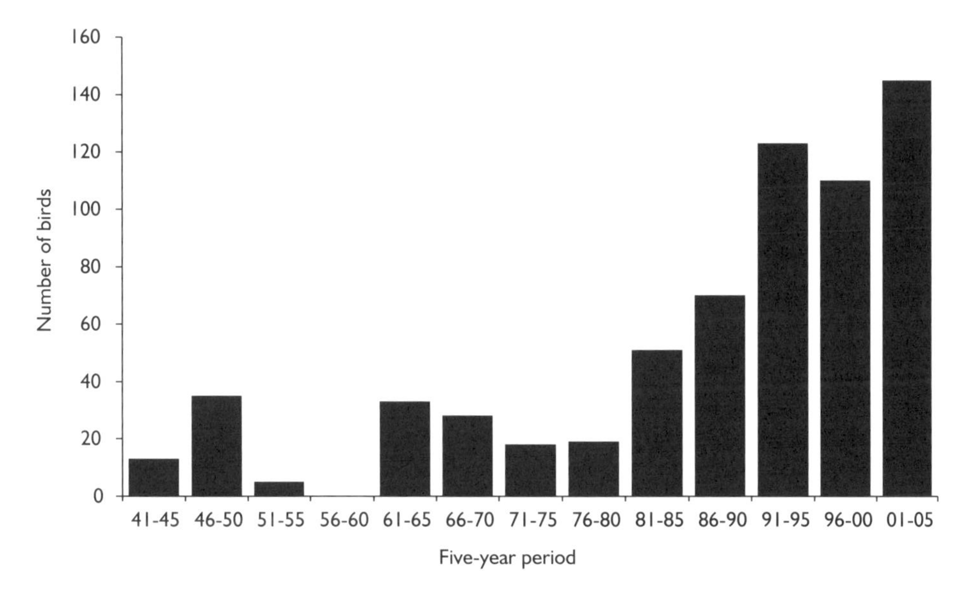

Figure 413: Estimated number of White Wagtails by five-year periods 1941–2005.

Most occur between mid-March and early May but the earliest was one at Thornton Reservoir on February 19th 1983, the only February arrival on record. In 1991 one lingered at an unspecified site until June 1st and in 1986 one was reported at Swithland Reservoir on June 20th.

Since the run of autumn reports mentioned above came to a halt in 1950, the White Wagtail has rarely been noted at this time of year and the only records, all of single birds unless stated, are:

- Eyebrook Reservoir, September 27th 1971.
- Rutland Water, August 13th 1983.
- Kirby Lakes, October 6th 1991.
- Swithland Reservoir, October 4th 1992.
- Whetstone, August 29th 1993.
- two, Trent Valley Pit, August 30th 1993.
- Rutland Water, September 7th 1997.
- Eyebrook Reservoir, August 29th and 30th 1998.
- Eyebrook Reservoir, September 10th 2000.
- four, Rutland Water, August 17th 2004.

There have been two winter reports, both of males: at Watermead Park on December 29th 1994 and at Kirby Lakes on five occasions between January 23rd and March 27th 2005. The latter bird was presumed to be the individual of this race reported at nearby Priory Water on October 17th 2004 but not seen again until 2005.

The White Wagtail is a resident breeder throughout most of western and southern Europe, the Levant and Asia Minor, but is only a winter visitor to parts of the Iberian peninsula and most of the Mediterranean islands. It is a summer migrant breeder in parts of Iceland, the Faroe Islands, Scandinavia and the remainder of Europe eastwards from Switzerland and Denmark. In winter most birds move into western and southern Europe, parts of the Middle East and the tropics and subtropics of Africa. Other races breed throughout most of northern and central Asia.

RED

Waxwing (Bohemian Waxwing) ***Bombycilla garrulus***

Rare to uncommon irruptive winter visitor.

During the 19th century Browne knew of occurrences in eight winters in Leicestershire, as follows:

1827 small parties of up to three or four around the county.
1835–36 'several' seen during the winter.
1850 'fairly plentiful', including single birds shot at Swannington, Stoney Stanton and Belgrave, Leicester, as well as one seen at Claybrooke Magna and three near Bagworth.
1868 one shot at Arnesby.
1878–79 one shot at Belgrave, Leicester.
1883 one shot at Anstey in late December.
1886 two shot during the autumn at Loughborough.
1895 single birds shot at Loughborough on January 12th and Laughton on February 13th.

In addition there were undated occurrences of one shot at Melton Mowbray and two seen at Broughton Astley, whilst a pair was apparently seen at Bradgate during the summer of 1883; in view of the known occurrence patterns of this species in the counties this latter record is probably best ignored.

In Rutland, Haines reported on occurrences in four winters during the 19th century:

1844–45 one within the Rutland border near Stamford.
1883 several at Bisbrooke on March 26th and one at Barnsdale on an unspecified date.
1885 one shot at Lyddington in February.
1898 one at Uppingham from March 2nd to about March 10th, when it was caught and put in a school aviary 'where it moped and soon died'.

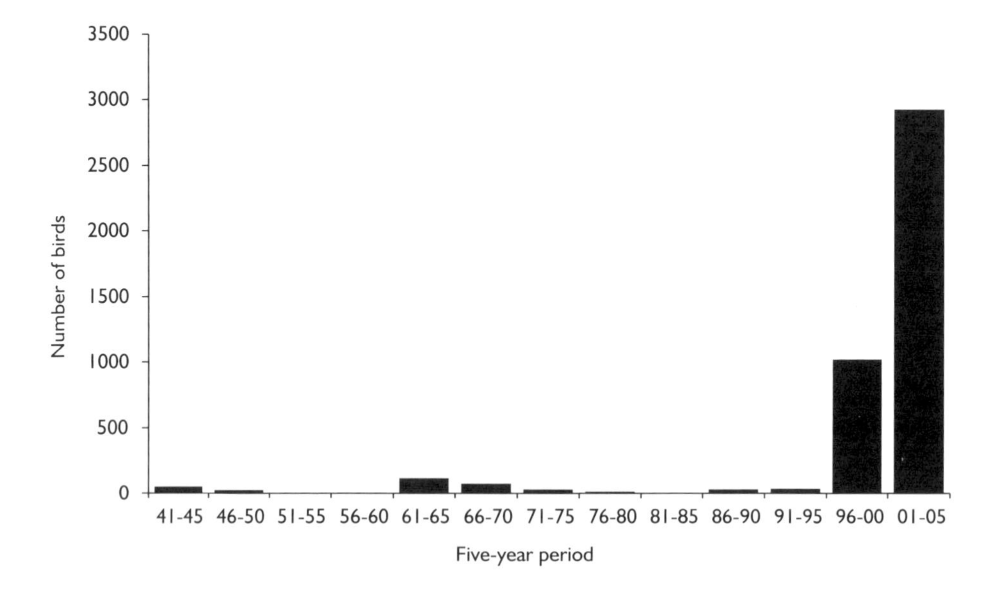

Figure 414: Numbers of Waxwings by five-year periods 1941–2005.

Haines also mentioned that 'several' were seen at Barnsdale in 1904, whilst the LROS archives detail early 20th century occurrences at Swithland in 1914, Queniborough in 1916, one shot at Peckleton on December 4th 1932 and one at Rothley in 1937.

The delightful Waxwing has always been an unpredictable visitor to the counties and was recorded in 38 of the 65 years from 1941 to 2005. On occasion there are long periods with very few reports; for example, there were only eight records (involving 12 birds) between February 1950 and November 1965, none were seen between December 1974 and January 1979 and there were just three records, all of single birds, between February 1979 and January 1987. Periodical irruptions are a feature of this species; modest influxes took place in the winters of 1965–66 and 2000–01 and major arrivals occurred in 1995–96 and 2004–05.

Prior to the 1965–66 influx there had only been three winters in which more than nine birds had been recorded: in 1941 at least ten were at Rothley and 14 were at Swithland on January 9th; in 1944 there were 25 at Preston on February 16th and three birds elsewhere in February and March and in 1947 there were records from six sites involving 14 birds, all of which were within or close to the city boundary of Leicester.

The 1965–66 influx began early, with records from six sites during November 1965 after the first at Oakham on November 14th. Unusually, the largest flocks of the influx occurred in this month: 30 to 40 at Ketton on the 24th and 40 to 50 at Mountsorrel Common at the end of the month. Other double-figure counts were up to 20 at Loughborough from the end of December to January 18th and 20 at Stanford Reservoir on January 2nd. Three birds lingered into April: at Woodhouse Eaves on the 10th, Leicester from the 23rd to the 28th and Countesthorpe on the 30th. In all, records came from 20 sites during the winter and involved at least 165 birds.

The winter of 2000–01 saw a similar-sized influx, with an estimated 153 birds occurring between December 28th 2000, when one was at Anstey, and April 21st, when 20 were at Bede Island, Leicester. Most birds occurred during January (at least 84), with counts in this month including up to ten at Markfield from the 20th to the 30th, up to 11 at Ravenstone from the 2nd to the 6th, 17 at Melton Mowbray on the 13th and 14th and 30 at nearby Melton Country Park on the 27th. Other double-figure counts during the winter were 14 at Loughborough on March 8th, up to 15 at Leicester Forest East on March 26th and 27th, 20 at Hinckley Road, Leicester on April 10th and Bede Island, Leicester on April 20th and ten at Ratby on April 17th and 18th. In total, records came from 17 sites during this influx.

The first of two major irruptions occurred in the winter of 1995–96. Single birds at Stanford Reservoir on December 26th 1995 and Markfield on January 28th 1996 were the only ones recorded before the main arrival took place in February, when there were records from 30 sites. Double-figure flocks were noted in four areas of

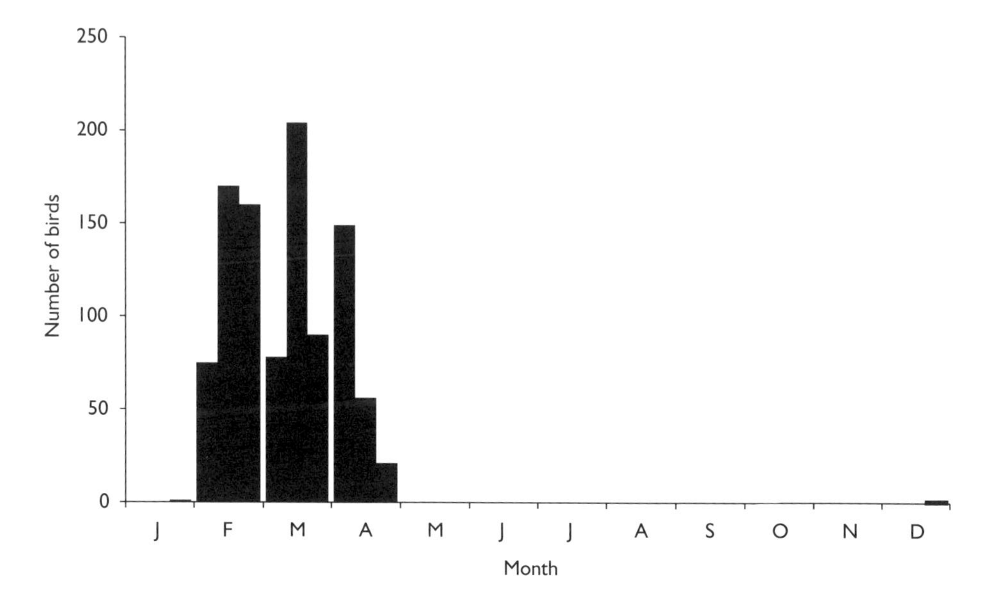

Figure 415: Monthly occurrence of Waxwings during the 1995–96 influx.

Leicester during the month: 90 in the West End area on the 18th increased to 107 the following day, 50 were at New Walk on the 27th and 28th, 29 were at Uppingham Road on the 17th and 13 were at Downing Drive the same day. Elsewhere in February, double-figure counts came from five sites: 50 at Leicester Forest East on the 20th, up to 36 at Shelthorpe from the 10th to the 16th, 12 at both Oakham on the 12th and Bushby on the 18th and 11 at Ryhall on the 3rd. March saw birds continue to arrive and three-figure flocks were recorded in three areas: the flock in the West End area of Leicester numbered 151 on the 9th and 187 on the 18th, 100 were at Rowlatt's Hill, Leicester on the 15th and 100 were at Glenfield on the 31st. Other sizeable counts during March included 60 at Loughborough from the 16th to the 19th, 53 at Braunstone Industrial Estate, Leicester from the 25th to the 29th, 30 at Evington on the 18th, 15 at Norris Hill on the 24th, 13 at Oakham on the 1st, 12 at Asfordby on the 8th and ten at Groby on the 29th. Numbers tailed off into April, although there were up to 107 at Glenfield until the 16th, up to 54 at Groby until the 20th, up to 29 at New Parks, Leicester until the 21st and 12 at Keyham on the 3rd, with smaller numbers at another four sites until the last bird was seen at Markfield on the 22nd. In total, records came from 45 sites during the winter and approximately 1,000 birds were involved in the invasion.

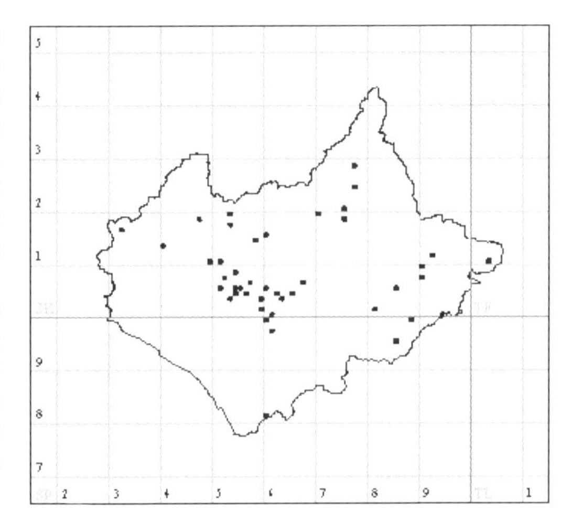

Figure 416: Distribution of Waxwings during the winter of 1995–96.

By far the largest irruption occurred during the 2004–05 winter. The first birds were 13 at Castle Donington on November 4th 2004, the earliest ever autumn arrival, although there were no more until December 17th when three were at Birstall. A total of 19 birds were seen at four sites before the end of December. In contrast to the 1995–96 invasion, when only one bird was seen in January, large numbers began arriving in January 2005 and records came from 14 sites during the month. The West End district of Leicester was a favoured area, as in 1995–96, and a flock of 57 on January 21st had built up to 120 by the month's end. Other sizeable counts

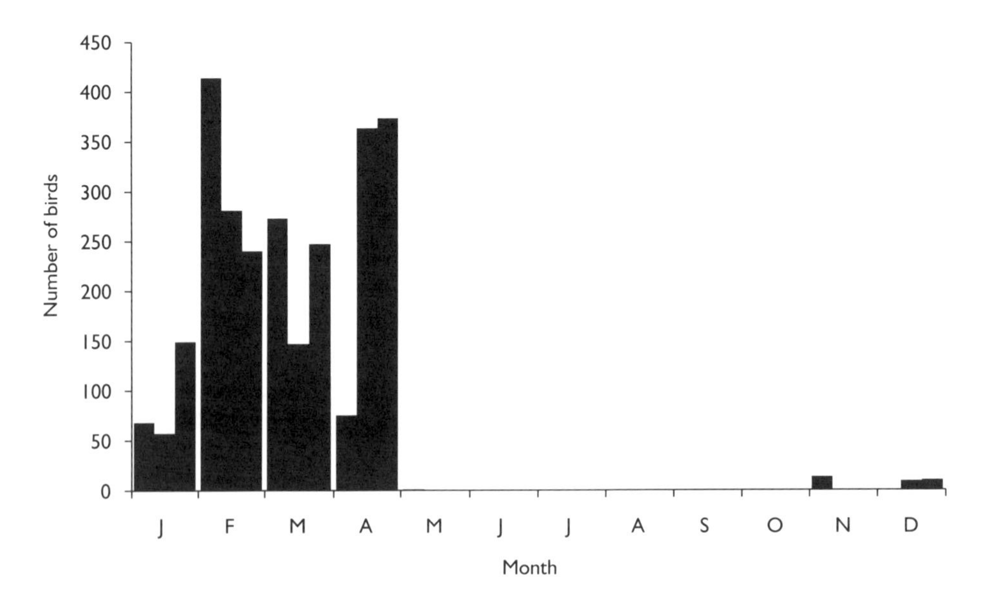

Figure 417: Monthly occurrence of Waxwings during the 2004–05 influx.

included up to 40 at Markfield from the 19th to the 24th, up to 30 at Highfields, Leicester from the 26th onwards and up to 15 at Loughborough from the 8th onwards. Most other groups in January were short-staying flocks and included 25 at Ratby Burroughs on the 1st and 18 at both Swithland Reservoir on the 6th and Birstall on the 12th.

The major arrival of the winter occurred in February and several large flocks frequented various parts of Leicester. The West End flock peaked at 232 on the 5th and then moved to the St. Nicholas Circle/High Street area of the city centre, where the maximum count of 270 on the 9th constituted the largest-ever flock recorded in the counties. Other groups within Leicester at this time included maximum counts of 220 at Eyres Monsell/Saffron Lane, 164 at Braunstone Frith, 154 at Victoria Park, 100 at Beaumont Leys and 40 at West Knighton; with so many birds roaming the city it was difficult to know exactly how many were involved, but the pattern of records suggested that as many as 950 were present in Leicester during the month (Fray 2007b). There were records from 11 sites away from Leicester during February; the majority were to the north of the city, very few were seen in the east of the counties and none were recorded to the west of Leicester. Double-figure flocks were noted at Whetstone (maximum 40 on the 15th), Loughborough (maximum 26 on the 26th), Quorn (20 on the 10th), Wigston (20 on the 13th) and Evington (20 on the 25th).

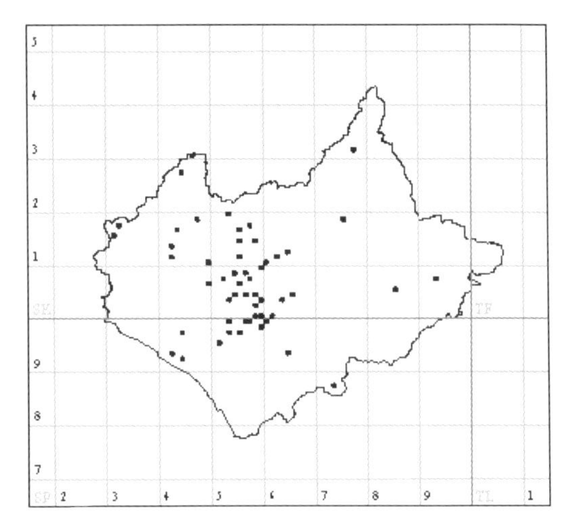

Figure 418: Distribution of Waxwings during the winter of 2004–05.

A noticeable shift northwards and westwards occurred during March, presumably as food stocks in Leicester were exhausted. The largest flock was at Groby, where numbers peaked at 125 on the 12th, whilst other good-sized groups in the north of the counties included 55 at Loughborough, 53 at Birstall, 50 at Coalville and 45 at Castle Donington. Towards the end of March the first flocks were found south of

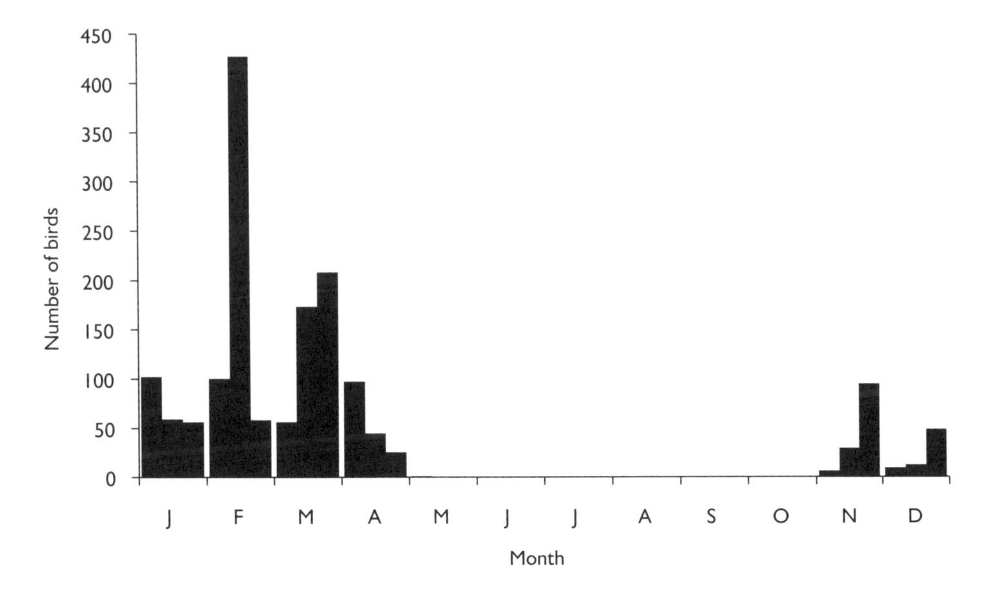

Figure 419: Monthly occurrence of Waxwings 1941 to 2004.*
* excludes the 2004–05 influx

Leicester, including 92 at Narborough and 22 at Fleckney all on the 29th. Numbers dipped dramatically during the first half of April, but from the 15th records came from 17 sites, nine of which were areas that had not previously been visited by this species earlier in the winter. Many birds were moving through the counties quickly, evidenced by flocks of 100 at Cropston on the 15th and Moira on the 20th which were seen on one day only. The south-west had its first records, with double-figure counts coming from Burbage, Hinckley, Croft and Barwell, but by far the largest count of the month was 250 at Trent Valley Pit on the 24th; many of the birds in this latter flock were heard singing. Up to six remained at nearby Castle Donington until May 6th and the final record involved one at Stocking Farm Estate, Leicester on May 9th. The total number of birds involved in this memorable invasion can only be speculated at; a conservative estimate would be 1,800, although a total of 2,700+ would seem more likely.

The earliest winter arrival was the flock of 13 at Castle Donington on November 4th 2004 mentioned above, although records prior to November 10th are rare and have only occurred on four occasions: single birds at Rutland Water on November 5th 1988, Hamilton, Leicester on November 9th 1957 and Old Dalby on November 9th 1974 and two at Heyworth Road, Leicester on November 9th 1961. April records are not unusual, although with the exception of 2005 there have only been three instances where birds have been seen in April later than the 25th: one at Leicester from April 23rd to 28th 1966, two at Quorn on April 26th 1958 and one at Countesthorpe on April 30th 1966. In April 2005 there were 40 at Queniborough until the 26th, 70 at Birstall and four at Melton Mowbray on the 28th, 15 at Hinckley on the 29th and eight at Syston on the 30th. Also in 2005, up to six lingered at Castle Donington until May 6th and one was at Stocking Farm Estate, Leicester on May 9th, but the latest spring record was one at Market Bosworth from May 7th to 13th 1992.

Two colour-ringed birds were located amongst the large flocks in Leicester on January 23rd 2005; both had been ringed in Aberdeenshire, one at Inverurie on November 8th 2004 and one at Bridge of Don on December 1st 2004.

Waxwings have a circumpolar distribution, breeding in high latitudes in Eurasia and North America. They are highly eruptive and move south in search of food when northern berry crops fail.

RMF

Dipper (White-throated Dipper) *Cinclus cinclus*

Rare vagrant from Europe: nine modern records involving ten individuals. Formerly a localised resident breeder. Two distinct subspecies have occurred.

According to Harley, who wrote in 1841, this species occurred on the brooks at Grace Dieu Priory and Copt Oak and was also shot on the stream in Bradgate Park. Later in the 19th century, Browne described the Dipper as 'formerly resident, now very rare' and detailed two occurrences after the days of Harley: a specimen in Leicester Museum which was shot near Syston or Queniborough in approximately 1880 and one shot at Noseley some time before 1882. He also mentioned that the keeper at Thornton Reservoir had apparently procured several specimens before 1885. In Rutland, Haines reported that one was killed in the spring of about 1880 at Empingham and that another was killed at Burley Fishponds shortly after 1889. This species was also reputed to have occurred 'on the Welland' and at Thorpe by Water.

During the 20th century there have been nine records, involving ten individuals, as follows:

1951	Barrow upon Soar, July 15th.
1964	Great Casterton, April 2nd.
1965	River Gwash, Tolethorpe, January and February.
1966	Swithland Wood, January 28th.
1973	two, Rothley, February 1st and 2nd.
1990	River Welland, Tinwell, December 2nd and 15th.
1997	River Wreake, Frisby on the Wreake, February 9th.
	River Gwash, Tolethorpe Mill, February 21st to 23rd.
2005	River Lin, Bradgate Park, July 19th.

The 1990 individual was of the nominate race, known as Black-bellied Dipper and was present in the area from November 20th 1990 into 1991; however, it spent most of its time over the county boundary in Lincolnshire and was only known to have been seen in Rutland on the two dates shown above. The Tolethorpe Mill bird of February 1997 was also of the nominate black-bellied race, whilst the Frisby on the Wreake individual of the same month belonged to the British race *C. c. gularis*, as did the 2005 Bradgate Park bird. Details on the first five records are sparse and it is not known to which race these reports referred; however, given the locations of the 1964 and 1965 individuals at least, it seems likely that these may also have been black-bellied birds.

Dippers are traditionally associated with rocks and waterfalls in mountain streams and breed in most suitable areas of mainland Europe, with isolated populations in north-west Africa and central Asia. Most populations are sedentary or undergo altitudinal movements, although the nominate black-bellied race is partially migratory. In Britain, the population is estimated to be between 7,000 and 21,000 pairs (Gibbons *et al.* 1993), the nearest breeding birds to Leicestershire and Rutland being in the Peak District of Derbyshire.

RMF

Wren (Winter Wren) ***Troglodytes troglodytes***

Abundant resident breeder.

The Wren is one of the most widespread species in Leicestershire and Rutland and arguably the commonest. Previous indications on its status have been provided by Browne, who described it as 'resident and common' in Leicestershire in the 19th century and Haines, who noted that it was 'very common and welcome everywhere' in Rutland during the same period. The first LROS Annual Report, in 1941, also indicated that the Wren was 'resident and common', whilst a little later in the 20th century it was noted as a 'very common and successful resident' in east Leicestershire (Otter 1965).

Wrens breed in all types of habitat in Leicestershire and Rutland wherever there is low cover and Warrilow recorded this species in 607 tetrads in the counties (95% of the total number of tetrads) during 1976–84, with breeding confirmed in 233. In suitable areas, Wrens breed at very high densities: a survey of 39 woodlands in east Leicestershire in 1987 and 1990 produced a mean territory density of 696 pairs per tetrad. Mature gardens also hold substantial populations, as evidenced by a census of the University of Leicester Botanical Gardens at Oadby in 1993 which found a mean territory density of 333 pairs per tetrad. Numbers on farmland are variable, but are generally lower, with local CBC data giving totals of 88 pairs per tetrad at Stoughton and 233 pairs per tetrad at Newton Harcourt. Fray *et al.* (1990) found Wren to be the second-commonest bird at four green sites within the city of Leicester in 1989, demonstrating how this species can thrive even in areas with little available habitat. The only parts of the counties that are avoided are extremely heavily built-up areas, or areas devoid of a field layer, and most of the tetrads where it is absent are in the intensive agricultural landscapes of east Leicestershire and north Rutland. Warrilow proposed a tentative estimate of between 100 and 160 pairs per occupied tetrad, equating to a county-wide population of 60,000 to 97,000 pairs.

Wrens are particularly vulnerable to prolonged spells of cold weather. After the severe winter of 1946–47, 'a serious decrease over practically the whole counties' was noted and numbers remained low throughout 1948 before approaching pre-1947 status the following year. Following the 1962–63 winter, Gamble (1965) wrote: 'few of us ever thought that we should find the ubiquitous little Wren so scarce as it was at the termination of this cold spell, for in many localities the species was practically non-existent', but by the summer of 1964 the species was reportedly 'not obviously less common than normal'. Although the reduction in numbers following these two harsh winters is merely anecdotal, it is noticeable that the lowest number of Wren territories detected on the CBC plot at Stoughton was in the survey's first year in 1964, after which numbers increased gradually and reached a peak in 1975. However, the hard winters of 1978–79 and 1981–82 were both followed by drastic reductions in breeding numbers at Stoughton, as well as at the Newton Harcourt CBC plot. Serious population crashes were also noted in 1991 and 1996 at these two CBC sites and these reductions were mirrored at the two Rutland CBC plots at Prior's Coppice and King's Hill Lodge, Uppingham. However, the run of mild winters in the late 1990s and early part of the 21st century has ensured that the Wren population has well and truly recovered. Large gains, which can probably be attributed to habitat management and the removal of predators as well as the recent mild winters, have recently been recorded at Loddington where, from 47 pairs in 1992, numbers increased to 141 pairs by 2001, an increase of 200%.

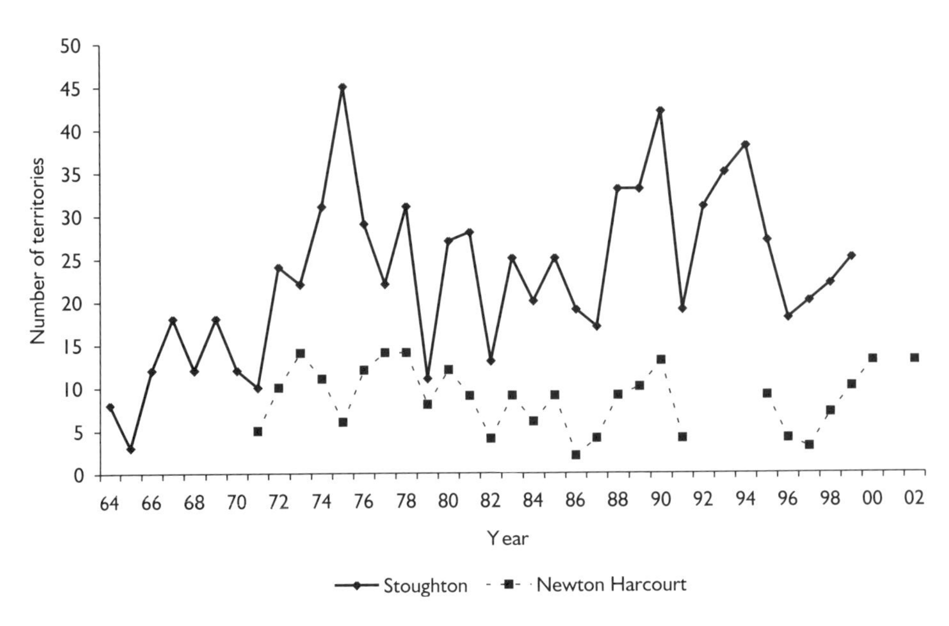

Figure 420: Number of breeding pairs of Wrens on two Leicestershire CBC plots 1964–2002.

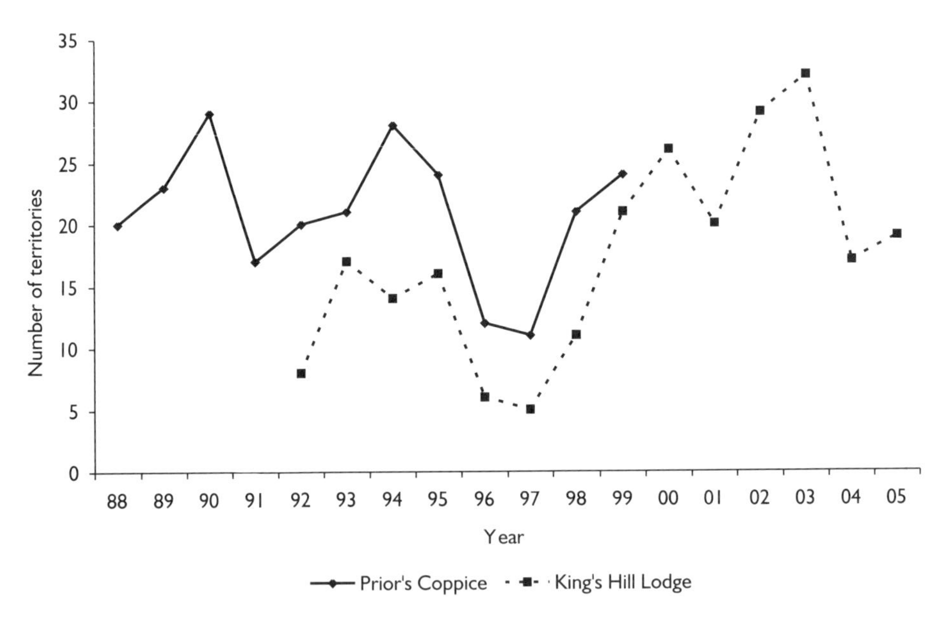

Figure 421: Number of breeding pairs of Wrens on two Rutland CBC plots 1988–2005.

Wrens are renowned for their communal roosting habits during cold weather periods and two such examples involve 27 entering a hole in the eaves of a summer-house at Desford in December 1981 and 15 roosting in a Grey Squirrel drey at Swithland Reservoir on January 4th 1982. Another endearing habit of the Wren is to pick unusual nest sites. Browne mentioned that Leicester Museum was presented with a nest that had been built in an old hat in a garden on Hinckley Road, Leicester in 1884, another was found in a dog muzzle at Long Clawson and a pair built a nest between the wings of a dead Carrion Crow hanging on a gibbet at Leicester City Farms in 1949.

Wrens breed right across the Palearctic from Iceland and Morocco to Japan and also in North America. They are very common and widespread in Britain, with a population estimated at 7,100,000 pairs (Gibbons *et al.* 1993). Most British Wrens are essentially sedentary, although some move south, especially during periods of severely cold weather. Three ringing recoveries involving Leicestershire and Rutland demonstrate this southerly movement: a juvenile ringed at Wanlip North Gravel Pits on July 5th 1985 was found dead 269km to the south at Burrington (Devon) on February 26th 1986, an adult ringed at Ingleby Greenhow (North Yorkshire) on July 24th 1992 was found dead at Leicester (a 200 kilometre southerly movement) on March 20th 1994 and a juvenile ringed at Rutland Water on August 21st 1998 was picked up freshly dead 163km to the south-west at Berkeley (Gloucestershire) on February 1st 2000. Moving in the opposite direction was an adult ringed at Icklesham (East Sussex) on October 7th 1999 which was found dead at Cottesmore on June 23rd 2002, a movement of 220km in a north-north-westerly direction. Conversely, the sedentary nature and surprising longevity of this species was demonstrated by a bird ringed at Quorn on September 17th 1980 which was retrapped at the same site almost five years later on January 17th 1985.

RMF

Dunnock (Hedge Accentor) ***Prunella modularis***

Abundant resident breeder and passage migrant.

The Dunnock is one of the more familiar breeding birds in Leicestershire and Rutland. Browne described it as 'resident and common' in Leicestershire in the 19th century and Haines considered it to be 'one of the commonest of the resident birds and subject to little or no variation in numbers' in Rutland at the same time. There had been little change in this status by the middle of the 20th century: the first LROS Annual Report, in 1941, described the Dunnock as 'resident and common', whilst it was considered 'a common resident in the gardens' within the city boundary of Leicester (Pochin 1954). Later descriptions of this species' status have been similar: Otter (1965) considered it to be 'an abundant resident' in east Leicestershire, whilst Mitcham (1984) described it as 'common in gardens, woodland and on farmland' in Rutland.

During 1976–84, Warrilow recorded this species in 623 tetrads (97% of all tetrads in the counties), with breeding confirmed in 303, making it the fourth most-widespread species in the counties. The unoccupied parts of the counties were mainly the intensively farmed areas of east Leicestershire and north Rutland, where habitat loss (particularly the destruction of hedgerows) has affected this species. Dunnocks are generally rather catholic in their choice of habitat, although they tend to favour mature deciduous and mixed woodlands with a well-formed shrub layer, as well as farmland hedgerows, mature gardens, urban parks, overgrown gravel pits and bushes bordering roads and railways. They are able to survive even in heavily built-up areas of the inner city of Leicester and a survey in 1989 of four green spaces within Leicester (Aylestone Meadows, Abbey Park, Knighton Park and Western Park) revealed it to be the fifth-commonest species overall (Fray *et al.* 1990). They do, however, avoid the dense interior zone of woodlands, preferring edge habitat or sites with open or semi-open canopy, as shown by a survey of 24 hectares of interior zone of east Leicestershire woods in 1987 and 1990 which produced just three breeding pairs. Local studies have shown that average territory densities vary, peaking in mature gardens: a total of 428 pairs per tetrad was recorded in 1993 at the University of Leicester Botanical Gardens at Oadby. The Leicestershire Garden Bird Survey found Dunnock to be the seventh most-frequent species during the period January 1996 to June 2005, visiting nearly 73% of all gardens. Elsewhere locally, densities range from 266 pairs per tetrad in woodland to between 117 and 174 pairs per tetrad on farmland (at the Stoughton and Newton Harcourt CBC plots respectively) and Warrilow estimated a total breeding population for Leicestershire and Rutland of 50,000 to 62,000 pairs.

Between 1973 and 1998, however, the national population of Dunnocks declined by 45% (Chamberlain & Vickery 2002) and therefore Warrilow's breeding estimate may now be a little on the high side. Local CBC data show this decline, especially at Stoughton where, from a peak of 49 pairs in 1975, numbers fell to only 16 pairs in 1979. The species had not recovered by the time CBC work at this site ceased in 1999 and had in fact continued to decline, with no more than 15 pairs recorded in any year from 1995 to 1999. A similar, although less dramatic, slump took place at Newton Harcourt, where 11 pairs were recorded in 1976 but no more than seven from 1991 to 2002. However, two recent CBCs have produced more encouraging results, perhaps indicating that Dunnocks are making a recovery, in some areas of the counties at least. At King's Hill Lodge, Uppingham, numbers showed an increase from nine pairs in 1992 to 23 in 2003, although this dropped to 12 pairs in 2005, whilst at Loddington a phenomenal increase of 213% was recorded between 1992 (46 pairs) and 2001 (144 pairs). The huge increases at the latter site are probably not typical of the counties as a whole and can be attributed to habitat management and the removal of a number of predators in the area.

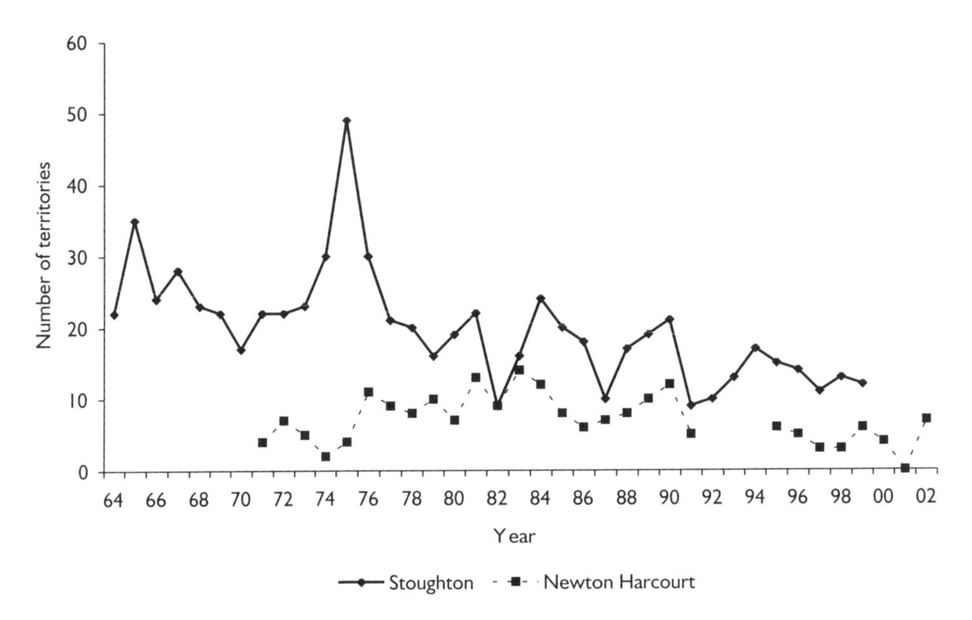

Figure 422: Number of breeding pairs of Dunnocks on two Leicestershire CBC plots 1964–2002.

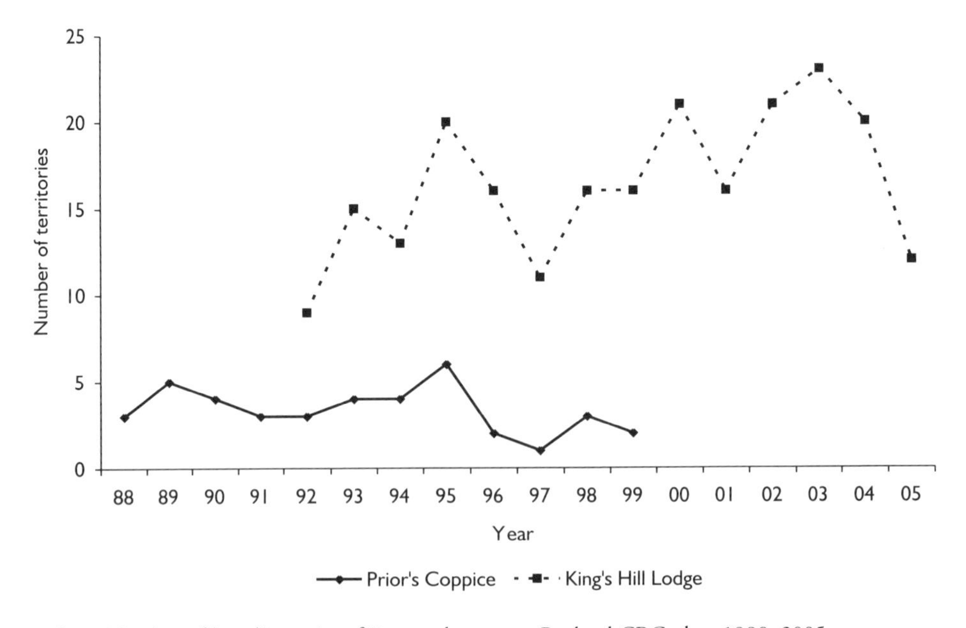

Figure 423: Number of breeding pairs of Dunnocks on two Rutland CBC plots 1988–2005.

Dunnocks can be badly affected by severe weather. After the cold winter of 1946–47, a marked decrease was noted in the Quorn and Willoughby Waterleys areas and numbers were reported as still below normal over most of the counties in 1948. The winter of 1981–82 seemed to hit this species particularly badly and CBC results at Stoughton and Newton Harcourt showed reductions of 59% and 30% respectively. The run of milder winters in the 1990s and early part of the 21st century may have helped to reverse these declines.

Dunnocks are not renowned for their agility, but birds have been seen attempting to feed from hanging nut feeders at Oadby on March 29th 1988, Leicester on December 27th 1996 and Whetstone on April 8th 2000.

Partially albino birds have been recorded on two occasions: Browne noted that one was shot at Thurmaston on September 27th 1889, whilst another was at Queniborough in 2004. Browne also recorded a creamy-white leucistic individual in the summer of 1886. A further leucistic bird, being silvery-grey in colour, was at Rabbit's Bridge, near Swithland Reservoir, on October 18th 1992 and a melanistic bird was at the Meridian Business Park, Braunstone on February 28th 1998.

The Dunnock breeds throughout northern and central Europe east to the Urals. It is a common and widespread species across most of Britain, with a population estimated at 2,060,000 pairs (Baker *et al.* 1997). However, CBC data has revealed a steady decline since the mid-1970s and because of this, the Dunnock has been added to the 'Amber List' of Birds of Conservation Concern (Gregory *et al.* 2002). The British population is generally sedentary, evidenced by the fact that of all the ringing recoveries of this species involving Leicestershire and Rutland, only three had moved more than 10km. The most notable of these was one ringed at Great Linford (Buckinghamshire) on September 21st 1975 which was retrapped at Frisby Gravel Pits on July 15th 1978, a movement of 75km. However, Scandinavian populations do move south in the autumn, so it is likely that some migrant Dunnocks appear in the counties. Records to support this assumption are few and far between, but include one over Loughborough in October 1990, two over Burrough Hill during the same month and two over Beacon Hill on October 6th 2001; all of these birds were flying high overhead. In addition, 40 were counted in a 200 acre area of the Soar valley around Narborough on October 3rd 1981, perhaps indicating an arrival of migrant birds.

RMF

Robin (European Robin) — ***Erithacus rubecula***

Abundant resident breeder, passage visitor and winter visitor.

The Robin is one of the commonest and most widespread birds in Leicestershire and Rutland and probably always has been. Browne described it as 'resident and common' in the 19th century and the description of its status in the first LROS Annual Report, of 1941, was identical. Other descriptions of this species' status in recent times have included 'a common resident' within the city boundary of Leicester (Pochin 1954), 'resident and abundant' in east Leicestershire (Otter 1965) and 'abundant resident breeder' in Rutland (Mitcham 1984).

Despite being one of our most familiar birds, the Robin is also one of the most poorly studied and recorded. During the period 1976 to 1984, Warrilow recorded this species in 603 tetrads (94% of the total number of tetrads in the counties), with breeding confirmed in 362. It was absent from some parts of east Leicestershire and north Rutland, an area where the destruction of hedgerows and intensive nature of the farmland has depleted available habitat. Warrilow found that Robins show a preference for mature broad-leaved or mixed woodland, gardens, parkland, hedgerows and shrubby margins along roads and railways. Unlike most other species, it sometimes reaches its highest densities in interior woodland zones. A study of 39 mixed deciduous woodlands in east Leicestershire in 1987 and 1990 found a total of 69 territories, making it the third most-numerous species in the area after Chaffinch and Wren. This study produced an average territory density of 556 pairs per tetrad, well above the average of 310 for British woodland. Densities can be even higher in mature gardens, as evidenced by the total of 619 pairs per tetrad in the University of Leicester Botanical Gardens at Oadby in 1993 and the Leicestershire Garden Bird Survey found Robin was the sixth most-frequent species during the period January 1996 to June 2005, visiting nearly 77% of all gardens. Farmland densities, however, are lower, with the CBC plots at Stoughton and Newton Harcourt giving 85 and 196 pairs per occupied tetrad respectively. Given this wide range of densities depending on habitat, producing an accurate population estimate for the counties is difficult, but Warrilow proposed a total of between 75,000 and 99,000 pairs, based on an average of between 125 and 165 pairs per occupied tetrad.

Although Robins are virtually absent from the inner city of Leicester, they will readily utilise available pieces of habitat in heavily built-up areas. In 1989, a study of four green spaces within Leicester (Aylestone Meadows, Abbey Park, Knighton Park and Western Park) found the Robin to be the fourth-commonest species after Blackbird, Wren and Blue Tit (Fray *et al.* 1990).

Local CBC data shows that the population of this species is stable and may be increasing slightly. At Stoughton, numbers remained fairly consistent at beween 15 and 20 pairs from 1964 to 1999, with unexplained peaks of 29 in 1975 and 31 in 1990, whilst at Newton Harcourt between four and eight pairs have been recorded in most years from 1971 to 2002. The two CBC plots in Rutland show some interesting results, as the rises and falls have mirrored each other despite one being a farmland site (King's Hill Lodge, Uppingham) and the other being woodland (Prior's Coppice). Both showed noticeable reductions in 1996 and 1997 of over 30%, followed by rapid and sustained increases to record levels. A major success has been recorded at Loddington, where 61 pairs in 1998 had increased by 80%, to 110 pairs, in 2001; this increase is no doubt linked to the habitat management carried out at this site and may not be typical of the counties as a whole.

Robins are opportunistic feeders and often show little fear of man and it is probably this attitude that means they do not appear to be as badly affected by severe winters as some other species. In the 1946–47 winter, numbers were 'well maintained', although territorial instincts were not evident during lengthy periods of frost. Numbers were reduced in some areas after the 1962–63 winter, but soon recovered and in 1978–79 Robins at Stanford Reservoir were 'hit by the hard winter but suffered to a lesser extent than Wren and Dunnock.' CBC totals at Stoughton and Newton Harcourt after the 1978–79 winter did not show any declines.

The first record of a Robin feeding from a hanging nut basket came from a Wigston garden on December 28th 1980, since when this habit has been reported with increasing frequency. Other novel feeding methods have included one taking insects by skimming the surface of the River Soar at Narborough during hard weather on January 20th 1985, and one taking sticklebacks from a pond at Scraptoft in 1990.

Leucistic or partially albino individuals have been noted on five occasions. Browne mentions an albinistic bird shot at Thurmaston some time around 1886, whilst Haines recorded a leucistic bird at Bisbrooke on September 28th 1882 and a partial albino at Ketton around 1886. More recently, another partial albino was at Thurnby on October 6th 1946 and a leucistic individual was at Leire on December 2nd 1984.

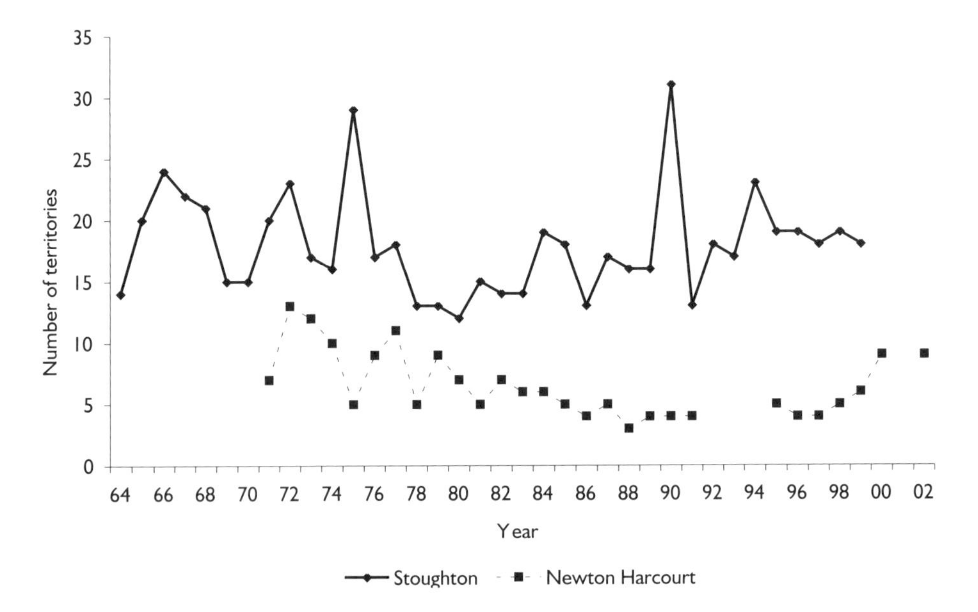

Figure 424: Number of breeding pairs of Robins on two Leicestershire CBC plots 1964–2002.

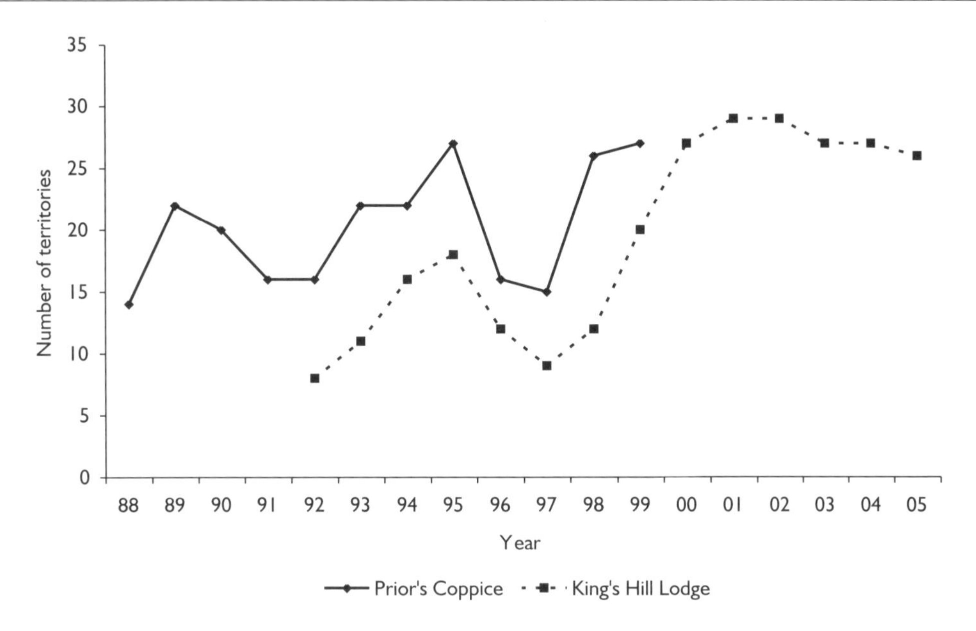

Figure 425: Number of breeding pairs of Robins on two Rutland CBC plots 1988–2005.

Robins breed over most of Europe, as well as in western Siberia, south-west Asia and north-west Africa. Most populations are largely sedentary, although those in eastern and northern Europe migrate south of the breeding range. Whilst firm evidence that continental birds appear in the counties is difficult to obtain, there have been several large autumn counts which suggest immigration, including 19 which were 'very obvious in hedges and plantations' on the Egleton Reserve at Rutland Water on November 7th 1992 and 32 at the same site on September 30th 2003. The highest count, however, was of 80 around Swithland Reservoir on November 4th 1998, which coincided with one of the largest-ever arrivals of this species on the east coast of Britain.

There have been two ringing recoveries which presumably involve continental immigrants, both of which were ringed on the English east coast during peak migration periods: one trapped at Spurn Point (East Yorkshire) on October 1st 1979 was found freshly dead at Syston 25 days later on October 26th and one ringed at Filey Brigg (North Yorkshire) on October 12th 1988 was found dead at Wymeswold on December 23rd the following year.

Most British Robins are sedentary but some move south-west in winter and there have been several recoveries of birds which were ringed whilst clearly breeding in Leicestershire and Rutland that have then moved south or south-west. The most extreme examples of this are of a juvenile ringed at Great Glen on July 14th 1972 which was retrapped in Dorset on September 11th the same year; an adult ringed at Owston Wood on July 24th 1972 which was found dead in south Wales at Milford Haven on August 28th 1972, and a pullus ringed at Woodhouse Eaves on May 22nd 1996 which was found freshly dead on St. Agnes (Isles of Scilly) on October 15th 1996. Other evidence of British Robins moving through the counties was noticed as early as the 1940s, when Pochin (1953) described a positive southward movement at Croft Hill which occurred during September, this being a month or so earlier than the majority of continental Robins arrive on the east coast. In the 1970s, intensive observations at Frisby Gravel Pits produced counts of 15 on both September 13th 1975 and September 12th 1976 which were considered to relate to migrant birds (Snape 1978).

RMF

Nightingale (Common Nightingale) *Luscinia megarhynchos*

Formerly a fairly common migrant breeder, now an uncommon migrant breeder.

During the 19th century the Nightingale was described by Browne as a sparingly distributed breeding summer migrant in Leicestershire; little detail was provided on localities used, although it nested within the city boundary of Leicester at Evington and Stoneygate in the 1850s and Braunstone in 1887 and a singing male was at Freemen's Common in 1887. In Rutland Haines considered it to be rare around 1840 and not common around 1870, but by the end of the century it was a common breeder and 50 pairs could be found within a five mile radius of Uppingham.

There is little information available on the status of the Nightingale during the first part of the 20th century. In spring 1905 at least 25 singing males were located near Market Harborough, whilst it was known to have bred at Humberstone, Leicester in 1915 and 1928 (Pochin 1954). The LROS archives describe this species as a summer visitor in irregular numbers, being common in some years and scarce in others. It was rarely heard in the Charnwood Forest area, although there were records from Greenhill in 1934, Cropston in 1938 and Markfield in 1939.

The first LROS Annual Report in 1941 described the status of the Nightingale as local but not abundant and commented that numbers fluctuated annually. This description was expanded in 1948, when it was considered to be fairly common in east Leicestershire and Rutland, sparingly distributed in Charnwood Forest and local in west Leicestershire. It certainly appeared to be at its peak in the 1940s in terms of numbers, the major concentration being in the east Leicestershire woodlands; several pairs were noted annually in such areas as Billesdon, Owston Wood, Tilton Wood, Tugby Wood, Loddington Reddish, Launde and John O' Gaunt and there were regular records further west towards Leicester from sites like Barkby Holt, Thurnby and Scraptoft.

This species was also widely distributed in Rutland at the time, with strongholds at Greetham Wood (where it was described as 'fairly common in 1943), Luffenham Heath, Coppice Leys and Wardley Wood. There were also numerous records from Charnwood Forest during the decade, with records in three or more years from Newtown Linford, Buddon Wood, Blakeshay Wood and Quorn. Elsewhere, there was a small cluster of records in the south-west of Leicestershire, where Ambion Wood, Higham Grange and Lindley were favoured sites, whilst in the north-east of Leicestershire there were regular records from the Grimston area and eight singing males were located at Belvoir in 1949. Within the city boundary of Leicester itself, singing males were recorded at Anstey Gorse, Braunstone and Leicester City Farms.

There is little information available regarding the distribution and numbers of this species in the 1950s and 1960s. The LROS Annual Report for 1950 reported an increase in Rutland and in 1951 stated that 'the increase noted last year has been maintained'. However, Warrilow thought that a steady decline began from about 1950. In 1960 it was noted that the Nightingale was rarely found away from east Leicestershire, Rutland and Charnwood Forest. Records from outside of what was considered to be the usual range included a pair which bred at Cloud Wood in 1961, a singing male at Hinckley the same year and singing males in 1969 at Oadby, Stanford Reservoir and Swannington. It appears that the Charnwood population had virtually disappeared by the end of the 1960s, the only records from this area after 1965 being of single singing males at Loughborough in 1966, Buddon Wood in 1967 and Ulverscoft in 1969.

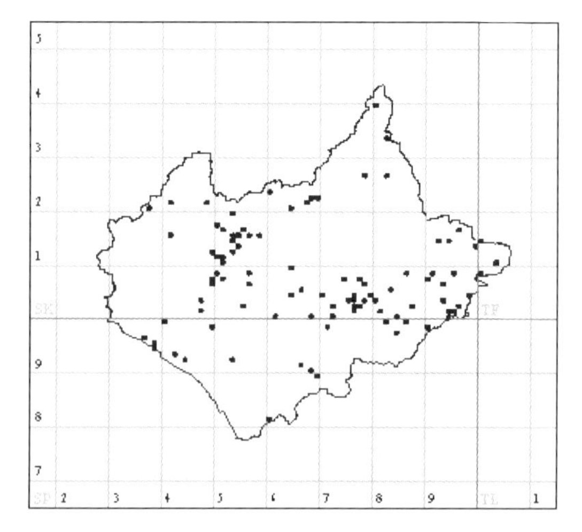

Figure 426: Distribution of Nightingales 1941–69.

By the early 1970s Nightingales were restricted almost exclusively to Rutland and east Leicestershire.

During 1976–84 Warrilow carried out his tetrad survey of the counties and believed that this species was lost as a regular breeder from the east Leicestershire woodlands during the early years of his work. LROS Annual Reports seem to confirm this, with the last record from this area being a singing male at Launde in 1978. A reasonable population still existed in Rutland in the mid-1980s, the largest numbers of singing males being six at Barnsdale Wood in 1985, four at Luffenham Heath in 1983 and three at Newell Wood the same year. Warrilow considered the breeding population to be just 15 to 25 pairs during most years of his survey. Other sites where singing males were recorded during 1970–85 were Ashby Pastures in 1971 and 1972, Countesthorpe in 1972, Ingarsby in 1976, Plungar Wood and Birstall in 1977, Stathern Wood in 1978 and 1983, Stanford Reservoir in 1980, Gopsall Park in 1982 and Melton Airfield in 1983. In addition, a pair bred at Wistow in 1972, a dead bird was found at Jewry Wall Museum, Leicester on July 20th 1977 and a passage individual was recorded at Rowley Fields, Leicester on May 1st 1988.

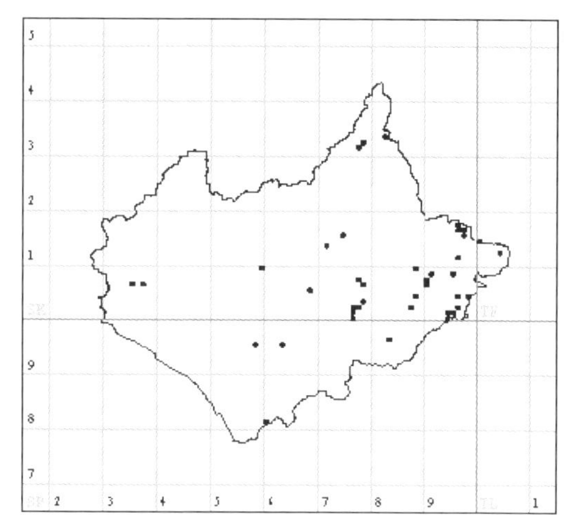

Figure 427: Distribution of Nightingales 1970–85.

Since 1985 the Nightingale has been confined almost entirely to Rutland. There have been records from 27 sites in Rutland during the period, the most regular sites being as follows:

- Barnsdale Wood: singing males recorded in 15 years between 1986 and 2004, the highest counts being four in 1989 and three in 1986, 1987 and 1990.
- Hambleton Wood: recorded in 15 years between 1987 and 2005, the highest count of singing males being five in 1992. There were still three singing males in 2005.
- Luffenham Heath: singing males recorded in 12 years, although no reports from this site since 1999. The highest counts were five in 1990 and 1997, four in 1987 and three in 1986, 1995 and 1999.
- Pickworth Great Wood: singing males recorded in ten years between 1988 and 2004, all involving single males except for two in 1989 and three in 2004.
- Egleton Reserve, Rutland Water: records of singing males in nine years between 1987 and 2005, including five in 1995 and four in 1997 and 2005.
- Lyndon Reserve, Rutland Water: one or two singing males in nine years between 1997 and 2005, with three in 2001.
- Ketton Quarry: records in nine years between 1987 and 2003, all of one or two singing males.
- Newell Wood: one or two singing males recorded in nine years between 1986 and 1998, with three in 1988.
- Coppice Leys: singing males recorded in eight years between 1988 and 1997, including five in 1992 and three in 1990, 1993 and 1994.
- Barrowden Fox Covert: singing males recorded in six years between 1986 and 1992, including five in 1989 and 1990.

It is not known whether the populations at Luffenham Heath, Newell Wood, Coppice Leys and Barrowden Fox Covert have disappeared or whether observers are no longer visiting these areas to look for Nightingales. The number of sites and singing males has dropped significantly during the first five years of the 21st century, with just five birds at two sites in 2001 and eight birds at three sites in 2005, although records of four singing males at Greetham Wood in 2004 and one singing at Stretton Wood in 2003 were the only ones from these prime-looking but underwatched areas during 1985–2005 and suggest that there may be more Nightingales in Rutland than is currently known. However, it is clear that this species is barely maintaining its presence in the counties and could be heading the same way as Common Redstart, Whinchat and Wood Warbler in becoming extinct as a breeding bird in Leicestershire and Rutland.

There have only been nine records away from Rutland since 1985, none of which have occurred in the 21st century. Eight of these records have been singing males, as follows:

- Sharnford, spring 1986.
- two, Cropston, spring 1990.
- Cropston, May 15th to 27th 1991.
- Frisby Gravel Pits, May 3rd to 19th 1992.
- Scraptoft, May 26th 1993.
- Loughborough, April 26th 1995.
- Braunstone Frith, Leicester, May 6th to 16th 1995.
- between Quorn and Loughborough, May 20th 1999.

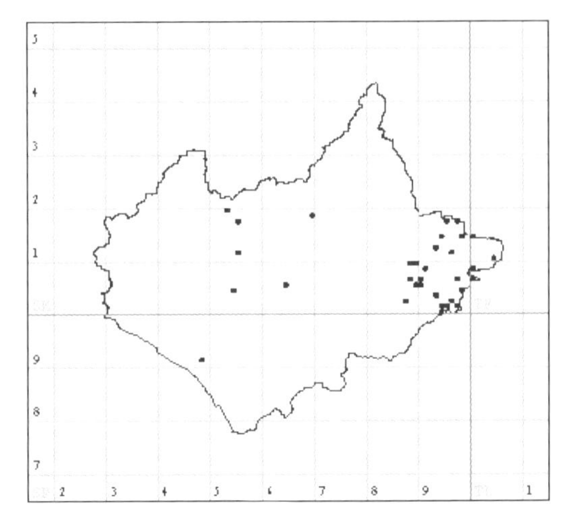

Figure 428: Distribution of Nightingales 1986–2005.

In addition, a most unusual record was of one reportedly flushed from a dense patch of nettles at Watermead Park on June 29th 1994.

The first singing birds are usually recorded during the last ten days of April. The earliest reports have occurred on April 14th: at Belton-in-Rutland in 1953, Ketton Quarry in 1993 and the Lyndon Reserve at Rutland Water in 1998, whilst arrivals on April 15th have been recorded in four years: at Ingarsby in 1952, the Lyndon Reserve in 1987 and 2003 and Barnsdale Wood in 1989. Despite this species becoming much scarcer in recent years, average spring arrival dates have remained consistent since the 1980s and during the first five years of the 21st century have become earlier.

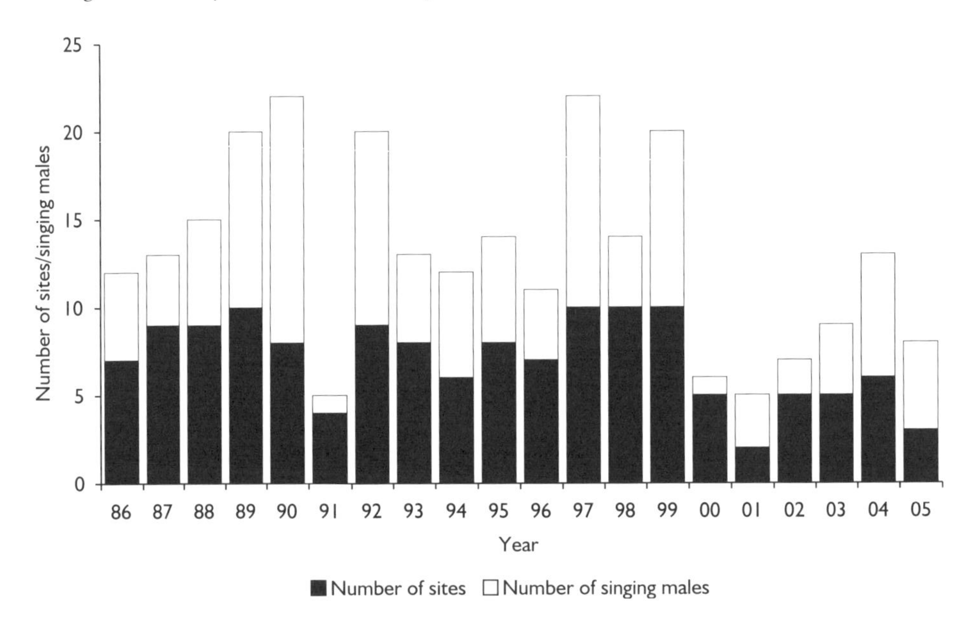

Figure 429: Numbers of singing Nightingales 1986–2005.

Once this species stops singing in late May it becomes difficult to find and late summer/autumn records are very rare. There have only been eight records in July and August, the latest of which was a rather bizarre report of one flying south with a flock of finches at Preston on August 25th 1944; this is nearly three weeks later than any other record and is perhaps best treated with a degree of caution. Other records in July and August, all of single birds, are as follows:

- Luffenham Heath, August 6th 1988.
- trapped and ringed, Belmesthorpe, August 2nd 1989.

- found dead, Jewry Wall Museum, Leicester, July 20th 1977.
- Lyndon Reserve, Rutland Water, July 20th 1997.
- Lyndon Reserve, Rutland Water, July 20th 2004.
- Ketton, July 18th 1993.
- juvenile trapped and ringed, Luffenham Heath, July 15th 1986.

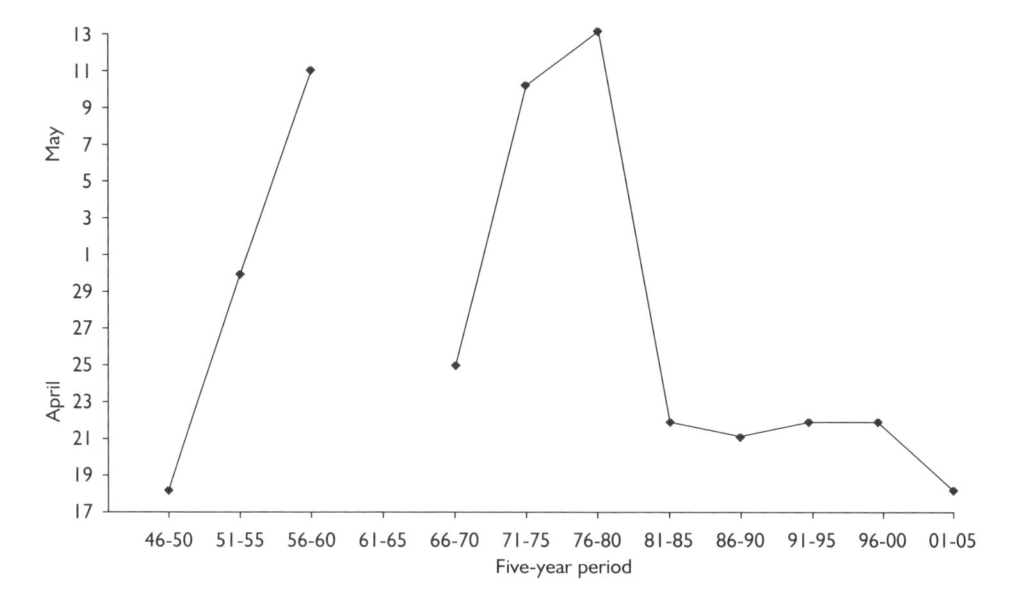

Figure 430: Average spring arrival dates of Nightingales by five-year periods 1946–2005.

The only ringing recovery involves a juvenile ringed at Ketton Quarry on June 30th 1994 that was controlled at Castor Hanglands (Cambridgeshire) on May 30th 1998.

Nightingales breed mainly in southern and central Europe as far north as England, as well as in north-west Africa and south-west and central Asia. They winter in tropical Africa. A BTO survey in 1999 (Wilson *et al.* 2002) showed a marked range contraction since the previous national survey in 1980, in line with the disappearance of this species from east Leicestershire and estimated the British population to be 6,700 males, an overall population decline of 8% since 1980. The likely causes of the decline are thought to relate to pressures on migration and in winter, reduction in coppicing, clearance of scrub and a decline in productivity; ringing data between 1984 and 1999 indicated a 59% decline in the number of juveniles trapped (Baillie *et al.* 2006, Brown & Grice 2005). In view of the range contraction mentioned above, the Nightingale has been added to the 'Amber List' of Birds of Conservation Concern (Gregory *et al.* 2002).

RMF

Bluethroat *Luscinia svecica*

Very rare vagrant from Europe: one record.

A female was trapped in the Lagoon III reedbed at Rutland Water on April 20th 1996. After being ringed and photographed, it was released and was never seen again.

Two previously published records have been reviewed and are no longer considered acceptable: single birds at Barwell on October 21st 1952 (Fray 2005) and Croft on August 31st 1954 (Mackay 1995a).

Bluethroats breed right across the Palearctic, from Spain and the Atlantic coast of France to the Pacific. The nominate, red-spotted race breeds in northern Europe and Siberia, whilst at least nine other races breed elsewhere, including *L. s. cyanecula* (the form most often referred to as 'White-spotted Bluethroat'), which is found over most of the central and southern European range. It winters around the Mediterranean, in tropical Africa and from the Middle East, through the Indian subcontinent to south-east Asia. Bluethroats are regular spring and autumn migrants to Britain in varying numbers, with arrivals in this country usually being dependent on the presence of easterly or south-easterly winds, particularly in the spring. The bulk of spring records are of the red-spotted form, which usually occur during May, whilst white-spotted birds are much rarer and usually appear earlier in the season, from late March to mid-April. Although females of each form are indistinguishable, it seems likely that the Rutland Water individual was of the white-spotted form given the relatively early date it was found on. It is also worth noting that, between March 23rd and April 20th 1996, an influx of 11 white-spotted birds was recorded in Britain.

RMF

Red-flanked Bluetail *Tarsiger cyanurus*

Very rare vagrant from north-east Europe or Siberia: one record.

A first-winter was trapped and ringed by three members of the Charnwood Ringing Group at The Brand, Woodhouse Eaves on October 19th 1997. After the somewhat stunned observers had photographed the bird, it was released into dense cover, never to be seen again (Fray 1998a, *BB* 91:501). This was a quite astonishing record of one of the most sought-after and enigmatic rarities on the British List and is perhaps the most extraordinary species to have occurred in the county. The bird arrived following several days of strong south-easterly winds, which had resulted in good numbers of Pallas's Warblers *Phylloscopus proregulus* appearing on the south and east coasts and, perhaps more pertinently, a Siberian Rubythroat *Luscinia calliope* in Dorset the same day. The Leicestershire bird represented only the 17th British record, although by the end of 2005 the total reported in this country had more than doubled to 36. With the exception of single birds in Cornwall and Dorset, all other British records have occurred along the east coast or in Shetland. Sixteen have arrived between October 10th and 20th: in the words of the BBRC Report for 1997 'entirely typical in date, but a quality addition to the Leicestershire list.'

Red-flanked Bluetails breed from north-east Europe through the Siberian taiga from west Russia to Japan. Northern populations, including those in Europe, winter in south-east Asia. The species has undertaken a westward range expansion since the late 19th century and a small breeding population of 200 to 300 pairs is now established in Finland.

RMF

Black Redstart *Phoenicurus ochruros*

Scarce spring passage migrant, rare autumn passage migrant and winter visitor; recorded in all months, with the majority in March and April. Very rare breeder; six confirmed breeding records.

According to Browne, the only 19th century record was of a male caught near Belgrave, Leicester on October 19th 1888 and presented to the Leicester Museum. There were just two other documented reports prior to the formation of LROS in 1941: single birds at Thurmaston in both April and November 1921.

Today, the Black Redstart is chiefly a scarce passage visitor, mainly during the spring. It occurs less frequently as an autumn migrant, with occasional wintering records, and has bred on at least six occasions. Since 1941, there have been records in 43 of the 65 years up to 2005. It is now occurring more regularly than ever, with the only blank years since 1968 being 1978, 1983 and 1998. Figure 431 shows that the highest numbers were found in the 1970s; however, these figures are distorted slightly in that several breeding pairs were recorded in this decade and their associated young are included in the annual totals. In most years, one or two passage birds are the norm, the highest annual total (excluding breeding birds) being seven in 1975.

The data show that Black Redstarts are most regular in the counties during late March and early April and almost one third of all arrivals have occurred between March 21st and April 10th. Records of presumed passage migrants are, however, very rare before this period, the only other March records being a male at Humberstone, Leicester on March 6th 1989, a female at Sapcote on March 19th 1992 and one at Ibstock on March 19th 2005. A smaller peak in occurrences is detectable during the last ten days of April, after which records tail-off and it

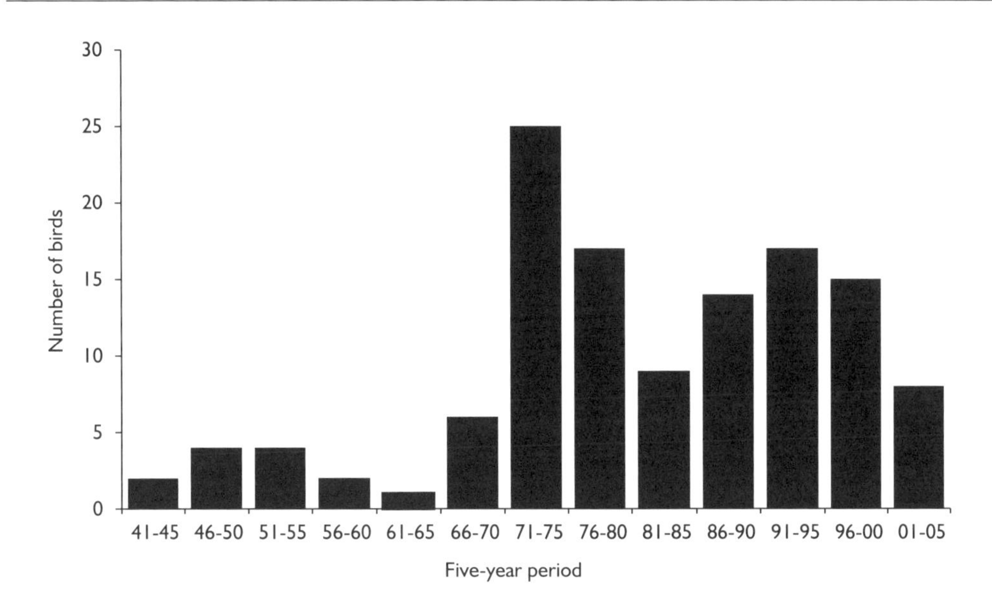

Figure 431: Numbers of Black Redstarts 1941–2005.

is difficult to say whether birds recorded in May are passage birds or potential breeders. Two of the four birds first noted during June were singing males, which had presumably arrived earlier in the year. The other two records, involving a female at Eyebrook Reservoir on June 19th 1949 and one at Swithland Reservoir on June 13th 1969, are more difficult to explain as there was no evidence in either case of breeding at or near the sites involved.

Autumn passage is much less pronounced than during the spring and is mainly restricted to the period from mid-October to early November. The earliest migrants have been single males at Market Bosworth on September 25th 1985 and Burbage on September 29th 1973; two August records, at Rutland Water on August 14th and 15th 1996 and Glaston on August 23rd 1975, were both of juveniles, which had presumably been bred nearby.

On passage, Black Redstarts may appear almost anywhere and many records have come from private gardens. The only sites to have recorded this species on more than two occasions (excluding breeding records) are Rutland Water, where there have been nine individuals, and Swithland Reservoir, which has five records to its name. It is interesting that over a quarter of all passage birds have occurred in the Charnwood Forest area.

A total of 11 birds have been found in January, February or December, but most have been short-stayers and only two have remained long enough to be considered as wintering: a male at Rutland Water from December 6th 1980 to January 15th 1981 and a female/first-winter at Sileby from December 19th 1992 to March 1st 1993.

Figure 432 excludes breeding birds when their arrival date is unknown, as well as fledged young.

Breeding has been confirmed on six occasions:

1974 a pair raised three young in old station buildings at Great Central Street, Leicester and another pair bred unsuccessfully at Holwell Quarry.

1979 a pair reared four young at Leicester Power Station on Burnmoor Street.

1988 a pair bred at Cliffe Quarry, Markfield, although the number of young reared remains unknown.

1993 a pair reared five young at Ketton Quarry.

1997 three recently fledged juveniles were found at Burley House during June.

Black Redstarts can be very unobtrusive when breeding in city centres and their rather quiet song is easily drowned out by traffic noise; it is therefore possible that breeding occurred in a number of other years in Leicester, with the most likely being as follows:

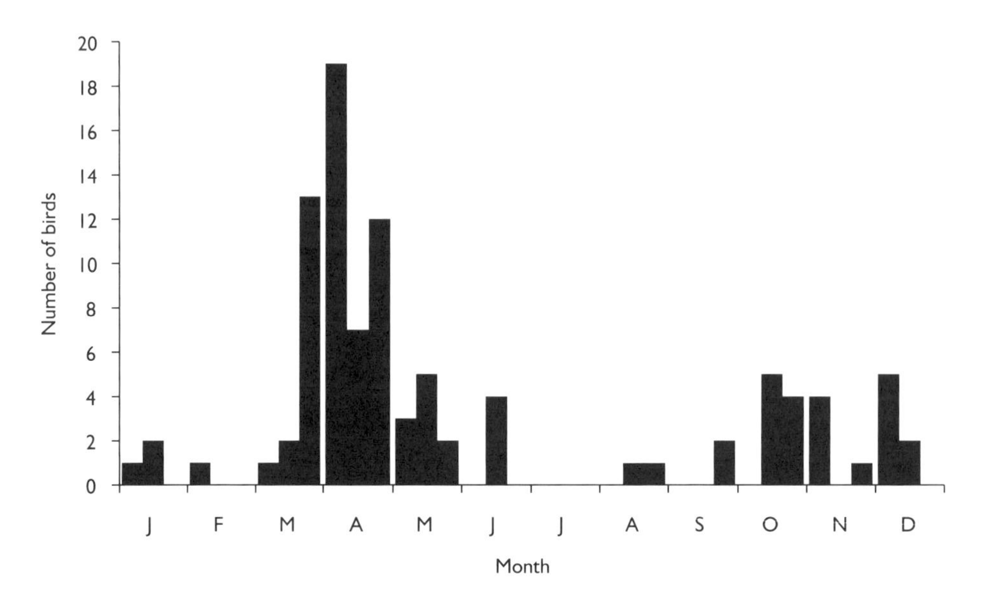

Figure 432: Monthly occurrence of Black Redstarts 1941–2005.

1971	a singing male was at Leicester Power Station from June 14th to 19th. This site was extremely difficult to access and breeding could easily have escaped detection.
1975	a male was at Leicester University during the third week of April and a pair remained at the previous year's breeding site at Great Central Street from April 27th to mid-June.
1979	singing males were in two areas of Leicester from May 15th to July 30th and on May 25th and 26th.
1995	a singing male frequented the Millstone Lane area from June 11th to 19th.
1999	a first-summer male sang regularly at Bede Island from April 6th to 26th.

It is clear that this species was at its most regular as a breeding species in the 1970s, a period when much re-development was taking place in Leicester and suitable derelict buildings and wasteground were plentiful. During the early part of the 21st century, Leicester is again undergoing substantial redevelopment and it is possible that more breeding records may occur in the near future; however, this species' predilection for changing sites in response to habitat change, and the fact that it occurs in locations frequently of little interest to bird-watchers, makes assessment of any breeding population difficult.

Black Redstarts breed throughout most of central and southern Europe as far north as southern Sweden, as well as in south-west and central Asia. European birds winter in western and southern Europe and north Africa. Britain is at the northernmost limit of this species' breeding range and the population usually numbers between 80 and 120 pairs (Gibbons *et al.* 1993). Due to the small number of breeding birds, this species has been added to the 'Amber List' of Birds of Conservation Concern (Gregory *et al.* 2002).

RMF

Common Redstart *Phoenicurus phoenicurus*

Uncommon passage migrant; formerly an uncommon to fairly common breeder.

During the 19th century the Common Redstart was described by Browne as a summer migrant to Leicestershire, sparingly distributed and breeding, although he thought it was not as common as it once was. He quoted Harley, who wrote in 1841, as saying it had bred within Leicester at the castle and the abbey. It appears that this species was more widespread in Rutland during the 19th century: Haines considered it common and reported that in some years it was so numerous that eight nests could be located within a radius of 50 yards at Exton Park.

From a seemingly stable position, the decline and ultimate demise of the Common Redstart as a breeding species in the counties is a depressing tale. The LROS archives mention that it was a summer visitor breeding in small numbers, especially in Charnwood Forest, during the first part of the 20th century. The first LROS Annual Report, in 1941, described this species' status as 'thinly distributed in favoured localities'; this was updated in 1948 to the more accurate 'fairly common in east Leicestershire and Rutland, sparingly distributed in Charnwood, uncommon elsewhere'. The 1940s appear to have been the time when Common Redstarts were at their most numerous in the counties, with the stronghold being east Leicestershire. Otter (1965) provided a good summary of its distribution in this area during the late 1940s. In 1949 he located a total of 90 singing males in an area bordered by Keyham to the west, the Rutland border to the east, Burrough Hill to the north and Glooston and Hallaton to the south. The majority of birds were concentrated around Owston Wood and along the Eye Brook from Tilton on the Hill to the Rutland border just east of East Norton. He noted that the numerous old ash trees and pollarded willows along the Eye Brook provided ideal nest holes. Other counts in east Leicestershire around this time included 20 pairs in the Tilton on the Hill/Tugby area in 1946 and 15 singing males around Tilton on the Hill in 1947.

Although this species was apparently common in Rutland during the 1940s the only published breeding sites were Wardley Wood, Stoke Dry Wood, Preston and Lower Hambleton. In Charnwood, the most regular breeding records came from Bradgate Park (maximum of three pairs in 1942 and 1943) and Bardon Hill (maximum of three pairs in 1942). At the former site a pair nested in a kettle placed in a tree in 1945. Buddon Wood, Blakeshay Wood, Charley Hall, Lea Wood and Blackbrook Reservoir also provided confirmed breeding records during the 1940s. Away from the three main areas of east Leicestershire, Rutland and Charnwood, breeding records in the 1940s came from a number of other sites, mainly in the north of Leicestershire. The south-west of the region was virtually shunned, although birds nested at Croft in 1945 and 1946 and Burbage Wood in the latter year. There was little published data regarding this species' status in north-east Leicestershire, although 12 singing males at Belvoir in 1949 suggested that a good population existed in this area.

Breeding data for the 1950s is sadly rather sparse; there were vague comments in the LROS Annual Reports noting an 'increase in Charnwood' in 1950, an 'increase in numbers and range' in 1951 and an 'increase in the Oakham area' in 1955, but no other details are available. New breeding sites in this decade included Market Bosworth (1951 and 1953) and Stoke Golding (1952), whilst in 1957 a pair bred in a hole above a window at Bardon Hall. Likewise, there is little information available for the first half of the 1960s, although there were 12 singing males at Owston Wood in 1963 and eight pairs at Charnwood Lodge in 1964. It appears that the first signs of a decline were noted in 1966, when numbers in Charnwood were reported to be well down on previous years. Rutland seemed to be faring better at this time; 20 breeding pairs were located in the south of the county in 1968, the majority of which were at Wardley Wood and Burley Wood and the following year 20 pairs were found in the Eye valley near Wardley. The situation in east Leicestershire during the late 1960s is not clear, although five or six pairs were present between Baggrave and Lowesby in 1969.

During the 1970s the majority of breeding records came from east Leicestershire, but in lower numbers than previously. The largest concentrations were of seven singing males at Launde Abbey in 1979, five singing males at Lowesby also in 1979, three or four pairs at Great Merrible Wood in 1970 and three pairs at both Billesdon Coplow in 1970 and Sauvey Castle in 1979. Other sites in this area utilised with some regularity during the 1970s included Tugby Wood, Baggrave Park and Owston Wood. The only sites occupied in Rutland during this decade were

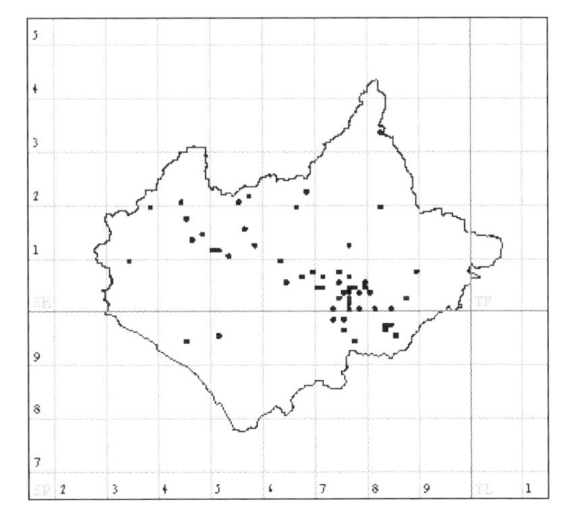

Figure 433: Distribution of breeding Common Redstarts 1941–49.

Burley Wood and Wardley Wood in 1970, Eyebrook Reservoir in four years between 1970 and 1977, Brake Spinney, Normanton in 1972 (Mitcham 1984) and Preston in 1972, although it is likely that this is an incomplete picture. The Charnwood population seems to have contracted substantially during the 1970s: the only regular site was Bradgate Park, where one or two pairs nested every year, with other breeding records from Charnwood Lodge in 1970, Ulverscroft in 1970 and 1971, Swithland Wood in 1975 and 1979 and Swithland Reservoir in 1979.

Away from the three main areas, a significant population existed in the south of Leicestershire at Stanford Park, where there were six pairs in 1979; breeding was also recorded at nearby Stanford Reservoir in 1977. Elsewhere, single pairs bred at Saddington Reservoir in 1970, Market Bosworth and Coalville in 1972, Waltham on the Wolds in 1975 and Enderby in 1979.

Warrilow carried out his tetrad survey during 1976–84 and located Common Redstarts in 35 tetrads in the counties, with breeding confirmed in 13 of them. Apart from Belvoir, where small numbers still persisted during this period, all records came from the three traditional areas. He estimated a county-wide breeding population at this time of between 50 and 75 pairs.

The distribution map showing breeding sites of this species in the 1960s and 1970s (Figure 434) reveals a similar pattern to that of the 1940s but with fewer records away from the core areas of east Leicestershire, Rutland and Charnwood.

This species' slide towards extinction as a breeding bird in the counties began in earnest in the 1980s. Apart from three pairs at Tilton on the Hill in 1983 and a singing male at Tugby Wood in 1988, all east Leicestershire records during this decade came from the upper Chater valley between Sauvey Castle and Launde, where nine singing males in 1980 had fallen to just two in 1986. From 1987 to 2000 numbers in this area varied from one to five singing males, but a pair carrying food in 1997 was the last indication that breeding had occurred and there have been no records from this site since 2000. Elsewhere in east Leicestershire there were five singing males at Tilton on the Hill and one at Launde Big Wood in 1990 and a pair bred at Langton Caudle in 1992, but there have been no further records from these areas.

The Rutland population was almost entirely restricted to Burley Wood from 1980 onwards, with peak counts of four or five singing males in 1986 and six in 1990. The last pair bred at this site in 1995, although single singing males were recorded in each of the next four years. At other sites in Rutland, single pairs bred at Ketton Quarry in 1989 and King's Hill Lodge, Uppingham in 1995, two singing males were at Wardley Wood in both 1990 and 1994 and a singing male was at Prior's Coppice in 1995.

A similar situation occurred in Charnwood, where only one site (Bradgate Park) provided regular records. Single pairs bred in 1981, 1989, 1991 and 1993, with probable breeding reported in 1988 and 1995 and singing males in 1990, 1994 (two) and 1997. Elsewhere in Charnwood, single singing males were at Stoneywell

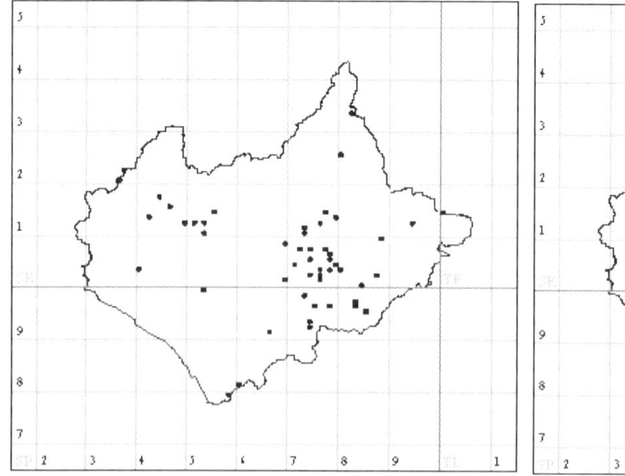

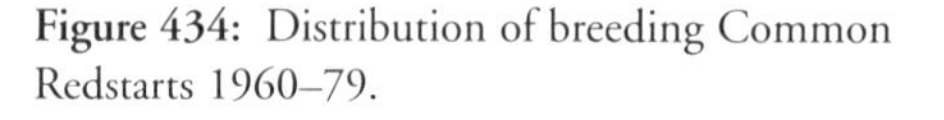

Figure 434: Distribution of breeding Common Redstarts 1960–79.

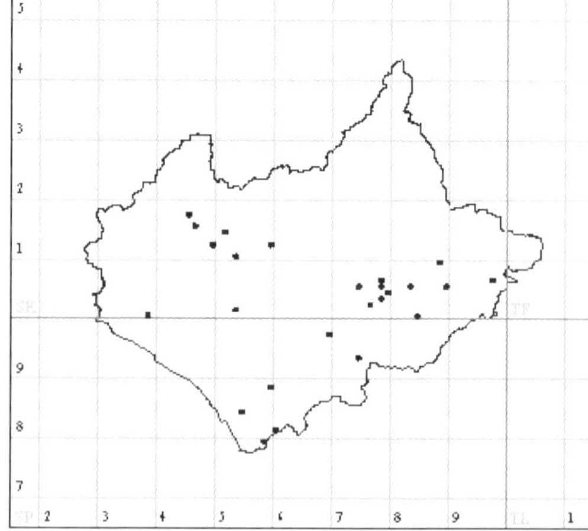

Figure 435: Distribution of breeding or singing male Common Redstarts 1980–2005.

Wood in 1980, Beacon Hill in 1989 and Ulverscroft in 1988, 1990 and 1991, a pair was present at the latter site in 1998 and juveniles at Blackbrook Reservoir in July 1995 and Beacon Hill in July 1997 may have been indicative of local breeding.

Sporadic breeding attempts occurred in other areas of the counties in the 1980s. There were still six singing males at Stanford Park in 1980 but there have been no further records from this site; in 1981, single pairs probably bred at Carlton Curlieu, Cossington Gravel Pits and Lubbesthorpe, singing males were at Bruntingthorpe Airfield and Lutterworth in 1988 and breeding was confirmed at Shenton in 1985 and Belvoir in 1997, the latter representing the last confirmed breeding record in the counties.

During the 21st century there have been only five instances of birds showing potential breeding behaviour. In 2000, a male at Rutland Water on June 17th was followed by a juvenile and a heavily moulting female on July 15th, whilst the following year two males sang at the Lyndon Reserve at Rutland Water until mid-May. In 2002, a female with a brood-patch was trapped and ringed at Stanford Reservoir on June 29th and subsequently single singing males were recorded at Charnwood Lodge on May 26th 2003 and Owston Wood on May 16th 2004.

Since the demise of the counties' breeding population, the status of the Common Redstart is now restricted to that of an uncommon passage migrant in Leicestershire and Rutland. The highest annual totals since 1996 have been 18 in both 2001 and 2003. There are usually more records during the autumn than the spring; 15 autumn records in 2003 represented the best recent year, whilst nine spring birds in 2001 is the highest recent total at that season. Just five birds (one in spring and four in autumn) were recorded in the counties in 2005.

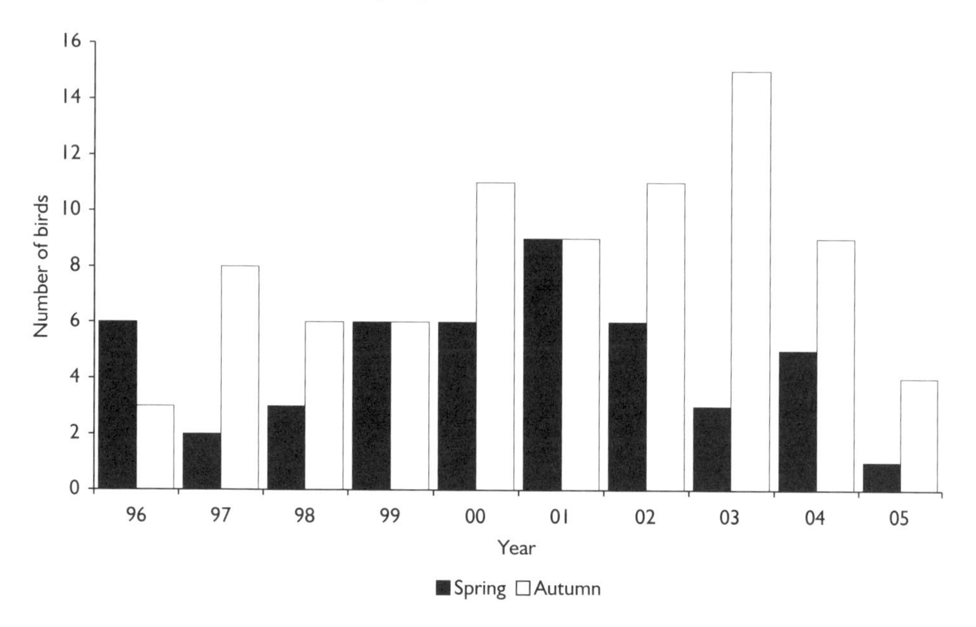

Figure 436: Number of passage Common Redstarts 1996–2005.

The first spring arrival is usually during the middle ten days of April, although the earliest was one at Eyebrook Reservoir on April 1st 1959. There have been a further seven records prior to April 8th, all of single birds, as follows:

- Great Glen, April 3rd 1958.
- Eyebrook Reservoir, April 4th 1948.
- Lutterworth, April 4th 1988.
- Rutland Water, April 6th 1985.
- Cropston, April 6th 2005.
- Great Glen, April 7th 1952.
- Eyebrook Reservoir, April 7th 1966.

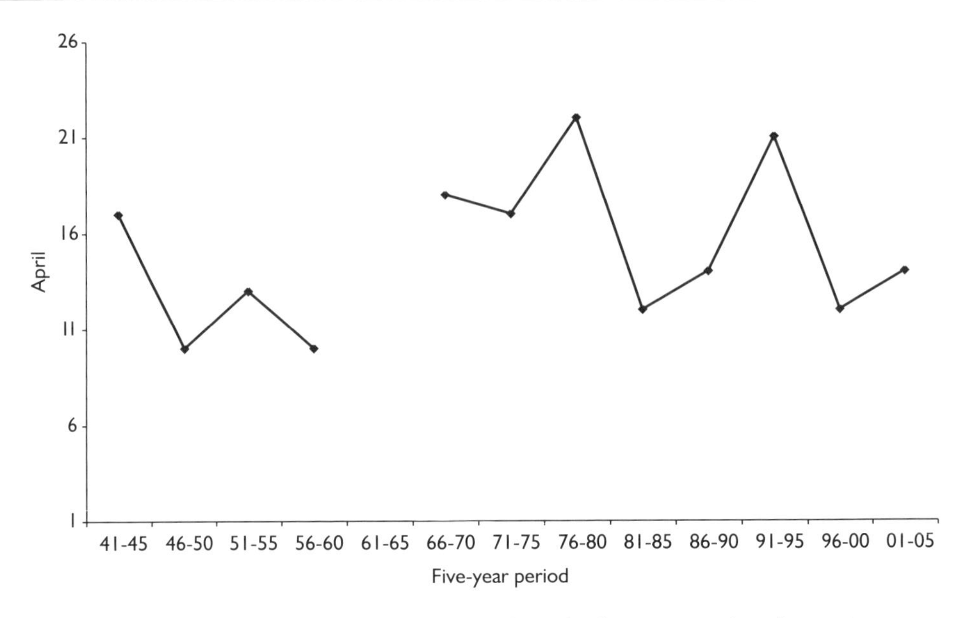

Figure 437: Average spring arrival dates of Common Redstarts by five-year periods 1941–2005.

Common Redstarts tended to arrive in the counties earlier in the spring when the breeding population was at its peak in the 1940s and 1950s, although unlike some other declining migrants such as the Turtle Dove, House Martin and Yellow Wagtail, recent arrival dates have not become significantly later.

During the autumn most birds have usually left the counties by mid-September. There have been October records in seven years, all of single birds unless stated:

- found dead, Wistow, October 28th 1965.
- Eyebrook Reservoir, October 25th 1959.
- Kilby Bridge, October 10th 1998.
- Saddington Reservoir, October 9th 1966.
- two, Croft, October 7th 1966.
- Wigston, October 6th 2001.
- Rutland Water, October 4th 1997.
- Allexton, October 1st 2003.

The latest record, however, is of one at Willoughby Waterleys on November 7th 1962. Again, in contrast to other declining migrants, the average departure date has not become earlier; indeed, since the mid-1980s it has become slightly later.

There have been two ringing recoveries involving Leicestershire and Rutland: a juvenile male ringed at Lincoln (Lincolnshire) on September 12th 1968 was found dead at Leicester nine days later and a pullus ringed at Ketton Quarry on June 8th 1989 was retrapped at Redhill (Surrey) on August 24th 1990.

Common Redstarts breed over most of Europe, as well as in western and central Siberia, the Middle East and north-west Africa. They winter in sub-Saharan Africa north of the equator. The British population, the most recent estimate of which was 101,000 pairs (Baker *et al.* 2006), declined in the late 1960s and early 1970s following severe drought conditions in the Sahel desert wintering area and there was a contraction of range of 20% in Britain between 1968–72 and 1988–91 (Gibbons *et al.* 1993), coinciding with the beginning of its disappearance from Leicestershire and Rutland as a breeding species. More recently the British population has fluctuated and has increased in some areas of England (Baillie *et al.* 2006); given this and the fact that the habitat at this species' favoured locations in Leicestershire and Rutland does not appear to have changed, the extinction in the counties as a breeding bird is something of a mystery, although Mitcham (1992) commented that, following the national decline beginning in the 1960s, eastern England was one of the areas where it did not

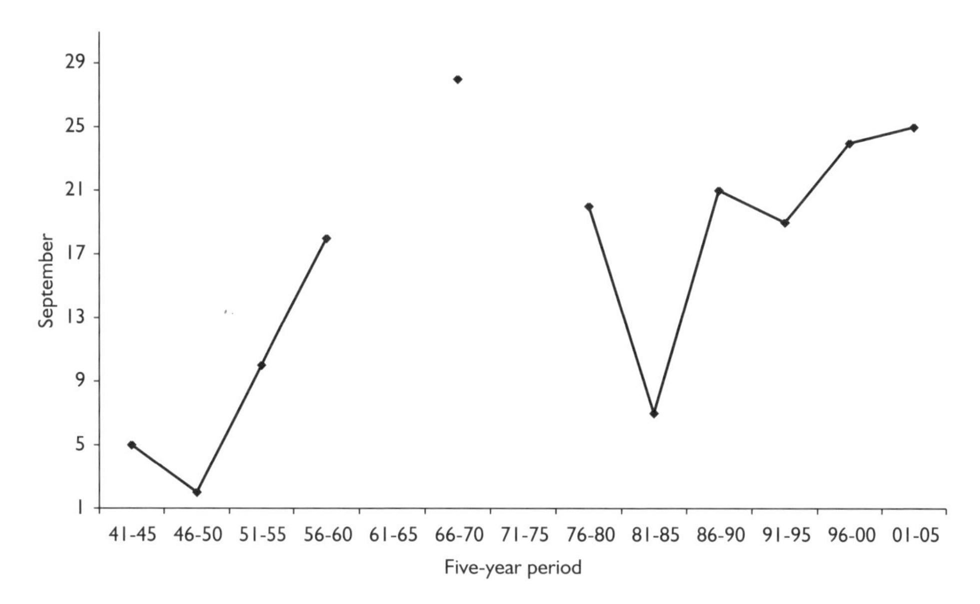

Figure 438: Average autumn departure dates of Common Redstarts by five-year periods 1941–2005.

increase in numbers again during the 1980s. Due to its unfavourable conservation status the Common Redstart has been added to the 'Amber List' of Birds of Conservation Concern (Gregory *et al.* 2002).

RMF

Whinchat *Saxicola rubetra*

Formerly an uncommon to fairly common migrant breeder, now an uncommon passage migrant.

The Whinchat was a fairly common summer visitor to the counties in the 19th century. It was described as 'generally distributed' in Leicestershire by Browne, who said that it nested 'in suitable positions throughout the county and not far from the town of Leicester.' Around the same time, Haines considered it to be a 'common migrant.'

The LROS archives, covering the early part of the 20th century, described the Whinchat as 'generally distributed in small numbers, invariably found in meadows along river valleys'. By the time of the first LROS Annual Report, in 1941, this species' status was noted as a 'summer visitor, locally common.' From 1941 to 1950, breeding reports came from a total of 46 sites; as can be from Figure 439, the Soar valley both north and south of Leicester was the stronghold, with nesting records from various other scattered sites around the counties. Some large densities were noted, including 24 pairs in the Quorn district in 1944, with 18 pairs there the following year; a pair every 100 yards along the Rutland bank of Eyebrook Reservoir in 1947, with an estimated 20 pairs at the same site the following year; seven pairs at Stanford Reservoir in 1948 and five pairs at Loughborough Big Meadow in both 1943 and 1947. In addition, at least 18 pairs bred alongside the River Soar between Zouch and Sileby in 1947 and in 1948 it 'bred along the whole length of the Soar valley'.

Details of this species' distribution in the 1950s are sparse, although it appears that a decline had set in early in the decade. In 1951 it was considered to be 'possibly slowly declining' and the next year 'declining numbers were reported from many widespread areas'. However, there were still 12 pairs by the River Soar at Aylestone in 1952 and five pairs at Lindley in 1956.

Evidence of a reduction in breeding numbers continued during the 1960s: nesting was recorded at 31 sites during the decade, with some areas of the Soar valley, particularly north of Leicester, being abandoned or only used sparingly. Amongst the more regular breeding sites around this time were Bradgate Park, where there were up to 12 pairs during the summer of 1964; Stoughton Airfield, where there were five pairs in 1966; Aylestone

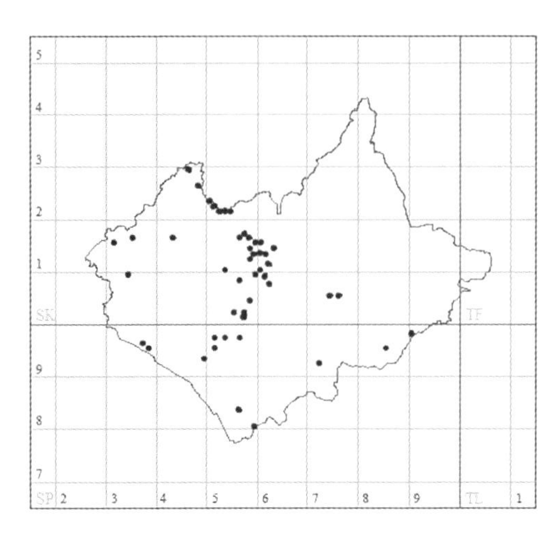

Figure 439: Distribution of breeding Whinchats 1941–50.

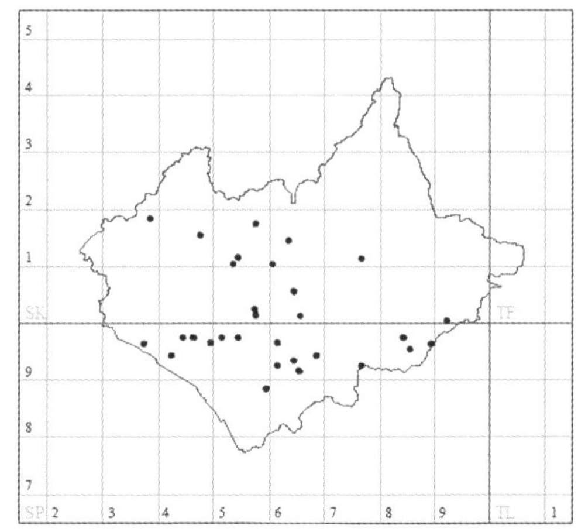

Figure 440: Distribution of breeding Whinchats 1961–70.

and Earl Shilton. By 1967, concern was expressed in the Annual Report thus: 'markedly declined over the last 20 years . . . more efficient use of land and increased mechanisation on farms has probably played a part in the decrease'.

Breeding was confirmed at 18 sites during the 1970s. Bradgate Park and Aylestone were again two of the most regular areas, with four pairs at the latter in both 1970 and 1975 and Kilby Bridge was occupied in seven years during the decade. Two pairs bred at Eyebrook Reservoir in 1975, the last time that this previous stronghold was used.

There were no confirmed breeding records in 1980, for the first time since the formation of LROS in 1941. Throughout the rest of the 1980s breeding was confirmed at only six sites: Bradgate Park, Enderby, Stoughton Airfield, Bittesby, Melton Airfield and Aylestone Meadows, and suspected at a further four: Hallaton, Stanford Reservoir, Wanlip Gravel Pits and Hinckley. Since 1989, when single pairs nested at both Aylestone Meadows and Stoughton Airfield, the only site where potential breeding behaviour has been noted is Sence Valley Forest Park, where an adult and three juveniles were seen on July 23rd 1997 and a pair was present in early July 1999.

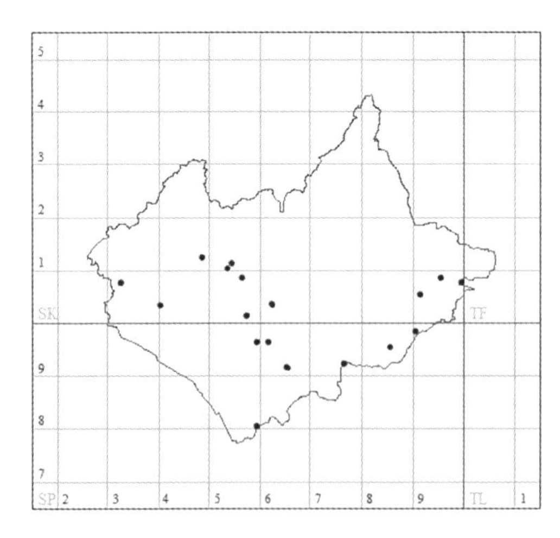

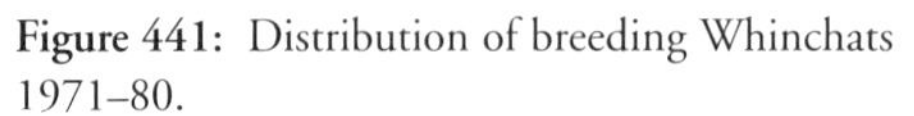

Figure 441: Distribution of breeding Whinchats 1971–80.

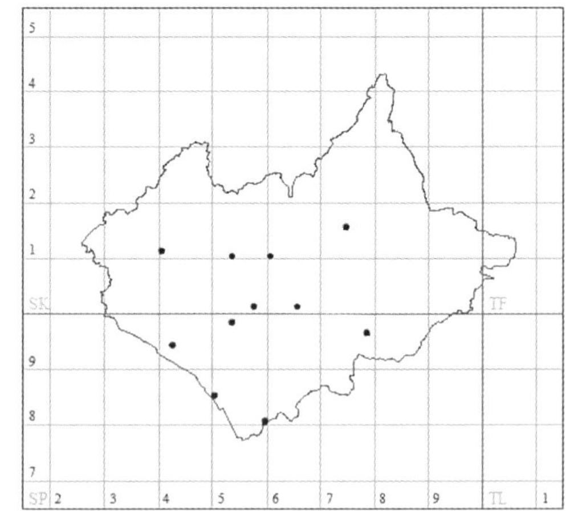

Figure 442: Distribution of breeding Whinchats 1981–2005.

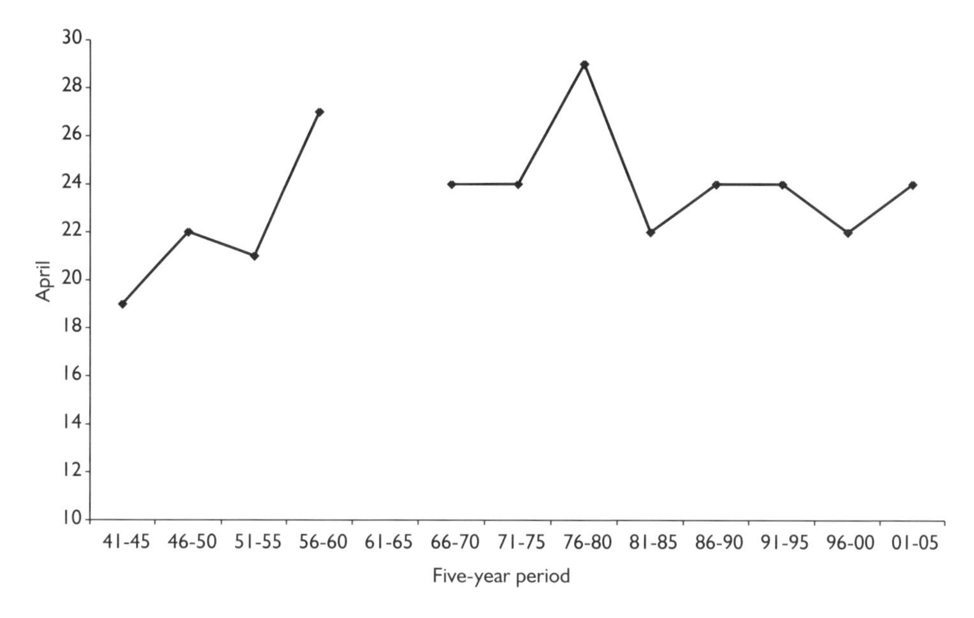

Figure 443: Average spring arrival dates of Whinchats by five-year periods 1941–2005.

With the demise of the counties' breeding population, the Whinchat is now restricted to the status of uncommon passage migrant. The earliest spring arrival was one at Eyebrook Reservoir on April 5th 1962 but the first spring report is usually during the last ten days of April and the only other records prior to April 16th are single birds at Eyebrook Reservoir on April 10th 1952, Ketton on April 13th 1968 and Wigston on April 15th 1952. With the exception of the period 1976 to 1980, the average arrival date has remained remarkably consistent since the mid-1960s, ranging between April 22nd and 24th. Spring passage usually finishes in mid-May, although there are occasional records into early June.

Autumn migrants usually appear from early August, with peak numbers in late August and early September. The final record is often during the last few days of September, although there have been October reports in 17

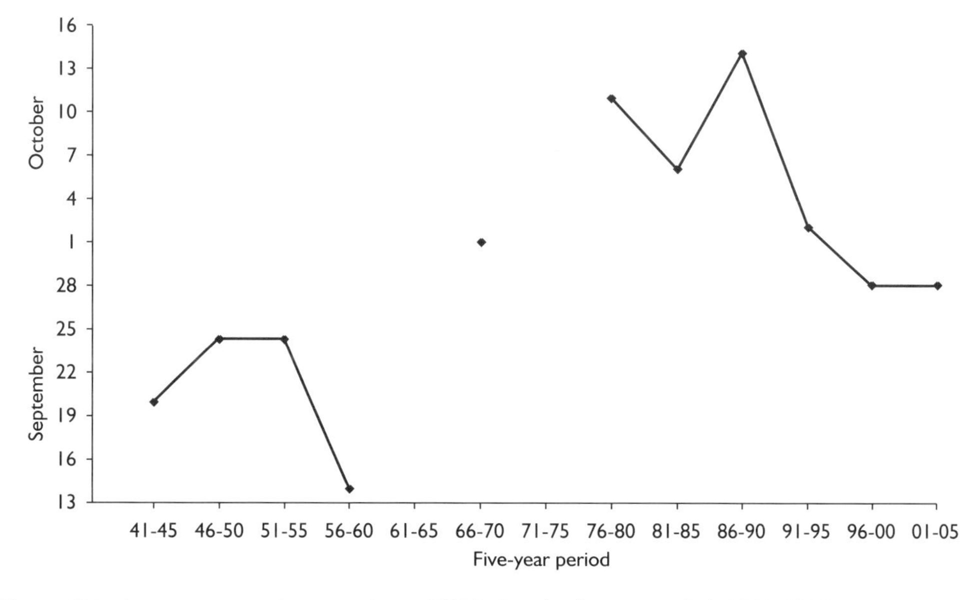

Figure 444: Average autumn departure dates of Whinchats by five-year periods 1941–2005.

years, the latest of which have been single birds at Rutland Water on October 14th 1990, Eyebrook Reservoir on October 17th 1968, Leicester City Farms on October 26th 1963 and Castle Hill Park, Leicester on October 30th 1985. There have, however, been two November records: single birds at Bradgate Park on November 6th 1977 and Rutland Water on November 18th 1986.

Whinchats are usually two to three times more numerous on passage in autumn than spring and in several recent years spring passage has been very light: 1990, for instance, produced just three spring birds. Most records at this time of year involve single birds or groups of up to four; the only higher documented spring counts are:

- seven at Burbage Common on April 23rd 1986.
- six at Oadby on May 3rd 1985.
- five at both Rutland Water on May 1st 1985 and Bruntingthorpe Airfield on April 23rd 1988.

Counts during the autumn are usually higher, with parties of up to seven birds not uncommon. Groups of eight have been seen on four occasions and higher counts are:

- 17 at Rutland Water on September 22nd 1989.
- 15 at Eyebrook Reservoir on August 6th 1959.
- 12 at Sence Valley Forest Park on September 2nd 2001.
- ten at Sence Valley Forest Park on September 7th 2005.
- ten at Wellsborough in late July and early August 1993.
- nine at Sence Valley Forest Park on both August 25th 1998 and August 30th 1999.
- nine at Shepshed on August 26th 1990.

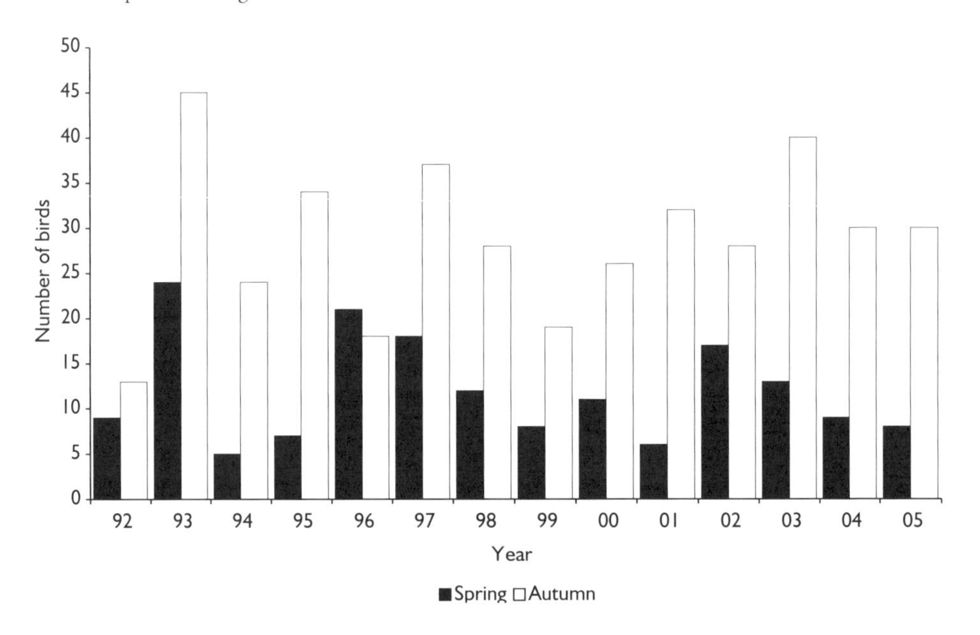

Figure 445: Numbers of Whinchats in spring and autumn 1992–2005.

Whinchats breed over much of Europe and winter in sub-Saharan Africa north of the equator. The British population is estimated at between 14,000 and 28,000 pairs (Baker *et al.* 2006). There has been a major range contraction from lowland England during the latter half of the 20th century, probably due to loss of marginal farmland habitats (Gibbons *et al.* 1993) and national BBS data show that a further decline took place in the 1990s (Baillie *et al.* 2006).

RMF

Stonechat (Common Stonechat) ***Saxicola torquatus***

Formerly a scarce to uncommon resident breeder, now a scarce to uncommon passage and winter visitor and very rare breeder.

During the 19th century the Stonechat was considered by Browne to be resident but sparingly distributed in Leicestershire, but was thought to be much rarer than the Whinchat. The only breeding record Browne knew of came from Charnwood Forest in 1849. In Rutland, Haines described this species as resident and fairly common until the middle of the 19th century and nesting wherever there was any extent of gorse; breeding localities mentioned included Uppingham, Ridlington, Bisbrooke and Wing. By the late 19th century Haines thought that the Stonechat could no longer be considered resident, although it was seen on migration every year and nested only at Barrowden and Luffenham Heaths. The LROS archives, describing the status of this species during the first 40 years of the 20th century, mention it as a regular visitor in small numbers in the early winter months and also refer to a male seen at High Sharpley on July 3rd 1936.

From the formation of LROS in 1941 until 1990, the Stonechat was a scarce passage and winter visitor. Numbers recorded annually remained relatively constant throughout the period, although it became much rarer from the mid-1950s to the mid-1960s, when the only two blank years occurred (1960 and 1963). Conversely, the early to mid-1970s saw much larger numbers and included the four highest annual totals during this period: 22 in 1975, 18 in 1974, 16 in 1977 and 15 in 1973. The only other double-figure annual totals were 14 in both 1944 and 1945 and ten in 1951.

Most records during this time were of one or two birds, although there were three at Cropston Reservoir/Bradgate Park on December 28th 1944, October 4th 1964 and December 31st 1972, and up to three were at Rutland Water from October 31st to December 5th 1981. Higher counts were four at Quorn on September 23rd 1945, six at Bradgate Park in late 1951 and seven at Stanford Reservoir on November 22nd 1970. There were also two odd records, of eight or nine juveniles at Cropston Reservoir on September 3rd 1944 and four or five at Eyebrook Reservoir on July 31st 1947; given the status of Stonechats during this period, the time of year and the fact that Whinchats were commonly breeding in the counties during the 1940s, these records are perhaps best treated with caution.

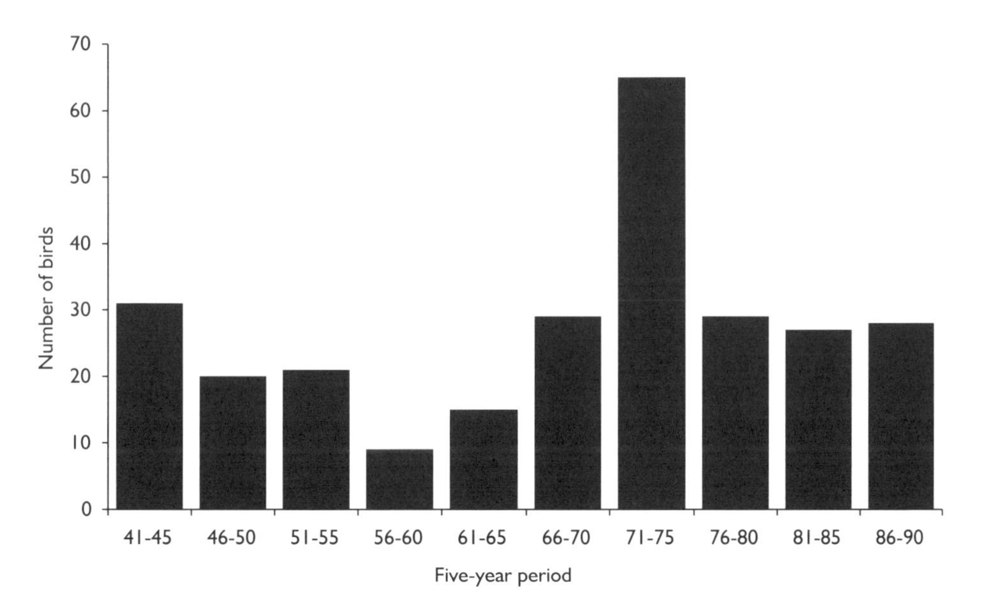

Figure 446: Numbers of Stonechats by five-year periods 1941–90.

The peak time for Stonechats during 1941–90 was late September to November, with smaller numbers remaining during the winter months and a detectable early spring passage movement in March. Records between April and August were rare and the majority occurred in the 1940s and early 1950s, as follows:

- male, Ratcliffe on the Wreake, May 24th 1944.
- male, Mountsorrel Common, June 24th 1945, with a female there on July 31st 1945.
- male, Six Hills, July 8th 1945.
- male, Stanford Reservoir, May 4th 1947.
- male, Eyebrook Reservoir, June 21st 1947.
- male, Eyebrook Reservoir, May 2nd 1948.
- pair, Beacon Hill, May and June 1950.
- female, Eyebrook Reservoir, August 5th to 8th 1950.
- singing male, Braunstone, Leicester, May 13th 1952.

The female at Eyebrook Reservoir in 1950 was reportedly feeding a brood of fledged young with a male Whinchat. From 1952 to 1990 the only records between April and August were single males at Eyebrook Reservoir on April 13th 1962 and Saddington Reservoir on both May 10th 1980 and April 13th 1981, and an unsexed individual at Rutland Water on April 14th 1979.

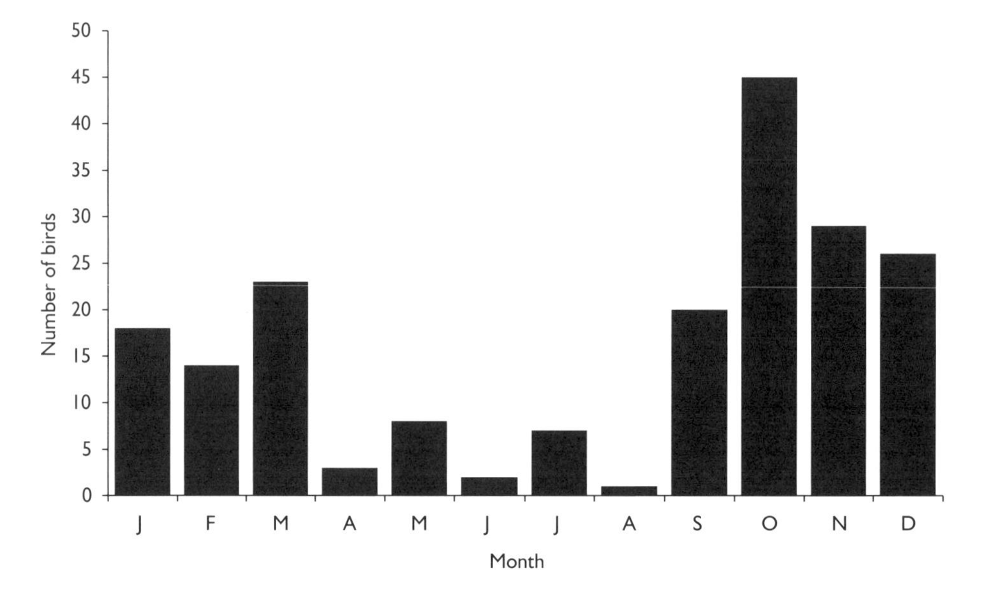

Figure 447: Monthly occurrence of Stonechats 1941–90.

The distribution map for 1941–90 shows a noticeable cluster in and around Charnwood Forest, where Bradgate Park/Cropston Reservoir was by far the favoured site. Away from Charnwood, the three most regular areas were Stanford Reservoir, Eyebrook Reservoir and Rutland Water, whilst Hemington Water Meadows and Aylestone Meadows both recorded six birds each.

Since the early 1990s Stonechats have increased markedly in England (Baillie *et al.* 2006) and this is reflected in reports from Leicestershire and Rutland, with double-figure annual totals being recorded in every year since 1990. The best years in the 1990s were 1994 and 1995 (34 individuals each), 1993 (27) and 1999 (26); since 2000 a further increase has been apparent, with annual totals of 41 in 2000, 77 in 2001, a record 86 in 2002, 52 in 2003, 55 in 2004 and 81 in 2005. The recent increase may also be due to the availability of more suitable habitat, particularly in the north-west of Leicestershire where regenerated coalfields such as Sence Valley Forest Park are favoured sites. Trent Valley Pit and Trent Farm Pool are now regular wintering areas, whilst Bradgate Park, Eyebrook Reservoir, Melton Country Park and Aylestone Meadows also provide records in most winters.

Four at Kirby Lakes on October 8th 1995 was the largest count since 1970, but subsequently there have been records of four together on 13 occasions involving 11 sites. The majority of higher counts have come from Sence Valley Forest Park, as follows:

- up to eight, January 1st to March 12th 2000.
- eight, October 5th and December 15th 2000.
- seven, January 25th 2001.
- seven, December 9th 2001.
- up to six early 1999.
- six, October 31st 2002.
- six, February 5th 2003.
- five, February 10th 2002.
- five, October 20th 2005.

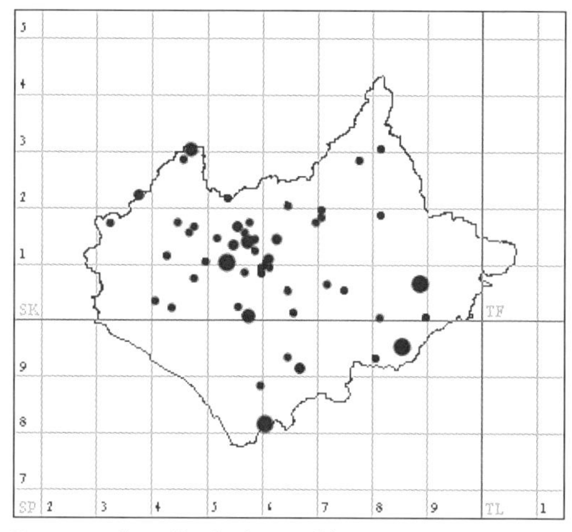

Dot = number of birds, 4 sizes of dot
1–2 (smallest), 3–4, 5–9, 10+ (largest)

Figure 448: Distribution of Stonechats 1941–49.

Counts exceeding four have been recorded at a further four sites: Eyebrook Reservoir, eight on October 16th 2002 and five on March 11th and 12th 2002; 'Conkers', Moira, six on November 2nd 2001; Trent Valley Pit, six on October 31st and November 10th 2002 and five on October 27th 2001 and October 8th 2004, and Trent Farm Pool, five on January 24th 2004.

The general pattern of occurrence has remained the same, with peak numbers arriving in October and November and passage individuals noted in March, although more birds are now remaining to winter. The first autumn arrival has been in September in all but three years since 1990 and every year since 1998, the earliest being single birds at Sence Valley Forest Park on September 2nd 1999 and Frolesworth Manor Lake on September 3rd 2001. Spring records after March are still rare, however, the only ones since 1990 being a female at Rutland Water on April 10th 1994, an unsexed bird at Saddington Reservoir on April 11th 1998, single males in 2004 at Charnwood Lodge on April 9th and Rutland Water on May 7th and a pair at Bradgate Park on May 5th 2005.

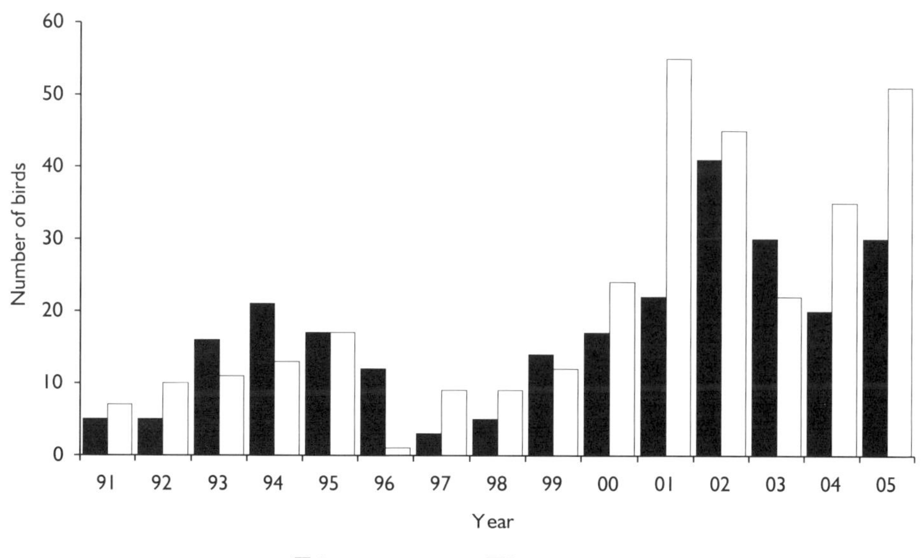

Figure 449: Numbers of Stonechats in each winter period 1991–2005.

A juvenile at Sence Valley Forest Park on July 13th 2001 hinted at local breeding and the following year this site provided the first confirmed breeding record of the Stonechat in the counties since the late 19th century, when a pair was seen with four juveniles on June 25th. A juvenile at Rutland Water on July 10th 2004 may also have been locally bred. With the large amounts of suitable new habitat in the counties and the increased numbers now appearing, further breeding records can be expected.

Stonechats breed across Europe, northern Asia and sub-Saharan Africa. The taxonomy of this species is complex; five subspecies are found in the Western Palearctic, some of which may warrant specific status. Those breeding in Britain belong to the race *S. t. hibernans*. Some European populations are migratory, moving south of their breeding range to winter. The British breeding range showed a substantial contraction between the early 1970s and late 1980s and during 1988–91 the population was estimated at 8,500 to 22,000 pairs (Gibbons *et al.* 1993). Its abundance appears to be affected by severe winter weather and the recent run of mild winters has contributed to the Stonechat increasing markedly since 1994; the latest British population estimate is now put at 19,300 to 49,400 pairs (Baillie *et al.* 2006). Due to this species' overall unfavourable conservation status, it has been added to the 'Amber List' of Birds of Conservation Concern (Gregory *et al.* 2002).

RMF

Northern Wheatear *Oenanthe oenanthe*

Formerly a rare migrant breeder; now an uncommon to fairly common passage migrant and very rare breeder.

During the 19th century Browne described the Northern Wheatear as a sparingly distributed summer migrant in Leicestershire that occasionally bred; nests were recorded at Bardon, Skeffington and Barlestone. Haines noted a similar pattern of occurrence in Rutland, with breeding recorded near Seaton, Caldecott, Edith Weston and Ketton. It would appear that regular breeding by this species ceased towards the end of the 19th century: the LROS archives mention that it was a scarce but regular spring and autumn migrant in the first part of the 20th century, but do not refer to any breeding records.

The Northern Wheatear is one of the earliest spring migrants to arrive in the counties, with the first record of the year usually occurring in mid to late March. A report of 20 at Tinwell on March 7th 1975 (Mitcham 1984) cannot be considered reliable, so the earliest on record relate to single birds seen on March 9th, at Eyebrook Reservoir in 1957 and Stanford Reservoir in 2003. There have been a further six records prior to March 13th, all of single birds unless stated:

- Saddington Reservoir, March 11th 1993.
- Fort Henry Ponds, March 11th 2000.
- three, Bruntingthorpe Airfield, March 12th 1989.
- two, Rutland Water, March 12th 1989.
- Eyebrook Reservoir, March 12th 1994.
- Rutland Water, March 12th 1994.

The average arrival date has become significantly earlier since the mid-1980s and there have only been two years since 1988 when the first bird has been seen later than March 20th.

Spring passage extends throughout March and April into early May, with a few stragglers into late May. Records in early June are rare: the last spring sightings in 1971 and 1972 were on June 12th and 11th respectively, but apart from one at Stoughton Airfield on June 3rd 1987 and a female at Rutland Water on June 2nd 1996, the only recent records in early June came in 1991, when there were single birds at Sapcote on the 1st, Eyebrook Reservoir on the 2nd and Saddington on the 4th.

Numbers passing through the counties in the spring can be highly variable. LROS Annual Reports have not always specified seasonal totals although from the data available it appears that it is now being seen in greater numbers than ever before; this may in part be due to increased observer coverage and interest. The spring totals in 2002 and especially 2005 were exceptional, and 2004 was probably equally as good since 67 individuals were recorded on April 17th alone. By contrast, just five birds were seen during spring 1957 and there were only eight recorded the year before.

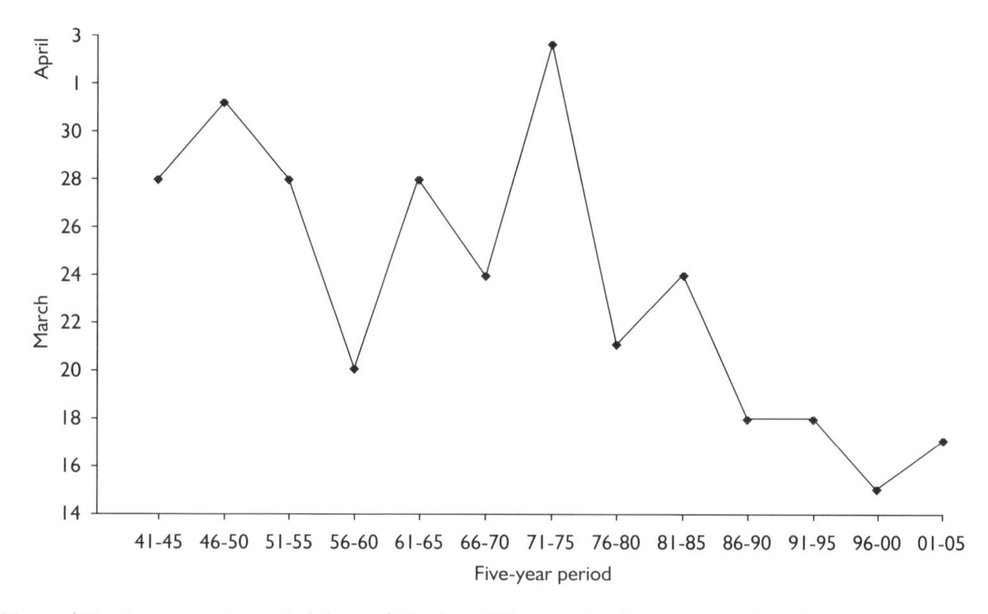

Figure 450: Average spring arrival dates of Northern Wheatears by five-year periods 1941–2005.

Table 36: Northern Wheatear records in spring 1991–2005. Bird totals given where available

Year	1991	1992	1993	1994	1995	1996	1997	1998
Sites	23	23	21	22	22	28	30	35
Birds	76	97	75	–	–	–	–	–
Year	**1999**	**2000**	**2001**	**2002**	**2003**	**2004**	**2005**	
Sites	28	34	22	34	29	36	40	
Birds	67	96	48	111	–	–	166	

Table 37: Northern Wheatear records in spring in selected years 1944–82. Bird totals given where available

Year	1944	1945	1946	1947	1948	1949	1956
Sites	–	5	5	10	12	16	4
Birds	19	–	–	–	–	–	8
Year	**1957**	**1958**	**1966**	**1967**	**1968**	**1979**	**1982**
Sites	3	7	–	–	–	15	12
Birds	5	–	35	38	60	26	25

Northern Wheatears can be encountered almost anywhere in the counties. Ploughed fields, disused airfields, waste ground and areas of short turf are favoured habitats, as are the margins of reservoirs and gravel pits. The regenerated coalfields and other industrial areas of north-west Leicestershire regularly attract passage birds; favoured sites in recent years have included Sence Valley Forest Park, Snibston Discovery Park, Albert Village Lake, Bagworth Heath and the disused power station at Castle Donington.

Spring records of Northern Wheatears often involve groups of up to eight birds. There have been four records of nine together and eight records of ten, with higher spring counts being:

- 17, Albert Village Lake, April 19th 2004.
- 15, Tilton on the Hill, April 1949.
- 15, Kilby Bridge, April 27th 1997.

- 15, Enderby Pool, April 19th 2004.
- 14, Fort Henry Ponds, March 29th 1995.
- 13, Snibston Discovery Park, April 24th 1998.
- 12, Eyebrook Reservoir, April 8th 1959.
- 12, Charnwood Lodge, April 21st 1993.
- 12, Snibston Discovery Park, April 4th 1994.
- 12, Bagworth Heath, April 23rd 1998.
- 12, Albert Village Lake, April 26th 2002.
- 12, Castle Donington, April 18th 2004.
- 11, Leicester City Farms, spring 1949.

Birds of the Greenland race *O. o. leucorhoa* have been reported during the spring regularly since the 1940s and it is likely that a good proportion of birds recorded later in the passage period are of this race. A male trapped and ringed at Bagworth Heath on April 28th 2000 was confirmed to be of this race (Smith 2002a) and others were trapped and ringed in 2001 at Raw Dykes Road, Leicester on May 2nd and Whetstone on May 11th. One found dead at Croxton Kerrial on May 7th 1952 was also confirmed as *leucorhoa* and the skin was deposited at the Leicester Museum.

Breeding has been confirmed or strongly suspected in six years since 1941:

1948	a pair at Eyebrook Reservoir from May 15th to 18th behaved as though they were breeding in the area and the female was regularly seen entering rabbit burrows. On August 19th a pair was seen feeding three fledged young at the site.
1949	two pairs were thought to have bred at Eyebrook Reservoir; on July 6th pairs were seen feeding two and one young respectively.
1972	a bird was seen carrying food into a heap of stones at North Luffenham on July 9th.
1974	a pair bred at Rutland Water whilst the reservoir was being constructed, raising two young.
1976	a female was seen carrying food at Clipsham on July 10th 1976.
1979	two nests were found at Desford and three young were known to have fledged.

In addition, a pair in the south-west of Leicestershire in late May 1982 behaved as though they were breeding and a pair was observed copulating at a site in north-east Leicestershire in early May 1998, but no further records were received from either area. Three juveniles at Beacon Hill on July 9th 1993 may also have indicated local breeding.

Autumn passage usually commences in early August and extends to late September, with a few birds seen in October most years. Prior to 1981 the first returning birds were noted in July in at least eight years, but since then there have only been four records in this month: two at Eyebrook Reservoir on July 2nd 1999 (where there had been a female on June 30th), single birds in 2000 at Eyebrook Reservoir on the 17th and Frolesworth on the 28th and one at Enderby Pool on July 20th 2005. Records in mid to late June, such as one at Loughborough Sewage Farm on June 29th 1957, three at Eyebrook Reservoir on June 18th 1966 and two between Seaton and Caldecott on June 22nd 1966 are more difficult to assign to a passage period and may have involved wandering non-breeders.

Numbers during the autumn are usually smaller than the spring although the two largest counts ever recorded in the counties, of 20 at Bruntingthorpe Airfield in autumn 1968 and 19 at Stoughton Airfield on August 19th 1986, have occurred during this season. With the exception of 15 at Bruntingthorpe Airfield during autumn 1949, all records during this passage period have been of fewer than ten and only seven counts have exceeded five:

- nine, Croft, August 14th 1942.
- nine, Lindley Airfield, August 22nd 1948.
- eight, Lindley Airfield, autumn 1949.
- eight, Sence Valley Forest Park, August 27th 2001.
- six, Stoughton Airfield, August 14th 1987.
- six, Sileby, August 30th 1993.
- six, Enderby Pool, September 25th 2002.

Given that the largest autumn numbers usually occur in late August and that autumn numbers are generally smaller than those in spring, a report of 35 at Ingthorpe on October 9th 1976 (Mitcham 1984) cannot be considered reliable.

As with the spring, LROS Annual Reports have not always specified seasonal totals, but from the data available it appears that the best recent year was 1999, when a total of 43 birds were recorded at 23 sites. 59 birds during the autumn of 1967 is the highest annual total.

Table 38: Northern Wheatear records in autumn 1991–2005. Bird totals given where available

Year	1991	1992	1993	1994	1995	1996	1997	1998
Sites	10	12	13	7	7	8	15	11
Birds	24	19	21	11	12	12	25	16
Year	**1999**	**2000**	**2001**	**2002**	**2003**	**2004**	**2005**	
Sites	23	16	15	12	16	19	11	
Birds	43	28	27	–	–	–	32	

Table 39: Northern Wheatear records in autumn in selected years 1944–82. Bird totals given where available

Year	1944	1945	1946	1947	1948	1949	1956
Sites	–	5	6	6	11	11	7
Birds	24	–	–	–	–	–	–
Year	**1957**	**1958**	**1966**	**1967**	**1968**	**1979**	**1982**
Sites	6	7	–	–	–	12	8
Birds	–	–	26	59	–	–	14

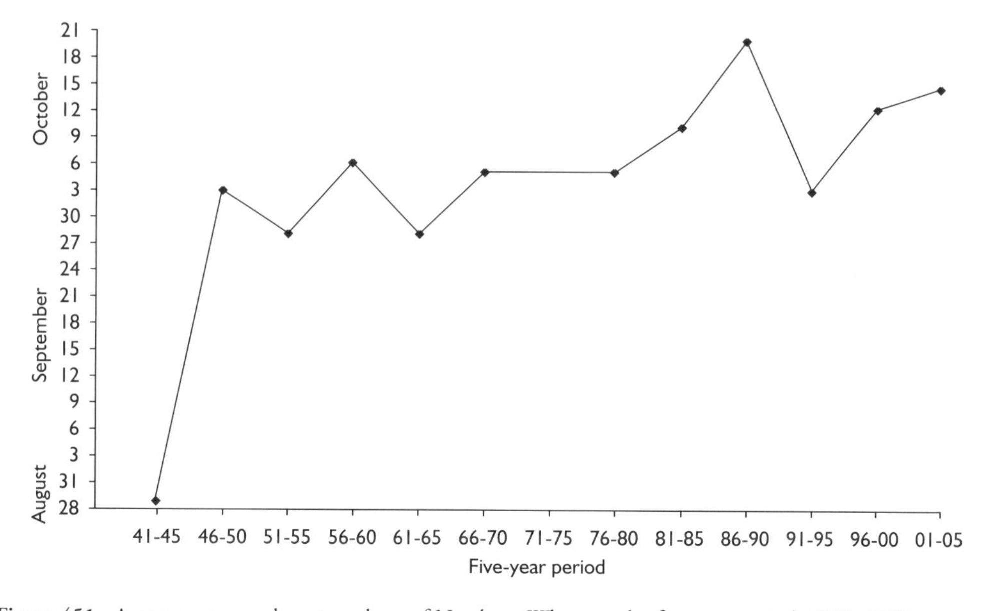

Figure 451: Average autumn departure dates of Northern Wheatears by five-year periods 1941–2005.

The last bird of the year is usually seen in early or mid-October. There have been eight records in October later than the 26th, all of single birds unless stated:

- Ratby Meadows, October 30th 1980.
- Castle Donington, October 29th 2004.

- Knossington, October 28th 1984.
- two, Melton Airfield, October 28th 1990.
- Eyebrook Reservoir, October 28th 1990.
- Cottesmore Airfield, October 28th 1991.
- Eyebrook Reservoir, October 28th 2005.
- Stoughton Airfield, October 27th 2001.

Four birds have been recorded in November: at Eyebrook Reservoir on November 1st 1975, at the Rutland Water construction site on November 26th 1972 (Mitcham 1984) and two individuals on the 27th, at Eyebrook Reservoir in 1960 (Mitcham 1984) and Outwoods in 1971.

Northern Wheatears breed throughout Europe, north-west Africa, south-west and central Asia, northern Siberia, Alaska, north-east Canada and Greenland. The nominate race breeds in northern Eurasia. The 'Greenland Wheatear' *O. o. leucorhoa* breeds in Greenland, Iceland and north-east Canada. All populations winter in tropical Africa. The latest British population estimate is 55,000 pairs (Baker *et al.* 2006).

RMF

Ring Ouzel *Turdus torquatus*

Formerly a scarce localised migrant breeder; now a scarce to uncommon spring and rare autumn passage migrant; recorded in all months except February, July and August, with the majority from late March to early May.

During the 19th century Ring Ouzels were uncommon and rarely observed except in late autumn and spring, though Browne records that they were known to breed near Whitwick and had occasionally bred at Market Bosworth. In Rutland, Haines found that they occurred in small numbers throughout the county in spring and autumn every year, but did not remain to breed. Whilst the high relict moorland and granite outcrops of Charnwood remain the most important area in the counties for the species there has been no evidence of breeding since the 19th century, although Ring Ouzels are now recorded as regular and increasing migrants, predominantly in spring.

From the formation of LROS in 1941 until 1980 this species remained a rare visitor to the counties, with records in 21 of the 40 years relating to a total of 37 individuals. There was only one record between 1946 and 1960 (of a female at Potters Marston on May 1st 1954) and only four years in which more than two birds were seen (three in 1973 and 1974, four in 1944 and five in 1976). A significant increase in numbers began from 1980 onwards and particularly from the mid-1990s; there were more individuals recorded between 1996 and 2005 than in the previous 55 years. The best year was 2003, when 16 birds were found, whilst other notable annual totals have been 12 in 2002 and 2005, ten in 1998 and 2000 and nine in 1988.

This increase is mainly a result of the discovery of several important spring stopover sites, the first of which was Snibston Discovery Park, where nine birds were recorded between 1994 and 1999. Bardon Hill has now been found to be the most important site in the counties for passage Ring Ouzels; they have been recorded in spring annually here since 1998, with 32 spring individuals between 1998 and 2005. Multiple arrivals, which were virtually unheard of prior to the late 1990s, are now regular at this site and have included five males and a female on April 17th 2003, three males and two females on April 16th 2001 and three males and a female on May 3rd 1998. Other areas of high ground in Charnwood may prove to be important passage sites in the future; records of two males and a female at Charnwood Lodge on both April 20th 1984 and May 4th 2002 and a male and two females at Ives Head on April 23rd 1989 hint at the potential of these two sites. High ground in other parts of Leicestershire and Rutland may also repay investigation; Croft Hill, for instance, has been visited by eight birds since 2000.

There have been eight birds recorded in March, the earliest of which was a male at Rutland Water on March 22nd 1981. All March records have been of single birds except for two females at Snibston Discovery Park from

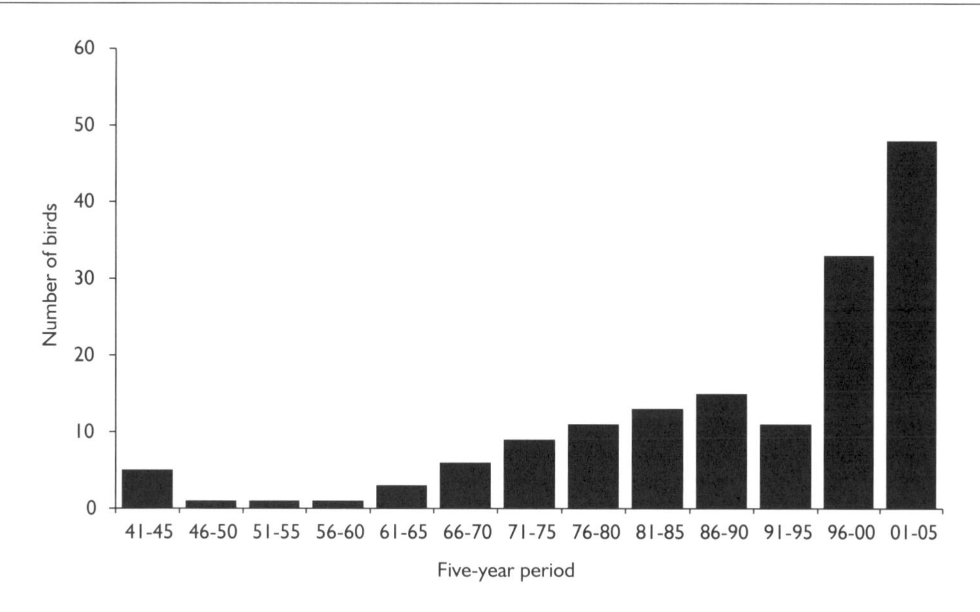

Figure 452: Numbers of Ring Ouzels 1941–2005.

March 27th to 29th 1996. Passage peaks in April and early May, with particular arrivals during the periods April 16th to 18th (25 individuals) and April 25th to 27th (18 individuals). Records after early May are unusual and the only ones later than May 10th are a female at Loddington on May 13th 2004, a male at Leicester on May 22nd 1946 and one at Kilby on the very unusual date of June 17th 1967.

Numbers are much lower in autumn than in spring. The earliest autumn record is of one at Exton on September 15th 1978, although the only other occurrence prior to October 10th is a male at Snarestone on September 26th 1944. Nine individuals have been recorded in October:

- male, Owston, October 10th 1985.
- Groby, October 14th 1962.
- male foud dead, Edith Weston, October 14th 1993.
- male, Rutland Water, October 16th to 19th 1988.
- male and three juveniles, Bardon Hill, October 22nd 2005.
- male, Freemen's Weir, Leicester, October 23rd 1992.

The latest in autumn was one at Swithland Reservoir on November 7th 1976; the only other fully accepted November record involved a male in an Ashwell garden on November 5th 2005.

Leverton (1993), following studies at a site in Sussex, found that migrants were much more numerous in autumn (especially October) than in spring, whereas the opposite is true in Leicestershire and Rutland. Although we lack ringing data to provide hard evidence about the origin of our migrants, the recent increase in records at a time when the British population is declining suggests that at least some of them are likely to be from the Scandinavian breeding population. This is especially likely to be true of spring records from mid-April onwards (the peak period for records in the counties) and autumn records in October. Earlier spring and autumn records may involve birds from the British breeding population.

Winter records, though exceptional, date back to 1888 when a female was killed with a catapult at Kibworth on January 6th; other than one at Huncote on December 25th 1943 the only other winter record involved a male at Rutland Water from December 28th 1996 until January 1st 1997. There are several winter records from nearby counties, sometimes following large arrivals of Fieldfares.

The average arrival date has become noticeably earlier since the mid-1980s, coinciding with increased numbers of birds visiting the counties. In light of previous fluctuations, more data will be required before we can be sure that the earlier average spring arrival date recorded during the past decade is a genuine trend.

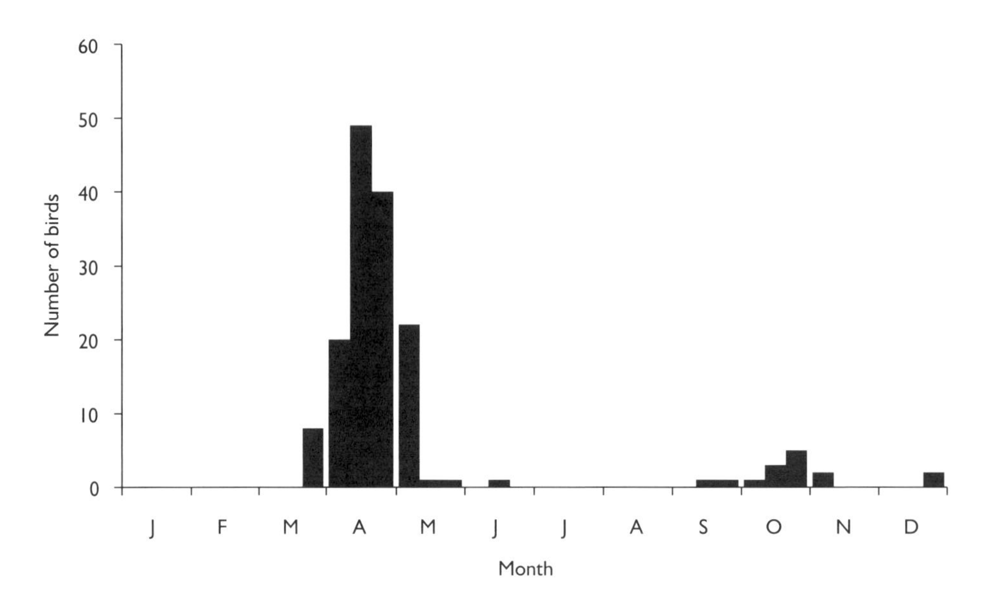

Figure 453: Monthly occurrence of Ring Ouzels 1941–2005.

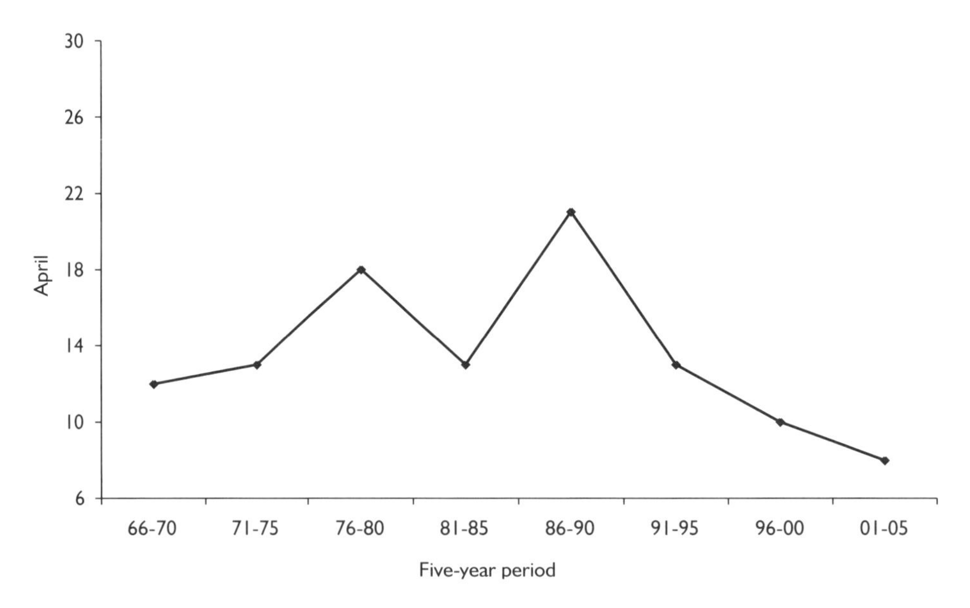

Figure 454: Average spring arrival dates of Ring Ouzels by five-year periods 1966–2005.

Following a review in 2004, two previously published records were found to be unacceptable: single birds at Narborough on January 19th 1944 and at Stoughton on April 24th 1994 (Fray 2005).

Ring Ouzels breed in mountainous areas in north-west and central Europe and south-west Asia and winter around the Mediterranean coast, especially in north-west Africa. The latest British population estimate is 6,157 to 7,549 pairs (Baker *et al.* 2006). Following a marked contraction in range and decline in numbers, this species has been added to the 'Red List' of Birds of Conservation Concern (Gregory *et al.* 2002).

AHJH

Blackbird (Common Blackbird) ***Turdus merula***

Abundant resident breeder and winter visitor.

The Blackbird is one of our most widespread and abundant species, made familiar as much by its beautiful song as by its distinctive appearance. Formerly restricted to woodlands, it now occupies a wide variety of habitats, including urban areas, where the mainly resident breeding population is joined in winter and during passage periods by birds from northern and central Europe.

Unsurprisingly, following a gradual spread into man-made habitats, this species was considered resident and common in the 19th century. Both Browne and Haines considered it to be resident, with no mention of autumn or winter influxes. Both recorded pied varieties, of which perhaps the most interesting was one with a white gorget found sitting on its nest at Bisbrooke in 1855 'and mistaken for a ring-ouzel.'

During 1976–84 Warrilow found Blackbirds present during the breeding season in all but six of the tetrads in Leicestershire and Rutland, occupying almost any habitat with scrub, trees and open spaces for feeding. On the basis of an average territory density of 190 to 300 pairs per occupied tetrad, he estimated that the total breeding population was likely to be 120,000 to 190,000 pairs, making the Blackbird the most numerous breeding bird in the counties. Mitcham (1992) recorded this species in all 117 tetrads in Rutland, with breeding proved in 93 (79%) of them. During the Leicestershire Garden Bird Survey between January 1996 and June 2005 Blackbird was the most frequently recorded species, occurring in 98% of gardens at an average of three birds per garden; likewise, a survey of four green spaces within the Leicester city boundary in 1989 showed that this species was the most numerous at all four sites and accounted for over 20% of all territories (Fray *et al.* 1990).

CBC results from Stoughton have shown a gradual but steady decline, from 53 pairs in both 1969 and 1975 to only 20 in 1997, a decline of 62%; in contrast, numbers have remained more stable at Newton Harcourt. At two Rutland CBC plots numbers have bucked the national trend by increasing, especially at the farmland site of King's Hill Lodge, Uppingham, where numbers have almost trebled. Given that numbers of this species on farmland CBC plots in England fell by 30% between 1967 and 1999 (Brown & Grice 2005), continued regular monitoring of the local breeding population is desirable.

All recent high counts have been during winter and passage periods and have included 120 roosting at Glen Parva on January 30th 1981, 111 at Abbey Park, Leicester on April 18th 1989, 120 at Kilby Bridge on November 3rd 1992 and 82 at Rutland Water on January 25th 2005.

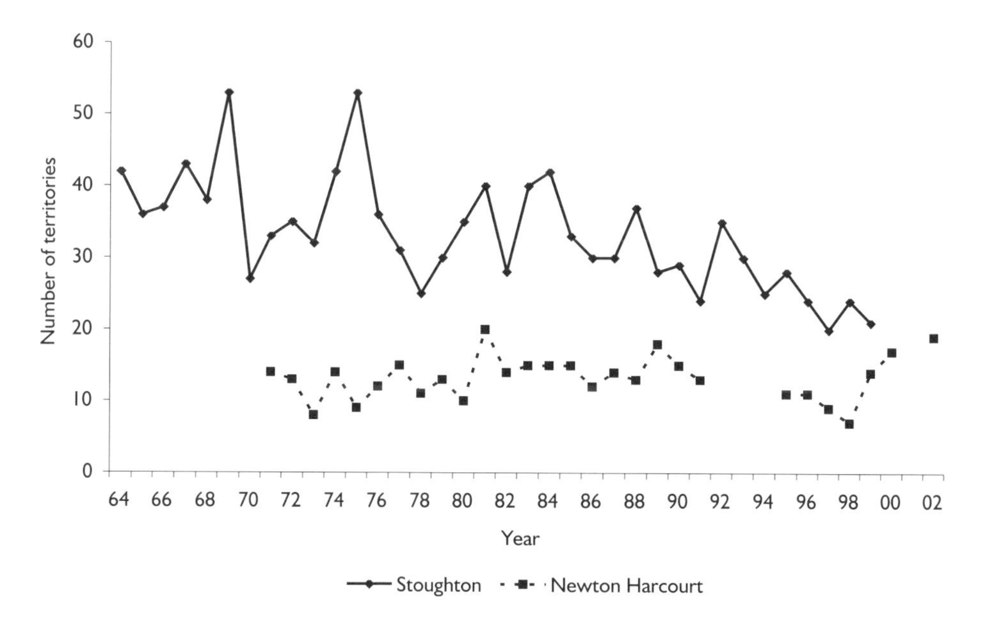

Figure 455: Number of breeding pairs of Blackbirds on two Leicestershire CBC plots 1964–2002.

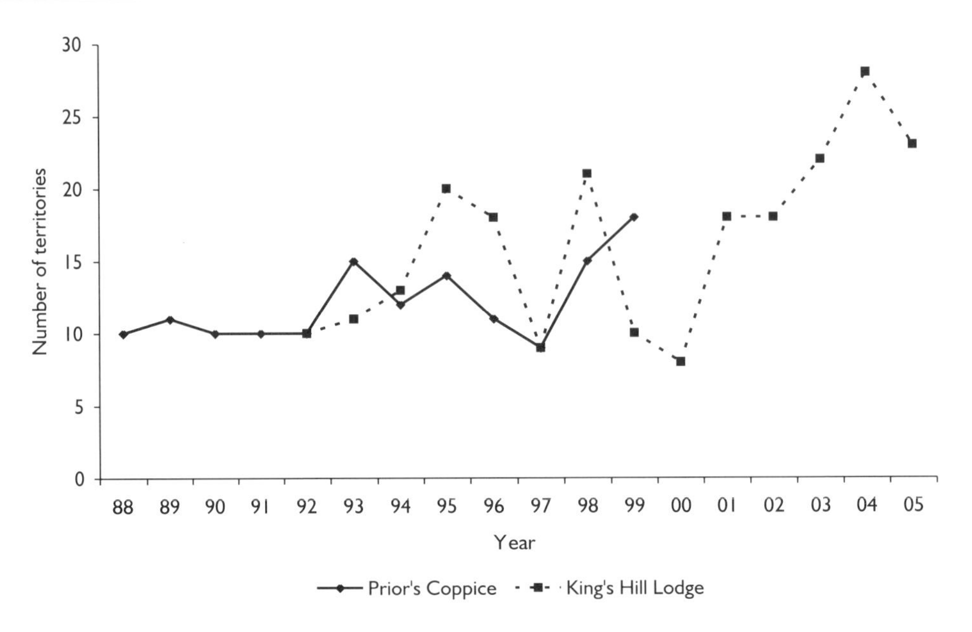

Figure 456: Number of breeding pairs of Blackbirds on two Rutland CBC plots 1988–2005.

Firm evidence of movement to and from the continent is provided by ringing recoveries. Birds ringed in Leicestershire and Rutland have been recovered in Finland, Norway (two), Sweden (seven), Denmark (two), Germany (five), the Netherlands (five), France (two) and Spain (one), whilst there have been local recoveries of birds ringed in Norway (two), Germany (one) and the Netherlands (four). All these birds were ringed during passage or winter periods, in keeping with the view of Wernham *et al.* (2002) that very few natives of Britain and Ireland move abroad. Unlike other thrushes, Blackbirds do not undertake significant hard-weather movements (Snow 1966).

Blackbirds breed over most of Europe and north-west Africa, as well as the Middle East, western Siberia and central and southern Asia. Northern and eastern populations are partially or wholly migratory, wintering south of their breeding range. The latest British breeding population is estimated at 4,620,000 pairs (Baker *et al.* 2006).

AHJH

Fieldfare — *Turdus pilaris*

Common winter visitor, rare in summer.

Browne and Haines in the 19th century described this species as a winter migrant which did not remain to breed. Its arrival in autumn seems to have been getting steadily earlier, though this may partly reflect increased recording: in Rutland, Haines noted that from 1736 to 1800 the average date of arrival recorded by T. Barker of Lyndon was October 29th to 30th, but from 1890 to 1905 it was October 22nd; Browne stated that it appeared about the middle of October in Leicestershire, with an exceptionally early bird at Lowesby on September 2nd 1877. There were some reports of late spring birds 'even onward until June', but Browne considered these to have involved misidentified Mistle Thrushes. He also mentioned a summer record of one which 'appears to have been shot at Kirby Muxloe on July 29th 1864'; his reservations about this record were probably strengthened because the same observer reported nesting Redwings in his grounds during the same summer. During the severe winter of 1878–79 Macaulay noted that they were 'seen by thousands and shot by scores' during the first fortnight, after which they entirely disappeared (no doubt to look for a safer environment!). Today the Fieldfare is predominantly a passage migrant and winter visitor which is occasionally recorded during the summer. Numbers fluctuate from year to year. Hickling considered this species less numerous than the Redwing, but in recent years the opposite has been true.

Birds are nowadays normally present from late September or early October until late April or early May. The average autumn arrival date has in general become earlier since the early 1960s, although this may be partly due to increased recording effort. Between 1941 and 1967 the only arrival prior to October was one at Quorn on September 22nd 1948, but since 1967 birds have arrived during September in 15 years, eight of which have been since 1992. Most of these September arrivals are during the last ten days of the month, although earlier records, all of single birds unless stated, have been as follows:

- Rothley, September 1st 1977.
- Uppingham, September 4th 1989.
- Aylestone Meadows, September 13th 1994.
- Charnwood Lodge, September 17th 2005.
- three, East Goscote, September 19th 2003.

The first arrival date can, however, be highly variable; for instance, the first birds in the autumn of 2002 were not recorded until October 16th and the first in 1999 arrived on October 18th. Early and late arrivals normally correspond with those of Redwings and are presumably influenced by prevailing weather patterns.

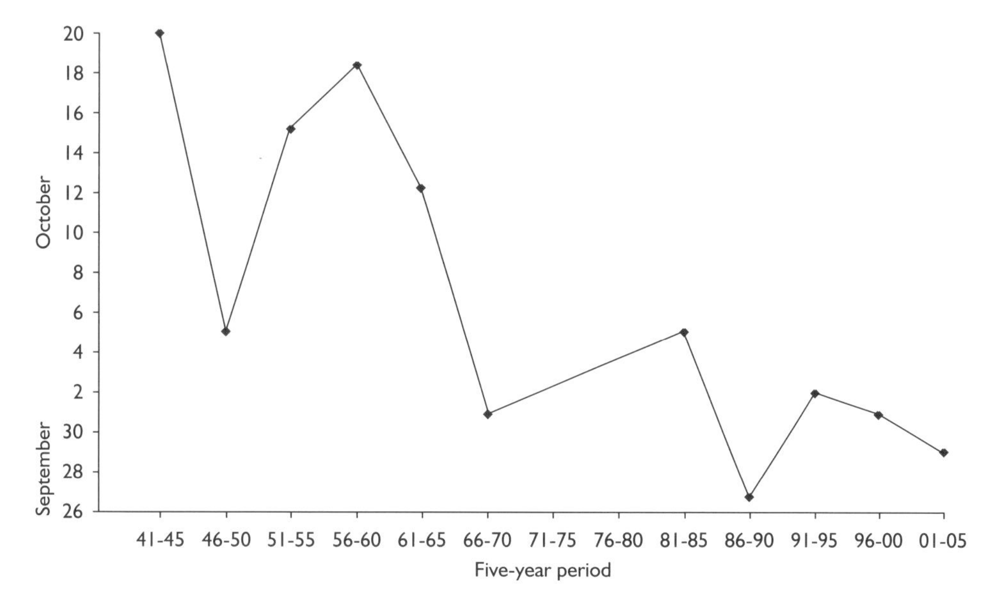

Figure 457: Average autumn arrival dates of Fieldfares by five-year periods 1941–2005.

Four-figure flocks were virtually unheard of before the 1980s, the only ones being 2,000 at Sileby on December 15th 1945, 1,000 at Stanford Reservoir on January 30th 1949 and an exceptional 4,000 at Barrow upon Soar on December 3rd 1949, a count that has only been exceeded once subsequently. There has been a notable increase in the numbers of birds recorded during passage and winter periods since the early 1980s: after 1,200 at Sharnford on March 29th 1982, four-figure flocks were recorded every year from 1986 to 2002, although oddly there have been none since. Most of these flocks have numbered fewer than 2,000, larger totals being:

- 5,000 at Priory Water on October 24th 1993.
- 3,500 at Harby on November 16th 1997.
- 3,000 at Priory Water on October 27th 1991.
- 3,000 at Priory Water on November 25th 2001.
- 2,800 at Enderby on November 17th 1997.
- 2,500 at Kilby Bridge on January 28th 1996.

- 2,350 at Rearsby on February 10th 1990.
- 2,000 to 2,500 at Market Bosworth from January 27th to 29th 1996.
- 2,000 to 2,500 between Walton and Bruntingthorpe on February 17th 1996.

Two particularly large influxes took place in the 1990s: in late January and early February 1996 there were six four-figure flocks recorded, including those mentioned above at Kilby Bridge, Market Bosworth and between Walton and Bruntingthorpe, whilst between November 7th and 18th 1997 another six flocks of 1,000+ were noted, including those mentioned above at Harby and Enderby.

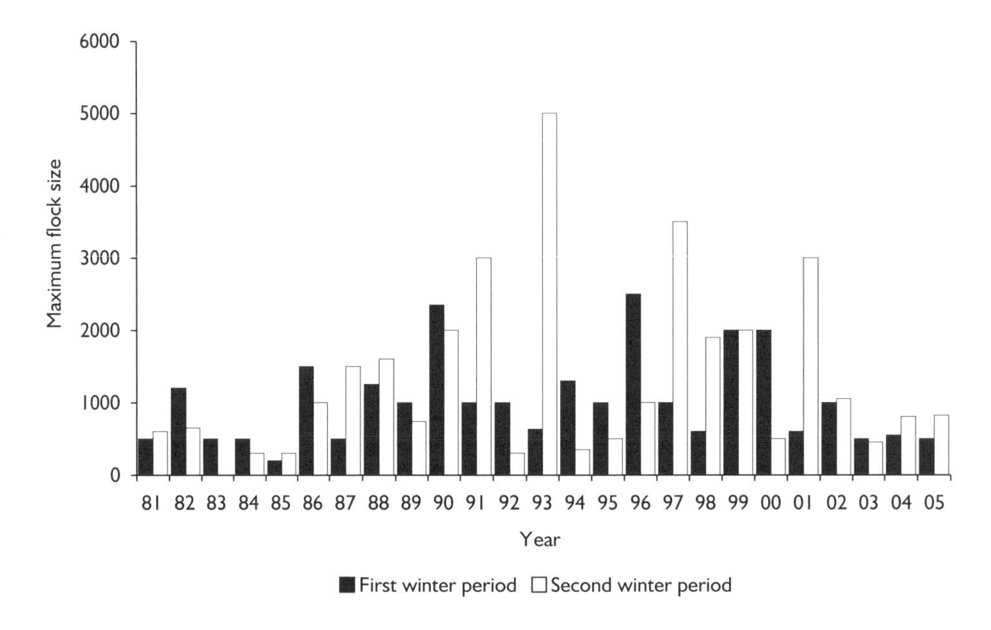

Figure 458: Maximum winter flock sizes of Fieldfares 1981–2005.

Most birds have usually departed the counties by mid-April, although there is often a distinct passage movement in this month; notable flocks have included 500 at Gopsall Park on April 17th 1954, 800 at Melton Country Park on April 9th 1995, 1,000 at Launde on April 15th 1995 and 1,200 at Withcote on April 15th 1996. There have been May records in 29 years since 1941, including six sizeable flocks:

- 350 at Tilton on the Hill on May 7th 1980.
- 300 at Peckleton on May 4th 1980.
- 250 at Launde on May 7th 1980.
- 111 at Launde on May 2nd 1999.
- 57 at Launde on May 8th 1991.
- 30 at Burton Overy on May 6th 1979.

It is interesting to note that the majority of large groups in April and May have been found in the area of east Leicestershire around Launde, Withcote and Tilton on the Hill.

Most May records occur prior to the 14th, although there have been five later than this date, all of single birds unless stated:

- five, Eyebrook Reservoir, May 30th 1967.
- Willoughby Waterleys, May 27th 1948.
- unspecified site, May 18th 1946.
- eight, Huncote, May 16th 1980.
- King's Hill Lodge, Uppingham, May 15th 2000.

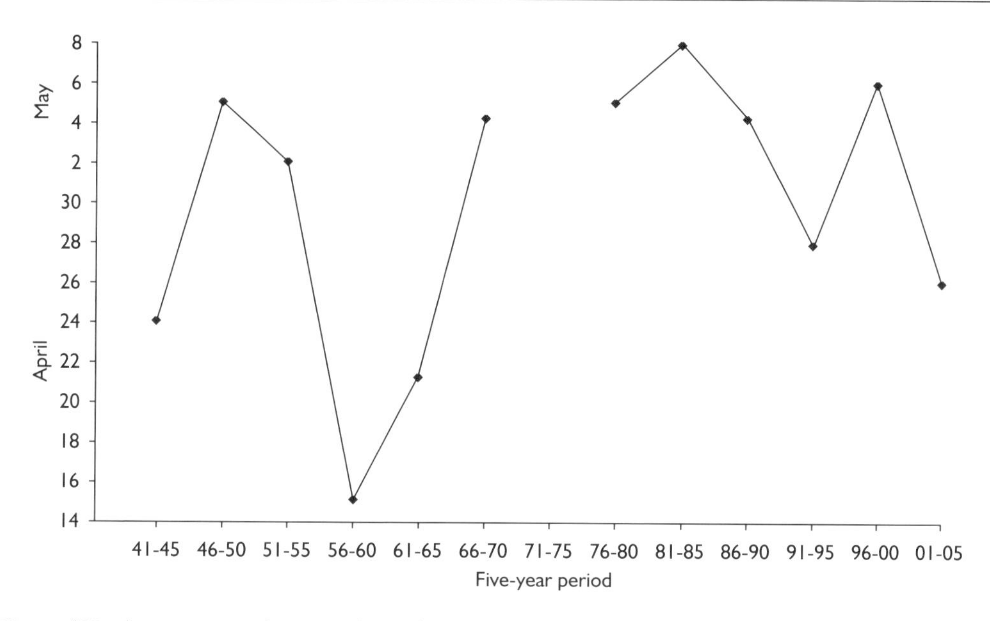

Figure 459: Average spring departure dates of Fieldfares by five-year periods 1941–2005.

There have been reports during the period June to August in nine years, although how much scrutiny these records received is not known:

- 1944: 15 to 20 at Keythorpe on August 17th and ten at Wistow on August 26th.
- 1969: one at Eyebrook Reservoir on July 27th.
- 1974: one at Aylestone on June 13th.
- 1975: one apparently 'summered' at Aylestone.
- 1976: one at Gaddesby on August 27th.
- 1980: one at Wing on August 7th.
- 1981: four at Narborough Bog on July 22nd and one at Eyebrook Reservoir on July 29th.
- 1983: one found dead at Bradgate Park on June 15th.
- 1998: one at Baggrave on July 14th, 20 at Barwell on July 29th and six at Belgrave, Leicester from July 31st until August 4th.

As there have been regular breeding records from both Derbyshire and Staffordshire (Brown & Grice 2005) it is possible that some of the above refer to birds which bred in England, but the large numbers in 1998 suggest an early arrival from northern Europe.

Birds ringed in Leicestershire and Rutland have been recovered in Finland (four), Norway (two), the Netherlands, France and Italy (two). Ringers at Leicester City Farms on November 11th 1961 had a very exciting and informative day when they trapped a bird which had been ringed as a nestling near Rovanieni (Finland) on June 17th 1960 and ringed another which was shot near Udine (Italy) just one month later on December 13th 1961. Partially albino birds were recorded at Saddington on January 14th 1980 and Wistow on April 19th 1980.

Fieldfares breed throughout central and northern Europe east to central Siberia. Northern populations are migratory, wintering in southern and western Europe. During 1988–1991 there were fewer than 25 pairs in Britain, mainly in northern England and Scotland (Gibbons *et al.* 1993). In 2005, however, Holling *et al.* (2008) reported only one suggestion of possible breeding (in Shetland). The small size of the British breeding population, combined with its recent decline, has resulted in the Fieldfare being placed on the 'Amber List' of Birds of Conservation Concern (Gregory *et al.* 2002).

AHJH

Song Thrush *Turdus philomelos*

Common resident breeder, recent decline; passage migrant and winter visitor.

In the 19th century Browne described this species as resident and common in Leicestershire, its ranks considerably increased during the autumn when the note of arriving birds 'may be heard during mild nights in October.' In Rutland, Haines noted that many migrated in hard winters, but that at other seasons it was very abundant. Albinism is relatively uncommon in this species, but Harley recorded three albino birds taken out of a nest at Aylestone.

During the first half of the 20th century the Song Thrush was regarded as our most abundant thrush, present in most habitats with trees or mature shrubs. Although a national decline began during the 1970s it was not commented on in LROS Annual Reports until 1993, perhaps because local farmland supports higher densities than the mean national value.

Recent distribution and population estimates have been provided by Mitcham (1992) and Warrilow. The former recorded the Song Thrush in 102 (87%) of the tetrads in Rutland and noted that the absence of birds from some farmland tetrads may have been related to the increasing practice of growing winter barley, which leads to a reduction of spring tillage where birds formerly fed. During the period 1976 to 1984, Warrilow found this species present in 605 tetrads in the counties (95% of the total number of tetrads), with breeding confirmed in 380. He noted that it was largely absent from smaller copses and the interior zones of the largest woods, where it was outnumbered by the Blackbird in a ratio of 3:1. Nonetheless, the average territory density in 39 woodlands surveyed in east Leicestershire in 1987 and 1990 was 158 pairs per tetrad, higher than the average British density of 103 pairs per tetrad. Mean densities in gardens can be even higher; for example 285 pairs per tetrad were located at the University of Leicester Botanical Gardens at Oadby in 1993. The mean territory density on farmland was 70 (Stoughton) and 100 (Newton Harcourt) per tetrad, a lot higher than the mean value for British farmland of 26 pairs per tetrad. Given an average of 60 to 80 pairs per occupied tetrad, he estimated a total breeding population of between 36,000 and 48,000 pairs, though the current population is almost certainly much lower than this.

Nationally, high population levels were followed by a steady decline from the late 1970s, accelerated by the harsh winters of 1978–79 and 1981–82. By 1984 the population level on farmland was half that of 1976,

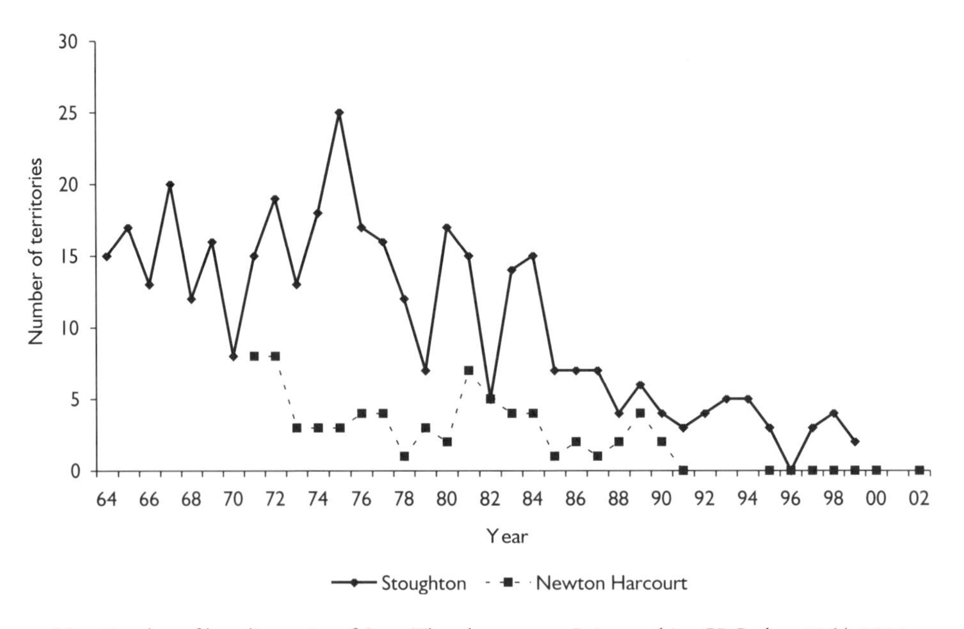

Figure 460: Number of breeding pairs of Song Thrushes on two Leicestershire CBC plots 1964–2002.

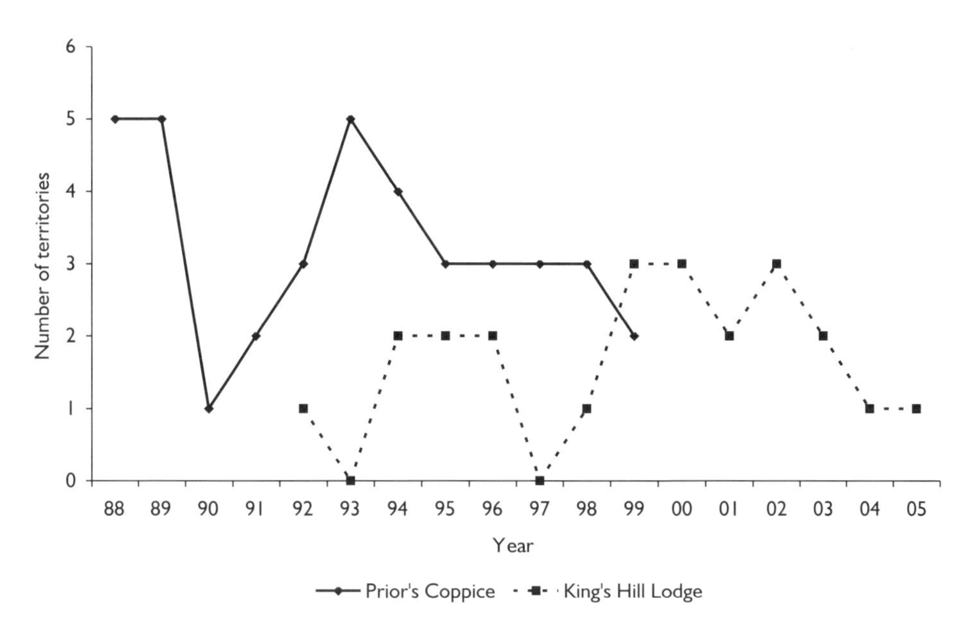

Figure 461: Number of breeding pairs of Song Thrushes on two Rutland CBC plots 1988–2005.

though the decline in woodland was less severe. Farmland declines have been attributed to changing farmland methods, for example the loss of spring tillage, use of pesticides and destruction of hedgerows. There has also been concern about molluscicides used to kill slugs which may affect suburban populations. Local CBC data confirm that numbers have continued to decline from the high levels of the early 1970s. Stoughton has seen the most dramatic decrease, where from a peak of 25 pairs in 1975 numbers fell to 15 pairs by 1984 (with noticeably low counts of seven pairs in 1979 and five pairs in 1982, following severe winters); from 1985 onwards, no more than seven pairs were located annually and in 1996 this species was not considered to have bred at the site. At Newton Harcourt there were eight pairs in 1971, but by 1991 Song Thrushes had been lost from the site. The two CBC plots in Rutland, at Prior's Coppice and King's Hill Lodge, Uppingham, began in the late 1980s and early 1990s; at this time the Song Thrush population nationally had already declined dramatically and thus the figures for these two sites are a little more stable.

The local breeding population is joined by birds from the continent during passage and winter periods, although the only significant counts published in recent Annual Reports which may have related to influxes from the continent are of several smaller flocks totalling 600 birds in the Carlton Curlieu, Shangton and Illston on the Hill area on January 11th 1981 and 106 at Croft Hill on October 7th 2002. Confirmation that continental birds occur was provided by the recovery at Long Clawson in January 1985 of a bird which had been ringed in the Netherlands the previous October. Distinguishing nominate *philomelos* from the resident British *clarkei* can be tricky, though the former tend to show colder grey tones: a helpful photograph and note were published in the LROS Annual Report of 2002 regarding several presumed *philomelos* trapped and ringed at Charnwood Lodge on October 19th 2002 (Judson 2004). The majority of ringing recoveries, however, show that birds from the local breeding population normally remain within Britain, though there are three recoveries from Ireland and one recovery from France which probably involved a migrant since the bird was ringed in November. Further studies of both breeding populations and migrant/wintering birds would be desirable.

Song Thrushes breed throughout most of Europe eastwards into central Siberia. Western European populations are largely resident, although most other populations are migratory, wintering mainly in western Europe and around the Mediterranean. The current British population estimate is 1,030,000 pairs (Baker *et al.* 2006) but the steady decline first noted in the mid 1970s has caused this species to be placed on the 'Red List' of Birds of Conservation Concern (Gregory *et al.* 2002).

AHJH

Redwing *Turdus iliacus*

Common winter visitor.

During the 19th century Browne described this species as a winter migrant to Leicestershire, generally distributed, but not remaining to breed and noted that its numbers fluctuated from year to year. It arrived about the middle of October and remained 'sometimes late into the spring.' Haines considered it to be a regular winter visitor to Rutland during the same period, although not in such numbers as the Fieldfare. He mentioned that it arrived during October and in mild winters remained until the second or third week of April, or sometimes later. Haines also noted that in hard weather this species soon starved.

Today, the Redwing remains a passage migrant and winter visitor, normally present from late September until early or mid-April. The average autumn arrival date is almost a week earlier than Fieldfare and has been becoming progressively earlier since the mid-1960s; there have been September records in 22 years since 1941, 15 of which have been since 1985. The majority have occurred during the last ten days of September, with earlier records being:

- one, Scraptoft, September 13th 2000.
- three, London Road, Leicester, September 13th 2000.
- two, Cropston, September 15th 1991.
- 20, Braunstone, Leicester, September 16th 1945.
- 15, Saddington, September 16th 1985.
- six, Priory Water, September 18th 2005.
- six, Priory Water, September 19th 1993.

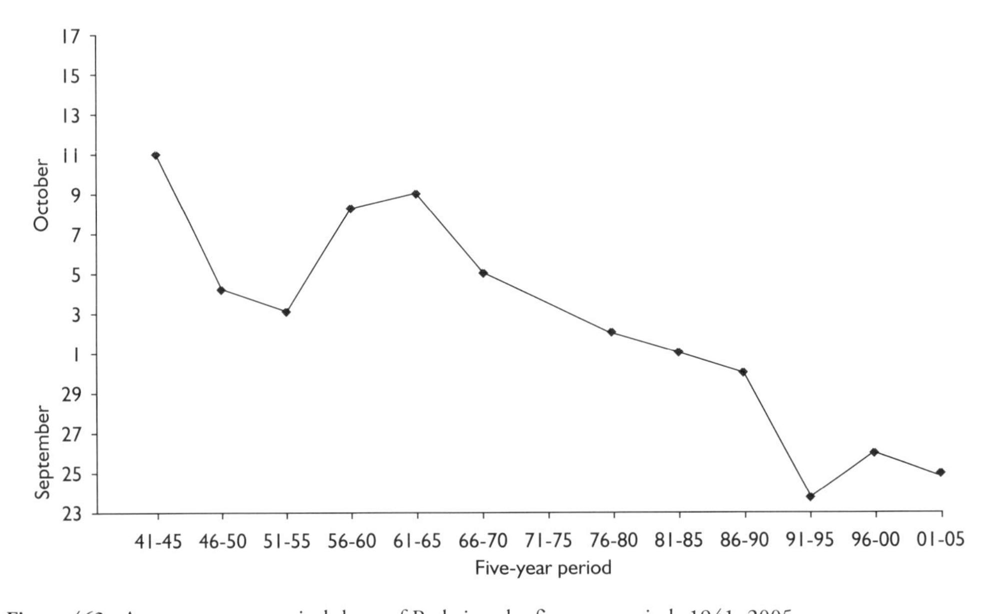

Figure 462: Average autumn arrival dates of Redwings by five-year periods 1941–2005.

There seems to have been a significant decline in the numbers of wintering birds during the last 50 years. Hickling considered that Redwings were usually much more numerous in winter than Fieldfares and this is backed up by the fact that the four largest totals on record, which all involved roost counts, occurred before the late 1970s: 20,000 at Barrow upon Soar in late 1960, 6,800 at Higham Grange on January 25th 1951, 5,000 again at Higham in 1960 and 3,000 at Huncote in February 1976. The only roost to hold over 1,000 birds in more recent years was at Lucas' Marsh, Oadby, where there were 1,400 on November 20th 1983. There have been six counts away from roosts of more than 1,000, as follows:

- 'thousands' at Leicester City Farms on October 13th 1962.
- 2,000 between Enderby and Narborough on February 3rd 1986.
- 1,500 in the Walton/Bruntingthorpe area on February 17th 1996.
- 1,300 at Priory Water on October 12th 1997.
- 1,200 at Hinckley on October 12th 2003.
- 1,200 at Deans Lane, Woodhouse on October 26th 2005.

The latter two totals were both recorded on visible migration watches and the majority of the most recent large counts have been recorded in similar circumstances; in 2005 there were 705 over Trent Valley Pit on October 16th and 660 over Rutland Water on October 25th, whilst at Deans Lane, Woodhouse a total of 3,099 was counted on 14 dates between October 13th and November 17th (Lister 2007b).

It is not clear whether the recent decline is the result of hunting pressure in France and Portugal, climatic change or other factors (Wernham *et al.* 2002).

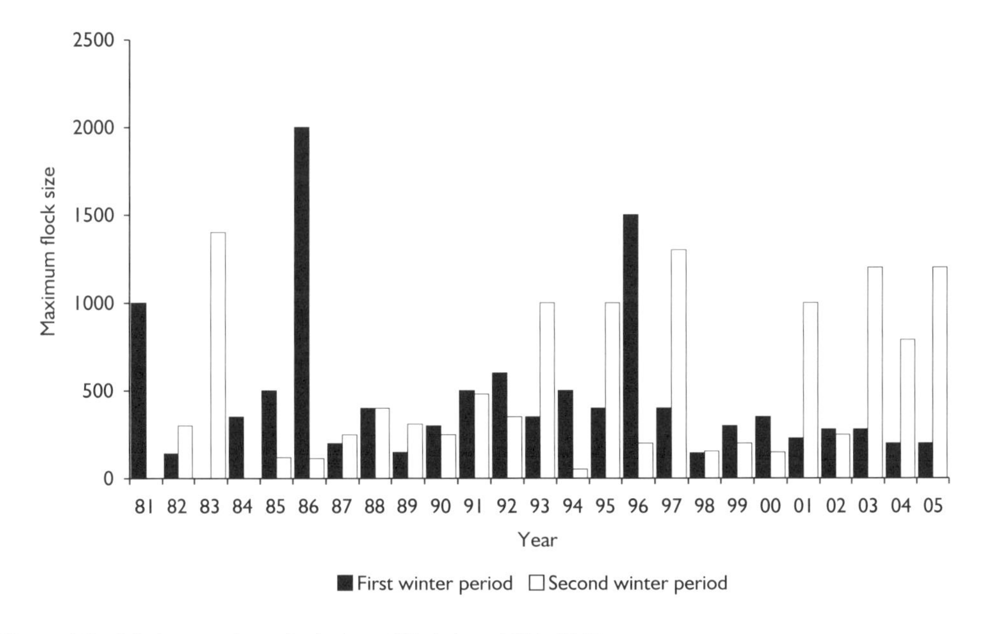

Figure 463: Maximum winter flock sizes of Redwings 1981–2005.

This species is prone to hard-weather movements, after which it may appear in urban environments including the city centre of Leicester. Browne also noted this behaviour in January 1888 and January 1889, when he saw birds within ten yards of the footpath on Aylestone Road. As mentioned by Haines, this species suffers badly during harsh weather: in the famously cold winter of 1962–63 'of the 30 or so species found dead in the two counties the Redwing was easily the most numerous' and 'starving birds allowed themselves to be approached to within a few feet' (Gamble 1965).

The majority of Redwings have left the counties by early April and, unlike Fieldfare, there are very few records of large passage flocks in this month; 450 at Kilby Bridge on April 6th 1996 is by far the biggest group recorded in April. The average departure date is usually about two weeks earlier than the Fieldfare and there have only been four records in May, all of single birds unless stated, as follows:

- two, Enderby, May 7th 1986.
- Groby, May 6th 1979.
- Stanton under Bardon, May 4th 1981.
- Oadby, May 4th 1985.

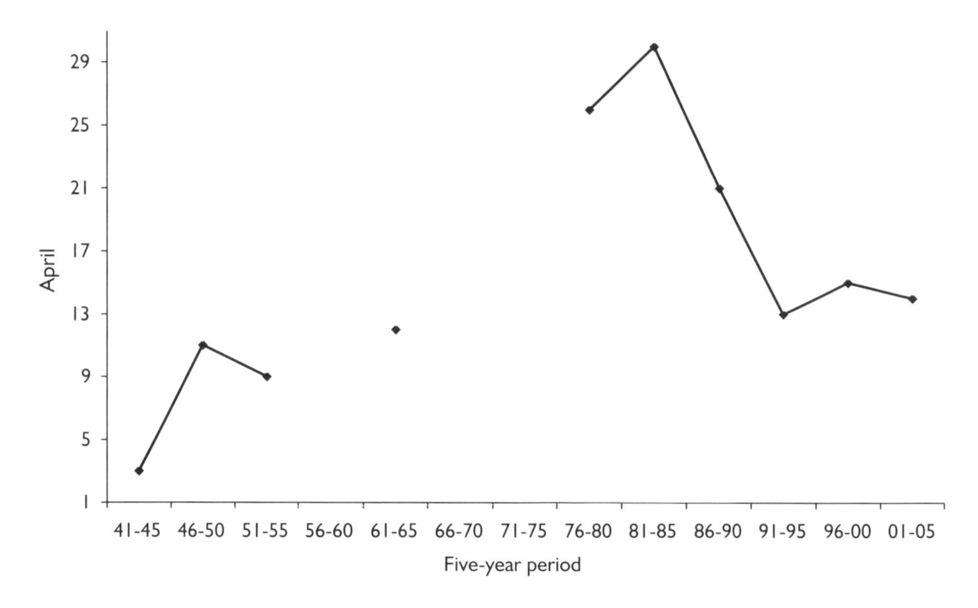

Figure 464: Average spring departure dates of Redwings by five-year periods 1941–2005.

Although there is anecdotal evidence that Redwings formerly bred in several English counties including Leicestershire (Browne refers to an unconfirmed record from Kirby Muxloe in 1864; cf. Brown & Grice 2005), none of these claims was ever proven and the only modern record during the summer months involved one at Market Bosworth on June 15th 1996. Unlike the Fieldfare, this species has never been recorded in the counties during July or August.

A partially albino bird was at Kilby Bridge in February 1997 and a leucistic individual was recorded at Priory Water on February 16th 2003.

Birds ringed in Leicestershire and Rutland have been recovered in Finland, Norway, France (two) and Italy, whilst one ringed in Finland on July 3rd 1997 was found dead near Bottesford on December 25th 2000. It is likely that most of our migrant and wintering Redwings come from Fennoscandia.

The nominate race of Redwing breeds throughout northern Eurasia and the slightly darker Icelandic race *T. i. coburni* breeds in Iceland and the Faroe Islands. All populations winter in southern and western Europe, north-west Africa and the Middle East. The small British breeding population, which reached a peak of 78 pairs in 1984 but only numbered between one and six pairs in 2005 (Holling *et al.* 2008), is found mainly in Scotland though breeding was also recorded in Kent during 1988–91 (Gibbons *et al.* 1993). The small size of the breeding population has resulted in this species being placed on the 'Amber List' of Birds of Conservation Concern (Gregory *et al.* 2002).

AHJH

Mistle Thrush *Turdus viscivorus*

Common resident breeder.

During the 19th century, the Mistle Thrush was considered resident and generally distributed (including in gardens in Leicester) by Browne, whilst Haines commented that it had 'increased very much in numbers since the beginning of the last century' in Rutland. The LROS archives describe this species as 'generally distributed' during the first half of the 20th century.

Our largest thrush, the sedentary Mistle Thrush is widespread at low densities. It occupies open woodland, woodland fringes, parkland and urban habitats including suburban gardens. Its extensive territories require mature trees for nesting and open grassy areas for feeding. During the period 1976 to 1984, Warrilow recorded

Mistle Thrushes in 420 tetrads in the counties (66% of the total number of tetrads), with breeding confirmed in 213. He found it most numerous in Charnwood, central and southern Leicestershire; it was sparingly distributed in the extreme west and north-east where suitable habitat is more limited. The relatively high population levels in Charnwood were confirmed by Webster (1997), who recorded definite or probable breeding in 62% of the 1–km squares surveyed, whilst the more sparse distribution in the east was confirmed by Mitcham (1992), who recorded Mistle Thrushes in only 59 (50%) of the tetrads in Rutland, where it was absent from some cereal-growing areas. In 1989 this species was found in four green spaces surveyed within the Leicester city boundary (Abbey Park, Aylestone Meadows, Knighton Park and Western Park), with two or three territories recorded at each site (Fray *et al.* 1990). The Leicestershire Garden Bird Survey between January 1996 and June 2005 found it to be the 21st most-frequent species, visiting 6% of gardens.

The average territory density of Mistle Thrush is considerably lower than that of Song Thrush and Blackbird in most habitats including woodland and farmland. A survey of 39 east Leicestershire woods, totalling 85 hectares, in 1987 and 1990 produced eight pairs, equivalent to 37 pairs per tetrad. The territory density on local farmland is lower than in woodland, for example 1.4 pairs on the Stoughton CBC plot, making it difficult to assess population trends there. Given an average of five to eight pairs per occupied tetrad, Warrilow estimated a breeding population of 2,100 to 3,300 pairs in Leicestershire and Rutland. Since the mid-1970s the national population has declined significantly, especially on farmland, although local CBC data from Stoughton, Newton Harcourt and King's Hill Lodge all show relatively stable populations at these sites, albeit in small numbers.

Late summer and early autumn flocks regularly number 40 or 50 birds and an exceptional 65 were recorded at Swithland Reservoir on September 7th 1997. Nonetheless, there is no evidence of long-distance movement: all those ringed in Leicestershire and Rutland have been recovered in the counties and the two recoveries of birds from outside the counties involved individuals from Nottinghamshire and Staffordshire.

Mistle Thrushes breed throughout most of Europe, north-west Africa and western and central Asia. Most are sedentary, although the more northerly populations are migratory. There were an estimated 230,000 territiories in Britain during 1988–91 (Gibbons *et al.* 1993) but a significant decline in the breeding population, which began in the mid-1970s, has caused this species to be added to the 'Amber List' of Birds of Conservation Concern (Gregory *et al.* 2002). The current population estimate is 205,000 pairs (Baker *et al.* 2006).

AHJH

Cetti's Warbler *Cettia cetti*

Rare to scarce visitor, mainly during the winter; recorded in all months except May, June and September: 16 individuals.

The first record for the counties involved one trapped and ringed by Tim Appleton in the Lagoon III reedbed at Rutland Water on February 2nd 1977. It was not until 1995 that the next occurred, but since 1997 there have been new arrivals in six of the nine years to 2005, though some may have involved returning individuals. Several of those at Rutland Water have been trapped during their long stays.

All records:

1977	trapped, Rutland Water, February 2nd.
1995	Rutland Water, November 29th to April 8th 1996 (trapped and ringed on November 29th 1995).
1997	Rutland Water, November 22nd to March 8th 1998 (trapped and ringed on December 28th 1997).
1998	singing male, Wanlip South Gravel Pits, February 14th to March 15th.
2001	Rutland Water, November 20th to January 12th 2002.
2002	Rutland Water, April 4th to 11th (trapped and ringed on the latter date).
2003	Trent Valley Pit, January 12th to February 8th.
	Rutland Water, March 18th to April 12th.
	singing male, Rutland Water, November 11th to April 24th 2004 (trapped on April 14th 2004).

2004 singing male, Wanlip South Gravel Pits, February 15th to March 9th.
male and female (additional to the bird above), trapped, Rutland Water, April 14th.
Rutland Water, July 30th to August 4th.
Rutland Water, October 25th to January 18th 2005, with two from October 26th to November 1st.
singing male, Lockington Marshes, December 29th to March 19th 2005.

Following the first county record in 1977 there was a surprisingly long gap before the second, though the species was also scarce in the West Midlands during the 1980s (Harrison & Harrison 2005). The regular records during winter and spring since the mid-1990s might be expected to be followed by breeding and further colonisation, which has already occurred in some nearby counties. Sites where willow and bramble scrub is invading the edge of reedbeds are most likely to be favoured and all records away from Rutland Water to date have all been in such habitat.

Cetti's Warblers breed throughout much of southern Europe and the Middle East and have expanded their range northwards over the last 50 years. The recent increase in records of this species in Leicestershire and Rutland precisely mirrors national trends. The first British record was as recent as 1961, but by 2005 there were over 1,330 singing males in the country (Holling *et al.* 2008). The former stronghold was in south-east England, but in more recent times this has shifted to south-west England and East Anglia (Wotton *et al.* 1998).

AHJH

Grasshopper Warbler *Locustella naevia*

(Common Grasshopper Warbler)

Uncommon migrant breeder.

Haines, writing about the 19th century status of this species in Rutland, said that for more than 50 years it had been described as a common summer migrant, but 'of late years it seems certainly to have decreased in numbers.' Browne described the Grasshopper Warbler as a summer migrant in Leicestershire, sparingly distributed and breeding, which he had not met with around Leicester. The earliest arrival date he recorded was April 11th in 1849.

Hickling described the Grasshopper Warbler as an uncommon summer visitor in markedly variable numbers, which remains an accurate summary of its status today. Its numbers have, however, declined significantly from the 100 pairs which he estimated in some years, probably by as much as 50% or even more.

During 1976–84, Warrilow recorded this species in 81 tetrads in the counties (13% of the total number of tetrads), with breeding confirmed in just 11. Favoured habitats include low tangled vegetation in both wet and dry locations, with newly planted conifers being especially favoured. The presence of loose colonies was noted in successive years at a few sites including Rutland Water, Stanford Reservoir, Ratcliffe on the Wreake and Stoughton Airfield. Warrilow estimated a breeding population of 30 to 40 pairs, though his data were collected at a time of low population levels.

Mitcham (1992), whose work followed a period of high population levels, found 24 occupied tetrads (21%) in Rutland where he estimated a breeding population of about 30 pairs. By contrast, Webster (1997) recorded Grasshopper Warblers in just three (2%) of the 1-km squares in Charnwood during 1992–94.

Because the favoured habitat of the Grasshopper Warbler is transient and forms a small proportion of local land use, numbers are likely to remain relatively low. In particular, there are few newly-planted conifer plantations in the counties. In 1990, following high population levels, one or two birds were even recorded singing from cereal crops in Rutland (Mitcham 1992), but this habit has not developed. During 1988 and 1989 up to 45 males were reported to LROS from up to 26 sites, with 15 at Rutland Water in 1989 at a time when young plantations there were ideal for Grasshopper Warblers. The highest single concentration in recent years involved 11 reeling males at Trent Valley Pit in 2004. Since this species is popularly reported, numbers recorded by LROS are likely to be more accurate than those relating to some other warbler species. If so, the local breeding population of this species in most years is probably less than half that known to Hickling, in keeping with a sharp national decline (Brown & Grice 2005).

Table 40: Grasshopper Warbler records 1996–2005

Year	1996	1997	1998	1999	2000	2001	2002	2003	2004	2005
Sites	14	14	22	13	13	15	15	13	22	13
Birds	20	18	26	15	18	24	25	20	46	17

Birds are most often recognised from their distinctive reeling song. The earliest spring arrival date on record is of two at Rutland Water on April 8th 1989, whilst arrivals prior to April 12th have been noted in a further four years: single birds at Rutland Water on April 9th 1993 and April 10th 2005, Ambion Wood on April 11th 1945 and Stanford Reservoir on April 11th 1981 (where there were six singing the following day). The average arrival date has remained relatively constant since the mid-1970s, ranging between April 15th and April 18th.

After the song period ends this species' skulking behaviour and crepuscular habits make it difficult to find so there are few autumn records. There have been reports during August in 18 years since 1941 and later autumn records, all of single birds, as follows:

- Stanford Reservoir, September 9th 1977.
- Priory Water, September 10th 1995.
- found dead, Stockerston, September 11th 1982.

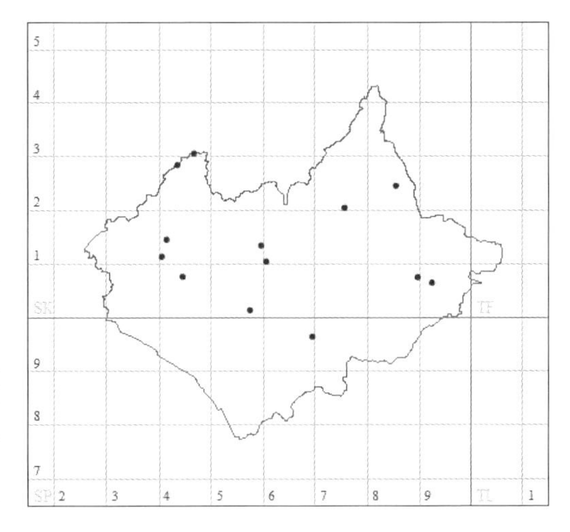

Figure 465: Distribution of Grasshopper Warblers 2005.

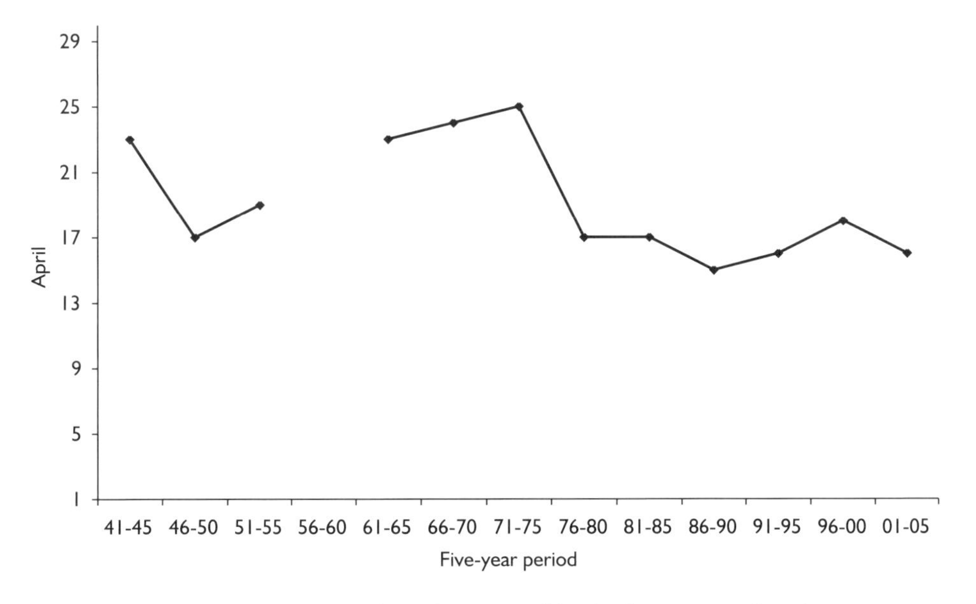

Figure 466: Average spring arrival dates of Grasshopper Warblers by five-year periods 1941–2005.

- Frisby Gravel Pits, September 19th 1984.
- Rutland Water, September 27th 1992.
- found dead, Packington, October 2nd 1988.

Grasshopper Warblers breed over most of Europe, south to northern Spain and Italy and north to Scotland and southern Scandinavia and east through Russia to central Asia and south-west Siberia. They winter in sub-Saharan Africa and in the northern Indian subcontinent. The British population was estimated at 10,500 pairs during 1988–91(Gibbons *et al.* 1993). Since then there has been a national decline of about 50%, so this species, which was previously 'Amber Listed', has been added to the 'Red List' of Birds of Conservation Concern (Gregory *et al.* 2002).

AHJH

Savi's Warbler *Locustella luscinioides*

Very rare vagrant from southern Europe: three records.

The first record for the counties was of a singing male seen and heard by Ralph Lockwood, Ian and Peter Gamble and Gerald Felstead at Frisby Gravel Pits from May 15th to 26th 1980 (*BB* 74:484). The bird maintained territory by singing from sallows and osiers adjacent to a flooded pit. In 1988, a singing male took up territory at Rutland Water. Originally found by Tim Appleton, it sang regularly in the reedbed by Lagoon III from April 19th to July 27th and was trapped and ringed on April 21st. The third record was strikingly similar; a singing male was again at Rutland Water, from April 13th to 24th 2005; it frequented the same area and was also found by Tim Appleton (*BB* 100:83).

A record of one at Kelham Bridge from May 2nd to 5th 1984 was originally published in the LROS Annual Report, but is now considered unacceptable following review in 2004 (Fray 2005).

Savi's Warblers breed discontinuously across much of western Europe and north Africa and winter in a narrow zone immediately south of the Sahara. This species has had a rather chequered history as a British breeding bird. It bred in small numbers in eastern England until the middle of the 19th century, when it became extinct. It then recolonised Kent in 1960 and subsequently spread. The population peaked at around 30 pairs during 1978–80 (coinciding with the Frisby Gravel Pits record), after which it declined again and by 2005 just seven singing males were reported (Holling *et al.* 2008). Due to the rapid decline and small size of the British breeding population, Savi's Warbler has been added to the 'Red List' of Birds of Conservation Concern (Gregory *et al.* 2002).

AHJH

Aquatic Warbler *Acrocephalus paludicola*

Very rare vagrant from eastern Europe: one record.

The only record of what is now one of the rarest and most threatened migrant passerines in the Western Palearctic dates back to when its breeding range was much more extensive. In 1864, an adult was obtained near Loughborough during the summer and constituted the second British record. The specimen was forwarded to J.E. Harting in the belief that it was a Grasshopper Warbler; however, after seeing the first British specimen of Aquatic Warbler in November 1866, Harting realised that the Leicestershire bird was also of this species (*Ibis* 1867: 468–469, *Zoologist* 1867: 946–947). The specimen is now held in Leicester Museum.

Hickling mentions a bird seen close to the River Soar at Zouch on July 10th 1945. This record was submitted to the editor of *BB*, who considered it to be probable only. Subsequent investigations have confirmed that this report cannot be considered reliable.

Aquatic Warblers breed from north-eastern Germany, Poland and Hungary eastwards through Russia to the Urals. Its winter quarters are poorly known, but western populations are believed to winter in west Africa south of the Sahara. This species is now globally threatened, having suffered drastically through habitat loss as a result of land drainage and has been added to the 'Red List' of Birds of Conservation Concern (Gregory *et al.* 2002). In Britain, it is a scarce autumn migrant, with the majority of records on the south coast of England during mid-

August. Although a summer occurrence such as that in Leicestershire now seems surprising, at the time Aquatic Warblers were known to breed in the Netherlands and also in France around Lille and Dieppe, so spring/summer occurrences would have been much more likely; following the recent contraction of breeding range a juvenile in August or September would provide a more typical record.

AHJH

Sedge Warbler *Acrocephalus schoenobaenus*

Fairly common to common migrant breeder.

According to Haines, this species was said to have been rare in Rutland until 1870 but by the end of the 19th century it was a common and, in some years, quite abundant summer visitor. Browne described it as a summer migrant to Leicestershire, generally distributed and breeding. The earliest arrival date he recorded was April 17th (in three years).

The Sedge Warbler remains a fairly common summer visitor which is easily recognised both by its distinctive appearance and by its loud song and display flight. It normally arrives in numbers from the second week of April onwards, one or two weeks ahead of the Reed Warbler. There has been a striking trend towards earlier arrivals in recent years, the average arrival date during 2001–05 being April 5th compared to April 22nd during 1971 to 1975. Prior to 1997 there had only been two arrivals before April 10th, of single birds at Ketton on April 4th 1967 and Rutland Water on April 9th 1987; since 1997, there have only been two years where the first date has been later than April 8th. The earliest on record is one at Rutland Water on March 29th 2003, whilst arrivals in early April have included single birds at Rutland Water on April 2nd 2002, Eyebrook Reservoir on April 3rd 1999, Wanlip South Gravel Pits on April 6th 2001 and Wing on April 7th 1997.

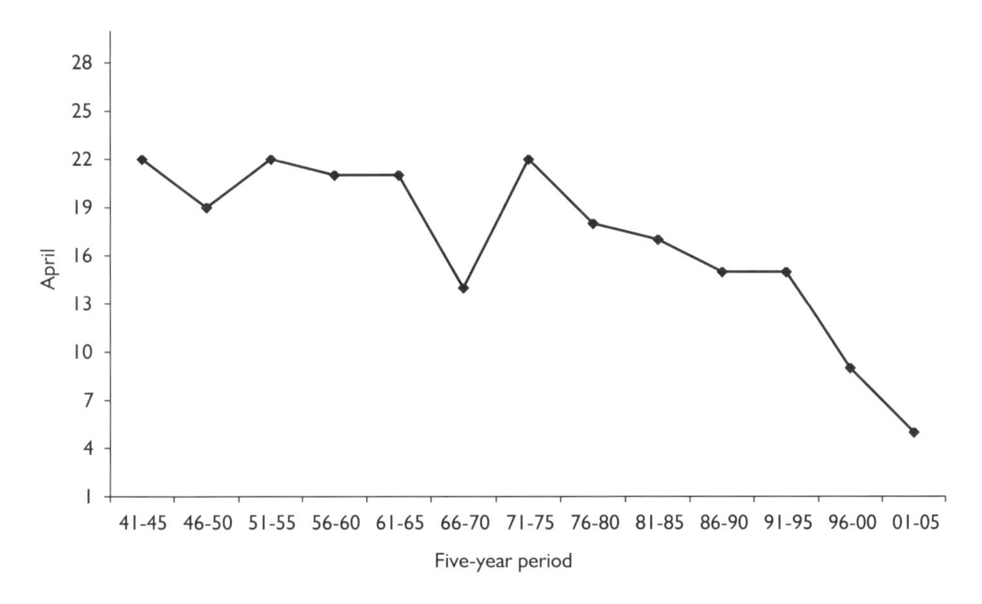

Figure 467: Average spring arrival dates of Sedge Warblers by five-year periods 1941–2005.

In autumn few are seen after September; there have been records in October in 15 years since 1941, four of them later than October 10th:

- Eyebrook Reservoir, October 24th 1966.
- Aylestone, October 16th 1997.
- Beeby, October 13th 2000.
- Priory Water, October 8th to 12th 1995.

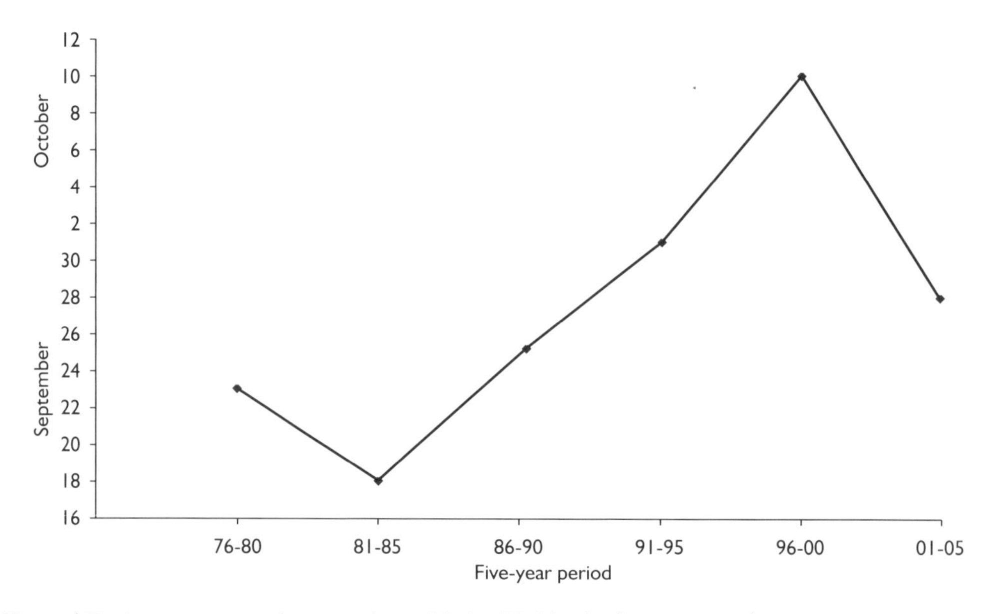

Figure 468: Average autumn departure dates of Sedge Warblers by five-year periods 1976–2005.

There is very little data available regarding departure dates prior to the mid-1970s; Figure 468 therefore only shows average departure dates from 1976 onwards.

The preferred habitat of the Sedge Warbler is low bushy vegetation close to water. Areas with shrubs of willow or hawthorn adjacent to reeds or beds of willowherb and nettles are especially favoured. During 1976–84 Warrilow recorded it in 167 tetrads in the counties (26% of the total number of tetrads), with breeding confirmed in 62. Small colonies were found at all the major wetland sites in the counties, including the canals, and this species was present in three times as many tetrads as Reed Warbler. Warrilow estimated a county-wide breeding population of 630 to 960 pairs. Mitcham (1992) found Sedge Warblers in 28 (24%) of the Rutland tetrads, with the main concentration around Rutland Water. There were few records from farmland or young plantations.

Sites with particularly high numbers have included Frisby Gravel Pits (43 pairs in 1976), a five-mile stretch of the Grantham Canal between Harby and Redmile (50 males in 1979), Birstall Gravel Pits (38 males in 1982), Priory Water (38 males in 1998), Rutland Water (101 males in 2002) and Trent Valley Pit (39 males in 2004). The highest number recorded by LROS is 281 males at 42 sites in 2002, which is well below Warrilow's population estimate and shows the importance of survey work in establishing accurate population figures for commoner species.

Ringing returns for this species have reflected its movements through Europe to wintering areas in western Africa. Birds ringed locally have been recovered in France (ten), Switzerland, Portugal, Mali and Ghana, whilst birds ringed in Belgium (two), France

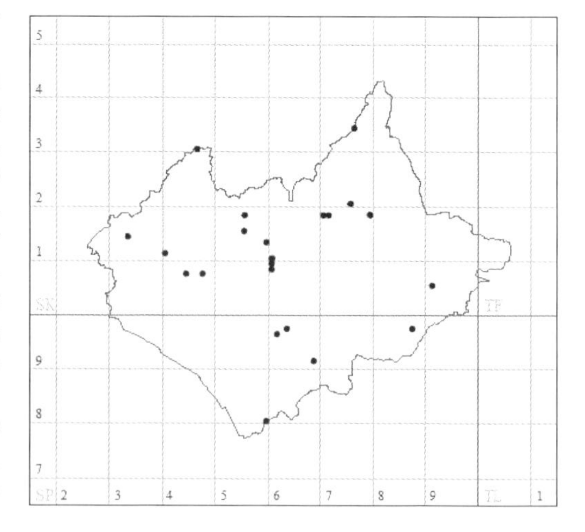

Figure 469: Distribution of Sedge Warblers 2005.

(four) and Spain have been recovered in the counties. The two African recoveries involved one ringed near Ratcliffe on the Wreake on 5th September 1979 which was controlled in Mali on 3rd April 1982, and one ringed at Rutland Water on 15th July 1981 and then found dead in Ghana on 27th September of the same year.

Sedge Warblers breed throughout much of the Western Palearctic, from the high Arctic to Greece and Turkey and from Ireland east to central Siberia. They winter south of the Sahara. The latest British population estimate is 297,000 pairs (Baker *et al.* 2006).

AHJH

Marsh Warbler *Acrocephalus palustris*

Very rare vagrant from Europe: eight records.

The first record for the counties was of one trapped and ringed by F.A. Bak in a garden at Stoneygate, Leicester on August 13th 1954. There have been a further seven accepted records of this tricky warbler, all involving birds singing or trapped.

All records:

1954 trapped and ringed, Stoneygate, Leicester, August 13th.

1982 a singing male was seen and heard by S.J. Moon at Foxton Locks on May 11th and a male was trapped and ringed at Shawell Gravel Pits on May 18th, remaining for about four days.

1984 a singing male was trapped and ringed at Stanford Reservoir on June 17th.

1996 a singing male was located by Ken Goodrich in an area of nettles and willowherb adjacent to the River Soar at Watermead Park on June 9th, where it remained until the following day and gave excellent views to many observers.

1998 a male was found singing by the River Soar at Wanlip South Gravel Pits by N.M. Sharp on May 23rd. This bird, which was only a mile or so away from the site of the 1996 individual, remained until the morning of May 25th, but had departed by the evening when a pair of Reed Warblers had moved into the area and possibly driven it off.

2000 a singing male was trapped and ringed at Stanford Reservoir on June 7th; then the first record for Rutland was of a singing male found by Tim Caldicott on the Egleton Reserve at Rutland Water on June 9th. The bird was seen briefly on several occasions by a number of observers, but was generally very elusive. The coincidence in date with the 1996 individual is noteworthy.

In addition, a record of one at Quorn on September 2nd 1981 was published in the LROS Annual Report as the second record for the counties, but was found to be unacceptable following review in 2004 (Fray 2005).

Marsh Warblers breed throughout large parts of the Western Paearctic, from Finland and Sweden southwards to Italy and the Balkan peninsula and south-eastwards to Turkey and Iran. They winter in south-east Africa as far south as Cape Province, South Africa. Although there has been a remarkable northwards expansion into Scandinavia in recent years (Brown & Grice 2005), the British population has declined markedly during the same period, so much so that this species has been added to the 'Red List' of Birds of Conservation Concern (Gregory *et al.* 2002). The former stronghold in the Avon valley (Worcestershire), which held up to 95 pairs in the 1960s, suffered badly in the mid-1980s, falling from 22 pairs in 1984 to just three pairs in 1987 (Kelsey *et al.* 1989). This population no longer exists and by 2005 fewer than ten pairs were thought to be breeding in the whole of Britain; these were mainly concentrated on the south-east coast of England, where a small, but slowly expanding, population is becoming established (Holling *et al.* 2008). In this context, it is likely that recent records in Leicestershire and Rutland involved migrants or overshoots from this growing population in south-east England rather than strays from traditional Worcestershire sites. The first 1982 record, at Foxton Locks, was exceptionally early: the earliest on record for the West Midlands was one on May 15th 1993, whilst the average date for first arrivals there over 48 years was May 30th (Harrison & Harrison 2005).

AHJH

Reed Warbler (Eurasian Reed Warbler) ***Acrocephalus scirpaceus***

Fairly common migrant breeder.

Haines stated that this species occurred in Rutland in some numbers as a summer migrant at Burley and Exton Ponds, but elsewhere in Rutland was very sparingly distributed, chiefly along the River Welland. Browne considered it unevenly distributed in Leicestershire, but referred to a thriving colony numbering about 20 pairs in Leicester itself, in reeds below the castle. Work on the flood control scheme which began in 1889 will have destroyed the habitat there and this species did not return to the city until 2005, when a pair successfully bred in a small reedbed by the River Soar at Evans' Weir.

Most birds arrive from mid-April onwards. Browne's earliest arrival date was April 17th (in two years) but it was not until 1995 that this date was equalled, when one was at Wanlip South Gravel Pits. Since then there have been five records earlier than this date, all of single birds unless stated:

- Wanlip South Gravel Pits, April 9th 2002.
- Watermead Country Park North, April 10th 2005.
- Rutland Water, April 12th 2005.
- Rutland Water, April 14th 2002.
- three, Stanford Reservoir, April 15th 2003.

Average arrival dates have become noticeably earlier since the early 1980s although there is little data on arrival dates of this species prior to the mid-1960s.

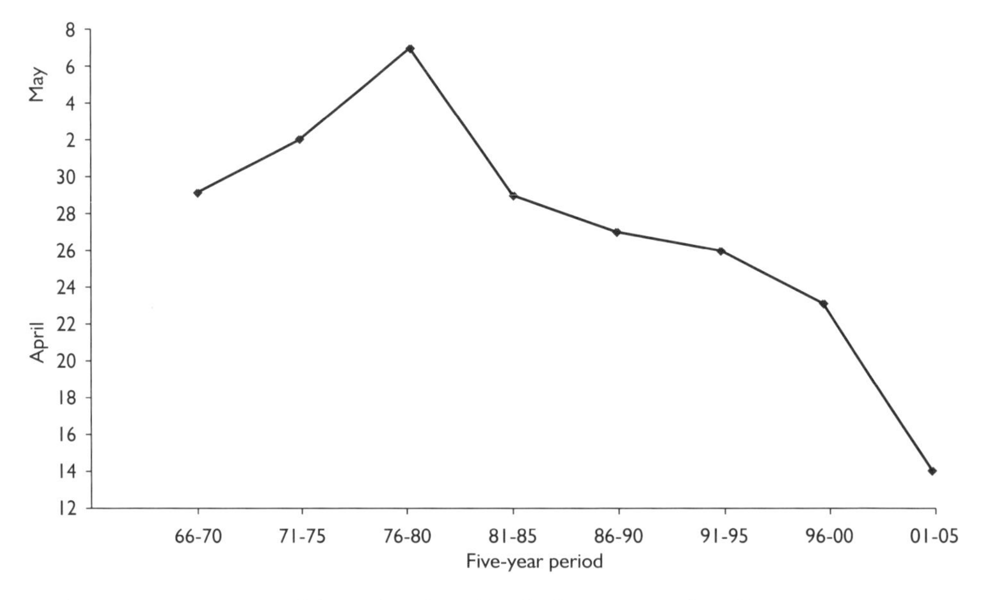

Figure 470: Average spring arrival dates of Reed Warblers by five-year periods 1966–2005.

In autumn most have gone by the end of September, although there have been ten October records, all of single birds unless stated:

- up to three, Groby Pool, throughout October 2002, with the last bird on the 28th.
- Rutland Water, October 14th 2002.
- two, Blaby, October 12th 1947.
- Cropston Reservoir, October 9th 1977.
- Stanford Reservoir, October 9th 1977.
- Groby Pool, October 7th 2004.

- Rutland Water, October 6th 1984.
- Rutland Water, October 4th 1980.
- Priory Water, October 3rd 1993.
- Birstall Gravel Pits, October 2nd 2005.

The latest record, however, involved one at Rutland Water on November 22nd 1992.

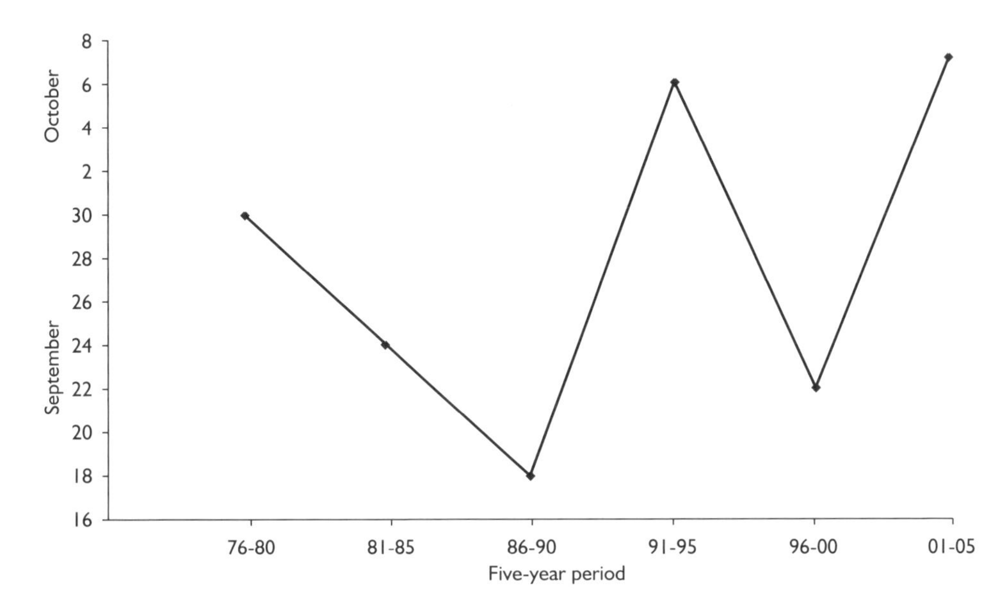

Figure 471: Average autumn departure dates of Reed Warblers by five-year periods 1976–2005.

Habitat loss since the Second World War was identified by Hickling as the main reason for a decline in numbers. As its name suggests, the Reed Warbler is closely associated with reeds and its distribution mirrors this. There are currently few extensive stands of reed in the counties. Warrilow estimated a breeding population of 200 to 450 pairs, though he noted that breeding sites remain under threat from infilling and the introduction of flood-prevention measures. A notable example of the impact of the latter was provided at Narborough Bog, where lowering the water table and the consequent drying out of the reeds led to the loss of an established colony: the only possible breeding record there since 1976 involved a male from May 10th to 17th 1981. Mitcham (1992) recorded this species in just six (5%) of the Rutland tetrads. The largest colonies have been found at Stanford Reservoir (rising from 23 males in 1972 to 50 males in 2002), Rutland Water (about 50 pairs in 1988 and 1989), Grantham Canal (74 males along the county length of the canal in 2003) and Watermead Country Park South/North (a combined total of 42 males in 2005). Continued monitoring and conservation of the main breeding sites will be needed to protect our relatively small breeding population.

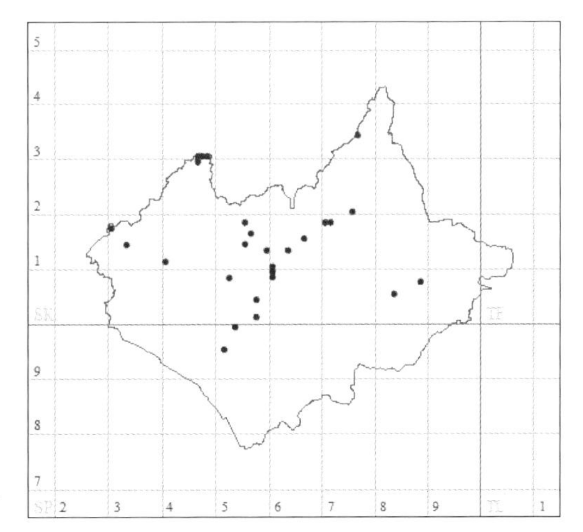

Figure 472: Distribution of Reed Warblers 2005.

Table 41: Reed Warbler records 1996–2005

Year	1996	1997	1998	1999	2000	2001	2002	2003	2004	2005
Sites	15	24	26	26	27	22	39	33	34	26
Singing males	58	60+	100+	103	104	?	234	208	213	185

As with the Sedge Warbler, ringing recoveries reflect migration to and from wintering grounds in western Africa, though as noted by Wernham *et al.* (2002) this species prefers to migrate in shorter stages. Birds ringed locally have been recovered in Belgium, France, Spain, Portugal (two) and Morocco (three), whilst there have been recoveries in Leicestershire and Rutland of birds ringed in Spain (two) and Senegal. The latter bird was ringed on April 10th 1993 in the Parc National du Djoudj and controlled at Rutland Water on July 10th 1994.

Reed Warblers breed throughout Europe and north-west Africa and winter south of the Sahara. The latest British population estimate is 60,800 to 122,000 pairs (Baker *et al.* 2006).

AHJH

Great Reed Warbler *Acrocephalus arundinaceus*

Very rare vagrant from southern Europe: one record.

A singing male was at Coleorton Fishponds from May 18th to July 5th 1963. First identified by J. Crocker, the bird was subsequently seen by many observers as it sang from reed-mace and reed (*BB* 57:273).

A further record, of one trapped and ringed at Stanford Reservoir on September 5th 1976, was accepted by the BBRC and published as being in Leicestershire (*BB* 71:520). However, it later transpired that this bird was caught on the Northamptonshire side of the reservoir.

Great Reed Warblers breed in North Africa and much of continental Europe east through Asia to the Pacific. European populations winter in tropical Africa. In large parts of the Western Palearctic, numbers have decreased dramatically due to habitat destruction and therefore, despite increased numbers of observers, this species is not occurring here any more frequently than it did in the past. By the end of 2005, there had been 223 accepted British records, the great majority of which have involved overshooting migrants in May and June; the Leicestershire record is therefore typical. With Northamptonshire having four records to its name and both Nottinghamshire and Warwickshire having two each, it is not unreasonable to expect another Great Reed Warbler to turn up in one of the county's reedbeds in future.

AHJH

Blackcap *Sylvia atricapilla*

Common migrant breeder, uncommon winter visitor.

This species seems to have been scarcer in the 19th century than it is now: Haines commented that it could not be considered plentiful in Rutland and was 'usually much scarcer than the garden-warbler'; Browne described it as a summer migrant in Leicestershire, sparingly distributed and breeding. He twice recorded the earliest arrival on March 31st. Macaulay, writing in 1881, stated that it usually arrived in the first week of April, but that he had heard the song as early as March 24th 1877. Haines found that it arrived about April 8th, though he believed that he once saw a female on March 23rd 1890.

The Blackcap has increased both as a breeding summer visitor and as a wintering bird in small but significant numbers. Its fluting, melodious song is one of the most characteristic sounds from the spring canopy of our woodlands. The preferred habitat of Blackcaps is mature deciduous or mixed woodland and although they prefer larger woods they are also found in small spinneys and mature suburban gardens. During the Leicestershire Garden Bird Survey from January 1996 to June 2005 it was the 26th most-frequently reported species (just ahead of the Goldcrest), occurring in more than 3% of gardens.

During 1976–84 Warrilow recorded this species in 370 tetrads in the counties (58% of the total number of tetrads), with breeding confirmed in 92, making it our third most-widespread warbler after Willow Warbler and Common Whitethroat and twice as widespread as Garden Warbler. It was absent from the Leicestershire wolds, the Wreake valley and parts of the extreme west of Leicestershire, where suitable habitat, particularly woodland, is in short supply. Based on an average of eight to 12 pairs per occupied tetrad, Warrilow estimated the

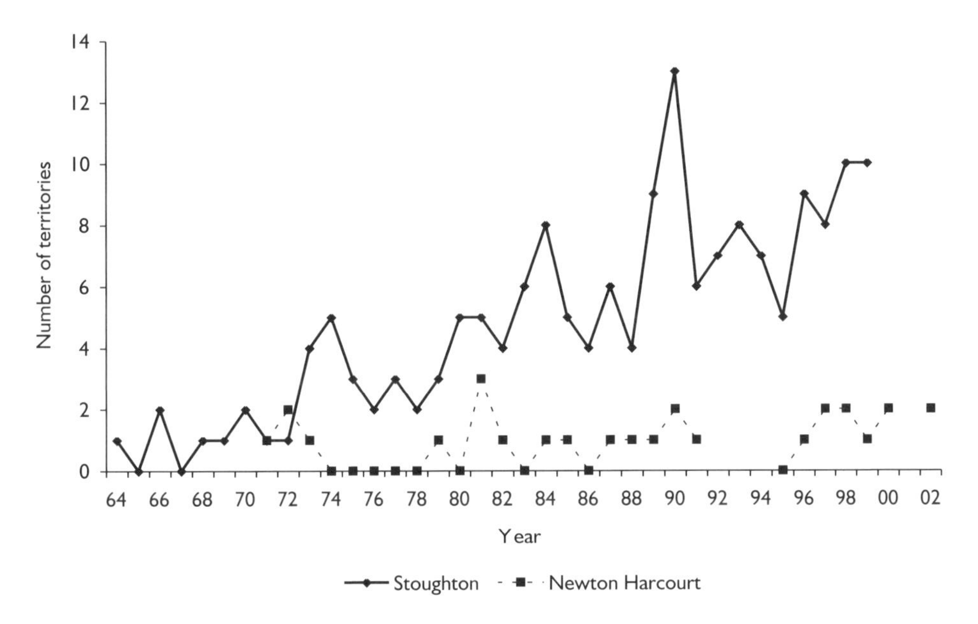

Figure 473: Number of breeding pairs of Blackcaps on two Leicestershire CBC plots 1964–2002.

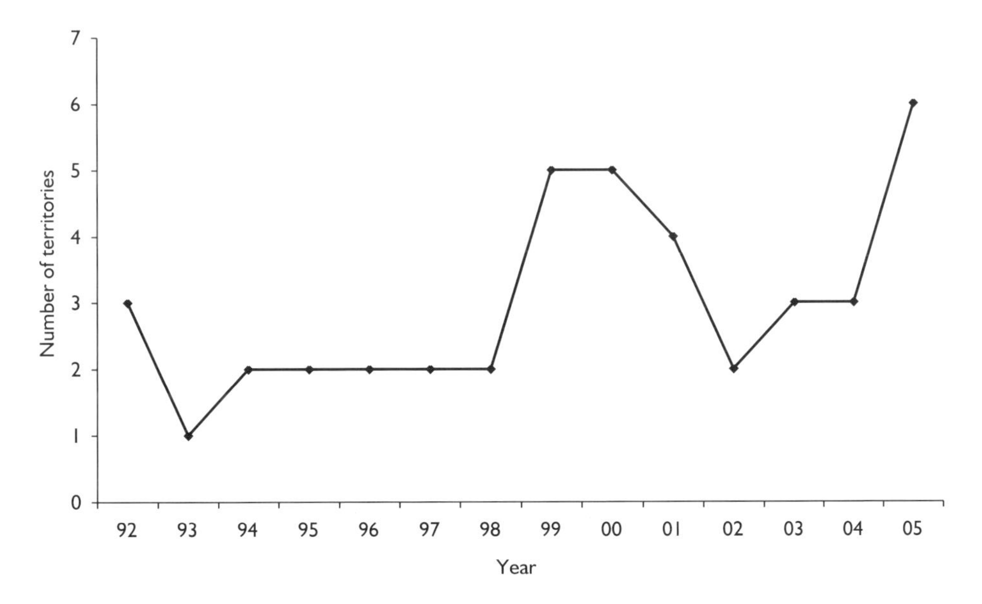

Figure 474: Number of breeding pairs of Blackcaps on the King's Hill Lodge, Uppingham CBC plot 1992–2005.

breeding population at 2,900 to 4,400 pairs. In Rutland, Mitcham (1992) recorded this species in 84 (72%) of tetrads, a figure very close to that in Charnwood where Webster (1997) recorded it in 71% of 1-km squares during 1992–94.

Unlike Garden Warblers, numbers of Blackcaps in England have increased markedly, especially since the 1980s (Brown & Grice 2005) and it is likely that Warrilow's estimate is now too low. CBC results from Stoughton illustrate this increase well, with numbers increasing steadily from one or two pairs in the 1960s and early 1970s to peaks of 13 pairs in 1990 and ten in both 1998 and 1999. A similar increase has been noted at King' Hill Lodge, Uppingham, where the estimated number of territories grew from one in 1993 to six in 2005.

From 2002 to 2005, LROS Annual Reports contained details on the number of sites where singing males were reported; the highest number was 238 males at 54 sites in 2002, which is obviously an underestimate of the true population. Notable concentrations of singing males have been recorded in recent years around Rutland Water, including 69 on April 27th 2002, 35 on April 22nd 2005, 32 on April 20th 2004 and 28 on April 18th 2003. Elsewhere, the highest recent counts of singing males have been 20 at Stathern Wood on April 10th 2005, 15 at Buddon Wood in April and May 1995 and 14 at Swithland Reservoir on May 2nd 1992.

Table 42: Blackcap records 2002–2005

Year	**2002**	**2003**	**2004**	**2005**
Sites	54	51	49	57
Singing males	238	158	154	178

The increase in the breeding population has corresponded with growing numbers of wintering birds, especially since the mid-1980s. The first record of wintering involved a female in a garden at Humberstone, Leicester from January 15th to March 27th 1955. Apart from one again at Humberstone on December 31st 1961, there were no further wintering records until 1967, when one was at Upperton Road, Leicester on February 23rd. Since then, however, wintering birds have been recorded in every year except 1970 and 1978. By 1988, 28 were recorded, 22 of which were during the first winter period. 31 were recorded during November and December 1995, 81 during January to March 1996 and numbers between these parameters are now normal.

In a short study, Davis (1998) discussed the increase in and movements of wintering birds. He found that almost twice as many males as females were recorded (supported by figures of 214 wintering males and 132

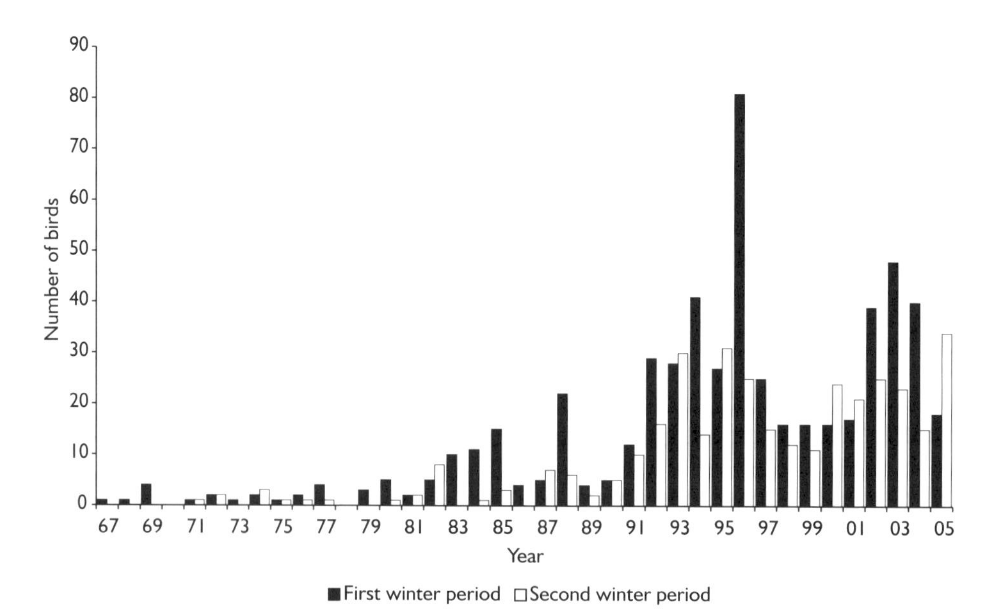

Figure 475: Wintering numbers of Blackcaps 1967–2005.

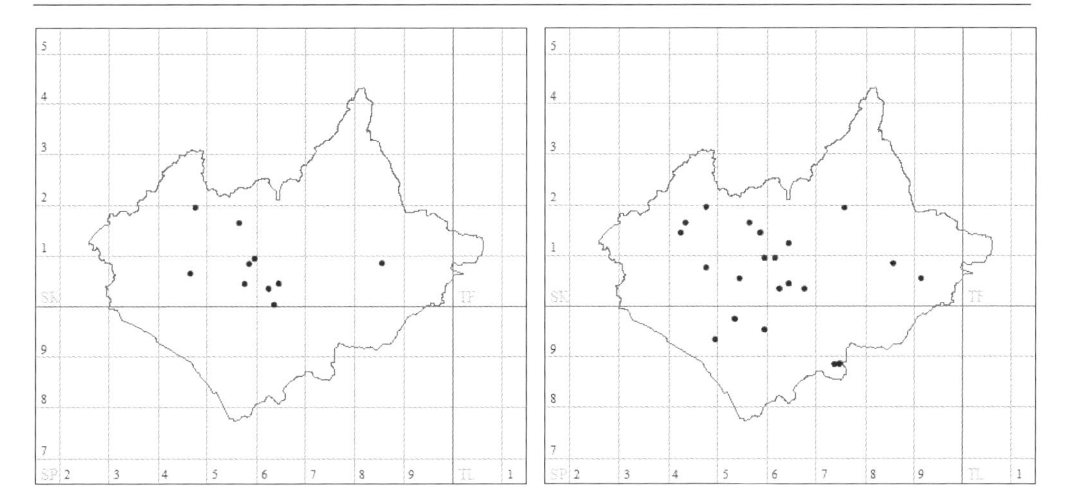

Figure 476: Distribution of Blackcaps during the first winter period of 2005.

Figure 477: Distribution of Blackcaps during the second winter period of 2005.

females during 1997 to 2005); they tend to feed on berries whilst these are available and thereafter (normally from late December onwards, when numbers recorded decline) rely on windfalls and food provided on bird tables. Urban gardens seem to be favoured by wintering Blackcaps and Figures 476 and 477 showing wintering birds during the early and latter parts of 2005 reveal that the area in and around Leicester is clearly favoured, though to some extent this reflects the distribution of observers.

The presence of so many birds during the winter months has made it impossible to maintain precise arrival dates for this species, but migration into Britain begins in early April (Wernham *et al.* 2002). Mason (1977) calculated an average arrival date of April 13th during 1942–1968; this was at a time when wintering birds were almost unheard of in the counties. Similarly, departure dates are now very difficult to calculate, but it would appear that most birds leave by early October.

Ringing recoveries reflect movements to and from the main wintering grounds in southern Iberia and north-west Africa: birds ringed locally have been recovered in Belgium (two), France, Spain (two), Portugal, Morocco (six) and Algeria and there are local recoveries of birds ringed in Spain and Norway. The last of these involved a bird ringed in Norway in May 1992 which was controlled at Ketton the following June; it is tempting to speculate that in 1993 it opted to remain and breed on the 'wintering' grounds.

Blackcaps breed in Europe, western Siberia, north Africa and south-west Asia. North-western populations winter in sub-Saharan Africa and around the western Mediterranean, whilst north-eastern populations move to south-east Africa to winter. Since the 1960s, a central European population has developed a new migratory direction, to the west-north-west, to winter in Britain and Ireland (Berthold 1995). The estimated British breeding population during 1988–91 was 580,000 pairs (Gibbons *et al.* 1993) but a rapid increase over recent years has resulted in a revised estimate of 916,000 pairs (Baker *et al.* 2006).

AHJH

Garden Warbler *Sylvia borin*

Fairly common migrant breeder.

The 19th century authors were in agreement that this species was then commoner than the Blackcap: Haines stated that in Rutland it arrived a fortnight later but was a much commoner bird, whilst Browne described it as a summer migrant in Leicestershire, generally distributed, breeding and more common than the Blackcap. His earliest arrival date was April 11th 1849, but normally it arrived during the latter half of April or early May.

Despite its name, the Garden Warbler is not commonly found in gardens. Its breeding range as a summer visitor is widespread, but it is now more thinly distributed than the familiar Blackcap. Whilst its song is rich, its nondescript appearance and unobtrusive habits make it less well-known to many people than some other members of the family.

Most birds arrive during the last week of April, though the earliest was one at Eyebrook Reservoir on April 7th 1959. A further six birds have been recorded earlier than April 14th:

- Owston Wood, April 11th 1961.
- Outwoods, April 12th 1947.
- Rearsby, April 12th 1987.
- Blaby, April 13th 1952.
- Stoughton Airfield, April 13th 1993.
- Desford, April 13th 2004.

The graph of average arrival dates below reflects population levels, with arrival dates becoming later from the mid-1960s to the mid-1970s as the national population declined then becoming steadily earlier as the population recovered to former levels.

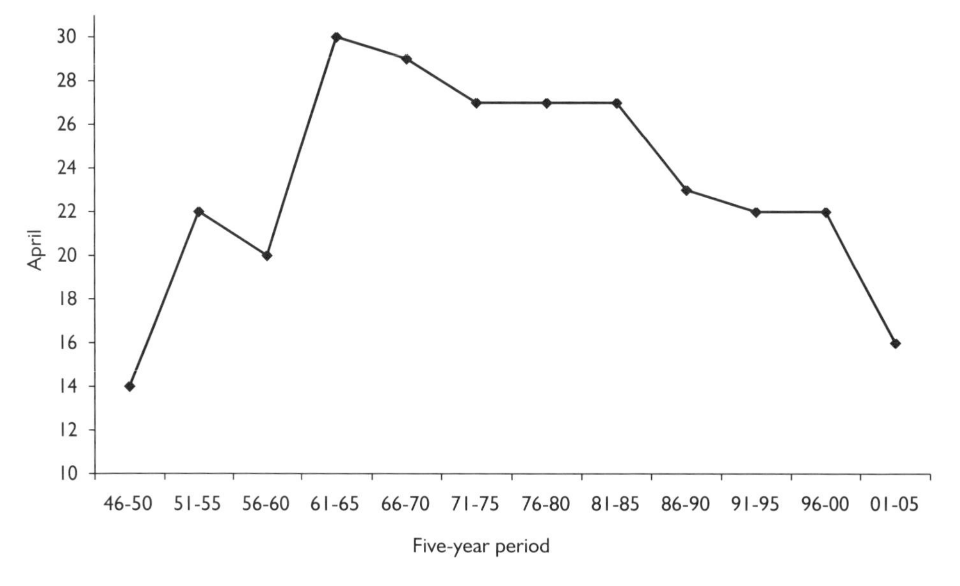

Figure 478: Average spring arrival dates of Garden Warblers by five-year periods 1946–2005.

In autumn few remain after mid-September. There have been three September records after the 24th: two at Rutland Water on September 25th 1982 and single birds at Kirby Bellars on September 25th 1983 and Rutland Water on September 26th 1992. The only October report is of one in 1993 at Kirby Lakes on the 10th but by far the latest on record was one trapped at Barleythorpe on November 4th 2000, which was retrapped eight days later.

Warrilow found that the two main breeding habitats of this species were open or semi-open mature deciduous or mixed woodland with a dense or extensive shrub layer and shrubby areas without mature trees which are more likely to be lost to agricultural 'improvement'. He recorded Garden Warblers in 201 tetrads in the counties (31% of the total number of tetrads), with breeding confirmed in 36. Local breeding densities have been shown to reach very high levels in optimum habitat: 24 pairs were located in 39 east Leicestershire woodlands totalling 85.6 hectares, equating to 112 pairs per tetrad, whilst based on a survey of 1.6 hectares of scrubland at Stoughton 1,250 pairs per tetrad is possible. As the average woodland and scrub cover in each tetrad in the counties rarely exceeds 5% of the land area, Warrilow calculated a county-wide breeding population of 600 to 1,000 pairs, based on an average of three to five pairs per occupied tetrad. Mitcham (1992) recorded Garden Warblers in 46 (39%) of Rutland tetrads and noted that the core of the population was present in the woodlands of central Rutland. In Charnwood, Webster (1997) recorded this species in 55% of 1-km squares during 1992–94, noting a preference

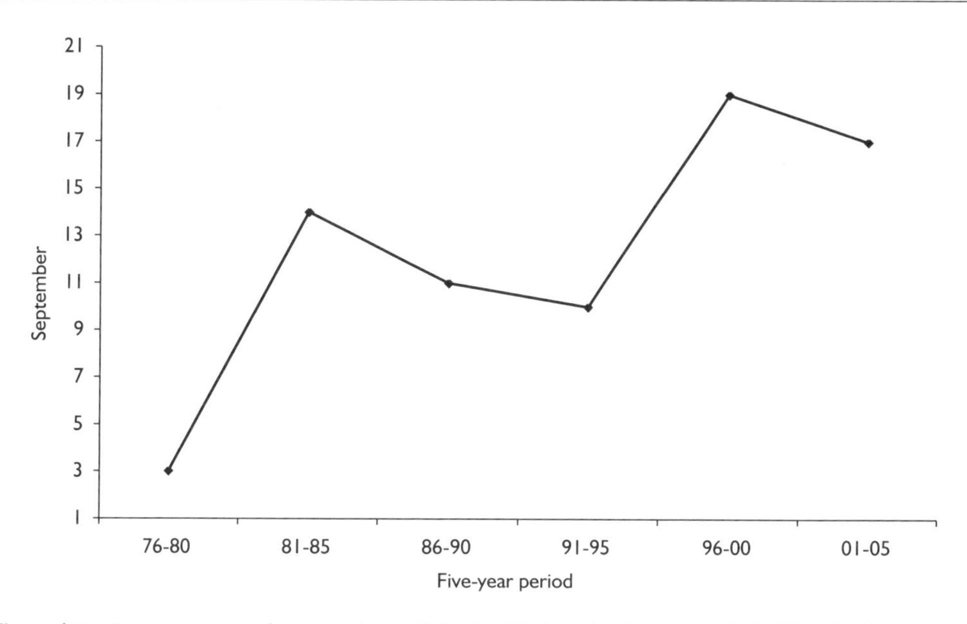

Figure 479: Average autumn departure dates of Garden Warblers by five-year periods 1976–2005.

for new plantations as well as open deciduous woodland with thick undergrowth.

Both Haines and Browne in the 19th century and more recently Otter (1965), considered that this species was more common than the Blackcap. Without comparable data it is difficult to make meaningful comparisons, but it is known that both woodland and farmland populations began to decline from the mid-1960s onwards (Brown & Grice 2005), perhaps as a result of the same drought conditions in the Sahel which affected Common Whitethroats. The highest numbers recorded by LROS in recent years have been 126 males at 61 sites in 2002 and 129 males at 37 sites in 2004. Rutland Water, where up to 62 males were recorded in 2004, is a stronghold.

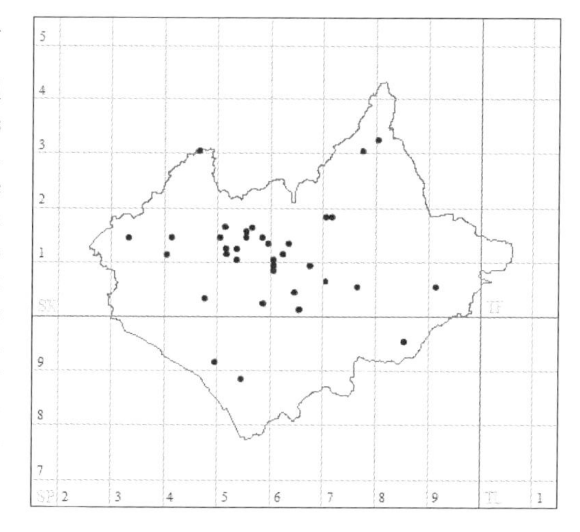

Figure 480: Distribution of Garden Warblers 2005.

Table 43: Garden Warbler records 1992–2005

Year	**1992**	**1993**	**1994**	**1995**	**1996**	**1997**	**1998**
Sites	32	27	25	24	33	25	35
Singing males	87	35	63	65	64	80	?
Year	**1999**	**2000**	**2001**	**2002**	**2003**	**2004**	**2005**
Sites	**29**	36	38	61	42	37	35
Singing males	**53**	65	67	126	98	129	116

Data from the Stoughton CBC plot suggest that the population is subject to moderate fluctuations from year to year. In most years the plot holds one to three pairs, the only exception being 1990 when the population inexplicably leapt to eight pairs.

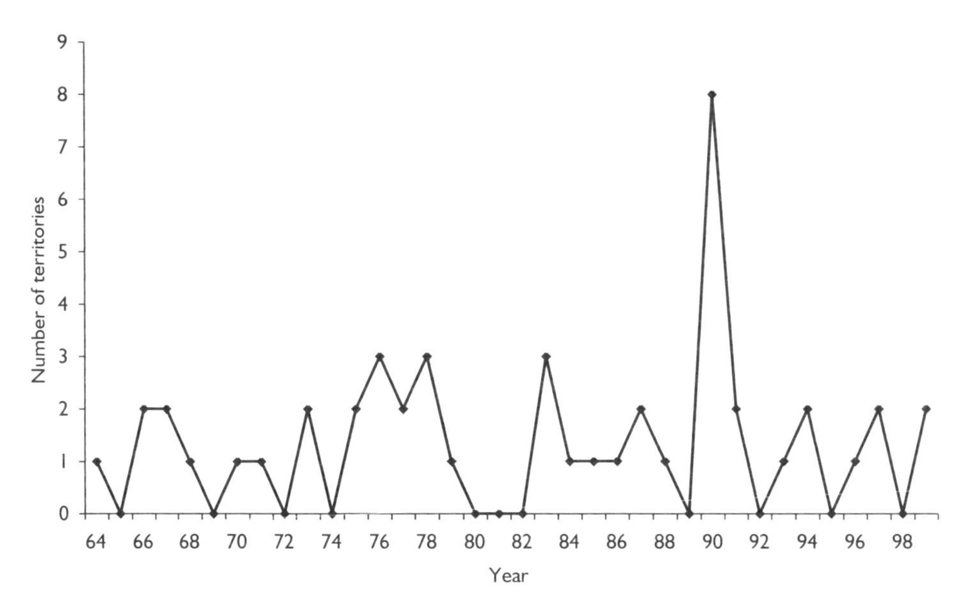

Figure 481: Number of breeding pairs of Garden Warblers on the Stoughton CBC plot 1964–99.

Ringing recoveries illustrate the migration route of this species to and from wintering grounds in western Africa: one from Spain, one from Morocco and two from Ghana (where a bird ringed at Swithland Reservoir on June 9th 1982 was shot on February 27th 1989 and another ringed at Wanlip on July 4th 1993 was found dead on December 12th 1998).

Garden Warblers breed in western, northern and central Europe and western Siberia and winter in sub-Saharan Africa. The latest British population estimate is 190,000 pairs (Baker *et al.* 2006).

AHJH

Lesser Whitethroat *Sylvia curruca*

Fairly common migrant breeder.

Browne described this species as a summer migrant in Leicestershire in the 19th century, sparingly distributed and breeding. He noted that Harley considered it very local. At the same time Haines considered this species to be about eight times scarcer than the Common Whitethroat in Rutland, a proportion similar to that revealed by recent surveys. Hickling described the Lesser Whitethroat as a fairly common but overlooked summer visitor. He considered that numbers may have declined, but if so they have recovered again more recently.

The distinctive rattling song of the Lesser Whitethroat is normally first heard during the last ten days of April, although the earliest arrival was one at Rutland Water on April 9th 2001 (only two days earlier than Browne's earliest arrival on April 11th 1879). There have been a further seven records of birds seen prior to April 16th, all single birds, as follows:

- Swithland, April 11th 1944.
- unspecified site, April 11th 1981.
- unspecified site, April 13th 1981.
- Swithland Reservoir, April 14th 2000.
- Ratby, April 15th 1961.
- Loughborough, April 15th 1989.
- Rutland Water, April 15th 1989.

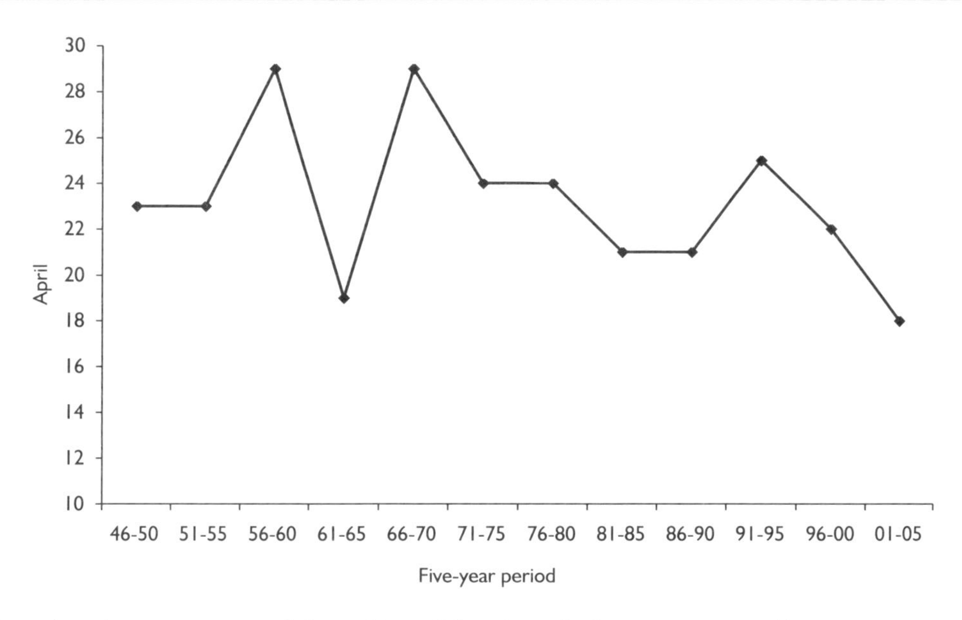

Figure 482: Average spring arrival dates of Lesser Whitethroats by five-year periods 1946–2005.

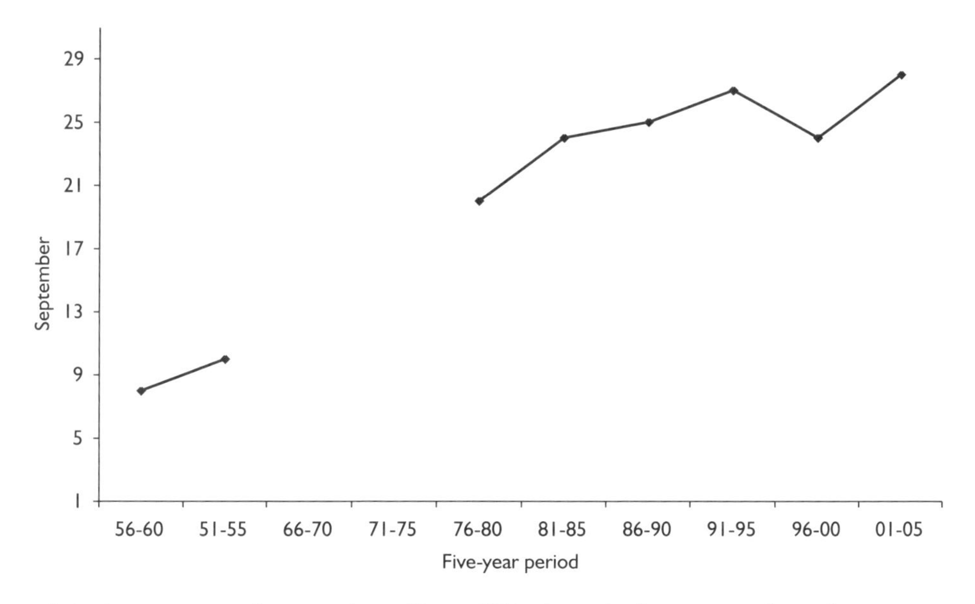

Figure 483: Average autumn departure dates of Lesser Whitethroats by five-year periods 1956–2005.

Although several of the earliest arrivals have been in recent years, this species has not shown a marked trend towards earlier arrivals in recent years, unlike some other migrant passerines.

In autumn most have gone by the end of September, although there have been five records during October, all of single birds unless stated:

- Peatling Magna, October 16th 1949.
- Kirby Lakes, October 10th 1993.
- Rutland Water, October 4th 1987.

- Rutland Water, October 2nd 1985.
- two, Melton Country Park, October 2nd 1993.

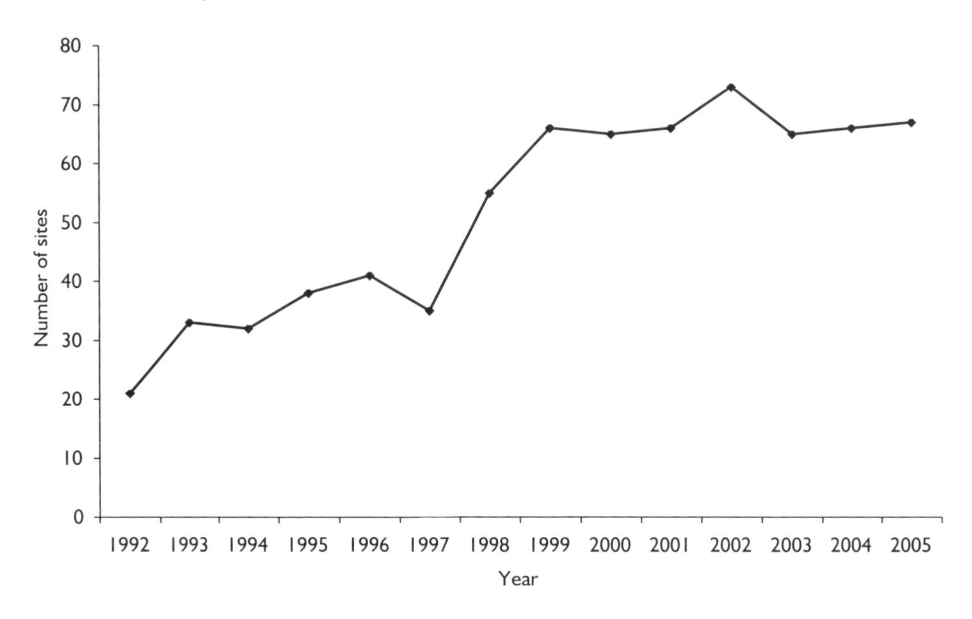

Figure 484: Number of sites with records of Lesser Whitethroats 1992–2005.

In contrast to spring, the average autumn departure date of this species has become markedly later since the mid-1970s.

A detailed study by Bonner (1946) found 243 pairs in Leicestershire and Rutland, a figure quite close to the 250 to 500 pairs estimated by Warrilow during 1976–84. Bonner found the species reasonably common over the counties except for Charnwood, the north-west and the area east and north-east of Melton Mowbray. Most birds were found below 130 metres in areas of boulder clay where lanes and bridle tracks were bordered by thick, tall hedgerows. Warrilow's data, collected up to four decades later, found the Lesser Whitethroat present in 247 tetrads in the counties (39% of the total number of tetrads), with breeding confirmed in 56. He concluded that the species had increased in Charnwood and the north-west (though Webster (1997) found it in just 13% of 1-km squares during his 1992 to 1994 survey of Charnwood), whilst the Vale of Belvoir (not visited by Bonner) also supported relatively high numbers. In Rutland, Mitcham (1992) found Lesser Whitethroats in 53 (45%) of local tetrads. Local CBC data does not reveal any particular trends as numbers on sites have always been small.

The highest number of singing males recorded by LROS in recent years is 94 in 2001. The number of sites at which birds have been recorded shows a marked increase since the late 1990s, the maximum being 73 in 2002; this may, however, be a reflection of increased observer interest and recording effort. The Egleton Reserve at Rutland Water, where up to 11 pairs have been located, is a particularly favoured site.

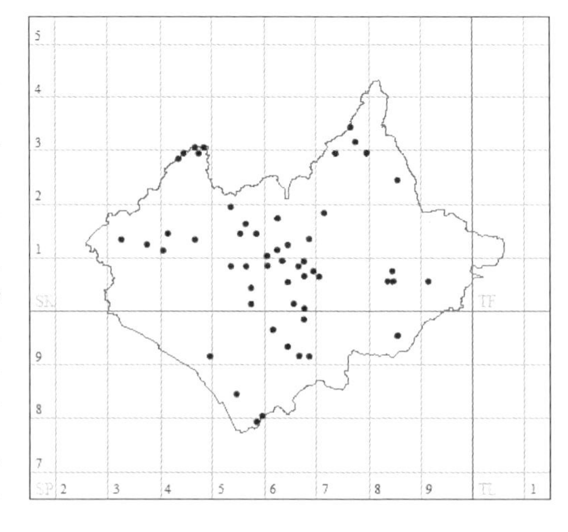

Figure 485: Distribution of Lesser Whitethroats 2005.

Ringing recoveries are from England with the exception of one ringed at Eyebrook Reservoir on

July 29th 2000 which was recovered 1,068km to the south-east at Bergamo (Italy) on September 12th of the same year. This example neatly illustrates the species' preferred migration route through the eastern Mediterranean to wintering grounds in north-east Africa (Wernham *et al.* 2002).

Lesser Whitethroats breed in the mid latitudes of Eurasia from Britain east to eastern Siberia, Mongolia and China. Western populations winter mainly in Ethiopia and Sudan, whilst eastern races winter in south-west Asia and the Indian subcontinent. 80,000 territories were estimated in Britain during 1988–91 (Gibbons *et al.* 1993) but a shallow decline since then has resulted in a more recent estimate of 64,000 pairs (Baker *et al.* 2006).

AHJH

Common Whitethroat *Sylvia communis*

Common migrant breeder.

In the 19th century, Haines described the Common Whitethroat as one of the commonest migrants in Rutland. Browne also described it as a commonly distributed breeding summer migrant in Leicestershire and noted that its song was often mistaken for that of the Sedge Warbler. His earliest arrival date was April 11th 1883.

The Common Whitethroat illustrates more vividly than any other species how factors in distant wintering and migration zones can have dramatic effects on our breeding populations. Described by Hickling as 'once our commonest and most delightful, summer visitor', its population crashed in 1969 by around 70% following severe drought in the Sahel to the south of the Sahara Desert. The impact of this crash was clearly illustrated by numbers on the Stoughton CBC plot, where the average number of breeding pairs fell from 18 before 1968 to four or five in subsequent years. Fortunately, the population has increased again since, though as the graph shows the recovery has been slow, following further setbacks during the winter of 1983–84 and in 1991 (the only year when there were no breeding pairs on the Stoughton CBC plot). Numbers have still not fully recovered to their pre-1969 levels. At Newton Harcourt, CBC work began in 1971 at a time when the Common Whitethroat population was at a low ebb; since then, numbers have slowly increased although have shown some fluctuations. Results from the CBC plot at King's Hill Lodge, Uppingham have shown a slow but steady increase since 1992.

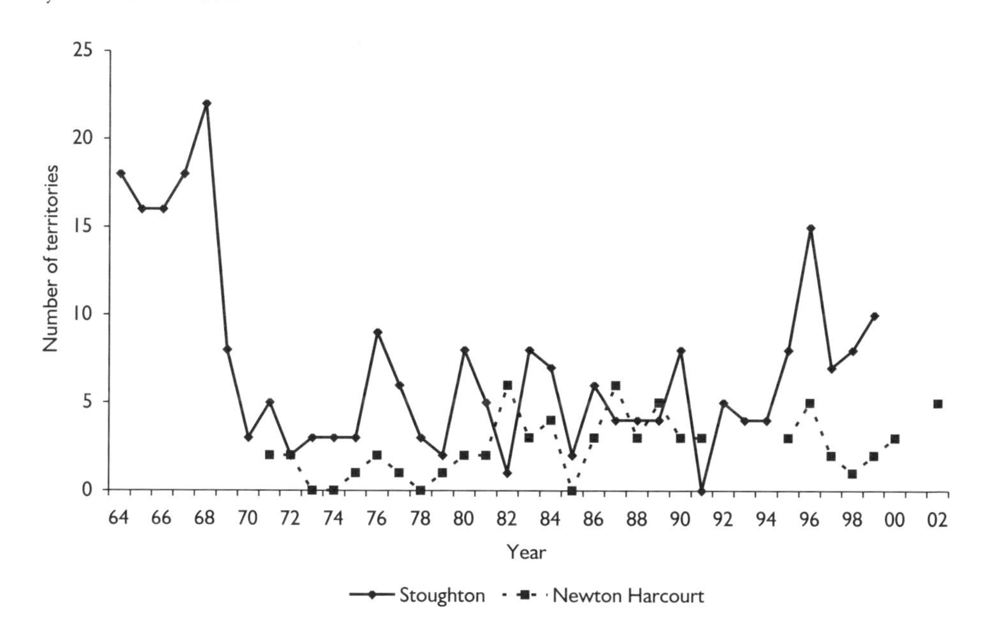

Figure 486: Number of breeding pairs of Common Whitethroats on two Leicestershire CBC plots 1964–2002.

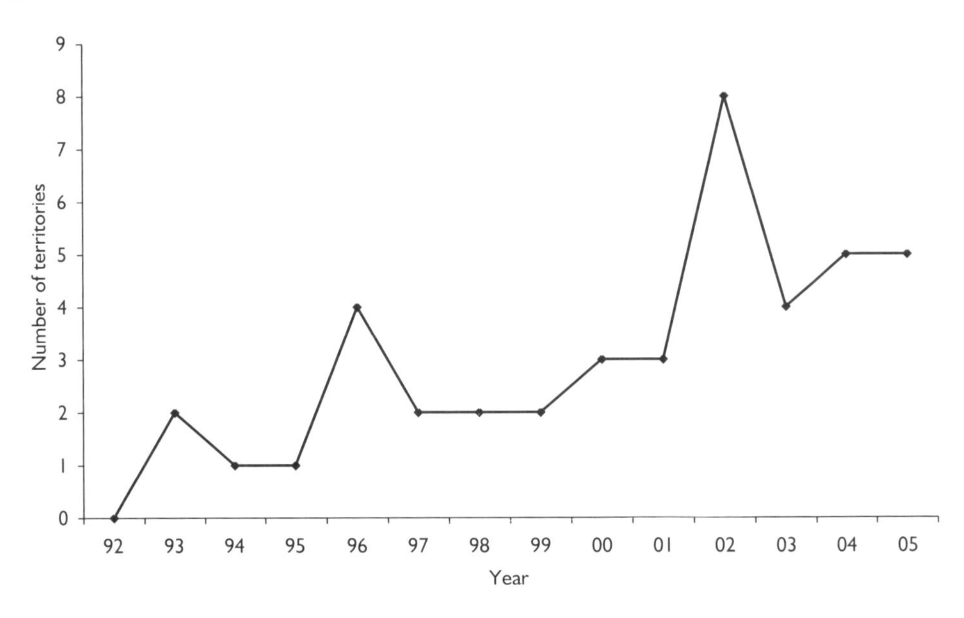

Figure 487: Number of breeding pairs of Common Whitethroats on the King's Hill Lodge, Uppingham CBC plot 1992–2005.

Warrilow, whose data were compiled during 1976–84, a time of relatively low population levels, nonetheless found this species in 425 tetrads in the counties (66% of the total number of tetrads), with breeding confirmed in 139, making it the second most-widespread warbler in the counties. By combining estimates from farmland and woodland, he arrived at a breeding estimate of approximately 2,800 pairs. The current population will now be significantly higher than this, as recent data has suggested that numbers on farmland increased by 100% between 1973 and 1998 (Chamberlain & Vickery 2002). Mitcham (1992) considered that the species had made an excellent recovery from the low ebb of 1969 and recorded 91 occupied tetrads in Rutland (77% of the total). In Charnwood, Webster (1997) recorded this species in 39% of 1–km squares during 1992–94 and noted that it was absent from the higher, more rugged areas. The preferred habitat of this species (scrub, woodland edge and hedgerows, including low, trimmed hedges) is widespread so local habitat loss is less critical than it is for some other passerines, though the complete removal of hedgerows is of course detrimental.

The highest numbers recorded by LROS in recent years have been 258 males at 64 sites in 2005 and 249 males at 95 sites in 2002. Notable concentrations of singing males have included:

- 26 at Stanford Reservoir on May 15th 2001.
- 25 at Castle Hill Park, Leicester in May 1986.
- 22 at Little Stretton on May 15th 2004, with 20 there on May 25th and 26th 2005.
- 20 at Stoughton Airfield on both May 6th 1987 and May 9th 1990.
- 20 at Trent Valley Pit on May 2nd 2004.

Table 44: Common Whitethroat records 1992–2005

Year	**1992**	**1993**	**1994**	**1995**	**1996**	**1997**	**1998**
Sites	35	33	37	44	47	40	47
Singing males	68	37	82	69	?	?	?

Year	**1999**	**2000**	**20011**	**2002**	**2003**	**2004**	**2005**
Sites	44	52	45	95	76	75	64
Singing males	**119**	175	120	249	167	203	258

Most birds arrive from mid-April onwards, although there have been reports in four years on April 11th (at Hoby in 1966, Stanford Reservoir in 1979, Melton Mowbray in 1982 and Stoughton Airfield in 2005) and earlier records, all of single birds unless stated, as follows:

- Thurmaston, April 2nd 1949.
- Rally Park, Leicester, April 4th 2005.
- two, Huncote, April 6th 1997.
- Rutland Water, April 6th 2002.
- Priory Water, April 7th 2002.
- Huncote, April 9th 1995.
- Aston Flamville, April 10th 1952.

Average spring arrival dates became later following the 1969 crash, but since population levels recovered there has been a trend towards earlier arrivals.

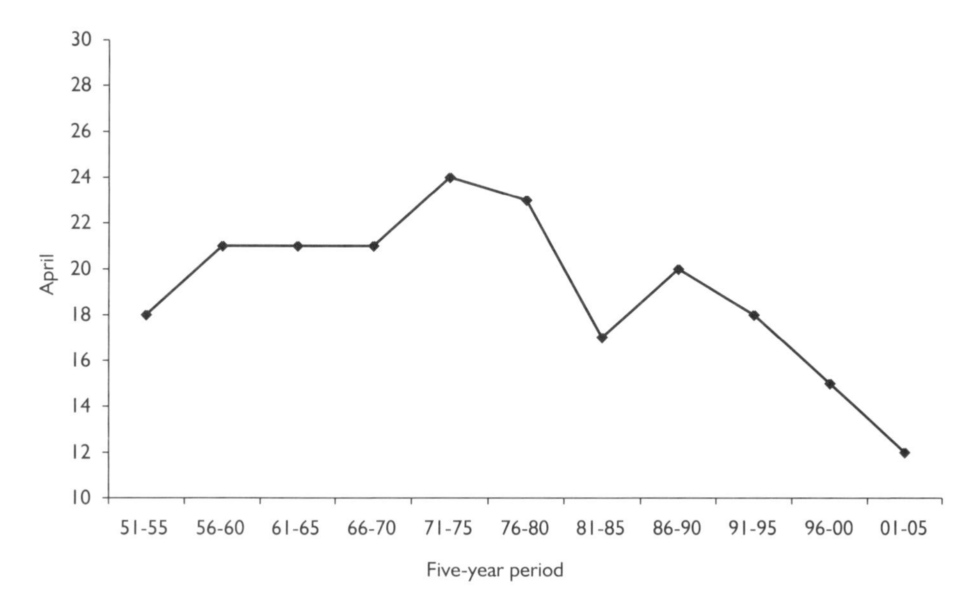

Figure 488: Average spring arrival dates of Common Whitethroats by five-year periods 1951–2005.

In common with other warblers most Common Whitethroats have gone by the end of September although there have been five October records, all of single birds:

- Swithland Reservoir, October 10th 1985.
- Rutland Water, October 8th 1989.
- Hinckley, October 7th 1945.
- Rutland Water, October 2nd 2005.
- Kilby Bridge, October 1st 1996.

The latest record, however, involves one trapped and ringed at Stanford Reservoir on November 11th 1978. There is also a truly exceptional winter record of one seen and photographed by several observers at Barlestone between February 8th and mid-April 1996.

Perhaps surprisingly, all the relatively few ringing recoveries of Common Whitethroats are from sites in England: a much larger sample will be required before we can draw conclusions about the movements of our breeding birds.

Common Whitethroats breed over much of Europe, north-west Africa, western Siberia and central and south-west Asia. They winter south of the Sahara. Drought in 1969 in the Sahel region led to dramatic declines

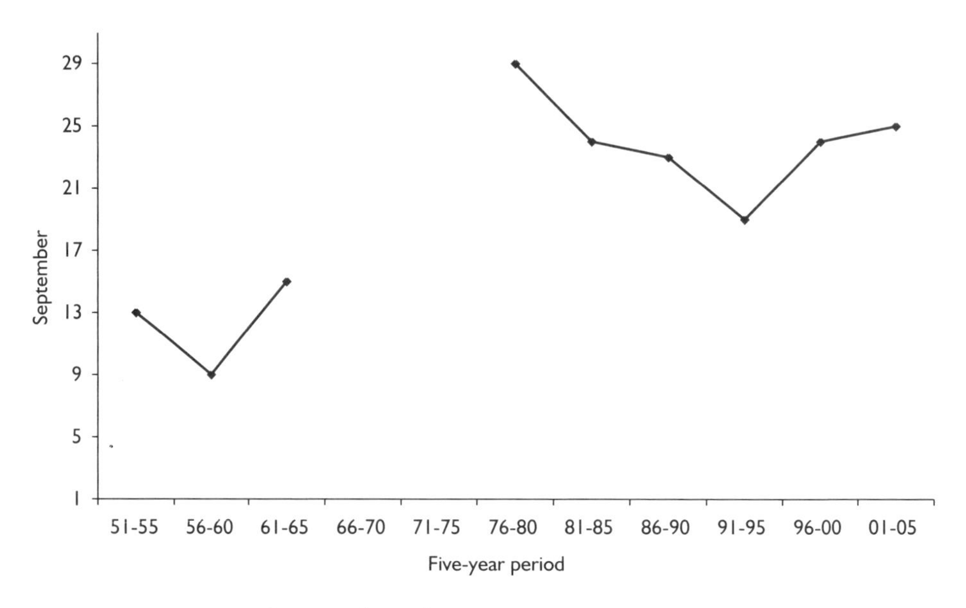

Figure 489: Average autumn departure dates of Common Whitethroats by five-year periods 1951–2005.

in western Europe; in Britain there has been some contraction of range, but in core areas populations have slowly recovered towards earlier levels. 660,000 territories were estimated in Britain during 1988–91 (Gibbons *et al.* 1993), but more recent estimates put the population at 931,000 pairs (Baker *et al.* 2006), indicating that this species is making a good recovery.

AHJH

Greenish Warbler *Phylloscopus trochiloides*

Very rare vagrant from north-east Europe: two records.

The Greenish Warbler was not widely predicted to turn up in Leicestershire and Rutland, so the appearance of two individuals in 1996 was totally unexpected. The first was found at Snibston Discovery Park on September 17th by Mick Jarvis, who heard what sounded like a Pied Wagtail calling from an area of sheltered bushes and, on tracking the bird down, was surprised to find himself looking at a *Phylloscopus* warbler (Jarvis 1998, *BB* 91:507). The second was found in similar circumstances by Dave Gamble at Priory Water on October 13th (Gamble 1998, *BB* 91:507). Unfortunately, despite thorough searches of the respective areas, neither bird could be relocated after the initial sighting.

There are three subspecies of Greenish Warbler and both Leicestershire records were of the European and west Siberian race *P. t. viridanus*, which is the westernmost subspecies of the complex. It breeds from north-east Europe east to central Siberia and south-east to Kashmir and winters in the south-east of the Indian subcontinent. Formerly a rare vagrant to Britain, with only 13 records prior to 1958, a westward expansion of the breeding range in Europe in the 20th century, coupled with the large increase in observers looking for rare migrants over the same period, has resulted in this species becoming a fairly regular visitor to these shores. By the end of 2005, with the species averaging between five and 15 records per year, the British total was over 445 and it was dropped from the list of species assessed by the BBRC. However, the Leicestershire birds are the only ones ever to be found inland, making the appearance of two in less than a month somewhat remarkable. The peak time for Greenish Warblers to arrive in this country is late August and early September, so the Priory Water individual, in particular, was extremely late; there have only been 14 other October records in Britain and just five have been found on a later date.

RMF

Yellow-browed Warbler *Phylloscopus inornatus*

Very rare vagrant from Siberia: four records.

The first county record was of one seen twice over the period of an hour by Ian Snape in a Melton Mowbray garden on October 28th 1985. This coincided with a large influx into Britain, with some 542 individuals reported during the autumn (Fraser & Rogers 2004) and was perhaps not totally unexpected. The second record, however, was much more unusual: one found on a housing estate at Ashby-de-la-Zouch by V. Bayliss on January 9th 1988, remaining until March 5th. This bird frequented a small stream adjacent to gardens and was seen by many hundreds of observers throughout its stay. Wintering records in Britain at the time were particularly unusual and this appeared to be only the ninth such occurrence. In 2005, two were recorded during October, beginning with one found by Andy Mackay at Evington Park on the 11th. This bird remained until the following day but was very elusive, being seen only by a small number of other observers. A more obliging individual was located by Matthew Berriman in the Sykes Lane car park at Rutland Water on the 23rd, remaining until the 25th and being seen by many people.

Interest in the Ashby-de-la-Zouch individual was rekindled in the late 1990s, following the decision by the BOURC to grant Hume's Leaf Warbler *Phylloscopus humei* full species status from Yellow-browed Warbler. Although the overall plumage of the bird was rather dull and the median covert wingbar was virtually absent, examination of photographs and a video recording supported the identification as a Yellow-browed Warbler (Fray & Harrop 2000). It was therefore something of a surprise when the BBRC, out of the blue, accepted this bird as a Hume's (*BB* 91:507), but they were asked to reconsider their decision and finally came to the conclusion that the bird was, indeed, a Yellow-browed Warbler (*BB* 94:493).

Two additional records have been published in the past, but both were reviewed in 2004 and found to be no longer acceptable: single birds at Thorpe Trussels on October 15th 1989 and Rutland Water on October 5th 2001 (Fray 2005).

Yellow-browed Warblers breed throughout Siberia and winter in south-east Asia. They are now regular migrants in Britain, averaging around 300 individuals per year; the vast majority of these arrive from late September to late October, with occasional wintering birds and a handful of spring records. Most are seen at the expected coastal sites, but inland records are on the increase, probably as a result of observers actively searching for scarce passerines inland during the autumn and winter. Further records in Leicestershire and Rutland are likely in the future but, as with the four previous records, they may well be at rather unexpected sites.

RMF

Wood Warbler *Phylloscopus sibilatrix*

Formerly a scarce to uncommon migrant breeder, now a scarce migrant and a rare breeder.

It appears that the Wood Warbler was a rare visitor to Leicestershire and Rutland during the 19th century. Browne knew of several reports from Leicestershire, but was sceptical about them: six at Tugby in 1891, with a pair there in May 1892, a pair at Knighton Spinney, Leicester in May 1889, a singing male at Stretton Hall on June 18th 1891 and single birds at Belvoir in May 1893, Hinckley in May 1898 and Market Harborough on April 27th 1899 and May 2nd 1903. The only Rutland records during this period quoted by Haines involved a nest found at Wardley Wood in June 1872, a pair at Tunneley Wood on June 6th 1888 and a pair at Empingham on June 14th 1905.

There is little data available on the status of the Wood Warbler in the counties during the early part of the 20th century, although the LROS archives state that it was 'not uncommon in most parts of Charnwood Forest'. By 1943, the status was described as a 'local summer resident in small numbers' (Jolley 1944). Records show that this species was commonest during the 1940s and from the mid-1970s to late 1980s, although there is very little data available for the 1950s.

During the 1940s, this species was recorded regularly in Charnwood Forest. Numbers varied from year to year, from a low total of four pairs or singing males in 1945 to ten pairs or singing males in 1943. The favoured area was Swithland Wood, where at least one pair bred each year; the best years at this site were 1943 and 1947, with five pairs in each year. Other regular areas were Outwoods, where at least one pair or singing male was

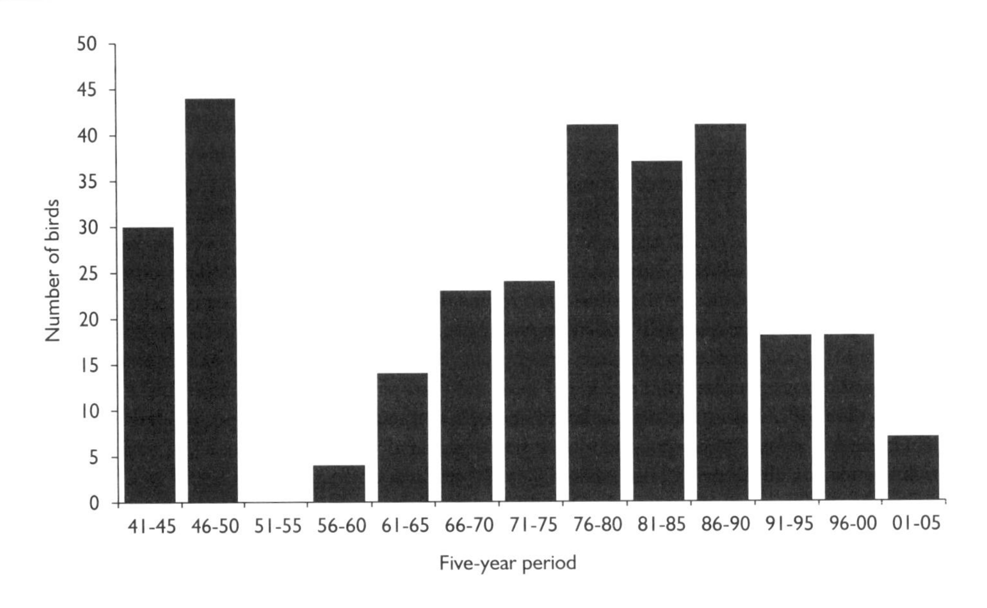

Figure 490: Number of singing Wood Warblers by five-year periods 1941–2005.

recorded in every year from 1944 to 1949 (maximum of three pairs in 1947) and The Brand, Woodhouse Eaves, where there was one pair in five years. Elsewhere in Charnwood, singing males were located at Warren Hills, Beaumanor, Longcliffe Wood, Whitwick, Bradgate Park, Swithland Reservoir, Beacon Hill and Maplewell Hall, all single pairs in one year only except for two pairs at Maplewell Hall in 1949. There were scattered records from 11 sites outside Charnwood Forest during this decade, including from Prestwold in four years and near Stanford on Soar in three years. Most birds were found in the western half of the counties, although there was a pair at Stapleford Park in 1948 and two pairs at both Wardley Wood and Belvoir in 1949.

It is difficult to provide meaningful comment on distribution during the 1950s as data is lacking, although it seems that this species became scarce from about 1955. They were no breeding records from 1956 to 1959 and the only records during this period were of single singing males at Higham Grange from May 7th to 11th 1956, Swithland Wood on May 4th 1956 and in May 1958 and Spencefield Lane, Evington on May 6th 1959.

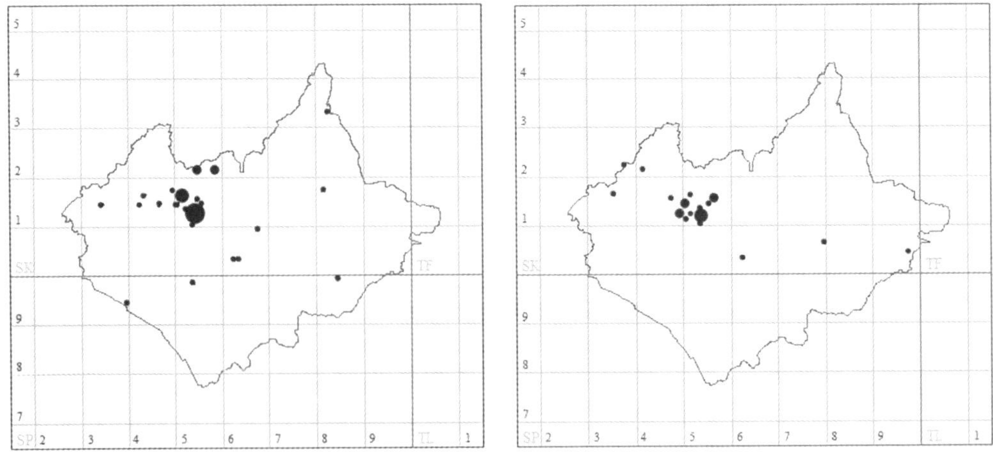

Dot = number of birds, 4 sizes of dot, 1–2 (smallest), 3–4, 5–9, 10+ (largest)

Figure 491: Distribution of singing Wood Warblers 1941–60.

Figure 492: Distribution of singing Wood Warblers 1961–70.

The 1960s produced fewer records than the 1940s. Again, the majority came from Charnwood Forest, although the best years (1964 and 1967) produced just five singing males. Only Swithland Wood could be classed as a regular site, with records in five years and a maximum of three singing males in 1967. Beacon Hill attracted single birds in three years and Buddon Wood and Poultney Wood produced records in two years; otherwise, all other records were of single birds in one year only, at Bradgate Park, Gisborne's Gorse, Benscliffe Wood, Stoneywell Wood, Outwoods and The Brand, Woodhouse Eaves. The only records away from Charnwood during the 1960s involved one at Evington on April 16th 1961, a pair nest-building at Cloud Wood on May 27th 1961 and single singing males at Owston Wood on May 13th and 14th 1967 and Staunton Harold Reservoir in May 1968.

The early 1970s saw similar numbers to those recorded in the 1960s, but a slump in the middle of the decade resulted in there being just five records from 1974 to 1976: a pair at Swithland Wood during the summer of 1974, one at Oadby on May 3rd 1975, two at both Swithland Wood on May 11th 1975 and Buddon Wood on May 18th 1975 and one at Eyebrook Reservoir on April 20th 1976. However, a noticeable increase subsequently occurred, with records from 12 sites involving 14 singing males in 1977, six sites (ten singing males) in 1978 and six sites (eight singing males) in 1979. Again, the prominent site throughout this decade was Swithland Wood, from where there were records in seven years, including confirmed breeding in 1970, three singing males in both 1972 and 1979 and four singing males in 1978.

A further 14 sites in Charnwood recorded this species during the 1970s, including areas such as Ulverscroft, Chitterman Hills, Copt Oak, High Sharpley, Martinshaw Wood and Blackbrook Reservoir which had not been used in previous decades. Most Charnwood sites were only occupied in one or two years throughout the 1970s, although the Buddon Wood/Swithland Reservoir area produced records in five years, including four singing males in 1977, and Poultney Wood, Ulverscroft and Outwoods each held single singing males in three years. Birds were seen away from Charnwood on more occasions during the 1970s than at any other time, with records from 16 widespread sites, although at none of these were birds recorded in more than one year. A significant number were found in the east of the counties, with single singing males at Ketton in 1970, Plungar Wood in 1971, Owston Wood in 1972, Melton Mowbray in 1977 and both Gumley and Launde in 1979, along with two singing males at Billesdon Coplow in 1978: where breeding was suspected. Elsewhere during the 1970s, singing males were recorded at Ashby-de-la-Zouch in 1970, Ashby Pastures in 1971 and Stanford Reservoir, Barlestone, Narborough Bog and near Stanford on Soar in 1977, with breeding confirmed at Staunton Harold Reservoir in the latter year.

The 1980s saw a continuation of the good numbers recorded in the 1970s, with records from Charnwood Forest in every year, including nine singing males in 1982, 1987, 1988 and 1989. The Swithland Wood population seemed well established; at least one singing male was recorded every year, with peaks of five in 1980, 1981 and 1988 and six in 1982. Breeding was confirmed at this site in 1981 and 1983. One or two singing males were found at Swithland Reservoir/Buddon Wood in six years, whilst Outwoods held birds in five years, including three singing in 1982. Records also came from Bradgate Park, Martinshaw Wood, Charnwood Lodge, Ulverscroft, Benscliffe Wood, Beacon Hill, Poultney Wood, Jubilee Wood and Kaye's Plantation, Quorn during this decade. Outside Charnwood, birds were reported during the spring from ten sites, the most notable being three singing at Barnsdale Wood in 1984 (where there had been one the previous year). The only other sites where birds were heard singing in more than one year were Narborough Bog (1985 and 1989) and Rutland Water (1986 and 1988); one-off records of singing birds came from Birstall Gravel Pits in 1983, Willesley Lake and Kelham Bridge in 1984, Lubenham, Sheepy Wood and Narborough in 1986

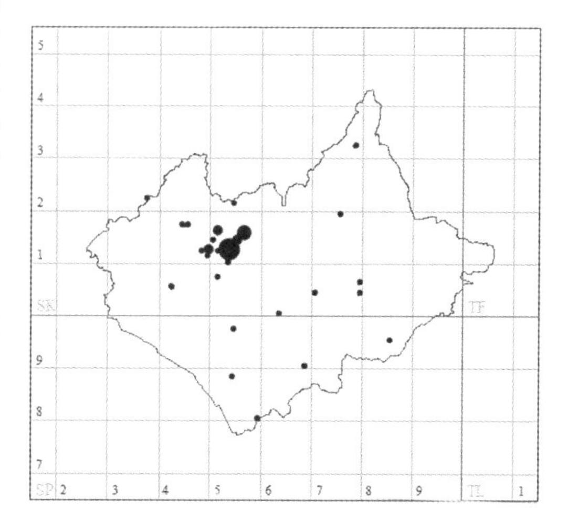

Figure 493: Distribution of singing Wood Warblers 1971–80.

and a passage individual was at Kirby Lakes on April 30th 1989.

From a seemingly stable situation in the 1980s, the Wood Warbler population in Charnwood declined rapidly during the 1990s and by the 21st century had all but disappeared. From 1990 to 2000 there were records from only ten sites in Charnwood, involving a total of 29 singing males. Beacon Hill took over as the most regular site, with records in five years involving seven birds; of these, single singing males from May 6th into June 1992 and April 9th to mid-June 1994 were two of only four birds during this period that remained on territory for any length of time. The Swithland Reservoir/Buddon Wood area held birds in five years and Swithland Wood produced records in four years, involving six birds, but all were relatively short-stayers. The only evidence of breeding came from Outwoods in 1994, when a pair was seen carrying food on June 12th; otherwise, all records in Charnwood involved short-staying birds, at Bardon Hill and Kaye's Plantation, Quorn in 1990, Bradgate Park in 1992 and 1994, Outwoods in 1996, 1997 and 2000 and Ulverscroft in 1998. Away from Charnwood, records came from ten sites between 1990 and 2000. With the exception of two at both Willesley Wood on May 11th 1991 and Burley Wood on May 11th 1996 and one at Piper Wood from May 2nd to 9th 1996, all records involved single singing males on one day only: at Glenfield in 1990, Eyebrook Reservoir in 1992, Launde in 1995, Dishley Pool in 1996, Newell Wood in 1998, Ravenstone in 1999 and Tyron Spinney in 2000.

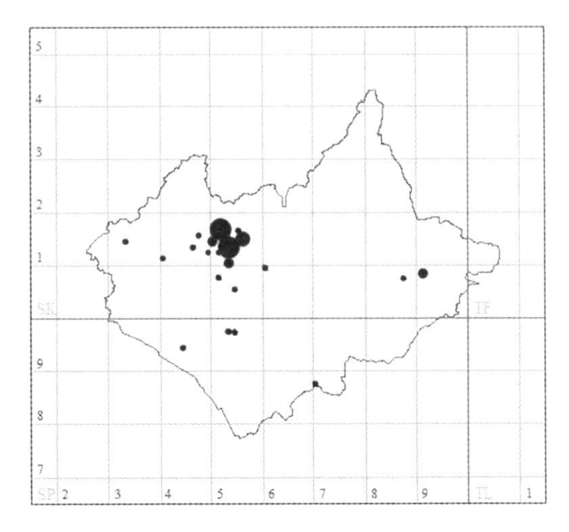

Figure 494: Distribution of singing Wood Warblers 1981–90.

Since 2000 there have been just eight records, all of single birds, as follows:

- Sheepy Wood, late April to May 8th 2001.
- Beacon Hill, April 25th 2002.
- Swithland Wood, April 26th to May 5th 2003.
- Evington Golf Course, April 26th 2004.
- Abbey Park, Leicester, April 14th 2005.
- Bardon Hill, April 17th 2005.
- Charnwood Lodge, May 1st 2005.
- Ingarsby, May 2nd 2005.

The reasons for the virtual disappearance of this species from the counties are not clear, although the Wood Warbler has declined significantly nationally since 1994 and has shown a retreat from south-eastern England during the same time (Baillie *et al.* 2006).

The earliest spring record involved one singing at Swithland Reservoir on April 6th 1984, but there have only been another four records prior to April 17th, all single birds unless stated:

- two, Beacon Hill, April 9th 1994.
- Beacon Hill, April 12th 1997.
- Abbey Park, Leicester, April 14th 2005.
- Evington, April 16th 1961.

It is worth noting that three of these records have occurred since 1994 and, in line with a number of

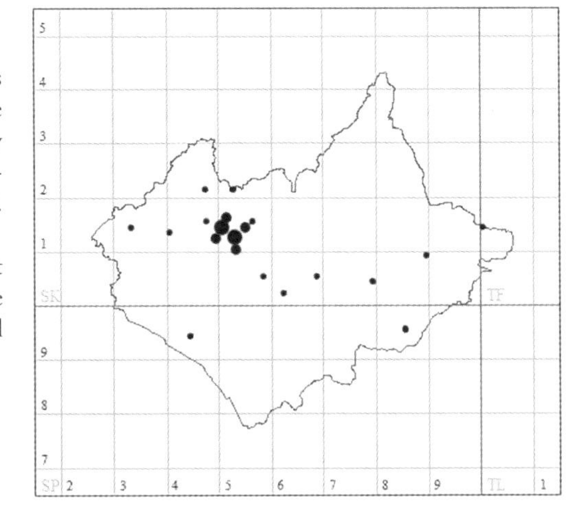

Figure 495: Distribution of singing Wood Warblers 1991–2005.

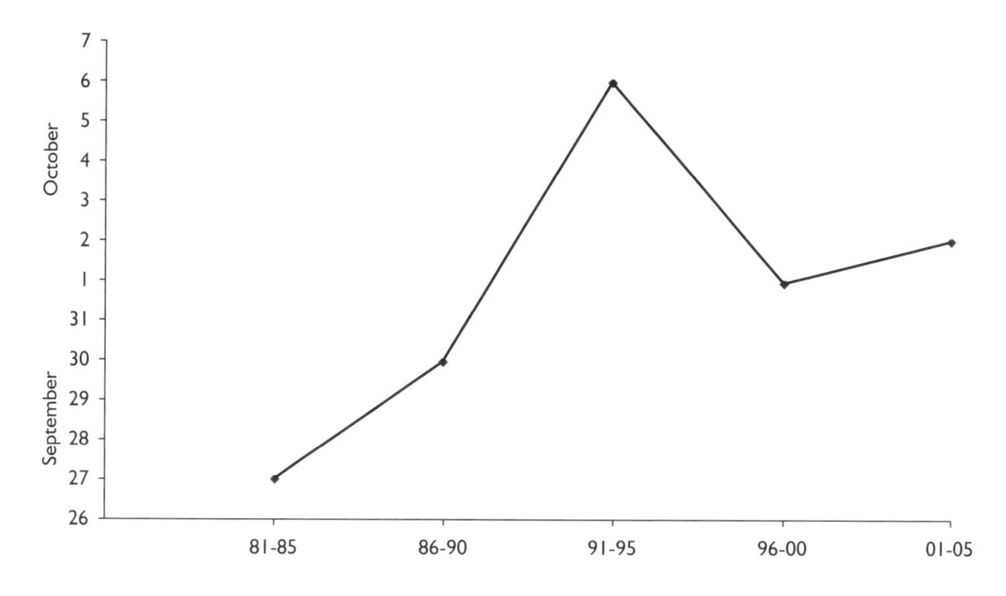

Figure 496: Average spring arrival dates of Wood Warblers by five-year periods 1951–2005.

other summer migrants, the average arrival date of Wood Warbler in Leicestershire and Rutland has become earlier in recent years.

The Wood Warbler is rare in Leicestershire and Rutland on autumn passage and there have only been 11 records at this time of year, all of single birds, as follows:

- Cropston Reservoir, 19th August 1962.
- Beacon Hill, August 4th 1963.
- Bradgate Park, August 5th 1963.
- Ketton, August 31st 1970.
- Eyebrook Reservoir, July 28th 1980.
- Stoughton Airfield, August 18th 1986.
- Rutland Water, August 31st 1991.
- trapped and ringed at Belmesthorpe, August 15th 1982.
- Saddington Reservoir, August 15th 1993.
- Rutland Water, August 20th 1997.
- Watermead Park, September 1st 2000.

Wood Warblers breed across much of Europe north to southern Lapland and winter in Africa south of the Sahara. The British population is estimated at 17,200 pairs (Baker *et al.* 2006) and, due to the recent decline noted above over recent years, this species has been added to the 'Amber List' of Birds of Conservation Concern (Gregory *et al.* 2002).

RMF

Chiffchaff (Common Chiffchaff) ***Phylloscopus collybita***

Common migrant breeder, uncommon winter visitor.

The 19th century status of the Chiffchaff was described in Leicestershire as 'a summer migrant, commonly distributed and breeding' by Browne and in Rutland as 'distributed over the county but nowhere numerous' by Haines. The earliest spring migrant was one in Rutland on March 16th 1893. Wintering records were virtually unknown at this time although Browne noted single birds at Langton on February 21st 1882 and Gumley on

November 11th 1882, whilst Haines mentioned one seen at an unspecified site in Rutland on 25th November 1900.

The Chiffchaff is traditionally one of the earliest summer migrants to appear. The first birds are usually recorded in mid-March although establishing exact arrival dates is now complicated by wintering birds. Despite these difficulties it would appear that the average arrival date has become significantly earlier since the early 1980s.

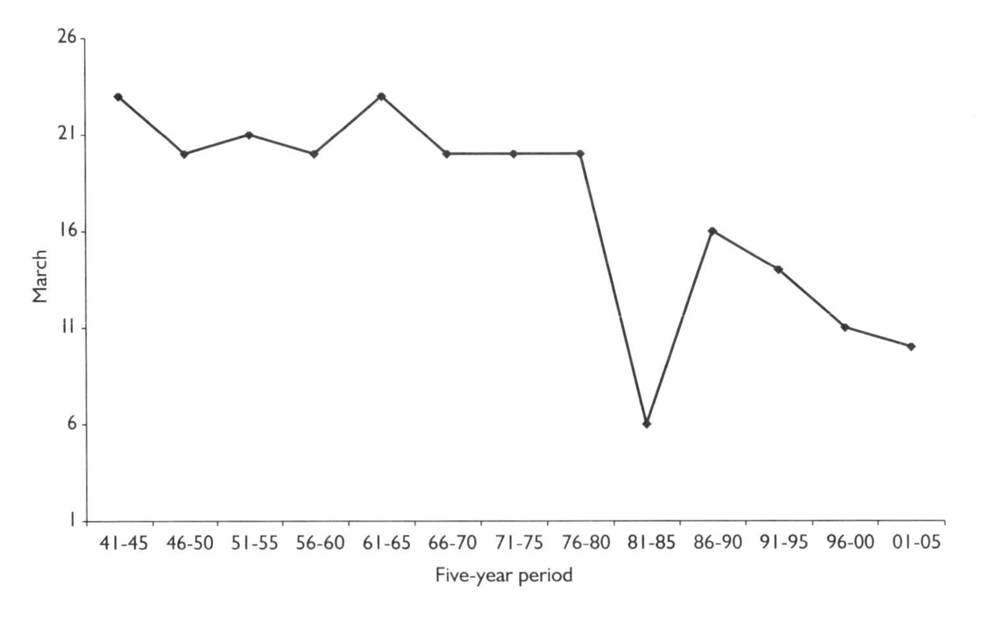

Figure 497: Average spring arrival dates of Chiffchaffs by five-year periods 1941–2005.

Very little is known about the breeding status of the Chiffchaff during the first half of the 20th century. The first LROS Annal Report in 1941 described this species as 'not numerous but well distributed' and evidence from Quorn in the 1940s suggested that it was increasing at this time: there were 41 pairs within a six-mile radius of the village in 1944, increasing to 55 pairs in 1947 and 66 the following year. In 1960 the LROS Annual Report amended the status of Chiffchaff to 'fairly common with uneven distribution'.

During 1976–84 Warrilow recorded this species in 269 tetrads in the counties (42% of the total number of tetrads), with breeding confirmed in 55, making it less than half as widespread as the Willow Warbler. It requires mature woodland with a shrub layer for breeding and was largely absent from parts of the north-east, especially the Leicestershire wolds and the Wreake valley. It was also unrecorded from most areas within the city boundary of Leicester and a survey in 1989 of four green spaces in the city found Chiffchaffs to be present at just one site, Knighton Park, where two pairs were located. Both pairs were found in Knighton Spinney within the park, a woodland habitat absent from the other areas surveyed (Fray *et al.* 1990). Surveys carried out in 1987 by Warrilow at a number of east Leicestershire woods found that Chiffchaffs tended to avoid copses smaller than two hectares and preferred larger woods of ten hectares or more. Here, territories were mainly found in the interior zone rather than along the woodland edges. Densities calculated per occupied tetrad included 35 pairs at Billesdon Coplow, 13 at Botany Bay Fox Covert, 41 at Owston Wood and 31 at Loddington Reddish. Numbers on farmland are much smaller (for instance an average of fewer one pair per tetrad was recorded at the Stoughton CBC plot). Based on these calculations Warrilow estimated a county-wide breeding population of 700 pairs.

Local CBC data does not reveal much information regarding the population since the time of Warrilow's work. Nationally this species has been increasing slowly since the 1980s and this is partly borne out by the results from Stoughton; from 1964 to 1988 the average number of breeding pairs was 0.68 but this increased to 2.2 pairs during 1989–99. However at Prior's Coppice, a woodland site with a more sizeable population of Chiffchaffs, numbers showed a steady increase from five pairs in 1988 to eight in 1995 and 1996 but then dropped to just four by 1999.

Since 1997 there have been ten records of 15 or more singing males at any one site; the largest counts have come from Rutland Water, where there were 59 on April 8th 2003, 54 on April 16th 2004, 35 on April 27th 2002, 20 on March 24th 2005 and 17 on April 1st 2000. Elsewhere, notable counts have included:

- 30 at Stathern Wood on April 10th 2005.
- 23 at Blakeshay Wood on April 13th 2003.
- 18 at Bardon Hill on April 17th 2004.
- 15 at Pickworth Great Wood on June 1st 2002.
- 15 at Aylestone Meadows on March 16th 2003.

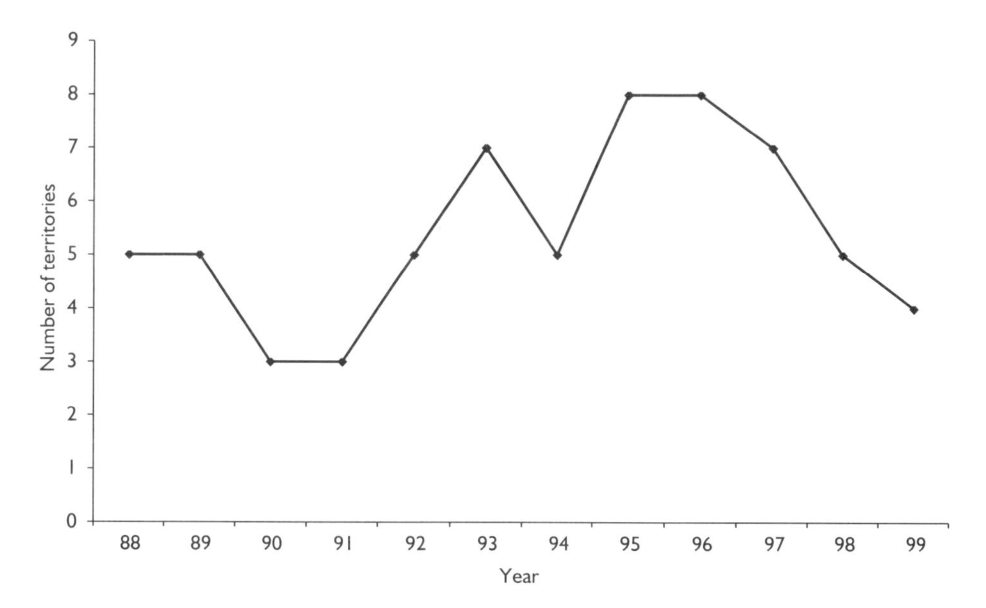

Figure 498: Number of breeding pairs of Chiffchaffs on the Prior's Coppice CBC plot 1988–99.

Autumn passage is protracted, lasting from mid-August to early October. As with spring, departure dates are now difficult to ascertain due to the presence of wintering birds but, where known, the last date is usually in the second or third week of October. Small concentrations of migrants are a feature of the autumn; the largest groups have been:

- 35 at Rutland Water on September 9th 2004.
- 30 at Croft Hill on September 22nd 2000.
- 25 at Rutland Water on 13th September 2003.
- 18 at Stanford Reservoir on September 10th 2001.
- 15 at Croft Hill on August 27th 1999.

Prior to 1982-83, records during the winter months were unusual and had only been noted on nine occasions. All records refer to single birds:

- Stanford Reservoir, November 19th 1944.
- Quorn, November 26th 1949 to January 16th 1950.
- Scraptoft, December 2nd 1956.
- Eyebrook Reservoir Plantation, January 1st 1969.
- Stanford Reservoir, December 12th 1971.
- Gaddesby, February 12th 1977.

- Rutland Water, December 16th 1977.
- Stanford Reservoir, November 25th 1978.
- Aylestone, January 26th 1981.

There were also seven winter records of unidentified *Phylloscopus* warblers between 1961 and 1982, all of which are likely to refer to Chiffchaffs. Since 1982–83 wintering by a small number of individuals has been recorded annually and has increased since the mid-1990s; the most productive winters have been 1994–95 (17 individuals at ten sites), 2005–06 (16 birds at 12 sites) and 2003–04 (15 birds at nine sites). The first record of two together was at Cropston Reservoir on January 3rd and 24th 1988, since when records of two have come from 11 sites. Larger counts during the winter have been:

- up to five at Kirby Lakes during the first winter period in 1995.
- five at Wanlip South Gravel Pits on February 29th 2004.
- up to five at Kirby Lakes from December 27th 2004 to February 27th 2005.
- up to four at Kirby Lakes from January 31st to March 17th 1993 (Gamble 1994).
- three at Aylestone Meadows on February 5th 1995.
- three at Rutland Water from December 2nd to 24th 1995.
- three at Kirby Lakes on January 4th 2004.
- up to three at Watermead Country Park South from March 6th to 19th 2005.
- three at Watermead Country Park South during the second winter period in 2005.

Kirby Lakes has been the most favoured site for wintering Chiffchaffs in the counties and the birds here are often found in the vicinity of a small sewage works (Gamble 1994). Other areas where this species has been found wintering with some regularity include Rutland Water, the Soar valley gravel pits and Trent Valley Pit; here the birds have often been found in or around reedbeds.

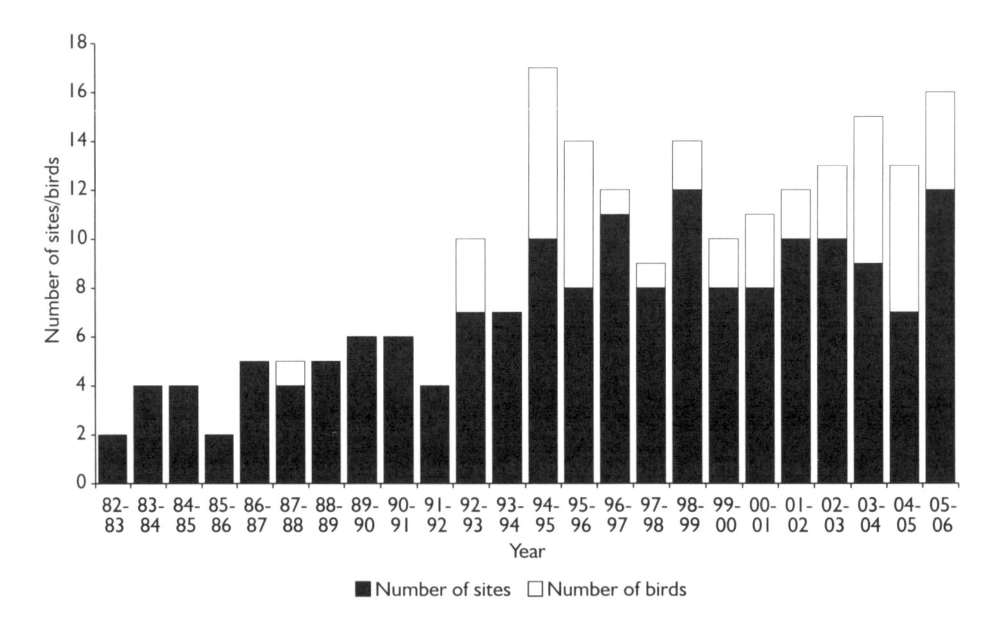

Figure 499: Numbers of wintering Chiffchaffs 1982–83 to 2004–05.

Individuals of the Scandinavian race *P. c. abietinus* have been reported in nine years since 1988, involving a total of 11 birds. All records have been of single birds, as follows:

- Narborough, September 24th to October 2nd 1988.
- Loughborough, December 22nd 1990.
- Kirby Lakes, 31st January intermittently to March 21st 1993 (Gamble 1994).

- Kirby Lakes, two dates in August and early September 1993.
- Swithland Reservoir, December 30th 1993.
- Kirby Lakes, March 20th 1994.
- Rutland Water, December 23rd 1995.
- Watermead Park, November and December 2000.
- Dishley Pool, December 14th 2003.
- Dishley Pool, October 17th 2004.
- Kirby Lakes, December 27th 2004 to February 27th 2005.

In addition, birds reported as either *abietinus* or *P. c. tristis* (often known as 'Siberian Chiffchaff') have been reported as follows:

- Eastwell, September 9th and 10th 1993.
- Kirby Lakes, November 13th 1994 to January 22nd 1995, with two on the latter date.
- Wanlip South Gravel Pits, February 11th 2004.

The only definite record of *tristis* in the counties was a singing bird at Loughborough from March 23rd to April 5th 2000. The racial identification of Chiffchaffs is something of a challenge and many of the reports of *abietinus* birds have not been subjected to detailed scrutiny by the Records Committee. Two birds recorded at Rutland Water in recent years demonstrate the difficulties involved. One from January 17th to 26th 1998 was initially thought to be *tristis*, but was subsequently trapped and ringed and found to exhibit characters more typical of *abietinus* or an intergrade, whilst a rather grey individual on April 4th 2003 was sound-recorded and its song contained elements of both *tristis* and *abietinus*. Although reports of *abietinus* should be treated with a degree of caution, it is clear from the pattern of records that this race is most likely to be encountered in the counties in late autumn or winter; the records from Narborough in September 1988, Kirby Lakes in August and September 1993 and Eastwell in September 1993 are therefore exceptional. Identification criteria for *tristis* are currently evolving and the situation regarding the occurrence of this race in Britain is somewhat confused, but it is likely to be a rare vagrant to the counties. Fortunately the Loughborough bird of 2000 was regularly heard singing; this is currently one of the only identification features recognised as being reliable.

Chiffchaffs breed throughout much of Europe and northern Asia to eastern Siberia. The nominate race is found in western and central Europe, *abietinus* breeds across much of Scandinavia east to the Urals and south to south-west Asia and *tristis* occurs east of the Urals. Most western populations winter around the Mediterranean and in sub-Saharan Africa although some winter in Britain, whilst northern and eastern populations move to eastern Africa and northern India. The current British breeding population, which is slowly but steadily increasing, is estimated at 749,000 pairs (Baker *et al.* 2006). All ringing recoveries involving the counties have been within England except for a juvenile ringed on Guernsey (Channel Islands) on August 13th 2000 which was found dead at Market Harborough on April 13th 2001.

RMF

Willow Warbler *Phylloscopus trochilus*

Abundant migrant breeder.

The Willow Warbler is the commonest and most widespread warbler in Leicestershire and Rutland. Previous indications on its status confirm that this has probably always been the case: in the 19th century, Browne described it as 'commonly distributed and breeding . . . the most abundant of our summer migrants', whilst Haines noted that in Rutland it was 'far more numerous than Chiffchaff, one of our commonest migrants'. The first LROS Annual Report, in 1941, indicated that the Willow Warbler was 'well distributed and fairly common'; by 1948, this status had been amended to 'abundant'. A little later, Otter (1965) described it as a 'very common visitor to east Leicestershire'.

The distinctive descending song of the Willow Warbler is one of the most eagerly awaited sounds of the spring. The first migrants usually arrive in late March or early April, with the main influx during mid-April. Haines mentions one by the Eye Brook on March 14th 1903 and Mitcham (1984) refers to one at Eyebrook Reservoir on March 7th 1959; in the absence of further information, neither of these reports can be considered reliable and the earliest acceptable arrival is one at Atterton on March 18th 1950. There have been a further seven records prior to March 25th, all of single birds, as follows:

- Melton Country Park, March 20th 2005.
- Anstey, March 21st 1946.
- Swithland Reservoir, March 21st 1989.
- Huncote, March 21st 1995.
- Swithland, March 23rd 1957.
- Eyebrook Reservoir, March 23rd 1961.
- Barkby, March 24th 1945.

In line with a number of other summer migrants, arrival dates of Willow Warbler are becoming earlier; there have been March records in 14 of the 18 years between 1988 and 2005, compared to in 14 of the preceding 47 years. The average arrival date during the four five-year periods since 1986 has been between March 28th and March 31st, whilst in the equivalent periods from 1961 to 1986 the average dates range from April 2nd to April 5th.

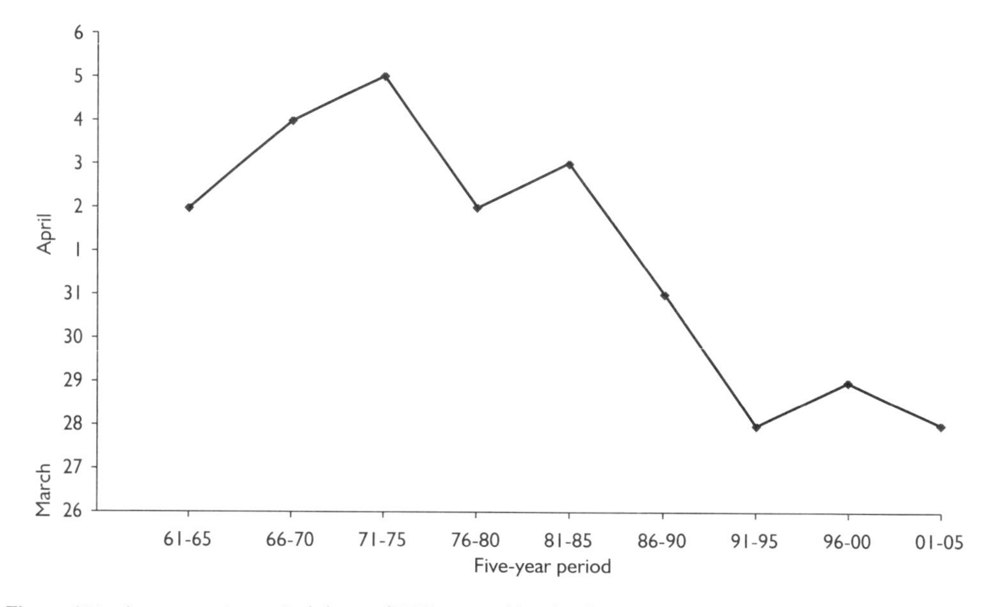

Figure 500: Average spring arrival dates of Willow Warblers by five-year periods 1961–2005.

During the autumn, a noticeable movement often takes place through the counties. This was first referred to by Pochin (1953) in his report on visible migration at Croft Hill, when he stated that 'large numbers pass through in August to mid-September'. In more recent times, concentrations have included 30 at Quorn Borrow Pit on August 20th 1989 and 20 at Kirby Lakes on August 15th 1983, Priory Water on both September 6th 1995 and August 19th 2001 and Croft Hill on August 20th 1999. By late September most birds have left the counties, although there have been October records in 25 years since 1941. The majority of these occur during the first few days, although there have been six October reports later than the 10th, all of single birds, as follows:

- Elmfield Avenue, Leicester, October 27th 1963.
- Thornton Reservoir, October 16th 1992.
- Normanton Park, October 15th 1967.
- Priory Water, October 14th 2001.
- Evington, October 12th 1964.
- an unspecified site, October 12th 1969.

The latest record, however, involves one found at Watermead Country Park South on the exceptional date of December 10th 2000. This bird, which appeared to be in poor health, remained until December 17th, when the onset of freezing conditions may have caused its demise. In addition, Haines mentions a report of one at an unspecified site on November 18th 1900, but in the absence of further information this is best ignored.

Average departure dates have become slightly later since the early 1980s, reflecting the increased incidence of October records in more recent years. The following graph shows the average departure date for the five-year periods from 1981 onwards only, as meaningful data does not exist prior to this; the exceptional winter record in 2000 is excluded.

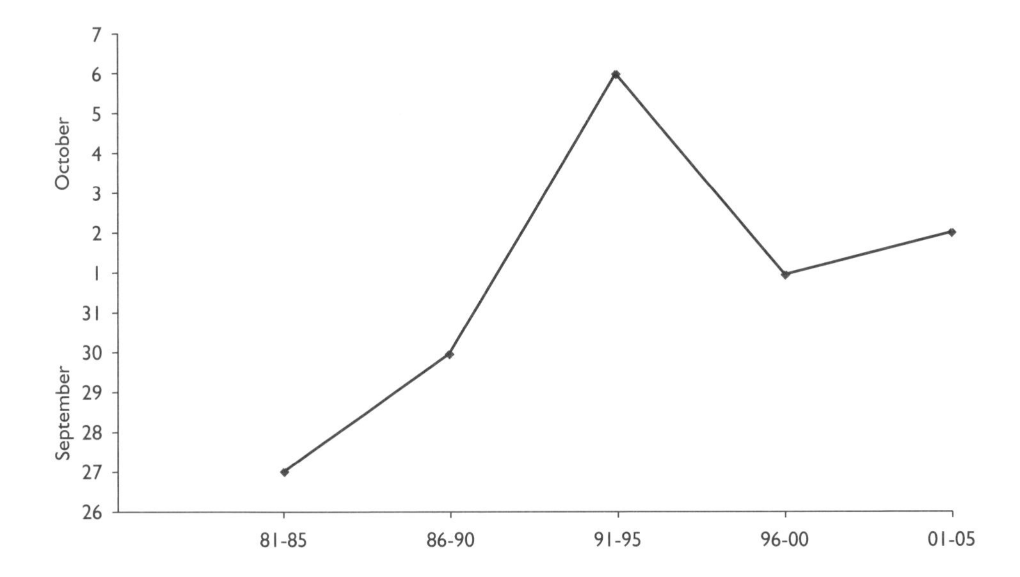

Figure 501: Average autumn departure dates of Willow Warblers by five-year periods 1981–2005.

Willow Warblers are found in a wide range of habitats including hedgerows with trees, golf courses, woodland edges and clearings, plantations, disused gravel workings, overgrown railway embankments and scrubby patches around former airfields. Local censuses carried out by Warrilow have demonstrated that the highest breeding densities are found in scrubby habitats: in 1990, a density of 3,000 pairs per tetrad was recorded in such habitat at Stoughton, whilst 23 pairs found in 1987 in 13 small scrubby woodlands with a total area of 8.8 hectares at Wistow gave a breeding density of 1,044 pairs per tetrad. Numbers appear to be lower in larger woodlands: Billesdon Coplow (11.4 hectares) and Botany Bay Fox Covert (14.9 hectares) had 120 and 256 pairs per tetrad respectively, concentrated along the woodland edge zone. Average densities on farmland are lower still, with the CBC plots at Stoughton and Newton Harcourt producing only 20 and 88 pairs per tetrad respectively. In all, Warrilow recorded this species in 558 tetrads in the counties (87% of the total number of tetrads) during 1976–84, with breeding confirmed in 201, making this species twice as common as the Chiffchaff and second only to the Swallow as the counties' most widespread summer visitor.

Of the few unoccupied tetrads, many were in the heavily built-up areas of Leicester, Loughborough, Melton Mowbray and Hinckley; however, Willow Warblers are able to utilise urban environments and nest readily in parks, mature gardens and cemeteries, albeit at lower densities than elsewhere. Pochin (1954) described this species as a 'common summer resident in suburbs and outskirts' of the city of Leicester, whilst Fray *et al.* (1990) found Willow Warblers present in four green spaces within the city boundary in 1989, including seven pairs at Aylestone Meadows. The wide variation in breeding densities makes estimating the counties' total breeding population difficult, although Warrilow proposed a tentative figure of between 30,000 and 38,000 pairs.

Away from the work of Warrilow, there are other examples of the abundance of this species. Brady (1944) found 14 pairs at The Brand, Woodhouse Eaves in 1940, with 16 pairs in 1943, making this the fifth commonest breeding species at the site. A survey of woodland and scrub at Lount in May 1985 found the Willow Warbler to be the third most abundant species after Blue Tit and Wren and the equal first most widespread with the latter. The highest densities were in immature deciduous (mainly birch) and hawthorn scrub, although there were almost as many birds in some coniferous areas; indeed, the Willow Warbler was the commonest and most widespread of all species in the coniferous areas (Smallshire 1986b).

Counts of singing birds during the spring also give some idea of the densities this species can attain. Otter (1965) mentions totals of 80 at Owston Wood, 42 at Loddington Reddish, 35 at Tugby Wood and 30 at Skeffington Wood, although does not reveal in which years these counts were made. Since 1966, LROS Annual Reports have detailed double-figure totals at 21 sites; of these, six have provided records involving 25+ singing males. Counts at Rutland Water have included 85 on April 27th 2002, 67 on April 18th 2003 and 66 on April 20th 2004, whilst elsewhere the highest counts have been:

- 34 at Stanford Reservoir in April 1982.
- 30 at Owston Wood in June 1978.
- 30 at Beacon Hill on April 12th 1987, April 24th 1999 and April 18th 2002.
- 28 at Barnsdale Wood in April 1982.
- 28 at Charnwood Lodge on April 19th 2004.

National CBC data shows that the Willow Warbler declined by 31% between 1974 and 1999 (Gregory *et al.* 2002) and local CBC data supports this, although some wide fluctuations have been noted. At Stoughton and Newton Harcourt, peak levels were reached in the early 1980s, since when both sites recorded noticeable declines. Similarly, the two CBC plots in Rutland show a slump in numbers; this is particularly evident at Prior's Coppice, where 15 territories in 1988 fell to just one by 1992. Conversely, large gains have recently been recorded at Loddington where, from 28 pairs in 1992, numbers increased to 47 pairs by 1998, an increase of 68%. These figures, which can possibly be attributed to sensitive habitat management and the removal of predators, are probably not representative of the county-wide situation. Given the declining numbers recorded at local CBC sites, it may be that Warrilow's estimate of 30,000 to 38,000 pairs is now optimistic.

Willow Warblers breed throughout much of Europe and winter in Africa south of the Sahara. Surprisingly, for such a common bird, Leicestershire and Rutland ringing returns for this species have only produced one continental recovery: a juvenile ringed at Rutland Water on August 7th 2000 was retrapped in France at Floirac,

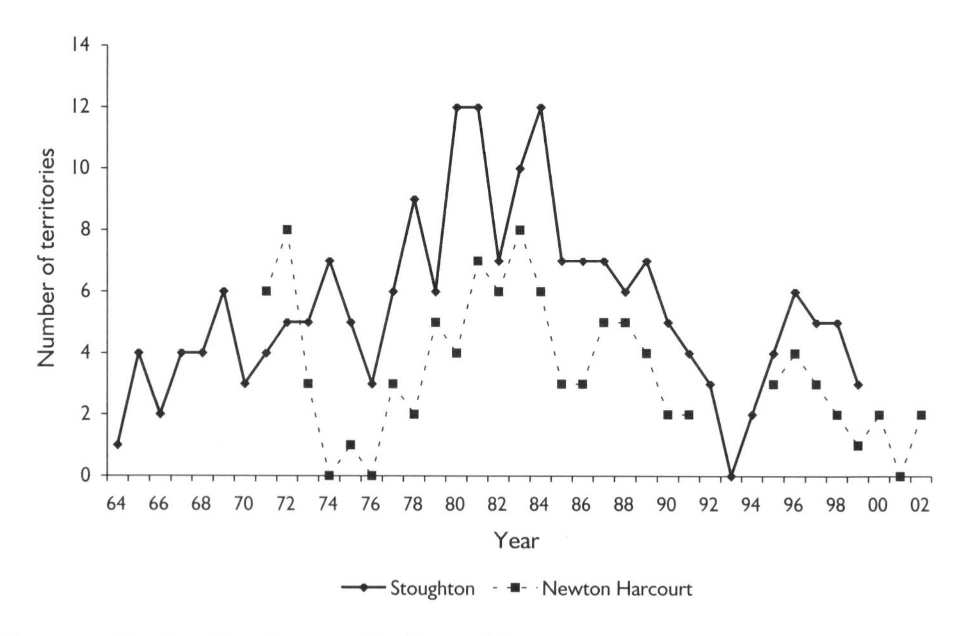

Figure 502: Number of breeding pairs of Willow Warblers on two Leicestershire CBC plots 1964–2002.

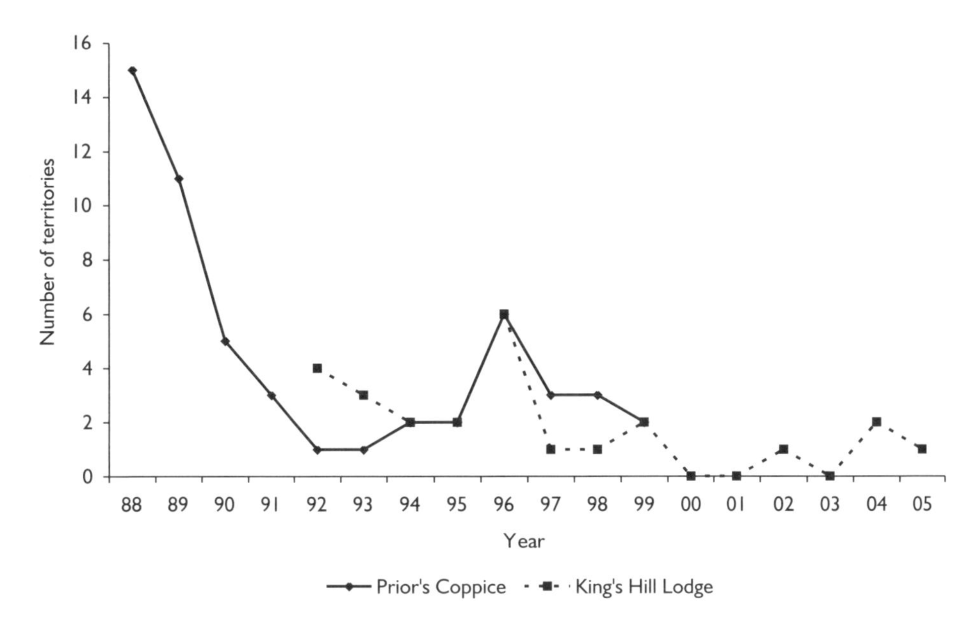

Figure 503: Number of breeding pairs of Willow Warblers on two Rutland CBC plots 1988–2005.

Charente-Maritime 22 days later. The British breeding population is estimated at 1,955,000 pairs (Baker *et al.* 2006) and, due to a moderate decline in breeding numbers over the last 25 years, the Willow Warbler has been added to the 'Amber List' of Birds of Conservation Concern (Gregory *et al.* 2002).

RMF

Goldcrest *Regulus regulus*

Fairly common to common resident breeder and winter visitor.

Despite being a relatively common and widespread species in the counties, the Goldcrest is rather poorly studied. Indications of its status in the 19th century were provided by Browne and Haines: the former described it as 'resident but sparingly distributed' in Leicestershire, whilst the latter stated that it was 'resident and by no means uncommon' in Rutland. Browne considered that this species was commoner during the winter and cited a concentration of 50 at Burbage Wood in January 1890. The first LROS Annual Report, in 1941, described the Goldcrest as 'resident and thinly distributed'.

It is known that this species steadily increased nationally throughout the first 70 years of the 20th century and then decreased from 1970 to 1995 (Gibbons *et al.* 1996). The little available evidence suggests this may also have been the case in Leicestershire and Rutland, although further studies would be needed to confirm this. A notable increase was recorded by Brady (1944), who found six territories at The Brand, Woodhouse Eaves in 1940 and 13 in 1943, whilst CBC data from Stoughton shows peak numbers in the early 1970s followed by a steady decline to such an extent that no pairs were thought to have bred after 1989. Unfortunately, other CBC plots in the counties do not provide any further clues as to the fortunes of this species, as Goldcrests were all but absent at each site.

Goldcrests suffer badly during extended periods of extreme cold and their numbers can take several years to recover. Strangely, the only written evidence to suggest this in Leicestershire and Rutland is provided by Mitcham (1984), who stated that this species was not seen in Greetham Wood between 1963 and 1967 following the infamous severe winter of 1962–63. Circumstantial evidence from the Stoughton CBC plot suggests that the same winter wiped out Goldcrests from this site as well; with the exception of a pair in 1966, there were no birds here from 1964 (the year that the survey began) to 1971, after which numbers built up steadily over the next few years.

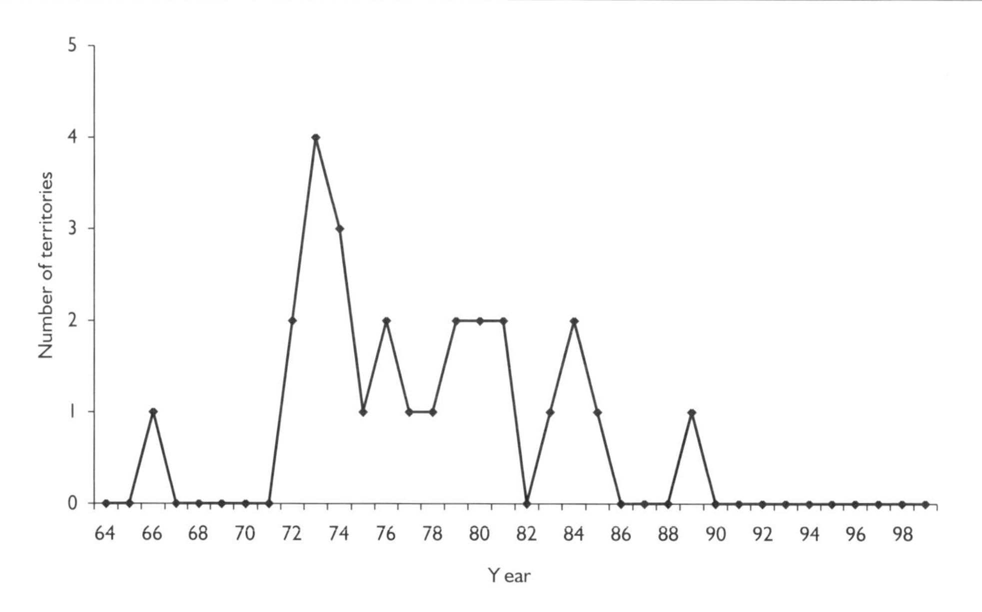

Figure 504: Number of breeding pairs of Goldcrests on the Stoughton CBC plot 1964–99.

Warrilow recorded Goldcrests in 201 tetrads in the counties (31% of the total number of tetrads), with breeding confirmed in 49. It is well known that this species shows a distinct preference for conifers and the distribution mapped by Warrilow closely matched that of Scots Pine trees, particularly in the Charnwood area. It was this region that was found to be the stronghold, although Goldcrests were scattered widely over the remainder of the counties; it was absent from large parts of the intensively farmed areas in east and north-east Leicestershire and north Rutland, where suitable breeding habitat does not exist. Some idea of this species' predilection for coniferous plantations is shown by two studies carried out in the 1980s: at Lount in 1985, the Goldcrest was found to be one of the foremost species in coniferous blocks (Smallshire 1986b) and the following year at the predominantly coniferous Martinshaw Wood it was found to be the fourth most abundant species (Holling 1987). At the latter site, 32 males were identified as holding territory in May 1985.

Goldcrests are not, however, strictly confined to coniferous plantations and are also associated with non-native conifers; they therefore breed in urban habitats such as large gardens, ornamental parks and cemeteries. Examples of such urban breeding habits include seven pairs at Narborough in 1983 that were 'all nesting in *Cupressus* trees, when other coniferous species were available', whilst in 1989 one or two pairs were located in each of Abbey Park, Knighton Park and Western Park, all sites within the city boundary of Leicester which contain ornamental coniferous trees (Fray *et al.* 1990). In addition, a survey by Warrilow in 1993 of the University of Leicester Botanical Gardens at Oadby found a density of 47 pairs per tetrad and the Leicestershire Garden Bird Survey placed the Goldcrest as the 27th most-frequent visitor, being recorded in just under 3% of all gardens between January 1996 and June 2005. Since 1996, a few birds have been recorded visiting peanut feeders.

Other habitats are also utilised as breeding sites and surveys by Warrilow in 1987 and 1990 of 85 hectares of mixed deciduous woodland in east Leicestershire produced 12 pairs, equivalent to a mean territory density of 56 pairs per tetrad. Given all the evidence, Warrilow proposed a county-wide breeding population of 1,000 to 2,000 pairs, based on an average of five to ten pairs per occupied tetrad. However, the population level at the time of Warrilow's work was thought to be at a low level following the hard winters of 1975–76 and 1978–79 and it is likely that numbers are currently higher following recent mild winters.

Large numbers of immigrants arrive from northern Europe each autumn to swell the resident population through the winter months. It is at these times that most of the largest counts have been recorded, the highest of which is 200 at Eyebrook Reservoir Plantation during the winter of 1959–60 (Otter 1965). 'Large influxes' were also recorded at this site in 1950 and 1967 (Mitcham 1984). There have been a further eight counts of 30+, as follows:

- 100, in two flocks of 50 each, at Outwoods on December 25th 1949.
- 50 at Stoke Dry Wood on October 15th 1962.
- 45 at Eyebrook Reservoir Plantation on April 21st 1989.
- 40 at Martinshaw Wood on January 1st 1983.
- 40 at Swithland Reservoir on December 2nd 1997.
- 40 at Outwoods on December 27th 1999.
- 35 at Eyebrook Reservoir Plantation on September 16th 1988.
- 35 at Croft Hill on September 22nd 2000.

Goldcrests breed over most of Europe and discontinuously across Asia as far as west Japan and China. The current British population estimate is 773,000 pairs (Baker *et al.* 2006) and due to the moderate decline in breeding numbers over the last 25 years this species has been added to the 'Amber List' of Birds of Conservation Concern (Gregory *et al.* 2002); this, however, may only be a temporary measure, as following the recent run of mild winters it is considered that the Goldcrest is likely to be increasing again (Baillie *et al.* 2006). The majority of British Goldcrests spend the winter on or near their breeding territories, but large numbers visit the country from northern Europe to swell the winter population. Although there are no foreign ringing recoveries involving Leicestershire and Rutland, there are four instances of birds which were trapped on the English east coast during the autumn and were later found in the counties, presumably indicating a continental origin:

- a female ringed at Gibraltar Point (Lincolnshire) on October 29th 1988 was retrapped 72km to the south-west at Belmesthorpe on November 27th of the same year.
- a male ringed at South Gare (Cleveland) on October 4th 1992 was controlled 226km to the south at Leicester on November 3rd 1992.
- a male ringed at Spurn Point (East Yorkshire), also on October 4th 1992, was retrapped 113km to the south-south-west at Ketton Quarry on March 6th 1993.
- a male ringed at Saltholme (Cleveland) on September 12th 1998 was controlled 223km to the south-south-east at Ketton Quarry on October 15th of the same year.

DJSG

Firecrest *Regulus ignicapilla*

Scarce passage migrant and rare winter visitor: 50 records involving 54 individuals.

Always considered a rare winter vagrant, Firecrests have increased significantly in recent years and are currently scarce passage migrants and winter visitors, with records in most years since 1992. The first on record is one 'handled' at Market Harborough on November 10th 1905. There were no further reports until one at Stoughton on May 6th 1942 and only eight more were recorded in the next 38 years. Frequency of occurrence increased steadily through the 1980s to the present situation. There were 54 records by the end of 2005, the best years being 1988 (five individuals), 1993 (four) and 2003 (five). Most sightings are of single birds, but there have been four occasions when two birds have been seen together:

- Peatling Parva on October 25th 1988.
- a pair at Swithland Reservoir from January 12th to March 21st 1989.
- a pair at Buddon Brook, Quorn on March 8th 1993.
- two first-winter males trapped and ringed at Charnwood Lodge on November 8th 2003.

In addition, one or two were at Great Glen on November 2nd and 3rd 1988.

The majority of records are during the winter and passage months, the earliest autumn arrival being one at Rutland Water on September 21st 2002 and the latest spring departure being the Stoughton bird on May 6th 1942. There is, however, an exceptional record of one singing in the plantation at Eyebrook Reservoir on June 8th 1986. Other singing birds have been recorded at Victoria Park, Leicester on May 3rd 1995 and Hambleton Wood on May 4th 1996. Wintering birds often remain for lengthy periods of time, the longest stays being:

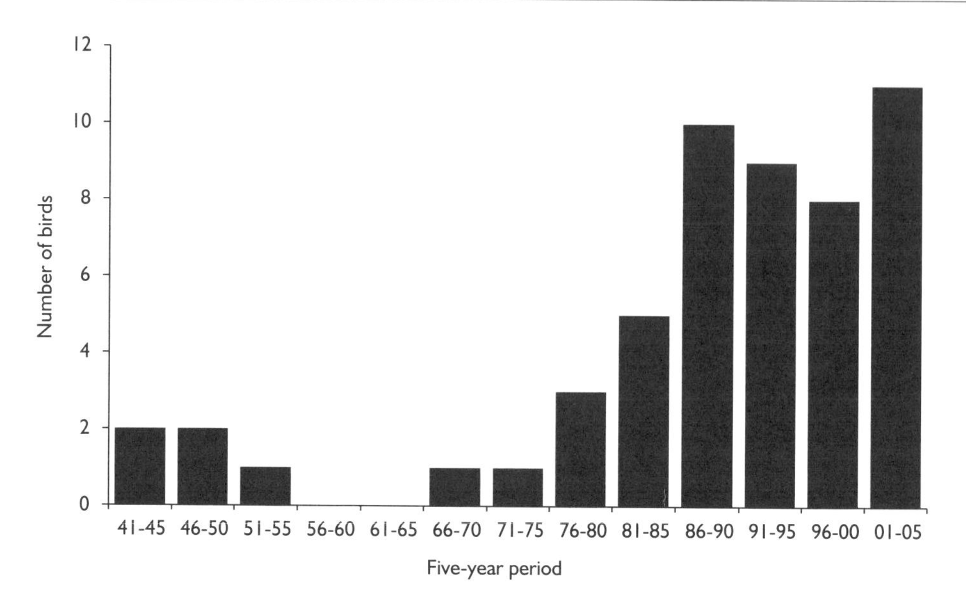

Figure 505: Numbers of Firecrests 1941–2005.

- a female at Swithland Reservoir from January 2nd to March 21st 1989.
- a male (with the above female) at Swithland Reservoir from January 12th to March 25th 1989.
- a female at Willesley Lake from January 13th to March 16th 1992.
- a male at Rutland Water from January 27th to March 5th 1997.

Figure 506 shows a preponderance of records in the first four months (peaking in January) and last two months and another peak (representing passage birds) in late September.

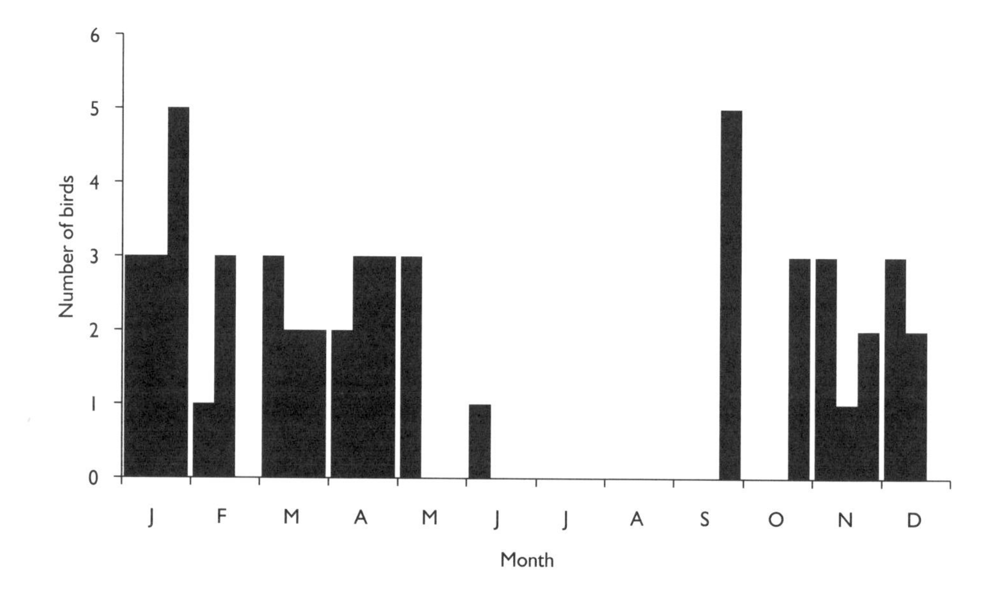

Figure 506: Monthly occurrence of Firecrests 1941–2005.

Firecrests have been found at a total of 33 sites. The most popular areas have been the Charnwood Forest area, with 21 records, six of which were at Swithland Reservoir, and the Rutland Water area, with six records.

Eight birds have been trapped and ringed, which is a high proportion of the birds recorded. This suggests that more are occurring in the counties than are being discovered.

The Firecrest has a European distribution. Northern and eastern populations are migratory, heading south and west to winter in the Mediterranean area and extreme west of Europe from Portugal north to Britain and Ireland. Its main breeding range in Britain lies in southern and eastern England and the Forest of Dean (Gloucestershire); the latest population estimate is between 80 and 250 singing males (Baker *et al.* 2006). On account of its small breeding population, the Firecrest is on the 'Amber List' of Birds of Conservation Concern (Gregory *et al.* 2002).

DJSG

Spotted Flycatcher *Muscicapa striata*

Fairly common migrant breeder, recent decline.

In the 19th century, Haines described this species as common throughout the county of Rutland and Browne considered it a commonly distributed summer migrant in Leicestershire, breeding even in gardens close to Leicester. He found it every year along New Walk by the Leicester Museum and nearly every year it nested in the ornamental stonework at the top of the Hollings Memorial. Browne noted first arrivals as early as April 27th and as late as June 13th.

The Spotted Flycatcher is one of the latest summer migrants to arrive. The main arrival is during May (3rd being the average first arrival date during the last ten years) and there are only 14 years in which the first record has been in April. Most of these have been after April 20th, the only earlier ones being:

- Quorn, April 5th 1949.
- Greetham, April 5th 1968 (Mitcham 1984).
- Narborough, April 14th 1997.

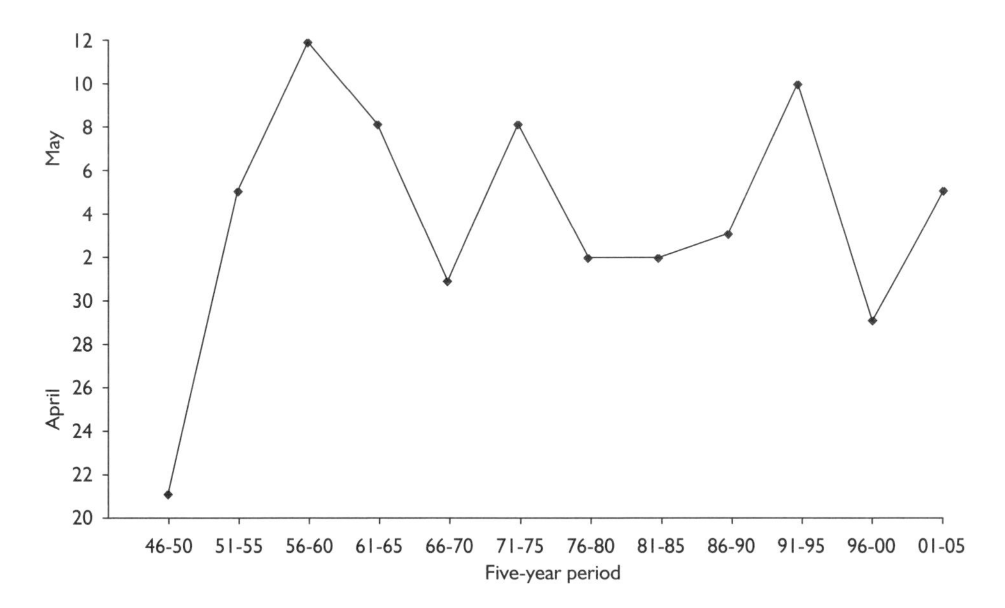

Figure 507: Average spring arrival dates of Spotted Flycatchers by five-year periods 1946–2005.

- unknown site, April 15th 1976.
- Rothley, April 19th 1945.

There are few records of spring concentrations and the largest have been ten at Carlton Hayes Hospital, Narborough on May 24th 1994 and six at both Eyebrook Reservoir on May 6th 1977 and Lowesby on May 29th 1979.

A bird of open woodland, woodland edge, parkland and large gardens, the Spotted Flycatcher was formerly a widely distributed common, if not abundant, breeding species in the counties, but numbers have declined considerably. Threats to this species are probably mainly centred in their wintering areas although they do seem to be particularly vulnerable to nest predation, with Grey Squirrels often quoted as the main culprits; the use of insecticides and a decline in the numbers of larger insects are also thought to be contributory factors.

Prior to the 1970s there is very little data on breeding densities of this species: 20 pairs were breeding in gardens in Uppingham in 1968, six nests were located at The Brand, Woodhouse Eaves on June 9th 1942 and four nests were found at Bradgate Park on June 25th 1942. During 1976–84 Warrilow recorded this species in 378 tetrads in the counties (59% of the total number of tetrads), with breeding confirmed in 172. Although widespread, Spotted Flycatchers were thinly distributed in the north-east, especially along the Wreake valley and on the Leicestershire wolds. A county-wide population estimate of 3,000 to 3,800 pairs was proposed by Warrilow, though this is now likely to be much too high. In Rutland, Mitcham (1992) found that 51% of tetrads were occupied whilst in Charnwood it was found in only 21% of 1-km squares during 1992–94 (Webster 1997).

There is little data on which to draw conclusions about local populations since the decline began; numbers on the counties' CBC plots have always been small and no meaningful patterns emerge. Records of breeding densities include 20 birds around Burton Lazars during 1991, eight pairs at both Narborough in 1991 and at the Egleton Reserve, Rutland Water in 1978 and seven pairs nesting at Carlton Hayes Hospital, Narborough in 1987. A survey by the RNHS in 2005 found that of 37 churchyards visited Spotted Flycatchers were absent from 17. It is also indicative that this species was ranked 34th during the Leicestershire Garden Bird Survey between January 1996 and June 2005, being found in less than 1% of gardens.

Records submitted to LROS from 1993 to 2005 suggest that there was a significant increase in the number of sites used during the late 1990s, but this almost certainly reflects observer interest and effort rather than an actual increase in numbers. The reduction in the number of sites since 2002 is probably a truer reflection on the fortunes of this species.

Table 45: Spotted Flycatcher records 1993–2005

Year	**1993**	**1994**	**1995**	**1996**	**1997**	**1998**	**1999**	**2000**	**2001**	**2002**	**2003**	**2004**	**2005**
Sites	29	36	37	34	48	65	61	62	56	63	53	49	41

Late summer and autumn passage concentrations used to be regular, but have become less noticeable as the species declines. The largest on record are:

- 30 at Rutland Water between August 26th and September 11th 1984.
- 20 at Rutland Water throughout August 1986.
- 20 at Stathern in mid-September 1997.
- up to 20 at Rutland Water between mid-August and September 4th 1983.
- 19 at Wistow Lake on August 30th 1987.
- 19 at Kirby Lakes on August 28th 1989.
- 18 at Narborough on September 12th 1983.
- 15 at Egleton Meadows, Rutland Water on August 24th 1997.

Most birds have departed by the end of September (27th being the average last departure date in the last ten years), but there have been seven records in October, all of single birds unless stated:

- Priory Water, October 9th 1994.
- Sharnford, October 6th 1975.

- two, Narborough, October 5th 1988.
- Narborough, October 4th 1982.
- Swithland Reservoir, October 3rd 1999.
- Allexton, October 1st 1987.
- Trent Valley Pit, October 1st 2000.

There are three foreign recoveries of birds ringed in the counties: one ringed at Burley Fishponds on July 20th 1988 was recovered 2,365km to the south-south-west near Safi (Morocco) on September 23rd 1990, one ringed at Shenton on July 16th 1953 was found dead 1,447km to the south at Benaguasil (Spain) on September 27th 1953 and one ringed at Great Casterton on June 29th 1979 was found freshly dead 612km to the south at Chinon (France) on May 10th 1982.

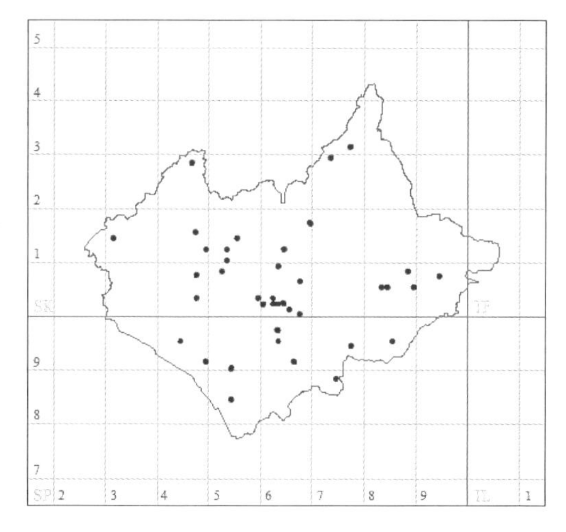

Figure 508: Distribution of Spotted Flycatchers 2005.

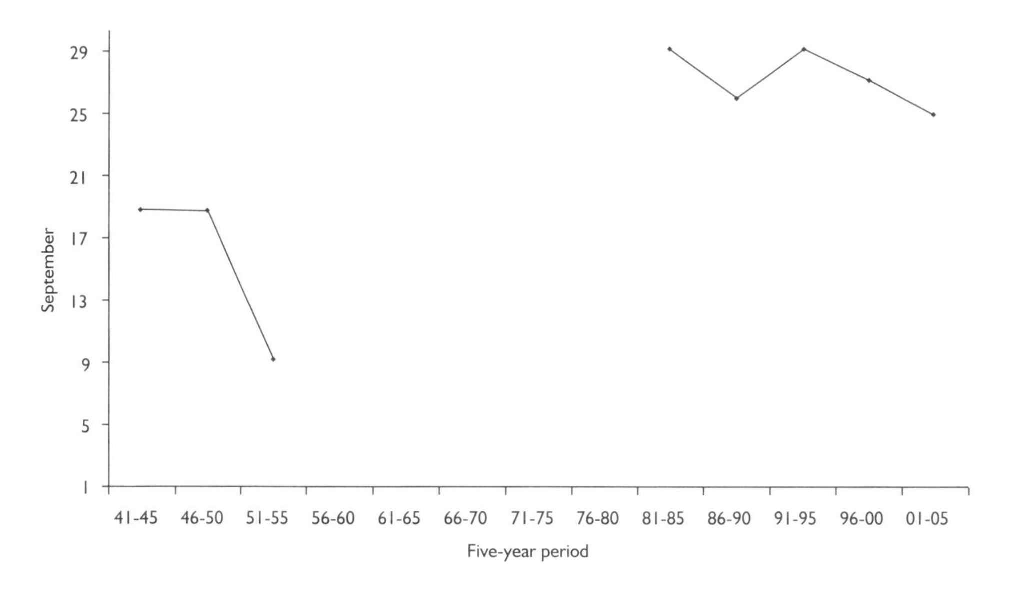

Figure 509: Average autumn departure dates of Spotted Flycatchers by five-year periods 1941–2005. No data is available for 1956–80.

Spotted Flycatchers are found from Europe east across the Ural mountains and in north-west Africa. They are long-distance migrants, the majority spending the winter in sub-Saharan Africa south of the equator. The British breeding population during 1988–91 was estimated at 120,000 territories (Gibbons *et al.* 1993), but the long-term decline which began in the early 1960s has unfortunately accelerated, a recent estimate putting the population at 58,800 territories (Baker *et al.* 2006). Accordingly, the Spotted Flycatcher has been added to the 'Red List' of Birds of Conservation Concern (Gregory *et al.* 2002).

DJSG

Pied Flycatcher *Ficedula hypoleuca*

Scarce passage migrant: recorded in all months between April and October, with the majority in April, May, August and September. One breeding record.

During the 19th and early part of the 20th century, the status of this species in Leicestershire appeared to be much as today. Browne details ten records, as follows:

1840	shot, Groby Pool, autumn.
pre-1859	shot, Bradgate Park, no date.
1859	male, shot, Markfield, April.
	Kibworth, May.
c1875	shot, Illston on the Hill, no date.
c1880	male, shot, Wanlip, no date.
1883	pair, Twyford, May 5th.
	male, shot, Bardon Hill, May 12th.
1898	male, shot, Laughton, April 29th.
1901	Cotesbach Hall, April 19th.

In addition, Browne mentions an undated record of one shot at Melton Mowbray, whilst a pair was apparently at Tugby on June 5th 1899; the latter report was not recorded by Browne but is detailed by Haines, who described the following passage migrants in Rutland during the same period:

c1872	male, Bisbrooke, no date.
1892	male, Uppingham, May 22nd.
1899	male, Exton Park, May.
1901	male, Ridlington, June.

In addition, Haines claims that Pied Flycatchers bred in Rutland. He describes a clutch of eggs taken by a Mr Rossiter at Ridlington some time around 1885, following which the same observer is said to have 'seen elsewhere over a dozen nests containing eggs or young birds'; in addition, Haines quotes Lord Gainsborough as saying that this species nested close to Exton village. It seems highly unlikely that Pied Flycatchers did actually

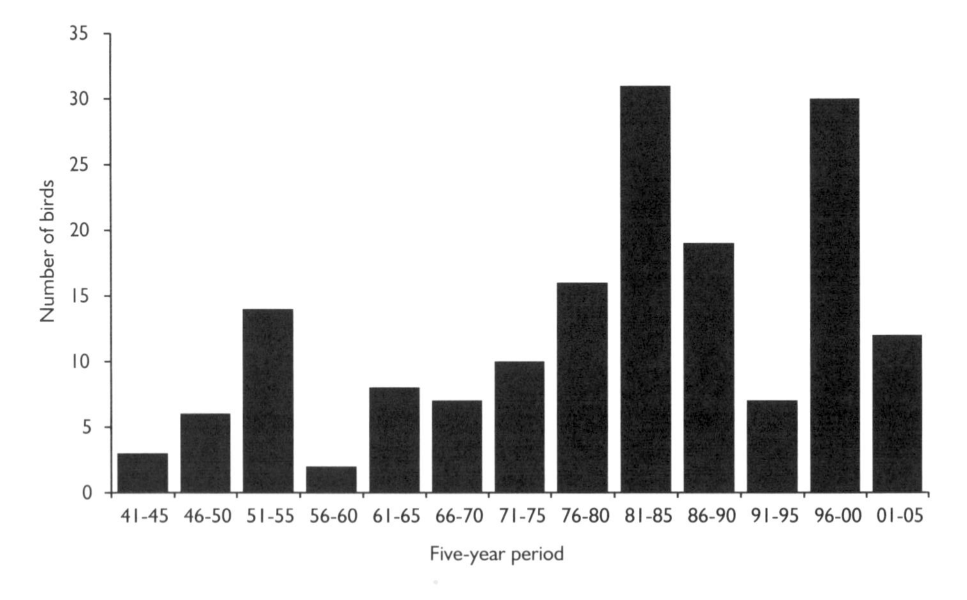

Figure 510: Numbers of Pied Flycatchers 1941–2005.

breed in Rutland at this time, especially as Holloway (1996) described the breeding range of this species during 1875 to 1900 as barely extending further west than Wales and further south than Yorkshire.

Prior to the formation of LROS in 1941, the only other documented records in the 20th century concerned a male at Burbage on April 28th 1912 and one at Barkby in 1930. Today, the Pied Flycatcher is a scarce spring and autumn passage migrant; since 1941, there have been records in 49 of the 65 years up to 2005. In general, occurrences have increased since the early 1980s, although there were no records in both 2003 and 2005, perhaps the first signs of a reversal of this trend. In most years there have been no more than four individuals, although there were six in 1951 and 1977, eight in 1984, 1985 and 1988, nine in 1997, ten in 1981 and a record 11 in 1996.

Pied Flycatchers are most regular in the counties during the spring, with 70% of all records having occurred at this time; the peak period is from April 20th to May 10th. The earliest spring record is of one at Huncote Sand Pit on April 10th 1975, although occurrences prior to April 15th are unusual, with the only ones being:

- a female at Stanford Reservoir on April 11th 1981.
- a male at Swithland Reservoir on April 12th 1953.
- a male at Narborough Bog on April 13th 1981.
- a male at Blackbrook Reservoir on April 14th 1948.
- a male at Stanford Reservoir on April 14th 1979.
- a male at Saddington Reservoir on April 14th 1981.

Passage usually ceases by the end of May, although there have been three records in early June: a female at The Brand, Woodhouse Eaves on June 2nd 1951, one at Higham Grange on June 5th 1961 and a pair at Kirkby Mallory from June 6th to 13th 1944.

Autumn passage is much less pronounced than during the spring, with the peak period being from mid-August to early September. There have, however, been five July records:

- a female at Little Bowden on July 19th 1998.
- one at Rutland Water on July 20th and 31st 1999.
- one at Croft Hill from July 25th to 28th 1953.
- a female at Fosse Meadows on July 25th 2000.
- a female at Stoneygate, Leicester on July 30th 1952.

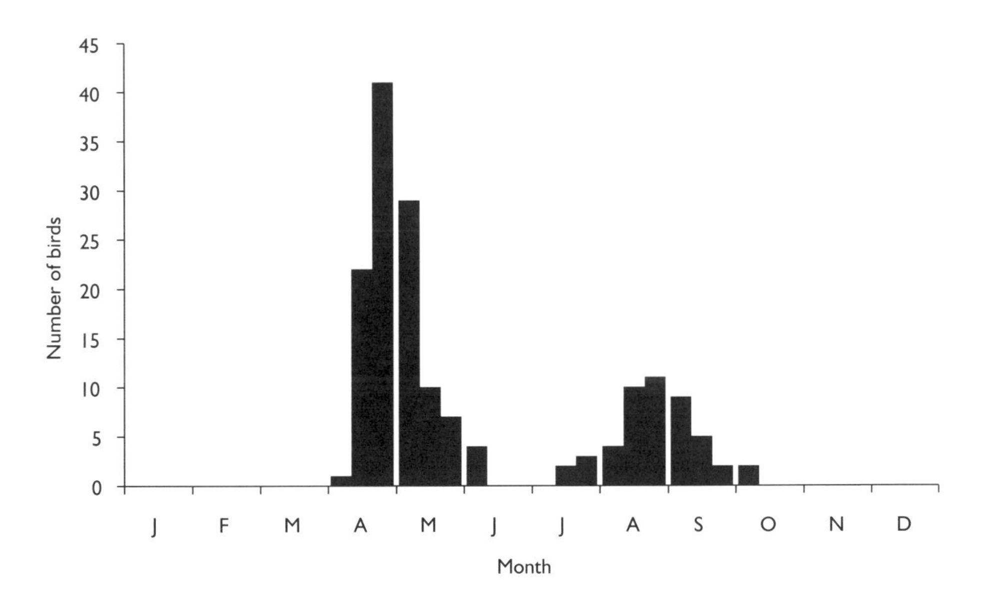

Figure 511: Monthly occurrence of Pied Flycatchers 1941–2005.

Birds have usually departed after September 20th and the only later records are a female at Groby on September 22nd 1996 and female/juveniles at Burbage Wood on September 27th 1996, Swithland Reservoir on October 1st 1978 and Gorse Close, Rutland Water on October 5th 2001. All autumn records have been of single birds, with the exception of two at Croft Hill from August 15th to 16th 1952, Stanford Reservoir on August 22nd 1977 and Whitwick on August 18th and 19th 2004.

On passage, Pied Flycatchers can appear almost anywhere and there have been a number of records from private gardens, including several within the city boundary of Leicester. Intensive watching of Croft Hill during the 1950s produced autumn records of five individuals between 1952 and 1954, suggesting that future searches of similarly-promising migration spots may reveal this species to be a more regular passage migrant than is currently believed.

There is one confirmed breeding record of a pair which fledged two young at Broombriggs in 1996 and during the same year two males and a female were at a nearby site at Woodhouse Eaves, with one of the males remaining until May 17th. This heralded the beginning of a period when subsequent colonisation of the Charnwood Forest area seemed likely, with records as follows over the next six years:

1997	up to five singing males at Beacon Hill from April 20th to June 1st, with a female there during late April; several of the males were seen inspecting nest-boxes.
1998	singing male at Beacon Hill from April 25th to May 25th.
1999	singing male at Beacon Hill from May 9th to 19th, with an additional male there on May 14th.
2000	singing male at Swithland Wood from May 5th to June 3rd.
2001	singing male at Beacon Hill on May 29th.
2002	singing male at Moira on May 4th.

However, there have been no singing birds found since 2002 and unfortunately this seems to be have been a temporary phenomenon. Prior to this period, there were several spring records of pairs, singing males or long-staying birds, as follows:

1941	a pair at Kirkby Mallory from June 6th to 13th, with the male again on July 20th.
1951	a singing male at The Brand, Woodhouse Eaves from May 30th to June 30th, with a female there on June 2nd.
1969	a pair at Swithland Reservoir on April 25th.
1971	a pair at Burley on April 25th.
1974	one at Charnwood Lodge from April 20th to mid-May.
1978	a pair at Market Bosworth on May 3rd.
1990	a singing male at Ulverscroft from May 4th to 6th.
1991	a singing male at Ulverscroft on April 28th.
1992	a singing male at Ulverscroft on April 23rd.

Pied Flycatchers breed in western, central and northern Europe, north-west Africa and Siberia and winter in west Africa. In Britain, they are restricted mainly to the north and west and any colonisation of Leicestershire and Rutland would be at the eastern edge of this species' range. The current population estimate is between 35,000 and 40,000 pairs and a small expansion has been noted in recent times, aided by the provision of nest-boxes (Gibbons *et al.* 1993).

DJSG

Bearded Tit *Panurus biarmicus*

Rare passage and winter visitor; recorded in all months between October and June, the majority in October: 27 records since 1965 involving 104 individuals and two records involving eight or nine individuals previously.

Hickling mentioned that it was vaguely reported to Browne that this species bred in reedbeds below the castle in Leicester and birds were often shot, but this is a habitat which has long since ceased to exist. Hickling then reported that the only certain record prior to the modern era was of two shot at Aylestone in 1870, although this is a rather simplified version of Browne's account, which states that a flock of six or seven was present at

Bede House Meadows, Leicester on November 10th 1870, three of which were shot (two males and a female). One of the males was purchased by Leicester Museum and remains there today, although is incorrectly labelled as having been obtained on October 3rd 1885; this is in fact the date that Browne purchased the specimen. In addition, Browne mentions a flock of 'about a dozen' at Groby Pool in July 1883, but he did not seem to give this sighting much credence, saying that 'many observers who see the Long-tailed Tit climbing about reeds mistake it for the Bearded Tit'; this record has been ignored by subsequent authors. A further record not mentioned by subsequent authors is that of two males shot at Burley Fishponds on January 18th 1905 and reported by Haines; there seems no reason to disbelieve this occurrence.

The first modern record came in 1965, with a pair at Wanlip Gravel Pits from February 20th to March 14th and two at Stanford Reservoir on October 16th. Since then, exactly 100 individuals had been located by the end of 2005.

All records since 1965:

1965	pair, Wanlip Gravel Pits, February 20th to March 14th.
	two, Stanford Reservoir, October 16th.
1967	two, Stanford Reservoir, November 19th, with one until November 26th.
1971	Stanford Reservoir, October 8th to 9th, with two from October 24th to 31st.
	two, River Gwash, Normanton Bridge, October 31st.
1972	Burley Fishponds, December 27th, with two on January 7th 1973.
1975	male and female, Ratcliffe on the Wreake, March 8th to 16th.
1976	pair, Rutland Water, January 27th to February 27th.
	four, Frisby Gravel Pits, October 10th.
	female, Rutland Water, November 19th to December 1st.
1977	17+, Ratcliffe on the Wreake, October 23rd with at least four until January 22nd 1978.
	seven, Frisby Gravel Pits, October 25th, with two until October 30th.
	three males and three females, Saddington Reservoir, October 30th.
1983	three males and four females, Wanlip Gravel Pits, January 3rd, with up to four until the end of January, two until early March and one male until March 12th.
	male, Birstall Gravel Pits, October 22nd to 23rd.
	one male and two female/juveniles, Rutland Water, October 27th to 31st.
1985	up to 12, Rutland Water, October 27th to February 3rd 1986.
1988	two, Rutland Water, October 30th, with seven from November 12th to December 31st, three throughout January 1989 and two until February 21st 1989.
1990	female, Rutland Water, May 28th to June 9th.
	pair, Rutland Water, November 29th to February 10th 1991.
1995	male, Rutland Water, October 21st to March 17th 1996.
1996	two females and two juveniles, Fort Henry Ponds, October 13th, with three to October 14th.
2001	four, Rutland Water, October 28th.
2002	pair, Trent Valley Pit, November 17th to February 22nd 2003.
2003	female, Rutland Water, March 6th.
2004	seven, Rutland Water, October 25th and 26th, with three until November 1st and one until November 9th.
2005	Rutland Water, April 8th.

Considering the relative lack of suitable habitat within the counties this is a remarkable number of records, although the extensive reedbed which has recently been established at Rutland Water could even lead to breeding in the future. Indeed, since October 1983 there have only been two records away from this site: at Fort Henry Ponds in October 1996 and Trent Valley Pit from November 2002 to February 2003; the latter is therefore the only record away from Rutland in the last 22 years.

Bearded Tits are known for their eruptive post-breeding movements during the autumn, which vary considerably in extent from year to year. The pattern of occurrence in the counties reflects this, with 70% of all arrivals having occurred during October; the vast majority of these have been during the last ten days of the month, although the earliest arrival was one at Stanford Reservoir on October 8th 1971. Another small peak is noticeable during mid-November, but apparent new arrivals are relatively scarce throughout the remainder of the winter and, given the often elusive nature of Bearded Tits, it is possible that these birds originally appeared during the main autumn arrival period and lurked undetected. Many of the birds that have been found during October and November have remained in their chosen reedbed for most of the winter, perhaps a further indication that those apparently appearing from December to February had actually arrived earlier. The latest spring record, of one at Rutland Water on April 8th 2005, is more difficult to explain, but could conceivably have been a pioneering bird searching out new breeding habitat. Even more unusual was the female at Rutland Water from May 29th until June 1st 1990; this individual had been ringed only a few days previously, on May 20th, 140km to the south-south-west at Brimpton Gravel Pits (Berkshire) and was clearly a wandering non-breeder.

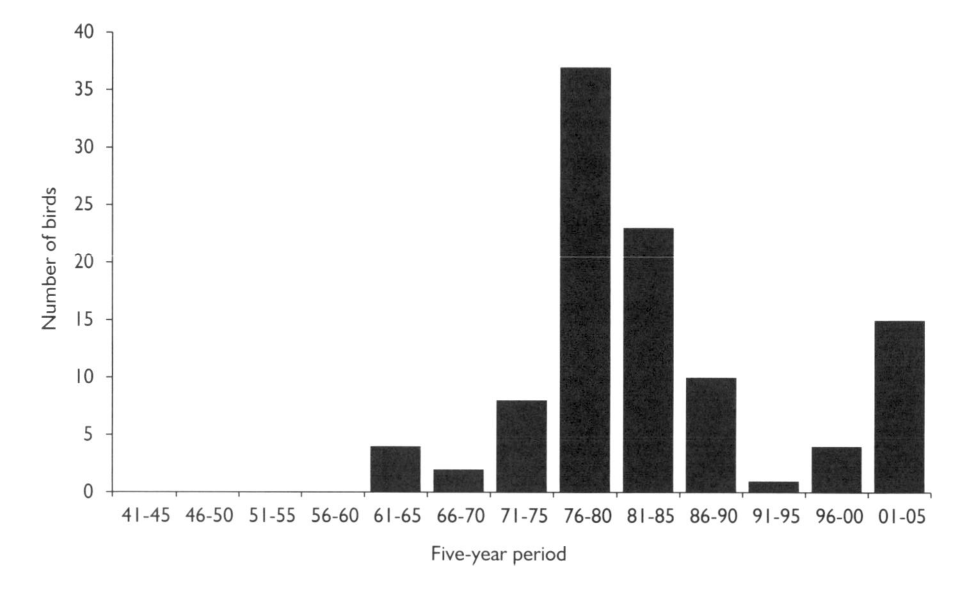

Figure 512: Numbers of Bearded Tits 1941–2005.

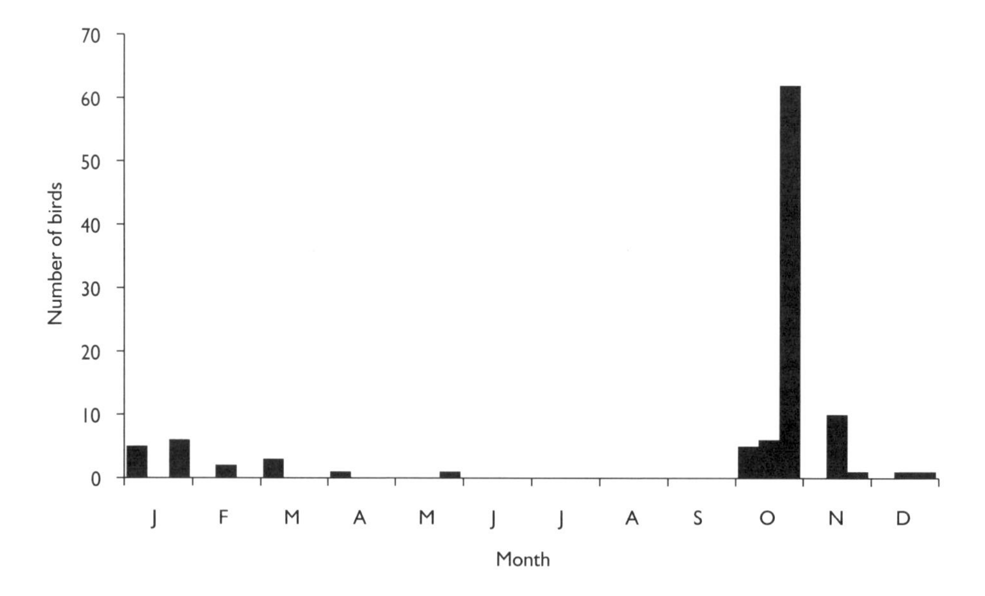

Figure 513: Monthly occurrence of Bearded Tits 1941–2005.

The influx during October 1977, which was mirrored in other inland counties, occurred at two sites where intensive ringing was being carried out at the time and provided information on where Leicestershire and Rutland's Bearded Tits originate. Of the flock of 17 at Ratcliffe on the Wreake, 12 were trapped and five were found to be already ringed; four originated from Blacktoft Sands (East Yorkshire) whilst the fifth had been ringed at Titchwell (Norfolk). It was thought likely that the Titchwell bird had arrived with the East Yorkshire party; some north Norfolk birds winter at Blacktoft Sands and it is possible that on arriving at Blacktoft it joined the eruption of locals to the south (Felstead 1978). At Frisby Gravel Pits, two of the flock of seven present in October 1977 had already been ringed and these were both discovered to have originated from Walberswick (Suffolk).

There have been three other ringing recoveries involving Leicestershire and Rutland. A male and female were ringed at Ratcliffe on the Wreake on March 16th 1975; the male was retrapped at Stodmarsh (Kent) on October 26th 1975 and controlled again on November 27th 1977 and the female was retrapped at Stodmarsh on the latter date. In 1983, a female controlled at Wanlip Gravel Pits on February 13th had been originally ringed at Blacktoft Sands on September 15th 1982.

Bearded Tits breed from west, central and southern Europe through central Asia to China, although they are rather localised due to their specific requirements for reedbeds. European populations are more or less sedentary, but, as mentioned above, are prone to post-breeding eruptive movements. The British population, which in 2005 numbered between 552 and 559 pairs (Holling *et al.* 2008), has expanded since the mid-1960s, although the main concentrations are in the coastal marshes from East Anglia to Kent. As more than 50% of the breeding population occurs in fewer than ten specified areas, the species is considered vulnerable and the Bearded Tit has been added to the 'Amber List' of Birds of Conservation Concern (Gregory *et al.* 2002).

DJSG

Long-tailed Tit — *Aegithalos caudatus*

Common resident breeder.

During the 19th century Browne described the Long-tailed Tit as 'resident but sparingly distributed' in Leicestershire and Haines thought it 'not uncommon' in Rutland. There is little information on the status of this species during the first half of the 20th century: the first LROS Annual Report, in 1941, described it as uncommon as a breeding species with numbers augmented in winter, Pochin (1954) noted that it was commonly reported on the outskirts of Leicester city centre and Otter (1965) considered it to be fairly common and widespread in east Leicestershire.

Long-tailed Tits suffer badly in hard winters and the LROS archives speak of 'great mortality' in the 1939–40 winter. However, the two famous severe winters of 1946–47 and 1962–63 did not seem to affect this species locally as much as might have been expected: in 1947, the Annual Report stated that there were 'possibly only slight reductions in numbers', whilst in 1963 'a small but adequate number survived' and the population recovered quickly (Gamble 1965).

During 1976–84 Warrilow recorded the Long-tailed Tit in 305 tetrads in the counties (48% of the total number of tetrads), with breeding confirmed in 128. It was found to be principally a bird of woodland margins and clearings, mature gardens, bushy overgrown hedgerows and shrubby areas and was fairly evenly distributed across the counties. However, it was generally more numerous in Charnwood and less common in north-east Leicestershire. A survey of 39 woodlands in east Leicestershire in 1987 and 1990 located a total of 11 Long-tailed Tit territories, giving an average breeding density of 51 pairs per tetrad. Numbers on farmland are lower, with only one pair per tetrad on the Stoughton CBC plot and 14 pairs per tetrad on the Newton Harcourt CBC plot. Based on all the available data, Warrilow proposed a county-wide population of between 2,500 and 4,800 pairs.

Local CBC data reveals little about current trends for this species as on all plots in Leicestershire and Rutland it has only ever bred in small numbers. The national situation is that Long-tailed Tits have shown a moderate increase over the last 30 years and this, combined with the recent run of mild winters, suggests that this species' population may now be greater than that estimated by Warrilow.

Long-tailed Tits do not usually visit heavily built-up areas and Warrilow found it to be virtually absent from the city of Leicester. A survey of four green spaces within the city boundary of Leicester in 1989 found it at

Aylestone Meadows and Knighton Park but absent from Abbey Park and Western Park and this may reflect the fact that the two former sites are located on the edge of the city (Fray *et al.* 1990). Long-tailed Tits will readily visit larger gardens and the Leicestershire Garden Bird Survey from January 1996 to June 2005 found that this was the 19th most-frequent species, visiting 10% of all gardens. Although a relatively infrequent visitor to garden feeding stations, they were first noticed on peanut feeders at Glenfield in 1982 and this habit has subsequently been noted with increasing frequency. However, foraging flocks have a tendency to move through their feeding areas rapidly and their visits to feeders are usually brief.

Flocks typically build up from June onwards, usually in the form of family parties of up to 20 birds. These frequently amalgamate into larger groups and the highest counts on record are:

- 200 at Willesley on January 19th 1958.
- up to 200 at Buddon Wood on March 9th 1958.
- 75 in three flocks at Swithland Wood on January 30th 1972.
- 69 in four flocks at Priory Water on December 16th 1990.
- 68 at Swithland Reservoir on November 25th 2002.
- 64 in five flocks at Hambleton Peninsula, Rutland Water on September 23rd 1995.
- 64 at Swithland Reservoir on November 22nd 2000.
- 62 at the Egleton Reserve, Rutland Water on June 13th 1998.
- 60 at Trent Valley Pit on November 29th 1998.

Long-tailed Tits are found throughout most of Europe as well as in Asia Minor and through Siberia and central Asia to China. There are many races recognised, the one found in Britain being *A. c. rosaceus*; the latest British population estimate is 261,000 pairs (Baker *et al.* 2006). Most Long-tailed Tits are sedentary although there are irregular autumn irruptions involving the nominate white-headed race from central and northern Europe. One at Eyebrook Reservoir in August 1950 was reported to be of the nominate race, although further confirmation would be required for this record to be considered acceptable, particularly given the early autumn date. Most ringing recoveries involving the counties have been relatively local, but one ringed at Gibraltar Point (Lincolnshire) on October 24th 1978 was found dead 104km west-south-west at Syston on March 20th 1979.

DJSG

Blue Tit *Cyanistes caeruleus*

Abundant resident breeder.

The Blue Tit is one of our most widespread and numerous species, a situation that has existed since at least the 19th century when Browne described is at 'resident and common' in Leicestershire. Haines noted that it was 'the commonest of our tits' in Rutland, calling it 'perky, pugnacious and not always honest'. Descriptions of this species' status in the first part of the 20th century are similar: the first LROS Annual Report, in 1941, described it as 'resident and common', it was considered to be a 'common resident' within the city boundary of Leicester (Pochin 1954) and in east Leicestershire was noted as an 'abundant resident' by Otter (1965).

The Blue Tit is another example of a common and familiar bird which is poorly studied in the counties. The most useful contribution to our knowledge of this species in Leicestershire and Rutland was provided by Warrilow, who found it in 622 tetrads in the counties during 1976–84 (97% of the total number of tetrads), with breeding confirmed in 438. This made the Blue Tit the fifth most-widespread species in the counties, after Blackbird, Starling, Yellowhammer and Dunnock. It was found in a wide range of habitats, from broad-leaved and mixed woodland to hedgerows, scrub, gardens and urban parks; it was at its lowest breeding density in areas where there had been major hedgerow removal or intensive hedgerow trimming. A total of 143 pairs were located in 85.6 hectares of woodland surveyed in east Leicestershire in 1987 and 1990, giving an average breeding density of 670 pairs per tetrad, although local farmland CBC data shows a much lower density of 80 to 200 pairs per tetrad. Based on an average of 90 to 150 pairs per occupied tetrad, Warrilow proposed a county-wide breeding population of 56,000 to 93,000 pairs.

Local CBC data shows that the Blue Tit population is stable or perhaps increasing slightly. At Stoughton numbers reached a peak of 29 pairs in 1974, but the severe winter weather of both early 1979 and early 1982 caused large declines to 14 and ten pairs respectively; since then, a run of milder winters helped the population increase to 22 pairs by 1999. A similar pattern was evident at Newton Harcourt, where the winter of early 1982 reduced the population there to just five pairs; however, unlike at Stoughton, numbers never really recovered from this low level. The two CBC plots in Rutland show some interesting results, as despite one being a farmland site (King's Hill Lodge, Uppingham) and the other being woodland (Prior's Coppice), both sites show

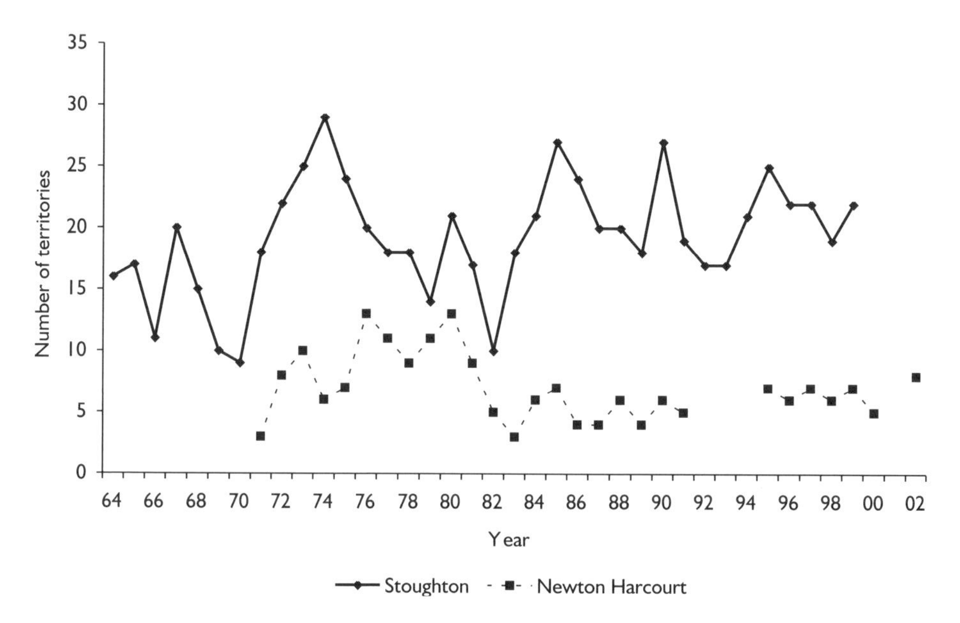

Figure 514: Number of breeding pairs of Blue Tits on two Leicestershire CBC plots 1964–2002.

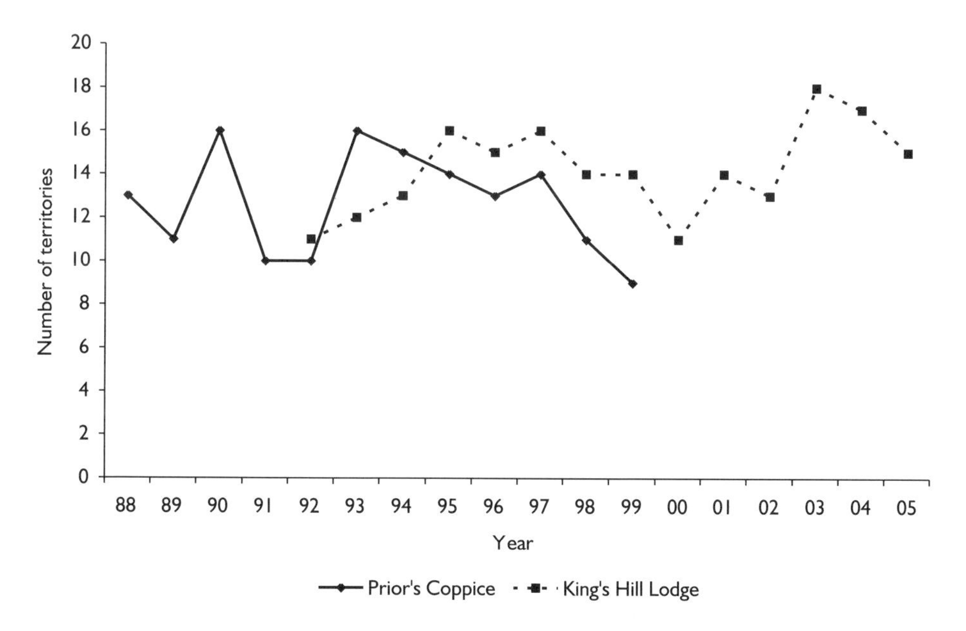

Figure 515: Number of breeding pairs of Blue Tits on two Rutland CBC plots 1988–2005.

similar decreases from 1995 to 1999. The Prior's Coppice survey ceased in 1999, but at King's Hill Lodge the population has recovered and by 2003 had reached record levels.

Blue Tits are well-known for visiting even the smallest of gardens and during the Leicestershire Garden Bird Survey of January 1996 to June 2005 this was the third most-frequent species, being recorded in over 88% of all gardens. During a survey in 1989 of four green spaces within Leicester (Abbey Park, Aylestone Meadows, Knighton Park and Western Park), Blue Tit was found to be the third-commonest species after the Blackbird and Wren (Fray *et al.* 1990).

Blue Tits flock regularly outside the breeding season, often in mixed groups with other tit species. Flock sizes are usually rather small and the largest on record are:

- 200 at The Brand, Woodhouse Eaves on August 27th 1989.
- 186 at Beacon Hill on June 29th 1997.
- 100 at Rutland Water in November 1975.
- 75 at Charnwood Lodge on August 3rd 2004.
- 70 at Rutland Water on January 20th 1982.

An abnormally-plumaged bird at Houghton on the Hill on May 14th 1999 had pale dove-grey upperparts, pure white cheeks, buttermilk-coloured breast and white underparts. There are two records of birds with deformed bills: one at Eastwell on March 12th 1995 had a long curved upper mandible similar to Treecreeper and a similar individual at Markfield in March 2000 had the upper mandible over 25 millimetres long and slightly decurved and the lower mandible marginally shorter.

Blue Tits are common and widespread over most of Europe and Asia Minor. Most populations are resident, although birds over central and northern Europe occasionally make eruptive movements. British birds are largely sedentary and ringing data shows that fewer than 1% travel more than 100km; therefore, a nestling ringed at Billesdon Coplow in June 1980 which was trapped the following December at Cheltenham (Gloucestershire) was exceptional, having travelled 114km to the south-west. The sedentary nature of this species is demonstrated by one ringed at Quorn on November 6th 1988 which was controlled at the same site over eight years later on December 31st 1996. British Blue Tit populations have increased in abundance, in parallel with those of Great Tits, with brief pauses in the long-term upward trend (Baillie *et al.* 2006); the latest British population estimate is 3,333,000 pairs (Baker *et al.* 2006).

DJSG

Great Tit *Parus major*

Abundant resident breeder.

The Great Tit has always been a common and widespread species in the counties. In the 19th century, Browne described it as 'resident and generally distributed' in Leicestershire, whilst Haines considered it 'abundant' but thought that it might be migratory to some extent. Descriptions of its status in the first part of the 20th century include 'resident and common' in the first LROS Annual Report of 1941, a 'common resident in the suburbs and frequent visitor to the built-up area' within the city boundary of Leicester (Pochin 1954) and a 'very common resident' in east Leicestershire (Otter 1965).

As with the Blue Tit, the Great Tit is a poorly studied bird in the counties. During 1976–84 Warrilow recorded it in 577 tetrads in the counties (90% of the total number of tetrads), with breeding confirmed in 335. It was found to be closely associated with almost any type of open or semi-open woodland, although areas with dense undergrowth were avoided. Scattered trees in hedgerows, parkland, scrubby margins alongside railways or roads, urban parks, gardens and cemeteries all provided suitable breeding habitat. The species was rather thinly distributed across the east and north-east of the region, where intensive farming has seen the removal of hedgerows and small copses and has limited the amount of breeding habitat available. A total of 63 pairs were found during a survey of 39 mixed deciduus woodlands in east Leicestershire in 1987 and 1990, roughly half the number of Blue Tits, giving an average territory density per tetrad of approximately 300 pairs. Local farmland CBC results produced average territory densities of between 30 and 75 pairs per tetrad. Taking this into account, Warrilow proposed an average of 40 to 80 pairs per occupied tetrad, giving a county-wide breeding population of 22,000 to 45,000 pairs.

Nationally, Great Tits have increased steadily since the 1960s, with the exception of two brief periods of stability or shallow decline during the mid-1970s and late 1980s (Baillie *et al.* 2006). Local CBC data follows this pattern. At Stoughton, numbers ranged from three to six pairs in the 1960s but had increased to ten pairs by 1975. A decline over the next few years led to only five or six pairs from 1977 to 1979, after which they more than doubled to 13 pairs in 1980 and 1981. A low count of six pairs in 1982 may have been due to the previous winter's severe weather, after which numbers quickly increased and remained at between 11 and 15 pairs until 1999, although there was a brief unexplained drop to six pairs in 1991. At Newton Harcourt numbers

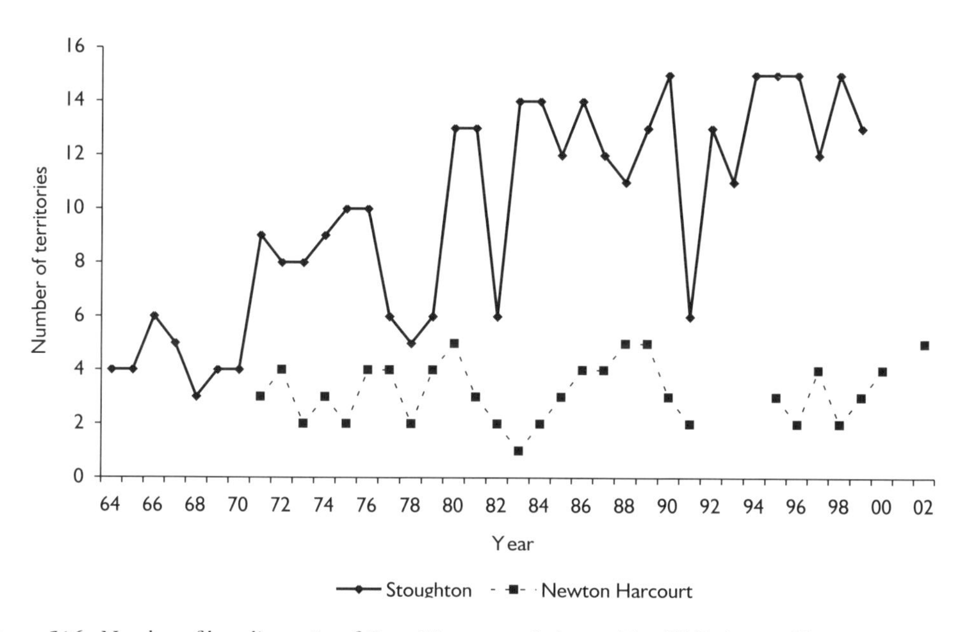

Figure 516: Number of breeding pairs of Great Tits on two Leicestershire CBC plots 1964–2002.

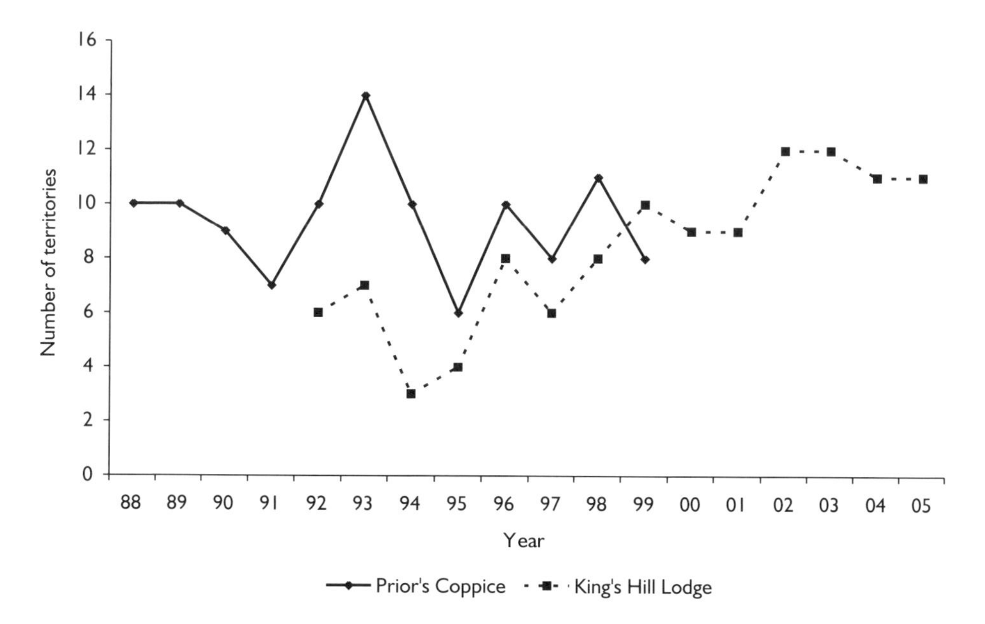

Figure 517: Number of breeding pairs of Great Tits on two Rutland CBC plots 1988–2005.

have fluctuated but the general trend is one of stability. The two CBC plots in Rutland almost matched each other regarding increases and decreases during 1992–99, when the survey at Prior's Coppice ceased; since that time numbers at King's Hill Lodge, Uppingham have continued to increase.

During the period January 1996 to June 2005 the Leicestershire Garden Bird Survey found the Great Tit to be the ninth most-frequent species, visiting almost 65% of all gardens. During a survey in 1989 of four green spaces within Leicester (Abbey Park, Aylestone Meadows, Knighton Park and Western Park) a total of 11 territories were located, making it the 13th commonest species (Fray *et al.* 1990).

Great Tits regularly form flocks during the winter, often in the company of other tit species, although numbers are usually much smaller than Blue Tits. The largest counts have been:

- 75 at Charnwood Lodge on August 3rd 2004.
- 70 at Rutland Water on January 20th 1982.
- 40 at Beacon Hill on January 1st 2003.
- 30 at Kilby Bridge on August 7th 1996.
- 30 at Ulverscroft on January 13th 2001.
- 27 at Prestwold Hall on December 5th 2005.
- 25 at Kilby Bridge on February 13th 1996.
- 22 at Watermead Country Park North on November 23rd 2005.
- 21 at Narborough on October 28th 1995.

A notable record came from Quorn in December 2005, where 20 were trapped and ringed in a garden during the month, demonstrating the continual turnover of birds at single sites.

A bird at Shepshed in March 2000 was unusually pale, with grey-blue upperparts and off-white underparts.

Great Tits are common and widespread throughout Europe, north-west Africa and western and central Asia east to China and eastern Siberia. Most European birds are resident, although irregular irruptive movements occur in northern areas. The majority of ringing data involving the counties confirms the sedentary nature of this species, although a male ringed at Donington Hall on December 7th 1990 was controlled at Tidworth (Wiltshire) on March 21st 1987. As mentioned previously, the British Great Tit population is increasing and the latest population estimate is 1,952,000 pairs (Baker *et al.* 2006).

DJSG

Coal Tit *Periparus ater*

Common resident breeder.

In the 19th century Browne described the Coal Tit as 'resident and generally distributed' in Leicestershire. Haines considered it fairly common in Rutland and mentions a report of the nominate European subspecies *ater* at Farleigh, Uppingham, in February 1904. However, further confirmation will be required before this subspecies can be added to the county list. It is perhaps worth noting here that another report of a 'continental' Coal Tit, at Wigston from October 25th to November 22nd 1996 (following a large arrival on the east coast during the last two weeks of September that year), was not accepted by the LROS Records Committee.

Coal Tits have been routinely under-recorded by county birdwatchers and one of the only sources of information available on breeding numbers and distribution is provided by Warrilow, who recorded this species in 229 tetrads in the counties (36% of the total number of tetrads), with breeding confirmed in 85. It was found to be closely linked with Scots Pine, larch and non-native exotic conifers and the highest densities were recorded in Charnwood Forest. It was also widespread throughout southern Leicestershire and parts of Rutland but was absent from large areas of east and north-east Leicestershire and north Rutland, where suitable habitat does not exist. Coal Tits were present in one-third of 39 mixed broad-leaved woodlands surveyed in east Leicestershire in 1987 and 1990, with conifers noted in all breeding territories. A total of 24 territories was recorded in 85.6 hectares of woodland investigated at this time, producing an average territory density of 112 pairs per tetrad. Farmland densities are much lower: for instance, just one to three pairs bred irregularly at Stoughton during 1964–99. Based on an average of four to eight pairs per occupied tetrad, Warrilow proposed a county-wide population of 900 to 1,800 pairs. The high density in Charnwood was confirmed by Webster (1997) who recorded confirmed or probable breeding in 54% of 1–km squares during 1992–94. In Rutland, Mitcham (1992) found that 34% of tetrads were occupied, with relatively few in deciduous woodland.

Coal Tits are regular visitors to garden feeding stations, although they tend to be dominated by other tit species. The importance of gardens is illustrated by the results of the January 1996 to June 2005 Leicestershire Garden Bird Survey, during which it was found to be the 15th most-regularly occurring species and was reported from 29% of gardens; its willingness to use gardens is probably one important factor in the relative success of this species compared with the next two species.

Although Coal Tits are not particularly noted for forming large feeding concentrations, significant flocks are occasionally reported, often in company with Goldcrests or feeding on the ground amongst leaf litter with Great Tits, Chaffinches and other species. The largest counts on record are:

- 40 at Martinshaw Wood on January 3rd 1983.
- 35 comprised of several family groups at Beacon Hill on July 17th 2002.
- 30 at Beacon Hill on December 26th 1988.
- 20 at Eyebrook Reservoir Plantation on December 6th 1992.
- 20 at Deer Park Spinney, Bradgate Park on December 26th 1993.
- 20 at Narborough on September 22nd 1994.
- up to 20 regular at Outwoods in October 1948.
- up to 20 at Quorn in November 1950.
- 17 at Old Dalby Wood on August 22nd 2002.
- 15 at Eyebrook Reservoir Plantation on June 6th 1997.

Coal Tits have a very extensive range in the Palearctic and parts of Asia. Nominate *ater* occurs in continental Eurasia south to France and eastwards across the plains of eastern Europe and west-central Asia, extending east as far as Manchuria. Other races are found elsewhere in Europe, in the Atlas and Caucasus mountains, in Cyprus, western and south-east China and Taiwan. The British race *britannicus* is endemic; the latest estimate of the British breeding population is 604,000 pairs (Baker *et al.* 2006) and considered to be stable. British birds are sedentary, but nominate *ater* is eruptive and in northern and eastern parts of its range is a fairly regular short-distance migrant. The most recent arrivals of large numbers in Britain were recorded in 1957, 1959 and 1996.

DJSG

Willow Tit *Poecile montana*

Fairly common resident breeder.

The Willow Tit was not distinguished from the Marsh Tit and described in Britain until 1900. It is not mentioned by Browne and Haines stated that the 'supposed sub-species' of Marsh Tit 'the so-called willow-tit' had not been recorded in Rutland. The LROS archives described this species as plentifully distributed during the first part of the 20th century, but records before the 1950s should perhaps be interpreted with some caution and since then there has been a significant decline in numbers.

In the early years of LROS, the distribution of the two species was still unclear. The first attempt to investigate the distribution of the Willow Tit in Leicestershire and Rutland was provided by Griffiths (1968), who noted that it appeared to have a more general distribution than the Marsh Tit and seemed to be the commoner species away from Charnwood Forest. He considered it more likely to be encountered in wetter habitats, conifer plantations, hedgerows and gardens than the Marsh Tit. We now know that this description of the habitat requirements of the Willow Tit is broadly correct; dry habitats are also utilised, but some element of water is usually present.

Warrilow recorded the Willow Tit in 230 tetrads in the counties (36% of the total number of tetrads) during 1976–84, with breeding confirmed in 72. It was found to be commoner in western and southern areas but largely absent from eastern Leicestershire and thinly scattered in the north-east and Rutland; he considered that this was partly explained by the distribution of birch trees. The breeding density of Willow Tits on local farmland

CBC plots is known to have varied between 16 pairs per tetrad at Newton Harcourt and the lower but more typical figure of up to two pairs per tetrad at Stoughton. Records from Stoughton between the late 1960s and the late 1990s reveal that one or two pairs were present in most years up to 1993, but since then breeding has not been recorded in most years (though a pair was again present in 1999). There are few other records of breeding densities, but three pairs bred in damp areas of Ambion Wood in 1947, two pairs bred at nearby Shenton Gorse in the same year and in 2005 a combined total of five or six pairs held territories on the reserves at Rutland Water. Based on an average of four to eight pairs per occupied tetrad, Warrilow estimated a county-wide breeding population of 900 to 1800 pairs during 1976–84; given the significant national decline that has taken place since, it is likely that this estimate is now much too high. In Rutland, Mitcham (1992) found 26% of tetrads occupied and noted that areas of willow scrub often provided habitat for this species. In Charnwood just 16% of 1-km squares provided records of confirmed or probable breeding during the 1992–94 survey (Webster 1997).

Records submitted to LROS from 1991 to 2005 suggest that there has been a significant increase in the number of sites used, but this almost certainly reflects observer interest and effort rather than an actual increase in numbers. Figures 518 and 519 show very little change between 1995 and 2005.

Table 46: Willow Tit records 1991–2005

Year	1991	1992	1993	1994	1995	1996	1997	1998
Sites	28	30	34	39	51	46	49	62
Year	**1999**	**2000**	**2001**	**2002**	**2003**	**2004**	**2005**	
Sites	53	56	40	67	58	54	58	

Family groups of Willow Tits invariably break up soon after the juveniles have fledged. Flocks are not formed outside the breeding season and the birds are usually to be found in pairs. However, these may become loosely associated with roaming flocks of Long-tailed Tits or other tit species. The only double-figure counts presumably refer to family groups, as they have all been recorded in the summer months: 14 at Tickencote on August 15th 1976 and ten at both Huncote on June 8th 1995 and Kelham Bridge on June 18th 1995. Two other relatively large counts, of six or seven at Willoughby Waterleys on June 25th 1947 and six at Eyebrook Reservoir Plantation on August 28th 1983 presumably also refer to family parties.

The highest counts outside the breeding season, some of which have been associated with artificial feeding stations, are:

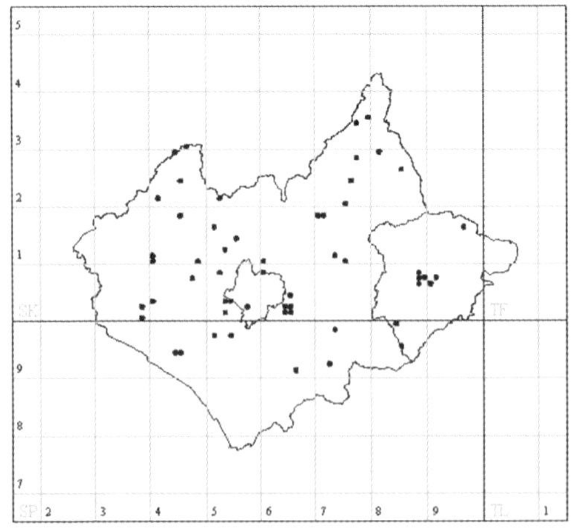

Figure 518: Distribution of Willow Tits 1995.

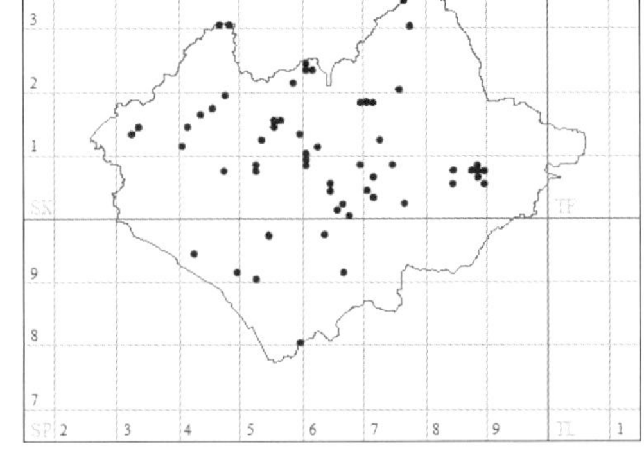

Figure 519: Distribution of Willow Tits 2005.

- eight in the Wymeswold area on November 23rd 2005.
- seven at Priory Water on October 13th 2002.
- six at Swithland Reservoir on January 30th 1987.
- six at Piper Wood on October 13th 2002.
- six at Melton Country Park on March 20th 2004.
- five at Castle Hill Park, Leicester on February 4th 1991.
- five at Dimminsdale on March 11th 1993.
- five at Huncote on October 31st 1993 and October 8th 1997.
- five at Priory Water on March 30th 2003.
- five at Fosse Meadows on November 29th 2003.

Most ringing recoveries involving Leicestershire and Rutland have been at or close to the ringing sites, as one would expect given that Sellers (1984) noted that of 114 recoveries only one was further than 50km and 78% were less than 5km; exceptions are:

- one ringed at Saddington Reservoir on June 29th 1980 was found freshly dead 8km to the south-east at East Farndon (Northamptonshire) on February 9th 1981.
- one ringed at Drakelow (Derbyshire) on August 19th 1995 was found dead 19km to the east at Griffydam on October 11th 1995.

The Willow Tit has a very extensive breeding range across northern Eurasia and a rather complex taxonomy. The British race *kleinschmidti* is endemic and sedentary, but some northern populations are eruptive. During 1988–91 the British breeding population was estimated at 25,000 territories, being outnumbered by Marsh Tits in both broadleaved woodland and farmland (Gibbons *et al.* 1993). A small decline was noted, probably related to more intensive cultivation of farmland and drainage of damp areas. Unfortunately a rapid and significant decline has since continued, the most likely causes being competition with other tit species, increasing nest predation by Great Spotted Woodpeckers and deterioration in the quality of woodland as feeding habitat for Willow Tits through canopy closure and increased browsing by deer (Baillie *et al.* 2006). The latest British population estimate is just 8,500 pairs (Baker *et al.* 2006), with the result that the Willow Tit has been added to the 'Red List' of Birds of Conservation Concern (Gregory *et al.* 2002).

DJSG

Marsh Tit — *Poecile palustris*

Fairly common resident breeder.

The Marsh Tit was described by Browne as resident but sparingly distributed in Leicestershire during the 19th century. Haines mentions this species as occurring in Rutland but does not give any details of distribution or abundance. It should be noted that at this time the Willow Tit had not yet been distinguished from the Marsh Tit.

The LROS archives described the Marsh Tit as thinly distributed during the first part of the 20th century and this is still the case today. Griffiths (1968) was the first to attempt to describe the distribution of this species and the Willow Tit seriously: he noted that it was reported three times as often as the Willow Tit in Charnwood Forest and was more common in mature deciduous woodlands. These findings were confirmed and added to by Warrilow, who during 1976–84 recorded this species in 140 tetrads in the counties (22% of the total number of tetrads), with breeding confirmed in 36. It was found to be closely associated with mature broad-leaved woodland and favoured the interior zone of larger woods. It was commonest in the most densely wooded parts of the counties, including Charnwood Forest, the east Leicestershire woods and central and eastern Rutland and was also well distributed in woodlands scattered between Lutterworth and Market Harborough.

Territory densities in the larger woods can be quite high: for instance, ten Marsh Tit territories were located in 85.6 hectares of woodland surveyed in east Leicestershire, providing a territory density of 46 pairs per tetrad. Local farmland densities are much lower; at the Stoughton CBC plot, it was just two pairs per tetrad. There are very few other records of breeding densities, although there were nine territories at Great Merrible Wood in 1986 and six territories at Prior's Coppice in 1988. Based on an average of four to eight pairs per occupied tetrad, Warrilow estimated a county-wide population of between 550 and 1,100 pairs; this figure may have been too low at the time since he considered it to be almost completely absent from the Belvoir Woods where it certainly occurs. However, since Warrilow's work there has been a significant national decline and it is likely that his original estimate is now too high. Mitcham (1992) found Marsh Tits in 23% of Rutland tetrads, with a preference for oak woods with a hazel shrub layer. Webster (1997) recorded confirmed or probable breeding in just 7% of 1-km squares in Charnwood during 1992–94, but this figure is surprisingly low and again suggests that some must have been overlooked.

Although essentially sedentary, birds frequently wander away from the main woodlands in the autumn and winter. At this time birds occasionally visit garden feeding stations and indeed feeding stations close to breeding habitat may be visited at any time of year. Problems of confusion with the similar Willow Tit can occur, but there is generally little overlap in habitat preference. Although Willow Tits may occur in the same woodlands, they prefer the edges and wetter areas and the greatest problems probably arise in the autumn and winter when Marsh Tits can be found in habitat more typical of Willow Tits. Most birdwatchers seem to have managed to get to grips with this difficult species-pair, but it is still suspected that a few are misidentified each year and these misidentifications may account for the few isolated dots on the distribution maps (Figures 520 and 521). These reveal little change in the general distribution of the Marsh Tit between 1995 and 2005 and show that it seems to be more widespread in the east of the counties than Willow Tit. Increased observer interest and effort needs to be taken into account when interpreting the distribution maps and the records submitted to LROS during 1991–2005, but they do suggest that the population has been relatively stable during the past ten years.

Table 47: Marsh Tit records 1991–2005

Year	1991	1992	1993	1994	1995	1996	1997	1998
Sites	17	21	31	32	37	46	50	62

Year	1999	2000	2001	2002	2003	2004	2005
Sites	50	55	50	63	57	44	53

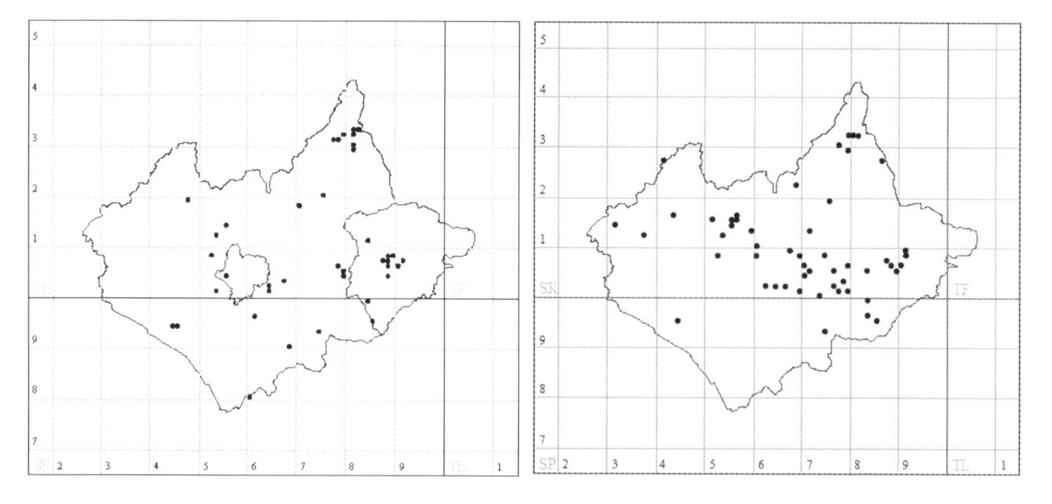

Figure 520: Distribution of Marsh Tits 1995.

Figure 521: Distribution of Marsh Tits 2005.

Marsh Tits are not noted for forming large flocks outside the breeding season, although they often join mixed feeding flocks of other species. Six together would seem to be a 'large' flock for this species and flocks of this size almost certainly refer to family groups. The only counts above eight have been:

- 14 at Botany Bay Covert on August 1st 2000.
- 12 at Swithland Wood on December 11th 1965.
- ten at Stathern Wood on April 10th 2005.

- ten at Burbage Common on November 20th 2005.
- nine at Belvoir on November 28th 1993.
- nine at Pickworth Great Wood on July 10th 2002.

Confirming the sedentary nature of this species, most ringing recoveries are of less than 6km and the only ones to exceed this are:

- one ringed at Rutland Water on July 12th 1988 and found dead 28km to the west at Leicester on August 28th 1988.
- one ringed at Saddington Reservoir on July 13th 1981 and found freshly dead 13km to the north at Stoughton on November 1st 1981.

The Marsh Tit has three main populations, one in the Western Palearctic and the other two in China, Korea and Burma. All three groups are polytypic. The race *dresseri* breeds throughout Britain and north-western France (the statement in *BWP* that birds in northern England and Scotland are of the nominate form requires confirmation). Most populations are sedentary, undergoing short-distance post-breeding dispersal. The British breeding population during 1988–91 was estimated at 60,000 territories, but a decline in numbers following cold winters was noted (Gibbons *et al.* 1993) and more recent estimates put the population at 52,800 pairs (Baker *et al.* 2006). Competition from Blue and Great Tits, which have adapted more readily to artificial feeding, may be another factor in the decline of Marsh Tits: neither Marsh nor Willow Tits appeared in the list of 34 most-frequently recorded species during the Leicestershire Garden Bird Survey. The rapid and significant decline of this species during the past 25 years has resulted in it too being added to the 'Red List' of Birds of Conservation Concern (Gregory *et al.* 2002).

DJSG

Nuthatch (Wood Nuthatch) — ***Sitta europaea***

Fairly common resident breeder.

In the 19th century, Browne described the Nuthatch as a sparingly distributed resident breeder of wooded areas, occurring as close to the city of Leicester as Knighton. In Rutland, Haines found it nowhere abundant except at Burley, Exton and Ketton and noted that it had almost disappeared from former sites near Uppingham. During the early part of the 20th century the LROS archives describe the Nuthatch as 'rather local, but common enough in really suitable localities'.

The Nuthatch is a characteristic bird of mature deciduous woodland, with oak and beech being particularly favoured, whilst a good understorey of hazel almost guarantees occupation. However, this species is not strictly confined to such areas; open parkland with scattered trees and large, mature suburban gardens are often occupied, whilst conifers adjacent to deciduous woodland are also used. There are also isolated sites with little woodland which have small populations.

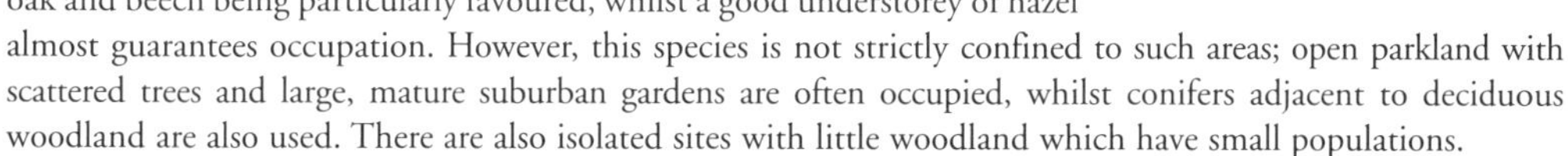

The traditional stronghold has always been the Charnwood Forest area and this situation remains today. Webster (1997) found this species in 43% of the 1–km squares visited during the 1992–94 survey and commented that he would choose the Nuthatch as the bird which for him symbolised the distinctiveness of Charnwood's birdlife. Swithland Wood is a highly favoured area and probably holds six to eight breeding pairs (Hickling). The Belvoir woods also hold significant numbers and good populations occur in such areas as the Burbage Common woods and some of the woodlands of Rutland. The woods of east Leicestershire do not seem to be particularly attractive: Warrilow reported on a survey of 39 woods in east Leicestershire which found only four occupied by a total of five pairs.

The BTO Breeding Atlas fieldwork of 1968–72 found Nuthatches breeding in 14 of the counties' main 29 10–km squares and indicated a population of below 100 pairs. Warrilow's local atlas project during 1976–84 found this species in 91 tetrads in the counties (14% of the total number of tetrads), with breeding confirmed in 38 and probable in another 31: the areas with likely breeding fell within 20 10–km squares and another three contained tetrads with possible breeding. This would suggest a marked expansion in range during the 1970s.

Using a population level of three to six pairs per occupied tetrad, Warrilow suggested a Leicestershire and Rutland population at that time of 270 to 540 pairs, well above that derived from the BTO survey. Mitcham (1992) found Nuthatches in just 14% of Rutland tetrads, with strongholds at Prior's Coppice and Pickworth Great Wood as well as Burley Wood and considered the Rutland population as below 40 pairs; Warrilow's data would broadly agree with this as he found nine Rutland tetrads with at least probable breeding birds, giving an estimate of 27 to 54 pairs. A survey organised by LROS in 1987 found 70 confirmed pairs breeding in Leicestershire; the true total would have been much higher (Fray 1988).

The newly planted areas of the National Forest in the west of Leicestershire could see further expansion when the woodlands mature as birds will be able to spread both west from Charnwood Forest and south from the woods along the Derbyshire boundary.

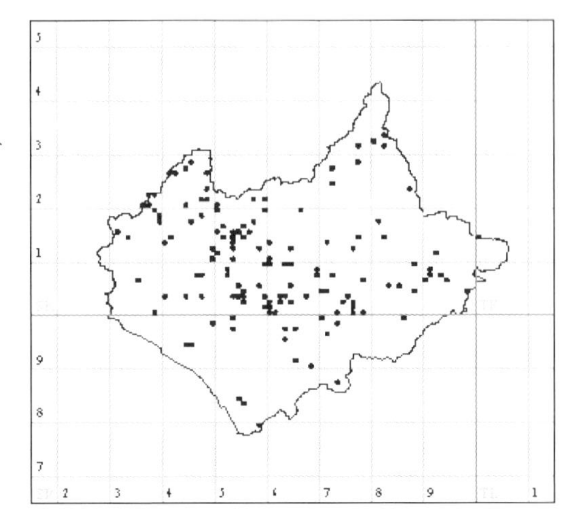

Figure 522: Distribution of Nuthatches 1941–2005.

Figure 522 brings together data from every year since 1941: as there has been no obvious contraction of range and all the evidence points towards an increase, it is probably fairly accurate.

Population densities are illustrated by the following counts, which give a good idea of numbers across the counties and show how populations in certain areas have changed little through the years.

- 20 at Swithland Wood in November and December 1949, on May 4th 1990 and March 17th 1996.
- 13 at Swithland Wood on February 15th 2004.
- 12 at Bradgate Park on June 23rd 1989.
- 12 at Piper and Oakley Woods in 1946.
- 12 at Burbage Wood on January 10th 1999.
- 11 at Bradgate Park on September 16th 1986.
- 11 at Ulverscroft on January 13th 2001.
- ten at Outwoods in November and December 1949.
- ten at Terrace Hills, Belvoir on August 16th 1992 and October 15th 2000.
- eight at Stanford Park in 1946.
- eight at Groby on June 3rd 1992.
- eight at Piper Wood in January 1997.
- eight in a Desford garden from September to December 2002.
- eight at Burbage Wood on January 13th 2003.

Nuthatches are almost sedentary but there is clear evidence of short movements outside the breeding season. Garden feeding stations well away from breeding areas are frequently visited: this species was the 28th most-frequently recorded during the Leicestershire Garden Bird Survey between January 1996 and June 2005, visiting over 2% of gardens.

There are very few ringing recoveries and all but one are local retraps or very short movements. The only recovery from outside the counties is of one ringed at Elvaston Park (Derbyshire) on May 23rd 1995 which was found freshly dead 13km to the south at Staunton Harold Reservoir on February 7th 1996.

Nuthatches breed from southern Britain, France and southern Scandinavia all the way across central Eurasia, with disjunct populations in Iberia and Morocco. Western populations are largely sedentary except that Scandinavian birds show a tendency for southerly eruptive and hard weather movements (Harrison 1982). The number of occupied 10-km squares in England increased by 10% between the periods of the two BTO breeding atlases in 1968–72 and 1988–91, with the population in the latter period estimated at 110,000 territories (Gibbons *et al.* 1993). The latest population estimate is 144,000 pairs (Baker *et al.* 2006). National CBC data for England has shown that numbers increased by 122% on woodland plots and by 97% on all plots between 1967 and 1999 (Brown & Grice 2005), so the local situation matches the national one.

DJSG

Treecreeper (Eurasian Treecreeper) ***Certhia familiaris***

Fairly common to common resident breeder.

During the 19th century the Treecreeper was considered by Browne to be 'resident and generally distributed' in Leicestershire and by Haines as 'resident and fairly common' in Rutland. The LROS archives describe it as 'generally distributed' during the first part of the 20th century.

Today Treecreepers are widely distributed across the counties in suitable habitat, ranging from the largest woodlands through small spinneys, shelter-belts, willow carr, large gardens and parkland to tree-lined farmland hedgerows. It is difficult to arrive at a fully comprehensive picture of the status of this species, because its unobtrusive habits and quiet song almost certainly cause it to be under-recorded. It is more catholic in its habitat requirements than the Nuthatch: examples of its catholic tastes include references to 'odd pairs' at Leicester City Farms (Mason & Pickering 1968), the findings that it was an 'occasional visitor' to Spinney Hill Park, Leicester, between 1960 and 1968 (Bradshaw 1969a) and was present in two green areas (Knighton Park and Western Park) within the Leicester city boundary in 1989 (Fray *et al.* 1990).

The most complete picture of this species' distribution was provided by Warrilow. During 1976–84 he recorded the Treecreeper in 262 tetrads in the counties (41% of the total number of tetrads), with breeding confirmed in 85; it was found to be widespread, though more thinly distributed in the north and east. Breeding pairs readily occupied woodland fragments as small as 0.2 hectares and of 13 small woodlands at Wistow ranging between 0.2 and 2.2 hectares in size which were surveyed in 1987, ten held breeding pairs. By contrast, in a comparison of two east Leicestershire woods, none were found at Owston Wood but there were three pairs at Great Merrible Wood. The absence from Owston Wood was probably due to a lack of mature timber and natural holes there (Jeeves 1987). Due to the sparse woodland cover in the counties, Warrilow proposed an average of four to eight pairs of Treecreepers per occupied tetrad, resulting in an estimated breeding population of 1,000 to 2,100 pairs. Nationally, the Treecreeper population has been roughly stable since about 1980 (Baillie *et al.* 2006), so it is likely that Warrilow's estimate is still valid today. Numbers on local CBC plots tend to be small: at Stoughton, where up to two pairs breed regularly, no obvious trends were recorded between the late 1960s and the late 1990s.

Two other sources provide some idea of the distribution of the Treecreeper in the counties. Mitcham (1992) found that 31% of tetrads in Rutland were occupied, but noted that this species may have been under-recorded: the survey revealed a curious lack of records from north-east Rutland where both Clipsham and Pickworth Great Woods would be expected to provide habitat for Treecreepers. Webster (1997) recorded this species as confirmed or probably breeding in 43% of 1-km squares in Charnwood during 1992–94.

Treecreepers are usually encountered singly or in pairs, although there have been the following relatively high counts:

- nine in the eastern third of Swithland Wood on May 18th 1997.
- eight at Burrow Wood on July 7th 1990.
- eight at Willesley Wood on February 25th 2003.
- seven at Beacon Hill on March 27th 1990.
- seven at Swithland Wood on November 17th 1998.
- seven at the Egleton Reserve, Rutland Water on September 16th 2003.
- seven at Swithland Wood on February 15th 2004.

Unusual nest sites have been noted three times: Haines reported that a pair at Exton Park placed a nest with five eggs between a window and the shutter and more recently there were successful nesting attempts in a crevice of a brick wall at Higham Grange in 1956 and within the wall of a corrugated iron garage at Enderby in 1988.

The Treecreeper has an extensive range in Europe and Asia. Most populations are sedentary, but some (including the northern, nominate, race *familiaris*) are partial migrants. British birds of the endemic subspecies *britannica* are highly sedentary. The latest estimate of the British breeding population is 204,000 pairs (Baker *et al.* 2006).

DJSG

Golden Oriole (Eurasian Golden Oriole) *Oriolus oriolus*

Rare vagrant from Europe; recorded from April to July and in September, the majority from mid-May to early June: 19 records involving 20 individuals.

Browne recorded that one 'of very doubtful occurrence . . . was seen about the railway gardens'; the site was thought to be near Melton Mowbray and the date was unknown. Subsequent authors have ignored this record and it is generally considered that this species was unknown in the counties until after the small breeding population became established in East Anglia in 1965 (Dagley 1994). The first record was of a pair seen by G.A. Down and G.M. Raske at Roundabout Spinney, Peckleton on May 29th 1974, since when there have been records in a further 14 years. Most have occurred in the spring and summer months, the majority between May 14th and June 14th; extreme dates are April 25th and July 31st. The only record outside this period was of one on September 22nd.

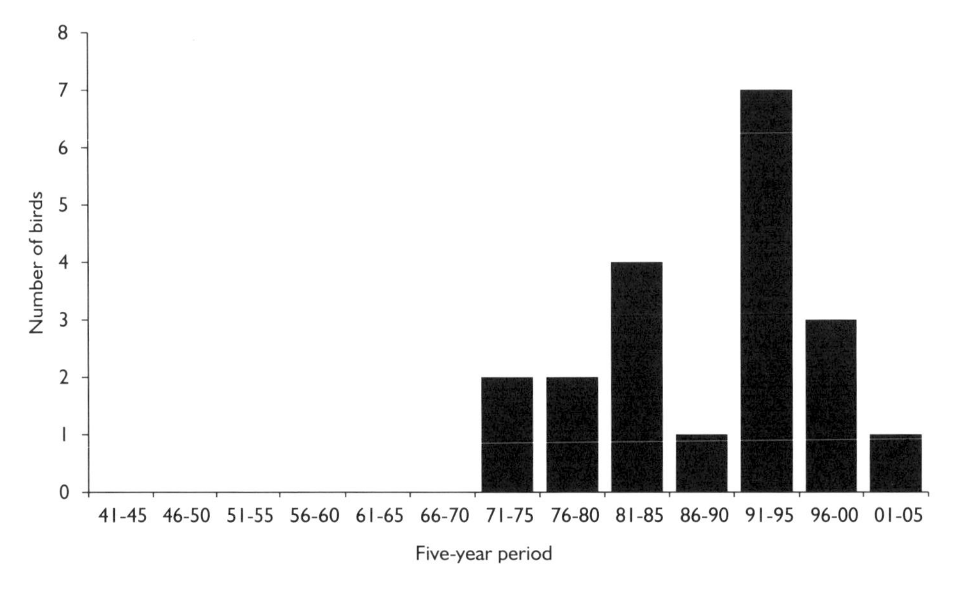

Figure 523: Numbers of Golden Orioles 1941–2005.

All records:

1974	pair, Roundabout Spinney, Peckleton, May 29th.
1979	singing male, Saddington Reservoir, June 9th.
1980	singing male, Stanford Park, June 1st.
1982	singing male, Newton Harcourt, June 5th.
	singing male, Eyebrook Reservoir, June 13th.
1984	male, Stanford Reservoir, May 4th and 6th.
	singing male, Barnsdale Wood, May 20th.
1990	singing male, Swithland Wood, May 14th.
1991	male, Bradgate Park, June 2nd.
1992	male, Clipsham, April 25th.
	female/first-year, Sapcote, July 31st.
1993	male, Wanlip South Gravel Pits, May 16th.
	female, Trent Valley Pit, June 22nd.
1994	singing male, near Lagoon I, Rutland Water, May 14th.
1995	singing male, Newton Harcourt, July 2nd and 3rd.
1996	male, Ingarsby, April 25th.
1997	singing male, Burley Wood, May 15th.

1998 female, Newton Harcourt, June 6th.
2002 female/juvenile, Stanford Res, September 22nd.

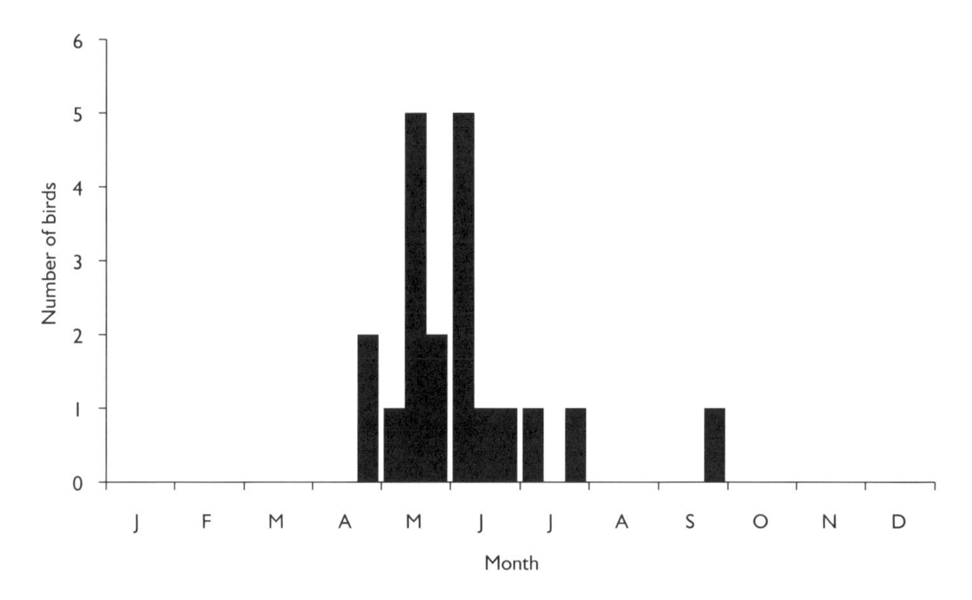

Figure 524: Monthly occurrence of Golden Orioles 1974–2005.

The remarkable run of occurrences in nine successive years between 1990 and 1998 has come to an abrupt halt and there has only been one record since. The Golden Oriole is very much a 'one-day' bird and only two have remained longer than this; the majority have been seen by their finders only and there has never been a twitchable individual in the counties. As can be seen from Figure 525, a large proportion of the records has occurred in the south and east of the counties.

A record of a pair at an undisclosed site in the south of the county from mid-May to early July 1995, originally published in the LROS Annual Report, was found to be unacceptable following review in 2004 (Fray 2005).

Golden Orioles breed across much of Europe, mainly south of the Baltic, eastwards into western Siberia and south into northern India and winter in sub-Saharan Africa and the Indian subcontinent. In Britain, small numbers breed in East Anglia, where they nest almost exclusively in hybrid poplar plantations. The British population is declining, with as few as eight pairs in 2004; there were between 20 and 30 pairs regularly during the 1990s (Holling *et al.* 2007a). Due to the small nature of the breeding population this species has been added to the 'Amber List' of Birds of Conservation Concern (Gregory *et al.* 2002). Golden Orioles are more frequent in this country as scarce passage migrants, the majority occurring as spring overshoots on the south and east coasts during May and June. In line with breeding numbers, they are currently occurring less frequently on passage than in the 1990s, with an average of 94 records per year from 2000 to 2002, compared to 132 per year between 1990 and 1999 (Fraser &

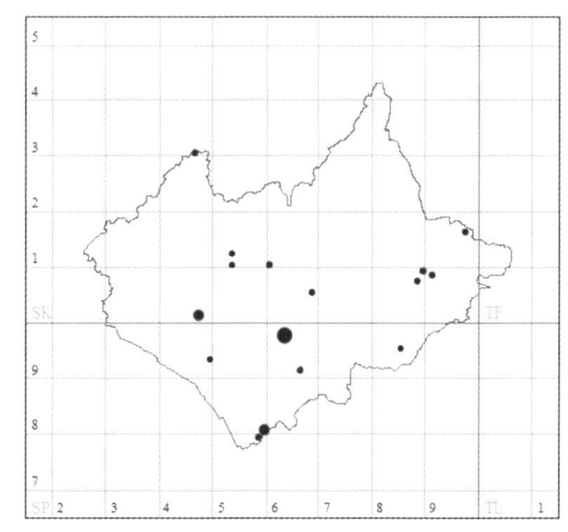

Dot = number of birds, 3 sizes of dot
1 (smallest), 2, 3 (largest)

Figure 525: Distribution of Golden Orioles 1974–2005.

Rogers 2004). The Leicestershire and Rutland records therefore fit the national patterns; a noticeable peak in occurrence during May and June and more records during the 1990s, at times of both higher breeding numbers and passage birds than during any other period.

DJSG

Red-backed Shrike *Lanius collurio*

Formerly a scarce to uncommon migrant breeder; now a very rare vagrant from Europe: six modern records.

Small numbers of Red-backed Shrikes bred in the counties annually in the first half of the 19th century, with reduced numbers in the latter half and in the early 20th century. Browne described it as 'sparingly distributed' in Leicestershire and noted that nesting occurred at Belgrave, Leicester in 1886, Billesdon in 1888 and Quorn in 1906. In addition, an egg and a male, both now retained at Leicester Museum, were apparently collected at Barkby in 1885. A similar situation was described by Haines in Rutland, where the first nest was recorded in 1870 near Tixover, followed by breeding records from, amongst others, Lyddington, Bisbrooke, Glaston and Uppingham; four nests were found in the latter area in 1902.

There is little information on the status of this species during the first 40 years of the 20th century. The LROS archives describe it as an 'uncommon and irregular summer visitor' and state that 'isolated pairs breed most years', whilst the first LROS Annual Report, for 1941, lists the Red-backed Shrike as 'an annual summer visitor, but sparsely distributed.' There are, however, no firm records to substantiate this, apart from an egg reported taken from a clutch at Ratby in 1944.

Between 1943 and 1950, the LROS Annual Reports listed a number of records, which all came from one observer, as follows:

1943	pair and four young, Six Hills, July 3rd.
1945	female, Swithland Reservoir, May 9th.
	male, Six Hills, July 8th and 13th.
1947	male, Beaumanor, May 27th.
1950	male, Swithland, May 1st.

Following a review in 1995, this series of records was considered unreliable and all were therefore rejected (Mackay 1995a). The only confirmed records remaining during the 1940s comprise single males at Sharnford from May 31st to June 12th 1942 and Bardon Hill on May 16th 1945.

The Red-backed Shrike was then absent from the counties for 40 years and is now a very rare vagrant. There have been four records since 1985, as follows:

1985	female, Ratby Burroughs, May 25th.
1988	male, Braunston-in-Rutland, September 17th to 19th.
1996	juvenile, Egleton, September 14th to 26th.
1998	first-winter, Eyebrook Reservoir, October 17th to 20th.

Two of these records occurred during large influxes of this species into the country: 1988 and 1998 have seen the two highest annual totals of Red-backed Shrikes in Britain in the last 20 years (Fraser & Ryan 1994, Fraser *et al.* 2000).

Red-backed Shrikes breed from western Europe to central Siberia but are absent from much of Iberia and northern Scandinavia. They spend the winter in eastern and southern Africa. This species has suffered a huge decline over much of north-western Europe over the last 150 years, the causes of which are not properly understood. It ceased to breed regularly in Britain in the late 1980s, although there have been occasional breeding attempts in Scotland since then. The status of the Red-backed Shrike in Britain is now restricted to a scarce spring and autumn passage migrant and due to the extinction of the breeding population this species has been added to the 'Red List' of Birds of Conservation Concern (Gregory *et al.* 2002).

DJSG

Great Grey Shrike *Lanius excubitor*

Rare passage and winter visitor; recorded in all months between October and April: 81 individuals since 1941 and at least 13 previously.

It is possible that this species occurred more frequently in the 19th century. Browne cites nine records which, with the exception of an undated bird shot at Anstey, all occurred in a ten-year period between 1882 and 1892; likewise, Haines knew of four Rutland records between 1883 and 1887. A total of 12 or 13 records within ten years is above the recent average and, given the relative lack of observers in the 19th century, it is probably safe to assume that many more occurred but were not seen.

The skins of four of the 19th century Great Grey Shrikes currently reside at Leicester Museum and two are of particular interest. One shot at Belvoir on February 8th 1885 has a convincing provenance and in some respects is a good match with the 'Siberian' Great Grey Shrike *L. e. sibiricus*, although further investigation has shown that the specimen lacks the prominent barring on the underparts typical of *sibiricus*, so is most likely to be either an atypical *excubitor* or an intergrade (Harrop 2006b). The form *sibiricus* is not currently on the British List, although there are two accepted records from Norway (in 1881 and 1891). A second individual, said to have been caught on allotments at Gipsy Lane, Leicester on November 9th 1891, matches the Steppe form of Southern Grey Shrike *Lanius meridionalis pallidirostris*; it has a pale bill and lores, pale grey crown and mantle and extensive white on the scapulars amongst other features suggesting this form, but the wing formula and pattern are consistent with Great Grey Shrike. The skin has been remade and its labelling changed at least once, so both its precise identity and provenance are questionable. It seems likely to be an eastern Great Grey Shrike but does not match any of the recognised subspecies perfectly (Harrop 2006b).

There were no 20th century records of the Great Grey Shrike in Leicestershire and Rutland until 1951, when one was at Uppingham on January 23rd. Since then there have been records in 37 of the 55 years up to 2005. The best years were all in the early and mid-1970s, with 40% of all records since 1951 occurring in the seven years from 1970 to 1976. There were eight individuals in 1974, six in 1976, five in 1972 and four in both 1971 and 1975; no more than three individuals have been reported in any other year. Since the mid-1970s this species

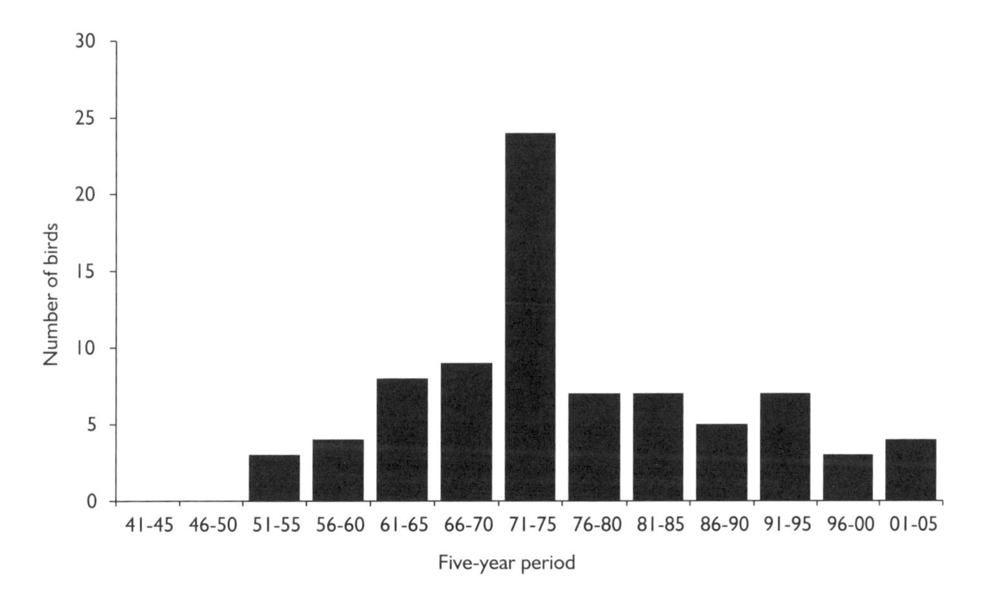

Figure 526: Numbers of Great Grey Shrikes 1941–2005.

has again become decidedly scarce in the counties, particularly since the mid-1980s; of the 18 blank years since 1951, nine have been since 1985. All records have been of single birds except for two at Orton-on-the-Hill on December 23rd 1962.

Great Grey Shrikes can appear in the counties at any time between October and April, although almost 30% have arrived between late October and mid-November. Records prior to October 21st are unusual, the only ones being:

- Stanford Reservoir on October 6th 1974.
- Rothley Sand Pit on October 9th 1982.
- Eyebrook Reservoir on October 10th 1998.
- Sproxton Heath on October 20th 1960.

Evidence of spring passage is provided by six birds that have appeared during the last ten days of March, with another three in early April: at Swithland Reservoir on April 3rd 1953, Eyebrook Reservoir on April 11th 1965 and Sapcote on April 11th 1981. Another four which had arrived earlier in the winter have lingered into April, including one at Bradgate Park which remained from March 23rd to April 11th 1991.

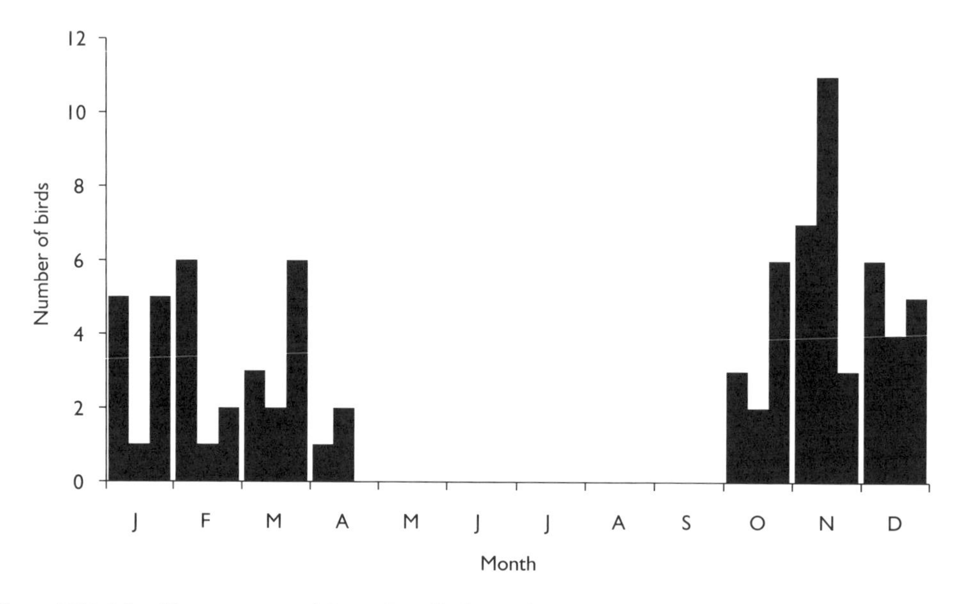

Figure 527: Monthly occurrence of Great Grey Shrikes 1941–2005.

Although most seem to be transient birds, with sightings on single dates only, a few have settled into winter territories and the longest staying birds have been:

- Stanford Reservoir from November 11th 1965 to March 17th 1966 (127 days).
- Swithland Reservoir from December 2nd 1972 to March 19th 1973 (108 days).
- Sapcote from February 8th to April 4th 1976 (57 days).
- Stanford Reservoir from October 6th to November 30th 1974 (56 days).
- Oakham from February 5th to March 19th 2005 (43 days).

A further 16 have stayed for periods ranging between four and 27 days.

Great Grey Shrikes have been seen at numerous widely scattered sites across the counties, although Figure 528 shows a distinct bias towards the south-east corner of Charnwood Forest and the nearby River Soar valley. Swithland Reservoir and the adjacent Buddon Wood is by far the most favoured area, with 15 records, although 11 of these occurred between 1965 and 1976 and at least some may have involved returning birds; there have not been any records from this area since 1983. Stanford Reservoir has six records to its name, all between 1965 and 1980; again, one or two returning birds may have accounted for some or all of these records. Six have been seen in the Cropston Reservoir/Bradgate Park area, but elsewhere the only sites to have recorded this species on more than one occasion are Eyebrook Reservoir (four individuals), Rutland Water (three) and Wanlip, Ratcliffe on the Wreake, Sapcote and Priory Water (two each). It is interesting that all of the six most-recent records have come from the east or north-east of the counties, four of them in Rutland.

Following a review in 2004, two previously published records were found to be unacceptable: single birds at Victoria Park, Leicester on May 6th 1943 and Swithland on May 15th and 18th 1954 (Fray 2005). The latter was undoubtedly a grey shrike but the evidence provided was inconclusive: see 'Unidentified shrikes' on page 596.

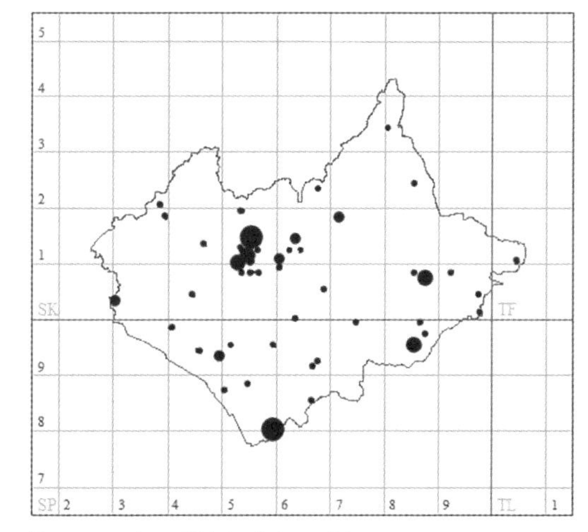

Dot = number of birds, 4 sizes of dot
1 (smallest), 2, 3–4, 5+ (largest)

Figure 528: Distribution of Great Grey Shrikes 1941–2005.

Great Grey Shrikes breed in central and northern Europe and across northern Asia, as well as in North America. Northern populations are migratory and move south to winter. Small numbers winter in Britain, with some returning to traditional sites each year. A study of the British status between 1986 and 1992 suggested that about 130 occurred each year, with 75 wintering and the others migrants (Fraser & Ryan 1995); numbers declined throughout the 1990s and only 76 were recorded in 2000 (Fraser & Rogers 2002).

DJSG

Woodchat Shrike *Lanius senator*

Very rare vagrant from Europe: two records.

The first county record was of a juvenile which frequented G.A. Todd's garden at Braunstone, Leicester from October 29th to November 3rd 1950. It was initially tentatively identified as a Lesser Grey Shrike *Lanius minor*, but a cine-film of the bird was sent to Georges Olivier, a French authority of the time on shrikes, who considered the bird to be a Woodchat Shrike, although he had reservations (Hickling 1952). The film, taken by Clifford Holt, has recently been tracked down and clearly shows the bird to be a juvenile Woodchat Shrike.

The second record soon followed and there was no confusion regarding this individual: an adult seen at Eyebrook Reservoir on June 6th 1953.

Haines mentions two records: one near Duddington in the spring of 1869 and another found dead 'near Stamford' during the same year. However, it was not known whether either of these actually occurred within Rutland, so neither is included within the county totals.

Woodchat Shrikes breed across much of southern Europe, North Africa and Asia Minor and winter in Africa south of the Sahara. They are regular spring and autumn visitors to Britain, currently averaging around 20 records a year. The species was removed from the BBRC list at the end of 1990. Spring records are usually between mid-April and early June and involve overshooting adults, whilst those in autumn usually relate to dispersing juveniles. Both county records therefore conform to the established pattern of vagrancy, although the Braunstone bird was exceptionally late in the year as most autumn records in this country are from mid-August to early October.

DJSG

Unidentified shrikes *Lanius sp.*

There have been two records of shrikes which have never been satisfactorily identified. In 1944, one was at Rowley Fields, Leicester from September 1st to 11th; it was seen and photographed by a number of observers, who considered it to be a Lesser Grey Shrike *Lanius minor*. All available evidence was submitted to Bernard Tucker, then the editor of *British Birds*, who had no doubt the bird was a Great Grey Shrike. Unfortunately, none of the photographs taken can now be traced and given the date (over a month earlier than any other Great Grey Shrike recorded in the counties and at a far more likely time of year for the Lesser Grey Shrike) there must be some element of doubt as to the identity of this bird.

An individual seen at Swithland on May 15th and 18th 1954 was originally published as a Great Grey Shrike. However, on review in 2004 it was found that the description provided did not rule out Lesser Grey Shrike (Fray 2005). As in the case of the 1944 bird, the date (this time over a month later than any other Great Grey Shrike recorded in the counties) favours Lesser Grey Shrike.

RMF

Jay (Eurasian Jay) *Garrulus glandarius*

Fairly common resident breeder; occasional autumn influxes.

Browne described this species as resident and generally distributed in Leicestershire during the 19th century, whilst in Rutland Haines declared that the Jay was 'surprisingly common still for a bird so conspicuous, so noisy and so detested by gamekeepers.' There is little data on the status and distribution of this species in the first 40 years of the 20th century, although it is known that nationally Jays steadily decreased during the 19th century, mainly due to persecution (hence the words of Haines), but then began to increase gradually from 1900 onwards. LROS Annual Reports during the 1940s reflected this, consistently referring to an increase in numbers and a spreading out of the population from the traditional strongholds in the counties. Increased tree planting and woodland management during the Second World War, along with the cessation of gamekeeping activities, meant that the population of Jays probably reached a peak in the counties at this time or shortly afterwards.

Today, Jays are rather shy and retiring birds of woodland, often being heard rather than seen. Both deciduous and coniferous woodlands are utilised, although mature broad-leaved woodland is favoured. Jays are noted for their close affinity with oaks but may also breed in areas of beech or horse chestnut and, in east Leicestershire, woods dominated by ash and maple are used. This species can also be found in large rural gardens, parkland and hedgerows, mainly outside the breeding season. Most urban and suburban areas are generally shunned and this species is rarely recorded within the Leicester city boundary; a study of four green spaces within Leicester in 1989 failed to locate any Jays (Fray *et al.* 1990).

Warrilow recorded this species in 200 tetrads (31% of the counties' total) during 1976–84 and suggested that the county-wide breeding population was between 400 and 800 pairs, based on an average of two to four pairs per occupied tetrad. A total of 121 occupied tetrads were to the west of Leicester and large parts of the north-east, south and south-east were unoccupied, probably due to a lack of suitable woodlands in these areas. The main concentration was in Charnwood Forest, but Warrilow noted that during the 20th century this species had spread outwards into suitably wooded areas, especially towards the south-west, but also eastwards as far as the edge of Leicester. Otter (1965) found that Jays bred in most east Leicestershire woods, but breeding surveys carried out by Warrilow in 1987 and 1990 of 39 woods in east Leicestershire located only three territories, all in large woods of greater than ten hectares. The fact that there has been no recent restocking of deciduous woodland or regular management of established woods may explain why the Jay is less common now than it was in the 1940s.

Little other recent data exists on breeding densities of this species. One or two pairs held territory at the Prior's Coppice CBC plot each year from 1988 to 1999, suggesting a stable population. Most other CBC surveys in the counties have been on farmland, where Jays are not usually found.

British Jays are essentially sedentary but continental Jays irrupt into western Europe periodically in autumn, their movements being triggered by food shortages to the north and east. The most well-known such influx occurred in 1983, when large numbers were recorded flying in off the sea in southern and eastern England during October (John & Roskell 1985). In Leicestershire and Rutland there were many sightings of ones and twos flying over open country and across roads and motorways and more than usual numbers in woodlands during October and November and into December, but the only specific counts in non-traditional Jay areas were of 11 at Aylestone Meadows on October 29th and at least ten at Rutland Water on October 22nd and 23rd. In 1996, another sizeable movement was noted from October onwards, with many records of birds from unusual areas or flying across open fields. Numbers remained high into the following year after each of these autumn influxes.

Apart from these influx years, counts of Jays are usually in single figures. A party of 40 to 50 on shocks of corn was reported in 1941, but unfortunately neither locality nor date is known. Otherwise, there have been ten counts of ten or more:

- 20 at Thornton on April 11th 1993.
- 17+ at Swithland Reservoir on November 2nd 1986.
- 17 at Swithland Reservoir on October 18th 2005.
- 15+ at Burbage/Sheepy Woods on April 6th 1987.
- 14+ at Groby on October 4th 1987.
- 14 at Martinshaw Wood on May 13th 1986.
- 14 at Stoke Dry Wood on February 2nd 1991.
- ten at Shenton Cutting on November 17th 1989.
- ten at Leicester Forest West on September 30th 1991.
- ten at Stathern Wood on October 31st 2004.

Jays are virtually ubiquitous throughout mainland Europe, being absent only from the extreme north, and also occur along a broad band across central Asia to the Oriental region In Britain they are widespread throughout England and Wales but more localised in Scotland and Ireland; the British population is estimated at 160,000 pairs (Baker *et al.* 2006). The generally sedentary nature of this species is evidenced by a bird trapped and ringed in a Quorn garden on August 17th 1968 which was retrapped in the same garden over seven years later on December 13th 1975.

DJSG

Magpie (Black-billed Magpie) ***Pica pica***

Common resident breeder.

Browne described the Magpie as 'resident and generally distributed' in Leicestershire in the 19th century, whilst in Rutland it was considered by Haines to be common, but less plentiful near Exton, Burley and Normanton. There is little data on the status and distribution of this species in Leicestershire and Rutland during the early part of the 20th century, although it is known that nationally Magpies steadily decreased throughout the 1800s before beginning a steady increase from the beginning of the 20th century (Gibbons *et al.* 1996). The first indication of the status of this species in the 20th century was provided in 1942, when a survey in Leicestershire considered the Magpie to be 'widely distributed, common and increasing in numbers as a nesting species, especially in the western half of the county, although not so predominant in the meadows of the Soar valley or uncultivated parks and heaths'. Breeding densities noted during this survey included at least one nest per square mile at Oadby, Croft, Quorn and Kirby Muxloe, nine nests per square mile in the Rearsby area and 12 nests in just over a square mile of Snarestone parish. Further evidence of an increase in numbers came from Quorn during the same decade: 66 breeding pairs were located within a six-mile radius of the village in both 1943 and 1944, increasing to 72 pairs in 1945 and 88 pairs in 1947. In 1948 23 nests were found within the three miles between Burton on the Wolds and Six Hills.

There is no doubt that this species is one of the present day avian success stories and the population continues to increase. Once confined almost exclusively to rural countryside, there has been a significant expansion, first into the suburbs and then into urban areas and they are now a common sight in Leicester city centre. A study of four green spaces within the Leicester city boundary in 1989 found Magpie to be the eighth-commonest species overall; densities were highest at Western Park and Aylestone Meadows, where it was the fourth- and fifth-commonest species respectively, with 14 pairs at each site (Fray *et al.* 1990). The Leicestershire Garden Bird Survey found Magpie to be the 11th most-frequent species during the period January 1996 to June 2005, visiting 59% of all gardens.

Chamberlain & Vickery (2002) found that, derived from national CBC results, the Magpie had increased by 57% during 1973–98 and local CBC data from two sites supports this. At Stoughton between one and four

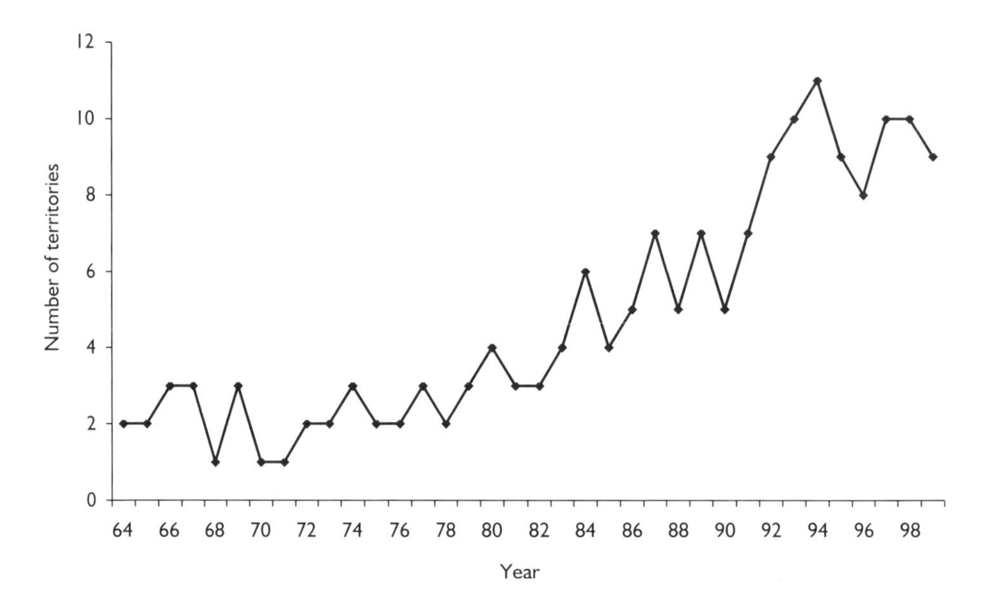

Figure 529: Number of breeding pairs of Magpies on the Stoughton CBC plot 1964–99.

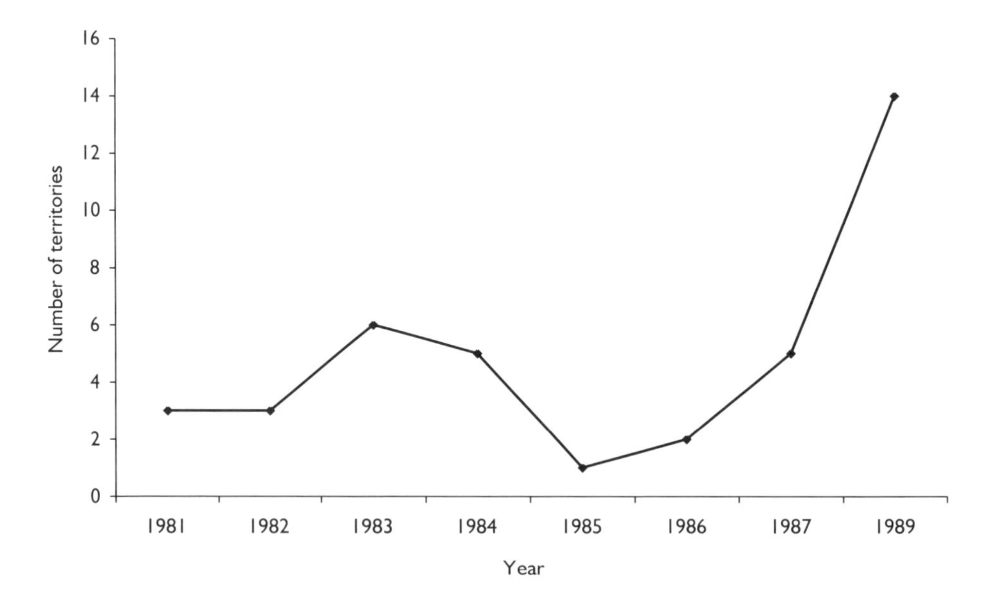

Figure 530: Number of breeding pairs of Magpies on the Aylestone Meadows CBC plot 1981–89.

pairs were recorded annually from 1964 to 1983, after which numbers rose sharply and reached a peak of 11 pairs in 1994, whilst at Aylestone Meadows only one territory was located in 1985 but there were 14 by 1989. However, other farmland CBC plots in Leicestershire and Rutland at Newton Harcourt and King's Hill Lodge, Uppingham do not show major increases, both recording between one and three pairs annually. Likewise, woodland CBC plots at Knighton Spinney and Prior's Coppice reveal very small and stable populations, reflecting the fact that this species does not readily utilise essentially wooded areas.

Warrilow recorded this species in a total of 509 tetrads during 1976–84, equating to 80% of all tetrads within the counties, with breeding confirmed in 301. There was an obvious trend from high breeding density in the west to lower in the east: only 43% of tetrads were occupied in the area to the north and east of Melton Mowbray and Oakham, largely reflecting the extent of rigorous gamekeeping in the eastern part of the counties. Warrilow proposed an average of 12 to 16 pairs per occupied tetrad (based on national CBC data), giving an estimated county breeding population of between 6,100 and 8,100 pairs. Since the completion of Warrilow's work, however, a relaxation in gamekeeping has allowed this species to return to many eastern areas and it is likely that the current population is now nearer 10,000 pairs.

Flocks of between 20 and 50 can occur at any time of year but particularly in winter and spring. The largest concentrations have been:

- 104 at Glenfield Sewage Works on March 17th 1991, with several counts of between 30 and 81 in the same area in the late 1980s and early 1990s.
- 80 at Glen Parva Gravel Pits on January 16th 2005, with 60 there on both September 30th 2002 and December 7th 2004.
- 73 at Glen Parva on February 27th 1994.
- 57 at Aylestone Meadows on July 5th 1987.

Unlike the black corvids this species does not seem particularly prone to albinism and the only aberrant bird that has been recorded was one with completely white secondaries at Glenfield on February 2nd 1992.

Magpies are widespread throughout Eurasia from Ireland to Japan; they also breed in north-west Africa and parts of the Middle East. In Britain, they are common and widespread throughout much of England and Wales, although more localised in Scotland. The total British breeding population is estimated at 590,000 pairs (Baker *et al.* 2006). They are relatively sedentary, as evidenced by the fact that most ringing recoveries from the counties are local retraps, although one ringed at Woodhouse Eaves on June 18th 1993 was found dead 46km to the north in Nottinghamshire on April 25th 1994.

DJSG

Nutcracker (Spotted Nutcracker) ***Nucifraga caryocatactes***

Very rare vagrant from north-east Europe or Siberia: two records.

During the second week of September 1948, one was seen by D. O. Thomas as it visited the rectory lawn at Stathern on three successive days, whilst another was found by A. B. Ritchie at Beacon Hill on September 8th 1968, where it remained until the 15th (*BB* 63:370). The 1948 bird was the only one to be seen in Britain that year and was in fact the sole record of this species in the country between 1946 and 1951. The 1968 individual, however, was part of a remarkable invasion into Britain which began in August and involved at least 340 birds of the slender-billed race *N. c. macrorhynchos*. The majority of reports came from East Anglia and Kent although 13 birds reached the Midlands; other counties to record the Nutcracker during this spectactular irruption included Staffordshire, Northamptonshire and Shropshire (Hollyer 1970).

The thick-billed nominate race breeds closest to Britain, in the mountains Scandinavia, central and south-eastern Europe and Russia. These populations are largely resident and British records are believed to have been of the slender-billed race, which breeds from north-east Russia east to the Pacific coast. Excluding the 1968 irruption there have been fewer than 100 British records, only four of them since 1987.

DJSG

Jackdaw (Eurasian Jackdaw) ***Corvus monedula***

Common resident breeder and winter visitor.

Browne described Jackdaws as resident and common in Leicestershire in the 19th century. They favoured old steeples and at St. Margaret's Church (Leicester) 'deposited their sticks in such numbers upon the upper steps of the belfry as to completely block up the passage and necessitate their being carted away.' In Rutland Haines considered it 'commoner than Magpie'. By 1941 the status of this species was described as 'common, particularly in old parks and estates which are its strongholds' in the first LROS Annual Report and it was considered 'resident and believed to be increasing' within the city boundary of Leicester (Pochin 1954).

During 1976–84 Warrilow recorded this species in 428 tetrads in the counties (67% of the total number of tetrads), with breeding confirmed in 160. The Jackdaw was widespread but, like the Rook, was absent from the far west for reasons which are unclear; it was also rather sparsely distributed in the north-east, with the exception of Belvoir and north Rutland. It bred in a variety of habitats with suitable large holes for nesting and open ground for feeding and was common in the central districts of major settlements, using chimneys of older houses or factories, traditional sites such as church towers and derelict properties. Unlike Rooks, with which they often feed on agricultural land, Jackdaws also regularly visit gardens and this was the 18th most-frequently recorded species during the January 1996 to June 2005 Leicestershire Garden Bird Survey, being recorded in over 12% of gardens. The adaptability of the Jackdaw is undoubtedly one reason for its success. Outside towns it uses quarries and natural holes. The highest breeding densities were found in parkland and woodland habitats and based on an average of 12 to 15 pairs per occupied tetrad Warrilow estimated a breeding population of 5,100 to 6,400 pairs.

Mitcham (1992) recorded Jackdaws in 73% of Rutland tetrads, with breeding proved in 51%. Perhaps surprisingly, Webster (1997) found a lower density (36% of 1–km squares) in Charnwood which is popularly believed to be a favoured area.

Local CBC data reveals little about current trends in the Jackdaw population as this species was either absent or present in very small numbers at the majority of sites. The only area where Jackdaws bred regularly was King's Hill Lodge, Uppingham, where the population declined from 26 pairs in 1993 to just six in 2004. This is rather surprising considering this species has been increasing nationally since the 1960s, although numbers had picked up to 16 pairs by 2005.

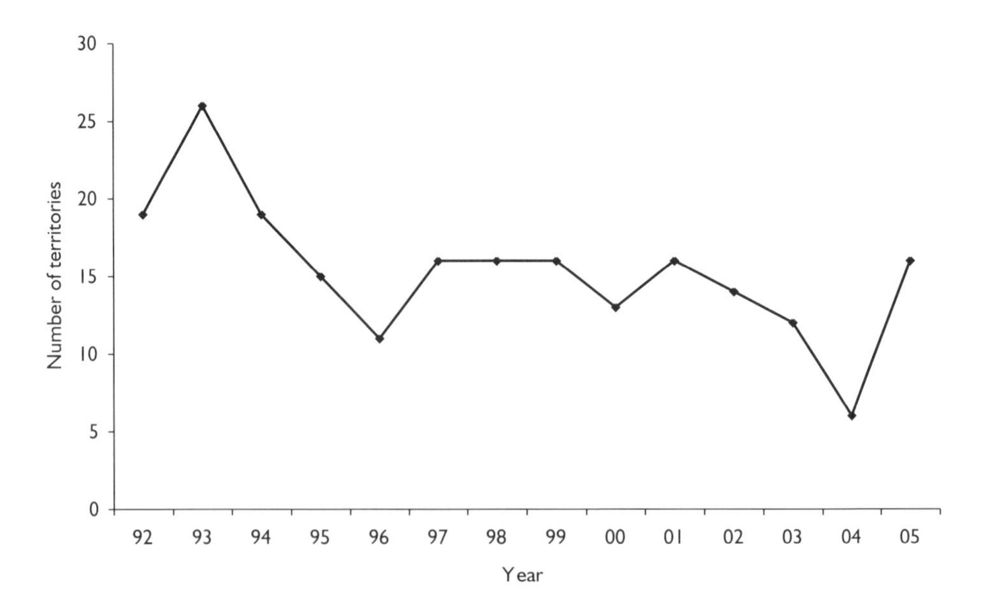

Figure 531: Number of breeding pairs of Jackdaws on the King's Hill Lodge, Uppingham CBC plot 1992–2005.

Large flocks congregate particularly in the autumn and winter and these often number in the high hundreds, whilst four-figure flocks are not unusual. Some of the largest flocks reported have been roost flights or pre-roost gatherings, often in association with Rooks. The largest on record is a mixed flock with that species of 15,000 to 20,000 roosting at Ambion Wood on October 29th 1954, with 13,000, again mixed, at the same site on November 20th 1955. The following four-figure flocks have been recorded:

- a pre-roost gathering of 4,500 at Knipton Reservoir on November 28th 1993.
- a pre-roost assembly of 4,000 at Buddon Hill on September 28th 1948.
- a pre-roost assembly of 2,000 at Belvoir on December 12th 1994.
- 2,000 at Teigh on December 28th 1998.
- regular roost flights of 1,000 to 2,000 at Quorn in the late 1940s and early 1950s.
- 1,550 in the Belvoir area on February 20th 2005.
- 1,100 at Branston on February 26th 1995.
- 1,000 at Belvoir on February 20th 2001.
- 1,000 at Wymondham on March 22nd 1997.
- 1,000 roosting in willows by the River Soar at Wanlip between March and November 1949.
- 1,000 feeding in stubble at Debdale Wharf on both January 7th and February 4th 1992.
- 1,000 at Belvoir on July 29th 2000.
- 1,000 at Branston on December 28th 1998.
- 1,000 at Whissendine on December 25th 1997.

In addition, 'several thousand' were noted roosting at Glaston Wood on October 22nd 1989.

As with other black corvids, this species is prone to albinism and the following have been recorded: an albino at Swepstone from September 4th to 10th 1944 which was pure white with a few chocolate flecks on the back and dull yellow bill, legs and feet; one with white wing coverts (site and date unspecified) in 1946 and similar birds at Leesthorpe on October 31st 1968 and Wistow on January 27th 1978; one with a white body and black wings at Swithland Reservoir on May 8th 1980; one with white blotches on the scapulars and belly at Groby Pool on February 12th 2000; one with a mainly white belly and a lot of white in the body and wings at Bradgate Park on July 30th 2005 and a similar bird at Billesdon on December 11th 2005. Haines also mentions three partially albino birds recorded in Rutland in the 19th century. More unusual was one at Little Dalby on January 17th and 18th 1997 which showed partial erythrism, with chestnut-brown wings, whilst one at Swithland Wood on April 29th 1984 had a deformed bill, with an elongated and decurved upper mandible.

The subspecies resident in Britain is *C. m. spermologus* and the vast majority of records refer to this race. However, birds showing characteristics of other races have been identified in recent years, as follows:

1999	one resembling the eastern European race *C. m. soemmerringii* was at Belvoir on December 5th and was joined on December 12th by a second bird which was either this race or an intergrade with the nominate Scandinavian race *monedula*. What was probably the former bird was also seen at nearby Branston on December 27th.
2000	one of the nominate race was at Egleton on January 30th, with presumably the same individual at nearby Rutland Water on both February 13th and 27th. Both of the 1999 birds were still at Branston on March 5th, with two more of the nominate race at Belvoir on March 11th and the original *soemmerringii* bird there on April 1st, when a nominate bird was at Stretton. Individuals that were either *monedula* or intergrades with *soemmerringii* were at both Egleton and Burley Fishponds on March 23rd.
2001	two poorly marked individuals of the nominate race were at Belvoir on February 20th.
2002	one of the nominate race was at Belvoir on March 25th.

Harrop (2000) is a useful reference for the identification of Jackdaw forms. Nominate *monedula* (often known as Nordic Jackdaw) is a regular winter visitor to Britain in varying numbers but there are as yet no fully proven records of *soemmerringii* (often known as Russian Jackdaw), though it is a possible vagrant.

Jackdaws are found in many parts of the Western Palearctic and western Asia, from Scandinavia south to Morocco and from Ireland east to Mongolia. Four subspecies are recognised by *BWP*. They are resident to migratory, tending to move west or west-south-west in winter, often accompanied by Rooks. The British population, which was most recently estimated at 503,000 pairs (Baker *et al.* 2006), has been increasing at a moderate rate since the 1960s; the increase has been associated with improvements in breeding performance and probably reflects the species' generalist feeding habits, which allow it to exploit diverse and ephemeral food resources (Baillie *et al.* 2006).

DJSG

Rook *Corvus frugilegus*

Abundant resident breeder.

In the 19th century the Rook was resident and common, indeed Haines described it as 'undoubtedly too numerous in this district.' He recorded flocks of 400 around Uppingham. Browne recorded breeding at Knighton, Stoneygate and Westcotes within the city of Leicester. Both he and Haines commented on variants with pale plumage tracts, though these are more commonly found in Carrion Crows.

The first comprehensive census of the Rook population in Leicestershire was carried out in 1928. Hickling discussed local population trends of this species, noting that it increased from 1928 to 1944 by 44% (though he acknowledged that early counts using unsophisticated methods may have been too low). Between then and 1975 the population declined by over 50%, possibly as a result of changes in agricultural practice which may have reduced available food, increased disturbance and loss of nesting habitat. Since the 1970s, however, there has been a welcome recovery in numbers by over 60%.

This species remains abundant and widespread across the counties and the clamour of a rookery provides one of the quintessential sounds of spring. These conspicuous nesting colonies mean that Rooks are one of the easiest species to census in the breeding season and surveys have been carried out in 1928, 1944, 1964–65, 1975 and 1986–87. Consequently, we probably have more data on breeding numbers of this than any other species. Census results are given in Table 48:

Table 48: Rookery census results

Year(s)	County	No. of nests	No. of rookeries
1928	Leicestershire	9,381	No data
1944	Leicestershire	13,639	422
	Rutland	3,657	83
	Total	**17,296**	**505**
1964–65	Leicestershire	10,652	No data
1975	Leicestershire & Rutland	7,475	327
1976–85	Leicestershire	8,720	No data
	Rutland	1,770	No data
	Total	**10,490**	**No data**
1986–87	Leicestershire & Rutland	12,261	421

The current trend seems to be upward and the present breeding population is probably back up to, or around, the 1944 level.

The most recent full survey in 1986–87 showed that there were 242 rookeries of between one and 25 nests, 115 of between 26 and 50 nests, 51 of between 51 and 100 nests and 13 of between 101 and 200 nests. Rookeries were widely distributed across the whole of the counties but were absent from urban areas such as Leicester, Loughborough, Coalville and Market Harborough; it was also noticeably scarce in the extreme north-east. The highest densities occurred to the south and east of Leicester between Melton Mowbray, Oakham and

Lutterworth and also in the Market Bosworth area (Holling 1988). Earlier surveys showed the highest nest density in east Leicestershire and Rutland, a region then dominated by pasture. During the recent recovery of this species, there has also been a shift towards larger rookeries. Most are small (fewer than 25 nests), but there has been an increase of 12% in the number of larger colonies (26 to 100 nests).

The largest rookeries recorded during the 1986–87 survey were:

- 200 nests at Wharf Farm, Market Bosworth.
- 175 nests at Barrowden.
- 159 nests at Lubbesthorpe.
- 157 nests at Crossburrow Hill, Cranoe.
- 150 nests at Osbaston Hall.

The only rookeries larger than those recorded in 1986–87 were two counted in 1944: 300 nests between Barlestone and Osbaston and 284 nests east of Wing.

From 1991 to 2003 the RNHS carried out an annual survey of rookeries in Rutland. This shows that the population has been fairly stable in recent years, though it has been noted that, whilst there is little change in the number of large rookeries, Rooks in smaller rookeries regularly relocate to new sites in response to changes of land use (for example, from spring to autumn ploughing). In Charnwood, where there is a much smaller proportion of pasture, Webster (1997) recorded breeding in only 18% of 1–km squares.

Table 49: Numbers of rookeries and nests recorded in Rutland by RNHS from 1994–2003

Year	**1994**	**1995**	**1996**	**1997**	**1998**	**1999**	**2000**	**2001**	**2002**	**2003**
Rookeries	56	62	73	56	63	74	69	n/c	74	78
Nests	1,453	1,960	2,123	2,147	2,044	1,981	2,283	n/c	2,099	2,009

There were worries in the late 1970s that the loss of elms through Dutch Elm disease would cause a decline in Rook numbers, as a significant proportion of nests were built in these trees. This has not been borne out and they have successfully switched to other tree species. Although the vast majority of nests are built in trees (usually deciduous, but occasionally conifers), there are several records of small rookeries on electricity pylons.

Large flocks are maintained outside the breeding season and often number in the high hundreds; the largest flocks recorded are:

- 3,750 at Eastwell on December 6th 1982.
- 3,000 at a pre-roost gathering at Kirkby Mallory on January 28th 1991.
- 2,000 at Dadlington on February 7th 1986.
- 1,650 at Branston on February 26th 1995.
- 1,600 at Teigh on December 1st 1989.
- 1,500 at a pre-roost gathering at Bottesford during the second winter period of 1996.

In addition a mixed roost, with Jackdaws, of 15,000 to 20,000 was at Ambion Wood on October 29th 1954, with 13,000, again mixed, at the same site on November 20th 1955 and several thousand, also mixed with Jackdaws, were roosting between Twycross and Orton-on-the-Hill in December 1949.

An aberrant bird shot at Noseley on May 20th 1942 was chocolate-brown in colour.

There are only six recoveries of ringed birds and just two had moved more than 10km: one ringed at Billesdon Coplow on April 5th 1990 was found shot 13km to the east-south-east at Stockerston on December 4th 1990 and one ringed at Market Bosworth on May 10th 1987 was found in similar circumstances 12km to the south-west at Atherstone (Warwickshire) on March 20th 1991.

Rooks are found from Europe and Asia Minor east to eastern Siberia, Japan, Korea and eastern China. The British breeding population was estimated at 853,000 to 857,000 pairs during 1988–91 (Gibbons *et al.* 1993) but a subsequent moderate increase has seen the latest estimate increased to 1,022,000 to 1,304,000 pairs (Baker *et al.* 2006).

DJSG

Carrion Crow *Corvus corone*

Common resident breeder.

Browne, writing in VH, described the Carrion Crow as 'resident and generally distributed, but not so common as formerly', although Haines said it was becoming commoner in Rutland towards 1900.

The first LROS Annual Report, for 1941, described this species as 'common and well distributed, particularly in east and south Leicestershire' and circumstantial evidence of it moving into new areas was provided by

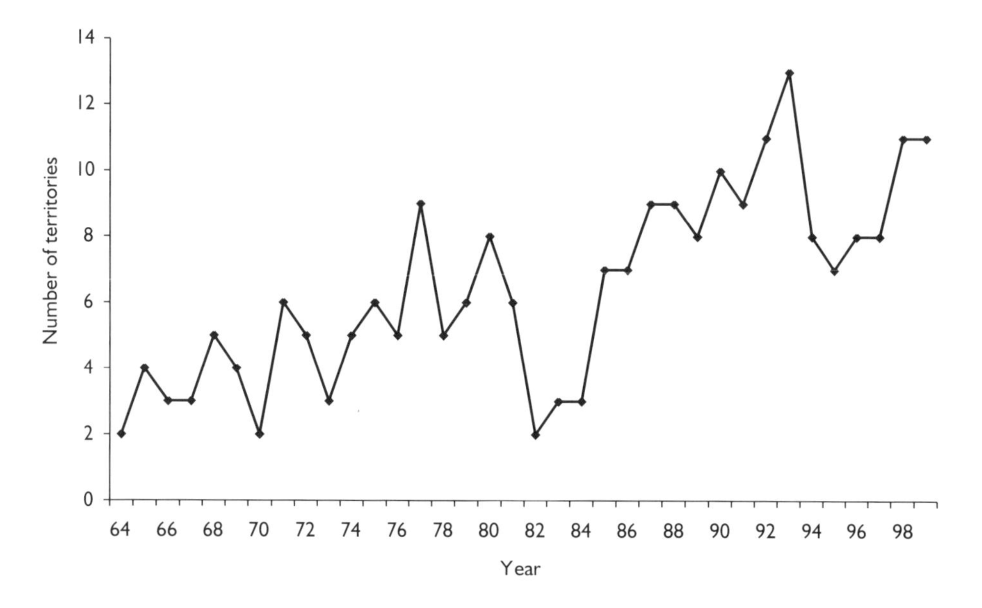

Figure 532: Number of breeding pairs of Carrion Crows on the Stoughton CBC plot 1964–99.

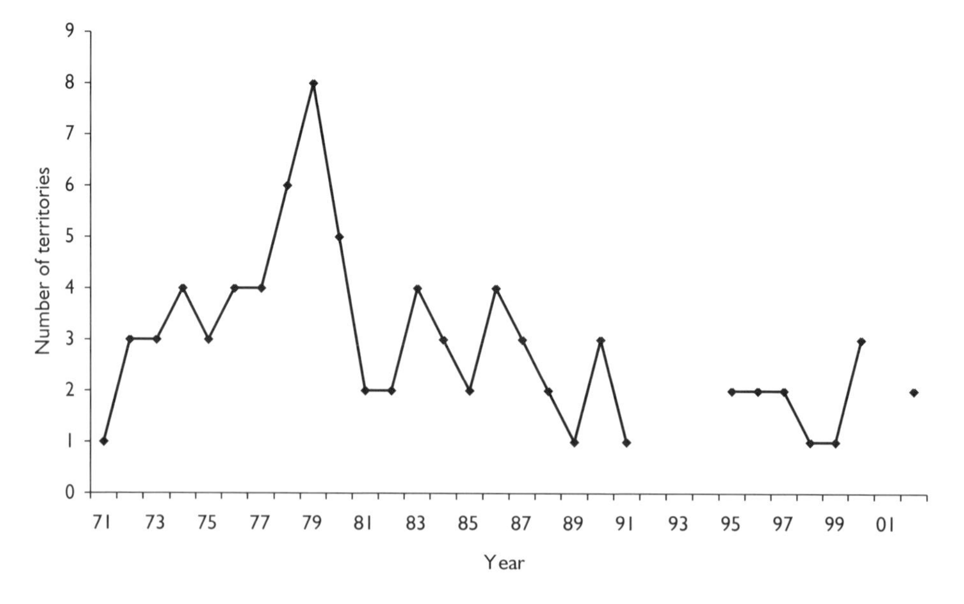

Figure 533: Number of breeding pairs of Carrion Crows on the Newton Harcourt CBC plot 1971–2002.

Brady (1944), who noted that the species was not recorded at The Brand, Woodhouse Eaves in 1940, but nested there in 1943. Little other data is available on breeding numbers during the early and middle parts of the 20th century, although 35 breeding pairs within a six mile radius of Quorn in 1943 increased to 38 pairs the next year and to 43 in 1945.

The widely held perception that Carrion Crows have become commoner during the latter part of the 20th century is borne out by the results of the long-term CBC study at Stoughton. From an initial two pairs in 1964, numbers increased steadily throughout the following two decades and peaked at 13 pairs in 1993. An even more dramatic rise was noted on the CBC plot at Newton Harcourt, where numbers increased from just one pair in 1971 to eight in 1979; a sudden downturn saw only two pairs breed at this site in 1981 and 1982, following which numbers there remained fairly stable.

Warrilow noted that Carrion Crows bred in a wide range of habitats throughout the counties, although they generally avoided larger towns and cities and extensive woodland interior zones. A total of 594 tetrads were occupied during 1976 to 1984, equating to 93% of all tetrads within the counties, with breeding confirmed in 446. There was a rather patchy distribution throughout Rutland and north-east Leicestershire and this was considered to be due to rigorous gamekeeping in these areas. A slight relaxation in these activities since has meant that this species has spread back into these areas. Warrilow estimated 25 to 35 breeding pairs per occupied tetrad, giving a total breeding population in the counties of 12,000 to 17,000 pairs in the period 1976 to 1984.

Large congregations of Carrion Crows can be found at any time of year, either as feeding flocks or communal roosts, the latter often associated with Rooks and Jackdaws. There have been many counts of between 100 and 200, with larger flocks as follows:

- 400 at Trent Valley Pit on December 18th 1993.
- 300 at Enderby Tip on January 5th 1992.
- 300 roosting at Buddon Wood on March 1st 1996.
- 220 at a pre-roost gathering at Thornton Reservoir on October 30th 1998.
- 200 at Charnwood Lodge on July 15th 2002.
- 200 at Houghton Lodge Farm on April 19th 2004.

As with other black corvids, this species can be prone to albinism, the most commonly occurring form having white bases to the flight feathers. The most extreme example of this was one at Anstey on April 5th 1988 which had all of the remiges pure white.

There are only four ringing recoveries involving Leicestershire and Rutland, two of which had moved away from the original ringing locality: one ringed at Rugby (Warwickshire) on June 4th 1933 was found at Desford, 28km to the north, in August 1933 and one ringed at Hallaton on May 27th 1994 was found freshly dead, shot, 8km to the west at Shangton on June 24th 1996.

In western Europe, Carrion Crows breed from southern Scotland south to Iberia and east to Germany and The Alps. A separate population is found in Asia. Most populations are sedentary, but some move south and west during the winter. In the United Kingdom, this species is common and widespread, although it is largely absent from Ireland and north-west Scotland. The breeding population in Britain is estimated at 790,000 pairs (Gibbons *et al.* 1993); national CBC data shows that it increased by 45% between 1973 and 1998 (Chamberlain & Vickery 2002).

DJSG

Hooded Crow *Corvus cornix*

Formerly a scarce winter visitor, now a rare vagrant; recorded in all months between October and April.

Historically the Hooded Crow was a regular winter visitor in small numbers. Browne cites numerous records from the 19th century, including six at Cossington on November 5th 1885 and three at Skeffington on December 5th of the same year; in addition, five or six pairs reportedly visited Belvoir every winter. He considered that this species generally arrived on about October 25th and departed around March 21st, a view shared by Haines in Rutland who said that 'it arrives very punctually about October 20th and leaves equally so about March 20th.' Haines thought that it had become more abundant during the second half of the 19th century and that it was 'always to be seen in the Welland valley from Barrowden to Seaton and inland to Morcott and Bisbrooke', with up to six seen at any one time.

It appears that the status of this species in the counties remained similar during the early part of the 20th century. The LROS archives mention that Hooded Crow was a winter visitor in small numbers during this period, mainly to the north-east of the county, although the only records specifically mentioned are single birds at Hathern in 1904, Swithland in January 1913, Stanford Reservoir in January 1936 and Barrow upon Soar in October 1938.

Since the formation of LROS in 1941 Hooded Crows have declined considerably and can now be considered no more than rare winter vagrants. Between 1941 and 1962 there were records in all years except 1957, with the best years all being in the 1940s: 13 were found in 1946, with nine in 1942 and seven in both 1943 and 1947. From 1963 to 1968 there were only two records, both of single birds and both, coincidentally, on January 26th, at Eyebrook Reservoir in 1964 and Eaton in 1967. Numbers increased between 1969 and 1976, with the only blank year being 1973 and notable annual totals of ten or 11 in 1976 and at least seven, possibly as many as 12, in 1975.

Since 1976 there have been records in just 12 years, involving 13 birds, only three of which have been since 1990. All records were of single birds, as follows:

1977	Barkby Thorpe, March 8th.
1978	Frisby Gravel Pits, December 7th.
1979	Swithland Reservoir, December 16th.
1982	Narborough, February 21st.
1984	Owston, February 29th.
1985	between Cold Overton and Somerby, December 30th.
1986	Swithland Reservoir, December 11th.
	Owston Wood, December 27th.
1987	Scraptoft, December 21st.
1990	Swithland Reservoir, November 19th to March 16th 1991; same, Cropston Reservoir, February 17th.
1993	Swithland Reservoir, December 9th.
1997	Huncote, November 24th to February 15th 1998; same, Enderby Tip, January 31st 1998.
2005	Eyebrook Reservoir, March 13th.

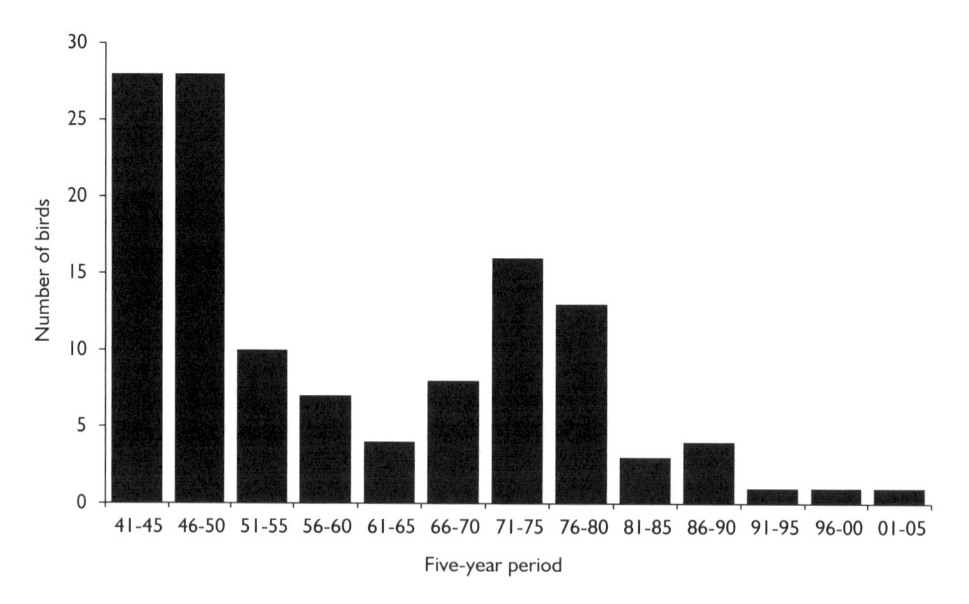

Figure 534: Numbers of Hooded Crows 1941–2005.

The vast majority of records have referred to single birds, but two have been seen together on seven occasions, four were at Willesley on February 16th 1946, six were at Kibworth on April 18th 1943 and seven were at King's Norton on February 13th 1942.

Haines' assertion that this species generally did not appear before October 20th is borne out by the fact that, in modern times, there have been only eight occurrences prior to this date. The earliest was one at Quorn on October 2nd 1950, with the others, all single birds, being:

- Horninghold, Ratcliffe on the Wreake and Quorn, all on October 11th 1975.
- Stanford Reservoir on October 13th 1946.
- Cropston Reservoir on October 15th 1944.
- shot at Swithland Reservoir on October 15th 1946.
- Houghton on the Hill on October 18th 1952.

Haines and Browne both mentioned that it had usually departed by around March 20th; again this remained roughly true throughout the 20th century, although there have been five records in April, all but one of single birds, as follows:

- Great Stretton on April 25th 1975.
- Quorn on April 24th 1946.
- six at Kibworth on April 18th 1943.
- Ab Kettleby on April 17th 1974.
- Leicester City Farms on April 14th 1956.

The apparent peak in mid-February shown on the accompanying graph is strongly influenced by the groups of seven at King's Norton in 1942 and four at Willesley in 1946. It is noticeable that with the exception of one at Eyebrook Reservoir on March 13th 2005 all birds since 1985 have arrived between November 19th and December 30th.

Hooded Crows have appeared at many scattered sites, although Figure 536 shows a distinct bias to the eastern half of the counties. Favoured sites have included Eyebrook Reservoir (14 individuals), King's Norton (nine), Swithland Reservoir (six) and both Quorn and Willesley (five each). Three of the last seven records have come from Swithland Reservoir.

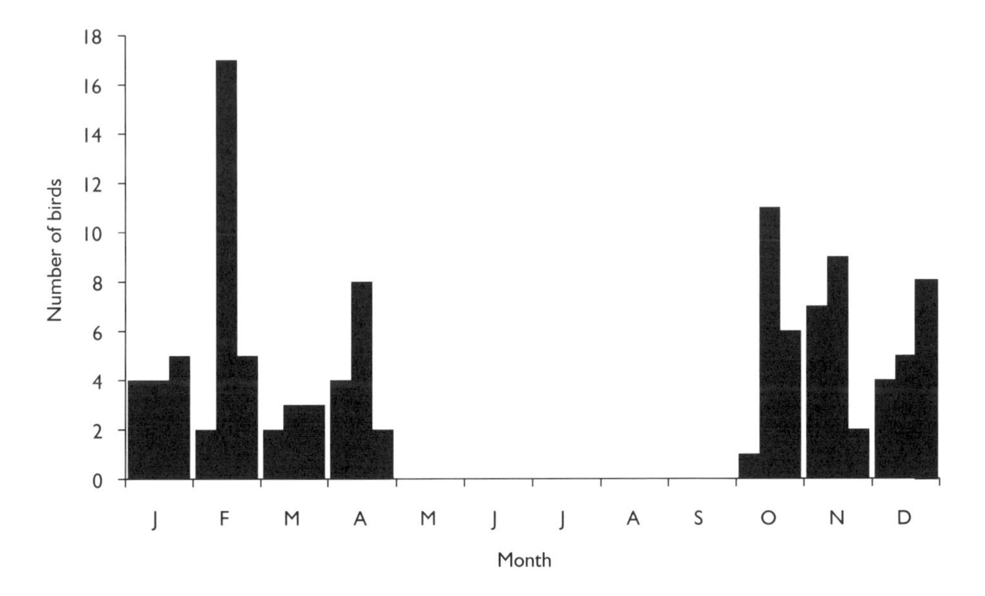

Figure 535: Monthly occurrence of Hooded Crows 1941–2005.

The Hooded Crow was long considered a subspecies of the Carrion Crow and was given full species status as recently as 2002. It breeds throughout northern, central and eastern Europe and replaces the Carrion Crow in Ireland and north and west Scotland; the latest British population estimate is at least 160,000 pairs, with another 53,900 in Ireland (Baker *et al.* 2006). The more northerly populations are partially migratory and move south and west in the winter, with most birds found in England originating in Scandinavia.

DJSG

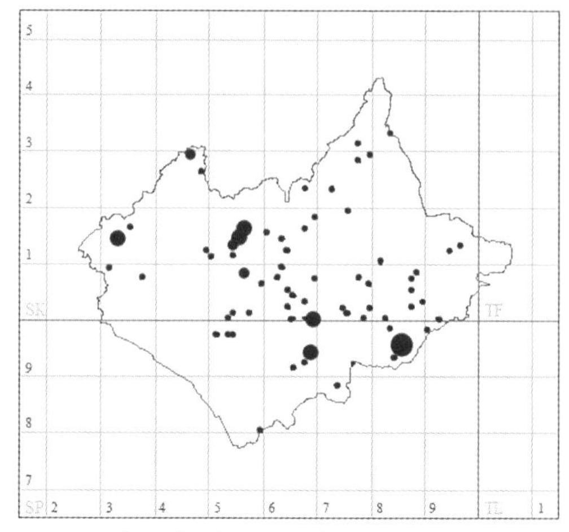

Dot = number of birds, 4 sizes of dot
1–2 (smallest), 3–4, 5–9, 10+ (largest)

Figure 536: Distribution of Hooded Crows 1941–2005.

Raven (Common Raven) ***Corvus corax***

Scarce resident, very rare breeder. Recent recolonist following extinction in the 19th century.

The Raven bred in more than one locality early in the 19th century, but it had almost entirely disappeared by the time of Browne and Haines. The last date of its occurrence known to Browne involved a record of one at Sharpley Rocks on October 26th 1848. Formerly, it had bred regularly at Bradgate Park. Haines stated that the last nests in Rutland were recorded about 1840 at Normanton and Exton, with subsequent records from Wardley Wood about 1855, Ridlington on October 12th 1898 and Empingham on April 20th 1905.

Apart from a report in the LROS archives of one at Wanlip in 1919 there followed a period of over 50 years without records, until the severe winter of 1963, when one flew over Thurcaston (not Thurmaston as erroneously stated in the 1988 and 1993 LROS Annual Reports) on January 6th. It was then another 25 years before the next sighting, of one being mobbed by a Sparrowhawk and Magpies as it flew south-west over Roundhill Road, Leicester on June 6th 1988. There were three records during the 1990s: two flew north-east over Kirkby Mallory on September 19th 1993, one was being mobbed by Carrion Crows over Burbage on June 6th 1994 and one flew over Evans' Weir, Leicester on November 18th 1996.

The reoccupation of Leicestershire began in 2000, when two were at Benscliffe Wood on March 25th. Up to four were then recorded regularly at various sites around Charnwood Forest until May 31st. Subsequent records in 2000 were two at Swithland Reservoir on both July 9th and October 22nd, one at Diseworth on July 16th and two at Bardon Hill on both September 23rd and October 22nd.

A similar pattern in 2001 saw two at Beacon Hill on January 4th, then regular ones and twos around Charnwood Forest (although none were reported in March) until May 8th and led to the comment in the LROS Annual Report that the species 'appears to be establishing a permanent foothold in the county'. There were then two at Bardon Hill on September 23rd and single birds at Thornton on September 29th, Buddon Wood on October 10th and Queniborough on October 25th.

In 2002, two again roamed Charnwood Forest between March 16th and April 28th, with Bardon Hill and Deans Lane, Woodhouse being particularly favoured. There were no further records until one at Markfield on September 20th and one was at Blakeshay Wood on September 29th, with two at both Swithland Reservoir on October 6th and November 22nd and Charnwood Lodge on October 20th.

The Charnwood pair was again resident in 2003, favouring the Charnwood Lodge and Bardon Hill areas and four were at both Newtown Linford on May 7th and Charnwood Lodge on July 12th, suggesting possible breeding. However, the first confirmed breeding record of Raven in Leicestershire and Rutland occurred at Breedon Quarry, where a pair successfully reared four young. Away from these areas there were single birds at Cossington Meadows on May 17th, Wanlip South Gravel Pits the next day and Tilton on the Hill on October 21st (the precursor of an eastwards extension of range).

In 2004 both semi-resident pairs were seen fairly regularly throughout the year. The pair at Breedon Quarry successfully raised three young, whilst the Charnwood pair was seen regularly from January to May, mainly in the Swithland Reservoir, Bardon Hill and Charnwood Lodge areas. Three were seen at the latter site on April 12th, suggesting that breeding may have occurred. Elsewhere, two were at Stoney Cove on April 27th with one there on May 25th, two were at nearby Croft Quarry on May 2nd and two were at Scraptoft on November 26th. A pair was at Stoke Dry Wood on December 27th, providing Rutland with its first record since 1905.

In 2005 the spread of Ravens back into former sites continued, with records from the east in both spring and late autumn/winter. Breeding was confirmed again at Breedon Quarry, where four young were raised. A pair was present again in the Charnwood area, though breeding was not proved. In the east, one was at Eyebrook Reservoir on April 16th and 17th and two were near Newbold on November 7th and December 3rd.

Two previously accepted records were found to be unacceptable when they were reviewed: two at Beacon Hill from June 11th to 14th 1950 (Mackay 1995a) and one at Dunton Bassett on February 22nd 1986 (Fray 2005).

The Raven has a very extensive global range. In the Western Palearctic it is found from Iceland south to Morocco and from Ireland east to Russia. It is also found continuously from the Western Palearctic to eastern Asia and in North America. BWP recognises 11 subspecies, some of which may warrant specific status following further taxonomic studies. The British population of Ravens (nominate *corax*) was estimated to be about 7,000 pairs during 1988–91, mainly in the west and north (Gibbons *et al.* 1993). Since then there has been an increasingly widespread return to sites in lowland England from which they were driven by farmers and gamekeepers during the 19th century. A more recent estimate put the British breeding population at 12,000 pairs (Baker *et al.* 2006). Ravens are also returning to former sites in neighbouring Midlands counties, so we can be fairly confident that they will again become established in Leicestershire and Rutland.

DJSG

Starling (Common Starling) ***Sturnus vulgaris***

Abundant resident breeder, passage migrant and winter visitor.

The Starling is an abundant and widespread breeding resident with numbers augmented in autumn and winter by continental migrants. In the 19th century Browne described it as resident and common in Leicestershire, breeding even in Leicester. He recorded several albinos and aberrants: in 1846, 1878, 1887 (two) and 1888. In Rutland Haines noted that it could be seen in flocks a thousand strong and described it as a 'too numerous species'. He too noted albinos and aberrants: in 1877, 1883 and 1898, plus another undated.

As with many of the counties' other common birds there is little data regarding breeding numbers of the Starling, particularly during the first half of the 20th century. The first LROS Annual Report in 1941 described it as 'common and the number augmented in the winter' and other indications of its status around this time included 'a common resident whose numbers are very much increased in winter' within the city boundary of Leicester (Pochin 1964) and 'a very common breeding species' in east Leicestershire (Otter 1965).

The best indication of the status of this species is provided by Warrilow, who found it widespread across the counties during 1976–84 due to its ability to colonise all habitats. Starlings were found anywhere where suitable nest holes were present and where open grassy or earth spaces for feeding were nearby. He found 632 of the counties' tetrads occupied (98% of the total number of tetrads), with breeding confirmed in 535, making the Starling the second most-widespread species in the counties (after Blackbird). The species' absence from a few isolated tetrads in Rutland was probably due to lack of suitable nest sites in the intensively arable landscape there. An average density of 27 pairs per tetrad is given by O'Connor & Shrubb (1986) for farmland in the East Midlands; allowing for the fact that this is likely to be too low for urban and suburban habitats and possibly too high for parts of east Leicestershire where there is intensive farming, Warrilow estimated 35 to 50 pairs per occupied tetrad to arrive at a breeding population of 22,000 to 31,000 pairs. Mitcham (1992) found Starlings in 94% of Rutland tetrads, a lower figure than that for the counties as a whole and noted a decline possibly attributable to a combination of the conversion of pasture to arable land and climatic change. In Charnwood the density of Starlings is lower, possibly because they are absent from higher ground: Webster (1997) found them in 79% of 1–km squares during 1992–94.

The abundance of breeding Starlings in Britain has fallen rapidly, particularly since the early 1980s and especially in woodland. Loss of the species' preferred feeding habitat (permanent pasture) and general intensification of livestock rearing are likely to be having adverse effects on farmland populations, which decreased by 51% between 1973 and 1998 (Baillie *et al.* 2006, Chamblerlain & Vickery 2002). Although Starlings are still relatively numerous and familiar in the counties, and were placed fifth in the Leicestershire Garden Bird Survey between January 1996 and June 2005, when they were noted in 79% of gardens, a measure of their decline as breeding birds is provided by local CBC data. At Stoughton the population rose to a peak in the early 1980s, when there were 14 pairs in 1980 and 16 in 1981, before declining to such an extent during the 1990s that no territories were recorded from 1993 to 1995. Although numbers have always been smaller at Newton Harcourt, a similar peak is apparent in the early 1980s followed by an almost total loss from the site by the mid to late 1990s. The two CBC plots in Rutland, at Prior's Coppice and King's Hill Lodge, Uppingham, have also both shown sharp declines thoughout the 1990s and into the 21st century.

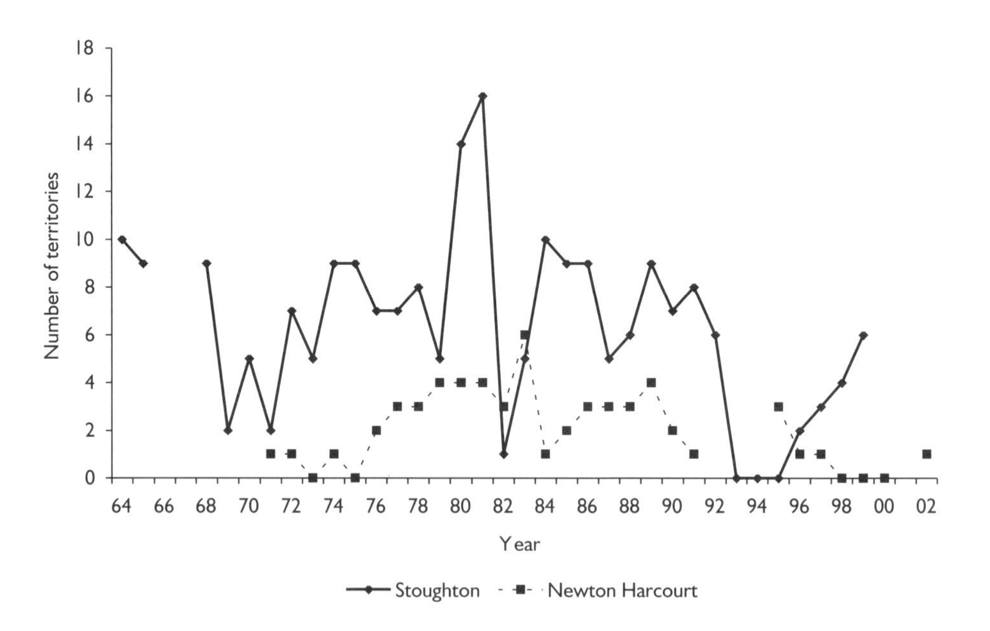

Figure 537: Number of breeding pairs of Starlings on two Leicestershire CBC plots 1964–2002.

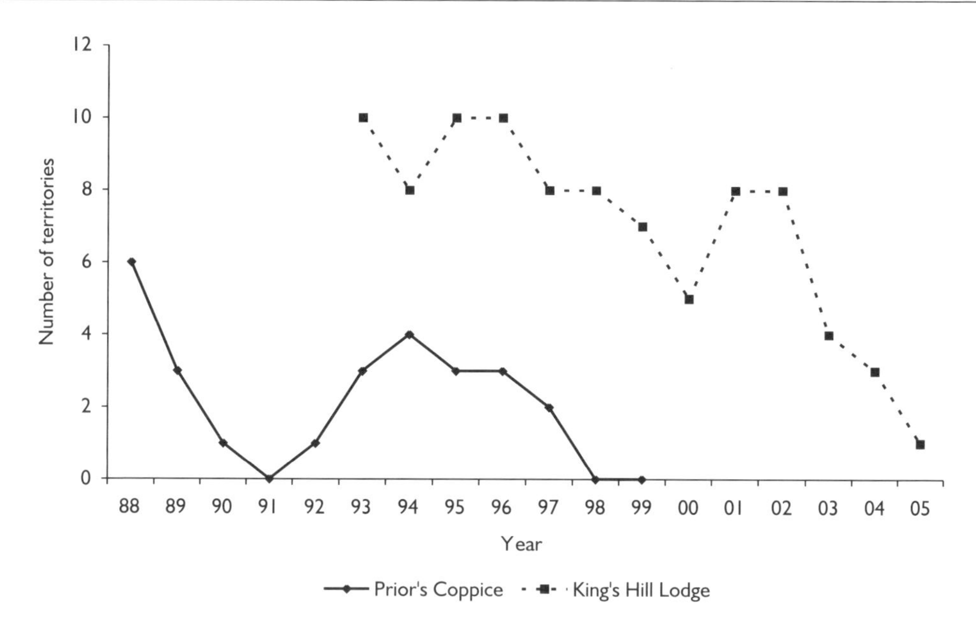

Figure 538: Number of breeding pairs of Starlings on two Rutland CBC plots 1988–2005.

A feature of this species is the huge roosting assemblies which often occur, drawing birds from a large area. Indeed, in some years the majority of birds feeding within the counties during the day may use roosts beyond the county boundary. These roosts can number anything from a few thousand to 250,000 or more. The largest and most well-known of these occurred at Abbey Park, Leicester each winter from December 1978 to the winter of 1986–87, where numbers peaked at between 500,000 and 1,000,000 in February 1984 (and it is thought that the upper limit was probably more accurate). This roost caused considerable nuisance and once it had become established studies were carried out by what became known as the 'Starling Squad' to investigate methods of dispersing the birds. Felstead (1980) described how, in early 1979 'the noise was tremendous until they settled down in complete darkness and when they were disturbed the wing sound was great. The droppings, which reeked foully, piled high on paths, inches high on ice and whitewashed bushes and the ground beneath the trees. Many evergreens were spoilt by droppings and falling leaves. At least two large branches were broken under the birds' weight'. Also in 1979, attempts were made to assess the distances travelled and the places of origin of the various flocks comprising the roost. The furthest that a flock was recorded to have come from was Uppingham, with others from well outside the city being seen passing over Melton Mowbray and Loughborough (Felstead 1980). Later studies by Peach & Fowler (1987) showed that the largest numbers of birds seemed to arrive from the south-west, west and north-east of the city. A total of 23 pre-roost assemblies were identified within the city boundary, the largest of which were at Braunstone Lane, New Parks Boulevard and Welford Road Cemetery.

Other research into Starling roosts was carried out during the 1953–54 winter, when it was found that at any one time few roosts were in use, but that each roost was used for only part of the winter (Hickling 1954). It has also been noted that some roosts are used for many years (for example, one at Sheepthorns Spinney, Kibworth was used for over 20 years up to about 1955), whilst others are short-lived.

Other large roosts over the years have included the following:

- several hundred thousand at Peatling Magna on March 23rd 1946.
- 250,000 at Misterton Gorse in December 1966.
- 250,000 at Whetstone in September 1983.
- 150,000 at Whetstone on September 6th 1990.
- 100,000 at Misterton in mid-February 1966.

- 100,000 at Carlton Curlieu from late November 1966 to early February 1967.
- 100,000 at Glen Parva on February 21st 2000.

In addition there have been roost counts of 'many thousands' at Willoughby Waterleys between January and mid-April 1947, Wistow in the second winter period of 1977 and Gilroes Cemetery, Leicester on January 11th and 25th 1988.

Feeding flocks into four-figures are regular and the largest on record is of 10,000 which 'blackened the fields' at Hoby on December 11th 1988.

Flocks of migrants are a common feature of late autumn, although there is very little data regarding numbers. At Deans Lane, Woodhouse in 2005, a total of 8,905 was counted on seven dates between October 9th and November 17th, including 3,080 on October 27th and 2,135 on October 29th; all passage was to the west (Lister 2007b). A similar record involved 1,628 heading west over Pickworth on October 28th 2004.

There are several continental ringing recoveries and controls from France, Finland, Belgium, Denmark, Norway, the Netherlands, Germany, Estonia, Sweden, Latvia, Lithuania, Belarus and Russia. Amongst these, 14 which were ringed in the counties were recovered over 1,000km away and eight over 2,000km away, whilst nine birds ringed abroad and recovered in the counties had moved over 1,000km. The furthest recoveries are:

- one ringed at Leicester on December 12th 1955 and recovered 2,625km to the east-north-east at Kubinka (Russia) on August 22nd 1956.
- one ringed at Leicester on February 22nd 1956 and found dead at Lesnoe (Russia) on April 26th 1957, a movement of 2,384km to the east-north-east.
- one ringed at Leicester on January 27th 1956 and recovered 2,380km to the east at Bryansk (Russia) on May 5th 1956.
- a male ringed at Leicester on December 21st 1955 and recovered 2,183km to the east at Mstsislavl (Belarus) on August 10th 1956.
- one ringed at Uppingham on January 27th 1974 and found dead near Vyborg (Russia) on May 20th 1976.
- one ringed at Stoneygate, Leicester on January 25th 1976 and found dead near Konakovo (Russia) on May 20th 1978.
- a male ringed at Stoneygate, Leicester on January 21st 1979 and found dead at Dubrovno (Russia) on May 15th 1982, a movement of 2,107km to the east.

The recoveries of foreign-ringed birds from furthest away involved one ringed as a pullus at Liminka (Finland) on July 4th 1968 which was retrapped at Stoneygate, Leicester on February 16th 1974 and one ringed at Zarasai (Lithuania) on May 20th 2001, which was found freshly dead at Freeby on March 13th 2002.

As in the 19th century, aberrant Starlings are often noticed today, usually in the form of albinos, partial albinos or birds with deformed bills. Between 1945 and 2005 there have been records of full albinos in nine years, partial albinos in ten years, other aberrant plumages in six years and birds with deformed bills (usually with overlong upper mandibles) in five years. Birds have occasionally occurred showing plumage patterns very similar to the Rose-coloured Starling, but with creamy to off-white rather than pink bodies.

The nominate subspecies *vulgaris* is found from Iceland, Britain (except Shetland and the Outer Hebrides, where *zetlandicus* breeds), Ireland and France east to European Russia. Other subspecies are found on the Faroe Islands, Azores, in Siberia and other parts of Asia. Introduced populations are found in North America, Australia, New Zealand and southern Africa. It is generally migratory in the north and west of the breeding range. The British breeding population was estimated at 1,100,000 territories during 1988–91 (Gibbons *et al.* 1993), but the most recent estimate of 737,000 territories is much lower (Baker *et al.* 2006). In light of this rapid decline, the Starling has been added to the 'Red List' of Birds of Conservation Concern (Gregory *et al.* 2002).

DJSG

Rose-coloured Starling (Rosy Starling) *Pastor roseus*

Very rare vagrant from south-east Europe and south-west Asia: four or five records.

Browne mentions three records: one seen near Foxton around 1870 by the Rev. H. Matthews; one shot near Enderby some time between 1870 and 1875 and an undated record from Castle Donington. The latter is particularly vague and subsequent authors have ignored it.

There have been just two further records. An adult was seen in a Blaby garden by Mrs J. Hickling on October 19th 1952 and in 2002 an adult male frequented gardens at Medbourne from August 16th to 31st. The latter bird, which was originally found by Steve Gamble, was enjoyed by many observers and was well photographed.

Three additional records have been published but on review were found to be unacceptable: single birds at Dishley Grange on October 1st 1944, Burton on the Wolds on December 31st 1949 and Leicester City Farms on September 17th 1954 (Mackay 1995a, Fray 2005).

The Rose-coloured Starling breeds from south-east Europe eastwards through western Asia to Iran and winter mainly in the Indian subcontinent. It is a regular migrant to Britain and was removed from the list of species considered by the BBRC at the end of 2001. In Europe this species is characterised by its erratic and highly variable irruptions to the west of its normal range after the breeding season and these are most likely to be driven by food availablility. A huge irruption occurred in the summer of 2002, with an estimated 14,000 extralimital pairs breeding in Romania, 2,000 pairs in Bulgaria and 10,000 non-breeding birds present in Hungary (Fraser & Rogers 2004). Britain shared in this influx, with over 180 individuals recorded, including the bird at Medbourne.

DJSG

House Sparrow *Passer domesticus*

Common resident breeder, recent decline.

During the 19th century House Sparrows were sufficiently numerous to be considered a pest. Browne described them as resident and 'far too common' in Leicestershire, whilst Haines echoed his words with the statement that they were 'far too numerous' everywhere in Rutland. Nests were found as early as January and as late as August. Partial abinos were also recorded, at Aylestone Road, Leicester on January 6th 1890 and Stoneygate, Leicester on September 30th 1890. A 'curious grey variety' was noted at Cosby on June 15th 1903.

This species has traditionally received relatively little attention from birdwatchers and although it has always been common and widespread, particularly in urban and suburban areas and around farm buildings, very little information can be gleaned from LROS Annual Reports. A nation wide decline, which was first noted in our area in the 1995 Annual Report, has engendered increased interest and consequently there is more information for the years since then than for all other years put together.

Warrilow recorded House Sparrows in 617 tetrads (96% of the total number of tetrads), with confirmed breeding in 515. He found this species closely linked with human habitation, ranging from dense inner urban areas to isolated farmsteads. Nests are usually in buildings. Its absence from some parts of east Leicesteshire and north Rutland reflects the lack of suitable habitat in areas used for intensive farming. Suburban populations, on the other hand, benefit from the provision of food, as shown by the fact that House Sparrow was the second most-frequently recorded species during the Leicestershire Garden Bird Survey of January 1996 to June 2005, occurring in 89% of gardens. As this species is a semi-colonial nester, estimating breeding numbers presents problems. Densities vary considerably from very high in suburban areas to very low in woodlands and on some farmland. Given 40 to 80 pairs per occupied tetrad, Warrilow estimated a population of 24,000 to 49,000 pairs. In Rutland, Mitcham (1992) found House Sparrows in a similar proportion of tetrads (97%). In Charnwood, House Sparrows were found in 53% of 1 km squares by Webster (1997), mainly in and around villages but also at farms and large houses.

It is likely that a combination of factors is contributing to the decline of this species. A study by Vincent (2005) suggested that breeding success depends on the abundance of invertebrate prey whilst, as with other species, lack of winter seed is believed to affect farmland populations. Another reason which could be put forward to help explain the recent decline is the increase in road traffic. Illustrating the toll which this can have on the population is a record from one observer who regularly cycled between Cropston and Anstey and counted 52 dead House Sparrows on the road during 1984, 26 of which were in September.

By far the highest counts on record are both of 1,000, at a well-established roost in a thicket at the junction of Anstey Lane and Glenfrith Way, Leicester on March 5th 1985 (unfortunately this habitat was subsequently destroyed by junction 'improvements') and at Essendine on January 11th 1976. Otherwise, the largest flocks on record are:

- 250 at Melton Country Park on both August 7th 1996 and August 9th 1998.
- 200 at Glenfield on both August 20th 2003 and October 29th 2004.
- 150 at Birstall during August 2005.
- 120 at Oakthorpe on September 10th 2000.
- 100 at Stoughton Airfield on December 25th 1988.
- 100 at Priory Water on September 5th 1993.
- 100 at Stockerston on January 21st 1999.
- 100 at Little Dalby on September 3rd and 12th 2001.

Aberrant birds are frequently recorded: at least eight albinos, 13 partial albinos, three leucistic birds, two melanistic birds and single erythristic and flavistic birds have been noted.

Hybrids with Tree Sparrows have been recorded: see 'Hybrids' (pages 676–684).

House Sparrows are found on almost all continents. The nominate race *P. d. domesticus* is found in northern Eurasia from Britain and Scandinavia east to the Sea of Okhotsk. Most races are sedentary. The British population was estimated at between 2,600,000 and 4,600,000 pairs by Gibbons *et al.* (1993), but a more recent estimate puts it at 1,950,000 to 3,450,000 pairs (Baker *et al.* 2006). Although House Sparrows remain relatively common, the recent rapid sharp decline in breeding numbers has caused the species to be added to the 'Red List' of Birds of Conservation Concern (Gregory *et al.* 2002).

DJSG

Tree Sparrow (Eurasian Tree Sparrow) ***Passer montanus***

Fairly common resident breeder, recent decline.

Browne considered this species to be resident but sparingly distributed over the woodlands of Leicestershire in the 19th century and Haines described it as common in Rutland at this time, where nests could always be found near Uppingham 'in holes of pollard trees or in the thatch of barns, even in old magpies' nests.' A flock of 50 was seen feeding in a stackyard close to Croft Quarry on April 17th 1900. Hickling stated that it was most frequently seen in Charnwood Forest, but that is certainly no longer the case.

Formerly a common and widespread resident breeder, mainly in farmland habitats, the Tree Sparrow has suffered a well-publicised decline, with the national population falling by 93% between 1973 and 1998 (Chamberlain & Vickery 2002). This decline was first noted locally in LROS Annual Reports in 1992. Some idea of former breeding numbers is illustrated by records of 40 nests on six 'telegraph' poles carrying power cables, the nests situated behind metal plates fixed to the extremities of the cross-members, at Sharnford on June 13th 1942 and 40 breeding pairs located within six miles of Quorn in 1944. The decline is most sharply illustrated by data from the Stoughton CBC plot. Between 1964 and 1968 there were over ten pairs in each year, with a peak of 20 pairs in 1965. Thereafter numbers began to decline, though there were 14 pairs as recently as 1980. The decline became most marked during the first half of the 1980s and since 1985 there have never been more than two pairs in any year. A similar situation is apparent at Newton Harcourt, where numbers have more than halved from a peak of 11 pairs in 1976, 1977 and 1980.

During 1976–84 Warrilow recorded Tree Sparrows in 470 tetrads in the counties (73% of the total number of tetrads), with breeding confirmed in 205. He found them closely associated with farmland hedgerows and mature deciduous woodlands. Large areas of north-east and east Leicestershire and north-east Rutland, which are intensively farmed, were unoccupied during the survey. This absence from the principal arable farming areas of the counties supports the view that the intensification of agriculture, including the widespread use of herbicides, reduction in winter stubble and the removal of hedgerow trees used as nest sites, was a major factor in the decline of the Tree Sparrow. Given an average of three to five pairs per occupied tetrad, Warrilow estimated a population of 1,400 to 2,300 pairs, an estimate which is now too high. Mitcham (1992) recorded Tree Sparrows in just 36 (31%) of Rutland tetrads, whilst in Charnwood Webster (1997) found them in just 15 (11%) of 1-km squares during 1992–94.

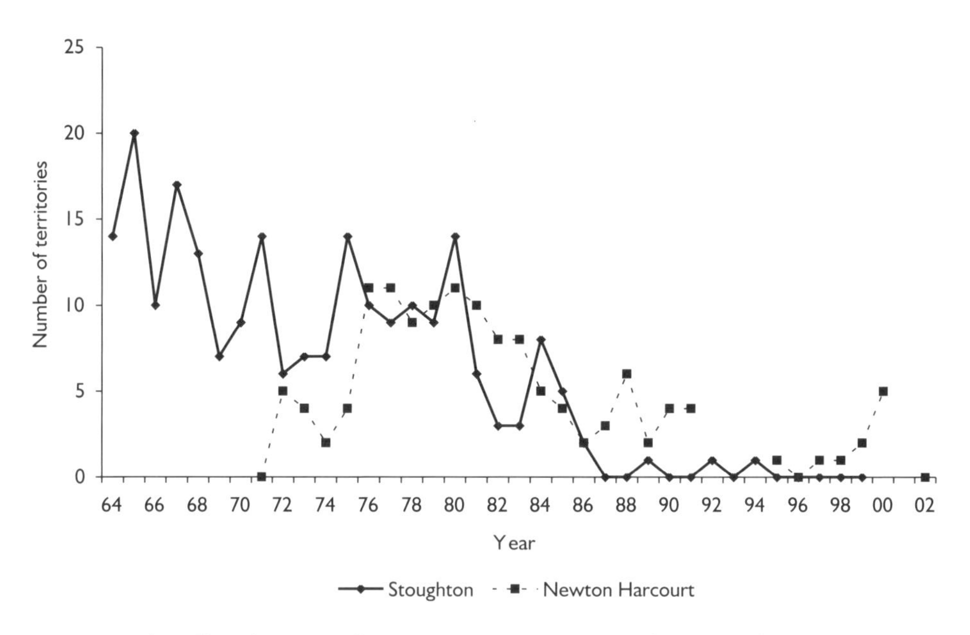

Figure 539: Number of breeding pairs of Tree Sparrows on two Leicestershire CBC plots 1964–2002.

There are still localised areas which hold good breeding numbers, such as at Wanlip North Gravel Pits, where 70 nestlings were ringed in 1999, 15 breeding pairs were present in 2001 and 16 pairs were located in 2002. A project was established at Rutland Water and Eyebrook Reservoir in spring 2000 to investigate the recent population decline and this project is still ongoing. At Rutland Water 229 young were fledged at the Egleton Reserve in 1999, 61 breeding pairs were found there in 2001 and 67 pairs were recorded in 2002, and 19 breeding pairs were located at the Hambleton Peninsula in 2001, with 16 pairs there in 2002. Eyebrook Reservoir held 16 breeding pairs in 2001 and 19 in 2002. The colony at Rutland Water is now one of the largest in the country, supported by the provision of nest boxes, a year-round supply of seed at feeding stations and the availability of insect food for nestlings from the wetland-edge habitats (Anderson 2002, Field & Anderson 2002).

Large autumn and winter flocks were once commonplace and have included:

- 'several thousand' at Rutland Water in the winter of 1976.
- 700 at Cotes on January 5th 1950.
- 600 at Sileby on December 15th 1945.
- 425 at Stoughton Airfield on December 20th 1986.
- 350 at Saltby on January 24th 1982.
- 300 at Rutland Water on March 1st 1981.
- 300 at Stoughton Airfield on January 5th 1989.
- 300 near Stanford on Soar on November 10th 1946.
- 250 at Stanford Reservoir on January 17th 1988.
- 250 at Stoughton Airfield on both January 28th 1986 and December 29th 1988.

In addition, there have been flocks of 200 at Loughborough Sewage Farm on March 8th 1947, Eyebrook Reservoir on February 10th 1965, Newtown Linford on January 20th 1968 and Belton on January 22nd 1991, 200 to 300 were at Leicester City Farms on November 15th 1942 and 'several hundred' were at Foston on September 27th 1947. There were also a further 19 flocks into three figures between 1941 and 1991, but the only three-figure flocks since then have been:

- 200 at Kilby Bridge on January 6th 2005.
- 120 at Frolesworth Manor Lake on December 3rd 2002 and March 7th 2003.

- 118 at Kilby Bridge on January 31st 2001, with 103 there on November 30th 2000.
- 110 at Braunston-in-Rutland on March 28th 1992.
- 100 at the Hambleton Peninsula, Rutland Water on November 7th 1993.
- 100 at Trent Valley Pit on March 2nd 1996.
- 100 at Marefield on August 27th 1999.
- 100 at Snarestone in January 2000.
- 100 at Queniborough on November 19th 2000.

Four ringing recoveries are worth listing: one ringed at Guildford (Surrey) on February 19th 1961 was found freshly dead 163km to the north at Oakham on July 2nd 1963; one ringed at Eyebrook Reservoir on July 26th 2001 was controlled 164km to the east-south-east at Iken Marsh (Suffolk) on February 16th 2002; one ringed at Rutland Water on May 4th 2002 was found freshly dead 102km to the east-south-east at Thetford (Norfolk) on December 18th 2002; and one ringed at Melton Spinney on March 21st 2003 was controlled at Mildenhall Fen (Suffolk) on January 8th 2004.

Aberrant birds have been recorded in two years: an albino at Eyebrook Reservoir on March 18th 1967 and a dilute bird, with plumage looking as though dusted with flour, at Thornton Reservoir on March 16th 1980.

Hybrids with House Sparrows have been recorded: see 'Hybrids' (pages 676–684).

Tree Sparrows are found extensively across the Palearctic and in Asia. Nominate *montanus* is found in Europe and Siberia from Norway, Ireland and Portugal east to the Sea of Okhotsk. Most populations are sedentary, though local movements occur. As mentioned previously, its numbers have crashed dramatically since the 1970s: during 1988–91 the British population, which was already in sharp decline, was estimated at 110,000 territories (Gibbons *et al.* 1993); more recent estimates put the population at 68,000 pairs (Baker *et al.* 2006). Not surprisingly, the Tree Sparrow has been added to the 'Red List' of Birds of Conservation Concern (Gregory *et al.* 2002).

DJSG

Chaffinch *Fringilla coelebs*

Abundant resident breeder, passage migrant and winter visitor.

The Chaffinch is one of the most common and widespread birds in Leicestershire and Rutland, breeding readily in woodlands, farmland hedgerows and suburban gardens. It would appear that this has always been the case: in the 19th century, Browne noted that the species was 'resident and common, breeding in gardens and plantations close to Leicester', whilst in Rutland Haines described it as 'one of our commonest species'. Otter (1965) considered it to be 'probably east Leicestershire's most numerous bird'.

Gibbons *et al.* (1996) noted that the Chaffinch decreased during 1940–69, due mainly to agricultural use of pesticides and toxic dressings, after which it steadily increased again. CBC data from farmland at Stoughton bears this out to some extent, with an average of 11.3 territories per year from 1964 to 1969 compared to 13.9 in the 1980s and 22.3 in the 1990s. However, numbers continued to slump in the 1970s, with an average of only 9.3 territories per year during this decade and lows of just five in 1973 and four in 1979; this was probably a reflection on the intensification of agriculture and loss of hedgerows at this site during the period. CBC data from two other farmland sites, at Newton Harcourt and King's Hill Lodge, Uppingham, also show steady gains in recent years, although numbers at the woodland site of Prior's Coppice show a slight decrease during 1988–99.

Warrilow recorded Chaffinches in 623 tetrads during 1976–84, equating to 97% of all tetrads within the counties, with breeding confirmed in 231. There was low density in some farming landscapes and densely built-up central urban areas were avoided; territory densities were at their highest in woodlands. A county-wide breeding population of between 50,000 and 100,000 pairs was proposed, based on an average of 80 to 160 pairs per occupied tetrad.

Given the common and widespread nature of this species, it is perhaps surprising to note that the Leicestershire Garden Bird Survey found the Chaffinch to be only the 12th most-frequent species during the period January 1996 to June 2005, visiting 55.6% of all gardens. Over recent years, Chaffinches have adapted to using feeding stations in gardens, although it was as long ago as 1957 that this species was first noted attempting to take food from nut feeders (Gimson 1959, Skelton 1959).

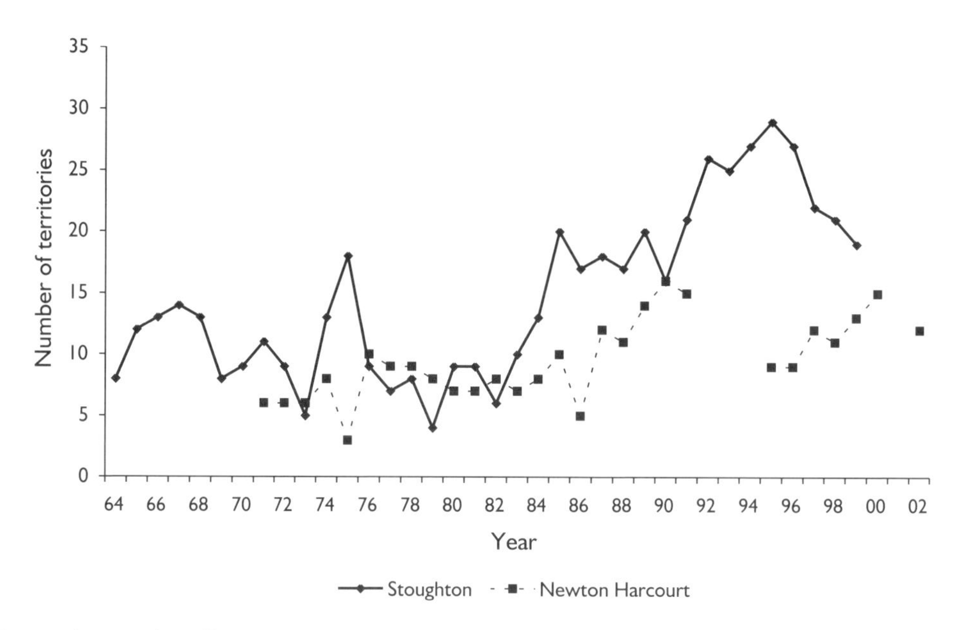

Figure 540: Number of breeding pairs of Chaffinches on two Leicestershire CBC plots 1964–2002.

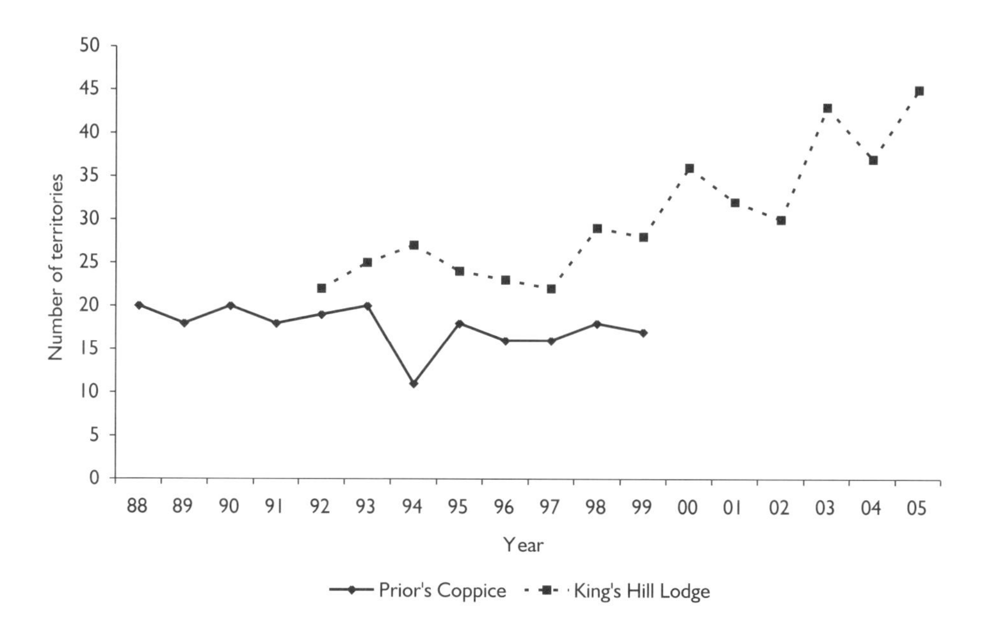

Figure 541: Number of breeding pairs of Chaffinches on two Rutland CBC plots 1988–2005.

A number of exceptional flocks were recorded in the 1940s and early 1950s, particularly at Quorn, where there were 'several thousand' in December 1947, 1,500 in December 1949 and 1,000 on December 17th 1950. Also around this time, 1,500 roosted at Woodhouse in December 1949 and 1,000 were at Bardon on March 21st 1942. However, the only large group reported between 1951 and 1980 was of a mixed flock of 'thousands', with Greenfinches, at Ragdale on November 1st 1969. Since 1980, three-figure flocks have become regular during the winter months, the largest being three groups of 500: at Oaks in Charnwood on December 11th 1987, Charley on January 15th 1992 and Barkby Holt on January 21st 2004. A flock of 400 to 500 was at South

Kilworth on November 28th 1995 and 450 were at Buckminster on February 11th 2001, whilst gatherings of 400 have been noted at Stoughton Airfield on both January 5th 1989 and December 6th 2005, Newtown Linford on January 15th 1992, Shepshed on January 15th and 16th 1994 and Barnsdale on January 20th 1996. These large winter flocks are often found feeding on beech mast.

Aberrant birds are occasionally recorded. A female nesting at Loughborough in 1967 was greyish-white with a dark centre to its tail, dark primaries and a dark carpal patch; one of the juveniles raised by this bird was also described as albino. Further albino individuals have been noted at Gaulby in 1960 and Bisbrooke on March 27th 1996, one with a white head was at Empingham on March 22nd 1992 and a leucistic bird was at Beacon Hill on December 19th 2004. A male at Newtown Linford on November 13th 2005 lacked the blue-grey cap and nape.

The Chaffinch breeds throughout Europe and over much of the rest of the western Palearctic. It is one of the most abundant and widespread species in Britain, the latest population estimate being 5,400,000 pairs (Gibbons *et al.* 1993). Although the species is resident over much of its range northern and eastern populations are migratory; Scandinavian birds move south and west during the autumn, augmenting the British winter population. This immigration is evidenced by the fact that there have been ringing recoveries relating to Leicestershire and Rutland birds involving Sweden, Norway, Denmark, the Netherlands and Belgium: six of them involved birds travelling over 1000km. The three birds which moved the greatest distance were all males: one ringed at Rutland Water on January 23rd 1987 was found dead 1,764km to the north-east at Sorsele (Sweden) on October 15th 1987; one ringed at Norra Rada (Sweden) on August 10th 1984 was found dead 1,218km to the south-west at Leicester on March 4th 1985 and one ringed at Cropston Reservoir on February 12th 1981 was found freshly dead 1,203km to the north-east at Elverum (Norway) on May 21st 1982.

DJSG

Brambling *Fringilla montifringilla*

Uncommon to fairly common irruptive winter visitor; recorded in all months between September and May, the majority from October to April.

In the 19th century, Haines described this species as a constant, though not very plentiful, visitor to Rutland in winter (November to mid-April), most commonly found around beech trees. He noted flocks of up to 20 at Exton and Normanton. Browne considered it a sparingly distributed winter visitor; it was abundant during the winter of 1843–44 and again in the winter of 1884. The LROS archives mention the Brambling as being an annual winter visitor in small numbers during the early part of the 20th century.

Numbers in each winter are very variable, being dependent upon the numbers entering the country in the autumn and local feeding conditions. The largest flocks are almost always associated with beech mast and are usually mixed with Chaffinches, making accurate counting difficult. Regular areas in recent years have been Beacon Hill, the Stanford Reservoir area, Barnsdale Avenue and an area of parkland at Exton. The Coleman Road area of Leicester also attracted large numbers, up to 150, in the early 1980s. Less important food sources utilised have been stubble fields, unharvested linseed crops and also garden feeding stations.

Large numbers were unknown in the 1940s and so 20 at Wanlip on February 4th 1948 evoked the comment 'a very large flock for Leicestershire'. A flock of 50 was at Stanford Reservoir on January 16th and 23rd 1949 and the first three-figure flock for the counties was 100 at the same site on February 8th 1952. Flocks of 100 or more have been recorded in a further 17 years since then, mostly numbering up to 150, but with larger ones being:

- 750 at Beacon Hill on December 27th 1997.
- 500 at Leicester City Farms in January and February 1967.
- 300 at Six Hills on January 13th 1955.
- 300 at Markfield on April 6th 1966.

- 300 at Outwoods in December 1968.
- 250 to 300 at Rutland Water in early January 1976.
- 220 at Beacon Hill on February 10th 1996.
- 200 at Ilston on the Hill on February 25th 1956.
- 200 at Eyebrook Reservoir and Wardley Wood between October and December 1966 (Mitcham 1984).

The 750 at Beacon Hill on December 27th 1997 was remarkably the only flock of more than ten in the early part of the 1997–98 winter and had built up from 40 on December 14th; 150 remained into January 1998 and flocks of 100 at Swithland Reservoir on February 25th and 50 at Quorn from January 14th to February 12th presumably derived from the flock dispersing.

Obviously the winters covered by the earlier list were some of the best for Bramblings in the counties: others that featured higher than normal numbers include 1980–81, 1985–86, 1993–94, 1996–97 and 2004–05. The five winters in the period 1998 to 2003 were all well below par, with only about 30 birds recorded during 2001 and hardly any more in 1999, when the largest flocks were of just four at both ends of the year. One of these groups was feeding on sycamore seeds at Rutland Water on November 7th, highlighting the link between low numbers and the lack of the main food source, beech mast.

The earliest autumn arrivals on record are two single birds on the exceptional date of September 5th, at Birstall in 1942 and at Rothley in 1948: the possibility of captive origin was suggested for the former and should be considered for both. Another very early date was September 15th 1963, when five were at Stanford Reservoir. There have been September records in just five other years and all but one have been on the 29th or 30th, most recently one caught and ringed at Melton Spinney on September 29th 2002. More typically the first records are in mid-October and in winters of low numbers, such as 2001, sometimes not until November. The average first arrival date for the last 30 years (1976 to 2005) is October 12th and that for the period 1941 to 1975 was October 20th but the difference is probably not significant as the average for the earlier period is heavily influenced by a preponderance of late dates in the early 1950s.

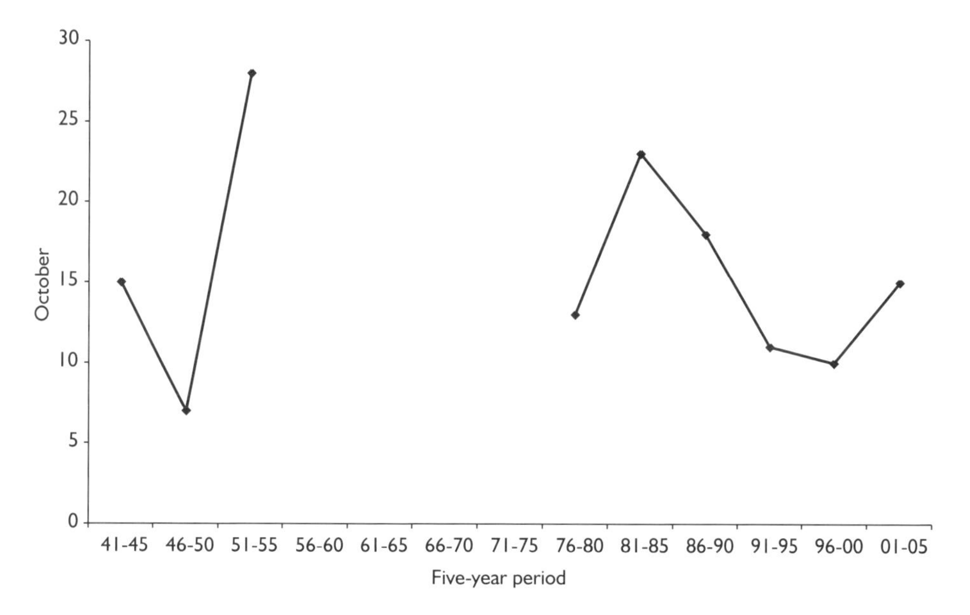

Figure 542: Average autumn arrival dates of Bamblings by five-year periods 1941–2005.

A visible migration study at Deans Lane, Woodhouse in 2005 recorded a total of 246 Bramblings migrating mainly west on ten days between October 26th and November 10th; the peak count was 95 on November 5th (Lister 2007b). It is interesting to compare this movement with those at bird observatories on the east coast: both Spurn (East Yorkshire) and Holme (Norfolk) recorded large numbers of passage Bramblings during the period October 15th to 18th but not at the same time as the Deans Lane observations, suggesting that the birds involved may either have been off-passage for around two to three weeks or may have crossed the coast undetected, possibly at night (Roadhouse 2006, Norfolk Ornithologists' Association 2006).

Records in April suggest that there may be a small spring passage through the counties and notable flocks in this month have included 300 at Markfield on April 6th 1966 and 150 at Swithland Reservoir on April 10th 1998. Small numbers quite often appear in gardens at this time, although this of course could just be in response to local feeding conditions. In some years April flocks are larger than earlier in the year: 1993 was such a year, with 25 at Rutland Water on April 14th and 11 at Burleigh Wood, Loughborough on the 13th. Males are occasionally heard singing in spring, for example one at Beacon Hill on April 20th 1996. The final observation of the spring is normally in late April, although the latest in the past 20 years was a female at Burbage on May 11th 1990; there have been records during the first four days of May in five years (1978, 1980, 1986, 1993 and 1997) and undated ones in this month in both 1977 and 1981. Old records of a male apparently paired with a female Chaffinch at Old Dalby on the very late date of May 31st 1950 and one at Swithland Reservoir on May 24th 1951 are now regarded as unreliable. The average final spring date for the last 30 years (1976 to 2005) is April 19th and that for the period 1941 to 1975 was April 8th, indicating that at least some Bramblings are lingering significantly later nowadays.

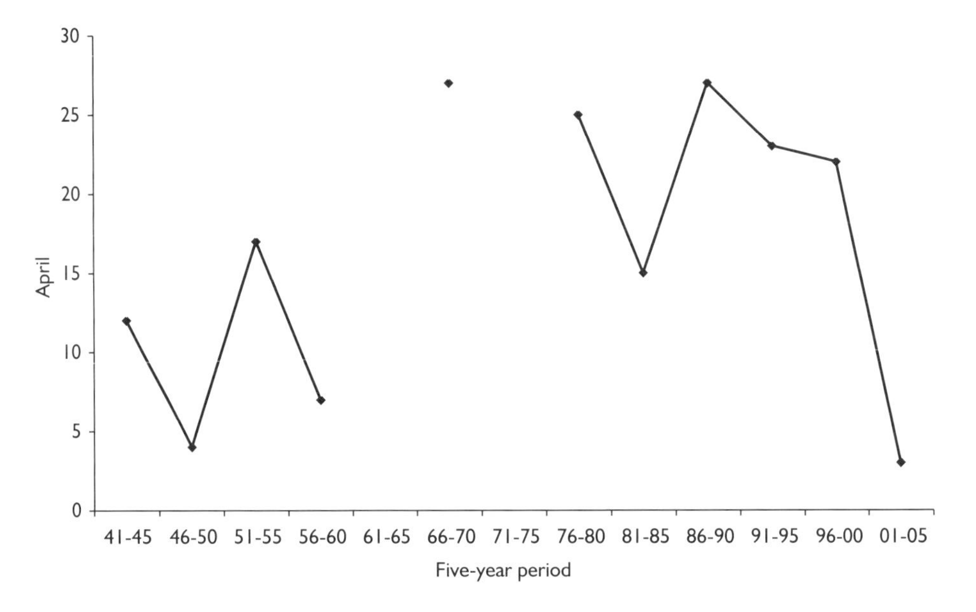

Figure 543: Average spring departure dates of Bramblings by five-year periods 1941–2005.

There are two interesting ringing recoveries. A male ringed at Groby on November 18th 1973 was controlled on spring passage 625km to the east-north-east on the island of Heligoland (Germany) on May 6th 1974 and a male ringed at Speke Hall (Merseyside) on February 22nd 1981 was controlled at Hugglescote (122km to the south-east) on January 8th 1982.

Bramblings breed across Northern Eurasia from Norway to the Pacific, mainly in the mixed and conifer forests of the subarctic and boreal zones. Birds from the western part of the range move south to winter throughout Europe and into north Africa. The winter population of Britain and Ireland probably varies between 50,000 and 2,000,000 birds (Lack 1986). Very small numbers have bred or at least attempted to breed in Scotland since the late 1970s but have failed to become established and the last confirmed case was in 2002 (Holling *et al.* 2008).

DJSG

Greenfinch (European Greenfinch) ***Carduelis chloris***

Common to abundant resident breeder, passage migrant and winter visitor.

The Greenfinch is a familiar bird of farmland and parkland and has adapted well to suburban environments. Previous comments on its status suggest that it has always been a common species in the counties: in the 19th century Browne noted it as 'resident and common in gardens and fields close to Leicester', whilst in Rutland Haines described it as 'resident and abundant everywhere'. In the 20th century the first indication of the status of the Greenfinch was in the 1941 LROS Annual Report, which stated it was 'common and well distributed'; a little later Otter (1965) considered it to be a 'common resident in all parts of east Leicestershire'.

Gibbons *et al.* (1996) noted that Greenfinches became less abundant on farmland from the 1960s onwards, due to the increased use of herbicides and the consequent reduction of the species' favoured food source of weed seeds. However, Leicestershire farmland CBC data does not bear this out: at both Stoughton and Newton Harcourt, total territories fluctuated from year to year, but by the conclusion of each survey (in 1999 and 2002 respectively) the number of pairs of Greenfinch at each site was similar to that recorded at the start of the census periods (1964 and 1971 respectively). More recent national CBC and BBS results indicate widespread population increases across the UK since the mid-1990s (Baillie *et al.* 2006) and CBC results at King's Hill Lodge, Uppingham tie in with this conclusion; numbers here have steadily increased from one pair in 1992 to 13 pairs in 2004. CBC data from Loddington shows huge increases, with 15 pairs in 1992 increasing to 57 by 1998 and 62 in 2001; sensitive habitat management and the removal of predators will no doubt have contributed to these results.

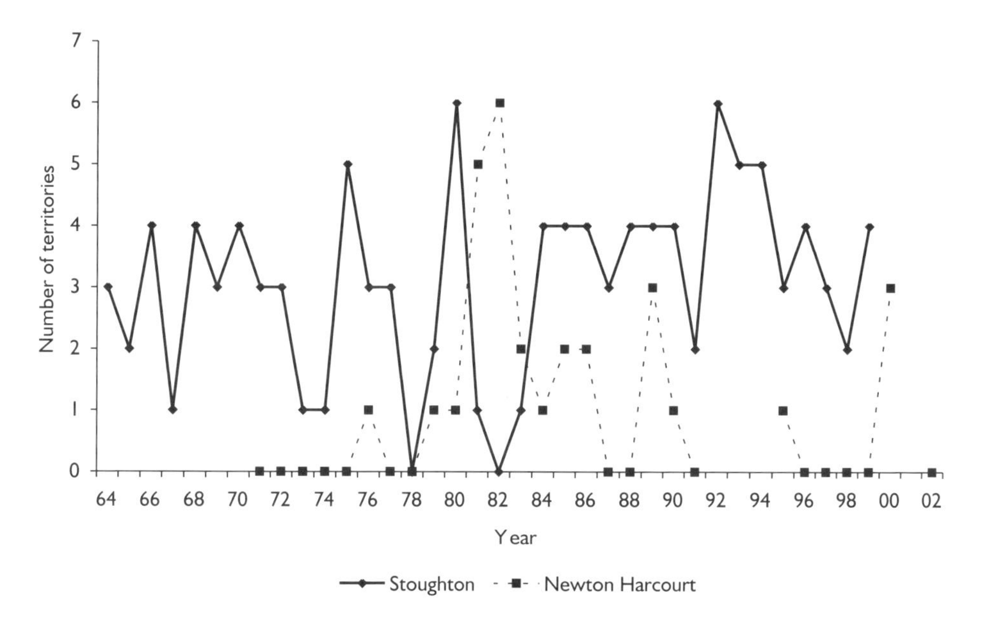

Figure 544: Number of breeding pairs of Greenfinches on two Leicestershire CBC plots 1964–2002.

Warrilow recorded Greenfinches in 534 tetrads during 1976–84, equating to 87% of all tetrads within the counties, with breeding confirmed in 188. The distribution of this species showed a marked concentration in the western half of the county, including the city of Leicester. It was rather sparsely distributed in the intensive agricultural areas of east and north-east Leicestershire and north-east Rutland, as well as in the extreme south of Leicestershire. Warrilow found that this species showed a preference for gardens, parkland, churchyards and overgrown hedgerows. Two CBCs demonstrated this habitat preference nicely: one comprising woodland patches and gardens in a suburban area of Leicester and another at the University of Leicester Botanical Gardens

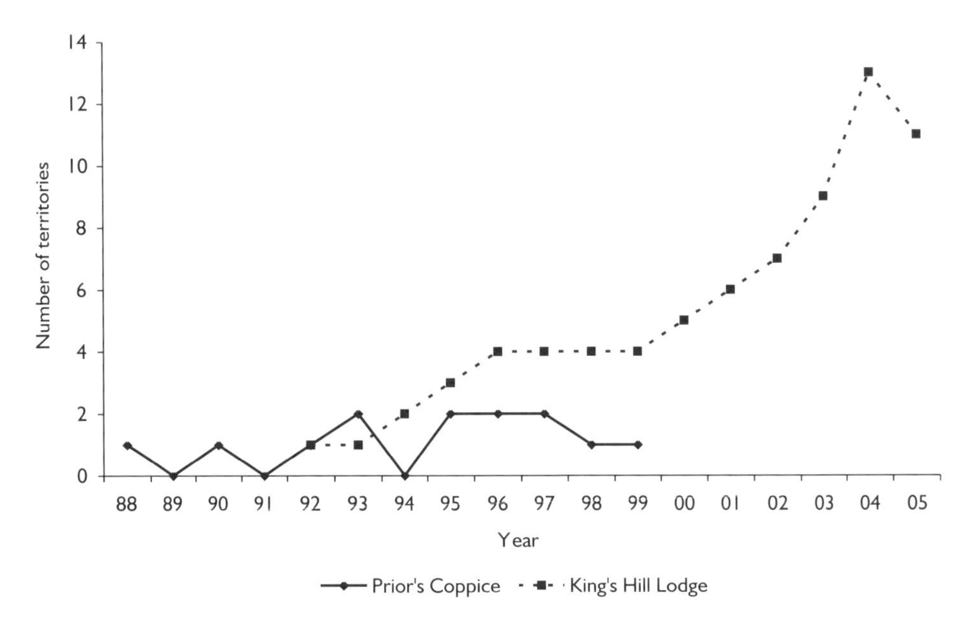

Figure 545: Number of breeding pairs of Greenfinches on two Rutland CBC plots 1988–2005.

at Oadby both showed the Greenfinch to be one of the foremost species present, with six and seven pairs respectively. A survey in 1989 of four green spaces within the city of Leicester (Abbey Park, Aylestone Meadows, Knighton Park and Western Park) found that the Greenfinch was the seventh–commonest species overall; a particularly large population was located in Abbey Park (16 territories), making it the fourth most-abundant species at this site (Fray *et al.* 1990). Another indication of this species' attraction to gardens and urban areas is provided by the Leicestershire Garden Bird Survey; during the period January 1996 to June 2005, the Greenfinch was the tenth most-frequent species, being recorded in 62% of all gardens. Its ability to make use of hanging nut feeders is well known and this behaviour was first noted in the LROS Annual Report of 1957 (Gimson 1959, Skelton 1959).

Further studies by Warrilow showed that this species tended to avoid closed canopy woodland: a survey of 24 hectares of the interior zone of mixed deciduous woods in east Leicestershire in 1987 failed to locate any breeding pairs. A similar survey at Wistow of nine small fragmented woods revealed nine breeding pairs, all of which were utilising the woodland edges. Based on all the available information, including local CBC data on farmland, Warrilow proposed an average of 15 to 22 pairs per occupied tetrad, giving a county breeding population of 8,000 to 12,000 pairs during 1976–84. It is possible that the population is now a little higher than this, given the recent increases noted both nationally and at the Loddington and King's Hill Lodge CBC sites.

Large flocks gather in the autumn and winter and there are records of three-figure groups in all months except July. The largest flocks on record are:

- 700 at Newtown Linford on October 25th 1962.
- 580 at Rutland Water dam on November 25th 1989, with 560 still there on January 14th 1990.
- 500 at Swithland in December 1949.
- 500 at Rutland Water in December 1975.
- 500 at Ridlington on September 11th 1987.
- 400 to 500 at Rearsby on October 6th 1968.
- 400 at Cotes in January 1950.
- 400 at Ratby Meadows on August 28th 1982.
- 400 at Houghton on the Hill on October 28th 1992.

It is noticeable that winter flock sizes have been smaller in recent years; there have been no counts of 350+ since 1995 and only three have reached 300 during this period. The change from spring to autumn ploughing of stubble fields is thought to be a contributing factor to these smaller numbers and as a consequence many birds have moved into gardens during the winter to take advantage of a ready supply of food (Gibbons *et al.* 1996).

The largest counts of Greenfinches, however, have occurred at roost sites. One of the largest was of up to 1,000 at Abbey Park, Leicester on March 17th 1979, with 750 there on February 4th 1984. A thorough investigation of a roost at Cropston Reservoir waterworks between February 1st and May 31st 1981 led to 1,081 being trapped and ringed. Although numbers using the roost each night apparently remained static at around the 1,000 mark, only 29 birds were retrapped, indicating a constant turnover of birds. Evidence obtained from recoveries of birds ringed in the roost supported the idea of a mobile population; of 23 recoveries, two were found in Melton Mowbray and one moved as far as Swaffham Heath (Norfolk), whilst the majority of others were found in gardens in Leicester. In addition, two birds trapped in the roost had previously been ringed in Nottinghamshire. It was estimated that as many as 27,000 birds may have used the roost during the four month period (Fowler 1982).

Greenfinches breed over much of Europe and parts of western Asia. The British population is estimated at 695,000 pairs (Baker *et al.* 2006), most of which remain in the country throughout the year, although a small proportion leave to winter on the continent or in Ireland. Three ringing recoveries involving Leicestershire and Rutland demonstrate this south or south-westerly movement, the most striking being that of a female ringed at Belmesthorpe on August 30th 1981 which was found dead at Caen (France) on February 6th 1982. A first-year male ringed at Melton Mowbray on October 9th 1999 was seemingly heading in the same direction as it was retrapped at Portland Bill (Dorset) just ten days later, whilst a female ringed at Belmesthorpe in May 1976 was controlled at Cirencester (Gloucestershire) in January 1980. Other than ringing data, evidence of immigration into or out of the counties is hard to come by, although a survey of visible migration at Deans Lane, Woodhouse in autumn 2005 produced a total of 244 Greenfinches on 14 days, with counts of 42 on both October 22nd and 27th (Lister 2007b).

DJSG

Goldfinch (European Goldfinch) ***Carduelis carduelis***

Common resident breeder and passage migrant.

Arguably our most attractive finch, the Goldfinch has increased in numbers markedly over much of Britain since the 19th century (Gibbons *et al.* 1996) and the available evidence suggests that this has also been the case in Leicestershire and Rutland. Browne considered this species to be resident but sparingly distributed in the 19th century, although by the start of the 20th century a Mr H. Davenport, writing in 1906, thought it was much more common than formerly. In Rutland, Haines described it to be rare up to 1850, then not common up to 1875 and becoming not scarce in summer and autumn by the end of the 19th century. The next indication of the status of the Goldfinch was provided by the first LROS Annual Report, in 1941, which considered it to be 'resident, not common'. At this time it only bred sparingly, being more numerous in the east of the county. By 1943, it was described as 'local, but increasing' (Jolley 1944).

The best indication of the recent local population is provided by Warrilow, who recorded Goldfinches in 456 tetrads during 1976–84 (71% of all tetrads within the counties), with breeding confirmed in 143. In contrast to the distribution noted in 1941, it was least common in the eastern half of the counties, where intensive farming now predominates, and was most numerous in the area of mixed and pastoral farming stretching from Charnwood Forest to Lutterworth and Market Harborough. It was also present in many areas within Leicester, where it was first noted nesting in gardens in the south of the city in the 1950s (Pochin 1954). Further studies within the city boundary recorded Goldfinches breeding at Abbey Park, Aylestone Meadows and Western Park in 1989 (Fray *et al.* 1990), whilst the Leicestershire Garden Bird Survey found it to be the 17th most-frequent species, being recorded in 16% of all gardens between January 1996 and June 2005. Use of garden feeding stations has been noted since 1997. County-wide, Warrilow discovered that densities were highest in mature gardens and small woodland fragments, with numbers reaching 60 pairs per tetrad during a survey of 39 woodlands in east Leicestershire, although on local farmland CBC plots between five and 45 pairs per tetrad was the norm. Based on an average of ten to 20 pairs per occupied tetrad, Warrilow estimated a county population of between 4,500 and 9,000 pairs. National CBC and BBS data shows that the abundance of this species fell sharply from the mid-1970s to the mid-1980s, coinciding with Warrilow's survey, although this decline has been followed by a significant population increase (Baillie *et al.* 2006); it is therefore possible that the county population is higher than Warrilow's estimate. However, local farmland CBC data from Stoughton does not show this pattern, with numbers fluctuating from no pairs to five during 1964–99 and no long-term trend apparent. Results from Newton Harcourt were similarly erratic, but did include a one-off peak of 14 pairs in 2000. Numbers of Goldfinches on other CBC plots in the counties are so small that no useful data can be obtained from them.

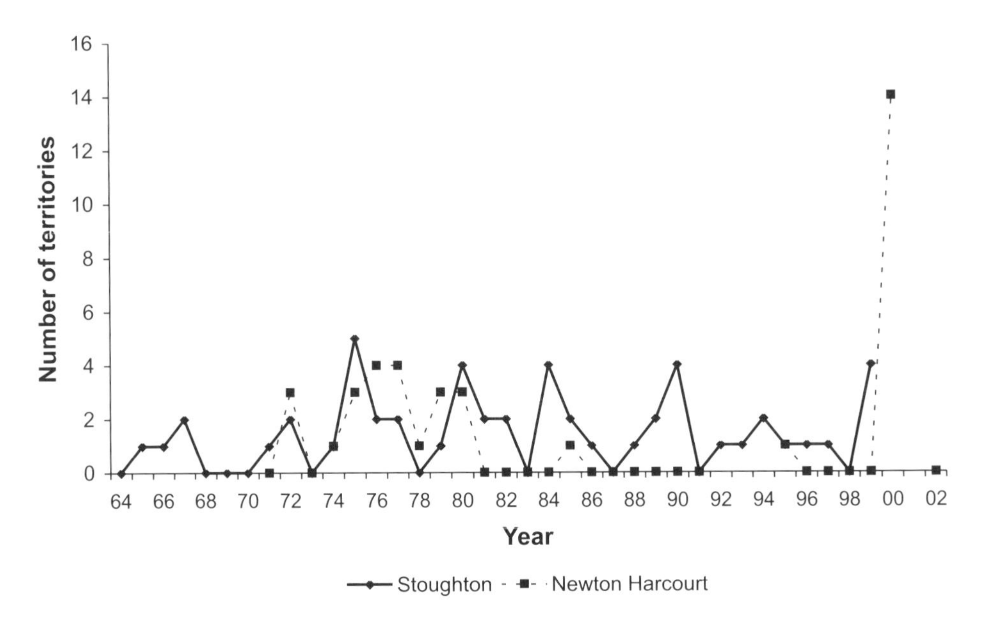

Figure 546: Number of breeding pairs of Goldfinches on two Leicestershire CBC plots 1964–2002.

Large 'charms' are a feature of the autumn and the collective noun well describes these flocks as they descend upon clumps of thistles, a favoured food plant. Other weed species and the seeds of alders and birches are also taken and it is not unusual to see this species feeding in mixed flocks with Siskins and Lesser Redpolls, particularly in alders. The highest autumn count is possibly of a mixed flock with Linnets totalling 1,000 at Syston Gravel Pits on October 15th 1983. In addition there are autumn records of 46 three-figure counts between 1941 and 2005, with the largest being:

- 400 at Foxton Locks on October 16th 1985.
- 300 in three flocks at Eyebrook Reservoir on October 24th 1948.
- 250 at Birstall on November 11th 1994.
- 250 at Narborough on September 9th 1985.

There have also been six records of flocks totalling 200 during the autumn period, at: Blaby on September 29th 1945; Eyebrook Reservoir on October 8th 1950 and October 16th 1996; Thurmaston Lock on September 28th 1990; Thornton Reservoir on August 31st 1999 and on the Hambleton Peninsula, Rutland Water on September 20th 2001.

Winter flocks are smaller as a large proportion of the counties' birds leave to winter further south. There are records of 38 flocks numbering between 25 and 80 during this period, along with eight three-figure flocks, the largest of which have been 200 at Swithland Reservoir on December 19th 1964, 128 in three flocks at Glen Parva on January 5th 1997 and 105 at Saltby on December 28th 1999. Groups of 100 have been seen at Rutland Water on February 1st 1992, Swithland Reservoir from November 26th 1998 to January 5th 1999,

Loughborough on February 14th 2001, Eaton on January 27th 2003 and Frolesworth Manor Lake on December 28th and 29th 2004.

Flocks have usually broken up by the spring but there are occasional large congregations at this time, with records of nine groups numbering between 25 and 80 and three into three-figures: 200 at Eyebrook Reservoir on March 31st 1954 and 100 at both Tickencote on March 1st 1998 and Rutland Water on April 21st 1990.

Goldfinches breed over most of Europe, as well as in northernmost Africa and western Asia. They are widely distributed across Britain, with the latest population estimate being just under 300,000 pairs (Baker *et al.* 2006). More than 80% of British birds move south in September and October to winter in Belgium, France and Spain and there have been two ringing recoveries involving Leicestershire and Rutland demonstrating this: one ringed at Leicester City Farms on August 7th 1974 was controlled 1,100km to the south-south-west at Santander (Spain) on January 19th 1975 and one ringed at Belmesthorpe on September 3rd 1977 was found dead 978km to the south in the Landes district (France) on October 25th the same year. Movement in the opposite direction in spring was shown by one ringed at East Grinstead (West Sussex) on February 11th 1997 which was found freshly dead 177km to the north-north-west at Whitwell on July 30th 1997.

DJSG

Siskin (European Siskin) ***Carduelis spinus***

Fairly common winter visitor and passage migrant, scarce in summer: very rare breeder.

Siskins have always been predominantly irruptive winter visitors, with numbers varying dramatically from year to year. Haines described it as an occasional winter visitor in the 19th century in all parts of Rutland where willows and alders were numerous, with Caldecott being a favoured locality. He noted that it had 'once or twice' been seen in summer at Uppingham, but attributed these records to escapes from the school aviary. Browne stated that it was an uncommon winter visitor in Leicestershire at this time. There were occasional influxes, since he records that Harley once met with some 400 or 500 Siskins at Oakley Wood and 'in the autumn of 1849 the species was frequently met with'.

In some years between the 1940s and 1970s annual totals barely reached double-figures; during the winter of 1942–43 there were no records at all and the winter of 1967–68 only produced four records involving just 14 birds. Three-figure flocks were recorded on 11 occasions between 1941 and 1979, all but one in the Charnwood Forest area, with the largest being:

- 300 at Hambleton Wood on October 19th 1973 (Mitcham 1984).
- 250 at Swithland Reservoir on January 23rd 1951.
- 200 at Quorn on February 20th 1949.
- 150 at Swithland Reservoir on March 8th 1971.
- 120 to 150 at Quorn on December 5th 1948.

Although numbers still vary annually, flocks in the trough years have generally been larger in more recent years and it is fair to say that the species is now much more common than formerly. The winter of highest numbers was 1985–86, when the four largest flocks totalled over 1,200 birds; other good winters were 1991–92, 1996–97, 2002–03 and 2003–04. Alder seeds are the favoured winter food and alder-lined streams often hold the highest numbers. Flocks of between 30 and 60 are regular in most years, although since 1979 there have been three-figure flocks recorded on 37 occasions, again mostly in Charnwood Forest. The largest flocks on record are:

- 600 at Glenfield on January 5th 1986.
- 300 at Glenfield on January 1st 1997.
- 300 at Buddon Brook, Quorn on January 23rd 2004.
- 250 at Castle Hill Park, Leicester on December 11th 1985.
- 200 at Bradgate Park on January 3rd 1986.
- 200 at Groby Pool on November 16th 2002.
- 200 at Swithland Reservoir on April 5th and 8th 2004.

Between January 8th and April 15th 1989 a trapping and ringing programme in a Quorn garden, where birds were attracted by peanuts in red net bags, showed a large turnover of birds, with a total of 250 (154 males and 96 females) being trapped (Gamble 1990). This was in a period when no flocks exceeding 40 were reported in the counties.

Birds are now normally present between September and April; this contrasts markedly with the status recorded in the LROS archives at the beginning of the 20th century, when the Siskin was considered to be a regular winter visitor in small numbers, normally from the end of January until early March. There is an increasing trend towards earlier arrivals and later departures and although data is lacking for a number of years, partic-

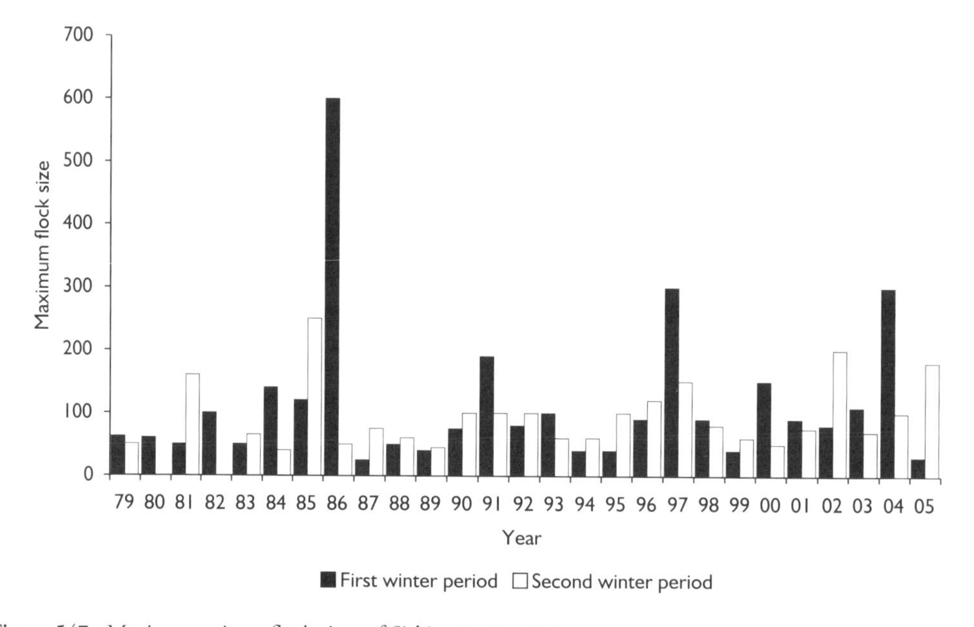

Figure 547: Maximum winter flock sizes of Siskins 1979–2005.

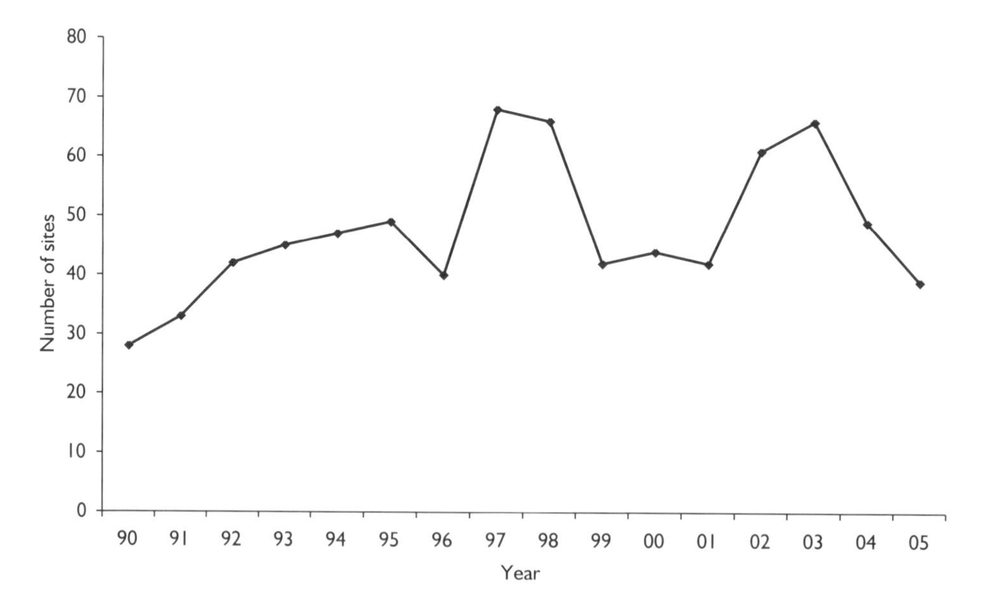

Figure 548: Number of sites with records of Siskins 1990–2005.

ularly from the mid-1950s to the early 1980s, this trend is confirmed by analysis of published arrival and departure dates. The average arrival date during 1941–70 was October 21st, whereas during 1985–2005 it was significantly earlier at September 17th. Average departure dates during the same two periods do not show such a large difference, being April 12th and April 19th respectively. The autumn 2005 visible migration survey at Deans Lane, Woodhouse recorded Siskins on most of the days covered between September 7th and November 5th with the largest numbers in October, of 28 on the 9th and 31 on the 26th (Lister 2007b).

Song-flight and courtship display were noted at Buddon Wood on April 11th 1948 and Outwoods on April 13th 1950, but there were no further indications that breeding was possible in the counties until the 1980s, when one was at an unspecified site on July 25th 1981, two were at Beacon Hill on June 17th 1985 and a male was at Burbage on July 25th 1986. Increasing numbers lingering in the spring and scattered summer records during the 1990s, plus the appearance of 28 birds at two sites in July 1991 and 40 at another two sites in early July 1997, led to speculation that Siskins may be about to colonise the counties, or may even have already done so. The first confirmed breeding record was eventually provided by a female with three newly fledged juveniles in a garden at Glenfield on June 19th 1998. Several juveniles at Benscliffe Wood on July 6th 1997 may also have been locally bred but recent years have seen migrants appearing even as early as June so summer presence alone is not a reliable sign of breeding. A pair successfully raised a brood in a Newtown Linford garden in 2000: breeding was also suspected at Thornton that year as a female with a brood-patch was trapped in a garden there on April 27th (Smith 2002b). Since 2000 there has not been any indication of further colonisation beyond a few birds singing in the spring each year, one example of courtship feeding, in a Groby garden in April 2003 and a group of ten, including juveniles, at Bardon Hill on July 10th 2005. It seems odd that all the likely breeding records have come from gardens when there is an abundance of prime habitat in the form of the conifer plantations of Charnwood Forest and elsewhere: perhaps more thorough coverage of the woodlands during May and June might reveal a small population already established.

Birds were first noted coming to garden feeding stations in March 1966, when five were attracted by hanging fat at Kirby Muxloe. They were first noted feeding on peanuts in 1978, in two Oakham gardens; this food source, particularly when provided in red net bags, has now become a major attraction. Non-natural food sources are not normally used until the second half of the winter. The importance of garden feeding stations at this time is shown by Siskin's 29th position in the Leicestershire Garden Bird Survey from January 1996 to June 2005, during which the species was recorded in 2% of gardens.

There are seven ringing recoveries involving Leicestershire and Rutland where birds have moved over 400km:

- a female ringed near Liepaya (Latvia) on October 1st 1975 was controlled at Quorn, 1,450km to the west-south-west, on April 4th 1976.
- a male ringed at Quorn on January 8th 1989 was found dead 1,000km to the east-north-east between Dalby and Sandby (Sweden) on April 15th 1989.
- a male ringed at The Brand, Woodhouse Eaves on April 5th 1992 was controlled 588km to the north-north-west at Ballchraggan (Highland) on August 8th 1993.
- a female ringed at Quorn on March 1st 1991 was found freshly dead near Fort William (Highland) on May 19th 1992, a movement of 533km to the north-north-west.
- a male ringed at Twyford on May 2nd 1983 was controlled 470km to the east at Wierum (Netherlands) just five days later.
- a male ringed at New Scone, Perth (Tayside) on January 29th 1994 was controlled at Rutland Water on December 14th 1997, a movement of 452km to the south-south-east.
- a female ringed at Quorn on February 8th 1989 was controlled 422km to the north-north-west at Killearn (Stirling) on March 1st 1990.

The four movements involving Scotland, along with two shorter distance recoveries in Borders and Northumberland, perhaps provide a pointer to the origins of the majority of the birds that winter locally. Clearly, some continental birds also feature in our winter flocks.

Siskins breed throughout forested parts of central, northern and eastern Europe plus scattered areas to the south and west: a separate population is found in eastern Asia. The more northerly components of the Western Palearctic population move south or south-west for the winter. In Britain the range has expanded from the former stronghold of the Scottish pine forests to include much of the forestry that has been planted further south. The British breeding population is currently estimated at 357,000 pairs (Baker *et al.* 2006).

DJSG

Linnet (Common Linnet) ***Carduelis cannabina***

Common resident breeder and passage migrant, less common in winter.

The Linnet is one of the counties' most widespread finches. During the 19th century Browne described it as 'resident and generally distributed' in Leicestershire, whilst in Rutland Haines considered it to be 'resident and plentiful except in hard winters'. The first LROS Annual Report in 1941 stated that this species was 'common in winter, but restricted to certain localities as a breeding species', a rather strange status which is at odds with all other available data. By 1948 it was considered 'common but local' and by 1960 this was amended to 'very common and widespread'. Otter (1965) described it as a 'very common resident' in east Leicestershire and Mitcham (1984) stated that it bred in suitable habitat throughout Rutland.

As is the case with several other farmland species, the Linnet has declined significantly in recent years. Chamberlain & Vickery (2002) noted a 47% decrease on national farmland CBC plots between 1973 and 1998, although there is evidence that the severest decline took place between the mid-1970s and mid-1980s and that the population is now more stable (Baillie *et al.* 2006). Linnets are more dependent on weed seeds than other finches and the application of herbicides is thought to be the major factor in this decline; in addition, the trimming and removal of hedgerows and other bushy habitats has robbed the species of nesting sites. Local CBC data from two farmland sites in Leicestershire appears to mirror the national picture. At Stoughton the highest numbers were recorded during the first 20 years of the survey (between 1964 and 1984), although even then there were erratic fluctuations. From the mid-1980s numbers were much lower although there were signs of a slight recovery towards the end of the 1990s. Newton Harcourt data shows that numbers peaked in the early 1980s, followed by a dramatic decline and subsequent slight recovery. CBC data from King's Hill Lodge, Uppingham suggests that this species is still prone to fluctuations; between 1992 and 2004 the number of territories ranged from one to seven, with no apparent pattern discernible. A success story has occurred at Loddington, where sensitive habitat management increased the population from ten pairs in 1992 to 21 in 1998 and 25 by 2001, an overall increase of 150% in less than ten years.

Warrilow found that during 1976–84 the Linnet was the second most-widespread finch in Leicestershire and Rutland after Chaffinch. It was recorded in 555 tetrads, equating to 87% of all tetrads within the counties, with breeding confirmed in 175. The main concentration was the western half of Leicestershire, with a sparser distribution noted in the intensive agricultural areas of east and north-east Leicestershire and north Rutland. It occurred throughout the city of Leicester, where habitats such as waste ground, allotments and parks are utilised;

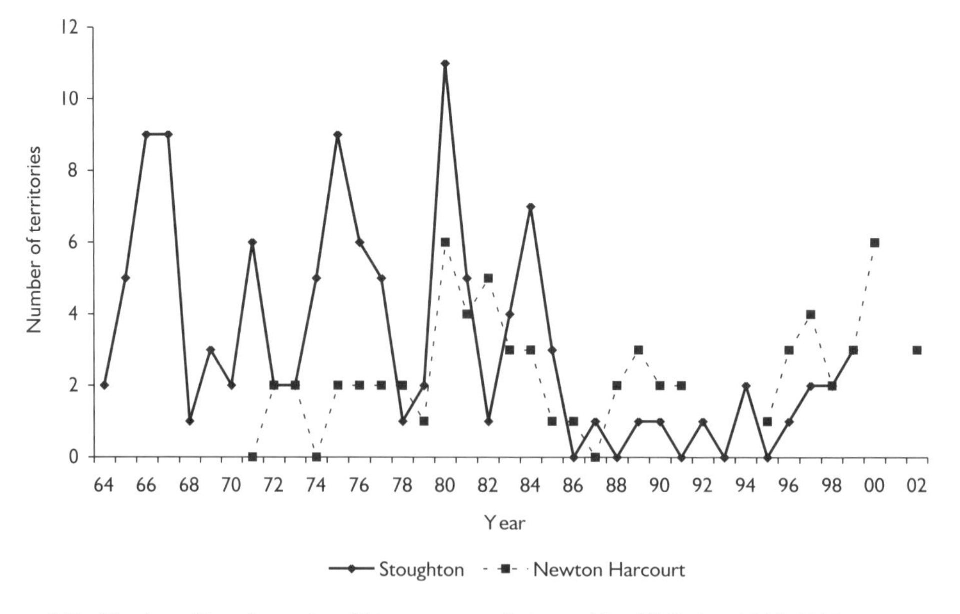

Figure 549: Number of breeding pairs of Linnets on two Leicestershire CBC plots 1964–2002.

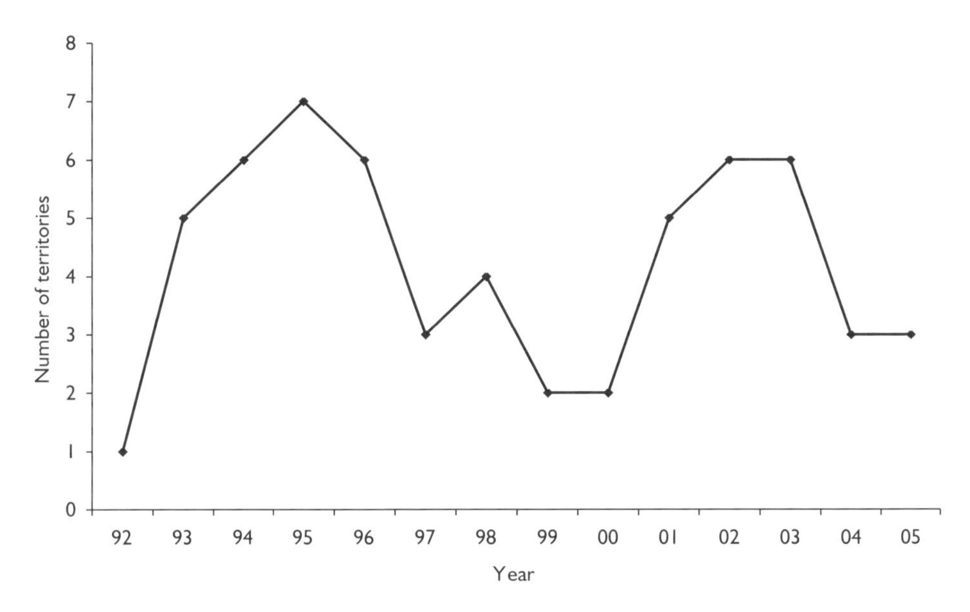

Figure 550: Number of breeding pairs of Linnets on the King's Hill Lodge, Uppingham CBC plot 1992–2005.

as an example, during a survey of four green areas within the city boundary in 1989, eight pairs were located at Aylestone Meadows, with six at Western Park and two at Knighton Park (Fray *et al.* 1990). At the time of Warrilow's work, local farmland CBC data gave an average of between 20 and 56 pairs per tetrad and he concluded that an average of between 18 and 38 pairs per occupied tetrad would give a total breeding population in Leicestershire and Rutland of between 10,000 and 21,000 pairs, qualifying the Linnet as an abundant breeding bird. However, given both the national and local declines noted since the mid-1970s, it is probable that this estimate is no longer appropriate.

Large flocks gather in the autumn. There are two records of four-figure autumn flocks: up to 2,400 at Enderby on August 26th 1980 and 1,000 at Stanford Reservoir on September 30th 1979, whilst a mixed flock of 1,000 Linnets and Goldfinches was at Syston Gravel Pits on October 15th 1983. Mason & Pickering (1968) noted that large Linnet flocks were a feature of the late 1950s and early 1960s at Leicester City Farms, with up to 1,000 being noted at times, although no specific dates are provided. There are also many records of autumn flocks numbering between 100 and 800, with the largest being:

- 800 at Frisby Gravel Pits on September 15th 1985.
- 600 at Ratby Meadows on August 8th 1982.
- 500 at Bruntingthorpe Airfield on October 10th 1948.
- 500 at Cropston Reservoir in August 1966.
- 500 at Stanford Reservoir on October 5th 1980.
- 500 at Eyebrook Reservoir between September 2nd and the end of October 1995.

Linnets are inconspicuous autumn migrants through the counties in small numbers. The 2005 survey of visible migration at Deans Lane, Woodhouse recorded a total of 211 on ten dates between September 28th and November 7th, with a maximum of 76 on October 9th (Lister 2007).

Winter flocks are of comparable size to those in autumn. The largest concentration on record is of 1,500 in several flocks in the Mountsorrel area on January 15th 1951 and the other highest counts are as follows:

- 1,000 at Frisby Gravel Pits on December 9th 1977.
- 800 at Rutland Water in the winter of 1975.
- 620 at Rutland Water on January 29th 1994.
- 450 at Rutland Water on January 23rd 1993.
- 400 at Hungarton on December 18th 2005.

- 350 at Cold Newton on January 15th 2002.
- 300 at Enderby Pool in December 2001.
- 300 at Rutland Water on December 14th 2002.
- 300 at Scalford Gorse on January 3rd 2005.

It is noticeable that the majority of these large flocks have occurred since the mid-1990s and this perhaps indicates that fewer birds are now moving south out of the counties for the winter; an alternative theory could be that rich feeding areas on farmland are now much reduced, thus concentrating birds into larger flocks in the fewer suitable areas.

There are fewer reports of large spring gatherings, the largest being 600 in two flocks at Enderby on April 5th 1986 and 350 at Groby on April 1st 2001. In addition flocks of 300 have been noted at at Quorn on April 12th 1950 and Enderby on April 7th 1985.

There is just one record of an aberrant bird: a partial albino at Eyebrook Reservoir in November 1995 which was all white except for a streaked breast patch and two symmetrical brown bars on the wings.

Linnets breed over much of Europe as far north as central Scandinavia and Russia as well as in west Siberia, northern Africa and parts of the Middle East. Northern populations are migratory and southern ones partly so. A proportion of British birds move south to winter in western France and Iberia and six ringing recoveries involving Leicestershire and Rutland demonstrate this:

- one ringed at Loughborough on May 20th 1949 was found dead 1,415km to the south at Cuenca (Spain) on November 28th 1949.
- one ringed at Leicester City Farms on October 1st 1964 was retrapped 800km to the south-south-west in the Landes district (France) on October 20th 1965.
- one ringed at Leicester on July 14th 1967 was controlled 1,563km to the south at Ciudad Real (Spain) on November 28th 1967.
- one ringed at Stanford Reservoir on August 14th 1976 was retrapped 800km to the south-south-west in the Pyrénées-Atlantiques district (France) on October 28th 1976.
- a male ringed at Belmesthorpe on June 14th 1981 was controlled 1,351km to the south at Valdetorres de Jarama (Spain) on October 16th 1981.
- a male ringed at Rutland Water on August 10th 1981 was found dead 1,404km to the south-south-west at Rozas de Puerto Real (Spain) on January 1st 1982.

The British breeding population is estimated at 535,000 pairs (Baker *et al.* 2006) and due to the rapid decline over the last 25 years this species has been added to the 'Red List' of Birds of Conservation Concern (Gregory *et al.* 2002).

DJSG

Twite *Carduelis flavirostris*

Formerly a scarce passage migrant and winter visitor; recorded in all months between September and April, the majority in February, March, October and November: 32 records involving 91 individuals. Now a rare vagrant unrecorded since 1996.

The only information available on the historical status of the Twite in the counties comes from Browne; he quotes Harley, writing in 1840, as stating that it 'appears here at times, at the close of autumn . . . its associates being the Linnet and Goldfinch'. The only other record known to Browne related to one shot near Hinckley in the autumn of 1889. Haines refers to a flock of 200 seen near Morcott on March 4th 1905 but this report seems distinctly unbelievable and is best ignored.

Between the formation of LROS in 1941 and the early 1960s the Twite was a very rare visitor to the counties, the only records being of at least one at Quorn Sewage Farm on February 21st and 22nd 1948 and four at Dadlington on February 27th 1955. A slight upturn in numbers was recorded in the 1960s, with records in three years during this decade: three at Stanford Reservoir on December 29th 1962; one at Eyebrook Reservoir on February 21st 1965, two there on March 21st the same year and at least five at Staunton Harold Reservoir from October 24th to 26th 1968.

During the 1970s the status of the Twite changed to that of a scarce passage and winter visitor, with records in every year from 1972 to 1979, as follows:

1972	nine, Stanford Reservoir, October 14th.
1973	up to six, Eyebrook Reservoir, March 24th to April 14th.
	two, Frisby Gravel Pits, September 30th.
1974	three, Cropston Reservoir, December 15th.
1975	five, Frisby Gravel Pits, January 12th.
	eight, Frisby Gravel Pits, March 1st, with three on March 8th.
	nine, Eyebrook Reservoir, October 4th to December 31st, with one until April 10th 1976.
	one, Frisby Gravel Pits, October 12th.
	three, Thornton Reservoir, December 24th.
1976	two, Frisby Gravel Pits, March 27th.
1977	one, Stanford Reservoir, April 17th.
	one, Eyebrook Reservoir, April 18th.
1978	two, Swithland Reservoir, March 11th.
1979	two, Stockerston, February 17th.
	one, Eyebrook Reservoir, March 18th.
	one, Stanford Reservoir, November 4th.

The run of regular sightings came to an abrupt halt at the end of the 1970s and since then there have been only ten records, involving 19 individuals and none since 1996. All were of single birds unless stated:

1981	Rutland Water, March 28th and 29th.
1986	three, Rutland Water, April 2nd.
1988	Stoughton Airfield, April 15th.
1990	Eyebrook Reservoir, October 6th.
1991	Rutland Water, April 1st.
1992	Rutland Water, March 29th.
	Stoughton Airfield, October 15th.
1995	two, Priory Water, January 1st.
1996	singing male, Leicester Forest East, January 27th.
	seven, Rutland Water, November 13th.

Given the current status of the Twite in the counties, the sequence of records in the 1970s may seem a little strange. However, this species regularly wintered at several inland sites in the late 1960s and 1970s, including

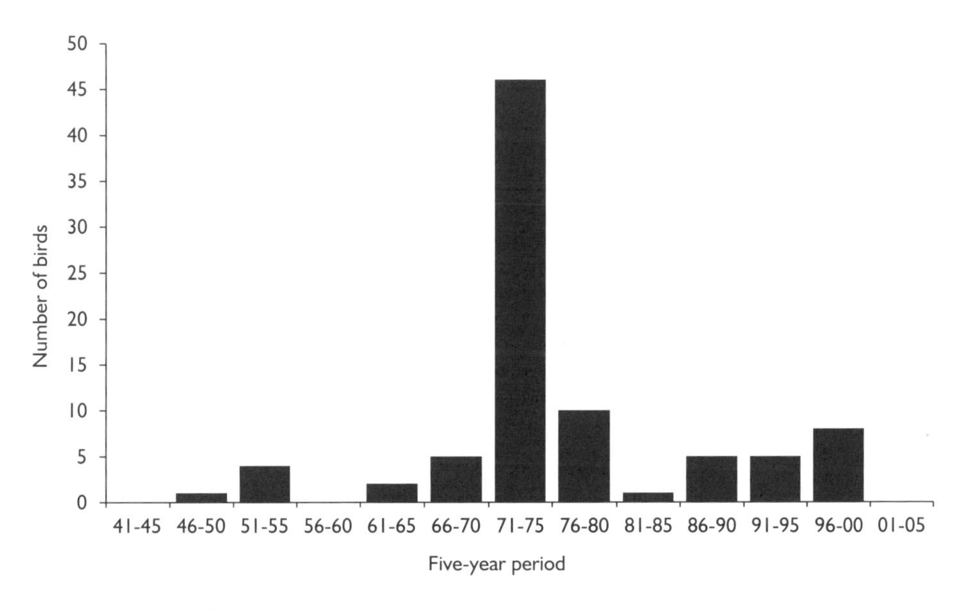

Figure 551: Numbers of Twite 1941–2005.

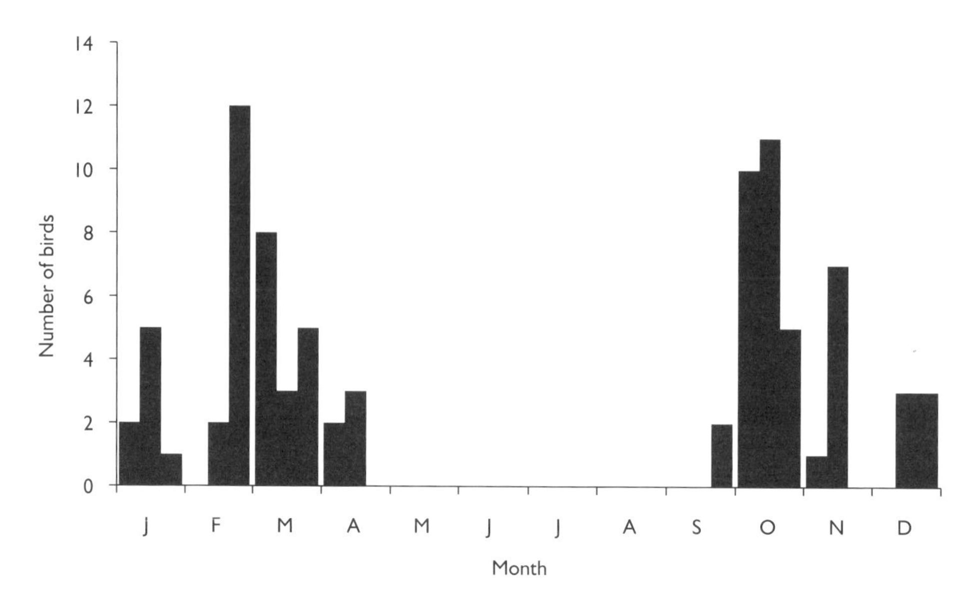

Figure 552: Monthly occurrence of Twite 1941–2005.

Chasewater (Staffordshire), where there were as many as 90 in 1968 and 1973, 95 in 1971 and 1972 and still 60 in 1980 (Hume 1983).

As the status of this species in Leicestershire and Rutland appears to have changed significantly in a relatively short space of time, a review of all records was carried out in 2004. This resulted in the following, which had previously been published in LROS Annual Reports, being found to be inadequately documented and no longer considered acceptable (Fray 2005):

- three (of a flock of six) at Thornton Reservoir on December 24th 1975.
- six at Rutland Water on February 6th 1980.
- one at Stanford Reservoir on May 16th 1980.
- 15 at Frisby Gravel Pits on October 21st 1980.
- five at Eyebrook Reservoir on January 15th 1981.

The Twite has a disjunct world distribution, with two breeding centres separated by over 2,500km. The main breeding range is in the uplands of central and south-west Asia, with other birds nesting on the Atlantic coastlines and mountains of north-west Europe, predominantly Britain and southern Scandinavia. British birds nest mainly in the coastal areas of north and west Scotland and on the moorlands of the Scottish Highlands and northern England, with smaller numbers in other areas including the southern Pennines. It is probably from the latter area that Leicestershire and Rutland receives its Twite, as these birds move to coastal areas, including The Wash, to winter whereas Scottish birds appear to be mainly sedentary (Gibbons *et al.* 1993). The British population is estimated at approximately 10,000 pairs (Baker *et al.* 2006) and as there has been a long-term decline in numbers the species has been added to the 'Red List' of Birds of Conservation Concern (Gregory *et al.* 2002).

DJSG

Lesser Redpoll *Carduelis cabaret*

Fairly common passage and winter visitor, rare breeder. Formerly a fairly common to common breeder.

The Lesser Redpoll was only formally separated from the Common Redpoll in 2001; consequently some records prior to that year could relate to the scarcer species as the LROS Annual Reports contained entries simply for 'Redpoll'. In the 19th century, however, it was known as Lesser Redpoll: Haines commented that this species seemed to have become much commoner as a breeding species in Rutland since 1860, with nests recorded at Preston, Seaton, Caldecott, Beaumont Chase and Glaston; in Leicestershire, Browne knew of breeding records from Bardon, Melton Mowbray and Kibworth.

This species was known still to be breeding in the counties during the early part of the 20th century but the last confirmed nest was in 1916. The LROS archives describe it as a winter visitor in small numbers from then until the formation of LROS in 1941 and this status description remained accurate until the late 1960s. Breeding was proved or strongly suspected a few times in this period: a juvenile was being fed by an adult at Spring Wood, Lount on June 17th 1944, a pair was at Swithland on June 6th the following year and singing birds were recorded on a number of occasions. Earliest autumn and latest spring records were published for 15 of the 18 years between 1942 and 1959, with the average autumn arrival date during this period being October 1st and the average spring departure date being April 21st. Winter flocks during this time were generally small, although between 1941 and 1963 there were six of more than 50, all in the general Charnwood area, as follows:

- 150, Quorn, November 28th 1948.
- 100, Quorn, October 1963,
- 80, Martinshaw Wood, December 1961.
- 75, Beacon Hill, March 7th 1954.
- 65, Groby, November 4th 1962.
- 50 to 100, Quorn, February 1947.

A pair probably bred at Pickworth Great Wood in 1967 and a singing male was at Ulverscroft on July 22nd the same year; this marked the beginning of a period of regular breeding records in the counties. The 1968 LROS Annual Report stated that it was 'strongly suspected that a few birds breed in most years' and a family party was observed at Buddon Wood that year. In 1970 fledged young were seen at Swithland Wood and in 1971 four nests were found at unspecified sites, when the LROS Annual Report considered that 'clearly it is now an established breeding species'. The first confirmed modern breeding records for Rutland came in 1972 when two pairs bred at Clipsham and the following year this species' status in the LROS Annual Report was upgraded to 'resident breeder, fairly common'.

There is little published data on breeding numbers of the Lesser Redpoll throughout the 1970s and 1980s. The best indication is provided by Warrilow, who carried out his tetrad survey during 1976–84, when numbers of this species were probably at their highest in the counties. He recorded Lesser Redpolls in 227 tetrads in the counties (35% of the total number of tetrads), with breeding confirmed in 44. Based on an average of three to five pairs per occupied tetrad this suggested a breeding population of 680 to 1,100 pairs, concentrated in Charnwood Forest and south to Market Bosworth, in the east Leicestershire and Rutland woods and in the Belvoir area; it was absent from most other areas. This figure was much higher than casual records proposed, although a comment in the LROS Annual Report for 1977 that '50 records, wide spread, confirm the spectacular increase of this species on both county and national level' suggested that local observers were aware at the time that the breeding population was being vastly under-recorded. Favoured breeding sites at this time included coniferous, especially larch, woods and birch woodland, but at their peak they were using such habitats as osier beds, overgrown hedgerows and abandoned railway cuttings and loose colonies were often formed.

This period of high breeding numbers in the counties was a short-lived phenomenon and a significant decrease began from the mid-1980s. This decline is illustrated by breeding numbers at the Egleton Reserve at Rutland Water, where there were 11 breeding pairs in both 1983 and 1984, up to 12 in 1985, but just five pairs possibly breeding in 1988 and 1989. The decline continued throughout the early 1990s until the local breeding population was virtually non-existent.

The majority of the largest flocks ever recorded in Leicestershire and Rutland occurred between 1968 and 1991, coinciding with the time of peak breeding activity in the counties. During this period, three-figure flocks were noted on eight occasions, with again the majority in the Charnwood Forest area, as follows:

- 300 at Staunton Harold Reservoir on December 30th 1968.
- 200 roosting at Swithland Reservoir in the winter of 1971.
- 100 at Poultney Wood on March 23rd 1971.
- 100 at Swithland Wood during the late autumn and early winter of 1971.
- 100 at Beacon Hill on January 22nd 1985.

- 100 at Longcliffe Golf Course on December 10th 1987.
- 100 at Beacon Hill on November 7th 1990.
- 100 at Swithland Wood on January 4th 1991.

Since 1991 the only three-figure counts occurred in 1997, when 100 or more were recorded at five sites:

- 200 at Outwoods on January 18th and March 1st.
- 150 at High Leys Farm, Branston on October 30th.
- 100 at Swithland Wood on February 8th.
- 100 at Beacon Hill on March 31st.
- 100 at Quorn Fields Farm on November 11th.

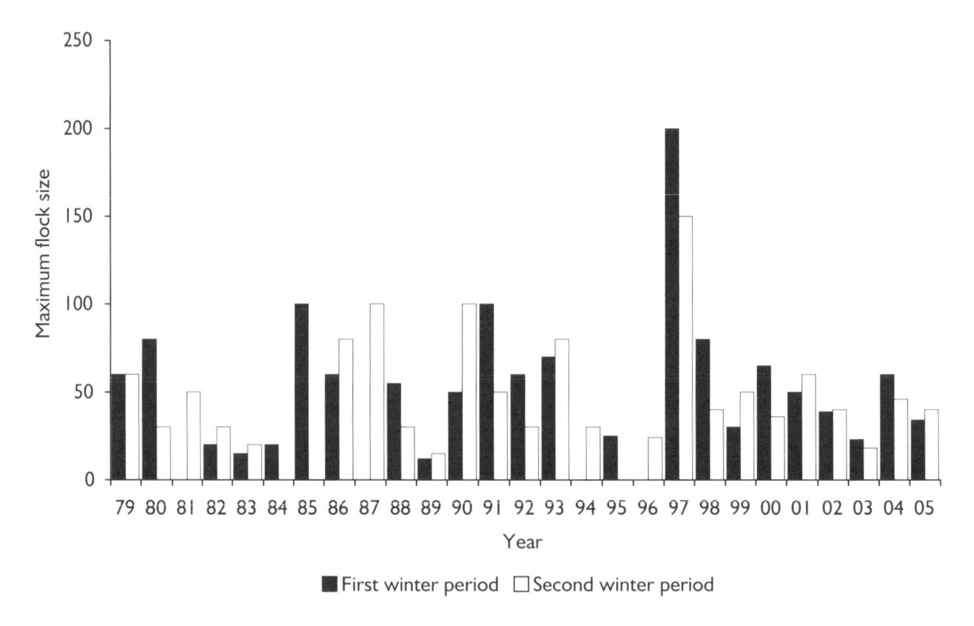

Figure 553: Maximum winter flock sizes of Lesser Redpolls 1979–2005. Gaps indicate lack of data, not of birds.

The present situation is that Lesser Redpolls are largely absent from the counties between early April and the middle of September. Pairs or single birds are sometimes noted displaying during April but the last confirmed breeding was as long ago as 1996, when there was a pair with young at Wigston in June. LROS Annual Reports were describing the species as a 'fairly common resident breeder' up to 1993 but in fact there was only one other proved case of breeding in the 1990s, at Oadby in 1995. It is hoped that the situation may improve as the large areas of maturing conifer plantations in Charnwood and elsewhere are harvested and replanted; the new woodlands of the National Forest in north-west Leicestershire may also provide suitable breeding habitat in the future.

Since regular breeding ceased the LROS Annual Reports have again been detailing first and last dates for this species. The average spring departure date for the period 1994 to 2005 is May 1st, although departures are getting earlier and the average for 2001–05 is April 25th. Likewise, autumn arrivals are becoming later: the average arrival date for 1994–2005 is September 14th, but for 2001–05 it is September 23rd. There have been no records between April and September since 2002 and the only summer reports during the 21st century have involved single birds at Rutland Water on July 8th 2000 and Wigston from July 27th to August 7th 2001. The visible migration survey at Deans Lane, Woodhouse recorded a total of 90 on 12 dates between September 22nd and October 29th with a maximum of 23 on October 22nd (Lister 2007b).

The number of sites where Lesser Redpolls have been recorded has remained fairly constant since the late 1990s, although whether this is a true representation is unclear as observer effort and interest in this species has understandably increased since it became much scarcer.

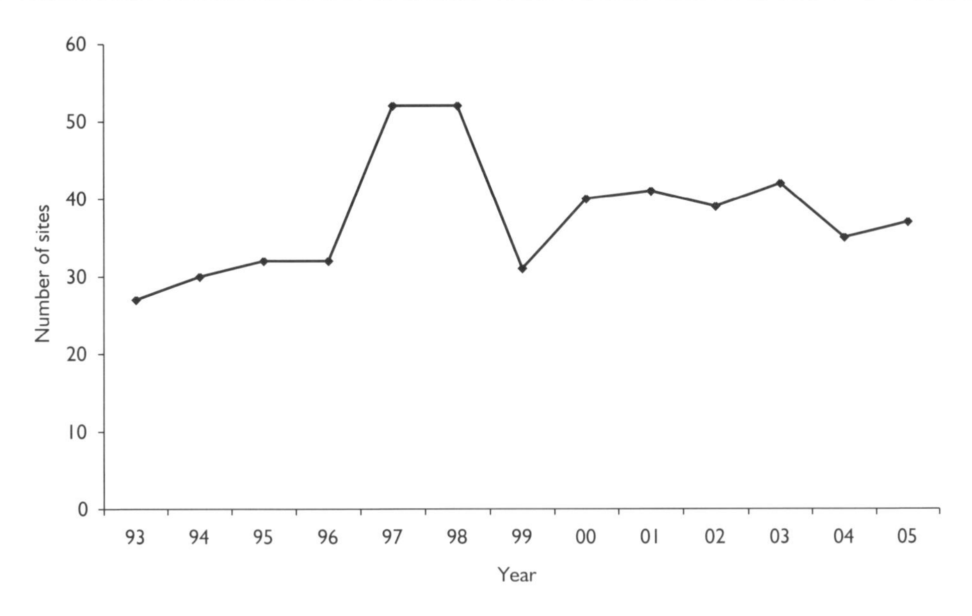

Figure 554: Number of sites with records of Lesser Redpolls 1993–2005.

There are two continental ringing recoveries, both of birds ringed in Belgium and controlled at Frisby Gravel Pits: a female ringed on November 3rd 1974 and controlled on June 3rd 1975 and a juvenile ringed on November 10th 1974 and controlled on October 29th 1977. Ringing has also shown that birds breeding in the Sherwood Forest area of Nottinghamshire move south to winter in Leicestershire.

Lesser Redpolls breed mainly in Britain and Ireland and in the Alps but increasingly also in coastal areas of north-western Europe. There is some movement south for the winter. The British population was estimated at around 160,000 pairs during 1988–91 (Gibbons *et al.* 1993) but more recent estimates put it at 25,300 pairs (Baker *et al.* 2006). The species is currently on the 'Amber List' of Birds of Conservation Concern as a result of the recent rapid decline (Gregory *et al.* 2002).

DJSG

Common Redpoll *Carduelis flammea*

Rare to scarce winter and passage visitor.

Popularly known as the Mealy Redpoll and long considered the nominate race of one species, this taxon was split from the Lesser Redpoll in 2001. The fact that this species has only been officially recognised for a few years may have resulted in some earlier records being ignored, but with increased observer numbers and awareness over recent years it is clear that the Common Redpoll remains a scarce, sometimes irruptive winter and passage visitor to the counties.

Neither Browne or Haines make any mention of this species and the only record prior to the formation of LROS in 1941 concerns two apparently 'caught by a bird-catcher' at Shenton on November 9th 1913. During the 1940s there were records in two years: 15 at Quorn on March 2nd 1947, with five there on April 9th and two at Buddon Wood on April 11th 1948. Except for 'several' at Buddon Wood in February 1964, there were no further records until the 1990s, beginning with two at Rutland Water on February 29th 1992.

A record influx into Britain in the winter of 1995–96 (Riddington *et al.* 2000) provided the vast majority of records. Several large flocks were reported, usually with Lesser Redpolls present as well, but the majority of birds were identified as Common Redpolls, as follows:

- 230 at Bradgate Park on January 15th 1996.
- 100 at Rutland Water from December 10th to 25th 1995, with 80 still there on January 7th 1996.

- 100 at Beacon Hill on November 12th 1995 and February 3rd 1996.
- 40 at Ibstock Opencast (now Sence Valley Forest Park) on December 10th 1995.

Other records of 'redpolls' during this period could well have referred to this species, although the only other bird specifically identified was one at Leicester Forest East on January 27th 1996.

Since this influx, there have been records in four years:

1997	15 at Rutland Water on January 26th.
	two at Swithland Reservoir on March 9th, with one there on March 15th.
2000	55 at Ulverscroft on May 13th.
2002	one at Sence Valley Forest Park on January 1st.
	a female at Rutland Water from March 2nd to 23rd.
	40 at Deans Lane, Woodhouse on May 1st.
	45 at Blakeshay Wood on May 2nd.
2005	one at Burrough Hill on October 23rd.
	two adult males at Watermead Country Park Birstall on December 26th.

The recent May flocks are difficult to explain and it remains to be seen whether spring records become more regular. There have been other large flocks of redpolls at this time of year which were possibly overlooked Commons, such as 20 at Barnsdale Wood on May 8th 1985 and 55 at Bradgate Park on May 5th 1988: such numbers of Lesser Redpolls still flocking in May would be very unusual.

Two records published in previous LROS Annual Reports were found to be unacceptable on review: a 'small flock' at Aylestone on January 25th 1941 and one at Swithland Wood on February 19th and March 12th 1949 (Fray 2005).

Common Redpolls breed throughout the Arctic and boreal zones of Eurasia and North America. The European population of the nominate race *C. f. flammea* ('Mealy' Redpoll) winters from northern Scandinavia as far south as central Europe, whilst 'Greenland' Redpoll *C. f. rostrata* breeds in southern Greenland and Baffin Island and winters mainly in Iceland. A further race, *C. f. islandica* ('Iceland' Redpoll) breeds in Iceland. All Leicestershire and Rutland records have presumably involved the nominate race.

DJSG

Arctic Redpoll *Carduelis hornemanni*

Very rare vagrant from the Arctic: five or six individuals.

A spectacular invasion of Common Redpolls towards the end of 1995 brought with them the counties' first Arctic Redpolls, with at least five and possibly six (two or three males, two females/first-winters and one first-winter) at Rutland Water. Following the first, found by Andrew Harrop and John Wright on December 10th, two were present between the 11th and 15th, with three from the 16th into 1996 and a final sighting on February 7th (Harrop 1996, *BB* 89:523 & 90:506). Two were trapped and ringed on December 11th. The birds were rather difficult to see well, as they associated with a highly mobile flock of Common Redpolls which moved between two favoured feeding areas, beside Lagoon III and Rushpit Wood. All birds were of the race *exilipes*, sometimes referred to as 'Coues's Redpoll'.

Arctic Redpolls breed in the tundra regions of Eurasia, Greenland and North America. The winter range depends upon the availability of suitable feeding areas and so is highly variable but can extend south to central Europe. The nominate race *C.h. hornemanni* ('Hornemann's Redpoll') breeds in north-east Canada and Greenland and is a very rare vagrant to Britain, whilst the smaller *exilipes* occupies the rest of the species' range and occurs annually in small numbers in Britain. Prior to the 1995 irruption there had been only one record in the Midlands (in Nottinghamshire in 1987), but several other nearby counties had their first records at the same time as the Rutland Water birds, most notably Derbyshire and Staffordshire (21 and 14 individuals respectively). The number of birds recorded in Britain during this influx was well over 400 (Riddington *et al.* 2000) and accounts for almost half of the British total of around 830. The Arctic Redpoll was dropped from the list of species assessed by the BBRC at the end of 2005.

DJSG

Common Crossbill *Loxia curvirostra*

Uncommon irruptive visitor, very rare breeder; recorded in all months, with the majority in June and July.

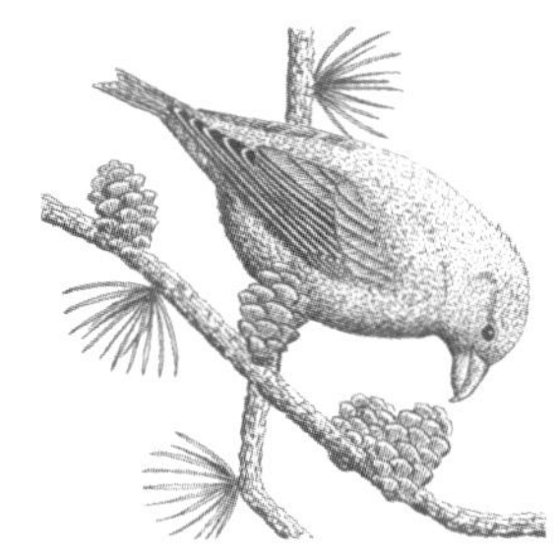

Browne described the Common Crossbill as an irregular and uncertain visitor in Leicestershire from autumn to early spring which had bred. There were big invasions in 1839–40 and 1854 and a pair bred in a fir plantation at Hallgates in 1839. In Rutland, Haines described it as 'a winter visitor, but not often seen.'

The LROS archives refer to a record at Barkby Holt in January 1931. The picture is clouded concerning the early years of LROS as several records were square-bracketed and as such cannot now be deemed acceptable. Indeed, the only positive record in the 1940s is of three at Farnham's Park, Quorn on March 27th 1949. There were records for just three years of the next decade: 1956, 1958 and 1959, which included 20 at Cropston Reservoir on December 9th 1958 and up to six at Eyebrook Reservoir Plantation in September and October 1959. Small numbers remained at the latter site into 1960, with up to ten from the beginning of the year until March 20th and breeding was strongly suspected.

There were records in six years during the 1960s. 1962 was an irruption year, with at least 46 birds recorded from late June onwards, including up to 14 at Eyebrook Reservoir Plantation from July onwards and 20 at Gisborne's Gorse on September 29th. Breeding was confirmed at Owston Wood where a nest with eggs was found, but unfortunately the eggs were taken. There were notable numbers recorded during the autumn and early winter of 1963 which may have related to lingering birds from the previous year's influx, including up to 11 at Eyebrook Reservoir Plantation from October 12th onwards, 12 at Cropston Reservoir on December 2nd and 20 at Beacon Hill on December 9th. Apart from a small influx in 1966, when birds were seen at six sites, numbers remained low for the following 25 years. The 1970s and 1980s saw records in five years in each decade and only small irregular flocks were noted, the largest of which were nine at Martinshaw Wood on May 6th 1979 and 20 at Charnwood Lodge on June 30th 1985.

The 1990s provided by far the highest numbers thanks to national influxes in 1990, 1991 and 1997 and only 1996 was a blank year. The 1990 influx saw records at five sites, all in Charnwood Forest, involving up to 37 birds. Most were found in autumn, including up to 21 at Benscliffe Wood from October 1st to November 11th and ten at Blakeshay Wood on October 7th. None were seen between November 1990 and March 1991, after which there were records from 18 sites by the end of 1991 involving an estimated 158 individuals. Juveniles at Blackbrook Reservoir, Eyebrook Reservoir Plantation, Rutland Water and Wigston may have been locally bred. The largest counts during 1991 were:

- 38 at Lea Meadows on June 16th, with 20 on July 7th.
- 25 at Blakeshay Wood on March 26th, with 15 on March 31st.
- 17 at Outwoods on April 13th and 14th.
- 15 at Blackbrook Reservoir on June 23rd.
- 12 at Beaumont Leys, Leicester on July 12th.

As can be seen from Figure 555 the influx was centred mainly on the coniferous woodlands in the Charnwood Forest area, with a few records from Rutland and occasional reports elsewhere.

By far the largest irruption occurred in 1997. The first birds were three at Snarestone on June 10th, but the main arrival was in late June and July and included the following flocks:

- 170 at Lea Wood on July 3rd.
- 80 at Benscliffe Wood on July 8th.
- 60 at Pickworth Great Wood on July 17th.
- 45 at Stathern Wood on July 17th.

- 35 at Leesthorpe on July 5th.
- 35 at Wardley Wood on July 16th.

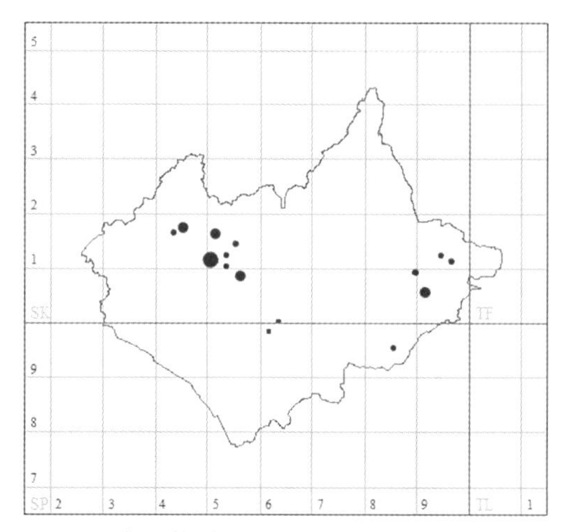

Dot = number of birds, 4 sizes of dot
1–9 (smallest), 10–24, 25–49, 50+ (largest)

Figure 555: Distribution of Common Crossbills in 1991.

There was some evidence of a further arrival during the autumn, when there were flocks of 20 at Ulverscroft on September 29th and 30th, 50 at Outwoods from October 14th to 18th, 15 at Rutland Water on October 18th, 20 at Beacon Hill on October 26th and up to 21 at Groby Pool from November 9th into 1998. In all, records came from 23 sites during the year and involved as many as 850 birds. As in 1991, the coniferous woodlands of Charnwood Forest were the favoured areas; the Rutland woods also produced a number of records, as did the Vale of Belvoir.

Following this irruption, numbers remained high into 1998; notable flocks included 67 at Outwoods on April 25th, 48 at Windsor Hill, Belvoir on February 22nd, 40 at Stathern Wood on February 1st and 30 at both Lea Meadows on February 15th and Newell Wood on April 26th. Singing birds were recorded at six sites, breeding was strongly suspected at a seventh and two recently fledged juveniles were at a site in the north of the county.

Into the present decade, numbers tailed off and the only records in 2000 were three at West Beacon Farm on January 16th, up to 15 at Bradgate Park on February 19th and 20th and 12 at Buck Hill on February 22nd. There may have been a new influx in 2001, with one at Lea Wood on July 28th and 20 at Swithland Reservoir the next day, with one at the latter site on September 4th. However, a sizeable irruption occurred in 2002, beginning on June 29th when 14 were at Fort Henry Ponds. Up to 180 birds were recorded from a total of 14 sites, the largest flocks being:

- 40 at Burley Wood on September 15th.
- up to 35 at Blakeshay Wood from September 14th to 29th.
- 30 at Exton Park on September 16th.
- 15 at Charnwood Lodge on July 14th.

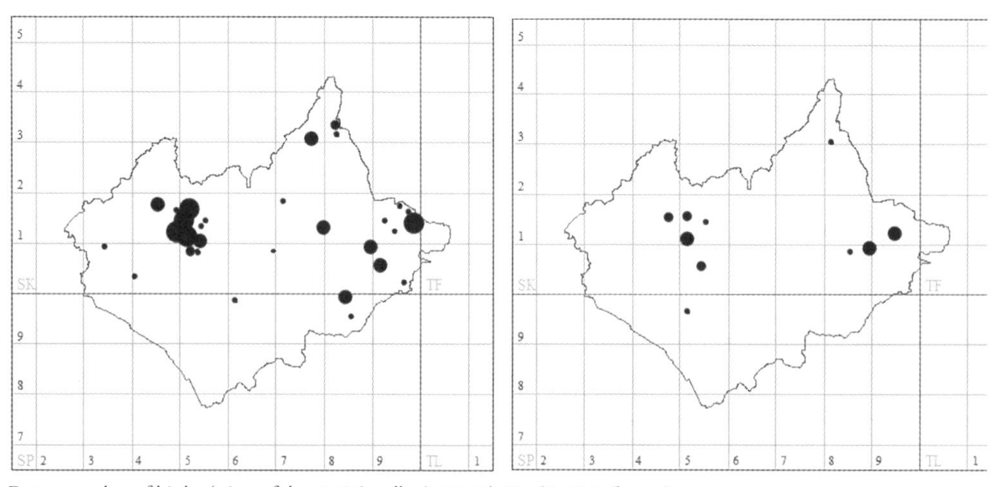

Dot = number of birds, 4 sizes of dot, 1–9 (smallest), 10–24, 25–49, 50+ (largest)

Figure 556: Distribution of Common Crossbills in 1997.

Figure 557: Distribution of Common Crossbills in 2002.

Numbers remained high and even increased at some sites in 2003, when it was thought that at least 275 birds were involved. The highest counts during the year were:

- 80 at Burley Wood on May 28th.
- 50 at Bardon Hill on March 19th.
- 30 at Barnsdale on February 8th.
- 30 at Charnwood Lodge on March 27th and April 13th.
- 29 at Blakeshay Wood on May 21st.
- 25 at Lea Wood on January 26th.

During 2003, courtship feeding was noted at Bardon Hill on March 19th, a recently fledged juvenile was at Blakeshay Wood on May 21st and two juveniles were at Deans Lane, Woodhouse on June 21st.

There were no records in 2004, but in 2005 there was a summer influx involving at least 160 birds, followed by a small passage of about 20 birds in the autumn. The highest counts during this period were 65 at Benscliffe Wood on July 9th, 24 at Bardon Hill the same day and 21 at Rutland Water on July 3rd.

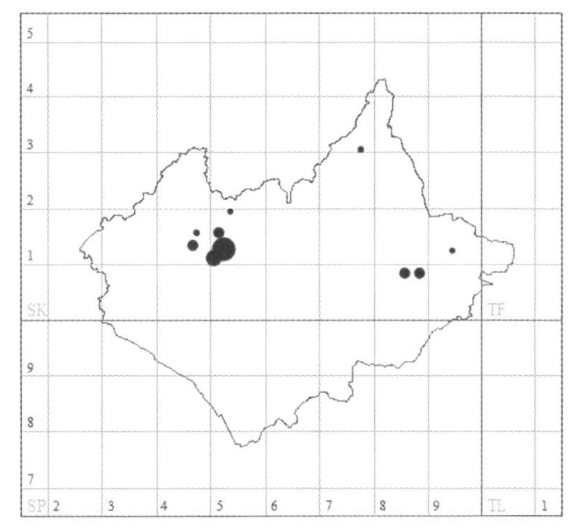

Dot = number of birds, 4 sizes of dot
1–9 (smallest), 10–24, 25–49, 50+ (largest)

Figure 558: Distribution of Common Crossbills in 2005.

As Figure 560 shows, irruptions are usually first noted in late June or early July and flocks may remain in suitable areas throughout the invasion year and into the following and sometimes subsequent years. However, numbers invariably decline and the birds eventually disappear. Many of the coniferous woods in the counties are privately owned with no public access and although breeding probably occurs in most invasion years, it is rarely confirmed. Numbers during irruption years are difficult to calculate exactly due to mobile flocks moving between sites.

There is just one ringing recovery: one ringed at The Brand, Woodhouse Eaves on July 28th 1991 was controlled 1,188km to the east-south-east at Gmunden (Austria) on November 29th 1991.

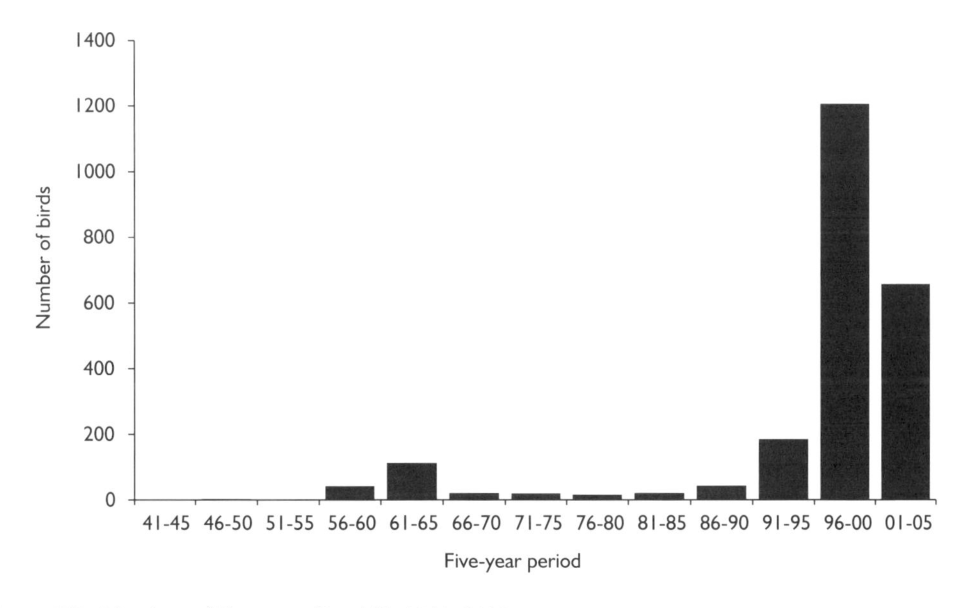

Figure 559: Numbers of Common Crossbills 1941–2005.

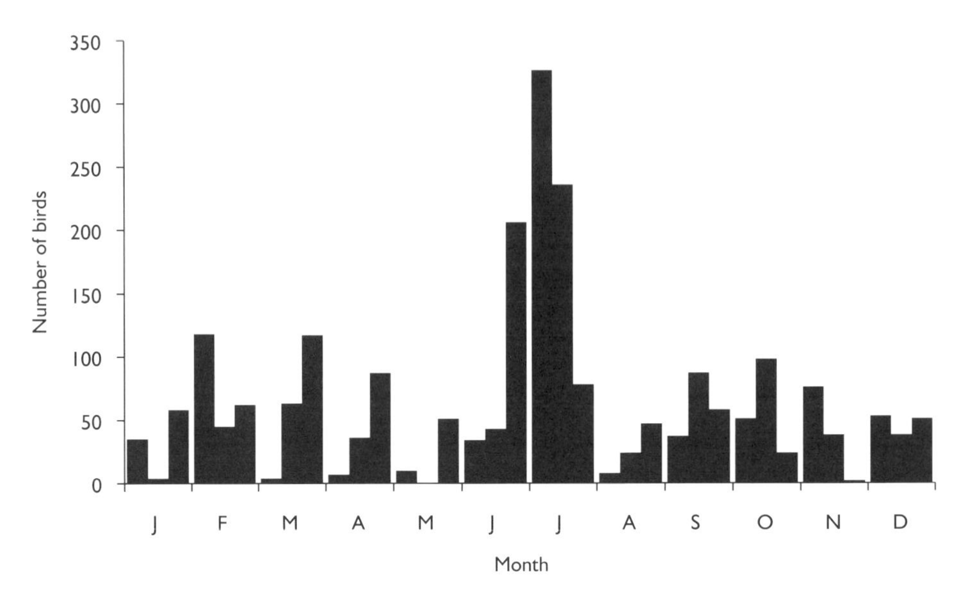

Figure 560: Monthly occurrence of Common Crossbills 1941–2005.

This species has a complex taxonomy and recent work on vocalisations has led to suggestions that several 'cryptic species' may be unrecognised by traditional treatments. According to the arrangement followed by *BWP,* nominate *curvirostra* is found in Eurasia from Britain to the Sea of Okhotsk, south to northern Spain, central Italy, the northern Balkan countries and European Russia. Other subspecies are found elsewhere in Eurasia and North America. Populations are resident and dispersive and are famously irruptive, covering up to 4,000km, mainly in one direction, in years when high population levels coincide with poor or moderate seed harvests. Common Crossbills live only in conifer woods and population estimates are made difficult by enormous variations in numbers from year to year. A recent estimate put the British population at between 1,000 and 20,000 pairs (Baker *et al.* 2006). Although we have some locally obtained museum specimens from the 1990 and 1997 irruptions (see Appendix 6), there is as yet no data about the vocal types involved in records from Leicestershire and Rutland.

DJSG

Bullfinch (Common Bullfinch) ***Pyrrhula pyrrhula***

Common resident breeder.

The Bullfinch is a quiet, unassuming bird of woodlands, hedgerows and mature gardens that manages to keep a low profile despite its bright colours. It is probably more numerous and widespread than records would suggest. During the 19th century, Browne considered it to be 'resident but unevenly distributed' in Leicestershire, whilst Haines thought it was 'plentiful' in Rutland. It is known that this species showed a marked increase nationally from 1940 to 1970 (Gibbons *et al.* 1996) and various published statements around this time accord with this view: in the first LROS Annual Report, in 1941, it was described as 'resident, well distributed, increasing, particularly in south-east Leicestershire', whilst Otter (1965) considered that there had been a 'steady increase in numbers for some years' in east Leicestershire.

In line with most finch species, the Bullfinch has suffered a rapid decline since the mid-1970s (Baillie *et al.* 2006). This decline has been more evident on farmland than in woodland and Chamberlain & Vickery (2002) noted a 70% decrease on national farmland CBC plots between 1973 and 1998. The major causes of the decline have been due to agricultural intensification, particularly hedgerow removal and the destruction of weed-rich field margins. Local CBC data from Stoughton and Newton Harcourt mirrors this situation to some extent;

both sites recorded their highest numbers during the 1970s, but the subsequent decline has not been as severe as the national trend suggests and during recent years populations appear to have stabilised. CBC data from two plots in Rutland show that on farmland at King's Hill Lodge, Uppingham numbers remained relatively static during the 1990s, whilst at the woodland site of Prior's Coppice the general trend between 1988 and 1999 was upwards. At the farmland site at Loddington, numbers increased from six pairs in 1992 to 12 by 2001, showing yet again what can be achieved with sensitive and responsible farming practices.

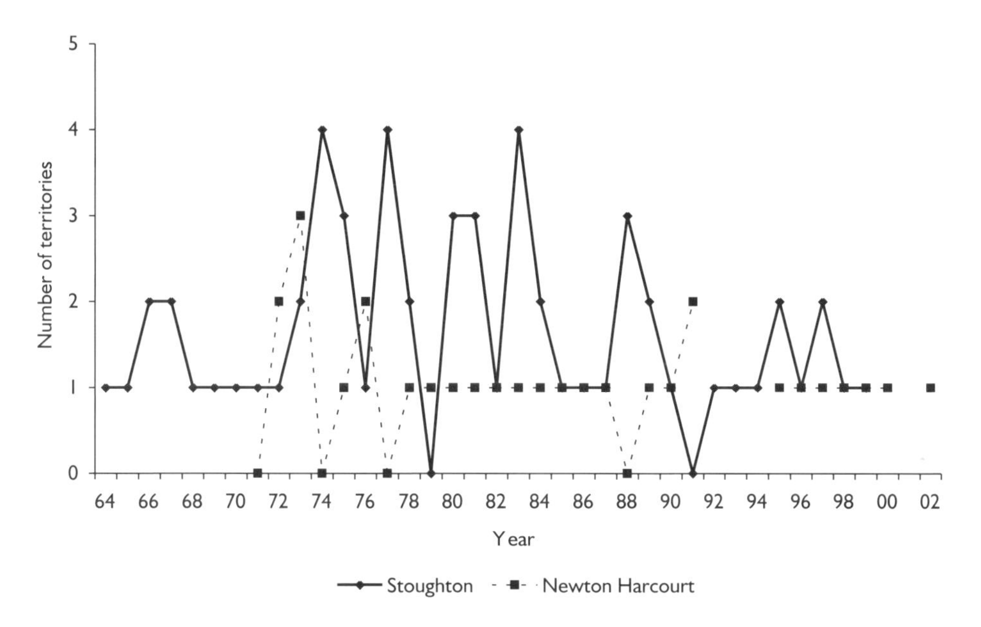

Figure 561: Number of breeding pairs of Bullfinches on two Leicestershire CBC plots 1964–2002.

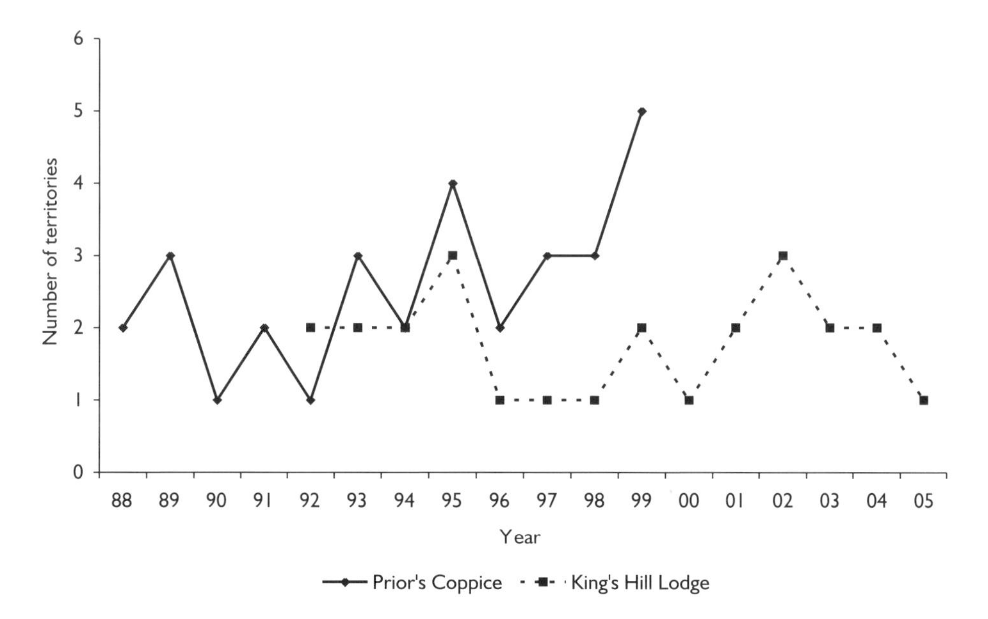

Figure 562: Number of breeding pairs of Bullfinches on two Rutland CBC plots 1988–2005.

Warrilow recorded the Bullfinch in 464 tetrads (73% of the total number of tetrads in the counties) during 1976–84, with breeding confirmed in 154. It was most common in the mixed and pastoral farming areas of west and south Leicestershire and was absent from intensively farmed sections of east Leicestershire and north Rutland. Figures from local CBCs showed the highest territory densities to be in woodland, followed by mature suburban gardens and finally farmland. Surveys carried out in 39 east Leicestershire woodlands during this time found that the average density was 65 pairs per tetrad, well above the national figure. Farmland figures varied from eight to 28 pairs. Based on an average of 12 to 25 pairs per occupied tetrad, Warrilow proposed a county-wide population of between 5,500 and 11,600 pairs, although given the dramatic declines noted nationally since the time of this estimate it seems likely that this figure is now well above the present level.

Unlike the majority of finches, this species is not prone to gathering in large flocks, although 100 feeding on haws at Ambion Wood on November 7th 1943 would suggest that this habit may have been more frequent in the past. More recently, a flock of up to 50 frequented the newly-formed Egleton Reserve at Rutland Water in late autumn 1976. Otherwise, there have been 60 counts of between ten and 17 and higher counts are as follows:

- 23 at Rutland Water on January 14th 2002.
- 23 at Western Park, Leicester on November 25th 2002.
- 22 at Western Park, Leicester on December 28th 2001 and October 1st 2003.
- 20 at Fosse Meadows on December 30th 2001 and January 23rd 2002.
- 19 at Rutland Water on January 17th 1982 and November 16th 2004.
- 18 at Rutland Water on December 15th 2001.

Most of these larger counts have occurred during the 21st century, probably as a result of changing recording habits rather than a change in the species' population levels.

Bullfinches breed over much of Europe apart from the south and in a wide band across the boreal and temperate zones of Asia. They are widespread over much of Britain, where the latest population estimate is 157,700 pairs (Baker *et al.* 2006). Due to the rapid decline in the population over the last 25 years, this species has been added to the 'Red List' of Birds of Conservation Concern (Gregory *et al.* 2002). British birds, which are of the endemic race *pileata*, are rather sedentary and this certainly applies to the local ones, evidenced by the fact that there have been only two ringing recoveries involving birds that have moved out of the counties: a female ringed at Banthorpe in August 1977 was retrapped at Peterborough (Cambridgeshire) in May 1978 and a male ringed at Belmesthorpe in October 1977 was killed by a cat at Leighton Buzzard (Bedfordshire) in February 1979. North European populations of the nominate race, especially those in Scandinavia, are occasionally eruptive and there are records of this race in Britain in most years, usually in the Northern Isles. A widespread arrival of 'northern' Bullfinches took place during the autumn of 2004 and one flying over Swithland Reservoir on January 19th 2005 was described as giving a plaintive '*beep*' call typical of this race; however, it is worth noting that the vast majority of birds recorded during this influx gave a quite different trumpeting call rather than the usual call associated with this race (Pennington & Meek 2006).

DJSG

Hawfinch *Coccothraustes coccothraustes*

Formerly a scarce resident breeder, now a scarce to rare passage migrant.

During the 19th century Browne considered the Hawfinch to be an occasional breeder which was quite frequent in winter and gradually increasing; he noted that it had nested at Bardon Hill, Coleorton, Hinckley, Woodhouse, Lubenham and near Loughborough. Harley, writing in 1840, said that it was abundant in the winters of 1820 and 1823 and that many were shot. Haines described it as very rare in Rutland until 1870 but well established by 1907; breeding had been recorded at Uppingham, Bisbrooke and Glaston and notable flocks included 13 at Oakham on January 23rd 1903 and six at Uppingham in January 1902. The assertions by Browne and Haines that this species was increasing towards the end of the 19th century are in line with the national trend at that time: Gibbons *et al.* (1996) noted that Hawfinches steadily increased in Britain between 1850 and 1940.

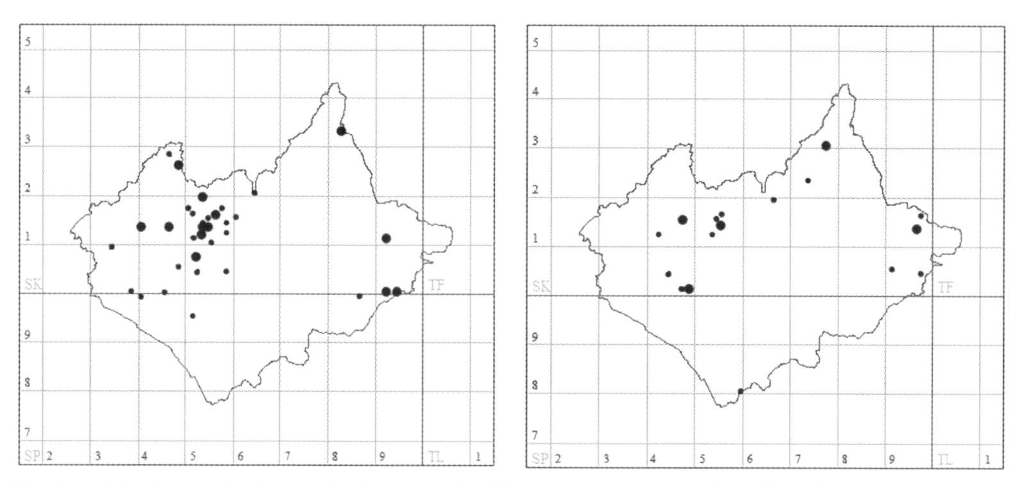

Two sizes of dot showing distribution, Smallest = non-bredding record, Largest = confirmed breeding record

Figure 563: Distribution of Hawfinches 1941–60. **Figure 564:** Distribution of Hawfinches 1961–80.

The LROS archives say that the Hawfinch was thinly distributed during the early part of the 20th century; nests had been found at Beacon Hill in May 1937, Knipton Reservoir in June 1937 and The Brand, Woodhouse Eaves (two pairs) in 1940. By 1943, it was described as 'resident locally, but not common' (Jolley 1944). Between 1941 and 1960 records came from 34 sites, with the majority in the Charnwood Forest area, a few in the Rutland woods and scattered pairs elsewhere. During this period breeding was confirmed at 13 sites, nine of which were in or near Charnwood Forest: the most regular area was Kaye's Plantation at Quorn, with others at The Brand, Swithland Wood, Loughborough, Swithland village, Groby, Bardon Hill, Ravenstone and Kegworth. Of the other four nesting sites, three were in Rutland, at Exton, Morcott and Barrowden; breeding was also confirmed at Belvoir.

During this period there were frequent references to 'several' and 'small parties' and significant counts included:

- 30 to 40 at Kirkby Mallory on December 7th 1941.
- 20 at Quorn in February 1945.
- 12 to 15 (including juveniles) at Bardon Hill on July 7th 1944.
- 12 at Quorn in February 1949.
- nine at Swithland on July 13th 1944.
- eight at Kaye's Plantation, Quorn on November 13th 1958.

From 1961 to 1980 Hawfinch records came from a total of 17 sites, exactly half the number in the previous 20 years. The general distribution of reports was similar to that found from 1941 to 1960, with a cluster of records in Charnwood Forest, a few in Rutland and odd ones elsewhere. No winter flocks were noted during this period. Confirmed or suspected breeding records came from only five sites: Tooley Spinney, Woolfox and Stathern Wood in 1969, Charnwood Lodge in 1973 and Swithland Reservoir in 1974, whilst one reported as 'probably a juvenile' at Holwell in July 1975 was perhaps indicative of local breeding.

A noticeable change in distribution occurred during 1981–2000; records came from a total of 21 sites, ten of which were in Rutland. The species became much scarcer and there were only two sites at which birds occurred with any regularity. There were records in seven years from Clipsham, including eight on January 24th 1995 and five on March 21st 1994; in addition, five juveniles were at this site in 1981, one of only two confirmed breeding records during this period, the other being at an undisclosed site in the east of the counties in 1988. Exton Park produced reports in six years, with Tunneley Wood being particularly favoured: a wintering flock from November 11th 1990 to April 11th 1991, peaking at 14 on January 13th 1991, was remarkable and six were also at this site on November 28th 1993. Away fom Rutland all records were of single birds on one day only, with the exception of the following:

- five at Swithland Reservoir on October 7th 1995.
- five at Stathern Wood on February 15th 1998.
- two at Wistow Hall on both November 13th 1985 and February 18th 1990.
- two at Newbold Verdon on March 17th 1991.

There were only three records from 2001 to early 2005, of single birds at Clipsham on January 1st 2001, Tugby on March 11th 2004 and Countesthorpe on April 2nd 2005. However, the autumn of 2005 saw an influx of presumed continental migrants, with records fom nine sites involving 15 individuals, as follows:

- one at Deans Lane, Woodhouse on October 9th.
- one at Charnwood Lodge on October 22nd.
- three at Rutland Water on October 25th.
- one at Oakham on October 28th.
- two at Deans Lane, Woodhouse on October 29th.
- one at Rutland Water on November 11th.
- one at Thornton Reservoir on November 12th.
- one at Loddington Reddish on November 22nd.
- one at Rolleston on November 28th.
- one at Lockington on December 10th.
- two at Eyres Monsell, Leicester on December 24th.

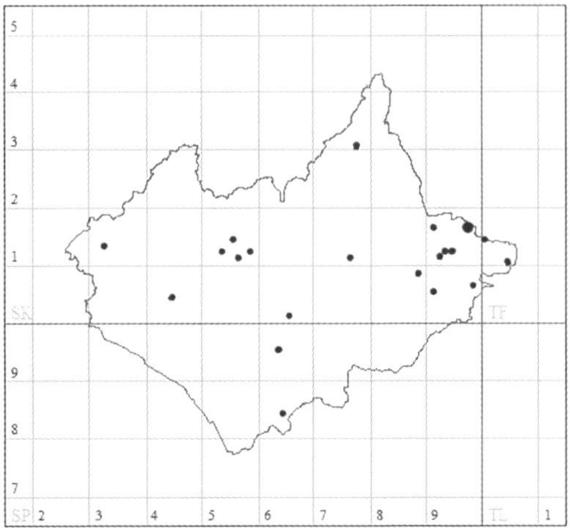

Two sizes of dot showing distribution
Smallest = non-bredding record, Largest = confirmed breeding record

Figure 565: Distribution of Hawfinches 1981–2000.

Hawfinches breed in suitable areas of Europe and Asia Minor from the Mediterranean to about 60° north; separate populations exist further east in Asia. European birds are largely sedentary, although some northern and eastern birds move south-west in the winter. The British breeding population is estimated to be between 3,000 and 6,500 pairs (Baker *et al.* 2006) and as there has been a moderate contraction of the breeding range in the country over the last 25 years this species has been added to the 'Amber List' of Birds of Conservation Concern (Gregory *et al.* 2002). A number of recent records in Leicestershire and Rutland, particularly those in spring and autumn at non-traditional sites, are assumed to involve birds of continental origin and clear confirmation of this was provided by the one ringing recovery: a female ringed at Stoughton Airfield on April 20th 1994 was controlled 788km to the north-east at Sokndal (Norway) on April 24th 1998 (Fowler 1999).

DJSG

Lapland Bunting (Lapland Longspur) ***Calcarius lapponicus***

Rare vagrant, mostly in autumn and winter: 11 records involving 12 individuals.

The first county record was of a female/immature found by Tim Appleton and Chris Park on the Egleton Reserve at Rutland Water on December 22nd 1981. It remained until December 27th and was attracted to grain, allowing several observers close views. There have been a further ten records, involving 11 individuals.

All records:

1981 female/immature, Egleton Reserve, Rutland Water, December 22nd to 27th.

1986 two females/immatures fed with a mixed bunting flock on the Rutland Water dam from February 9th to 23rd.

1990 one was heard calling over the Egleton Reserve, Rutland Water on November 10th.

1993 one flew south over the Hambleton Peninsula, Rutland Water on January 23rd.

1994 a summer plumaged male was seen on the dam at Rutland Water briefly on April 7th before it flew off south-west. During the autumn, one flew north over Eyebrook Reservoir on November 5th.

1995	one flew south-west over Rutland Water on October 22nd, whilst another was found associating with a large flock of Sky Larks near Eastwell on November 12th.
1996	one flew north over Trent Valley Pit on November 26th.
1998	a male was flushed at Aylestone Meadows on October 1st.
2002	one was found feeding with Meadow Pipits on the Rutland Water dam on November 26th.

Rutland Water is easily the most favoured site for this species, with eight individuals recorded there. The grassy slopes of the dam are particularly attractive and all records there have involved birds seen on the ground, although only the 1986 birds remained long enough to be enjoyed by more than one observer. The majority of other records, both from Rutland Water and elsewhere, have been of birds in flight that have initially been detected by their distinctive call; only those at Eastwell in 1995 and Aylestone Meadows in 1998 were seen on the ground and even then both soon took flight and disappeared.

Late autumn appears to be the best time to find Lapland Buntings in the counties and half of all the records have occurred between October 22nd and November 26th. Those recorded in midwinter, most notably the 1981 and 1986 individuals, have arrived during particularly harsh weather conditions. The male in April 1994 is quite extraordinary, being the only spring record.

Lapland Buntings breed from the Scandinavian mountains through Arctic and sub-Arctic Russia to Siberia and also in Alaska, Arctic Canada and Greenland. The Greenland birds travel south-westwards to winter in North America, whereas those from Scandinavia mainly head south-east into eastern Europe and central Asia with smaller numbers wintering around the southern North Sea. Small numbers, usually 200 to 500, regularly winter on the English east coast; they arrive between mid-October and mid-November, neatly tying in with the majority of records in Leicestershire and Rutland.

DJSG

Snow Bunting *Plectrophenax nivalis*

Rare to scarce passage and winter visitor; recorded in all months between October and April, the majority from late October to late December: 65 records involving at least 159 individuals since 1941 and 17 records involving at least 26 individuals previously.

The 19th century status of the Snow Bunting appeared to be the same as it is today, that of a rare and irregular winter visitor. Browne detailed nine records for Leicestershire during this period:

c1838	shot, Whitwick, undated.
c1854	four or five, Glenfield, undated.
c1865	killed, Laughton, undated.
1870	'large flock', Abbey Meadows, Leicester, undated.
1881	four, shot, Burton Overy, February.
c1881	shot, near Hinckley, undated.
1885	shot, Braunstone Lane, Leicester, November 7th.
1894	caught, Croft, November.
	Market Bosworth, November 28th.

Haines knew of three occurrences in Rutland during the 19th century: one shot at Tixover Grange in 1883, one at Cottesmore some time the same year and three at Ayston in 1895.

The LROS archives contain details of five records in the early part of the 20th century: two shot at Swithland on November 25th 1909, the specimens of which were sent to Leicester Museum and single birds at both Croft and Hinckley in 1913, Thurmaston in 1921 and Market Harborough in 1929.

Since the formation of LROS in 1941 there have been records in 41 of the 65 years up to 2005. As Figure 566 shows, peak numbers occurred in the late 1940s and late 1950s, although the totals in both of these periods were heavily influenced by several large flocks. In reality only one or two records per year is the norm and only six years have produced three or more records; there were five records in 2002, making this the best year for individual sightings. Most reports have involved one or two birds, with three records of three together and higher counts of:

- 40 between Morcott and Glaston on October 27th 1949.
- 20 at Eyebrook Reservoir from December 20th to 22nd 1959.
- at least ten at Swithland Reservoir on January 17th 1960.
- five at Leicester City Farms on January 10th 1960.
- five at Eyebrook Reservoir from January 9th to 23rd 1965.
- four at Eyebrook Reservoir on December 20th 1969.

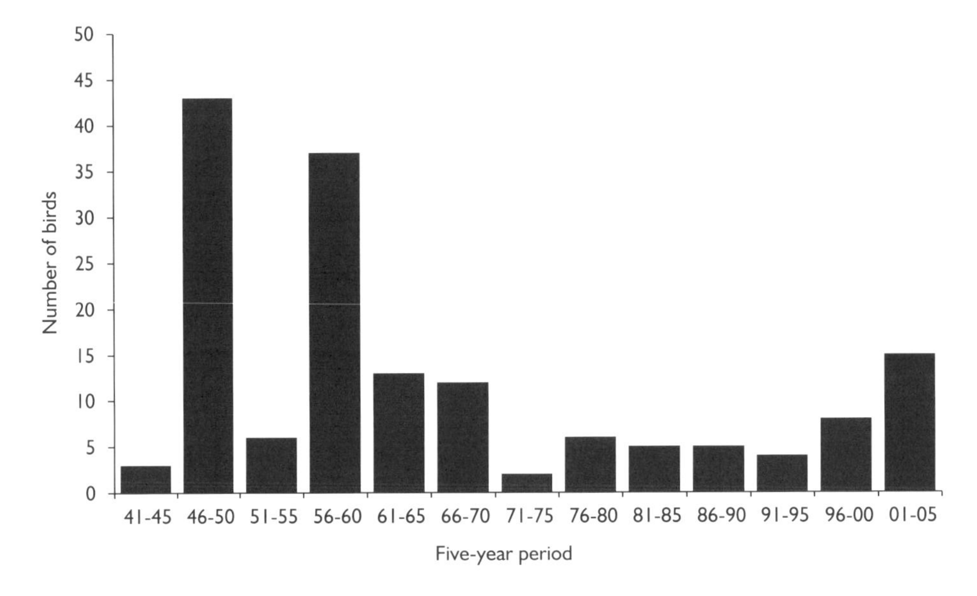

Figure 566: Numbers of Snow Buntings 1941–2005.

Most birds have occurred between late October and late December, although the large flocks somewhat distort the data and mid-November has produced more individual records than any other time of year. Sightings prior to October 25th are rare, the only ones being a male at Hemington Gravel Pits on October 8th 1961, a female/immature at Eyebrook Reservoir on October 17th 1976 and a first-winter male at Stanford Reservoir on October 12th 1980. Birds that have appeared during January and February have often been associated with cold weather. There is very little evidence of early spring passage through the counties and the only arrivals after the end of February are single adult males at Eyebrook Reservoir on March 8th 1997 and April 10th 2004.

A large proportion of Snow Bunting records in the counties have involved birds flying over, when they are usually located by their distinctive call. Of the 65 records since 1941 only 16 have related to birds that have lingered for more than a day and, of these, just six records (involving 11 birds) have been of individuals remaining for longer than ten days:

- one at Quorn from January 1st to 15th 1950.
- two at Stoughton Airfield from February 20th to March 6th 1955.
- one at Eyebrook Res from November 6th to 19th 1961.
- up to five at Eyebrook Reservoir from January 9th to 23rd 1965.
- a female at Rutland Water from January 4th to 17th 1981.
- a first-winter male at Rutland Water from February 13th to March 2nd 1994.

It is noticeable that long-stayers have become something of a rarity in recent times; indeed, since 1994 only four individuals have remained for more than a day.

Snow Buntings, particularly those that are merely flying over, can be encountered anywhere in the counties and records have come from 26 widespread sites. Just six sites have more than one record to their name. Two, Bruntingthorpe Airfield and Beacon Hill, have recorded it only twice. Stanford Reservoir and Hemington

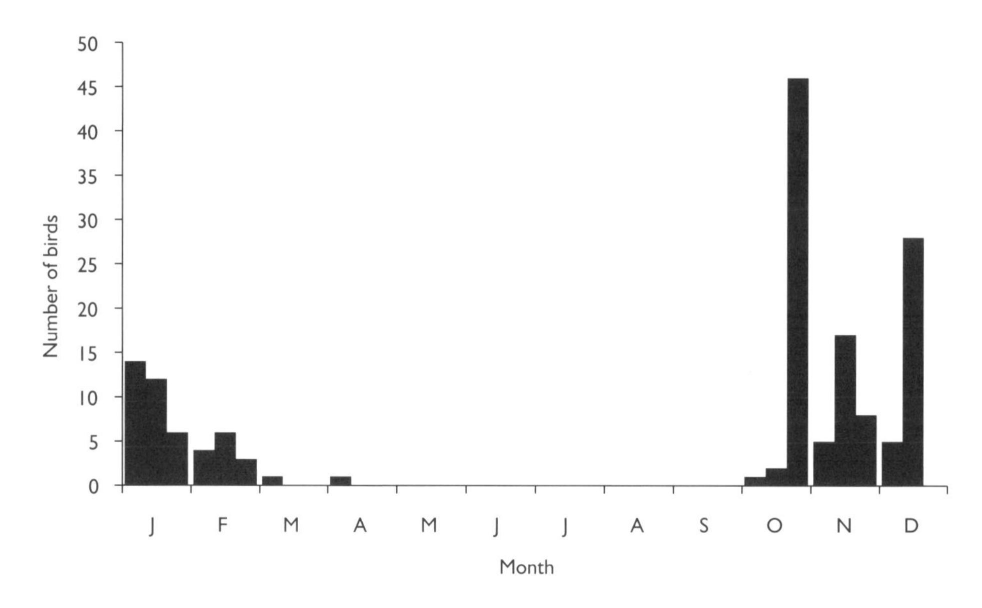

Figure 567: Monthly occurrence of Snow Buntings 1941–2005.

Gravel Pits/Trent Valley Pit have three records each but the two sites which dominate are Rutland Water and Eyebrook Reservoir: the former accounts for 21 records, involving 23 individuals, whilst the latter has had 17 records involving 45 birds.

Snow Buntings have a circumpolar, mainly Arctic, breeding distribution, with the southern limit being the Scottish Highlands and southern Norway. Most winter south of the breeding range and this species is then a familiar bird of the British east coast shorelines; an estimated 9,000 to 13,500 winter in Britain (Baker *et al.* 2006). The breeding population in Scotland is estimated at between 70 and 100 pairs (Baker *et al.* 2006) and due to the small size of this population the species has been added to the 'Amber List' of Birds of Conservation Concern (Gregory *et al.* 2002).

DJSG

Yellowhammer *Emberiza citrinella*

Common to abundant resident breeder, recent decline.

This species has always been a common and widespread breeding bird of the counties' farmland and heaths. During the 19th century it was described by Browne as 'resident and common' in Leicestershire, whilst Haines considered it to be one of the commonest resident birds in Rutland. The next indication of its status was provided in the first LROS Annual Report in 1941, when it was categorised as 'resident and common'. A little later Otter (1965) described it as a 'very common resident' in east Leicestershire.

The Yellowhammer has suffered one of the most dramatic and well-publicised declines of all species in recent times, beginning in the mid-1980s and continuing ever since; Chamberlain & Vickery (2002) noted a 45% decrease on national farmland CBC plots between 1973 and 1998. Reductions in winter seed food availability as a result of agricultural intensification, including the loss of winter stubble, are widely believed to have contributed to population declines (Baillie *et al.* 2006). Local CBC data from two areas of farmland in Leicestershire follow this trend. At Newton Harcourt this was the commonest species during 1971–82, averaging 16.9 pairs annually, decreasing to an average of 15.1 pairs from 1983 and 1990 and 11.75 pairs from 1991 to 2002, a decline of 30%. Data from Stoughton makes even more depressing reading; during 1964–79 Yellowhammer was the third most-numerous species, averaging 25.1 pairs annually, but from 1980 to 1989 this figure fell to an average of 17.5 pairs and from 1990 to 1999 slumped to just 8.5 pairs, a total decline of 66%. Another example of the downward spiral this species appears to be on comes from Rutland Water, where there were 47 territories in both 1976 and 1978 but only nine by 1989. A notable exception to this rather bleak picture is provided by CBC data from King's Hill Lodge, Uppingham, where numbers have increased from six pairs in 1992 to 20 in 2005.

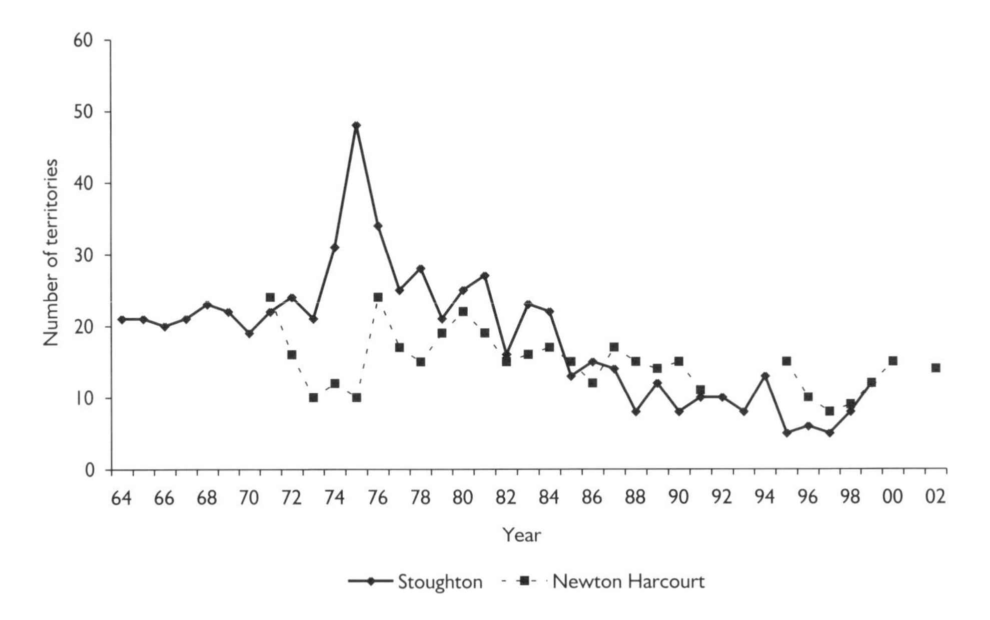

Figure 568: Number of breeding pairs of Yellowhammers on two Leicestershire CBC plots 1964–2002.

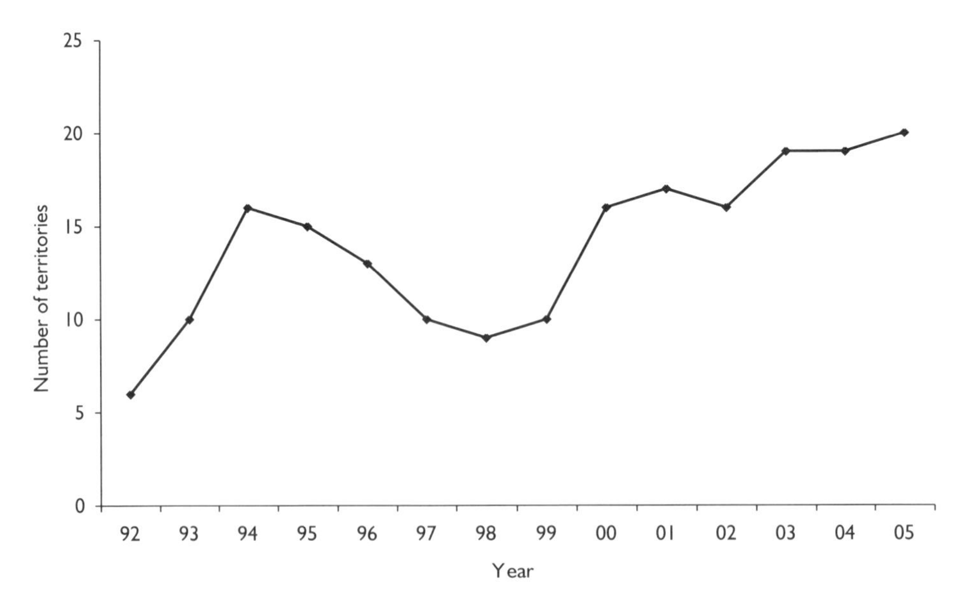

Figure 569: Number of breeding pairs of Yellowhammers on the King's Hill Lodge, Uppingham CBC plot 1992–2005.

Warrilow found the Yellowhammer to be one of the four most-widespread breeding species in Leicestershire and Rutland; it was recorded in a total of 627 tetrads during 1976–84 (98% of all tetrads within the counties), with breeding confirmed in 274 of these. It was absent from the large settlements of Leicester, Loughborough and Hinckley and there were fewer confirmed breeding records from the intensively farmed areas of north Rutland and north-east Leicestershire. At that time local farmland CBC data showed that the average territory density varied from 115 to 397 pairs per tetrad, well above the national average which in 1982 was 44 pairs per tetrad. Allowing for low densities in woodland and absences from built-up areas and assuming that the local CBC numbers were exceptional, Warrilow proposed an average of 50 to 120 pairs per occupied tetrad, giving a total breeding population in the range of 31,000 to 75,000 pairs. Given the subsequent large declines noted at Stoughton and Newton Harcourt, it would be reasonable to assume that Warrilow's estimate is now out of date and it is possible that the current population is less than half of what he suggested. However, this species remains widely distributed and may still exceed the 10,000 pairs mark required to qualify it as 'abundant'.

Yellowhammers tend to remain in rural habitats throughout the year, although small numbers may visit gardens on the edge of countryside, particularly in hard weather. Flocks build up during the winter months and as well as stubble fields and other farmland habitats, the new plantings of the National Forest have attracted large numbers recently. The largest flock was 600 at Rutland Water in January 1980 and there have been a further ten records of groups exceeding 200, as follows:

- 400 at Bagworth Heath on December 28th 1995.
- 300 at Rutland Water in November and December 1975.
- 300 at Anstey on December 29th 2001.
- 250 at Rutland Water in December 1983.
- 250 at Shenton on January 24th 1986.
- 250 at Ryhall Heath in January and February 1996.
- 250 at Sence Valley Forest Park on December 27th 1999.
- 250 at Lockington Marshes on February 8th 2003.
- 212 at Great Bowden on January 5th 2005.
- 210 at Stoughton Airfield in the winter of 1986.

Despite the well publicised decline, it is encouraging to note that most of the larger flocks have been in more recent years.

There have been three records of aberrant birds, all partial albinos: one with white primaries at Thurcaston on February 11th 1945; one with white wing-coverts at Croft also in February 1945 and one with a large area of white on the lower back at Ambion Wood on August 21st 1947.

Yellowhammers breed across most of Europe and as far east as central Siberia; some populations are partially migratory, with northern areas of the breeding range being abandoned in winter. The current British breeding population is estimated at 792,000 pairs (Baker *et al.* 2006) and due to the rapid decline mentioned above this species has been added to the 'Red List' of Birds of Conservation Concern (Gregory *et al.* 2002). The majority of British birds are relatively sedentary and this is reflected in ringing data concerning Leicestershire and Rutland. Of ten ringing recoveries, only three have have involved sites outside the counties: one ringed at an unspecified site in Leicestershire and Rutland on July 31st 1976 was found freshly dead 20km to the east in Northamptonshire on January 1st 1977; a male ringed in the counties on March 24th 1977 was found dead 26km to the north-west in Derbyshire on June 9th 1987 and a female ringed at Belmesthorpe on August 3rd 1980 was controlled 19km to the north at Kirkby Underwood (Lincolnshire) on January 1st 1982.

DJSG

Cirl Bunting *Emberiza cirlus*

Formerly a very rare breeder and visitor. No accepted records since 1948.

Browne recorded that this species had 'occurred but once, on the authority of Harley, who writing between 1840 and 1855 said that he had met with it in company with the Yellow Bunting at Thurmaston'. Haines reports that one was shot near Uppingham some time between 1870 and 1873, a pair was seen in the same area about a year later and an egg of this species was found near Lyddington in May 1872. In addition, a nest and eggs was recorded by A.R. Horwood near Leicester in the *Naturalist's Journal, 1896*, whilst a nest with three eggs was reportedly found near Melton Mowbray on May 3rd 1920. The clutch was taken and identified by Mr H.S. Davenport, who reported it to *BB* (Davenport 1920). Apparently, Jourdain then confirmed the authenticity of the nest.

Between 1944 and 1951, the LROS Annual Reports listed a whole host of records, which all came from one observer, as follows:

1944	pair and three young, Six Hills, August 2nd.
1945	male, Wymeswold, May 14th.
	pair and one young, Six Hills, September 10th.
1946	male, Whissendine, October 5th.
1947	male, Ulverscroft, April 10th.
	male, Quorn, June 21st.
	male, Wymeswold, June 30th.
1948	male, Lea Wood, June 7th.
1949	male, Waltham on the Wolds, April 16th.
	male, Prestwold, April 17th.
	pair, Bradgate Park, May 8th.
	at least two, Quorn, December 6th.
1950	nest and three eggs, Beacon Hill, June 8th.
	male, Beacon Hill, July 13th.
1951	male, Buddon Hill, unspecified date.
	male, Beacon Hill, unspecified date.
	male, Hangingstone Rocks, unspecified date.
	pair with young in nest, Beacon Hill, early July.

Following review in 1995, this series of records was considered unreliable and all were therefore rejected (Mackay 1995a). The only remaining records since the formation of LROS in 1941 are of a male at Aylestone on November 12th 1944, a pair at Bradgate Park on March 27th 1946 and at least two males at Eyebrook Reservoir on February 19th 1948.

Holloway (1996), in describing the distribution of this species in the period 1875 to 1900, showed it as occurring 'occasionally' as far north as Warwickshire and Northamptonshire, whilst Sitters (1982) reported that this species' range, which only reached as far north as the south Midlands anyway, began contracting to the south during the early part of the 20th century and breeding ceased in the Midlands and Wales in the 1930s. Witherby *et al.* (1938) mapped the Cirl Bunting's distribution as extending only as far north as Gloucestershire. Given all this evidence, the decision to reject the majority of Leicestershire records between 1944 and 1951 seems sound, as this would have been an extremely isolated population had it existed.

The status of the Cirl Bunting in Leicestershire and Rutland is therefore somewhat debatable. No documentation exists for any of the remaining records in the 1940s which, as already mentioned, occurred at a time when this species' range was contracting southwards. Cirl Buntings are also generally rather sedentary and are not renowned for moving long distances. The detail available regarding the earlier records is sketchy at best and it is perhaps debatable whether the Cirl Bunting's place on the county list is warranted.

Cirl Buntings breed mainly around the western Mediterranean with their range extending throughout Iberia and France and east through the Balkans into Asiatic Turkey. The British population is now estimated at just under 700 pairs, all of which are located in Devon except for a recent introduction scheme in Cornwall (Wotton *et al.* 2004). Due to the rapid contraction of the species' breeding range it is on the 'Red List' of Birds of Conservation Concern (Gregory *et al.* 2002).

RMF

Reed Bunting *Emberiza schoeniclus*

Common resident breeder and passage migrant, recent decline.

The Reed Bunting was long thought of as a breeding bird of wetland edges and river, stream and canal sides. In the 19th century, Browne described it as 'resident and generally distributed', whilst in Rutland Haines considered that Reed Buntings could 'be seen throughout the county along all the streams and watercourses'. The next statement on this species' status was in the LROS Annual Report, which described it as 'resident and common in suitable localities'.

The first signs of Reed Buntings expanding into drier habitats came in 1945, when it was noted that 'small numbers often feed in cornfields from late July onwards'. In 1950, increases were noted in Charnwood Forest, where many nests were found in willow clumps and clear-felled woods; during the same year, a pair nested at Blaby in dry scrub a mile from any water. By 1961, birds were breeding away from water in east Leicestershire cornfields and the abandoned farmland at the site of Rutland Water was soon colonised in 1971 (Mitcham 1984).

Gibbons *et al.* (1996) noted that the British Reed Bunting population remained stable from the late 1960s to the mid-1970s, after which a drastic decline of over 50% took place before numbers stabilised again from the early 1980s. CBC data from farmland at Stoughton shows a similar pattern, with peak numbers during the mid-1970s followed by a sharp decline; however, the downward trend at this site continued to such an extent that, apart from one pair in 1992, this species was not thought to have bred in any year after 1987. Nationally, the decline in Reed Buntings was attributed to food shortages caused by the introduction of herbicides, whilst the complete loss of this species from Stoughton was probably due to the intensification of agriculture and loss of habitat which characterised this site in the 1980s and 1990s. CBC data at Newton Harcourt better reflects the national picture, with numbers remaining relatively stable during the early and mid-1980s; however, as at Stoughton, a decline occurred after 1987 and this species maintained only a precarious presence during the 1990s. Elsewhere, birds do still persist in arable areas; during 1998, all records of Reed Buntings were requested and it was found that those breeding on farmland mainly utilised fields of wheat or oilseed rape.

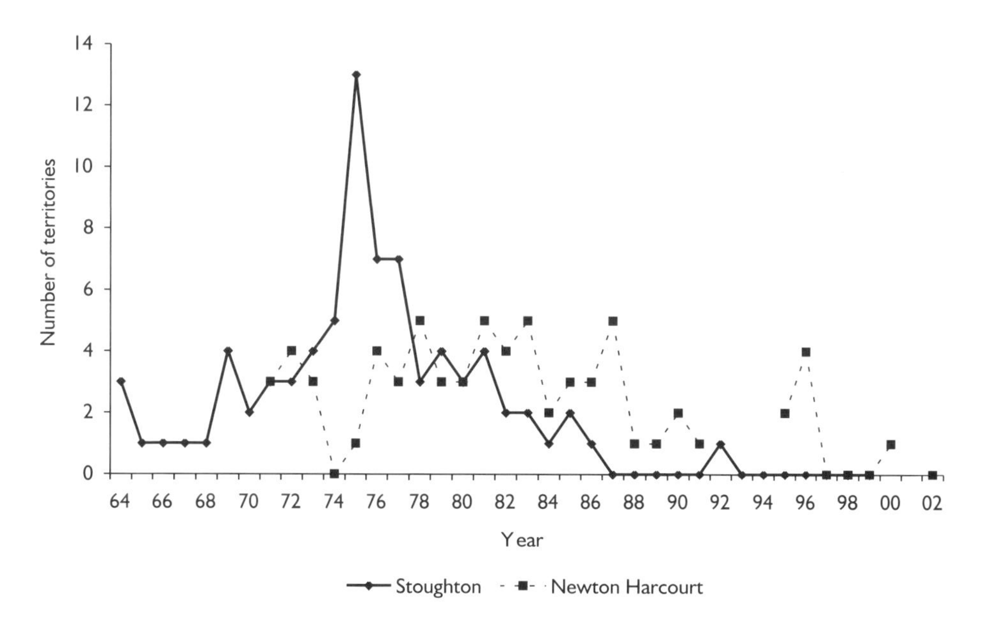

Figure 570: Number of breeding pairs of Reed Buntings on two Leicestershire CBC plots 1964–2002.

Warrilow recorded Reed Buntings in 448 tetrads during 1976–84, equating to 70% of all tetrads within the counties, with breeding confirmed in 157. The species was widely distributed, with more in the south and west, although it was absent from large parts of east Leicestershire, north-east Leicestershire and Rutland, where intensive farming predominates. Reed Buntings were also absent from Leicester city centre, although a survey of four green spaces within the city boundary in 1989 found five pairs at Aylestone Meadows (Fray *et al.* 1990). High breeding densities can be achieved in optimum habitat, with examples including 74 pairs at Stanford Reservoir in 1972, 44 pairs at Frisby Gravel Pits in 1976 and 90 pairs on the Egleton Reserve at Rutland Water in 1985. These figures are obviously the upper limit and Warrilow proposed a total county population of between 2,250 and 4,500 pairs, based on an average of five to ten pairs per occupied tetrad. Considering the declines noted on Leicestershire CBC plots since the time of Warrilow's work, it is likely that this estimate is now well above the current level.

Although the Reed Bunting is generally considered to be a resident species, there is evidence of a clear early spring passage. This was first noted as long ago as the 19th century by Browne, who thought that the Reed Bunting was 'much scarcer in winter than in spring, when its numbers are increased by immigrants'. In 1944, regular counts at Stanford Reservoir showed that numbers built up from just two on February 24th to 30 by March 18th, peaking at 200 on March 23rd and falling to 30 again two days later. Large numbers noted at Eyebrook Reservoir in March and April 1960 were considered to be on passage and in the same year 66 were ringed in a Groby garden in February and March, with no retraps, indicating that birds were continually moving through the area. Stanford Reservoir again provided records of spring passage in the 1970s, with 158 there on April 8th 1976 and 70 on March 27th 1977. There has been little evidence in recent years of movement throughout the counties, probably due to a lack of observers noticing or reporting this phenomenon; however, studies at Trent Valley Pit between 1992 and 2002 showed marked increases in numbers during March and April, as well as in September, suggesting that autumn passage also occurs (Fray 2004).

As with other buntings, this species flocks in the winter. Flock sizes tend to be fairly small, 20 to 50 being the norm and 60 to 150 less common, although 400 were at Stanford Reservoir on October 4th 1980. The largest counts have been at roost sites and have included 800 at Rutland Water in the winter of 1976 and 300 at the same site in November and December 1975. An investigation at a roost at Sutton Cheney in 1980 involved trapping and ringing birds on six dates between October 19th and December 7th; this resulted in a total of 330 ringed, with very few retraps and it was estimated that about 2,000 birds used the roost during the period (Fowler 1981).

Reed Buntings are prone to being affected by severe winter weather and national CBC results showed that the winters of 1978–79 and 1981–82 accelerated the steady decline which began in the mid-1970s. There is no evidence in the CBC data from Stoughton and Newton Harcourt to suggest that this was the case in Leicestershire and Rutland, although this species 'more than any other suffered a chronic reduction in numbers by virtue of the hard winter at Stanford Reservoir in 1979. During the famous severe winter of 1946–47 it was noted that Reed Buntings 'joined the finches round the chaff heaps and stacks', whilst in the similarly harsh winter of 1962–63 birds were seen more frequently in urban gardens (Gamble 1965). This latter habit was first noted in 1962 and for the following 20 years or so was considered to be a response to extreme weather conditions. However, from the 1980s onwards small numbers have regularly been seen in many urban and suburban gardens; this change in behaviour is thought to be related to food shortages in the more usual wintering areas on arable farmland (Gibbons *et al.* 1996). The Leicestershire Garden Bird Survey between January 1996 and June 2005 found the Reed Bunting to be the 30th most-frequent species visiting gardens.

Reed Buntings breed over most of Europe, as well as over much of Siberia and central Asia as far east as northern Japan. Northern and eastern European populations are migratory, mainly wintering within the breeding range. The British population is estimated at approximately 176,000 pairs (Baker *et al.* 1997), but due to the rapid decline of over 50% over the last 25 years this species has been added to the 'Red List' of Birds of Conservation Concern (Gregory *et al.* 2002). Around 60% of British Reed Buntings move less than 5km between summer and winter (Lack 1986) and some evidence of this is provided by the fact that of 35 ringed at Leicester City Farms during 1974 and 1975, 20% were recaught at a roost at Cropston Reservoir between October and December 1975. Fewer than 10% of British Reed Buntings move further than 100km during the winter, mainly to the south-west (Lack 1986) and there are five ringing recoveries involving Leicestershire and Rutland birds which have moved at least this far, although only two conform well with the south-westerly winter movement theory. A female ringed at Lashford Lane Fen (Oxfordshire) on February 17th 2000 and found freshly dead 119km to the north-north-east at Frisby on the Wreake on March 22nd 2000 was perhaps a Leicestershire breeder returning from the south-west during the spring, whilst a male ringed at Donna Nook (Lincolnshire) on October 13th 1985 and controlled 120km to the south-west at Hemington Gravel Pits on December 27th 1987 shows that birds may move to the counties during the winter as well as leave them. Birds presumed to be moving in a generally southerly direction from the counties in the winter have included a male ringed in Leicestershire on August 21st 1976 which was controlled 100km to the south-east in Hertfordshire on December 11th the same year and another male ringed in the county on September 11th 1976 which was controlled 156km to the south in Hampshire on January 9th 1977. Finally, a male ringed at Tewinbury (Hertfordshire) on October 12th 1980 and controlled 120km to the north-west at Sutton Cheney on January 22nd 1981 appears to have moved in completely the opposite direction than would be expected.

DJSG

Black-headed Bunting *Emberiza melanocephala*

Very rare vagrant from south-east Europe or south-west Asia: one record.

A male was found by M. Morris at Hilton Gravel Pits, near Hemington, on July 1st 1967. It frequented hedgerows and telegraph wires and sang from the tops of heaps of gravel (Morris 1968). The record was accepted by the BBRC, but with the proviso that the date made it possible that the bird was an escape from captivity (*BB* 61:359).

The Black-headed Bunting breeds in south-east Europe, Asia Minor and south-west Asia and winters in India. It is a relatively regular vagrant to Britain, with over 175 records by the end of 2005; unfortunately, these numbers have been clouded somewhat by the escape potential as it is a fairly common species in captivity, hence the BBRC's comments relating to the Leicestershire individual. However, it is now clear that late May to June is firmly established as the best time to find this species in Britain, as records of vagrants usually relate to overshooting adults; this species does not arrive on its breeding grounds until May, explaining the late spring occurrences in this country. July 1st is well within the known occurrence pattern, although inland records are extremely unusual: the only other ones have been single birds at Nuneaton (Warwickshire) in May 2004, Chesterton (Cambridgeshire) in May 1993, Mansfield (Nottinghamshire) in May and June 1976 (although this bird was very tame and considered probably to be an escape) and Radcliffe on Trent (also Nottinghamshire) as long ago as June and July 1884.

DJSG

Corn Bunting *Emberiza calandra*

Uncommon resident breeder, recent decline.

The distribution of the Corn Bunting was fragmented in the 19th century. In Leicestershire, Browne considered it to be a resident, sparingly distributed and more common in winter, especially near farm buildings where it consorted with sparrows and other birds. Haines described it as resident and common in many parts of Rutland, though rare in others. On the east side of Uppingham 20 could be seen in a day, but it was rare near Empingham and Normanton.

This species has always been considered of rather localised distribution, with numbers never matching the amount of suitable habitat available. Between the 1940s and 1960s, the main area of distribution seems to have been across the northern part of Leicestershire, centred on the Soar valley around Loughborough and extending across the wolds towards Six Hills. Hickling mentioned a well-known colony at Loughborough Big Meadow, where there were ten singing males in 1965. A good population seems to have been present in Rutland at this time, mainly in the south and east, for example 19 singing males within a three-mile radius of Uppingham in 1948 and 24 singing males within a similar area in 1968. Figure 571 shows that singing males were recorded at a wide variety of sites during this period.

Between the 1970s and 1990s there seems to have been a population shift, with the main breeding area being in the west of Leicestershire. A census during July 1995 of this area found a total of 23 singing males, mainly

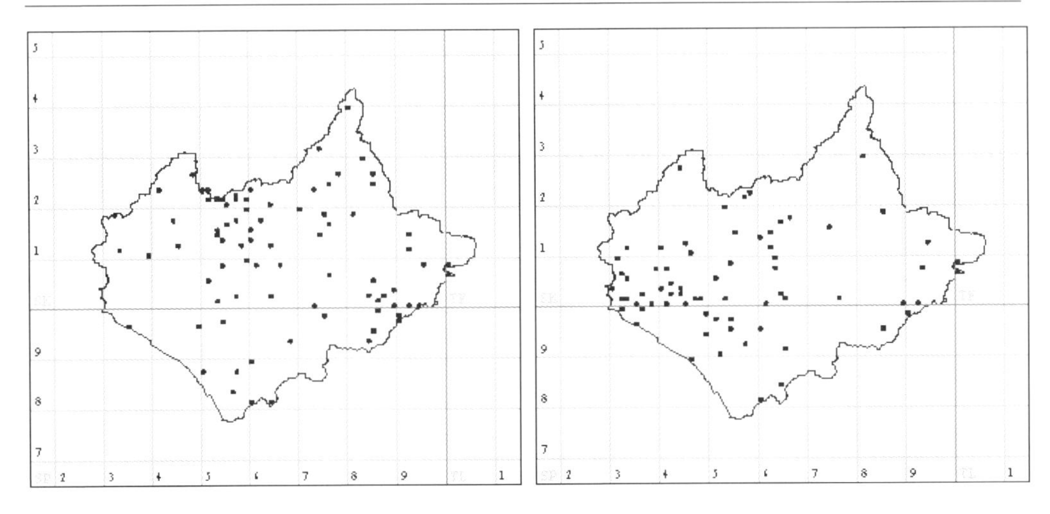

Figure 571: Distribution of singing male Corn Buntings 1941–69.

Figure 572: Distribution of singing male Corn Buntings 1970–99.

in the vicinity of Appleby Magna, Orton-on-the-Hill and Sheepy Magna (Dixon 1996), whilst the following year up to 36 singing males were located. The Rutland population remained much the same but in reduced numbers and contracted towards the east.

Warrilow's work was carried out during this period (1976–84) and, in common with other authors, he noted that this species was closely associated with barley. He recorded it in 156 tetrads in the counties (24% of the total number of tetrads), with breeding confirmed in 17. It occupied three main areas: west and south-west Leicestershire, north Leicestershire across the wolds to Hamilton,s and Rutland. By estimating an average of two to four pairs per occupied tetrad he calculated a countywide breeding population at this time of 300 to 600 pairs, an estimate which is now sadly much too high. The Rutland population was surveyed a few years after Warrilow's work: Mitcham (1992) recorded breeding in 23% of Rutland tetrads, with the stronghold on the Jurassic limestone in the east and estimated that about 30 singing males were then present.

Nationally, Corn Buntings declined very steeply between the mid-1970s and mid-1980s, with local extinctions across large sections of their former range. Although the causes are not fully understood the decline is often attributed to autumn sowing of barley and wheat. Subsequently the decline has continued, but at a much-reduced rate (Baillie *et al.* 2006). Locally, however, the full extent of the decline of this species was really felt from the beginning of the 21st century and at the present time the Corn Bunting would appear to be heading inexorably towards extinction as a breeding bird in the counties.

Table 50: Corn Bunting records 2000–2005

	2000	**2001**	**2002**	**2003**	**2004**	**2005**
Total number of sites	6	11	11	7	8	8
Sites holding singing males	4	8	5	2	2	6
Total number of singing males	9	23	16	16	7	17

There are only two areas where Corn Buntings currently breed regularly. Numbers in east Rutland appeared to be holding their own until 2002, when 11 singing males were at Great Casterton, but this had fallen to five in 2005. Also in Rutland, Exton Park had three singing males in 2001 and two in 2005 and one was at the Lyndon Reserve at Rutland Water in 2002. The extreme west of Leicestershire still holds a small population, although this too appears to be in decline. The former stronghold in the Orton-on-the-Hill area contained eight singing males in 2005, much reduced from the 36 recorded in 1996, whilst the area around Oakthorpe and Measham had 12 singing males in 2003, but this had halved to six the following year and only four in 2005. Two previously well-established populations elsewhere in Leicestershire, at Foston and Hoby/Thrussington, both disappeared after

2001. The only other site where singing birds have been recorded in the 21st century is Prestwold Hall, where there were two in 2001.

Flocks can be difficult to locate outside the breeding season and they often occur away from traditional breeding sites. By far the largest numbers on record occurred at the site designated for the construction of Rutland Water as large areas of suitable habitat became available: 100 roosted there in 1975, rising to 300 in the next two years. However, numbers quickly declined as the rising water levels flooded their favoured areas and an extensive tree-planting programme was put into place. The largest flocks elsewhere have been:

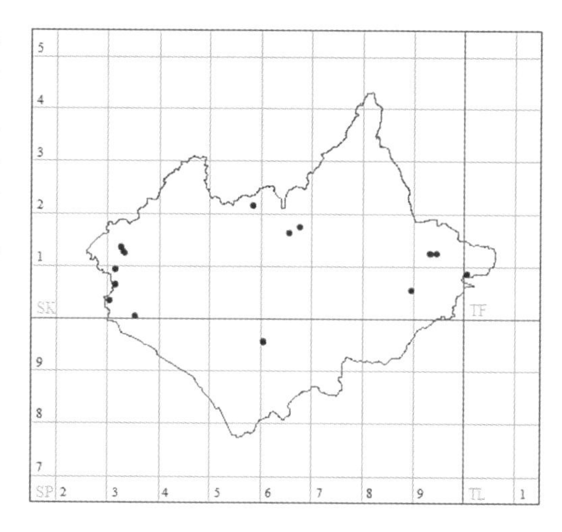

Figure 573: Distribution of singing male Corn Buntings 2000–2005.

- 64 at Mountsorrel on January 30th 1987.
- 60 roosting regularly at Ratcliffe on the Wreake in 1978.
- 60 at Wistow on December 1st 1983.
- 50 at Frisby Gravel Pits on December 12th 1976.
- 50 at Aylestone Meadows from December 29th 1983 to January 1st 1984.
- 50 at Oakthorpe on January 18th 2001.
- 40 at Stretton en le Field on January 18th 2002.
- 41 at Oakthorpe on December 27th 2004.
- 40 at Oakthorpe on February 20th 2003.
- 40 at Lockington Marshes on January 23rd 2000.
- 40 at Oakthorpe on December 31st 2000.
- 40 at Muston on December 28th 2002.

The recent run of sizeable winter flocks is a rare chink of light in a dismal story, although even these seem to be disappearing: a regular wintering group at Lockington Marshes has not been seen since the winter of 2002–03 and the only record during the first part of 2005 was of three at Terrace Hills, Belvoir on February 20th.

Nominate Corn Buntings are found in Europe east to the Caucasus, Asia Minor and the coastal Levant, with two more subspecies recognised in western Ireland and western Scotland and eastwards from the interior Levant to western China and Afghanistan. Most populations are resident or partially migratory. As mentioned previously, this species has suffered a huge decline since the mid-1970s. Gibbons *et al.* (1993) estimated the British population to be up to 160,000 territories during 1988–91, although considered that this was too high; CBC data showed that the population index had fallen by 60% since the previous Atlas in 1968 to 1972 (Sharrock 1976). The latest British population estimate is just 8,500 to 12,200 pairs (Baker *et al.* 2006) and not surprisingly the Corn Bunting has been added to the 'Red List' of Birds of Conservation Concern (Gregory *et al.* 2002).

DJSG

CATEGORY D SPECIES

by Dave Gamble and Andrew Harrop

Species in Category D are those that have occurred in Britain for which there is sufficient doubt that they have occurred in a wild state. The majority of species on Category D are potential vagrants, but are generally also widely held in captivity; they do not form part of the British List. Nomenclature, scientific names and the sequence of species follow the official British List, as published by the BOU (1992) and updated in their journal *Ibis*.

Ruddy Shelduck *Tadorna ferruginea*

Origin: North-west Africa, south-eastern Europe, southern and central Asia.

The first published record of this species related to a female at Kirby Bellars Gravel Pits from October 1976 until January 1977. Since 1977 there have been reports in 17 of the 28 years up to 2005, involving approximately 43 individuals. Most records have been of one or two birds, but three were at Watermead Park and Birstall Gravel Pits from September 29th to October 11th 1992, flocks of four were at Rutland Water from September 1st to 23rd 1979 and at Rutland Water and Eyebrook Reservoir from August 12th until October 23rd 1989, and five which flew into Leicestershire from Derbyshire near Castle Donington on July 15th 2005 were presumably the birds then seen at Swithland Reservoir fom July 22nd to 30th 2005.

A male which became more or less resident at Rutland Water from 1991 until 1997 paired with an Egyptian Goose, and on May 18th 1996 two hybrid young were recorded (Harrop 1998). Following the disappearance of this resident male, however, there were no further records until 2003, when a pair at Rutland Water from June 9th until August 6th was followed by two females there from September 7th to 21st and on October 30th. Subsequently, a pair was at Eyebrook Reservoir, Fort Henry Ponds and Rutland Water from April 17th to July 30th 2004, three were at Eyebrook Reservoir on September 3rd 2004 and the group of five mentioned above was seen in 2005.

The majority of reports have come from either Rutland Water or Eyebrook Reservoir. Apart from those already mentioned, the only records from other sites have been a female which visited Groby Pool, Swithland

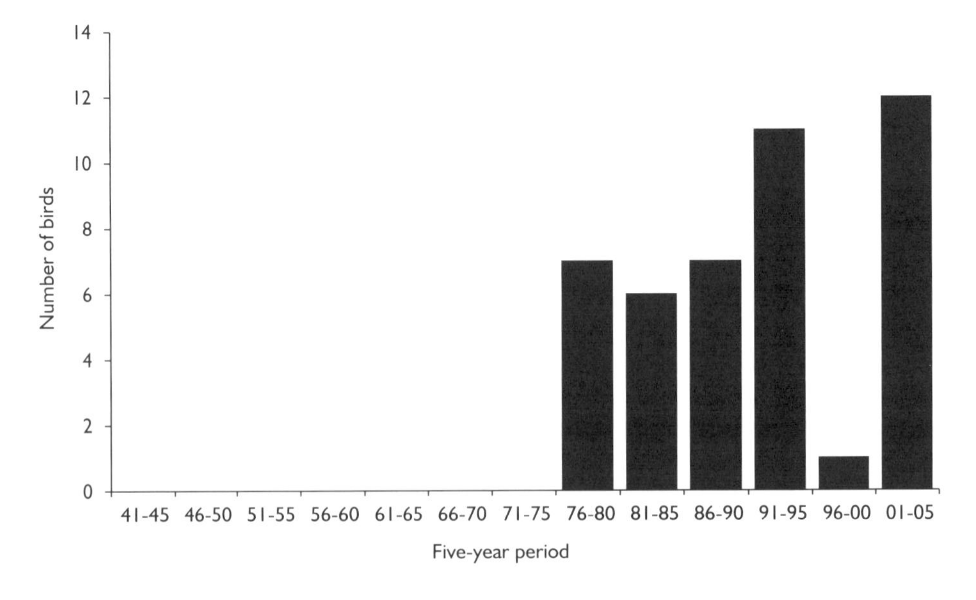

Figure 574: Number of Ruddy Shelducks by five-year periods 1941–2005.

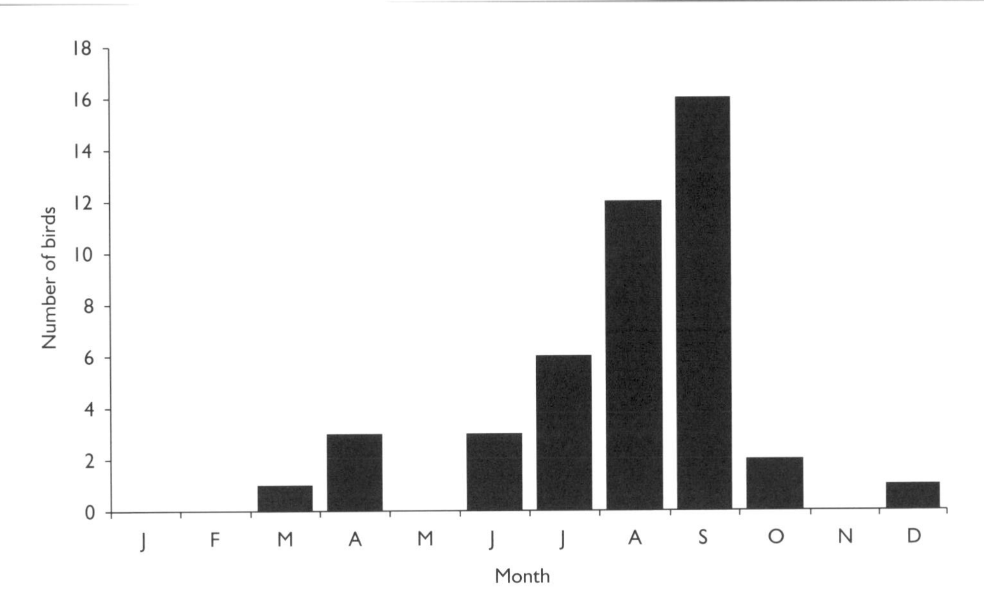

Figure 575: Monthly occurrence of Ruddy Shelducks 1941–2005.

Reservoir, Cropston Reservoir and Thornton Reservoir from September 18th 1985 to April 14th 1986, two at Watermead Gravel Pits from December 1st to 17th 1985, with the male until April 5th 1986, a female at Cadeby Quarry on August 28th 1986 and one at Saddington Reservoir on April 19th 1993.

Although there is a possibility that wild birds occasionally appear in Britain, all records of Ruddy Shelduck in Leicestershire and Rutland are considered to involve birds of captive or feral origin. It is, however, interesting to note the obvious peak in arrivals during August and September.

Hybrids with Egyptian Goose, South African Shelduck and Common Shelduck have been recorded: see 'Hybrids' (pages 676–684).

Falcated Duck *Anas falcata*

Origin: South-east Siberia and Mongolia to Kurile Islands and northern Japan.

A male associated with a flock of 70 Eurasian Teal at Cropston Reservoir from December 27th 1975 to March 20th 1976 (*BB* 87:567).

Baikal Teal *Anas formosa*

Origin: Eastern Siberia, wintering in south China and Japan.

An adult female was at Fort Henry Ponds from September 5th to 14th 1990 (*BB* 87:570).

Marbled Duck *Marmaronetta angustirostris*

Origin: Southern Spain and North Africa through the Middle East to western China.

Three individuals have been recorded. One, possibly a juvenile, was at Rutland Water from June 16th to 20th 1990, when it was found dead (*BB* 88:555); only the wings and feet remained, and irregular growth of the wings suggested that there had been a check in feather growth, perhaps at the time when it was first capable of flight.

In the same year, one was at Cropston Reservoir from August 28th to September 11th. A third individual was at Rutland Water on August 31st 1996; this bird had orange staining on its tail, a hole in its upper mandible, and hobbled, but despite its disabilities it managed to move from South Muskham (Nottinghamshire), where it had been on August 26th and 27th, and then return there from September 1st to 5th (*BB* 90:518).

White-headed Duck *Oxyura leucocephala*

Origin: South-west Mediterranean to north-west China.

There have been six records of this endangered species, possibly involving only four birds.

All records:

1978 female, Eyebrook Reservoir, September 21st to December 5th. This bird had previously been seen in Northamptonshire from August 5th to September 17th, and was possibly one of two birds which escaped from Slimbridge (Gloucestershire) in 1977.

1995 female or juvenile, Eyebrook Reservoir, September 13th to 29th; same bird, Rutland Water, October 10th (*BB* 89:531 and 90:521).

2002 male, Stanford Reservoir, September 10th to 22nd (*BB* 96:609 and 98:693).

2003 female or juvenile, Stanford Reservoir, October 3rd to 12th; possibly the same bird, Swithland Reservoir, October 12th to 18th (*BB* 98:693).

2004 male, Rutland Water, October 31st and November 1st (*BB* 98:693). This could conceivably have been the bird recorded at Stanford Reservoir in 2002.

In addition, a male reported at Swithland Reservoir on November 21st 1981 and again in April and May 1982 was later identified from photographs as a hybrid between White-headed Duck and Ruddy Duck; this was presumably the bird that had been reported earlier in 1981 in Somerset and Staffordshire (*BB* 75:143), and was perhaps the offspring of one of the birds which escaped from Slimbridge in 1977.

Formerly on Category E of the British list, a recent review of records resulted in the White-headed Duck being placed on Category D by the BOU. Potential vagrants were traditionally considered most likely to involve birds from the more migratory eastern populations, but the recent increase in numbers in Spain (and records of apparently wild birds in France) makes a southern origin for vagrants possible. Nonetheless, this species is relatively numerous in captivity, and assessment of records is further complicated because the Spanish population now includes introduced birds.

Saker Falcon *Falco cherrug*

Origin: Central Europe through Asia to China.

There have been four published records, all of single birds, at: Rutland Water on December 26th 1990 (which was certainly an escaped falconer's bird as it was carrying bells); Narborough on September 6th 1992; Priory Water on August 22nd and November 28th 1999, and Ives Head on May 1st 2005.

In addition, a bird first reported as this species at Swithland Reservoir on December 12th 2001 may have been the same as one subsequently identified as a hybrid between Saker Falcon and Gyr Falcon which remained in north-west Leicestershire until at least March 2005.

Although this species is on Category D of the British List, observers are unlikely to have records accepted unless they can prove the identification to the exclusion of similar falconers' hybrids. Even then, most records (including those above) are likely to involve escapes.

CATEGORY E SPECIES

by Rob Fray and Dave Gamble

The definition of Category E is 'species which have been recorded as introductions, transportees or escapees from captivity and whose breeding populations (if any) are not thought to be self-sustaining'.

It may seem strange to list non-native birds in a county avifauna, and a lot of birdwatchers do not bother to report exotic species. Although the vast majority of species in the following list will never be more than an occasional curiosity, who knows which will be the next to emulate the likes of the Greater Canada Goose, Mandarin Duck and Ruddy Duck and gain a firm foothold?

Also included in the following section are several species which are on either Category A or C of the British List, but have only ever been recorded in Leicestershire and Rutland as certain escapes; where this is the case, it is made clear in the text. Details of species which have occurred in the counties both naturally and as escapes are given in the main Systematic List.

The list follows the sequence and nomenclature of Gill & Wright (2006), *Birds of the World: Recommended English Names*. It should be noted that 'Category E' records are not subjected to the same level of scrutiny as those species detailed in the main Systematic List.

Helmeted Guineafowl — *Numida meleagris*

Origin: Africa.

The majority of records of this widely domesticated species probably refer to birds which have wandered away from their respective farmyards, rather than true escapes. Single birds were at Cropston Reservoir on September 26th 1989 and Belvoir on February 28th 1993, whilst in 1997 six were near Rothley Park Golf Course on March 3rd and one was at King's Hill Lodge, Uppingham on April 27th and June 9th. Four near Burbage Common on April 9th 1999 included one which 'attacked a horse' (!). During 2000, two were at Cosby for much of the year and one was at Thurlaston on September 4th. Separate flocks of 14 and five were at Old Dalby Wood on March 16th 2002, with the flock of five seen again on June 3rd and August 22nd the same year. Also in 2002 one was seen wandering around near the Co-op in Melton Mowbray on June 3rd. In 2005, nine were at Stonepit Spinney, near Wartnaby, on January 3rd; seven (including an albino bird) were at Donington Hall on March 19th and three were at Billesdon Coplow on December 18th.

Chukar Partridge — *Alectoris chukar*

Origin: South-east Europe through Asia to China.

During the 1980s and early 1990s, it became common practice to release this species alongside, or instead of, Red-legged Partridges, and between 1986 and 1996 records came from a total of 27 sites. The first to be noted were males paired with Red-legged Partridges at both Meridian Business Park, Braunstone and Newton Harcourt between April and June 1986, after which this species, and hybrids with Red-legged Partridges, became common. The highest counts recorded were 21 at Cossington on November 3rd 1991, 19 at Leicester Forest East on December 15th 1992, 17 at Cossington South Gravel Pits on November 12th 1989 and 11 at Swithland Reservoir on February 4th 1989.

Once the release of this and other exotic species became illegal, numbers quickly dwindled and no pure bred birds have been recorded since a pair with a juvenile at Knipton on August 27th 1996. However, a few hybrids lingered until 2000.

Barbary Partridge — *Alectoris barbara*

Origin: North Africa.

According to Browne, one was picked up dead at Edmondthorpe in April 1842.

Japanese Quail *Coturnix japonica*

Origin: East Palearctic.

One was at Huncote on February 19th 2004.

Silver Pheasant *Lophura nycthemera*

Origin: South-east Asia

A male was at Priory Water on February 10th 1996, with a female there from March 26th to April 11th of the same year.

Reeves's Pheasant *Syrmaticus reevesii*

Origin: North and central China.

There have been four records: single males at Gumley on September 2nd 1999, Deans Lane, Woodhouse from October 14th 2001 to May 12th 2002 and Cloud Wood in early March 2004, and a female at Groby Pool on December 17th 2000.

Golden Pheasant *Chrysolophus pictus*

Origin: China. Category C of the British List.

There have been two records, both of single males: at Husband's Bosworth on September 1st 1976 and Barleythorpe on April 13th 1991. This gaudy gamebird is indigenous to the mountains of central China, and has been introduced to Britain since the late 19th century; several self-sustaining populations are now established, especially in East Anglia. The two Leicestershire and Rutland birds, however, are more likely to have escaped locally rather than moved from one of the established populations.

Lady Amherst's Pheasant *Chrysolophus amherstiae*

Origin: South-west Asia. Category C of the British List.

There have been four records: one at Market Harborough on June 2nd 1973, single males in 1995 in gardens at Coalville and Oadby on May 20th and June 2nd respectively, and a male at King's Hill Lodge, Uppingham, in July and September 2000. This spectacular pheasant breeds in the mountain forests of south-west East Asia and was introduced to Britain in the early 20th century. The main population in this country is centred on Bedfordshire and Buckinghamshire, but very few now remain. As with the Golden Pheasant, the Leicestershire birds are likely to have escaped locally.

Indian Peafowl *Pavo cristatus*

Origin: Indian subcontinent.

A female was in gardens at Melton Mowbray in May 1999, a male was at Priory Water on June 10th 2001 and two were at Great Easton on March 30th 2005.

White-faced Whistling Duck *Dendrocygna viduata*

Origin: Tropical South America and Africa.

An adult was at Swithland Reservoir from May 5th to 10th 2001.

Fulvous Whistling Duck *Dendrocygna bicolor*

Origin: Southern USA south to north and east South America, Africa, Madagascar and Indian subcontinent.

Four adults appeared at Cropston Reservoir on September 30th 1992, and then commuted between here and nearby Swithland Reservoir until October 25th, when one disappeared. The remaining three continued to be seen until November 27th, and two were noted the following day, after which there were no further reports.

Swan Goose *Anser cygnoides*

Origin: Eastern Asia.

Four of the common domesticated form, often referred to as Chinese Goose, were at Stanford Reservoir on August 12th 1975. All other records probably refer to just one wandering individual, which was seen at Thornton Reservoir, often in the company of a feral Barnacle Goose, from September 5th to 13th 1999, December 23rd to 31st 2000 and in September 2001, and also visited Cropston Reservoir on September 25th 1999 and Bagworth Heath on October 29th 2000.

A hybrid with Greylag Goose has been recorded: see 'Hybrids' (pages 676–684).

Lesser White-fronted Goose *Anser erythropus*

Origin: Arctic Eurasia. Category A of British List.

An adult was at Rutland Water from December 10th 2004 to January 9th 2005.

This species, which breeds in Arctic Eurasia and winters southern Europe, India and China, occurs in Britain less than annually; by the end of 2005 there had been 131 records. Most vagrants arrive with flocks of White-fronted Geese and a large proportion has been found at Slimbridge (Gloucestershire).

Bar-headed Goose *Anser indicus*

Origin: Central Asia.

This goose, along with Black Swan, is the most frequently occurring species of escaped wildfowl in the counties. The first published record was of two at Eyebrook Reservoir from August 30th to October 26th 1969, although there were no further reports until two were at Rutland Water on May 21st 1980; since then, there have been records in all but six years up to 2005. Reports have come from a total of 17 sites, with the favoured ones being Rutland Water (records in 12 years involving some 21 birds), Eyebrook Reservoir (approximately 19 individuals over the course of 12 different years) and Stanford Reservoir (seven records of nine birds). Most reports have been of single birds, but two have been seen together on nine occasions, three were at Rutland Water from January 30th to February 5th 2000 and five were at the same site on June 14th 2004. The majority of birds do not remain at one site for long, and there have only been three records referring to individuals staying for more than three months: one at Priory Water from January 3rd to April 24th 1998, two at Eyebrook Reservoir from June 6th

1997 to February 1998, and possibly the same two again at Eyebrook Reservoir from June 17th to September 17th 1998.

A hybrid with either an Emperor Goose or a Barnacle Goose has been recorded: see 'Hybrids' (pages 676–684).

Snow Goose *Chen caerulescens*

Origin: North America. Category A of the British List.

Although wild vagrants from North America occur elsewhere in Britain, all records of this species in the counties relate to birds of captive or feral origin. The first involved a bird at Wanlip Gravel Pits on April 11th 1976 and since then there have been records in all but five years up to 2005.

Following one at Eyebrook Reservoir on January 1st 1978, which was seen in the Welland valley on February 5th, three main arrivals of feral birds have accounted for most records. Four white morph birds appeared at Eyebrook Reservoir on December 9th 1978 and remained until March 13th 1979; three of them relocated to Stanford Reservoir on April 29th 1979 before returning to Eyebrook Reservoir from October 21st 1979 to February 25th 1980. Presumably the same three returned to Eyebrook Reservoir with four juveniles on October 25th 1980 and were joined by four more white adults on November 30th, all 11 remaining until March 15th 1981. Up to five were still present in April 1982, with four until February 1983 and one until February 2nd 1985.

Four white morphs arrived at Rutland Water on May 17th 1986, although four 'blue morphs' which joined them from August 27th the same year were subsequently identified as Snow Goose x Barnacle Goose hybrids. All four white birds remained at either Rutland Water or Priory Water until 1995, with three throughout 1996 and just two from 1997. In 1993, two of the birds which had arrived in 1986 bred at Rutland Water. A chick hatched on June 10th but died on July 6th. The following year, two young fledged. In 1996, four young hatched on May 31st but by August 10th only one survived. During the same period, 21 Snow x Greylag hybrids fledged at Priory Water following mating between one or two of the male Snow Geese which arrived in 1986 and local Greylag Geese. The last two birds which had arrived in 1986 died as the 20th century came to a close: one was not seen after September 1999 and the final bird was found dead at Rutland Water on April 16th 2000.

During the long periods mentioned above when various birds were resident in the counties, the only records which may not have related to these birds, all involving single white morph individuals unless stated, were as follows:

- Groby Pool from July 18th to 20th 1983.
- a blue morph individual at Stanford Reservoir and Stanford Park from January to August 1987 and again at Stanford Reservoir on July 29th 1989 (although there is a possibility that these records relate to one of the Snow Goose x Barnacle Goose hybrids originally seen in 1986, as it was not until 1990 that they were identified as hybrids).
- Swithland Reservoir on February 7th 1987 and Groby Pool from February 21st to March 15th 1987.
- Stapleford Park on March 26th 1991 and April 10th 1992.
- Dishley Pool on October 20th 1996.
- an adult and two second-years at Rutland Water on May 3rd 1997 were considered different from the then-resident birds, with the adult moving to Eyebrook Reservoir from May 6th to 8th 1997.
- Stanford Reservoir on January 14th 1997.
- two at Quorn Borrow Pit from December 6th to 22nd 1998.

Since the demise of the final resident bird in 2000, the only record was one which arrived at Priory Water on June 5th 2003 and stayed for just three days.

Hybrids with Greylag Goose and Barnacle Goose have been recorded: see 'Hybrids' (pages 676–684).

Snow Geese breed in the Arctic in north-west Greenland, Canada, Alaska and north-east Siberia and winter mainly in the south-western United States. They are rare winter visitors to Britain, although the species' status is confused by the large number of escaped birds in the country; breeding by feral birds has occurred regularly in Hampshire and on Coll (Argyll) since 1996 (Holling *et al.* 2008).

Ross's Goose *Chen rossii*

Origin: Arctic Canada.

An adult was at Bosworth Water Park from September to November 1997, and had probably been present for several months previously.

Emperor Goose *Chen canagica*

Origin: North-east Siberia and western Alaska.

One was at Belvoir Lakes on November 12th 1995 and seven visited Rutland Water on March 13th 2005. In addition, hybrids with Bar-headed Goose and Barnacle Goose have been recorded: see 'Hybrids' (pages 676–684).

Lesser Canada Goose *Branta hutchinsii*

Origin: Greenland, Canada and Alaska.

Two birds considered to have been Cackling Canada Geese *B. h. minima* were recorded at Eyebrook Reservoir in late December 1985, on February 22nd and 23rd 1986 and on September 13th 1989.

The Lesser Canada Goose (with subspecies *hutchinsii*, *leucopareia*, *minima* and *taverneri*) was only recognised by the BOU in 2005. The Greater Canada Goose is currently on Category C of the British List, but vagrants have probably occurred so it is currently under active consideration for addition to Category A. Following the recent taxonomic split, the Lesser Canada Goose is also under active consideration for addition to Category A since vagrants have probably occurred.

Red-breasted Goose *Branta ruficollis*

Origin: Siberia. Category A of the British List.

The only record relates to an adult bird with a plastic ring on its right leg which was first recorded at Priory Water on November 10th 2002. It was relocated at Rutland Water on November 25th, where it remained (with occasional short absences) until May 28th 2003. It then moved to Eyebrook Reservoir on June 1st and finally to Trent Valley Pit on August 25th 2003.

This species, which breeds in Siberia and winters in various parts of Europe, occurs in Britain just about annually; by the end of 2005 there had been 72 records. Most vagrants arrive with flocks of either Brent or Barnacle Geese.

Black Swan *Cygnus atratus*

Origin: Australia and Tasmania.

This species, which is commonly held in captivity, is one of the most frequent escapes to occur in the county. Since the first published record, of one at Eyebrook Reservoir on February 18th 1980, there have been reports in all but five years up to 2005. Records have come from a total of 22 sites, with the favoured ones being Eyebrook Reservoir (15 records of at least 25 birds), Rutland Water (12 records of some 19 birds) and Priory Water (five records involving 13 individuals). Most reports have been of single birds, but two have been seen together on 13 occasions and three were at Rutland Water on February 23rd 1994 and February 8th 2005. Groups of four were at Priory Water on February 5th 1992, Eyebrook Reservoir from August 11th to September 11th 2001 and Willesley Lake on January 28th 2003, whilst parties of five have been noted at Priory Water from November 18th to 20th 1991 and Rutland Water on August 15th 1999; the latter birds then moved to

Eyebrook Reservoir, where they remained from August 19th to September 30th 1999. Birds often linger at one site for lengthy periods, and several have remained for up to eight months; the longest stayers have been single birds at Evans' Weir on the River Soar in Leicester from October 2001 to July 6th 2002, Priory Water from November 6th 1995 to January 4th 1997 and Groby Pool from August 7th 2002 until August 25th 2005.

South African Shelduck *Tadorna cana*

Origin: South Africa.

There have been records in seven years, although with the exception of one at Eyebrook Reservoir in October 1975 and a male which visited Cropston Reservoir, Groby Pool and Swithland Reservoir between September 12th and 26th 1999, it is likely that all reports have referred to just one returning female, which was first seen at Eyebrook Reservoir on August 18th 1992, before moving to Rutland Water from August 24th to September 19th. It returned to the latter site in four of the next five years, being seen from May 21st to August 29th 1993, June 25th to August 25th 1994, July 30th to September 10th 1995 and June 8th to July 16th 1997. The same individual has also been noted at Priory Water from September 18th to October 31st 1993 and at Fort Henry Ponds on June 26th 1994.

A probable hybrid with a Ruddy Shelduck has been recorded: see 'Hybrids' (pages 676–684).

Australian Shelduck *Tadorna tadornoides*

Origin: Southern Australia.

A male was at Rutland Water on April 10th 2000, with perhaps the same bird from July 6th to September 28th 2002, December 20th 2002 to August 19th 2003, and on January 14th and November 6th 2004.

Paradise Shelduck *Tadorna variegata*

Origin: New Zealand.

There have been two records: a female at Eyebrook Reservoir on August 13th 2000 and a pair at Rutland Water on March 6th 2003.

Muscovy Duck *Cairina moschata*

Origin: Central and north-eastern South America.

This rather ungainly duck is widely domesticated and it is likely that there are more of the domestic form at liberty in the counties than records suggest. Indeed, there is a possibility that this species will be considered for admission to Category C of the British List in the near future (Dudley 2005).

In 1984, one was at Thornton Reservoir on April 1st, with two there on May 19th, and one was at Eyebrook Reservoir on December 15th. One was at Freemen's Weir, Leicester from September 12th to 20th 1995, with presumably the same bird again from January 1st to October 24th 1996. There were two at Ibstock Opencast (now Sence Valley Forest Park) on August 11th 1996, single males at Rutland Water on March 15th 1997 and Groby Pool on November 15th 2005, and one at Rutland Water from December 18th to 24th 2005. There are two breeding records: a female with four young at Barkby Brook on both July 20th 2000 and June 26th 2001.

Haines, writing in 1907, mentions that the 'Musk Duck' was semi-domesticated at Burley Fishponds, and that a nest was built in a tree there.

A hybrid with a Mallard has been recorded: see 'Hybrids' (pages 676–684).

Wood Duck *Aix sponsa*

Origin: North America.

The first published record was of two males at Swithland Reservoir from May 8th to 12th 1983, and what was presumably one of these birds was then seen either there or at Cropston Reservoir intermittently until October 19th 1985. One of only three females to have been seen in the counties was also recorded around the same time, at Swithland Reservoir on April 10th and 11th 1984 and then Cropston Reservoir from April 15th to 29th of the same year. Apart from three pinioned males at Groby Pool from October 8th 1989 to January 14th 1990, with two until March 9th 1991, and pairs at Priory Water on May 29th 2005 (with the drake again on June 12th) and Croft Quarry on December 28th 2005, all subsequent records have been of single drakes, at: Birstall on April 7th 1988; Aylestone Meadows from February 16th to the end of May 1993, with presumably the same bird there on May 2nd 1994 and at nearby Freemen's Weir on June 19th 1994 and throughout 1995; Rutland Water on September 14th and from October 10th to November 28th 1993; Barrowden in May and June 1999; Heather Fishponds on December 12th 1999; Charnwood Water on May 2nd 2000; Wistow Lake from May 16th to June 10th 2001, and Priory Water on September 30th and October 28th 2001.

Ringed Teal *Callonetta leucophrys*

Origin: South-central South America.

There have been three records, involving five individuals: a pair at Eyebrook Reservoir on August 31st 1985, two males at Swithland Reservoir on March 17th 1992 and a female at Rutland Water on October 3rd 1993.

Cape Teal *Anas capensis*

Origin: Eastern and southern Africa.

There have been two records: one at Melton Country Park on September 18th 1994 and an adult at Rutland Water on June 30th 1996.

Chiloe Wigeon *Anas sibilatrix*

Origin: Southern South America.

The first published record was of one at Swithland and Cropston Reservoirs on September 15th 1974, but it was not until February 17th 1985 that the next bird was found, at Rutland Water. There have been records in 12 subsequent years, but it is possible that as few as ten individuals have been responsible for these reports. After one at Abbey Park, Leicester from February 18th to March 1st 1986, records of single birds at Rutland Water on June 2nd 1990, from September 5th to 9th 1990 and on January 6th 1991, and at Priory Water on November 25th 1990, probably all related to the same bird. Likewise, one roaming male probably accounted for reports at Priory Water from December 10th to 17th 1995, Rutland Water on January 7th and February 4th and 10th 1996, and Fort Henry Ponds on January 14th and 20th 1996. A male at Swithland Reservoir on April 27th and 28th 1998 may well have been the same bird then noted at Groby Pool from December 21st 1998 to January 1999, and was possibly the male seen at Sence Valley Forest Park on October 15th and 16th and November 10th 2000. Further drakes were noted at Priory Water on March 31st 2002, Rutland Water on April 18th 2003, Eyebrook Reservoir from September 6th to 13th 2003, Thornton Reservoir from April 20th to 26th 2004 and Groby Pool on May 1st 2004, and three were at Eyebrook Reservoir on August 20th 2005.

Hybrids with American Wigeon have been recorded: see 'Hybrids' (pages 676–684).

Philippine Duck *Anas luzonica*

Origin: Endemic to the Philippine Islands.

One was seen on the River Soar at Abbey Park, Leicester on December 27th 1982 and from February 25th to March 1st 1986; it had presumably originated from the captive wildfowl collection within the Park.

Yellow-billed Duck *Anas undulata*

Origin: Eastern and southern Africa.

One was at Swithland Reservoir intermittently from April 17th 1982 to January 8th 1983, when it was shot.

Red Shoveler *Anas platalea*

Origin: Southern South America.

Two females were at Cropston Reservoir on August 1st 1990, with one still present the following day, and a male was at Groby Pool from April 27th to 30th 2005.

Chestnut Teal *Anas castanea*

Origin: Southern Australia.

There have been records in four years, involving four or five individuals, beginning with a male at Staunton Harold Reservoir on February 6th 1993; perhaps the same bird was then at Dishley Pool later the same year, on November 28th. A female frequented Rutland Water from June 25th to 27th 1995, and then a male visited Eyebrook Reservoir, Priory Water and Rutland Water between April 8th and May 4th 1997. Finally, one was at Rutland Water on August 2nd 1999.

A hybrid with a Shoveler has been recorded: see 'Hybrids' (pages 676–684).

White-cheeked Pintail *Anas bahamensis*

Origin: West Indies, Galapagos and South America.

There have been 12 records, all of single birds unless stated, at: Rutland Water from October 11th to 18th 1987 and on November 9th 1990 and July 8th 2005; Melton Country Park on May 1st 1994, with a leucistic individual there on July 15th 1995; Priory Water, possibly the same leucistic bird on March 26th 1996; Eyebrook Reservoir from July 14th to 27th 1997, from September 8th to 11th 1998 and from June 10th to 16th 1999, Watermead Park from September 13th to 23rd 1998; Trent Valley Pit on May 7th and 8th 2005, with presumably the same bird nearby at Lockington Gravel Pits on May 17th 2005, and Groby Pool from October 17th to November 18th 2005, with three there from November 19th to 23rd 2005. The leucistic form of this species is commonly held in captivity.

Speckled Teal *Anas flavirostris*

Origin: Western and southern South America.

There have been four records, probably involving three individuals: single birds at Cropston Reservoir from October 18th to November 8th 1990 and Eyebrook Reservoir on August 28th 1993, and a male at Priory Water on August 28th 2000, with probably the same bird returning there on August 26th the following year.

Yellow-billed Pintail *Anas georgica*

Origin: Southern South America.

The only record is of one at Eyebrook Reservoir on December 15th 1985, although a presumed hybrid with an unknown species has also been recorded: see 'Hybrids' (pages 676–684).

Eaton's Pintail *Anas eatoni*

Origin: Kerguelen Island, southern Indian Ocean.

One at Swithland Reservoir on November 25th 1992. It is often considered to be a race of Pintail.

Rosy-billed Pochard *Netta peposaca*

Origin: Southern South America.

An immature male was by the dam at Rutland Water on November 22nd 2002.

Canvasback *Aythya valisineria*

Origin: North America. Category A of the British List.

A very tame male was reported at Priory Water on October 14th 1995, although as no descriptive notes were provided the possibility of a hybrid cannot be fully excluded. This North American duck was added to the British List in 1996, since when there have been six accepted records.

Hooded Merganser *Lophodytes cucullatus*

Origin: North America. Category A of the British List.

There have been two records: a male by the dam at Rutland Water on March 17th 1985, and a female on the Grantham Canal between Harby and Plungar on May 22nd 1997; the latter bird had previously been recorded at various sites in Nottinghamshire from November 16th 1996 to February 18th 1997 (*BB* 90:521 and 91:517).

Lake Duck *Oxyura vittata*

Origin: Southern South America.

A wandering male was probably responsible for all records, at: Rutland Water on March 28th 1999, Melton Country Park from July to September 2000, April 8th to August 11th 2001 and August 8th to 15th 2004 and Priory Water from July 25th to August 1st 2004 and April 13th to 17th 2005. However, several similar species exist, including the African **Maccoa Duck** *Oxyura maccoa* and the Australian **Blue-billed Duck** *Oxyura australis*, whilst the possibility of this bird being a dark-headed Ruddy Duck cannot be entirely ruled out.

Chilean Flamingo *Phoenicopterus chilensis*

Origin: Central to southern South America.

There have been records of single birds in six years, at: Cropston Reservoir on September 27th 1970; Eyebrook Reservoir from July 11th to 18th 1971; Rutland Water from October 23rd to 27th 1985; Eyebrook Reservoir from August 9th to 11th 1989; Rutland Water from December 14th 1991 to May 16th 1992, and Stanford Reservoir on July 12th and September 16th 1992.

Unidentified flamingos *Phoenicopterus sp.*

Unidentified flamingos have been reported at Stanford Reservoir on October 13th 1968, Cropston Reservoir on September 21st 1974 and Eyebrook Reservoir on April 27th 1979.

Sacred Ibis *Threskiornis aethiopicus*

Origin: Africa.

An immature bird, first seen at Rutland Water on April 5th 1999, was at Priory Water later the same day and on the 6th.

Unidentified ibis

An unidentified ibis was at Eyebrook Reservoir on July 4th 1963.

Pink-backed Pelican *Pelecanus rufescens*

Origin: Africa.

One with a strap around its leg and various missing primaries was at Eyebrook Reservoir from October 16th to 20th 2003.

Unidentified pelican *Pelecanus sp.*

An unidentified pelican was at Eyebrook Reservoir on January 31st 1965.

Turkey Vulture *Cathartes aura*

Origin: Southern North, Central and South America.

An adult was seen over Burley Wood on December 28th 2003 and April 16th 2004.

Lanner Falcon *Falco biarmicus*

Origin: Southern Europe, Middle East and Africa.

A juvenile, with jesses, was at Eyebrook Reservoir on November 9th 1997, and single birds were at Frolesworth Manor Lake on January 19th 1999 and Stoke Dry Wood on January 26th of the same year. An adult, complete with jesses and a bell, was at Western Park, Leicester on October 24th and 25th 2002.

Unidentified falcon *Falco sp.*

A large juvenile falcon, considered to be either a Lanner Falcon or a Saker Falcon, was seen circling high over Swithland Reservoir on August 24th 1988.

Harris's Hawk *Parabuteo unicinctus*

Origin: Southern USA through Central America to South America.

An immature, wearing jesses, at Kirby Lakes on March 22nd 1998 had escaped whilst being flown at nearby Burton Lazars, whilst one, also with jesses, was at Groby Pool on April 7th 2001. Single birds were at Rutland Water on April 21st 2001, Manton on March 17th 2002 and Pickworth on October 5th 2003, one with jesses was at Felicity's Wood, near Nanpantan, on May 15th 2004, and perhaps the same bird was at Swithland Reservoir on March 25th 2005.

Red-tailed Hawk *Buteo jamaicensis*

Origin: North and Central America and West Indies.

One, wearing jesses, was at Burley Wood from March 31st to April 7th 2001, with presumably the same nearby at Tunneley Wood on June 24th of the same year. One, also trailing jesses, over Burley Wood on April 20th 2003 may have been the same bird.

Unidentified Crowned Crane *Balearica regulorum/pavonina*

Origin: Africa.

One was at Wellsborough on January 1st 1965, two were in the Kibworth area in September 1969 and three were between Kirby Muxloe and Newtown Unthank on July 30th 1970; the latter trio had apparently been seen elsewhere around the county in the previous few weeks.

Formerly considered subspecies, this species pair has only recently been split and it is not known which taxon was involved in the above records.

Demoiselle Crane *Anthropoides virgo*

Origin: Central Asia.

A ringed individual was seen near Cottesmore on September 21st 1976.

Unidentified crane *Grus sp.*

One at Bruntingthorpe Airfield on June 21st 1968 was probably a **Sarus Crane** *Grus antigone.*

Blacksmith Lapwing *Vanellus armatus*

Origin: Southern Africa.

One was at Eyebrook Reservoir from June 22nd to 28th 1981. Although an unlikely candidate for natural vagrancy, it caused a fair bit of interest at the time and was seen by many observers.

Grey-headed Gull *Chroicocephalus cirrocephalus*

Origin: The southern halves of Africa and South America.

An adult frequented the Egleton Reserve at Rutland Water from April 19th to 24th 2000.

African Collared Dove *Streptopelia roseogrisea*

Origin: North-central Africa

The widely domesticated form *risoria*, referred to as **Barbary Dove** and only known in captivity, is believed to derive from the African Collared Dove. There have been three records: one singing at Swithland Wood on June 1st 1975, two at Birstall in October 1977 and one at Rothley on March 8th 2004.

Diamond Dove *Geopelia cuneata*

Origin: Australia.

This tiny dove has occurred in three years: one found dead in a Blaby garden on September 27th 1996; one caught by hand at Saffron Lane, Leicester on August 25th 1998, and single birds in 2001 at Newtown Linford on April 6th and Hinckley from June 3rd to 10th.

Cockatiel *Nymphicus hollandicus*

Origin: Australia.

This popular cagebird seems to have a particular propensity for escapology, although there is a theory that their incessant, shrill shrieking causes their owners to release them deliberately.

The first published record was one at Mowmacre, Leicester on September 29th 1986 and, with the exception of 1987 and 1988, there have been reports in every subsequent year. There have been records from a total of 46 sites, involving some 84 birds; 'favoured' areas have been Leicester city centre, with 12 individuals (including five in the Great Central Street area), Beaumont Leys, Leicester (seven birds), and both Priory Water and the Aylestone area (five birds each). The majority of records have been of single birds, but two were at Beaumont Leys on October 6th 1991 and Asfordby on August 22nd 1999. There are often several records in a year, and the 'best' years have been 1994 and 1995, with eight reports each, whilst there were seven records in each of 1991, 1999, 2000 and 2002.

Red-fronted Parakeet *Cyanoramphus novaezelandiae*

Origin: New Zealand.

One was in an Osgathorpe garden for about five weeks from April 3rd 2002.

White-cheeked Rosella *Platycercus adscitus*

Origin: South-east Australia.

There have been three records of this attractive parakeet, all of single birds, at: Aylestone Meadows on July 16th 1987; Hamilton Pool, Leicester from September 17th to October 5th 1993, and Melton Mowbray on December 16th and 17th 1996 (found dead on the latter date).

Budgerigar *Melopsittacus undulatus*

Origin: Australia.

As the most popular cagebird, it is surprising that more Budgerigars have not been recorded at liberty; it is likely that many have gone unreported.

The first published record was of one at Enderby on May 6th 1984, since when there have been records in all but five subsequent years. The vast majority of reports refer to single birds, but there were two at Loughborough University on March 7th 1996 and a mass break-out of five at Huncote on September 5th 1991. In total, birds have been noted at 23 sites, involving some 39 individuals, with 'favoured' sites including Rutland Water (four records) and Swithland Reservoir and Beaumont Leys, Leicester (three records each).

This species does not always fare well once at large, as evidenced by feathers found beneath a Tawny Owl roost at Swithland Reservoir in 1996, and single birds taken by Sparrowhawks at Whetstone Pastures on May 2nd 1996 and Thurnby on May 26th 2004.

Plum-headed Parakeet *Psittacula cyanocephala*

Origin: Indian and Sri Lanka.

One was at Burrough on the Hill on June 24th 1988.

Rosy-faced Lovebird *Agapornis roseicollis*

Origin: South-west Africa.

There have been five records: single birds at Huncote on August 7th 1984, Narborough (an immature) from July 21st to August 1st 2000, Beaumont Leys, Leicester on May 27th and 28th 2001 and Market Harborough on August 15th 2002, and two at Anstey on September 28th 2003.

Fischer's Lovebird *Agapornis fischeri*

Origin; East Africa

One was at Melton Mowbray on March 15th 1999.

Parakeet sp.

Four unidentified parakeets have been recorded: single birds at Shepshed on November 5th 1983, Oadby on June 28th 1987, Thurmaston several times during 1987 and Wigston on September 20th 1994 and February 8th 1995.

Senegal Parrot *Poicephalus senegalus*

Origin: West Africa.

One was at Loughborough University on August 5th and September 2nd 1997.

Scarlet Macaw *Ara macao*

Origin: Central and northern South America.

One flew over Eyebrook Reservoir on December 16th 1998.

Turquoise-fronted Amazon *Amazona aestiva*

Origin: Central and South America.

A male frequented gardens in the Narborough and Enderby area from November 14th 2004 to April 10th 2005.

Amazon parrot sp. *Amazona sp.*

Origin: Central and South America.

One at Birstall on November 12th 2001 was, from the description supplied, either a **Mealy Amazon** *Amazona farinosa* or a **Yellow-crowned Amazon** *Amazona ochrocephala*.

Parrot sp.

There have been records of four unidentified parrots: single birds at Ullesthorpe from October 4th to 26th 1991 and Scraptoft on November 5th 2002, two at Aylestone/Glen Parva from mid-September to late December 1995 and two in a Blaby garden on February 8th 1997.

Eurasian Eagle Owl *Bubo bubo*

Origin: Europe and Asia.

One of two of the race *bengalensis*, which escaped from Greetham Falconry Centre in the winter of 1993–94, was still at large nearby in the Stretton area in the summer of 1994, whilst one of the European race *bubo* was on a house roof at Wigston on September 16th 1996.

Spotted Eagle Owl *Bubo africanus*

Origin: Southern half of Africa and Arabian peninsula.

One was photographed on a garden fence at Shepshed on May 25th 2003.

Red-billed Blue Magpie *Urocissa erythrorhyncha*

Origin: Himalayas, China and south-east Asia.

One was seen on a bird table in a Market Harborough garden on June 21st 2001.

Red-vented Bulbul *Pycnonotus cafer*

Origin: Indian subcontinent.

On was in a Little Dalby garden on June 21st and 22nd 2002.

Ashy Bulbul *Hemixos flavala*

Origin: South-east China.

One was at Thornton from March 16th to 20th 1999.

Red-billed Leiothrix — *Leiothrix lutea*

Origin: Indian subcontinent and China.

A male of this popular cagebird, often referred to as Pekin Robin, was at Rutland Water on April 13th 2004.

Common Myna — *Acridotheres tristis*

Origin: Central and south-east Asia and Indian subcontinent.

One was at Stoughton Airfield on August 14th 2000.

Myna sp.

Unidentified mynas were at New Parks, Leicester on December 1st 1997 and Evington on July 15th and 29th 2003.

Greater Blue-eared Starling — *Lamprotornis chalybaeus*

Origin: Africa.

One was seen perched on a TV aerial at Blaby on October 26th 1982.

Superb Starling — *Lamprotornis superbus*

Origin: Sudan to Somalia and Tanzania.

One was at Queen's Park, Loughborough on November 4th 2005.

White-capped Redstart — *Chaimarrornis leucocephalus*

Origin: Central Asia and India.

One was in a Glenfield garden on August 18th 1990.

Village Weaver — *Ploceus cucullatus*

Origin: Africa.

Single birds were in gardens at Great Glen in June 1995 and Stathern on November 9th 1996, and a male in a Theddingworth garden from March 8th to the end of April 2003 was joined by a female from March 17th to early April.

Black-headed Weaver — *Ploceus melanocephalus*

Origin: Africa

A male was in a Bottesford garden on June 24th 2005.

Golden-backed Weaver *Ploceus jacksoni*

Origin: East and central Africa.

Single males were recorded at Ibstock on October 6th 1999 and Sheepy Magna on July 21st 2001.

Red-billed Quelea *Quelea quelea*

Origin: Africa.

A male was in an Oakham garden for two weeks in late October 1997.

Yellow-crowned Bishop *Euplectes afer*

Origin: Central and East Africa.

A male was at Eyebrook Reservoir from August 20th to 28th 2000.

Southern Red Bishop *Euplectes orix*

Origin: East and central Africa.

A male was at Melton Mowbray on June 22nd 1999.

Zebra Finch *Taeniopygia guttata*

Origin: Australia.

After the first published record, of one at Markfield on August 5th 1989, there have been a further nine individuals reported. Single birds were at Ravenstone on July 22nd 1990, Huncote on June 16th 1997, Swithland Reservoir on November 30th 1997, Cropston Reservoir on September 13th 1998, Aylestone Meadows on October 16th 2000 and Leicester on June 29th 2001, whilst three were at Beaumont Leys, Leicester on March 17th and 18th 1991.

White-rumped Munia *Lonchura striata*

Origin: India and south-east Asia.

A female was caught by hand in a garden at Beaumont Leys, Leicester on February 5th 1991. This species is also sometimes referred to as Bengalese Finch.

Pin-tailed Whydah *Vidua macroura*

Origin: East and central Africa.

A male was at Trent Valley Pit from August 6th to 8th 1999.

Atlantic Canary *Serinus canaria*

Origin: Canary Islands, Azores and Madeira.

There have been ten reports of at least 11 individuals of this popular cagebird, in eight years between 1988 and 2003. The first published record was of one at Thurnby on September 4th 1988 and all subsequent reports have been of single birds, with the exception of two which were apparently nest-building (!) at Loughborough on July 27th 1990. As with Budgerigar, this species is almost certainly under-recorded once at large in the county.

Rufous-collared Sparrow *Zonotrichia capensis*

Origin: Central and South America.

A juvenile was in a Thurmaston garden on June 13th and 14th 1998.

Red-crested Cardinal *Paroaria coronata*

Origin: South America.

One was at Wanlip Gravel Pits on May 25th 1982.

Northern Cardinal *Cardinalis cardinalis*

Origin: North America.

One was in a garden at Humberstone, Leicester from March 1st to 25th 1969.

HYBRIDS

by Rob Fray and Dave Gamble

It is relatively unusual for species to hybridise in a natural environment, although there are exceptions, Herring Gull x Glaucous Gull being a well known example. The vast majority of hybrids recorded in the county are wildfowl; indeed, 41 of the 43 hybrid types listed below are *Anatidae* and it is probable that most originate from the unnatural confines of wildfowl collections. However, certain hybrids, such as Eurasian Wigeon x Eurasian Teal and Common Pochard x Tufted Duck may have come about in a natural situation. All except one of the hybrids recorded in the county are non-passerines.

Most hybrids are between members of the same genus, such as Common Pochard *Aythya ferina* x Tufted Duck *Aythya fuligula*. However, there are 12 instances listed below of cross-generic hybridisation. Hybrids tend to be infertile but it has been shown that Greylag Goose x Snow Goose hybrids are certainly fertile, whilst it is suspected that Greylag Goose x Greater Canada Goose hybrids, which are products of cross-generic hybridisation, are infertile.

Positive proof of parentage has been established for only a few hybrids: for most, educated guesswork applies. Consequently, in the majority of cases, the species pairings should not be taken as certain.

Hybrids are still under-recorded or treated dismissively by many observers, and the paucity of published literature on the subject does not help this situation. However, an understanding of at least some of the commoner hybrids is important, if not essential, if an observer wishes to identify certain species, particularly some of the *Aythya* ducks, correctly. The most important work as far as wildfowl are concerned is Gillham & Gillham (1996), *Hybrid Ducks*, and in the accounts below an attempt has been made to compare those hybrids recorded in Leicestershire and Rutland with the published information in Gillham & Gillham's work.

Chukar Partridge x Red-legged Partridge — *Alectoris chukar* x *Alectoris rufa*

Chukar Partridges were widely released for shooting in the 1980s and early 1990s and hybridised readily with Red-legged Partridges. The first hybrid noted was a male paired with a Red-legged Partridge at Meridian Business Park, Braunstone between April and June 1986, after which there were regular records until 1995. The majority of reports came from the Vale of Belvoir, an area well-known for large releases of game birds, particularly Red-legged Partridges; however, it is likely that during the late 1980s and early 1990s, large numbers of *Alectoris* partridges at large in other parts of the counties were also hybrids. The highest counts of presumed hybrids during this period were 13 at Oaks in Charnwood in October and November 1987, 12 at Shepshed on January 23rd 1990 and eight at Belvoir on February 7th 1993.

Once the release of Chukar Partridges (and other exotic species) became illegal, records of this hybrid dwindled rapidly, and the only reports after 1995 were of one at Waltham on the Wolds on June 1st 1997, two at Branston on February 15th 1998 and a male at Buckminster on April 25th 2000.

White-fronted Goose x Greylag Goose — *Anser albifrons* x *Anser anser*

In 1992, one was seen at Rutland Water from June 24th to August 28th, Eyebrook Reservoir on October 4th and Fort Henry Ponds on October 11th. One was again at Rutland Water on June 19th and 20th 1993. All sightings probably relate to the same bird.

White-fronted Goose x Greater Canada Goose *Anser albifrons x Branta canadensis*

One was at Ibstock Opencast (now Sence Valley Forest Park) on November 17th 1996, with perhaps the same bird at Knipton Reservoir on December 14th of the same year. A further individual (or, given the apparent rarity of this hybrid, maybe the same bird returning) was at Sence Valley Forest Park on January 1st 1999.

White-fronted Goose x Barnacle Goose *Anser albifrons x Branta leucopsis*

Two individuals of this unusual hybrid consorted with feral Barnacle Geese at Rutland Water from March 28th to 31st 1997.

Greylag Goose x Swan Goose *Anser anser x Anser cygnoides*

One at Blackbrook Reservoir on March 24th 1997 is the only record.

Bar-headed Goose x Emperor Goose *Anser indicus x Anser canagicus*

One, considered to be either of this parentage or, less likely, Bar-headed Goose x Barnacle Goose, was at Eyebrook Reservoir on May 7th and 8th 1997, and then at Rutland Water the following day.

Snow Goose x Greylag Goose *Anser caerulescens x Anser anser*

All records emanate from Priory Water, where a Snow Goose gander bred with a Greylag Goose in 1993, producing four hybrid young. Four goslings were also reared in 1994, with six in 1996. A second Snow Goose gander also bred with a Greylag Goose in 1997 and the two mixed pairs raised seven young between them. Consequently, these two Snow Geese were responsible for a total of 21 hybrids. To complicate matters, the hybrids proved to be fertile and several have interbred with Greylags over the years, producing an unknown number of second generation and beyond hybrids. These birds did not stay confined to Priory Water, and regularly wandered to Rutland Water, although the only records away from these two sites were of three at Quorn Borrow Pit in January 1999, one at Carlton Park, Narborough on January 15th 2001 and two at Cossington Meadows on January 10th 2004. The highest count at any one time was of 12 at Priory Water in August and September 1997.

The two Snow Geese died in 1999 and 2000 respectively, but have left a legacy of their genes within the local Greylag population which will last for generations to come. By 2005, only one first generation hybrid remained, but several birds from the second generation and beyond were still going strong.

Snow Goose x Barnacle Goose *Anser caerulescens x Branta leucopsis*

Four birds resembling blue Snow Geese were with four white Snow Geese at Eyebrook Reservoir on August 27th 1986. They were soon relocated at Rutland Water and were still all together on January 2nd 1988. Since then, one has been seen regularly into 2005, usually at Rutland Water, but with occasional visits to Eyebrook Reservoir and Priory Water. It was not until 1990 that it was realised that the one remaining 'blue Snow Goose' (now affectionately nicknamed Percy) was actually a hybrid between Snow Goose and a small-billed species of goose, most probably Barnacle Goose.

Apart from the regular bird, two different Snow Goose x Barnacle Goose hybrids were at Eyebrook Reservoir on June 2nd 1996 and another was at Hermitage Lake, Whitwick on July 28th 2000. In addition, three at Rutland Water on September 25th 1999 were considered to be either Snow Goose x Barnacle Goose or Emperor Goose x Barnacle Goose hybrids.

Emperor Goose x Barnacle Goose — *Anser canagicus x Branta leucopsis*

One at Eyebrook Reservoir on January 18th and February 15th 2003 was thought to be of this parentage or, less likely, Emperor Goose x Brent Goose.

Greater Canada Goose x Greylag Goose — *Branta canadensis x Anser anser*

This cross-generic hybrid is certainly the most commonly encountered and is one of the few for which we have absolute proof of parentage. The first mention of this hybrid was in 1988, when it was reported as 'increasingly recorded particularly at Rutland Water and Priory Water'. Consequently, there are clearly several 'missing' records from earlier years and it is thought to still be under-recorded. Birds have been recorded in all years since 1990, from a total of 18 sites. The favoured areas have been Priory Water and Rutland Water; at the former, the only blank years since 1990 have been 1997 and 2005, whilst at the latter there have been records every year since 1990 with the exception of 1999. Other sites where this hybrid has been recorded in three or more years are Trent Valley Pit (seven years), Eyebrook and Swithland Reservoirs (four years each) and Quorn Borrow Pit (three years).

Mixed Greater Canada Goose/Greylag Goose pairs have reared young at Priory Water in two years: five young in 1999 and six in 2000. The highest count came from this site, where there were ten on May 28th 2000. Elsewhere, the only counts in excess of two have been: up to five at Rutland Water throughout 1995, with four there in 2004; four at both Ibstock Opencast (now Sence Valley Forest Park) from November 1995 to February 1996 and Eybrook Reservoir on December 14th 1996, and three at Willesley Lake on March 23rd 1993.

This hybrid has been known to pair with both Greylag and Canada Geese and eggs have been laid, but no successful nests are known, suggesting that the hybrids may be infertile.

It may seem strange that these two species, one *Anser* and one *Branta*, should interbreed so readily. The most likely scenario is that when both species are breeding at the same time, the large crèches of goslings become accidentally intermixed before the imprinting process has taken place and some of the young become imprinted upon the wrong species.

Greater Canada Goose x Barnacle Goose — *Branta canadensis x Branta leucopsis*

There have been records in eight years, all but two of which were between 1990 and 1998. The number of birds involved is open to debate; it is possible that as few as five birds were responsible for all records since 1990.

All records:

1977 one, Eyebrook Reservoir, October 9th to 27th.
1990 one, Priory Water, May 20th.

1991	one, Rutland Water, February 3rd.
	four, Rutland Water, April 13th.
1993	one, Frisby Gravel Pits, April 25th.
	three, Priory Water, June 19th.
1995	one, Dunton Bassett, October 14th and November 4th; same, Frolesworth Manor Lake, December 24th.
1996	one, Rutland Water, January 7th to August 10th.
	three, Priory Water, May 26th.
1998	one, Eyebrook Reservoir, January 24th.
2005	one, Eyebrook Reservoir, January 1st.
	one, Rutland Water, April 14th and 19th.

This is a fairly common hybrid and, although variable, can look superficially like one of the races of Lesser Canada Goose; they do, however, usually show a dark breast.

Greater Canada Goose x ? *Branta canadensis x ?*

One at Rutland Water on January 14th 2003 was 'an obvious Canada Goose hybrid, but had a broad white eye-ring and narrow white band of feathering around the bill'. A similar bird (or perhaps the same one) was at Rutland Water from March 8th to May 3rd 2005, with two on the latter date.

Egyptian Goose x Common Shelduck *Alopochen aegyptiacus x Tadorna tadorna*

One was at Rutland Water on April 24th 2000.

Ruddy Shelduck x Egyptian Goose *Tadorna ferruginea x Alopochen aegyptiacus*

Two young from a male Ruddy Shelduck and a female Egyptian Goose pairing were at Rutland Water between May 18th and August 10th 1996, with one returning to the same site between July and September 1997. This was apparently the first time that hybridisation between these two species had been recorded (Harrop 1998).

Ruddy Shelduck x Common Shelduck *Tadorna ferruginea x Tadorna tadorna*

Single birds were at Rutland Water in May 1999 and on June 22nd 2002. According to Gillham & Gillham, this is a not uncommon hybrid pairing.

Ruddy Shelduck x South African Shelduck *Tadorna ferruginea x Tadorna cana*

One at Rutland Water from July 11th to August 31st 1997 was considered by some observers to be this hybrid, although others thought it was a pure-bred Ruddy Shelduck. These two species are very closely related and similar in appearance, and it is worth noting that this hybrid pairing is not mentioned by Gillham & Gillham.

Muscovy Duck x Mallard *Cairina moschata x Anas platyrhynchos*

One was at Groby Pool on November 13th 2005. Gillham & Gillham recorded three occurrences of this hybrid.

Mandarin Duck x *Anas sp.* *Aix galericulata x Anas sp.*

A male was at Priory Water on September 30th and October 28th 2001, and again on four dates between June 2nd and November 24th 2002, with a second, similar, bird also present on July 28th and November 11th. Two were again at this site on March 22nd 2003, with one on April 27th and August 24th. Both were very strange looking birds, with probably Mandarin Duck, but possibly Wood Duck, as one parent and an unknown *Anas* species (on bill shape) as the other. They were usually consorting with Mandarin Ducks, although when first seen a male Wood Duck was also present.

Interestingly, Gillham & Gillham describe Wood Duck as having successfully hybridised in captivity with 11 different species of *Anas*; Mandarin Duck is only detailed as having hybridised with one (Laysan Duck *Anas laysanensis*), and this attempt was unsuccessful as the two ducklings produced were born without eyes and both died within two months.

Eurasian Wigeon x Eurasian Teal *Anas penelope x Anas crecca*

A male was at Priory Water from November 26th 1989 to March 24th 1990, with presumably the same bird returning from December 9th 1990 to March 3rd 1991 and on September 15th 1991, whilst another was at Birstall Gravel Pits on November 19th 2000. Gillham & Gillham list five examples of this hybrid, one of which was the Priory Water individual. A bird at Sence Valley Forest Park on February 5th 1990 was possibly a second generation hybrid involving a Eurasian Wigeon x Eurasian Teal crossed with a Eurasian Wigeon.

American Wigeon x Chiloe Wigeon *Anas americana x Anas sibilatrix*

A controversial first-winter male, which was originally identified as an American Wigeon, was at Stanford Reservoir from December 24th 1995 to January 1st 1996, and then moved to Eyebrook Reservoir from January 10th to April 3rd 1996 (Mackay 1996b). A male was also at Eyebrook Reservoir on May 8th 1997, and then at Rutland Water from May 23rd to June 9th. Gillham & Gillham detail 11 examples of Eurasian Wigeon x American Wigeon hybrids, and 12 of Eurasian Wigeon x Chiloe Wigeon, both of which are relatively common and can resemble pure American Wigeons, but do not list any known examples of American Wigeon x Chiloe Wigeon.

American Wigeon x Cinnamon Teal *Anas americana x Anas cyanoptera*

A male was on Lagoon III at Rutland Water on March 23rd and 29th 2002. This hybrid pairing was unrecorded by Gillham & Gillham.

Gadwall x Eurasian Teal *Anas strepera x Anas crecca*

A female at Priory Water from December 27th 1994 to February 5th 1995, and again from November 5th 1995 to January 7th 1996, was thought to be this hybrid, and a male was at Swithland Reservoir on November 23rd 2005. As with the previous two pairings, this combination was unrecorded by Gillham & Gillham.

Gadwall x Mallard *Anas strepera x Anas platyrhynchos*

Single males have been seen at three sites, although all records could conceivably refer to the same bird: Priory Water from November 9th 1997 to January 4th 1998; Birstall Gravel Pits from December 21st 2000 to February 11th 2001, and again on January 18th 2002, and Trent Valley Pit from April 20th to 26th 2003. Nine examples of this hybrid combination are cited by Gillham & Gillham.

Gadwall x Pintail *Anas strepera x Anas acuta*

Single males, perhaps the same individual, were at Rutland Water on August 9th 1989 and September 30th 1991. It appears that this is a fairly unusual hybrid combination; Gillham & Gillham record just three known examples.

Eurasian Teal x Green-winged Teal *Anas crecca x Anas carolinensis*

A male was at Rutland Water on March 8th and 9th 1997. The bird superficially resembled a pure Green-winged Teal, but the white line at the sides of the breast was shorter (only on the 'shoulder'), and it had diffuse pale scapular lines. This hybrid is not mentioned by Gillham & Gillham, although at the time of the publication of their work Green-winged Teal had not been granted full species status. However, two similar birds were seen at Chew Valley Lake (Somerset) in early 1991 (Vinicombe 1994).

Mallard x Pintail *Anas platyrhynchos x Anas acuta*

A male was at Rutland Water on November 11th 1992. Despite just the single county record, this would appear to be a rather common hybrid; Gillham & Gillham note 85 instances (albeit most in captivity), whilst four were recorded at Belvide Reservoir (Staffordshire) between 1974 and 1983 (Smallshire 1986a).

Mallard x Tufted Duck *Anas platyrhynchos x Aythya fuligula*

One was at Priory Water on December 4th 2005. Ten instances of this rather surprising-sounding hybrid are recorded by Gillham & Gillham.

Yellow-billed Pintail x ? *Anas georgica x ?*

A bird at Rutland Water on July 8th and 22nd 2005 was similar to a pure Yellow-billed Pintail but showed some hybrid features, although no speculation was made as to the other parent.

Pintail x Red-crested Pochard *Anas acuta x Netta rufina*

A male was at Rutland Water on August 30th and October 6th 1990 and during August 1991 (Harrop 1993b) and two were at the same site on July 8th 2005. Gillham & Gillham cited six records of this hybrid pairing, including the first of the Rutland Water records detailed above.

Shoveler x Chestnut Teal *Anas clypeata x Anas castanea*

A male of this hybrid pairing, which was unrecorded by Gillham & Gillham, was at Rutland Water from May 31st to June 6th 1998.

Red-crested Pochard x Common Pochard *Netta rufina x Aythya ferina*

Up to three were at Cropston Reservoir between October 29th and December 18th 1989, with one again on January 31st 1990. A male was at Rutland Water on August 25th 2003, with presumably the same bird at Eyebrook Reservoir on September 21st of the same year. Nine instances of this hybrid were cited by Gillham & Gillham, including the three Cropston Reservoir birds detailed above.

Common Pochard x Ring-necked Duck *Aythya ferina x Aythya collaris*

A female thought to be this hybrid was at Groby Pool from November 8th 1997 to late January 1998, with the same bird at Swithland Reservoir on February 1st 1998. Gillham & Gillham record just one example.

Common Pochard x Ferruginous Duck *Aythya ferina x Aythya nyroca*

Although this hybrid has been recorded in nine years, it is likely that only five individuals have been involved. One was at Swithland Reservoir from August 11th to 22nd 1989, and then at Cropston Reservoir from November 6th to 22nd 1989 and September 18th to 25th 1990. A male noted at Cropston and Swithland Reservoirs and Dishley Pool on various dates from 1992 to 1995 may also have related to the individual mentioned above. A female at Groby Pool from December 5th to 12th 1999 was possibly a second generation hybrid, and another female was at the same site on October 16th and from November 24th to December 1st 2001. In 2005, a female was again at Groby Pool from January 27th to February 17th, with presumably the same returning bird returning from December 10th to 18th, and a male was at Swithland Reservoir on November 6th. Gillham & Gillham found this to be a relatively frequent hybrid; it is interesting that they recorded more examples of this cross than of Tufted Duck x Greater Scaup, which has apparently occurred in the county with much greater regularity.

Common Pochard x Tufted Duck *Aythya ferina x Aythya fuligula*

The first published record of this hybrid was a male at Rutland Water on September 9th 1984, and since 1989 there have been reports, all of single birds, in all but one of the subsequent years. Records have come from a total of ten sites; Rutland Water and the Charnwood reservoirs have been the most favoured, with records in most years from these areas since 1989. Eyebrook Reservoir has, for some reason, not proved particularly attractive to this hybrid compared to other waters, with records in only six years, whilst other waters with just one record each are Cossington South and Wanlip South Gravel Pits, Trent Valley Pit and Melton Country Park. Estimating the number of birds involved in all county records is virtually impossible, as some birds have been known to roam the county for lengthy periods. Gillham & Gillham found this to be easily the most frequent *Aythya* hybrid, being around five times more numerous than Common Pochard x Ferruginous Duck and nearly seven times commoner than Tufted Duck x Greater Scaup.

Ferruginous Duck x Tufted Duck *Aythya nyroca x Aythya fuligula*

An immature was at Kirby Lakes on January 31st 1998, a male was at Rutland Water on August 26th and December 22nd 2001 and a female, apparently paired with a Tufted Duck, was at Cossington Meadows on June 5th 2003. In addition, a male at Rutland Water on August 1st and 2nd 1998 was either this hybrid or a Common Pochard x Tufted Duck. The relatively few records of this cross in the counties is reflected in Gillham & Gillham's work; they found this to be one of the least numerous *Aythya* hybrids.

Ferruginous Duck x ? *Aythya nyroca x ?*

One at Thornton Reservoir on August 29th 1987 clearly had one parent as a Ferruginous Duck, but the other could not be distinguished. Hybridisation by Ferruginous Duck with both Common Pochard and Tufted Duck has been recorded in the counties.

Tufted Duck x Greater Scaup *Aythya fuligula x Aythya marila*

The first published record of this hybrid was of a female at Swithland Reservoir on May 20th and 21st 1988. Since then, there have been records in all but one year up to 2005, making this hybrid almost as frequent as Common Pochard x Tufted Duck. This situation seems a little strange, as Gillham & Gillham found Tufted Duck x Greater Scaup to be substantially less common that Common Pochard x Tufted Duck, and even noted more instances of Common Pochard x Ferruginous Duck. As has been mentioned previously, a lot of educated guesswork goes into hybrid identification, and this hybrid is probably the best example when it is said that parentage should not be taken as absolute gospel.

Published records have come from 13 sites and, as with Common Pochard x Tufted Duck, Rutland Water and the Charnwood reservoirs and lakes account for a large majority of reports. Other sites where this hybrid has been reported include Priory Water, Melton Country Park, the River Soar in Leicester, Eyebrook Reservoir, Syston, Watermead Country Park South and Cossington Meadows.

A description and photograph of a drake at Thornton Reservoir, which was tentatively identified as a Tufted Duck x Greater Scaup, appeared in the LROS Annual Report for 2000 (Wright 2002).

Unspecified *Aythya* hybrids

There have been seven records, of eight individuals, in 1985, 1987, 1993 and 2000, which were probably either Tufted Duck x Greater Scaup or Common Pochard x Tufted Duck hybrids.

Ruddy Duck x White-headed Duck *Oxyura jamaicensis x Oxyura leucocephala*

A male, originally reported as a White-headed Duck, was at Swithland Reservoir intermittently from November 21st 1981 to May 15th 1982.

Saker Falcon x Gyr Falcon *Falco cherrug x Falco rusticolous*

One was at Eyebrook Reservoir on August 27th and 31st 2001. A large, pale falcon which roamed various sites in the north-west of the county in the spring of 2002 was generally considered to be a Saker Falcon; however, what may have been the same bird was seen regularly at Whitwick Quarry in November and December of the same year and was then considered to be a hybrid. The same individual was at Breedon Quarry from February 12th to April 27th 2003; it returned to this site early in 2004, where it remained intermittently until at least March 2005, although occasionally went wandering in 2004 and was seen at Swithland Reservoir on March 3rd and during July, and at Bardon Hill on May 1st. A different individual, with jesses, was seen at Wanlip Meadows on September 26th 2005. In addition, a large pale falcon at Lockington Marshes on January 15th 2005 was likely to have been a hybrid involving these species, although was considered to be a different bird to that which was resident at Breedon Quarry at the same time.

Confidently identifying escaped large falcons is fraught with difficulties, given the sometimes bizarre hybrids produced by falconers.

Herring Gull x Glaucous Gull *Larus argentatus x Larus hyperboreus*

A first-winter was at Swithland Reservoir on January 18th 1992, a fourth-winter at Eyebrook Reservoir from December 11th to 16th 1994 returned as an adult from November 25th to December 16th 1995 and other first-winters were at Swithland Reservoir on November 5th 2000 and Rutland Water on February 11th and 15th 2005, with the latter bird appearing at Eyebrook Reservoir on March 1st 2005. Large numbers of this hybrid are reputedly present in Iceland, so their occurrence here is not entirely surprising.

House Sparrow x Tree Sparrow *Passer domesticus x Passer montanus*

One was in a Market Bosworth garden from September 30th 1995 to March 31st 1996, with two there on January 21st and March 11th and three on March 1st. The only other records were of single birds at Enderby Tip on October 15th 2000 and Shepshed on August 10th and 18th 2005.

UNCONFIRMED AND OTHER UNACCEPTABLE RECORDS

by Rob Fray

There have been published records of the following species or races in Leicestershire and Rutland, but these are considered unproven or otherwise unacceptable; none of these species or races is currently on the county list.

Harlequin Duck *Histrionicus histrionicus*

Browne records that, according to Harley, a pair was shot at Groby Pool during the early months of 1845. However, Browne was of the opinion that a mistake had been made, saying 'I have heard several ducks styled 'Harlequin', the last time the term being applied to the Long-tailed Duck.' He was surely correct, as a pair of inland Harlequin Ducks would be unprecedented; subsequent authors have wisely ignored this record.

Glossy Ibis *Plegadis falcinellus*

Browne records the following for this species: 'The 'Bickley Collection' in the Museum contains a fine specimen of this bird, for which the late Mr Widdowson told me £3 3s was paid by Mr Bickley to the fortunate sportsman who brought it to him. Mr Macaulay stated (*Mid. Nat.* 1882, page 77) in reference to this specimen: 'I have been recently informed by the donor's brother that it was killed on the border of the county and within it.' This however, is an error, for on the back of the case it is thus labelled 'this rare and valuable specimen was shot near the Derby Railway Station in February 1842."

American Kestrel *Falco sparverius*

A specimen record from Leicestershire apparently obtained 'about 1899' was considered and rejected by the BOURC in 2001 on the basis of doubts about its provenance (BOURC 2001).

Buff-breasted Sandpiper *Tryngites subruficollis*

Two reported at Belvoir on September 7th and 8th 1964 were originally accepted by the BBRC (*BB* 58:361) and remained as the only county record for 40 years. However, when the original description was tracked down in 2004, there were elements within it that seemed incorrect for this species. The BBRC was asked to re-evaluate the record and agreed; the record was therefore rejected and Buff-breasted Sandpiper was deleted from the county list (Fray 2005, *BB* 97:580).

Bonaparte's Gull *Chroicocephalus philadelphia*

Haines recounts the tale of a gull shot by C. Masters at Burley Fishponds in 1897 which was apparently identified by a William Hine as a Bonaparte's Gull. Hine had experience of the species from Canada, and after identifying the bird he took the wings away with him, but these were then lost. Haines made enquiries of other persons present when the bird in question was shot, but the only descriptive comments he received were from a gunsmith of Oakham named Mr Whitehouse, who said the bird 'had black on its head, grey back, wings crossed with black.'

Subsequent authors appear to have ignored or disregarded this record; as the only description provided could equally well refer to Little Gull or Kittiwake, and as this would have been one of the first British records of this North American species, it seems safest to regard this occurrence as unproven at best.

Passenger Pigeon *Ectopistes migratorius*

Browne quotes a Mr Widdowson as having written: 'one killed in Scalford village street some years ago. The same year I saw accounts of several killed near Liverpool.' According to Browne, there was little doubt that the Liverpool birds had escaped from captivity, and he considered it highly probable that the Leicestershire specimen had been from the same source.

This species is not on the British List and is, of course, long extinct, having been last recorded in the wild in 1899.

Scops Owl (Eurasian Scops Owl) *Otus scops*

Haines mentions a record of one killed within the Rutland border near Duddington some time around 1846. The bird was preserved by a John Taylor of Barrowden and seen by A.C. Elliott, who retrospectively identified it as a Scops Owl after being shown the skins of various owls by Lord Lilford.

Again, subsequent authors have disregarded this record, probably wisely given the rather vague details provided.

Tawny Pipit *Anthus campestris*

One reported at Bradgate Park on the unusual date of July 15th 1990 was originally published as the first (and only) county record, but was reviewed several years later and found to be unacceptable; the species was therefore deleted from the county list (Mackay 1996a).

Sykes's Wagtail *Motacilla flava beema*

The following records, all of single males, have been published in LROS Annual Reports:

1991	Rutland Water, April.
	Thornton Reservoir, May 5th.
1992	Cropston Reservoir, April 29th to May 25th.
1996	Priory Water, early May to June 2nd.
1997	Priory Water, April 15th to 24th.

Given the difficulties caused by variants and hybrids in identifying vagrant races of 'Yellow' Wagtails, this race was deleted from the county list following a review in 2004 (Fray 2005).

Alpine Accentor *Prunella collaris*

This species is listed by Browne but he quite clearly did not consider it worthy of further investigation; his only comment was: 'this more-than-rare bird is, I believe, credited to Rutland – but!'

American Robin *Turdus migratorius*

Dymond *et al.* (1989) make reference to a record of this species in Leicestershire some time between 1876 and 1937. However, it is not known where this information came from and there has been no other published reference of this record.

Dartford Warbler *Sylvia undata*

Browne noted that this species had been included in previous local lists as having occurred at 'Melton Mowbray in Leicestershire', but goes on to say that the example supposedly captured in the county had in fact been obtained in Cambridgeshire.

Haines quotes A.C. Elliott, writing in 1883, as noting 'Barrowden Heath as the breeding place of the Dartford Warbler.' However, Elliott then goes on to say: 'It has the exact resemblance to the Redbreast [Robin], only for colour. It jumps up the same, jerks the same, uses that quite (*sic*) but quick bob in feeding.' Haines placed this record in square-brackets, commenting that the description may have referred to a Stonechat; he was almost certainly correct in that assumption.

Hume's Leaf Warbler *Phylloscopus humei*

A bird present at Ashby-de-la-Zouch from January 9th to March 5th 1988 was widely considered to be a Yellow-browed Warbler, and a review of its identification was published in the 1999 LROS Annual Report (Fray & Harrop 2000). However, the BBRC accepted and published the record as a Hume's Leaf Warbler (*BB* 91:507), only to reverse their decision a couple of years later following representation at county level (*BB* 94:493).

Red-breasted Flycatcher *Ficedula parva*

One reported at Evington on October 3rd 1947 was accepted as the only county record, and brief details were published in *British Birds* soon after the occurrence (Bak 1948b). Upon review in 2004, however, certain details contained within the description appeared incorrect and as such Red-breasted Flycatcher was deleted from the county list (Fray 2005).

Parrot Crossbill *Loxia pytyopsittacus*

Browne records the following for this species: 'Harley wrote: 'on the authority of Mr Bickley, of Melton Mowbray, it appears the Parrot Crossbill made a visit to Leicestershire in 1849.' With reference to this statement, the late Mr R. Widdowson wrote me: 'a pair of Parrot Crossbills, killed close to Melton, are in the Bickley collection.' Unfortunately, however, the specimens in the Bickley collection are unlabelled.' Browne clearly did not believe this record, partly because he did not regard Parrot Crossbill as a valid species, and subsequent authors have made no further comment on it.

Ortolan Bunting *Emberiza hortulana*

One reported at Cadeby Quarry on August 28th 1988, and then nearby at Newbold Verdon the following day, remained the only county record until 2004; on review, the details provided were considered to be inconclusive and the species was deleted from the county list (Fray 2005).

Browne mentions two 'killed with larks, both young'. He was unsure of the locality, but thought it may have been near Melton Mowbray; the record was also undated, but was supposedly during the winter months. Browne only published this record in square brackets and, as the circumstances are both vague and somewhat unbelievable, this record has never received widespread acceptance.

ADDITIONAL RECORDS FROM RUTLAND

by Andrew Harrop and Rob Fray

The following records have been published in the past but have never been formally assessed and do not form part of the official statistics for the counties. Unless stated, records are from Rutland Water and appeared in *The Birds of Rutland Water* (Appleton 1978a & b, 1984, 1985, 1986, 1987a & b, 1990, 1991, Appleton *et al.* 1996).

Whooper Swan: six records, including 34 on January 15th 1994.

Bean Goose: eight on February 2nd and March 1st 1983 and one on April 2nd and 3rd 1987.

European White-fronted Goose: 19 on December 1st 1985 and 37 on December 22nd 1985.

Dark-bellied Brent Goose: seven on November 20th 1988, four on January 2nd 1989 and one on October 23rd 1990.

Ring-necked Duck: one (male) on September 30th 1989.

Long-tailed Duck: one on October 16th 1987.

Velvet Scoter: one on February 3rd 1985.

Red-throated Diver: single birds on February 23rd 1978, November 12th 1986, from January 17th to 25th 1987 and on November 7th 1993.

Black-throated Diver: single birds on January 17th 1987 and February 18th 1989.

Great Northern Diver: single birds on August 3rd 1993 and March 19th 1994.

Slavonian Grebe: single birds on April 13th 1985, February 2nd to 22nd 1986, September 11th 1987, November 20th 1988 and December 21st 1988.

Fulmar: single birds on April 26th 1979 (Mitcham 1984), June 5th 1983, August 14th 1985, September 23rd 1988 and June 11th and 12th 1992.

Manx Shearwater: one on September 17th 1980 (Mitcham 1984).

Gannet: single birds on September 28th 1986 and August 21st 1990.

Shag: single birds at Eyebrook Reservoir on July 8th 1965 (Otter 1965, Mitcham 1984) and Rutland Water on September 6th 1977, August 26th 1984 and from January 1st to 13th 1985.

Bittern: single birds on September 3rd 1985, December 16th 1986, October 10th 1989, November 20th and December 1st 1992, March 12th 1995 and November 11th to 17th 1995.

Spoonbill: four on April 10th 1983.

Hen Harrier: 15 single birds between 1977 and 1995.

Goshawk: single birds on August 3rd 1983, May 13th 1986, November 23rd 1986, September 24th 1992 and April 16th 1995.

Merlin: nine single birds between 1986 and 1994.

Common Crane: two on May 5th 1985.

Stone Curlew: single birds at Eyebrook Reservoir on April 13th 1952 (Otter 1965) and August 11th 1964 (Otter 1965, Mitcham 1984).

Avocet: two on May 21st 1992.

Temminck's Stint: one on August 23rd 1989.

Pectoral Sandpiper: single birds on August 2nd and September 3rd 1983.

Purple Sandpiper: single birds on October 3rd 1977, October 15th 1978 and September 20th 1990.

Wood Sandpiper: one on April 21st 1987.

Red-necked Phalarope: single birds on September 8th 1983 and from September 8th to 14th 1986.

Arctic Skua: eight records involving nine individuals between 1978 and 1995.

Great Skua: one on July 10th 1980 (Mitcham 1984).

Sabine's Gull: single birds on August 18th 1980 (Mitcham 1984) and October 18th 1987 (*BB* 82:202).

Iceland Gull: one on February 24th 1980 (Mitcham 1984).

Glaucous Gull: single birds on February 22nd 1977, January 12th 1983 and April 16th 1983.

Little Tern: eight records involving 12 individuals.

White-winged Black Tern: one on August 21st 1988.

Sandwich Tern: 19 reports involving 44 individuals between 1977 and 1994.

Nightjar: single birds at Barnsdale Wood on May 17th 1985 and Rutland Water on May 10th 1990.

Wryneck: single birds at Eyebrook Reservoir on September 3rd 1966 (Mitcham 1984), Oakham on September 3rd 1977 (Mitcham 1984) and Rutland Water on September 17th 1978.

Water Pipit: single birds on November 18th 1982 (Mitcham 1984) and December 15th 1989.

Dipper: single birds near Collyweston in September 1960 (Mitcham 1984) and Ketton in January 1965 (Mitcham 1984).

Black Redstart: single birds on April 4th 1983, April 9th 1985, April 26th 1985, May 8th 1986 and August 11th 1990.

Ring Ouzel: single birds on April 19th 1987, April 19th 1988, October 16th to 19th 1988 and November 26th 1988.

Savi's Warbler: one on June 16th and 17th 1994.

Firecrest: single birds at Barnsdale Wood on March 23rd 1983 and November 4th 1992.

Bearded Tit: up to two from October 18th to 24th 1989.

Red-backed Shrike: one at Barrowden in 1950 (Mitcham 1984).

Great Grey Shrike: one on April 8th 1977.

Hooded Crow: one on December 12th 1975.

Twite: two on October 8th 1975, ten on October 23rd 1978 and one on October 16th 1994.

Common Redpoll: two from January 15th to March 18th 1985.

Snow Bunting: a flock of nine sometime in 1975, two on December 7th 1985 and single birds on November 19th 1988, March 1st 1989 and November 19th 1989.

Leicestershire & Rutland

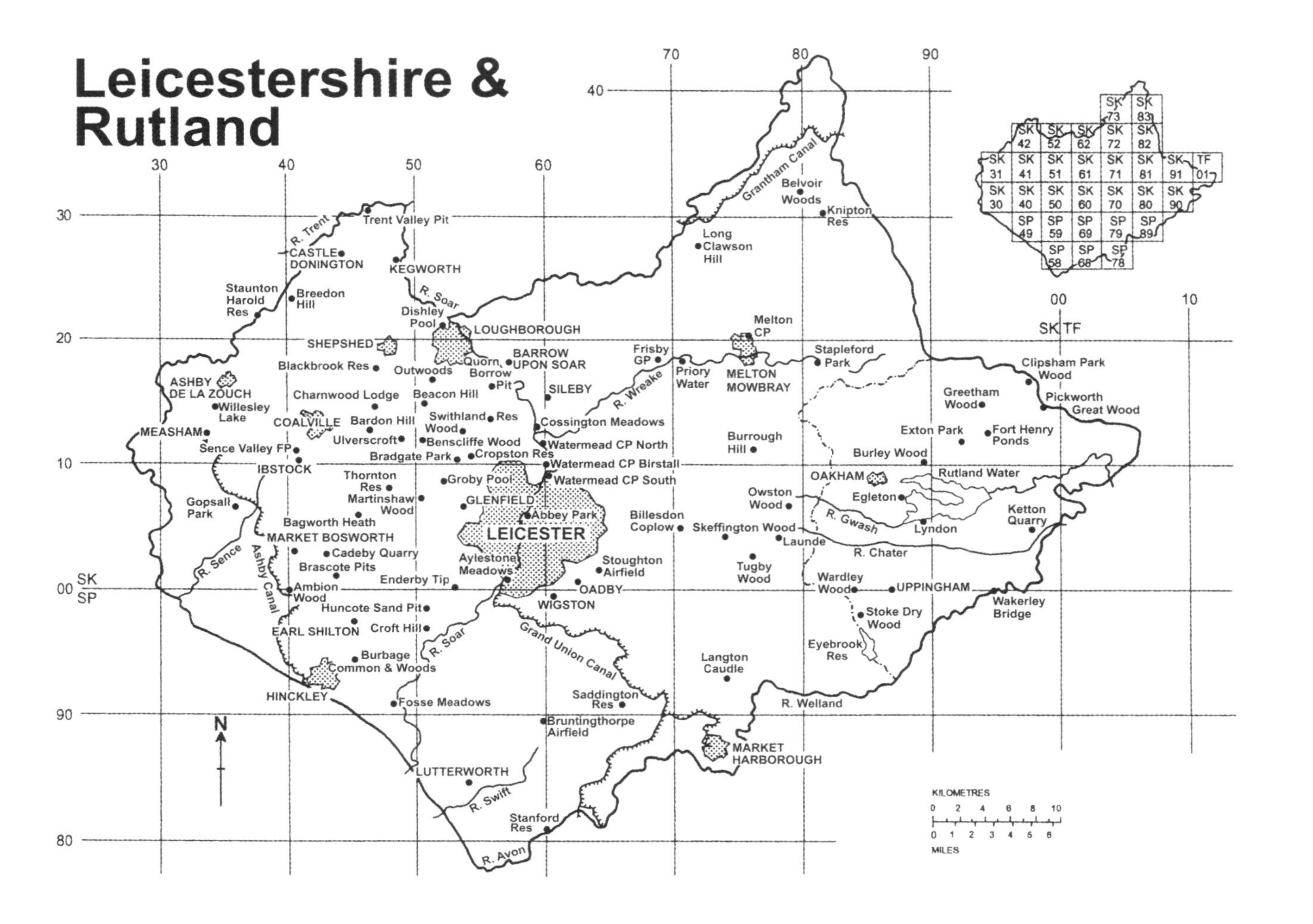

APPENDIX 1: GAZETTEER

All sites in Leicestershire and Rutland which are mentioned in the text are listed here. Sites shown in italics are either no longer in existence (such as filled-in gravel pits) or have been the subject of a name change; in the former case, the reason for the disappearance of the site is given, whilst in the latter case the name in current usage is shown alongside. Names usually conform to those on Ordnance Survey maps (either 1:50,000 or 1:25,000 series), although sites which are known locally by more than one name have both names shown. Where possible, a six-figure grid reference is given, but for larger sites a four-figure reference is given. The four-figure reference is intended to allow the site to be found on a 1:50,000 Ordnance Survey map, and does not imply that the site is wholly within that one-kilometre square.

Ab Kettleby	SK 725 230
Abbey Park, Leicester	SK 587 057
Abbey Meadows, Leicester	SK 587 064
Abney Street, Leicester	SK 604 039
Albert Village Lake	SK 305 175
Aldgate	SK 984 043
Allexton	SK 817 004
Ambion Wood	SP 402 996
Anstey	SK 54 08
Anstey Gorse (now developed)	*SK 564 069*
Anstey Lane, Leicester	SK 570 062
Appleby Magna	SK 316 097
Arnesby	SP 616 922
Asfordby	SK 705 190
Asfordby Gravel Pits (now Priory Water)	*SK 713 185*
Ashby-de-la-Zouch	SK 35 16
Ashby Folville	SK 706 120
Ashby Magna	SP 563 906
Ashby Pastures	SK 718 137
Ashwell	SK 866 137
Aston Flamville	SP 462 926
Atterton	SP351 982
Aylestone	SK 57 00
Aylestone Meadows	SK 57 01
Aylestone Mill	SK 577 025
Ayston	SK 861 010
Baggrave	SK 698 085
Baggrave Park	SK 694 088
Bagworth	SK 446 080
Bagworth Heath	SK 450 068
Bagworth Park	SK 447 077
Banthorpe	TF 061 109
Bardon	SK 451 128
Bardon Hall	SK 461 127
Bardon Hill	SK 461 132
Bardon Quarry	SK 455 130
Barkby	SK 636 097
Barkby Brook	SK 643 094
Barkby Gravel Pits (now filled in)	*SK 625 071*
Barkby Holt	SK 672 095
Barkby Lane Tip, Leicester (now closed)	*SK 615 078*
Barkestone Wood	SK 793 325
Barlestone	SK 425 056
Barleythorpe	SK 848 097
Barnsdale	SK 902 091
Barnsdale Avenue	SK 910 100
Barnsdale Wood	SK 912 088
Barrow upon Soar	SK 57 17
Barrow upon Soar Gravel Pits (now filled in)	*SK 569 167*
Barrowden	SK 946 002
Barrowden Heath (also known as Luffenham Heath)	SK 96 02
Barrowden Fox Covert	SK 966 021
Barwell	SP 44 97
Baxter Gate, Loughborough	SK 537 197
Beacon Hill	SK 511 147
Beaumanor	SK 536 157
Beaumont Chase	SP 840 990
Beaumont Leys, Leicester	SK 56 08
Bede House Meadows, Leicester (now developed)	*SK 578 032*
Bede Island, Leicester	SK 579 037
Beeby	SK 663 082
Belgrave, Leicester	SK 59 06
Belgrave Marina, Leicester	SK 587 063
Belmesthorpe	TF 042 102
Belton	SK 447 205
Belton-in-Rutland	SK 818 013
Belvoir	SK 822 338
Belvoir Castle	SK 819 336
Belvoir Lakes	SK 830 328
Belvoir Woods	SK 820 334
Billesdon	SK 720 026
Billesdon Coplow	SK 710 046
Birch Coppice, Lount	SK 392 186
Birstall	SK 59 09
Birstall Gravel Pits (also known as Watermead Country Park Birstall)	SK 603 095
Bisbrooke	SP 885 996

Bisbrooke Gorse	SP 884 998
Bittesby	SP 505 858
Bitteswell	SP 537 858
Bitteswell Airfield (now Magna Park Industrial Estate)	*SP 51 84*
Bitteswell Hall	SP 537 856
Blaby	SP 56 97
Blackbrook Reservoir	SK 458 173
Blakeshay Wood	SK 515 115
Bosworth Park	SK 412 028
Bosworth Water Park	SK 383 030
Botany Bay Fox Covert	SK 704 045
Bottesford	SK 805 390
Bradgate Park	SK 53 10
Bradgate Tip	SK 512 088
Brake Spinney, Normanton (now submerged under Rutland Water)	*SK 922 061*
The Brand, Woodhouse Eaves	SK 538 132
Branston	SK 810 293
Braunston-in-Rutland	SK 883 068
Braunstone, Leicester	SK 55 02
Braunstone Frith, Leicester	SK 54 04
Braunstone Industrial Estate, Leicester	SK 541 041
Braunstone Lane, Leicester	SK 563 022
Breedon on the Hill	SK 407 228
Breedon Quarry	SK 406 232
Bridge Road, Leicester	SK 608 051
Briery Wood	SK 821 330
Brooksby	SK 672 162
Broombriggs	SK 518 137
Broughton Astley	SP 53 92
Bruntingthorpe	SP 603 898
Bruntingthorpe Airfield	SP 595 885
Buck Hill	SK 508 164
Buckminster	SK 879 231
Buddon Brook, Quorn	SK 556 159
Buddon Hill	SK 563 156
Buddon Wood	SK 560 155
Burbage	SP 44 92
Burbage Common	SP 447 951
Burbage Wood	SP 449 941
Burleigh Wood, Loughborough	SK 507 176
Burley	SK 883 106
Burley Fishponds (now part of Rutland Water)	*SK 880 086*
Burley House	SK 883 103
Burley Wood	SK 888 095
Burrough on the Hill	SK 757 107
Burrough Hill	SK 761 120
Burrow Wood	SK 476 145
Burton Lazars	SK 768 169
Burton on the Wolds	SK 590 211
Burton Overy	SP 678 980
Bushby	SK 651 040
Cadeby	SK 425 022
Cadeby Quarry	SK 433 028
Caldecott	SP 867 937
Campbell Street, Leicester	SK 592 042
Carlton Curlieu	SP 694 974
Carlton Hayes Hospital, Narborough	SP 537 984
Carlton Park, Narborough	SP 539 982
Carlton Street, Leicester	SK 587 038
Casterton (correctly known as Great Casterton)	TF 001 088
Castle Cement Works, Ketton	SK 984 056
Castle Donington	SK 44 27
Castle Donington Power Station (now demolished)	*SK 432 282*
Castle Hill Park, Leicester	SK 56 09
Cavendish Bridge Gravel Pits (now filled in)	*SK 448 295*
Charley	SK 478 147
Charley Hall	SK 479 147
Charnwood Lodge	SK 468 158
Charnwood Water	SK 548 183
Chitterman Hills	SK 496 115
Church Langton	SP 723 932
Claybrooke Magna	SP 492 886
Cliffe Quarry, Markfield	SK 475 107
Clipsham	SK 969 161
Clipsham Ford	SK 955 095
Clipsham Park	SK 973 165
Clipsham Park Wood	SK 974 168
Clipsham Quarry	SK 978 153
Cloud Wood	SK 417 214
Coalville	SK 42 13
Coleorton	SK 402 172
Coleorton Fishponds	SK 399 171
Coleorton Hall	SK 392 174
Coleman Road, Leicester	SK 616 048
Coney Hill Plantation, Noseley	SP 733 984
Congerstone	SK 367 052
Coppice Leys	SK 954 013
Coppice Plantation, Bradgate Park	SK 540 110
Copt Oak	SK 482 129
Cosby	SP 54 95
Cossington	SK 605 135
Cossington Gravel Pits (now known as Cossington South Lakes)	*SK 598 129*
Cossington North Gravel Pits (now known as Cossington Meadows)	*SK 597 134*
Cossington Meadows	SK 597 134
Cossington Mill	SK 595 129

Cossington South Gravel Pits (also known as Cossington South Lakes)	SK 598 129
Cossington South Lakes (also known as Cossington South Gravel Pits)	SK 598 129
Cotes	SK 555 206
Cotesbach Hall	SP 537 823
Cottesmore	SK 901 136
Cottesmore Airfield	SK 90 15
Countesthorpe	SP 58 95
Cranoe	SP 760 951
Croft	SP 515 955
Croft Hill	SP 510 967
Croft Quarry	SP 512 964
Cropston	SK 555 110
Cropston Reservoir	SK 545 109
Crossburrow Hill, Cranoe	SP 752 952
Croxton Kerrial	SK 837 293
Croxton Park	SK 824 274
Dadlington	SP 404 980
Deans Lane, Woodhouse	SK 506 152
Debdale Wharf	SP 694 916
Deer Park Spinney, Bradgate Park	SK 537 105
Desford	SK 47 03
Dimminsdale	SK 376 217
Dishley	SK 513 212
Dishley Grange	SK 512 213
Dishley Mill	SK 516 210
Dishley Pool	SK 520 215
Donington Hall	SK 420 268
Donington Park	SK 420 260
Dover Street, Leicester	SK 590 040
Downing Drive, Leicester	SK 638 036
Duke's Drive, Clarendon Park, Leicester	SK 601 028
Dunton Bassett	SP 545 905
Earl Shilton	SP 46 97
Earl Shilton Sewage Farm	SP 475 976
East Goscote	SK 640 134
East Norton	SK 784 003
East Park Road, Leicester	SK 609 047
Eastwell	SK 774 285
Eaton	SK 796 290
Edith Weston	SK 928 052
Edmondthorpe	SK 857 177
Egleton	SK 877 073
Elmesthorpe	SP 467 962
Elmfield Avenue, Leicester	SK 601 030
Empingham	SK 953 087
Empingham Reservoir (now Rutland Water)	*SK 87 05 – SK 94 09*
Enderby	SP 53 99
Enderby Pool	SP 551 998
Enderby Quarry (now filled in)	*SK 538 001*
Enderby Tip (now filled in)	*SK 538 001*
Essendine	TF 047 126
Evans' Weir, Leicester	SK 579 047
Evington	SK 630 032
Evington Golf Course	SK 623 026
Evington Park	SK 627 034
Exton	SK 926 112
Exton Park	SK 940 127
Exton Park Lake	SK 918 115
Eyebrook Reservoir	SP 85 95
Eyebrook Reservoir Plantation	SP 858 957
Eyres Monsell, Leicester	SP 574 995
Far Coton	SK 386 020
Farnham's Park, Quorn	SK 561 158
Felicity's Wood	SK 504 154
Fenny Drayton	SP 350 969
Fergusson's Spinney, Birstall	SK 592 089
Filbert Street, Leicester	SK 582 033
Fleckney	SP 647 935
Fort Henry Ponds	SK 950 120
Fosse Meadows	SP 490 910
Fosse Road, Leicester	SK 574 041
Foston	SP 603 948
Foxton	SP 701 901
Foxton Locks	SP 691 895
Freeby	SK 804 200
Freemen's Common, Leicester	SK 586 026
Freemen's Weir, Leicester	SK 579 029
Frisby Gravel Pits	SK 693 181
Frisby on the Wreake	SK 696 177
Frog Island, Leicester	SK 580 052
Frolesworth	SP 507 903
Frolesworth Manor Lake	SP 496 906
Gaddesby	SK 688 131
Garendon Park	SK 502 196
Garthorpe	SK 833 209
Gaulby	SK 695 010
Gilroes Cemetery, Leicester	SK 561 066
Gipsy Lane, Leicester	SK 610 065
Gisborne's Gorse	SK 469 154
Glaston	SK 898 003
Glaston Wood	SK 900 014
Glen Hills, Leicester	SK 576 000
Glen Parva	SP 56 99
Glen Parva Gravel Pits	SP 556 984
Glenfield	SK 54 05
Glenfield Sewage Works	SK 530 057
Glenfrith Way, Leicester	SK 559 068
Glooston	SP 750 958

Glooston Wood	SP 753 967
Goadby Marwood	SK 781 263
Goadby Marwood Pools	SK 776 266
Gopsall Park	SK 350 065
Gopsall Wood	SK 338 065
Grace Dieu	SK 437 180
Grace Dieu Priory	SK 436 183
Great Bowden	SP 747 888
Great Casterton	TF 001 088
Great Central Street, Leicester	SK 582 047
Great Dalby	SK 745 145
Great Easton	SP 848 931
Great Fenny Wood (now destroyed)	*SK 562 174*
Great Glen	SP 656 979
Great Glen Lake	SP 659 974
Great Merrible Wood	SP 835 964
Great Stretton	SK 657 004
Greenhill	SK 44 13
Greetham	SK 928 144
Greetham Wood	SK 94 14
Griffydam	SK 413 185
Grimston	SK 685 218
Groby	SK 52 07
Groby Pool	SK 521 081
Groby Quarry	SK 526 082
Groby Road, Leicester	SK 568 059
Grove Park, Enderby	SK 550 000
Gumley	SP 682 900
Gwendolen Road, Leicester	SK 613 039
Hallaton	SP 789 966
Hallgates	SK 542 114
Halstead	SK 750 057
Hambleton (correctly known as Upper Hambleton)	SK 901 075
Hambleton Wood	SK 908 068
Hamilton, Leicester	SK 635 072
Hamilton Park, Leicester	SK 625 075
Hamilton Pool, Leicester	SK 625 072
Hangingstone Rocks	SK 523 151
Harby	SK 746 311
Harston	SK 839 317
Hathern	SK 503 223
Heather	SK 390 108
Heather Fishponds	SK 393 104
Hemington	SK 456 281
Hemington Gravel Pits (now filled in)	*SK 454 288*
Hemington Pools	SK 462 294
Hemington Water Meadows (now Trent Valley Pit)	*SK 465 305*
Hermitage Lake, Whitwick	SK 430 154
Heyworth Road, Leicester	SK 573 024
High Leys Farm, Branston	SK 807 318
High Sharpley	SK 447 170
High Street, Leicester	SK 584 045
Higham Grange	SP 389 947
Higham on the Hill	SP 383 954
Highfields, Leicester	SK 597 038
Hilton Gravel Pits (now Hemington Pools)	*SK 462 294*
Hinckley	SP 42 93
Hinckley Road, Leicester	SK 56 04
Hoby	SK 669 173
Holwell	SK 736 236
Holwell Quarry	SK 733 236
Horninghold	SP 806 972
Hoton	SK 573 225
Houghton Lodge Farm	SK 663 023
Houghton on the Hill	SK 678 035
Hugglescote	SK 424 124
Humberstone, Leicester	SK 61 05
Humberstone Gate, Leicester	SK 588 046
Humberstone Park, Leicester	SK 619 050
Humberstone Road, Leicester	SK 600 051
Huncote	SP 517 975
Huncote Sand Pit	SP 512 982
Hungarton	SK 690 073
Husband's Bosworth	SP 642 843
Ibstock	SK 40 10
Ibstock Opencast (now Sence Valley Forest Park)	*SK 403 113*
Illston on the Hill	SP 708 994
Ingarsby	SK 685 051
Ives Head	SK 477 170
Jewry Wall Museum, Leicester	SK 581 044
John O' Gaunt	SK 741 096
Jubilee Wood	SK 511 166
Kaye's Plantation, Quorn	SK 561 162
Kegworth	SK 48 26
Kelham Bridge	SK 407 121
Ketton	SK 980 043
Ketton Hall	SK 986 044
Ketton Hall Lake	SK 980 041
Ketton Quarry	SK 973 062
Keyham	SK 670 063
Keythorpe	SK 767 003
Kibworth Beauchamp	SP 68 93
Kilby	SP 621 953
Kilby Bridge	SP 610 970
Kilthorpe	SK 985 033
King Lud's Entrenchments	SK 861 278
King Richard's Road, Leicester	SK 576 043
King's Hill Lodge, Uppingham	SP 843 990

King's Mills	SK 417 274
King's Norton	SK 688 005
Kirby Bellars	SK 717 177
Kirby Bellars Gravel Pits (now Priory Water)	*SK 713 185*
Kirby Lakes	SK 706 183
Kirby Muxloe	SK 520 044
Kirkby Mallory	SK 456 007
Knighton, Leicester	SK 59 01
Knighton Park, Leicester	SK 605 006
Knighton Spinney, Leicester	SK 605 008
Knipton	SK 826 313
Knipton Reservoir	SK 817 304
Knossington	SK 802 085
Langham	SK 845 111
Langton Caudle	SP 745 935
Langton Hall	SP 714 931
Laughton	SP 660 891
Laughton Hills	SP 662 878
Launde	SK 795 042
Launde Abbey	SK 797 043
Launde Big Wood	SK 786 038
Launde Park Wood	SK 803 036
Lawn Wood	SK 505 095
Lea Meadows	SK 506 115
Lea Wood	SK 502 114
Leesthorpe	SK 790 134
Leicester	SK 58 04
Leicester Abbey	SK 584 059
Leicester Castle, Leicester	SK 582 041
Leicester City Farms, Leicester (now developed)	*SK 56 08*
Leicester Forest East	SK 530 033
Leicester Forest West	SK 499 018
Leicester Market Place, Leicester	SK 587 044
Leicester Museum, Leicester	SK 591 038
Leicester Power Station, Leicester (now disused)	*SK 582 030*
Leicester University, Leicester	SK 593 029
Leighfield	SK 828 040
Leire	SP 525 901
Lindley	SP 366 953
Lindley Airfield	SP 37 96
Lindridge Wood	SK 467 044
Little Bowden	SP 747 872
Little Casterton	TF 019 099
Little Dalby	SK 776 142
Little Stretton	SK 668 001
Lockington	SK 467 278
Lockington Gravel Pits	SK 477 300
Lockington Grounds	SK 477 300
Lockington Hall	SK 470 282
Lockington Marshes	SK 48 30
Loddington	SK 790 023
Loddington Reddish	SK 774 022
London Road, Leicester	SK 607 021
Long Clawson	SK 725 273
Long Whatton	SK 480 234
Longcliffe Golf Course	SK 495 174
Longcliffe Wood	SK 496 167
Loughborough	SK 53 19
Loughborough Big Meadow	SK 538 218
Loughborough Road, Birstall	SK 591 089
Loughborough Sewage Farm (now disused)	*SK 530 213*
Loughborough University	SK 513 185
Lount	SK 385 193
Lount Tip (now filled in)	*SK 381 184*
Lower Hambleton (now submerged under Rutland Water)	*SK 897 071*
Lowesby	SK 724 075
Lubbesthorpe	SK 535 015
Lubenham	SP 704 872
Lucas' Marsh, Oadby	SP 620 997
Luffenham	SK 94 02
Luffenham Airfield	SK 94 04
Luffenham Heath (occasionally referred to as Barrowden Heath)	SK 96 02
Lutterworth	SP 54 84
Lyddington	SP 874 971
Lyndon	SK 908 044
Magna Park Industrial Estate, Bitteswell	SP 51 84
Manton	SK 881 045
Maplewell Hall	SK 522 132
Marefield	SK 746 079
Market Bosworth	SK 406 031
Market Harborough	SP 73 87
Market Harborough Sewage Farm	SP 758 890
Market Overton	SK 888 163
Markfield	SK 490 100
Martinshaw Wood	SK 510 074
Measham	SK 33 11
Medbourne	SP 800 931
Melbourne Road, Leicester	SK 600 043
Melton Airfield	SK 748 158
Melton Country Park	SK 758 207
Melton Mowbray	SK 75 18
Melton Sewage Farm (also known as Sysonby Sewage Farm)	SK 737 185
Melton Spinney	SK 766 223
Meridian Business Park, Braunstone	SK 547 010
Millstone Lane, Leicester	SK 585 041
Misterton	SP 558 838

Misterton Gorse	SP 560 825
Moira	SK 318 158
Morcott	SK 923 006
Mountsorrel	SK 58 14
Mountsorrel Common	SK 571 146
Mountsorrel Osiers (now destroyed)	*SK 587 154*
Mountsorrel Tip (now closed)	*SK 577 147*
Mowmacre, Leicester	SK 580 082
Mowsley	SP 648 890
Muston	SK 828 378
Nailstone	SK 417 071
Nanpantan	SK 505 172
Nanpantan Reservoir	SK 507 170
Narborough	SP 53 97
Narborough Bog	SP 549 978
Narborough Road, Leicester	SK 56 02
Nether Broughton	SK 695 258
New Parks, Leicester	SK 55 05
New Parks Boulevard, Leicester	SK 550 048
New Walk, Leicester	SK 593 038
Newbold	SK 765 090
Newbold Verdon	SK 44 03
Newell Wood	TF 003 114
Newton Harcourt	SP 635 970
Newton Harcourt CBC plot	SP 634 981
Newton Harcourt Pool	SP 632 971
Newtown Linford	SK 520 097
Newtown Unthank	SK 489 043
Normanton	SK 946 062
Normanton Bridge (now submerged under Rutland Water)	*SK 929 066*
Normanton le Heath	SK 377 127
Normanton Park	SK 935 063
Normanton Thorns, Bottesford	SK 820 426
Normanton Turville	SP 492 987
Norris Hill	SK 327 166
North Luffenham	SK 935 034
Noseley	SP 738 987
Nowell Spring Wood	SK 503 121
Oadby	SK 61 00
Oakham	SK 85 05
Oakham Sewage Farm	SK 873 086
Oakley Wood	SK 484 215
Oaks in Charnwood	SK 473 163
Oakthorpe	SK 324 131
Oakthorpe Flash	SK 321 136
Old Dalby	SK 673 237
Old Dalby Wood	SK 679 229
Orton-on-the-Hill	SK 306 037
Osbaston	SK 426 044
Osbaston Hall	SK 425 045
Osgathorpe	SK 430 196
Outwoods	SK 512 165
Owston	SK 776 077
Owston Wood	SK 78 06
Oxey Crossroads, Loddington	SK 778 035
Oxford Street, Leicester	SK 585 039
Packington	SK 363 145
Packington Sewage Farm	SK 354 140
Pasture Wood	SK 424 213
Peatling Magna	SP 594 926
Peatling Parva	SP 589 895
Peckleton	SK 472 011
Pickworth	SK 996 138
Pickworth Drift	TF 005 133
Pickworth Great Wood	SK 985 147
Pilton	SK 915 028
Piper Wood	SK 477 217
Plungar	SK 768 339
Plungar Wood	SK 786 321
Potters Marston	SP 498 963
Poultney Wood	SK 494 129
Preston	SK 872 025
Preston Gorse	SK 862 026
Prestwold	SK 576 215
Prestwold Hall	SK 579 215
Prior's Coppice	SK 830 051
Priory Water	SK 713 185
Queen's Park, Loughborough	SK 533 194
Quenby	SK 698 062
Queniborough	SK 64 12
Quorn	SK 55 16
Quorn Borrow Pit	SK 555 181
Quorn Fields Farm	SK 560 184
Quorn Sewage Farm	SK 561 180
Rabbit's Bridge	SK 553 143
Ragdale	SK 662 198
Rally Park, Leicester	SK 578 048
Ratby	SK 51 05
Ratby Burroughs	SK 493 060
Ratby Meadows	SP 557 997
Ratcliffe on the Wreake	SK 629 143
Ravenstone	SK 403 136
Raw Dykes Road, Leicester	SK 583 028
Rearsby	SK 651 143
Redmile	SK 797 354
Ridlington	SK 847 027
Robin-a-Tiptoe Hill	SK 773 043
Rolleston	SK 732 004
Rothley	SK 58 12
Rothley Park Golf Course	SK 573 118

Rothley Sand Pit	SK 567 123
Rough Park, Lount	SK 392 182
Roundabout Spinney, Peckleton	SK 489 004
Roundhill Road, Leicester	SK 609 031
Rowlatt's Hill, Leicester	SK 625 045
Rowley Fields, Leicester	SK 569 020
Rushpit Wood	SK 900 095
Rutland Water	SK 87 05 – SK 94 09
Anglian Birdwatching Centre	SK 879 071
Barnhill Creek	SK 924 069
Burley Fishponds	SK 880 086
Dam	SK 943 078
Egleton Reserve	SK 88 06 – SK 88 07
Fieldfare hide	SK 886 066
Gibbet Gorse	SK 901 058
Gorse Close	SK 887 061
Hambleton Peninsula	SK 90 07
Lagoon I	SK 882 070
Lagoon II	SK 883 074
Lagoon III	SK 887 079
Lagoon III reedbed	SK 888 081
Lyndon Reserve	SK 88 05 – SK 89 05
Mallard hide	SK 879 070
Manton Bay	SK 88 05
Normanton Church	SK 932 062
North arm	SK 89 08
Plover hide (now demolished)	*SK 879 071*
South arm	SK 89 06
Sykes Lane car park	SK 937 083
Whitwell Creek	SK 926 082
Ryhall	TF 034 105
Ryhall Heath	TF 019 130
Saddington	SP 658 918
Saddington Reservoir	SP 664 911
Saffron Lane, Leicester	SK 582 039
Saltby	SK 850 262
Saltby Heath (occasionally known as Sproxton Heath)	SK 874 260
Saltersford Flash	SK 320 136
Sandringham Road, Wigston	SP 580 981
Sanvey Gate, Leicester	SK 583 050
Sapcote	SP 490 935
Sauvey Castle	SK 789 052
Sawley Gravel Pits (now filled in)	*SK 463 297*
Sawley Marina	SK 472 308
Scalford	SK 762 242
Scalford Gorse	SK 748 224
Scalford Lodge	SK 750 232
School Lane, Birstall	SK 593 088
School Lane Spinney, Birstall	SK 592 089
Scraptoft	SK 64 05
Scraptoft Lane, Leicester	SK 623 053
Seagrave	SK 618 175
Seaton	SP 902 982
Sence Valley Forest Park	SK 403 113
Shackerstone	SK 374 067
Shacklewell Hollow	SK 977 078
Shangton	SP 715 962
Sharnford	SP 480 918
Sharpley	SK 448 171
Sharpley Rocks	SK 447 168
Shawell	SP 544 802
Shawell Gravel Pits	SP 540 803
Shawell Tip	SP 540 806
Shearsby	SP 623 907
Sheepthorns Spinney, Kibworth	SP 701 951
Sheepy Magna	SK 326 014
Sheepy Parva	SK 332 014
Sheepy Wood	SP 447 947
Shelthorpe	SK 53 17
Shenton	SK 384 002
Shenton Cutting	SK 399 991
Shenton Gorse	SK 376 015
Shepshed	SK 47 18
Shoby	SK 682 204
Sileby	SK 60 15
Six Hills	SK 645 207
Skeffington	SK 741 028
Skeffington Wood	SK 756 035
Sketchley, Hinckley	SP 420 923
Smeeton Westerby	SP 677 927
Snarestone	SK 346 094
Snibston	SK 412 132
Snibston Discovery Park	SK 417 142
Somerby	SK 777 105
Somerville Road, Leicester	SK 569 023
South Croxton	SK 689 102
South Kilworth	SP 604 818
South Luffenham	SK 941 018
Spencefield Lane, Evington	SK 633 037
Spinney Hill Park, Leicester	SK 604 043
Spring Wood	SK 379 225
Spring Wood, Lount	SK 386 184
Sproxton Heath (correctly known as Saltby Heath)	SK 874 260
St. Margaret's Bus Station, Leicester	SK 587 050
St. Margaret's Church, Leicester	SK 585 050
St. Mary's Hospital, Melton Mowbray	SK 758 193
St. Nicholas Circle, Leicester	SK 582 044
St. Peter's Lane, Leicester	SK 583 046
Stanford Park	SP 584 793
Stanford Reservoir	SP 60 80

Stanton under Bardon	SK 466 103
Stapleford	SK 810 182
Stapleford Park	SK 81 17
Stapleton	SP 435 985
Stathern	SK 771 311
Stathern Wood	SK 782 316
Staunton Harold Hall Lakes	SK 380 209
Staunton Harold Reservoir	SK 376 236
Stockerston	SP 835 978
Stocking Farm Estate, Leicester	SK 580 073
Stoke Dry	SP 855 968
Stoke Dry Wood	SP 845 976
Stoke Golding	SP 400 972
Stonepit Wood, Wartnaby	SK 705 237
Stonesby Heath	SK 813 250
Stoney Cove	SP 492 941
Stoney Stanton	SP 490 948
Stoney Stanton Jetski Centre	SP 501 940
Stoneygate, Leicester	SK 60 02
Stoneygate Road, Leicester	SK 606 026
Stoneywell Wood	SK 499 120
Stoughton	SK 641 021
Stoughton Airfield	SK 65 01
Stoughton CBC plot	SK 63 01
Stoughton Lodge Farm	SK 637 027
Stretton	SK 950 158
Stretton en le Field	SK 304 119
Stretton Hall	SP 652 995
Stretton Wood	SK 956 169
Sutton Ambion	SK 989 002
Sutton Cheney	SK 416 004
Swannington	SK 415 159
Swan's Nest Weir, Belgrave, Leicester	SK 590 066
Swepstone	SK 369 106
Swinford	SP 568 794
Swithland	SK 548 132
Swithland Reservoir	SK 558 140
Swithland Water Works	SK 555 148
Swithland Wood	SK 539 125
Sysonby Sewage Farm (also known as Melton Sewage Farm)	SK 737 185
Syston	SK 62 11
Syston Grange	SK 639 108
Syston Gravel Pits	SK 615 122
Teigh	SK 867 160
Terrace Hills, Belvoir	SK 800 321
Theddingworth	SP 665 855
Thistleton	SK 913 179
Thornton	SK 468 073
Thornton Reservoir	SK 473 075
Thorpe Arnold	SK 771 201
Thorpe by Water	SP 892 966
Thorpe Langton	SP 743 925
Thorpe Trussels	SK 727 130
Thringstone	SK 42 17
Thrussington	SK 649 160
Thurcaston	SK 567 108
Thurlaston	SP 501 991
Thurmaston	SK 61 09
Thurmaston Gravel Pits (now Watermead Floodplain)	*SK 602 092*
Thurmaston Lock	SK 608 094
Thurnby	SK 64 04
Tickencote	SK 989 095
Tilton on the Hill	SK 743 056
Tilton Wood	SK 760 041
Timberwood Hill	SK 470 146
Tinwell	TF 003 063
Tixover	SK 973 008
Tixover Grange	SK 979 017
Tolethorpe	TF 022 103
Tolethorpe Mill	TF 021 105
Tonge	SK 419 232
Tooley Park, Desford	SK 48 00
Tooley Spinney	SK 476 002
Trent Farm Pool	SK 434 287
Trent Lock	SK 489 311
Trent Valley Pit	SK 465 305
Tyron Spinney	SK 769 031
Tugby	SK 762 009
Tugby Wood	SK 767 021
Tunneley Wood	SK 932 121
Tur Langton	SP 713 945
Twycross	SK 338 050
Twyford	SK 730 102
Ullesthorpe	SP 507 877
Ulverscroft	SK 492 126
Ulverscroft Priory	SK 501 127
Ulverscroft Road, Leicester	SK 600 056
University of Leicester Botanical Gardens, Oadby	SK 616 013
Upperton Road, Leicester	SK 574 034
Uppingham	SP 86 99
Uppingham Road, Leicester	SK 603 052
Vale of Belvoir	SK 80 33
Vaughan Way, Leicester	SK 584 048
Victoria Park, Leicester	SK 597 031
Wakerley Bridge	SP 955 998
Waltham on the Wolds	SK 802 250
Walton	SP 595 870
Walton on the Wolds	SK 592 197
Wanlip	SK 600 107

Wanlip Gravel Pits (now part of Watermead Country Park North)	*SK 60 10*
Wanlip Meadows	SK 603 105
Wanlip North Gravel Pits (also known as Wanlip North Lakes)	SK 602 118
Wanlip North Lakes (also known as Wanlip North Gravel Pits)	SK 602 118
Wanlip South Gravel Pits (also known as Watermead Country Park North)	SK 60 10
Wardley	SK 832 002
Wardley Wood	SP 839 997
Warren Hills	SK 460 148
Watermead Country Park North	SK 60 10
Watermead Country Park South	SK 599 083
Watermead Gravel Pits (now part of Watermead Country Park South)	*SK 599 083*
Watermead Park (also known as Watermead Country Park South)	SK 599 083
Welford Road, Leicester	SK 594 019
Welford Road Cemetery, Leicester	SK 591 030
Welham	SP 765 925
Welland valley	SP 88 95
Wellsborough	SK 364 024
West Beacon Farm	SK 501 152
West Bridge, Leicester	SK 581 043
West End, Leicester	SK 57 04
West Knighton, Leicester	SK 59 00
Westcotes, Leicester	SK 573 037
Western Park, Leicester	SK 558 044
Westleigh, Narborough Road, Leicester	SK 572 033
Wharf Farm, Market Bosworth	SK 378 059
Whatborough Hill	SK 767 059
Whetstone	SP 55 97
Whetstone Pastures	SP 562 941
Whetstone Pastures Farm	SP 561 939
Whissendine	SK 825 142
Whitwell	SK 923 088
Whitwick	SK 43 16
Whitwick Quarry	SK 448 159
Wigston	SP 60 99
Wigston Sewage Farm	SP 593 967
Willesley	SK 340 146
Willesley Lake	SK 338 147
Willesley Wood	SK 336 141
Willoughby Waterleys	SP 575 925
Windsor Hill, Belvoir	SK 815 323
Wing	SK 893 030
Wistow	SP 638 959
Wistow Hall	SP 641 958
Wistow Lake	SP 642 958
Withcote	SK 797 058
Withcote Hall Lake	SK 797 056
Woodhouse	SK 540 154
Woodhouse Eaves	SK 530 143
Woolfox	SK 963 132
Wycomb	SK 774 249
Wyfordby	SK 793 189
Wymeswold	SK 603 234
Wymeswold Airfield	SK 58 22
Wymondham	SK 851 186
Wymondham rough	SK 832 174

APPENDIX 2: SCIENTIFIC NAMES OF PLANTS AND ANIMALS REFERRED TO IN THE TEXT

Flowering plants

Alder *Alnus glutinosa*
Ash *Fraxinus excelsior*
Beech *Fagus sylvatica*
Birch *Betula* spp.
Blackthorn *Prunus spinosa*
Copper Beech *Fagus sylvatica 'atropunicea'*
Cypress *Cupressus* spp.
Eel grass *Zostera marina*
Elm *Ulmus procera*
Hawthorn *Crataegus monogyna*
Hazel *Corylus avellana*
Horse Chestnut *Aesculus hippocastanum*
Larch *Larix decidua*
Maple *Acer campestre*
Nettles *Urticaceae*
Oak *Quercus* spp.
Oilseed rape *Brassica napus*
Osier *Salix* spp.
Poplar *Populus* spp.
Reed *Phragmites australis*
Reedmace *Typha latifolia*
Rye Grass *Lolium perenne*
Sallow *Salix* spp.
Scots Pine *Pinus sylvestris*
Sycamore *Acer pseudoplatanus*
Thistles *Cirsium* spp.
Wheat *Triticum aestivum*
Whitethorn *Crataegus oxyacantha*
Willow *Salix* spp.
Willowherb *Epilobium* spp.

Fish

Pike *Esox lucius*
Stickleback *Gasterosteus* spp.

Mammals

Brown Hare *Lepus europaeus*
Common Shrew *Sorex araneus*
Deer spp. *Cervus* spp.
Field Vole *Microtus agrestis*
Grey Squirrel *Sciurus carolinensis*
American Mink *Mustela vison*
Mouse sp. *Mus* sp.
Rabbit *Oryctolagus cuniculus*
Red Fox *Vulpes vulpes*
Wood Mouse *Apodemus sylvaticus*

Molluscs

Swan Mussel *Anodonta cygnea*

APPENDIX 3: CONTRIBUTORS TO LEICESTERSHIRE AND RUTLAND BIRD REPORTS 1941 TO 2005 AND POSITIONS HELD

compiled by Steve Lister

The total number of contributors listed in the LROS Annual Reports between 1941 and 2005 has reached an astounding 2,132. The vast majority, 2,100 to be exact, are individual contributors and the other 32 are made up of a variety of natural history groups, bird clubs, conservation organisations, etc. All are listed here as an acknowledgement of the recording effort, large or small, that each has made.

Individual contributors

All contributors are listed alphabetically, along with the years that their names were included in the Annual Reports. Short breaks of one or two years in a series of annual contributions have been ignored, so someone who submitted records from 1950 to 1956 and from 1959 to 1970 will have been listed simply for 1950–1970. Observers who have made regular contributions over a period of ten years or more are highlighted in bold.

At the suggestion of Frank Pickering, current President and a true stalwart of the Society since 1948, it was decided to include details of those contributors that have also served on the committee or held office as President, Chairman, Vice-Chairman, Treasurer, Secretary, Honorary Vice-President, Recorder, Referee or Wildfowl Count Organiser, along with their relevant periods of service. Frank was very helpful in supplying details of committee members for the years in which no information was included in the Annual Report.

I apologise for any errors in names. In some cases the same person's name has been printed with different spellings in different years' reports, and where I could not resolve the difference I have used the more recent spelling. There may also be mistakes arising from an observer using different initials on their record slips in different years, and I may have wrongly 'lumped' two people with the same name. I am grateful to Keith Allsopp, Rob Fray, Dave Gamble, Jean Ironside and Frank Pickering who all checked my original compilation in an attempt to minimise such errors.

D.J. Abbott (1987), G.H. Acklam (1956), J. Adams (1994), P. Adcock (1966), P.H. Adcock (1997, 2001), C. Adkin (1990), N. Adkin (1990, 2004), R. Adkin (1973–74), H.G. Alexander (1952–56), W.B. Alexander (1949–50), Mrs Alexander (1991), J. Allcott (2005), **A.S. Allen** (1995–2005), D.M. Allen (1955–56), **D.M. Allen** (1987–95, 2001), G. Allen (1952), M.J. Allen (1968, 1990), O.J. Allen (1989–93), P.J. Allen (1989–93), R. Allen (2000), T. Allen (2000), W.D. Allen (1946–47), **E.M.P. Allsopp** (1962–73: Committee 1969–73), **K. Allsopp** (1962–2004: Committee 1966–76; Recorder 1970–75), Mr and Mrs M.L. Allsopp (1966–67, 1978–79), M. Allured (1987), A. Amery (2002, 2004), P. Amos (1998), D.A. Anderson (1990–98), G.Q.A. Anderson (2000–02), K.R. Anderson (2005), I.G. Andrew (1963–66), P. Andrew (1976), D.G. Andrews (1944), K. Andrews (1977–80), S.A. Andrews (1977–80), S.M. Andrews (1987, 1992), F.H. Anscliffe (1944), Mr and Mrs Ansell (1975), Mr Anson-Smith (1943), R. Appleby (1961), R.A. Appleton (1966), **T.P. Appleton** (1975–2005: Referee 1985–2003), W. Appleyard (1979), Mr Archer (1989), L.C. Archibald (1994), D.T. Armitage (1971), **D.W. Armstead** (1976–2003), P. Armstrong (1985), R. Armstrong (1985), G.A. Arnold (1952–55), M.A. Arnold (1953–55), P.W. Arnold (1965), A. Ash (1982), **P. Asher** (1981, 1986–94, 2003: Committee 1991–93), **M. Aspinall** (1984–96), N. Aston (1979–80), J. Atkins (1944), D.L. Atkinson (1984), J.D. Atkinson (1957), P.R. Atkinson (1992–93, 2004–05), **R.W. Atkinson** (1984, 1992–94, 2000–05), W.E. Atkinson (1984–85), C. Avery (2001).

J.C. Badcock (1951–54, 1962–70), C.R. Bagshaw (1980–86), **C.D. Baggott** (1992–2005: Committee 2000–05; Vice-Chairman 2003–05), D. Bailey (1998), D.E. Bailey (1952–54), K. Bailey (1961–62), M. Bailey (2002–05), S.F. Bailey (1941–44), Mr and Mrs Bailey (1965), J.G. Baines (1999–2003), L.P. Baines (1999–2003), **F.A. Bak** (1947–57, 1961, 1973: Committee 1946–59 and 1965–81; Secretary 1946–48; Vice-Chairman 1949; Chairman 1950; President 1965–81; Recorder 1964), J. Bak (1948, 1956–57), **A. Baker** (1975–81, 1998–2005), C. Baker

(1974), C.P. Baker (1998), J. Baker (1983–87), J.M. Baker (1983–87), M. Baker (1986), **N.E. Baker** (1971–81: Committee 1975–78), **R.F. Baker** (1971–2005: Committee 1977–86; Recorder 1982–86), V. Baker (1997), G.R. Balchin (1968), A. Baldock (1986–88), A.D. Baldwin (1988, 2004), N.R. Baldwin (1971), S.J. Baldwin (1985–86), D. Ball (1997), H. Ball (1986), P. Ball (1991–92), V. Ball (1988), D.K. Ballance (2004), E. Ballard (1995), C.P. Bancroft (1988), S. Banks (1990–94, 2002–03), T. Banks (1990), Mrs Barby (1989), Mr and Mrs O.R. Barclay (1979), P.V. Barford (1974), K. Barker (1997), K.R. Barker (1957), P. Barker (1996), D. Barlow (2001), B.A. Barnacle (1978–82), K. Barnacle (1978–82), D. Barnett (1943), M. Barnett (2000–01), B. Barfield (1941), D.A. Barratt (1965), N. Barratt (1978), **W.H. Barrow** (1941–50, 1956–58, 1961–66: Referee 1941–42), I. Bartlett (2002–04), J. Barwell (1988), H. Basford (1979), G.M. Basil (1984), A. Bates (2001), F. Bates (1997), J.K. Bates (1949–50), L. Batt (1984–85), G. Bayes (1980), J. Bayldon (2002), R.G. Bayldon (2001–05), S. Baylis (2000–03), V. Bayliss (1988–90), W. Baynes (1987), W.R. Baynes (1994), T. Bays (1998), S.R. Beal (1975–77), D. Bealks (1961), M.A.S. Beaman (1968–69), R. Beardsley (1995), D. Beckerton (1993), C. Beckett (1992), D.M. Bednall (1972–79), M. Beelets (1992), B.D. Bell (1967), J.B. Bell (2003), W.M. Bell-Richards (1941), F.G. Bellamy (1949), S. Bellamy (1990), D. Bennett (1988), S.J. Benneworth (2001), E. Beresford (1951), R.H. Beresford (1990), A. Berridge (1964–71), **M.G. Berriman** (1995–2005), P. Berry (2000), J.G. Beswick (2004), R. Betjemann (2005), G. Beven (1945), P. Beveridge (2002), C.T. Beverley (1960–67: Committee 1961–67; Vice-Chairman 1966–67), A.J. Biddle (2003–04), L. Biddle (2003), **E.M. Bielby** (1976–87), **J.H. Bielby** (1976–89: Committee 1977–90; Treasurer 1977–90), M.J. Biggs (1976), J.I. Billings (1977–84), M. Billings (1992), M.T. Billings (1977–84), N.M. Billsdon (1982–84), P.F. Billson (1986), G. Binder (2003), **K. Bindley** (1986–92, 1998–2005), K. Bindley (1999), **D. Binns** (1949–58), N.S. Birch (2005), R. Bird (1974–78), R.S. Bird (2000–04), B.E. Birkin (1991), B. Bishop (1965–67), D. Bishop (1951), E. Black (1976), **O.H. Black** (1958–65, 1971–75, 1988–90), R. Black (1975–76), R. Black (1996–98), W.M. Black (1946), C.M. Blackburn (1978–79), G. Blackburn (1994, 2000–05), P.J. Blackburn (1977–79: Committee 1979–80; Secretary 1979–80), G. Blackett (1992), J.S. Blair (1941), Mrs Blake (1997), D. Blake (2005), **D. Blakesley** (1974–83), J. Bleby (2003–04), G. Blow (1967), D. Boden (1983), G.A. Boden (1983–86), M. Body (1984), G.F. Bolton (1953), M. Bolton (1983), P. Bolton (1981–83), D.K. Bond (1968), T.K. Bond (1969), M. Bone (1989), **A. Bonner** (1941–89: Committee 1941–51; Vice-Chairman 1941–45 and 1947; Referee 1946–51), **G.J. Boobyer** (1978–91), M.J. Boobyer (1983–91), S.G. Boobyer (1983), M. Boothby (1986), R. Boothby (1986, 1998, 2004), F.M. Boston (1951), K. Bosworth (1996), E.M. Botterill (1979), A.R. Bottrill (1966), M. Bottrill (1969–74), J. Boulter (2000–03), S. Boulter (1964–66), G. Bovey (1975), K.G. Bowcock (1967, 1973–75), P.W. Bowcock (1962), C.G.R. Bowden (1980), P.F. Bowden (1967–69), J. Bowen (1993), S. Bowley (1990–91), R.M. Box (1998), J.C. Boyes (1966), C. Bradley (1984), C.J. Bradley (1995), **G.D. Bradley** (1989–2001, 2004–05: Committee 1991–94), P. Bradley (1987), **H. Bradshaw** (1946–48, 1960–68, 1997–2005), Mr and Mrs Bradshaw (1988), F. Brady (1941–45: Committee 1941–44; Chairman 1941–44), J. Braker (1997, 2001–02: Committee 1999–2005), M.F. Braker (1997–2005), A.D. Bramley (1974), J. Branscombe (1994, 2000), A. Branson (2005), N.C. Braund (1976–79), A. Bray (1987), B. Bray (1994), M. Brayshaw (1952–55), **A.S. Brett** (1986–2005: Referee 1997–2005), **R.G. Brett** (1987–2005), R. Brisland (1992–93), R. Britton (1964), M. Broadbent (1953), P.F. le Brocq (1970–71), J. Brogan (1959), D.R. Bromwich (1976–78), A. Brook (1961–65), P.R. Brook (1986), S.B. Brook (1966), J.E. Brookhouse (1967–71: Committee 1968–71), D. Brooks (1999), G.R. Brooks (1951–55), J. Brooks (1992, 2000–01), J.A. Brooks (1952–53), S. Brooks (1999), W. Broom (1992), M. Broome (1971), W. Broome (1980), D. Broughton (2003), **E.E. Broughton** (1959–69), G.R. Broughton (1979), H.E. Broughton (2005), **R. Broughton** (1941–45, 1955–58: Committee 1958–64; Vice-Chairman 1958–59; Chairman 1959–60), A. Brown (1985–90), A.M. Brown (1974–77), A.R. Brown (1993–99), B.M. Brown (1977), F.R. Brown (1974), K.F.C. Brown (1974–76), K.F.J. Brown (1988–95), L. Brown (1998), L.A. Brown (1955–57), M. Brown (1975), R.S. Brown (1961), S. Brown (2003), S. Browne (1991), W.G. Browne (1944–45), A. Browning (2002, 2004), A. Brownett (1970), E.C. Bruce-Gardner (1969), A. Bryan (1943), P. Bryan (1999, 2005), M. Bryant (1982), D.M. Bryce (1941–48), E.M. Bryce (1944–45), B.M. Buchanan (1950), J. Buchanan (1985), S.R. Buck (1979), A.F. Buckingham (1981), L. Buckingham (1996), H.A. Buckler (1956–60), H. Buckley (1988), M. Buckley (1988), D. Budworth (1988), A. Bull (1961), H. Bull (1998), S. Bullard (1971), D.J. Bullock (1989), R.W. Bullock (1977), F. Bunker (1995), G.J. Burbage (1977–81), A. Burdett (1986, 1991–97), P. Burgess (1997, 2004–05), M. Burn-Murdoch (2002), D. Burrows (2000–01), G. Burrows (2000–01), E.M. Burton (1944–48), F. Burton (2004), J. Burton (1986), J.L. Burton (1965), K.G. Burton (1984), L. Burton (2004), G. Busby (1997, 2004–05), G. Buswell (1987), J. Butchart (1985), R. Butchart (1985), J. Butcher (1992), C.J. Butler (1980–81), R. Butler (1957), R.K. Butler (1971), C. Butters (1999), M.A. Buxton (1958), R.S. Buxton (1969–70), R. Bye (2004), B.M. Byrne (1988).

T. Caldicott (1995–2005), J.R. Calladine (1977), R.A. Calladine (1977), E. Calow (1987–90), M.J.D. Campbell (1976–81), R. Campsall (1996, 2000), S.J. Campsall (1985–90), R.M. Carey (1944), A. Carling (1987–90, 2000), S. Carling (2000), M. Carr (2005), R.H. Carr (1945), **H.R. Carter** (1961–94, 2000–01: Committee 1968–78), K.E.

Carter (1962–94: Committee 1972–78), M. Carter (1974), **A.J. Carty** (1977–91), G. Cassell (1988), **M.T. Cassidy-Walker**, formerly Cassidy (1987–2005), D. Caswell (1986), J. Cato (1988–92), B.S. Cave (1964), Rev D.J. Cawte (1980), **K.J. Chamberlain** (1979–2005), N.M. Chambers (1983), L. Chandler (2005), R.J. Chandler (1979), H.E. Chantler (1984), E.R. Chapman (1951, 1956), R.A. Chapman (1972–75), Mrs Chapman (1988), P. Charge (1944), A.J. Charity (2003), C.E. Charity (2003), K.G. Charity (1994–96, 2002–05), S.E. Charity (1995, 2003), D. Charles (1992, 1998), J. Charles (2003), M. Charles (1992, 1998), J. Chase (1984), H.M. Chatfield (1947–48), **R.F. Chatfield** (1945–58), R.M. Cheney (1994–96, 2002–05), **H.G. Cherry** (1947–89: Committee 1952–72 and 1976–84; Vice-Chairman 1956–57, 1963–64 and 1967–69; Chairman 1969–72; Secretary 1965–68 and 1980–84; Treasurer 1961–65), **M.J. Chester** (1973–2005), A.P. Chick (2001, 2004), A. Chope (1944), B. Church (2003), A.E. Clark (1941), A.J. Clark (1951–56), P. Clark (1977–78), **R.G. Clark** (1969–85), C. Clarke (2001), F. Clarke (2003), G. Clarke (2001), J. Clarke (1961–65: Committee 1965–66), J.D. Clarke (1983), R.A. Clarke (1961–65), R.E. Clarke (1974), S.W. Clarke (1943–47: Committee 1945–46), E.I. Clay (1982, 1987: Committee 1976–86; Chairman 1982–85), P.N. Clay (1977–83), **M.S. Clayson** (1976, 1984–2005), T. Cleeves (1974), T.M. Clegg (1969), **H.A.B. Clements** (1947–64, 1970: Committee 1958–60), G. Clewes (2002), A. Clifton (2002–04), **S.J. Close** (1984–97), P. Clough (2003), J.R. Coates (1951), D.R. Coda (1951–56: Committee 1956–57; Secretary 1956–57), D. Coe (2003), B.A. Cohen (1987), **D.A. Cohen** (1974–96: Committee 1985–97; Vice-Chairman 1985–88; Chairman 1988–91), P. Cohen (1986), **S.E. Cohen** (1986–95: Committee 1990–96; Secretary 1990–93), J. Cole (1990, 1998), M. Cole (1984), S. Cole (2003), S.W. Cole (1972–74, 1979), J. Coleman (1995, 2002, 2004), J.C. Coleman (1961–62), R. Colenso (1976), M. Coles (1988–90), B. Coley (1995), D.R. Coley (1995), D. Collingham (2005), D.R. Collins (1983), H. Collinson (1941–47), H. Collinson (1972), G.M. Collis (1968), H.R. Colman (1944–49), W. Colver (1977), J. Colvern (1995), R.J. Cook (1987), C.H. Cooke (1941), J.D. Cooksey (1970–74: Committee 1969–77; Chairman 1975–77), M.B. Coole (2002), C.W. Cooper (1966), D.R. Cooper (1989–90, 1995), K.L. Cooper (1959–64: Committee 1965–66 and 1968–69), S.G.R. Cope (1986–87), D. Copley (2005), I. Copley (2005), A. Copson (1994), C.A. Cornish (1989–94), M.L. Cornish (1992–94), C. Corrigan (1981), R. Cosgrove (1984), **S. Costa** (1984–88, 1993–99), A. Costello (1976, 1983–85), **J. Cotton** (1987–96, 2002–05), P. Coulson (1991–92), D.L. Coultas (1990), J. Courty (1975), J. Cousins (1996), W. Cove (2001, 2005), **D. Cox** (1986–2005), D.J. Cox (1963–66, 1971–74), J. Cox (1991), P. Cox (1977–81), R.A.F. Cox (1984), **R.E. Cox** (1971–81, 2003: Committee 1976–82; Recorder 1975–80), R.F. Cox (1947–52), T. Cox (1988), T.R. Cox (1988), N. Coy (1983), P.J. Craddock (1979), D.R. Cragg (1996), J. Crane (1986), K. Crane (1983), **J.G. Cranfield** (1976–86, 2003), Rev. M. Crawshaw (1943), Mr and Mrs F.J. Croft (1976–77), **E.G. Croman** (1978–90, 2000), M. Cross (1976–83), R. Cross (2002), **R.J. Cross** (1976–88), B. Crouch (1997, 2005), R.A.N. Croucher (1971–74), S. Crowdell (1982), **W. Crowdell** (1977–86), M. Crowther (1943–47), B. Croxtall (2002–05), L. Croxtall (1953, 1970), L. Csizmazia (2002), K. Culbert (1946–47), M. Cullen (1944–45), B. Culley (1997), A.A.H. Cunningham (1960–81).

A.W. Dakin (1993), M.N. Dale (1974–76), L.K. Dallaston (1950–54: Committee 1954–57), A.M. Dally (1979–84), **P.G. Dams** (1975–76, 1997–2005), K.J. Daniels (1995–97), G. Dann (2001), M.S. Davenport (1968–69), D. Davenport-Handley (1985–88), P. Davey (1977), M. Davidson (2005), T.C. Davies (1980–87), C.M. Davis (1985, 1992–95, 1999), P.G. Davis (1972, 2000), H.M. Davis (1993, 2000), K. Davis (2005), **R. Davis** (1977–93, 1998–2000), **R.E. Davis** (1973–2005: Committee 1977–94; Recorder 1986–94), V. Davis (1979, 1989–91), T. Davison (1987, 2000–05), P.C. Daw (1965–68), J. Daws (1981), I.K. Dawson (1974), J.E. Dawson (1982–84, 1990–91), E.R. Day (1971), H.V. Day (1953), **P. Dayman** (1990–2005), A. Deacon (1988), Mrs Deacon (1999), J.M. Deag (1966), G. Densham (1988), **J. Denman** (1991–2005), **N. Denman** (1993–2005), R. Denman (1993–99, 2004), M.D. Dent (1973), L.S. Dewey (1948), R.A. Dewhirst (1943), J.D. Dexter (2002), G. Dickens (2003), K. Dickens (2002), T. Diebel (2001–05), S.V. Digger (1947), P. Dillon-Hopper (2005), V. Dilworth (1984), A. Dixon (1980–84), **D. Dixon** (1989–2002), G.F. Dixon (1946), H. Dixon (2001), **H.F. Dixon** (1950–64: Committee 1961–63; Vice-Chairman 1962–63), J. Dixon (1994–96), M. Dixon (1980–81), A. Dobbs (1956–59), G.W. Dodds (1996–99, 2004: Committee 1997–99), J.E. Dodds (1997–99), S. Dodds (1986), B. Dodsworth (1999), D.W.R. Doggett (1977–81), G.P. Dolby (1950–51), D.R. Doleman (1964), J.F. Doleman (1953), J.F. Doleman (1988), C. Dolphin (1987–90, 1998, 2002–05), S. Doughty (1990), N.R. Dove (1966), **G.A. Down** (1969–80, 1991–2004), R.A. Down (1994–2000), G.C. Downs (1984), J.C. Doyle (2005), V.A. Drake (1974), C. Drew-Edwards (1968), F. Drummond (1981), D. Duckett (2004), S.P. Dudley (1991), **E.A. Duffey** (1941–55: Committee 1946–49; Referee 1946–49), **A. Duffield** (1971–89, 2000–05), E.J. Duffield (2002), P. Duncan (1989), T. Dunkley (1983, 1998–99), **D.A. Dunn** (1971–81, 1986–87, 1991–2000, 2004–05): Committee 1972–77), J. Dunn (1991–92), W.M. Duthie (1968), P.H.R. Dutton (1951), R. Dyster (2003–05), H.J. Dytham (1941).

J.C. Eames (1977–80), B. Earp (2001), F. East (1957–58), D. Easton (1997–2004), J.D. Easton (1948, 1954), D.W. Easton (1954), Mr Easton (1987), G.A. Eastwood (1998), J. Eastwood (1998), A. Eaton (1984), D.E. Eaton (2000), J.J. Eaton (1971–76: Committee 1976–77), A. Eaves (1984), R. Eckton (2000), R. Edgar (1966), J.E.F. Edwards (1990–91), L. Edwards (1965), M.J. Edwards (1990–91), S. Edwards (1998), N.E. Eggington (1985), S. Eggington (1995–99), G. Eldridge (1974–77), P. Elkington (1966), G. Elliott (1976–79), J.M. Elliott (2004), **M.A. Elliott** (1987–2005), S.E. Elliott (1974), B. Ellis (1941), B. Ellis (1997), D. Ellis (1975), J. Ellis (2005), P.W. Ellis (1976–79), Mrs Elliott (1991), D. Elmer (1986), T.R. England (1986–87), **I.M. Evans** (1962–74, 1986–89), P. Evans (1981–84), **P.A. Evans**, formerly Candlish (1964–67, 1973, 1977, 1986–89), M. Everett (1993), J.A. Ewan (1958), H. Eyden (1976), J. Eyden (1976).

A. Fairbrother (1997, 2004), E.J. Fairbrother (1997–99, 2004), B.J. Fallon (2002–05), P. Farbridge (1998–2005), E.M. Farmer (1946), J.B. Farmer (1978), M.R. Farmer (1978), M. Farnsworth (1989), E. Faulkner (1973), A. Fear (2005), M.W. Feely (1987, 2003), **D. Felstead** (1944–59), **G. Felstead** (1943–62, 1972–91, 1996–2004: Committee 1948–54, 1980–81; Vice-Chairman 1980–81: Referee 1951–54), P.G. Fennell (1949), K.G. Fenton (1992), N.J. Ferriman (1977), **V.N. Ferriman** (1976–2005), **M.B. Fewkes** (1946–50, 1955–57, 1993–2004), R.H. Field (2001–02), R. Fieldman (1987), G.L. Finch (1980), P.J. Findon (1977–78), M.J. Finnigan (1974–75), D. Fisher (1979), J. Fisher (1953), R. Fletcher (1988), C. Flint (2002–05), Miss Flint (1988), R.H. Follows (2001–05), A.M. Folwell (1981–82), S.W. Folwell (1982), C.J. Ford (1977–79), M. Ford (2002), R.G. Ford (1976–79), **D.B. Forgham** (1987–2002), **J.A. Forryan** (1986–2005: Referee 1999–2005), D.W.J. Foster (1999, 2004), W.H. Foulds (1961), G. Foulkes-Williams (1993–94), **J.A. Fowler** (1970–89, 1994–98: Committee 1982–90), R. Fowles (2001), D. Fox (2003–04), **J.R.L. Fox** (1972–99), R. Fox (1977), **V. Fox** (1972–99: Committee 1990–92), T. Foxell (1988), D. Foxwell (1961), C. Francis (1982–85), C.P. Francis (1974–75), C. Frankham (2000), Mr Franks (1993), R. Frankum (1967), I. Fraser (1994, 2001), M.C. Fraser (2005), C.R. Fraser-Jenkins (1968), L. Fray (2004), **M. Fray** (1985, 1994–98, 2001–05), M.E. Fray (1995–2000, 2004), **R.M. Fray** (1984–2005: Committee 1986–2005: Vice-Chairman 2000–03; Chairman 2003–05; Recorder 1995–2005: Referee 1994–2005; Wildfowl Count Organiser 1992–94), **R.P. Fray** (1986–2002: Committee 1994–2002), K.S. Frazer (1979–87), M. Freeman (1991), O. Freer (1970), B. Frost (1995), C.D. Frost (1943), **J. Frost** (1985–2004), **M.V. Frost** (1986–98), R.A. Frost (1979–80, 1987), E.M. Fulford (1995), R.D. Fulford (1993–95).

A. Galasinski (2000–02, 2005), C. Galbraith (2005), T. Gale (2005), A. Gallimore (1984), C. Gallimore (1984, 2002), **D.J.S. Gamble** (1976–2005: Committee 1984–2005; Referee 1986–92; Wildfowl Count Organiser 1990–92), G. Gamble (2005), **I.B. Gamble** (1975–89, 1998–2003, 2005: Referee 1987–90), J. Gamble (1992–93, 2001–02), M. Gamble (2004), P. Gamble (2004), **P.H. Gamble** (1944–2005: Committee 1949–61, 1986–90; Referee 1950–57, 1990–2003), **R.P. Gamble** (1987–88, 1993–2005), S.R. Gamble (2000–05), P. Garbett (1989, 2002), N. Gardner (1991–92), **M.J. Garner** (1965–78, 1985–86, 1996), **S.S. Garner** (1958–78, 1985–86, 1996: Committee 1960–74; Vice-Chairman 1961–62; Chairman 1962–63), R.P. Garnett (1988, 1995–98), A. Garton (1999–2002), L. Gascoigne (1990–97), M.W. Gaunt (1958–65, 1972), R.W. Gaunt (1958–64), F.M. Gauntlett (1955–57, 1994), K. Gayton (1987), **A.H. Gearing** (1966, 1981–97, 2001–03), **M.M. Gearing** (1981–87, 2001–03), L. Gearing-Bell (2000–03), S. Gee (1992, 1997), D. Gent (1994), B. Geoghegan (1987), D. Gibbons (1976–79), E. Gibbons (1975–79), E. Gibbons (1976), J.R. Gibbons (1975–79), D.G. Gibbs (1982), R.G. Gibbs (1963–66: Committee 1964–67), A.G. Gibson (2001), J. Gibson (1984), Mr Gibson (1993), **M.J. Gibson** (1994–2005), **S.A. Gibson** (1995–2005), A. Gilbert (1990–93, 1998–2004), J.A. Gilbert (1992–93), R. Gilbert (1997), G. Giles (1943–44), R.T. Giles (1998), J. Gill (2004), **J.S.B. Gill** (1971–2005: Committee 1969–95; Vice-Chairman 1975–76, 1994–95; Chairman 1976–78; Treasurer 1989–93), R. Gill (2005), M.J. Gillham (1988–92, 1997–99, 2005), C. Gimson (1957–60), S. Ginns (1966), P. Giovannini (2004), D.J. Glass (2001), F.I. Glen (1980), C. Glenn (1986–89, 2005), N. Glenn (1992), A.M. Glenton (1985–91, 2005: Committee 1990–94), **F.I. Glenton** (1985–96, 2005), A. Goadby (1959–60), R. Goater (2002), D. Goddard (1984, 2004), M. Godwin (2005), A. Gomersall (1967–68), C. Goodall (1987), Miss Goode (1985), T. Goodlife (2002–05), N. Goodman (2004), **J. Goodrich** (1982–97, 2005), **K.G. Goodrich** (1981–2005: Committee 1984–2005), G.H. Goodwin (1969), **D.J. Gordon** (1971–81), **N.E. Gordon** (1996–2005), J.M. Goslin (1998), R.W. Gossage (1962–65), J. Gostelow (1949: Committee 1948–50), A. Gould (2000–01), D.M. Gould (1980–81), **C. Graham** (1953–62: Committee 1958–62), C. Graham (1987–89), H.T. Graham (1941, 1950–51), **J. Graham** (1987–2005: Committee 1989–2005: Chairman 2000–03), S. Graham (1995–98, 2004: Committee 1989–2005: Vice-Chairman 2005), J.G. Grahame (1943–45), G.A. Grain (1948–52, 1959), G. Grant (1961, 1966), G. Grant (1997), G.R. Grant (1951, 1969–72, 1994), H.G. Grant (1969), I. Grant (1994–95), J. Grant (1961–63), P.J. Grant (1976–80), Mr and Mrs Grant (1987), G. Grass (1974), H. Graves (1944), A.F. Gray (1978–79), **D. Gray** (1994–2005: Committee 1997–2003 and 2005), **L. Gray** (1945–58), H. Greatorex (1941),

A. Greatrex (2005), J.W. Greaves (1964), **C.S. Green** (1984–88, 2000–05), G.A. Green (1958), J. Green (1984, 1991), M. Green (1987–88), M. Green (2002), L. Greenberg (1994), M. Greenhill (2000), P.G. Greenhill (1998–2005), Mr and Mrs Greenhill (1978), J. Greenwood (1988, 1994–95), J.T. Greenwood (2005), M. Greenwood (1986), Lord Gretton (1965), G. Griffin (2004), J.B. Griffiths (1998–2005), L.R. Griffiths (2003–04), **M.E. Griffiths** (1961–71: Committee 1965–70), J. Griggs (2002), K. Grove (1996), **T.P. Grove** (1992–2005: Committee 1996–2005), **S. Grover** (1985–90, 1995–99: Committee 1994–2000), A.A. Groves (1951–52), A.P. Groves (1943), R. Gunby (2005).

P. Hack (1968), A.R. Hackett (1978–80), J.P. Hackett (1993–95), P.S. Hackett (1978–80), B. Hackney (1977–78), J.R. Haddon (1968), J.T. Hagarty (1958–59), **N.W. Hagley** (1979–82, 1987–91, 2000–04), J.M. Hague (1993–2000, 2005), P. Haldan (1949), R.W. Hale (1975–80), F. Hales (1970), A. Hall (1998), A.S. Hall (2004–05), L.E. Hall (2004–05), M. Hall (2002–04), **M.C. Hall** (1988–2004), **N.A. Hall** (1958, 1968–2005), R. Hall (1967), D.C. Hames (1985), G. Hames (1982–86), G. Hamilton (1994), S. Hamilton (1975), **W.J. Hamilton** (1975–84), A. Hamm (1985), H. Handley (1970), N. Hando (2005), **D.R. Hands** (1968–69, 1979, 1984–88, 1995–98), Mr Harcourt (1951), B. Harding (2001), A.R. Hardwick (2005), J. Hardwick (1961), J. Harley (1995), E. Harper (1979, 1984, 1993–96), J. Harper (2003), **K.G. Harper** (1984–86, 1994–2005), P. Harper (1978–82, 1992), R.E. Harper (1984), T. Harper (1978–82, 1992), **D.W.B. Harrald** (1981–90: Committee 1987–92), L. Harrald (1987–90), J. Harriman (1992), S. Harrington (1993), J. Harris (1991, 2000, 2005), P.R. Harris (1941–47: Committee 1945), S. Harris (1991–92), D. Harrison (1980), R. Harrison (1999–2005), R.W. Harrison (1980–86), **A.H.J. Harrop** (1989–2005: Referee 1991–99; Wildfowl Count Organiser 1994–2005), **R.D. Harrup** (1964–68, 1972–75, 1987–98), W.R. Hart (1974), P. Hartley (1963), K.R.J. Hartwell (1993), T.A. Hasdell (1977–78), T. Hawke (2002), **J.A.D. Hawker** (1982–2005: Committee 1993–99; Treasurer 1994–97), **R. Hawker** (1988–97, 2001, 2005), S. Hawker (1997), J. Hawkes (1988), H. Hawkesworth (1981), C.A. Hawkins (1975–77), G.A. Hayes (1943–45), H.T. Hayes (1943–49: Committee 1946–49; Vice-Chairman 1946), Mr Hayes (1989), L.A. Hayhurst (1988–89), J. Hayley (1988), A. Haynes (1997–2000), K. Hayward (2005), T. Hayward (2005), C.G. Haywood (1959), Sir A Hazlerigg (1941), The Hon. E. Hazlerigg (1961–68, 1978), I. Heaps (1996), K. Heath (1977), R. Heath (1977), T. Heath (1981), **A. Heaton** (1992–2005), R. Heaton (2000), R. Hemsley (1985), G.H. Henderson (1977), T. Henderson (1989), S. Henson (2003), E.V. Heppell (1966–68), D. Herbert (1975), T. Hering (2000), J. Heritage (1966), P. Herrick (1984–87), A. Herridge (2005), **D.G. Herringshaw** (1980, 1985–88, 1994–99), K.P. Herton (1984), J. Hickling (1952–56), **R.A.O. Hickling** (1946–94: Committee 1947–75, 1981–97; Secretary 1947–56; Chairman 1957–58, 1963–66; Referee 1950–55; President 1981–97; Honorary Vice-President 1998–2004), J. Hickman (2001), C. Hicks (2000), B.C. Higgins (1979–80, 1995, 2002), C. Higgins (1995–2001), G. Higgins (1996), H. Higgins (1993–98), J. Higgins (1993–98), R.C. Higgins (1959–61), **J.B. Higgott** (1982–88, 1994–96: Committee 1985–89), M.A. Higgott (1984, 2001), C. Hill (2005), D. Hill (1988), E.J. Hill (1968), M.S. Hill (1987–88), P.J.M. Hill (1946–48), **T.A.M. Hill** (1941–54), G. Hills (2000), J. Hipwell (1947), S. Hitchings (2003–05), S.P. Hitchins (1999), Mr Hoare (1945), G.M. Hobson (1979–80), M.H. Hoccom (1979), R.J. Hoccom (1979), K.C. Hockridge (1979–80), J. Hodgkinson (1969), R.C. Hodgkinson (2000–02), J.C. Hodkinson (1972), D.P. Hodson (1985–91: Committee 1991–92), N.L. Hodson (1956, 1964), T. Hodson (1947), C. Holden (1989), V. Holgate (1985–87), S. Hollidge (1987–89), **M. Holling** (1983–94: Committee 1984–88), K. Hollingshead (1985), J. Hollingsworth (1997, 2001–05), W. Hollingsworth (1992, 1997, 2001–05), D. Holloway (1979), D. Hollyoak (1979), **D. Holman** (1986, 1993–2002), D.A. Holmes (1960–61), G.O. Holmes (1943–47), M.A. Holmes (2005), **C.W. Holt** (1944–92, 2004: Committee 1946–79, 1992–2005: Chairman 1948 and 1966–69; Vice-Chairman 1965–66; Honorary Vice-President 1998–2005), L. Holton (1987), A. Holyoak (2005), D. Holyoak (1962–67, 2005: Committee 1967–68), T. Holyoak (1980), A. Homer (2002–04), G. Hood (1989), J. Hood (1998), G. Hooke (1945), P.A. Hooper (1990–92), P.A. Horne (1983), **V.A.J. Horsey** (1995–2004), S. Horsman (1996–2003), J.M. Horwood (1986), S.J. Houghton (1989, 2001–05), K. Howard (1988), M.K. Howarth (1947–52), A. Howes (2002–05), M.G. Howitt (1946), C. Hubbard (1981–84, 1991–92, 2005), G. Hubbard (1974), J.L. Hubbard (1966), C. Huckle (1975), C. Hughes (1995–2002, 2004), N. Hughes (2004–05), J. Hughes (1962), H. Hulland (2003), J.F. Humphries (1985–86), **G.H. Hunt** (1941–51: Referee 1946–48), P. Hunt (2001), S.E. Hunt (2000–01), T. Hunt (2001), T.J. Hunt (2001), F. Hunter (1945), J.R. Hunter (1951–55), R. Hunter (1999), C. Hunting (1968–72), A.J.K. Hurst (1945–47), L. Hurst (1968), G.R. Huskison (1974–76), R.O. Hutchinson (1995), P. Hutchinson (2005), Dr Hutton (1964), R.A. Hutton (2005), J. Huxley (1953).

M. Ianntuoni (1984), H. Ikin (1984), R. Iliffe (2001), R.J.C. Ingall (1967–68), D.V. Ingleby (2000), **E.R. Ingles** (1951–71: Committee 1955–66 and 1968–72; Secretary 1957–65), **B. Ingram** (1988–2000, 2005), R. Ingram

(1964), M.J. Inskip (1990), **J. Ironside** (1961–2003: Committee 1961–78 and 1992–2005; Honorary Vice-President 1998–2005), M.J. Izzard (1999).

M.C. Jackman (1977–79), P.S. Jackman (1975–79), C. Jackson (1988), C.D. Jackson (1952), F.A. Jackson (1954), M. Jackson (1986–94), S. Jackson (1980), Mr Jackson (1989), N. Jaggard (1998–2000), A. James (1991), C. James (1943), D. James (1976), R.M.R. James (1990, 2000–05), P. Jankovic (2005), C. Jarvis (1988), **M.J. Jarvis** (1980–2005), R. Jarvis (2003), H.R. Jasper (1941: Committee 1941–42; Referee 1941–42), J. Jaybell (2004), D.E. Jebbett (1950–60), **B.V. Jeeves** (1969–2005), **M.B. Jeeves** (1969–91, 2004–05), D.E. Jefferson (1987), A.P. Jeffery (1992), R.I. Jenkinson (1996), C. Jennings (2003), S. Jennings (2003), S. Jervis (1969–70), S. Jervis (1995), P. Jesson (1983), A.W.G. John (1984), A. Johnson (1992), C. Johnson (1995, 2004), C.G. Johnson (1976), F.J. Johnson (1995), **G.F. Johnson** (1968, 1972–83), J.R. Johnson (2001), L.S. Johnson (1977), N. Johnson (1976), N. Johnson (1987–88), R, Johnson (1974), S. Johnson (2004), S.F. Johnson (1956–58, 1964), **T.W. Johnson** (1965–2005: Committee 1972–78), P. Johnstone (1999–2003), **A.E. Jolley** (1941–52: Committee 1941–50; Secretary 1941–45; Honorary Vice-President 1948–50), D.M. Jolley (1943–46), R. Jolliffe (1974–75), B.W. Jones (2002–05), E.L. Jones (1956–58), G. Jones (2002), G.H. Jones (1993–94), I. Jones (2000), J. Jones (1999), L. Jones (1979–80), N.S. Jones (1971), P. Jones (1986), P. Jones (1996), P.H. Jones (1975), P.S.D. Jones (1977), **P.W. Jones** (1945–80, 1997–99, 2005: Committee 1950 and 1958–76; Treasurer 1965–72), R. Jones (1989, 2000, 2004), R.S.M. Jones (1963), S.J.R. Jones (1968), W.A. Jones (1945–46), P. Jordan (1973–81), J.M. Joslin (1997–98), S.L. Joyner (1974), J. Judge (2005), N.S. Judson (1995, 1999–2001, 2004–05: Committee 1999–2000; Treasurer 1999–2000), A. Jurgis (1975–78).

P. Kavanagh (1986), A. D. Keates (2000), D.R. Keates (1995–2002), **N. Keeling** (1994–2003), P. Keeling (1974–76), A.J. Keeping (1960), D. Keith (2004), S.A. Keller (1992), J. Kellett (1944–46), L.A. Kellett (1944–46), T.L. Kelsey (1944–48, 1962), J.E. Kendall (1941), A. Kennedy (2000), H. Kennedy (2004), S. Kent (1991–93), P.J. Keogh (1991–98, 2005), **M. Ketley** (1979–2005), **R.W. Key** (1960–61, 1968–70, 1977–80, 1987, 1995–96, 2000–05), J. Khan (1993–95), A. Kibble (1988), **D.J. Kightley** (1969, 1982–99), J.M. Kightley (1982–88), P. Kightley (2005), S. Kightley (1984), P. Killinger (1976), J. Kimpton (2001), J. King (1969), R. King (1997, 2002–05), L. Kirby (2005), S. Kirby (2005), W. Kirby (2003), T.A.W. Kirk (1954–57, 1969), **M.D. Kirkman** (1968–85), J. Kirkwood (1999), J.F.W. Knifton (1991), S. Knifton (2005), K.L. Knight (2002), M.G. Knight (1987–90), M.J. Knight (1988–91), **T.A. Knott** (1980–84, 1995–2005), D. Kramer (1965–66), T.A. Krawczyk (1977, 1981–83, 1993), T. Krik (1975–77).

E.E. Lacy (1975), G.K. Lacy (1975–77), G. Laffar (1992–94), N. Lakin (1975–77, 1991), E.C. Lamb (1974), F.M. Lamb (1974), N. Lamb (1998–2001), R. Lambert (2004–05), J.E. Lamming-Smith, formerly Lamming (2000–05), A.E. Land (1971), K. Land (2003), G.H. Lander (1968–69), S.M. Lander (1969), A.T. Lane (1998–2003), B.T. Lane (1992–94), J.R. Langford (1979–81), H. Langston (1989), P.J. Langston (1999–2002), **H. Lapworth** (1943–63, 1969: Committee 1947–61; Vice-Chairman 1952–53; Chairman 1953–54; Referee 1950–57), G. Large (1974), D. Latham (1980), V.E. Laughton (1954), M.K. Laverick (1961–66), A. Lawson (1990–91), N. Lawson (1968), N. Lawson (2000), N. Lawton (1990–92), T. Layton (1997), I.H. Leach (2001), **J. Leahy** (1976–79, 1985–87, 1992–94), M.A. Leamon (1977–82), B. Lee (1992), C. Lee (1979), D. Lee (2004), F. Lee (2004), G.F. Lee (2005), H.B. Lee (1972), M.P. Lee (1973–77), R.W.M. Lee (1947–50), S.A. Lee (2005), A.C. Lees (1994–99, 2004), E. Leese (2005), W. Lemmon (1974–85), A. Leon (1970), P.M. Leonard (2004–05), D. Leslie (1993), P. Leslie (1993), C.J. Lester (1989), G. Lester (1980–91), J. Lester (1990–96), **L. Lester** (1975–2005), **L.S. Lester** (1979–81), **M.P. Lester** (1979–2005), N. Lester (1996), **S. Lester** (1975–2005), A. Lever (1972), F. Levis (1950–54), C. Lewic (2005), L. Lewis (1977–80), N. Lewis (1988), Mrs Lewis (1987–88), J. Lindsey (1960), A.J. Lines (2005), A.A. Lisney (1943), **S.M. Lister** (1988–2005: Committee 2003–05; Referee 1993–2005), A.J. Litchfield (1980), D. Litchfield (1980–81), M. Litjens (1979–83), **F.P. Littlemore** (1962–2002: Committee 1968–77 and 1980–2002; Chairman 1972–75; President 1997–2002; Referee 1982–91), B. Lloyd (1998), K.W. Lloyd (1987), **E.J. Locker** (1988–2002), **R.G. Lockwood** (1976–95, 2001), **D.R. Lomas** (1984–97), K.M. Lomas (1992–97), P. Longland (1975), G. Longson (1990), **E.C. Loosmore** (1966–2000, 2005), D. Lott (2001–03), J. Lount (1991), G. Louth (1999–2000), A.J. Love (1988), A.M. Love (1988), C. Lowe (1979), T. Ludbrooke (1967), J.D. Ludlam (1951–52), S. Ludlam (1982), B.C.H. Luker (1950: Committee 1952), D. Lummins (2002–03), D. Lund (2005), J. Lund (2005), R. Lund (2005), W.J. Luton (1974, 1988, 1995), C. Lynn (1984–85, 1995, 2000–02), **C.P. Lythall** (1977, 1984–88, 1992–95, 2000–05), H. Lythall (1996), J. Lytollis (1981–88).

I.H. Macalpine-Leny (1964–66), I.P. MacEwen (1951), A. MacFarlane (1992), **A.M. Macfarlane** (1947–57, 1961–62, 1967–68), E.H. Mackay (1992–95), V. Mackay (1987–89, 1995), **A.J. Mackay** (1984–2005: Committee 1988–2003; Recorder 1994–95; Referee 1992–97 and 2005), I.E. Mackay (1951), **D. MacKenzie** (1984–2002), E.K. Mackley (2002), B. MacLean (2004), R.C. MacLean (1974), J. Magrath (1974), P. Mahiques (1995–96), J.D. Malin (2005), M.K. Malin (2005), R.J. Malin (1983, 2005), A. Mallet (1954), P. Mallett (1987–89), R.A. Mann (1965), Mrs Mann (1989), D. Mansfield (1995–97, 2005: Committee 1995–98; Secretary 1996–98), D. March (2001), **R. Marjoram** (1990–2002), M. Markham (2005), G.D. Marlow (1986), L. Marlow (1991), R.E. Marlow (1997), P.R. Marshall (1956), C. Martin (2003), J. Martin (1977–79, 2000–03), J.G. Martin (1974), M. Martin (2002, 2005), P. Martin (1984), Sir R.E. Martin (1954–57), S. Martin (2001), **C.F. Mason** (1960–71, 1990: Committee 1967–71), J. Mason (1988, 1998), **L.R. Mason** (1958–67), M. Masters (2004–05), I.J. Matson (2004–05), **A. Mattock** (1974–82, 1988), K.J. Matts (2004–05), M.S. Mawson (1975–77, 1983–85), C. Maxwell (2001), E. Maydwell (1986), H. Mayer-Gross (1996), W.E. Mayes (1941–43: Committee 1941–44; Referee 1941–42), F. L. Maylam (1954), N.W.D. McCausland (1983), A. McClung (1981), J. McCormack (1975), A. McDonald (2004), **O. McGarry** (1983–94: Committee 1988–89), T. McIlroy (1968–69), D. McLean (1944), **J.M. McMeeking** (1947–56, 1969), **D.A.C. McNeil** (1969–79, 1994–98), P. McNeil (1966), J.R. McPhail (2002), A. McPherson (1998–99), **J.A. Mead** (1979–2005), A.E. Meades (1941–43, 1950), P. Mear (1990), **C. Measures** (1974–88: Committee 1984–91; Secretary 1984–89), J.F. Measures (1947–48: Committee 1946–48), S. Measures (1980, 1987–88), Miss Medcalf (1993), J. Medland (1973–78), J. Mee (2001), I. Meigh (1978–83), A. Melia (1984), A.N. Mellor (1957–63, 1973), D. Meredith (1987–90, 2005), G. Merrell (1992), **I. Merrill** (1982–2005: Referee 2003–05), A.W. Merritt (2005), M.J. Merritt (2004–05), W. Merritt (1964–65), P.R. Messant (1975–76), J.C. Metcalf (1976–79), J. Michalik (2002–03), N. Michelson (1984), C. Midgley (2005), J.S. Mighell (1972), A. Miller (1998), S. Miller (1984), J.G. Milligan (1992–96), C.H. Mills (1987, 2004), D.R. Mills (1978), R. Mills (1997–2001), C.A. Milner (1970, 1976), P. Mitcham (1991), **T. Mitcham** (1977–2005: Committee 1986–90; Referee 1985–91), C. Mitchell (1989), D. Mitchell (2000–05), M. Mitchell (1999), R. Mitchell (1986–88), I.F. Mollart (2002–05), P. Monihan (2002), J. Montgomery (2002–05), H.P. Moon (1970), S.J. Moon (1982), **A.M. Moore** (1986–2001), **B. Moore** (1991–97, 2001–02, 2005: Committee 2004–05), C. Moore (1966), C.M. Moore (2005), D. Moore (1952), I. Moore (1973), J.L. Moore (1961), K. Moore (2002), R.J. Moore (1958–59, 1979–80, 1985), G. Morley (2002), J. Morley (1987), J. Morris (2002), M. Morris (1967), R. Morris (2002), W.R. Morris (1981–87), J. Morrison (1990–91), G. Mortimer (1943), J. Morton (1947), J.S. Morton (1980), K.G. Morton (1986), G.H. Moulden (1984–86, 1991), **K. Moulton** (1978–93, 1998–2004), **N. Mound** (1989–2000, 2004), E.C. Mount (1941), H.J. Mousley (1987), W.D. Mudie (1987), K. Munday (1997), P. Murphy (1994), J.N. Muscott (1943–49), M.A. Muse-Hodgson (2005), D.J.R. Myles (1951).

J.B. Nadin (1981–83, 2000), E. Nash (1958), D.W. Naylor (1982–85), D. Needham (1985, 1990), **C. Nelson** (1990–2005: Committee 1992–2005; Secretary 1993–1996; Vice-Chairman 1996–97; Chairman 1997–2000), D.L.W. Neusholme (1961), P. Neville (2005), A. Newberry (1963), A. Newman (1996), S. Newman (1996), R. Newson (1981–89), C.D. Newton (1999–2005), D.A. Newton (2004–05), **P.A. Newton** (1993–2005), K. Nicholls (1990–91, 1996), R.K. Nicholls (1983, 1989–96), W.P. Nicholls (1983), A. Nichols (1972–73), **H.R. Nichols** (1941–51, 1961), S.C. Nichols (1977–83, 2002–04), J.B.W. Nisbet (2004–05), **D. Noakes** (1974–2005: Committee 1984–93), V. Noakes (1996, 2002–03), N. Norledge (1956), B. Norman (1988), D. Norman (1974–75), **T.E. Norman** (1977–93), C.A. Norris (1947), S. Northwood (2005), J.H. Norwood (1991–92: Committee 1992–95; Treasurer 1993–94), S. Norwood (1999), L. Nottage (1976), J.W. Nourish (1989–93, 2000–04).

P. Oakman (1997–99, 2005), W.E. Oddie (1984), J. O'Keefe (1976), **B. Oldham** (1992–2002, 2005), K. O'Leary (2003), B.N. Oliver (1996–98), G.C.S. Oliver (1966–68), S. Oliver (1990), J. Ormerod (1968), E. Orr (1993), **H.J. Orridge** (1991–2003: Committee 1996–2000 and 2004–05), L. Orridge (1996), N. Orridge (1999), W. Orridge (1999), B.R. Orton (1996–97), G.J. Orton (1996), R.S. Orton (1997–2002), D. Osborne (2005), **D.M. Osborne** (1985–93, 1998–2003), **R.A. Oswald** (1958–70), J. Oswin (1987), J.C. Oswin (1948–51, 1959: Committee 1950), **G. Otter** (1983–90, 1996–2000), **J.L. Otter** (1946–60, 1974: Committee 1947–61; Vice-Chairman 1948 and 1957–58; Chairman 1958–59; Referee 1950–57; Honorary Vice-President 1998–2003), V. Otter (1949), P. Overson (1999), C.E. Owen (1967–71).

C.J.M. Packe (1944), J.B. Paice (1967), J.P. Paige (1944–45), C. Painter (1976), **J.R. Painter** (1973–84: Committee 1971–77; Treasurer 1971–77), **L. Painter** (1974–84), M. Paling (1986), M. Palling (1992), J.E. Palmer (2000, 2005), R. Palmer (2001), **S.B. Palmer** (1984–91, 2000, 2005), P.J. Palmer (1998), C. Park (1980–86, 1992), L. Park (2005), A. Parker (2005), R.H. Parker (1985, 1990), T. Parks (1987), A.S. Parnell (1987), L. Parnell (1987), **J. Parry**

(1994–2003), **R.L. Parry** (1994–2005: Committee 2000–05; Treasurer 2000–05), H. Partner (1982–84), D. Partridge (2001–04), C. Pask (1964), R. Pask (1980), M.E. Pass (1996–97), J. Patrick (1993–98), D. Patterson (2005), D. Payne (1972), D.N. Payne (1953), J.E.R. Peach (1958), W. Peach (1986–87), W.S. Peach (1958), J. Peachy (1996), **D.A. Peacock** (1976–88, 1998–2005), M.J. Pearce (1977–85, 1993: Committee 1985–87), S.M. Pearce (1954), A.K. Pearce-Smith (1968, 1977), R. Pearcy (2005), J. Pearson (1978–84), Mrs Pearson (1988), W.M. Peet (1951–56), B.W. Pegg (1987), J.A. Pegg (1979), J.T. Pegg (1977–79), R. Pegg (1969), M.J. Pendery (1982–84), B. Penman (1987), M.G. Pennington (1981–82), R.J. Penson (1993, 2005), G. Peplow (1991), A. Pepper (2005), R. Pepper (2005), C.J. Peppiatt (1995–98), **J.D. Periam** (1979–93, 2002), S. Perkins (1990), P.A. Perry (1984–85, 1996, 2000), R. Perry (2002–04), J.L. Petcher (1945–47, 1954: Committee 1946–57; Vice-Chairman 1951–52; Chairman 1952–53), M. Pettifer (2000), S.J. Petty (1958–63), N. Philips (1964–66), J. Phillips (1993), A.C. Pickering (1966), C. Pickering (1966–68, 1995–97, 2004), **F.C. Pickering** (1948–2005: Committee 1958–2005; Vice-Chairman 1960–61, 1974–75 and 1991–94; Chairman 1961–62 and 1994–97; President 2003–05), M.E. Pickles (1944: Committee 1946–47), P.C. Piggott (2005), N. Pilcher (1996), S.H. Pilgrim (1941), S.L. Pimm (1968), N.A. Pinckard (1982–88, 2002–03), M.L. Piper (1986–87), K.T. Pipes (1975), **A.G. Pitches** (1976–86), **D.A. Pither** (1976–87, 1998–2005), J. Plackett (1982–84), C. Plant (1987), B. Platt (1986), D. Player (1961), **H.R. Player** (1951–63, 1969: Committee 1954–57), R. Player (1994), **C. Playfair** (1986, 1994–96, 2000–05), E.C. Plummer (1952), **B.K. Pochin** (1966–2005: Committee 1968–83 and 1996–2005; Secretary 1970–76), **R.E. Pochin** (1941–58: Committee 1945–64; Chairman 1945; President 1946–64; Referee 1950–55), **A. Pocock** (1991–2005: Committee 1999–2005), P. Pocock (1992), D. Pollard (1995–97), L. Pollard (1972–74), P. Ponsford (1974), M.J. Pont (1994), A.C. Poole (1984–86, 1999–2000), **S.A. Poole** (1977–86, 1994–2000), B. Porteous (2005), **D.B. Porter** (1962–71), D.I. Porter (1980), J. Porter (1950–51), M. Portsmouth (1946–47), B.C. Potter (1960), C. Potter (1977–78), M. Potter (2005), N. Potter (1998–2002), R.D. Potter (2003), **K.M. Potterton**, formerly Kirton (1956–77, 1982–2004: Committee 1956–69 and 1971–72; Recorder 1968–70), **P.J. Powell** (1975–87, 2005), W.H. Power (1941), A. Prasad (1994), L.A. Pratt (1968–69), S.G. Pratt (1987), M. Preston (1995, 1999–2000), A.W.S. Price (1962), D. Price (1991), M.E. Price (1959), T. Pridmore (1977), **D. Prime** (1990–2005), **D. Primrose** (1987–95, 2003–05: Committee 1990–92), **L. Primrose** (1987–95, 2003–05), D. Prior (1996, 2003–04), H. Prior (2003–04), **F.I. Privett** (1977–90), **H.L. Privett** (1977–90), L.J. Proctor (1978–80, 1992–95), G Pullan (2002–03), F. Purvis (1997), R. Puxley (2005), B.A. Pye (1941–45).

B. Quille (1998), S. Quincy (1966), M. Quinlan (2005).

P. Radley (1974), M. Rae (1996), T.L. Rae (1996), A. Raeder (1984), **B.A. Raine** (1970–92: Committee 1974–78 and 1982–91; Vice-Chairman 1982–85; Chairman 1985–88), C.P.E. Raine (1968), M. Ralphs (2001–04), M. Ramsell (1999), P. Randall (1977–80), W.T.C. Rankin (1966), **G.M. Raske** (1961–76), P. Ratcliffe (1995), **R.B. Ratcliffe** (1962–87, 1995, 2004–05), M. Rawlins (1969), S. Rawlinson (2002–03), **A. Rayfield** (1987–2005), J. Rayfield (1987), J.B. Rayner (1972), A. Read (1991), S. Reayer (2001), J. Redmayne (1993), M.N. Reeder (1987–88), K. Reeves (2001, 2004), G.A. Reffin (1999–2005), K. Reid (1987), T. Reid (1987), R. Revell (1997), A. Reynolds (1985), D. Reynolds (1996), A.A. Rhodes (2002–03), **A.C.E. Rhodes** (1972–83), A.W. Rhodes (1995–97, 2002–05), D. Rhodes (1987), E. Rhodes (1997), B. Richards (2000), J. Richards (1963), C.W. Richardson (1977), G. Richardson (1993), J. Richardson (1987), P.M. Richardson (1952–54, 1961: Committee 1952–57), P.W. Richardson (1986), R.A. Richardson (1974), V. Richardson (2000), T.A. Rimmington (1956), J. Rippin (2005), A.B. Ritchie (1967–70), I. Ritchie (1995–96), **D.J. Robbins** (1991–2005), S. Robbins (1993–99, 2004–05), B. Roberts (2000–04), D.C. Roberts (1999–2004), E. Roberts (1990–91, 2003–05), E.L. Roberts (1949–50, 1956, 1987), K.F. Roberts (1987), G.E. Roberts (1998–2005), **G.R. Roberts** (1989–90, 1995–2003), R. Roberts (1990), W. Roberts (1945), W.N. Roberts (1954), D. Robertson (2000), K. Robertson (2000), A.C.H. Robinson (1943), C. Robinson (1972–73), D. Robinson (2000–01), J.A. Robinson (2003), M.C. Robinson (2001–03), S. Robinson (2000), C. Robson (1974–78), D.J. Robson (2000–01), E. Robson (1965), J. Robson (2001–04), W. Robson (1976), J. Rodgers (2005), J.S. Rodgers (2005), A. Roebuck (1943–45, 1951: Committee 1941–42), J. Rogers (1977), J.S. Rogers (1989), M.J. Rogers (1985), P. Rogers (1963), P. Rogers (2000–05), T. Rogers (1999–2002), **D.S. Roizer** (1994–2005: Committee 1995–97), P. Rollin (2001), M. Roome (2003), A. Root (2005), B. Rose (2003), D. Rose (2003), B.W. Roseman (1977), **M.T. Rossell** (1993–2005: Committee 1996–2000), J. Rounsefell (1979–81), M. Rouse (1997), **G. Rowbottom** (1947–70), G. Rowden (2001–03), J. Rowley (1980), L. Rowley (1993), L. Royd (1987), P. Rudkin (1977, 1984), J. Rumball (1987–90, 2001–05), J.A. Rumball (2003), **K.A. Rush** (1984–93: Committee 1986–99: Vice-Chairman 1988–91; Chairman 1991–94), L.E. Rushall (1969), A.P. Russell (2001), B.P. Russell (1962–66), The Hon. M. Russell (1944–46), M.D. Russell (1994), M.P. Rust (1956), J. Rutherford (1959–60), M. Ryan (1992–94), N. Ryley (1994, 2004), R. Ryley (2004).

J. Sainsbury (1965–68), G. Salisbury (1999), P. Salmon (1965), K. Sanderson (1976–77), D.E. Sargeant (1976–79), M.R. Sarson (1958–59), A. Saunders (1983), A. Saunders (1996), D. Saunders (2004–05), S.E. Saunders (1995–96, 2000–05), A.D. Savage (1989–97), A.W.R. Savage (1991–95), C. Savage (1996), H. Savage (1941), J.S. Savage (1989–96), R. Savage (1995), S.B. Scargill (1952–54: Committee 1950–57; Vice-Chairman 1954–55; Chairman 1955–56), G.W. Schaeffer (1971–72: Committee 1965–69), P. Scharenoeval (2004), A. Scott (1967), **D.J. Scott** (1973–2005: Committee 1980–86; Referee 1982–85), **M.E. Scott** (1956–73: Committee 1959–72; Vice-Chairman 1959–60; Chairman 1960–61), **R.E. Scott** (1993–2005), S. Scott (1967–70, 1976), J. Sears (1949), A. Seaton (1974), N. Seaton (2001), R.A. Seddon (1985), G.H. Sellars (1990), D. Sewell (1991–98), P. Sewell (1989), S.J. Sewell (1979–81), P. Sharman (1970, 2003), N.M. Sharp (1997–99), J. Sharpe (2005), **J.A. Sharpe** (1988, 1992–2005), C.H. Shave (1950–51), A. Shaw (1986–88), P. Shaw (1975–77), C. Shaw-Brown (1976–79, 1987–90), **R. Shaw-Brown** (1975–93), N. Shearer (2005), R.Shearer (2005), G.A. Sheler (2003), N. Shelton (2004), P. Shelton (2002), M.J. Sheppard (1974), R.C. Shergold (1996, 2002–05), M. Sherwood (1998), T. Sherwood (2005), D.M. Shilcock (1983–87), K.W. Shilcock (1981–87), R.G. Shilton (1992), W. Shipley (1979–80), A. Shipman (2003), A. Shorrock (1998–2000, 2005), K.F. Shorrock (1987–89), F. Shouler (2005), H.W. Sibson (1966–69), M. Sibson (1968), G. Siddons (2005), K.W. Siggens (1987), J. Sills (2000), N. Sills (1969), A. Simmonds (2003–04), B.N. Simmonds (1955–56), E.D. Simmons (1977–78: Committee 1977–78), K.E.L. Simmons (1992), E. Simms (1947, 1985, 1993–98), J. Simons (1943), A.N. Simpson (1964), I. Simpson (1975–80), R. Simpson (1999), W.H. Sims (1972), H.R. Singleton (1988–90), **K.N. Sivell** (1987–2005), Mr and Mrs Skeet (1965), **H.M. Skelton** (1943–68), **M.P. Skevington** (1992–2002: Committee 1998–2002), **P.A. Skidmore** (1987–2005), M. Skinner (1998–2000, 2004–05), P.D. Slack (1987–88), S.H. Slack (1985–88), D.J. Slater (2001–02), E. Slater (1958), G. Slater (1952), J.E. Slater (1984), Mr Slater (1974), M.J. Smalley (1978), T. Smalley (1997, 2002), **R.F.A. Smallshaw** (1979–90, 1999), D. Smallshire (1983–86: Committee 1984–86), B.R. Smeaton (1968), W.H. Smedley (1944–45), **A. Smith** (1985–95), **A.D. Smith** (1987–2005: Committee 2000–05), B. Smith (1996), C.A. Smith (2001–03), C.H. Smith (1947), E. Smith (2001), G. Smith (1998–2001, 2004–05), G.M. Smith (1958), G.W. Smith (1958), H. Smith (1984–87, 1993: Committee 1984–89), H.J. Smith (1981), H.K. Smith (2002–03), H.P. Smith (1997–99), H.S. Smith (1973–76), J. Smith (1960), J. Smith (1990), J. Smith (2001–02), J.D. Smith (1992), L. Smith (1992, 1997–99), L.B. Smith (1958), M. Smith (1984, 2000, 2005), Miss Smith (2004), P.C. Smith (2002–05), P.E. Smith (1998), P.H. Smith (1979), R. Smith (1983, 1988–90), S.C.H. Smith (1967–74), T. Smith (2001–05), T.G. Smith (1980, 1987), D. Smithurst (1983), **I. Snape** (1972–80, 1985), P. Snook (1998–2005), R. Snook (2002–05), W. Soar (2003–05), A.A. Sorrell (1996, 2004), J.M. Sorrell (1996, 2004), T.J. Sorrell (1996), C.G. Southall (1997), T.J. Southall (1990–97), H. Southwell (1949–55), D. Southwich (1979), D.E. Southwick (1969–72), S.C. Spalding (1990–93), B.E. Spence (1978–79, 1988, 1999, 2002, 2005), B.R. Spence (1960–61), A.E. Spencer (1948), H. Spencer (1982), M. Spencer (1988), L.D. Spendley (1966–71), R. Spiers (1987), P. Spivey (1987), **K. Spriggs** (1971–82, 1988–92, 2005), M. Springall (1960), B. Squire (2005), A.C. Squires (2005), **J. Stacey** (1941–50), A. Stafford (2004–05), A. Staley (2005), B. Staley (2005), P. Stancliffe (1987), R. Stanesby (1987), A. Stanley (1969, 1973), **A.D. Stanley** (1954–63), **J.M. Stanley** (1966–68, 1989–2005), M. Stanley (2003), W. Stanley (2003), R. Stansfield (1976), J. Stapleford (2005), J. Stapleton (1968–70), J.R. Stapleton (1977), J. Starie (1982), P. Stark (1946–47: Committee 1946–47), E. Staunton (2001), T.W. Steed (1997), D.R. Steele (1983–89), M. Steele (1997), M. Stevens (1984), P.A. Stevens (1944–47: Committee 1945–46), J. Steward (2002), I.R.K. Stewart (1987, 1994–95), C. Stoate (2001–02), B. Stokes (1997), H. Stokes (1989), P. Stokes (1989), Mr Stokes (1963), W. Stone (1941), R. Storer (1943–48, 1953), A. Strang (1995–96), J. Strang (1989), F. Stratford (1996), C. Straw (2004), J. Strong (1996), **N. Sturgess** (1980, 1985–2002), R. Sturgess (2005), D. Sulch (2000–02), D. Summerfield (1998–2005), **A.J. Summers** (1979–2005), **M.J. Summers** (1973–89), P.O. Summers (1945), M.J. Sutters (1999–2000), Mr Sutton (1982), W. Swaine (1949), J. Swinfen (1981), M. Swinfen (1965), G.N. Syer (1943–44), J. Sylvester-Bradley (1985–88), K.W. Symington (1947), S.P. Symington (1952).

T. Talbot (1979), Mr Talbot (1991), C. Talbot-Kelly (1947), D.L. Talbott (2004–05), B.W. Tallis (1999), R. Tallis (2003–04), R.W. Tallis (1962–66), W. Tallis (1983, 2003–04), K.J. Tapp (1991–96), H.W. Tassell (1966), A. Tate (1981–86: Committee 1982–90), Sir H. Tate (1962, 1971), Lady N. Tate (1967–71), A.H. Taylor (1991, 2000–05), **C.C. Taylor** (1970–81, 1995), **D. Taylor** (1975–76, 1981–89, 1997–99), D.J. Taylor (1968), E.L Taylor (1977: Committee 1973–79; Secretary 1974–79), F.J. Taylor (1982, 1990–96), J.E. Taylor (1966), L.S. Taylor (1969), P. Taylor (1982), P.G. Taylor (1977), S. Taylor (1991), T. Taylor (2002), N. Teall (1985), D. Tebbs (1948), C.F. Tebbutt (1964–69), S. Telling (1987), J.R.M. Tennent (1946–47), H. Tharp (1979), **J.C.F. Thatcher** (1975–2005: Committee 1975–86; Vice-Chairman 1978–79; Chairman 1979–82), D.O. Thomas (1948), M. Thomas (1949–50), M. Thomas (1975–77), M.D. Thomas (2000–04), A. Thompson (1993), D. Thompson (1965), D. Thompson (2000), P.M. Thompson (1984), R.G. Thompson (1953, 1960), J. Thorley (1991), P. Thornton (2002), **A.F.M. Thrower** (1995–2005), W. Thurley (2001), P. Thwaites (1993), **I.M. Tidmarsh** (1983–93), S.C. Tilley (1987, 1995,

2002–03), C. Timmins (1946), R.C. Timms (1977–84, 1991), R.M. Timms (1977–84, 1991), **J.J. Tinning** (1979–92, 2005), L.G. Tinning (1990), S.J. Tinning (1984–91), J. Tirrell (1987), E. Todd (1996), **G.A. Todd** (1941–54: Committee 1946–47; Recorder 1947), T. Tomkins (2005), D. Tomlinson (1984, 1993), J. Tomlinson (1993), S. Tomlyn (1998), A. Tompkins (1944), B. Tompkinson (1960), G. Toone (1990), R.M. Toseland (2000–01), **C.D. Towe** (1969–82, 2003–04), M.A. Towle (1952: Committee 1952–54), **M.J. Townsend** (1977–86), P. Traynor (2004), P. Trewerne (1997), M. Tricker (2000–01), E.P. Tromans (1981–86), B.W. Tucker (1949), J. Tucker (2005), Mr Tuckey (1963), E.H. Tunnicliffe (1995), F.H. Tunnicliffe (1974), R.F. Tupper (1966), M. Turland (1984), N. Turland (1984), C.F. Turnell (1979–86), R.D. Turnell (1979–80, 1986–88), D.M. Turner (1970–71, 1982), G.J. Turner (1995, 2002–04), C. Turtle (1974), D.W. Twiss (1991), D. Tyers (2000–01, 2005), J.N. Tyers (1972–73), E. Tyler (1964), M.W. Tyler (1985), P. Tyler (1996–2000).

J. Ugrinic (1976–83), M. Ugrinic (1974–79), J. Underwood (1984).

A.F. Valentine (1966, 2000–03), P. Vendy (1986), M. Vernon (1984), P. Vernon (1952–54), P. Vernon (1982–84), B. Vickers (2005), **M.A. Vincent** (1986–2005: Committee 1998–2005; Secretary 1999–2005).

T.A. Wadds (1951), T. Wade (1984), J. Wagstaff (1957–60, 1969), A. Wain (2000, 2005), F.E. Wainwright (1968), J.R. Waite (1978), N.R. Waite (1978), G. Wakefield (1996), R. Wakeling (1984, 1993–97, 2001, 2004), **G.L. Walford** (1971–81), A.J. Walker (1992–94, 2003–05), C.G. Walker (1975–82), E.T. Walker (1943), J. Walker (1993), **J.W. Walker** (1975–2005: Committee 1986–96), Rev. M.E. Walker (1962), P.J. Wallace (1944–48, 1957), M. Walpole (1959), J.R. Walsh (2004), G. Walters (1983), K. Walton (1998–99, 2004), **L.P. Walton** (1983–2005), S. Walton (1987–94), C. Ward (1976–77), D.A. Ward (1991), J. Ward (1978–79, 1984), J.N. Ward (1948), M.R. Ward (1976), P. Ward (1990), T. Ward (1966), W. Ward (1943–44), A.S. Wardle (1984), N. Wardle (1984–87), A. Ware (1991), D. Waring (1969–74), J.R. Warner (1957–58), B. Warren (1967–68, 1979), **G.J. Warrilow** (1975–83, 1995), P. Warwick (1984), J.O. Wastnage (1946–48), Mr Waterfield (1966), R. Watkins (1994–95, 2003), D. Watkinson (2001), Mr Watkinson (1989), D.C. Watson (1988), J.W. Watson (1943–44), M. Watson (1998–2000), M.K. Watson (1985), I. Watt (2002), I.B. Watt (1977), J. Watt (1957–58), R. Watt (1957–58), A. Watterson (2005), **C.J. Watts** (1992–2005), R. Webb (1979), Rev. G. Webster (1968), I.H. Webster (1958–60, 2003: Committee 1958–62), J.R. Webster (1967, 1976–79), **M.B. Webster** (1968–76, 1987, 2003–04: Committee 1972–78), P. Webster (1997), B. Wehrle (2004), G. Wehrle (2004), Mr Wells (1964), I.E. Wesley (1941–47: Committee 1941–47; Chairman 1946), J. Wesson (1974), A. West (1985), D.H. West (1944–47), P.W. West (1945–46, 1955), R. West (1984), R.F. West (2005), C. Weston (1941–46), S.J. Weston (1960), T. Weston (1996), W. Weston (2000–01), L. Wheatland (1984), H.J. Wheatley (1954–56), J. Wheeler (2005), D. Whelan (1998–2002), B. White (2003–05), G.S. White (1976–79), S.M. White (1979), S.M. Whitehouse (1993), M.J. Whiteman (1990–91), D. Whiting (1999–2003), D.J. Whiting (1998–2003), P. Whittaker (1991), S. Whittaker (1957), H.F. Whittall (1966), P.H. Whittall (1965), T.E. Whittall (1965–66), K. Wiblin (1991, 2001), A.E. Wignall (1968), K. Wilcox (2003), A.W. Wildig (1970), D.R. Wiles (1977), A. Wilkin (2002–04), **D.R. Willett** (1964–2001: Committee 1967–77; Secretary 1971–72), **A.E. Williams** (1946–47, 1952–71: Committee 1946–71; Vice-Chairman 1955–56 and 1969–70; Chairman 1956–57; Referee 1956–57), J. Williams (1996–97), J.G. Williams (1988), **P.D. Williams** (1984–2005: Committee 1993–2005), R.J. Williams (1943), S. Williams (1985), S.A. Williams (1989), D. Williamson (1998–99), S. Williamson (1976), W.E. Williamson (1943–47, 1952, 1962), **B.M. Willis** (1983–88, 1992–99), J.T. Willmott (1972, 1976), H. Wills (1941–45), O.S. Wilshere (1941–43), B. Wilson (1996), I.M. Wilson (1965, 1991–95), J.M. Wilson (1990–93), K.A. Wilson (1989–95), L. Wilson (1986), M. Wilson (1997), P. Wilson (1996), P.H. Wilson (1951, 1956), M.P. Winser (1943–48), M. Winship (2005), W. Wisdom (1989), M. Wiseman (2005), J. Withall (1987), D.J. Withers (1985–87), **M.B. Withers** (1977–91), J. Wolloff (1979), **D.J.L. Wood** (1980–89), **M.R. Wood** (1979–89), P. Wood (1987–91), B.A. Woodcock (1967–68), T.F. Woodcroft (1977–78, 1987–90), B. Woods (1983–85), D. Woods (1986), G.E. Woods (1986, 1993), S.L. Woollard (1990–95), A. Woolley (1958), R. Woolley (1993), Q. Worley (1958), L. Worth (1947), D.W. Wragg (1980), A. Wright (2005), B. Wright (1998), **D. Wright** (1987–88, 1993–2005), J. Wright (1974), **J. Wright** (1991–2005), K. Wright (1991), M. Wright (1987, 1992), P. Wright (1996–2001), R. Wright (1990–91, 1998), R.P. Wright (1966–69, 1974), T. Wright (1982), J. Wyatt (1990), D. Wynch (1994).

G. M. Yates (1981–82), H. Yates (1998), J.R. Yates (1977), T. Yates (1990), W. York (2001), M. Yorke (1974–75, 1982), R. Young (1988–90).

Clubs, groups and organisations

The following bodies have all contributed records or information at some time. Some may have changed their names since the time of their contribution and some no longer exist at all.

Bedfordshire Natural History Society
British Birds Rarities Committee
British Trust for Ornithology
Charnwood Ringing Group
City Wildlife Project
Conkers Staff
Corby Natural History Society
Derbyshire Ornithological Society
East Bedfordshire RSPB Group
Hinckley and District Naturalists Club
Kingswood School
Leicestershire and Rutland Wildlife Trust
Leicestershire Wildfowlers' Association
Limehurst School Natural History Society
Loughborough Naturalists' Club
Market Harborough Natural History Society
Northampton Natural History Society
Nuneaton Bird Watchers' Club
Oakham School Field Society
Oxford Ornithological Society
Royal Society for the Prevention of Cruelty to Animals
Royal Society for the Protection of Birds
Rugby School Natural History Society
Rutland Natural History Society
Rutland Water Ringing Group
Rutland Water WeBS Team
South Nottinghamshire Ringing Group
Stanford Ringing Group
Trent Valley Bird Watchers
University of East Anglia
Uppingham School Field Society
Wildfowl and Wetlands Trust

APPENDIX 4: SURVEYS CARRIED OUT IN LEICESTERSHIRE AND RUTLAND

Both LROS and the RNHS have carried out various surveys over the years, as shown in the following Table.

Year	LROS survey	RNHS survey
1944	Sand Martin	
1945	Lesser Whitethroat	
1952	Wintering gulls	
1953	Starling roosts	
1958	Nuthatch (north and east of Ashby-de-la-Zouch)	
1965	Rookeries	
1967	Marsh Tit and Willow Tit	
1968	Tree Pipit	
1969	Meadow Pipit	
1971		Kestrel (1967–1971 survey results)
1974	Wintering gulls	
1983	Mute Swan; wintering gulls	
1985	Warblers	
1986	Cormorant (Rutland Water)	Red-legged Partridge and Grey Partridge
1987	Nuthatch; rookeries	Nuthatch
1988	Wintering Golden Plovers	
1990	Mute Swan	
1991	Introduced geese	Rookeries
1993	Wintering gulls	
1994		Rookeries
1995	Corn Bunting (west Leicestershire)	Rookeries
1996		Rookeries
1999	Peregrine Falcon	Rookeries
2000	Tree Sparrow (Rutland Water); Peregrine Falcon	Rookeries
2001	Cormorant (Rutland Water); Osprey (Rutland Water); Tree Sparrow (Rutland Water)	
2002	Cormorant (Rutland Water)	Rookeries
2003	Cormorant (Rutland Water)	Rookeries
2004	Cormorant (Rutland Water)	
2005		Spotted Flycatcher

APPENDIX 5: COMMON BIRDS CENSUS DATA

All species that have held territory at least once are listed in the table. Numbers are the number of estimated territories, 'p' represents species recorded but not thought to be holding territory, – signifies that the species was not recorded during census visits and nc stands for not counted (usually used for species which are difficult to census correctly such as Wood Pigeon and Starling).

Stoughton

Table 1: Common Birds Census results at the Stoughton CBC plot 1964–1999

	1964	1965	1966	1967	1968	1969	1970	1971	1972	1973	1974	1975
Mallard	–	–	–	–	–	–	–	–	–	–	–	1
Red-legged Partridge	1	2	1	2	–	1	1	p	–	–	–	p
Grey Partridge	3	4	4	1	4	1	p	3	3	1	1	3
Pheasant	1	2	2	4	3	3	2	2	2	p	4	3
Sparrowhawk	–	–	–	–	–	–	–	–	–	–	–	–
Kestrel	–	p	p	p	–	–	–	–	–	–	–	1
Hobby	–	–	–	–	–	–	–	–	–	–	–	–
Stock Dove	–	–	p	p	p	–	–	p	–	–	–	p
Wood Pigeon	6	nc	nc	nc	nc	nc	nc	nc	nc	nc	nc	nc
Collared Dove	–	1	3	6	2	6	1	2	p	–	3	8
Turtle Dove	p	2	1	p	1	3	2	1	1	1	–	3
Cuckoo	1	2	1	1	1	p	1	3	p	1	2	2
Little Owl	–	–	–	p	1	1	p	–	–	–	1	1
Tawny Owl	–	–	–	p	1	–	–	–	–	–	–	1
Green Woodpecker	–	–	–	–	–	–	–	–	–	1	p	1
Great Spotted Woodpecker	–	–	–	–	–	–	–	–	p	–	–	p
Lesser Spotted Woodpecker	–	–	–	–	–	–	–	–	–	–	–	–
Sky Lark	19	17	16	15	15	13	15	20	15	18	28	24
Swallow	–	p	p	p	–	–	1	–	–	1	1	2
Yellow Wagtail	p	p	p	p	p	3	p	5	p	2	3	4
Pied Wagtail	–	p	–	1	–	–	–	–	–	–	–	2
Wren	8	3	12	18	12	18	12	10	24	22	31	45
Dunnock	22	35	24	28	23	22	17	22	22	23	30	49
Robin	14	20	24	22	21	15	15	20	23	17	16	29
Blackbird	42	36	37	43	38	53	27	33	35	32	42	53
Song Thrush	15	17	13	20	12	16	8	15	19	13	18	25
Mistle Thrush	p	–	p	2	–	1	–	p	–	–	1	1
Grasshopper Warbler	–	p	–	–	–	–	–	–	–	–	–	1
Sedge Warbler	1	p	p	p	–	–	–	–	–	–	–	–
Blackcap	1	–	2	p	1	1	2	1	1	4	5	3
Garden Warbler	1	p	2	2	1	p	1	1	p	2	–	2
Lesser Whitethroat	p	–	p	p	p	p	p	p	–	–	p	1
Common Whitethroat	18	16	16	18	22	8	3	5	2	3	3	3
Chiffchaff	–	1	1	1	1	1	1	–	2	1	1	2
Willow Warbler	1	4	2	4	4	6	3	4	5	5	7	5
Goldcrest	–	p	1	p	p	–	p	p	2	4	3	1
Spotted Flycatcher	–	p	p	–	–	p	p	–	–	1	–	1
Long-tailed Tit	–	1	2	–	–	–	–	1	–	1	p	–
Blue Tit	16	17	11	20	15	10	9	18	22	25	29	24

Great Tit	4	4	6	5	3	4	4	9	8	8	9	10
Coal Tit	–	–	p	p	p	p	–	–	1	1	1	p
Willow Tit	–	–	p	–	–	1	1	p	–	1	1	1
Marsh Tit	–	p	1	–	–	5	–	–	p	1	–	–
Treecreeper	–	–	–	–	p	p	1	p	p	1	–	p
Jay	1	1	p	1	–	–	p	–	–	1	–	–
Magpie	2	2	3	3	1	3	1	1	2	2	3	2
Jackdaw	–	p	–	p	–	–	–	–	–	–	–	–
Carrion Crow	2	4	3	3	5	4	2	6	5	3	5	6
Starling	10	9	nc	nc	9	2	5	2	7	5	9	9
House Sparrow	p	p	p	p	p	p	p	p	–	–	–	–
Tree Sparrow	14	20	10	17	13	7	9	14	6	7	7	14
Chaffinch	8	12	13	14	13	8	9	11	9	5	13	18
Greenfinch	3	2	4	1	4	3	5	4	4	1	1	5
Goldfinch	p	1	1	2	–	p	–	1	2	–	1	5
Linnet	2	5	9	9	1	3	2	6	2	2	5	9
Lesser Redpoll	–	–	–	–	–	–	–	–	–	–	–	–
Bullfinch	1	1	2	2	1	1	1	1	1	2	4	3
Yellowhammer	21	21	20	21	23	22	19	22	24	21	31	48
Reed Bunting	3	1	1	1	1	4	2	3	3	5	5	13
Corn Bunting	–	p	–	–	–	1	–	p	–	–	–	–
Total species holding territory	29	31	33	32	31	34	32	31	29	38	36	43
Total number of territories	241	263	246	287	252	250	181	245	251	243	325	443

	1976	1977	1978	1979	1980	1981	1982	1983	1984	1985	1986	1987
Mallard	–	–	–	–	–	–	–	–	p	p	p	1
Red-legged Partridge	p	1	p	1	p	1	p	–	p	1	2	2
Grey Partridge	3	4	4	2	2	2	1	1	–	1	1	p
Pheasant	2	1	–	1	4	–	1	2	3	3	2	3
Sparrowhawk	–	–	–	–	–	–	–	–	1	p	1	1
Kestrel	1	1	1	1	1	1	p	p	1	p	1	1
Hobby	–	–	–	–	–	p	–	–	–	p	p	p
Stock Dove	1	1	1	–	1	3	1	1	2	3	1	3
Wood Pigeon	nc	nc	nc	nc	nc	nc	nc	nc	9	11	16	20
Collared Dove	7	2	1	–	1	1	1	1	3	1	1	1
Turtle Dove	1	2	p	2	1	1	p	2	1	1	1	1
Cuckoo	p	1	1	2	2	2	2	1	1	1	3	2
Little Owl	1	p	1	–	1	–	p	1	1	p	–	1
Tawny Owl	1	–	p	–	p	p	p	p	p	p	–	1
Green Woodpecker	p	p	p	–	1	1	1	1	p	1	p	p
Great Spotted Woodpecker	–	–	p	–	–	–	–	p	p	p	p	p
Lesser Spotted Woodpecker	–	p	p	–	p	p	–	–	–	p	–	p
Sky Lark	21	27	19	12	17	13	1	6	4	4	4	5
Swallow	1	2	–	1	–	–	–	–	–	–	–	–
Yellow Wagtail	2	2	1	5	1	3	1	4	2	1	p	1
Pied Wagtail	1	–	p	–	1	1	p	–	p	p	1	–
Wren	29	22	31	11	27	28	13	25	20	25	19	17
Dunnock	30	21	20	16	19	22	9	16	24	20	18	10
Robin	17	18	13	13	12	15	14	14	19	18	13	17
Blackbird	36	31	25	30	35	40	28	40	42	33	30	30
Song Thrush	17	16	12	7	17	15	5	14	15	7	7	7

Mistle Thrush	p	p	p	–	1	1	–	–	1	1	1	p
Grasshopper Warbler	–	–	p	–	–	–	–	–	–	–	–	–
Sedge Warbler	1	–	–	–	–	–	–	–	–	–	–	–
Blackcap	2	3	2	3	5	5	4	6	8	5	4	6
Garden Warbler	3	2	3	1	p	–	p	3	1	1	1	2
Lesser Whitethroat	p	1	–	p	p	1	–	–	1	1	1	p
Common Whitethroat	9	6	3	2	8	5	1	8	7	2	6	4
Chiffchaff	1	p	p	–	3	2	p	p	–	–	–	p
Willow Warbler	3	6	–	6	12	12	7	10	12	7	7	7
Goldcrest	2	1	1	2	2	2	–	1	2	1	p	p
Spotted Flycatcher	1	1	4	1	2	2	–	3	1	2	1	–
Long-tailed Tit	p	–	–	–	–	–	–	–	–	1	1	–
Blue Tit	20	18	18	14	21	17	10	18	21	27	24	20
Great Tit	10	6	5	6	13	13	6	14	14	12	14	12
Coal Tit	1	1	p	p	3	2	–	1	1	p	2	1
Willow Tit	p	1	1	1	2	1	–	1	2	2	1	–
Marsh Tit	p	–	p	–	p	–	–	–	–	1	1	p
Treecreeper	p	p	2	1	1	p	–	1	1	1	–	p
Jay	p	–	p	–	p	–	–	p	1	–	–	p
Magpie	2	3	2	3	5	4	4	4	6	4	5	7
Jackdaw	–	–	–	–	p	p	–	–	p	2	p	1
Carrion Crow	5	9	5	7	8	6	2	3	3	7	7	9
Starling	7	7	8	5	14	16	1	5	10	9	6	5
House Sparrow	–	–	–	–	–	–	–	–	–	–	–	p
Tree Sparrow	10	9	10	9	14	6	3	3	8	5	2	p
Chaffinch	9	7	8	4	9	9	6	10	13	20	17	18
Greenfinch	3	3	p	2	6	1	p	1	4	4	4	3
Goldfinch	2	2	p	1	4	2	–	2	4	2	1	p
Linnet	6	5	1	2	11	5	1	4	7	3	p	1
Lesser Redpoll	–	–	–	–	–1	p	–	p	–	–	–	p
Bullfinch	1	4	2	–	3	3	1	4	2	1	1	1
Yellowhammer	34	25	28	21	25	27	16	23	22	13	15	14
Reed Bunting	7	7	3	4	3	4	2	2	1	2	1	–
Corn Bunting	–	–	–	–	–	p	–	–	–	–	–	–
Total species holding territory	40	39	32	34	41	38	28	36	40	42	40	35
Total number of territories	310	280	245	198	318	292	143	254	298	267	247	235

	1988	**1989**	**1990**	**1991**	**1992**	**1993**	**1994**	**1995**	**1996**	**1997**	**1998**	**1999**
Mallard	p	p	–	–	p	p	p	p	p	p	p	p
Red-legged Partridge	1	p	p	p	p	p	–	–	p	p	p	p
Grey Partridge	p	1	1	p	p	p	p	1	p	p	–	p
Pheasant	p	3	2	3	3	4	3	3	4	3	4	5
Sparrowhawk	1	1	1	1	p	1	1	1	1	1	1	1
Kestrel	1	1	1	1	1	1	1	1	1	1		1
Hobby	–	1	p	–	–	–	1	p	–	p	–	–
Stock Dove	1	3	1	1	p	p	1	3	1	2	3	2
Wood Pigeon	18	17	16	18	15	21	19	13	21	20	18	16
Collared Dove	p	–	p	p	1	p	1	2	1	1	p	1
Turtle Dove	–	2	p	p	p	–	p	–	–	–	–	–
Cuckoo	2	1	2	1	3	3	2	2	1	p	1	1

Little Owl	1	2	p	–	–	–	–	p	–	–	–	–
Tawny Owl	2	1	1	p	1	–	–	p	p	–	p	p
Green Woodpecker	p	p	–	p	p	p	p	p	–	1	p	p
Great Spotted Woodpecker	p	2	1	1	p	1	1	p	p	1	p	2
Lesser Spotted Woodpecker	–	–	p	p	–	–	p	–	–	p	–	1
Sky Lark	6	9	4	4	3	3	4	5	2	3	6	p
Swallow	–	–	–	–	–	–	p	p	p	p	–	p
Yellow Wagtail	2	2	1	1	p	p	p	2	–	p	–	p
Pied Wagtail	p	1	1	p	p	p	p	p	p	p	p	p
Wren	33	33	42	19	31	35	38	27	18	20	22	25
Dunnock	17	19	21	9	10	13	17	15	14	11	13	12
Robin	16	16	31	13	18	17	23	19	19	18	19	18
Blackbird	37	28	29	24	35	30	25	28	24	20	24	21
Song Thrush	4	6	4	3	4	5	5	3	p	3	4	2
Mistle Thrush	p	p	1	p	p	1	3	p	2	3	2	2
Grasshopper Warbler	1	–	–	–	p	–	–	–	–	–	–	–
Sedge Warbler	–	–	–	–	–	–	–	–	–	–	–	–
Blackcap	4	9	13	6	7	8	7	5	9	8	10	10
Garden Warbler	1	p	8	2	p	1	2	p	1	2	–	2
Lesser Whitethroat	1	p	1	p	p	2	1	1	1	2	2	3
Common Whitethroat	4	4	8	p	5	4	4	8	15	7	8	10
Chiffchaff	–	4	2	1	1	1	2	1	3	3	3	3
Willow Warbler	6	7	5	4	3	p	2	4	6	5	5	3
Goldcrest	p	1	p	–	–	p	p	p	p	–	p	p
Spotted Flycatcher	1	1	–	p	p	p	p	p	–	–	p	p
Long-tailed Tit	p	1	1	–	p	p	1	2	2	2	2	2
Blue Tit	20	18	27	19	17	17	21	25	22	22	19	22
Great Tit	11	13	15	6	13	11	15	15	15	12	15	13
Coal Tit	1	2	1	1	1	1	1	1	p	1	p	p
Willow Tit	1	2	1	1	1	p	–	p	p	p	–	1
Marsh Tit	p	p	p	–	–	–	p	p	p	p	1	2
Treecreeper	p	1	p	p	1	p	1	1	–	1	p	p
Jay	p	–	–	p	p	–	–	–	–	–	–	–
Magpie	5	7	5	7	9	10	11	9	8	10	10	9
Jackdaw	2	1	1	p	p	–	p	2	p	2	2	3
Carrion Crow	9	8	10	9	11	13	8	7	8	8	11	11
Starling	6	9	7	8	6	nc	nc	p	2	3	4	6
House Sparrow	p	3	p	p	1	p	p	p	p	3	p	p
Tree Sparrow	p	1	p	p	1	p	1	p	–	–	p	–
Chaffinch	17	20	16	21	26	25	27	29	27	22	21	19
Greenfinch	4	4	4	2	6	5	5	3	4	3	2	4
Goldfinch	1	2	4	p	1	1	2	1	1	1	p	4
Linnet	p	1	1	p	1	p	2	p	1	2	2	3
Lesser Redpoll	p	–	–	–	–	p	–	p	–	–	p	–
Bullfinch	3	2	1	p	1	1	1	2	1	2	1	1
Yellowhammer	8	12	8	10	10	8	13	5	6	5	8	12
Reed Bunting	p	p	p	p	1	–	–	–	p	–	–	p
Corn Bunting	–	–	–	–	–	–	p	–	–	–	–	–
Total species holding territory	35	44	39	28	333	28	36	33	31	37	29	36
Total number of territories	248	282	299	196	248	243	272	246	241	234	243	253

Table 2: Species recorded but not holding territory at the Stoughton CBC plot 1964 to 1999

	Years recorded
Greater Canada Goose	1991, 1992, 1993, 1995, 1996, 1998, 1999
Quail	1988
Grey Heron	1994, 1995, 1996, 1997, 1998
Moorhen	1967, 1976, 1986, 1988, 1989, 1990, 1995, 1997, 1998
Lapwing	1966, 1967, 1975, 1986, 1988, 1989, 1990, 1991, 1992, 1994, 1995
Common Snipe	1981
Curlew	1991, 1995, 1997
Green Sandpiper	1967
Lesser Black-backed Gull	1995
Herring Gull	1995, 1999
Feral Pigeon	1996, 1997, 1998, 1999
Barn Owl	1964
Common Swift	1967, 1968, 1975, 1981, 1986–1999
House Martin	1995
Tree Pipit	1972
Meadow Pipit	1967, 1976, 1980, 1981, 1985, 1986, 1987, 1988, 1991, 1994, 1995
Common Redstart	1966, 1984, 1994
Stonechat	1965
Northern Wheatear	1985, 1990, 1991, 1992
Fieldfare	1995, 1996
Pied Flycatcher	1984
Nuthatch	1992, 1996, 1997
Rook	1967, 1984, 1985, 1986, 1987, 1988, 1989, 1990, 1992, 1993, 1996, 1997
Brambling	1994
Siskin	1994

Newton Harcourt

Table 3: Common Birds Census results at the Newton Harcourt CBC plot 1971–2002

	1971	1972	1973	1974	1975	1976	1977	1978	1979	1980
Mallard	–	–	1	–	p	–	1	–	1	–
Red-legged Partridge	–	p	–	–	p	1	p	1	–	p
Grey Partridge	3	2	2	2	1	2	3	1	1	2
Pheasant	p	1	–	p	1	p	p	1	p	1
Kestrel	–	–	p	1	p	1	–	p	–	–
Hobby	–	–	–	–	–	–	–	p	–	1
Moorhen	1	1	1	p	–	p	–	–	–	–
Lapwing	–	–	p	1	p	1	–	p	2	p
Stock Dove	–	–	p	p	p	–	–	p	–	–
Wood Pigeon	nc	nc	nc	nc	nc	nc	nc	nc	nc	nc
Turtle Dove	–	–	p	1	p	p	–	p	p	–
Cuckoo	–	1	p	1	1	1	1	1	1	–
Little Owl	–	–	–	p	–	–	–	–	–	–
Tawny Owl	–	–	–	–	–	p	p	1	1	1
Great Spotted Woodpecker	–	–	–	–	–	–	–	–	p	1
Lesser Spotted Woodpecker	–	–	–	–	–	–	–	–	p	p
Sky Lark	7	13	14	13	12	20	20	20	21	22
Swallow	–	–	p	p	p	p	p	p	p	–
Yellow Wagtail	1	–	–	1	1	1	2	4	7	9

Pied Wagtail	–	–	p	2	p	–	–	–	–	–
Wren	5	10	14	11	6	12	14	14	8	12
Dunnock	4	7	5	2	4	11	9	8	10	7
Robin	7	13	12	10	5	9	11	5	9	7
Blackbird	14	13	8	14	9	12	15	11	13	10
Song Thrush	8	8	3	3	3	4	4	1	3	2
Mistle Thrush	–	–	p	p	p	–	p	–	p	p
Sedge Warbler	–	–	–	–	–	–	–	p	–	p
Blackcap	1	2	1	p	p	p	p	–	1	p
Garden Warbler	–	–	–	–	–	–	–	p	p	–
Lesser Whitethroat	1	2	2	–	1	–	p	2	1	2
Common Whitethroat	2	2	p	–	1	2	1	p	1	2
Chiffchaff	–	–	1	–	–	–	–	–	–	–
Willow Warbler	6	8	3	p	1	p	3	2	5	4
Spotted Flycatcher	–	–	p	–	–	–	1	–	p	1
Long-tailed Tit	p	1	1	1	1	1	p	–	–	–
Blue Tit	3	8	10	6	7	13	11	9	11	13
Great Tit	3	4	2	3	2	4	4	2	4	5
Willow Tit	–	1	1	p	p	1	–	p	p	2
Treecreeper	–	–	p	–	–	p	–	p	p	2
Jay	1	1	1	p	–	1	–	–	–	–
Magpie	1	3	2	2	2	2	3	2	1	1
Carrion Crow	1	3	3	4	3	4	4	6	8	5
Starling	1	1	p	1	p	2	3	3	4	4
House Sparrow	nc	nc	nc	nc	nc	nc	nc	nc	nc	nc
Tree Sparrow	p	5	4	2	4	11	11	9	10	11
Chaffinch	6	6	6	8	3	10	9	9	8	7
Greenfinch	p	–	–	p	p	1	p	p	1	1
Goldfinch	–	3	–	1	3	4	4	1	3	3
Linnet	p	2	2	p	2	2	2	2	1	6
Lesser Redpoll	–	–	p	–	–	–	–	–	–	–
Bullfinch	p	2	3	p	1	2	p	1	1	1
Yellowhammer	24	16	10	12	10	24	17	15	19	22
Reed Bunting	3	4	3	p	1	4	3	5	3	3
Corn Bunting	–	–	–	–	1	–	–	–	–	–
Total species holding territory	22	29	26	23	25	29	25	25	29	32
Total number of territories	103	143	115	102	85	157	158	135	159	171

	1981	1982	1983	1984	1985	1986	1987	1988	1989	1990
Mallard	p	–	p	p	–	1	–	–	p	p
Red-legged Partridge	1	1	1	p	1	2	3	p	2	1
Grey Partridge	1	p	1	p	–	–	p	1	p	–
Pheasant	3	3	1	p	1	1	2	2	2	2
Kestrel	p	p	–	–	–	–	1	p	–	p
Hobby	–	p	–	–	–	1	p	–	–	1
Moorhen	1	–	–	p	–	–	p	–	1	1
Lapwing	p	–	–	p	p	p	–	p	p	p
Stock Dove	–	p	p	1	1	2	2	1	2	3
Wood Pigeon	nc	nc	nc	nc	nc	1	3	nc	5	3
Turtle Dove	p	p	p	–	1	1	–	–	–	–
Cuckoo	1	–	1	1	1	1	1	–	2	1

Little Owl	–	1	–	–	–	–	–	–	–	–
Tawny Owl	p	1	p	1	1	–	p	–	p	–
Great Spotted Woodpecker	p	p	p	–	p	p	p	–	p	–
Lesser Spotted Woodpecker	1	–	p	–	–	–	–	–	–	–
Sky Lark	21	10	15	16	9	12	17	17	19	16
Swallow	5	6	12	8	9	7	5	5	6	6
Yellow Wagtail	1	–	–	1	1	1	2	4	7	9
Pied Wagtail	–	–	–	–	p	p	–	–	–	–
Wren	9	4	9	6	9	2	4	9	10	13
Dunnock	13	9	14	12	8	6	7	8	10	12
Robin	5	7	6	6	5	4	5	3	4	4
Blackbird	20	14	15	15	15	12	14	13	18	15
Song Thrush	7	5	4	4	1	2	1	2	4	2
Mistle Thrush	–	–	p	–	p	p	1	–	–	p
Sedge Warbler	2	4	–	1	–	–	–	–	–	p
Blackcap	3	1	p	1	1	p	1	1	1	2
Garden Warbler	–	1	p	1	2	1	2	1	2	1
Lesser Whitethroat	1	1	1	p	2	1	2	1	1	1
Common Whitethroat	2	6	3	4	p	3	6	3	5	3
Chiffchaff	–	–	–	–	–	–	1	–	p	–
Willow Warbler	7	6	8	6	3	3	5	5	4	2
Spotted Flycatcher	p	1	1	–	–	p	–	p	p	1
Long-tailed Tit	p	p	–	–	1	–	p	p	–	p
Blue Tit	9	5	3	6	7	4	4	6	4	6
Great Tit	3	2	1	2	3	4	4	5	5	3
Willow Tit	1	p	1	p	p	p	1	1	p	1
Treecreeper	1	p	–	–	p	–	–	–	–	p
Jay		–	–	p	–	–	–	–	–	–
Magpie	2	1	p	1	p	p	3	p	1	p
Carrion Crow	2	2	4	3	2	4	3	2	1	3
Starling	4	3	6	1	2	3	3	3	4	2
House Sparrow	nc	nc	nc	nc	nc	p	p	–	2	p
Tree Sparrow	10	8	8	5	4	2	3	6	2	4
Chaffinch	7	8	7	8	10	5	12	11	14	16
Greenfinch	5	6	2	1	2	2	p	p	3	1
Goldfinch	p	p	p	p	1	p	–	–	–	–
Linnet	4	5	3	3	1	1	p	2	3	2
Lesser Redpoll	p	–	–	–	–	–	–	p	–	–
Bullfinch	1	1	1	1	1	1	1	p	1	1
Yellowhammer	19	15	16	17	15	12	17	15	14	15
Reed Bunting	5	4	5	2	3	3	5	1	1	2
Corn Bunting	–	–	–	–	–	–	p	1	–	–
Total species holding territory	32	30	27	27	29	30	32	27	31	32
Total number of territories	176	141	149	133	121	104	140	125	153	145

	1991	1995	1996	1997	1998	1999	2000	2002
Mallard	p	–	p	p	1	p	p	1
Red-legged Partridge	p	p	1	p	1	p	p	–
Grey Partridge	p	–	–	–	–	–	–	–
Pheasant	1	3	2	1	2	1	2	1
Kestrel	–	1	–	p	p	–	–	p

Hobby	1	1	–	p	–	p	–	–
Moorhen	–	–	–	–	–	–	–	–
Lapwing	–	p	–	p	–	p	–	–
Stock Dove	1	p	–	p	1	p	2	3
Wood Pigeon	4	3	4	3	2	3	3	6
Turtle Dove	–	–	–	–	–	–	–	–
Cuckoo	2	–	1	–	–	1	–	–
Little Owl	–	–	–	p	p	–	1	1
Tawny Owl	-	–	–	–	–	–	p	–
Great Spotted Woodpecker	–	–	p	p	p	p	p	1
Lesser Spotted Woodpecker	–	–	–	–	–	–	–	–
Sky Lark	14	12	12	11	11	12	14	13
Swallow	p	p	p	p	p	p	1	p
Yellow Wagtail	7	2	3	2	3	4	3	2
Pied Wagtail	–	–	–	–	p	p	p	–
Wren	4	9	4	3	7	10	13	13
Dunnock	5	6	5	3	3	6	4	7
Robin	4	5	4	4	5	6	9	9
Blackbird	13	11	11	0	7	14	17	19
Song Thrush	p	p	–	p	p	p	p	p
Mistle Thrush	p	–	p	p	–	p	1	p
Sedge Warbler	–	p	–	–	–	–	–	–
Blackcap	1	p	1	2	2	1	2	2
Garden Warbler	p	–	–	p	p	–	–	–
Lesser Whitethroat	p	–	–	–	–	–	p	–
Common Whitethroat	3	3	5	2	1	2	3	5
Chiffchaff	–	–	–	–	p	p	–	–
Willow Warbler	2	3	4	3	2	1	2	2
Spotted Flycatcher	–	–	–	–	p	–	–	p
Long-tailed Tit	–	–	2	–	p	–	1	1
Blue Tit	5	7	6	7	6	7	5	8
Great Tit	2	3	2	4	2	3	4	5
Willow Tit	–	–	1	–	–	p	–	–
Treecreeper	p	–	–	–	–	–	–	p
Jay	–	–	–	–	–	–	–	–
Magpie	1	2	1	1	1	1	1	2
Carrion Crow	1	2	2	2	1	1	3	2
Starling	1	3	1	1	p	–	p	1
House Sparrow	–	–	–	–	–	–	–	–
Tree Sparrow	4	1	–	1	1	2	5	–
Chaffinch	15	9	9	12	11	13	15	12
Greenfinch	p	1	p	p	p	p	3	p
Goldfinch	–	1	p	p	p	p	14	p
Linnet	2	1	3	4	2	3	6	3
Lesser Redpoll	–	–	–	–	–	p	–	–
Bullfinch	2	1	1	1	1	1	1	1
Yellowhammer	11	15	10	8	9	12	15	14
Reed Bunting	1	2	4	p	–	p	1	p
Corn Bunting	–	–	–	–	–	–	–	–
Total species holding territory	25	25	25	21	23	21	28	25
Total number of territories	107	107	99	84	82	104	151	134

Table 4: Species recorded but not holding territory at the Newton Harcourt CBC plot 1971–2002

	Years recorded
Mute Swan	2000
Great Canada Goose	1976, 1989, 1997, 1998, 1999, 2000, 2002
Cormorant	1988
Grey Heron	1989, 1991, 1997, 1998, 1999
Sparrowhawk	1986, 1988, 1996, 2002
Coot	1984
Common Snipe	1976
Whimbrel	1985
Curlew	1982, 1990, 1996, 1997
Black-headed Gull	1986, 1987, 1996, 1999
Common Gull	1986, 1990, 1998
Lesser Black-backed Gull	1986, 1987
Herring Gull	1999
Common Tern	1999
Feral Pigeon	1990, 1991, 1995, 1996, 1997, 1998, 1999, 2000, 2002
Collared Dove	1977, 1980, 1982, 1983, 1985, 1987, 1989, 1990, 1991, 1996, 2002
Common Swift	1974, 1976, 1977, 1978, 1979, 1980, 1986–2002
Green Woodpecker	1976, 1980, 1984, 1987
House Martin	1976, 1979, 1986, 1987, 1988
Meadow Pipit	1976, 1986, 1987, 1988, 1989, 1995, 1996, 1997, 1998, 1999, 2000, 2002
Common Redstart	1983, 1989, 1996
Whinchat	1979, 1983, 1989, 1990, 1998
Northern Wheatear	1974, 1976, 1983, 1984, 1985, 1988, 1997, 1999, 2000
Ring Ouzel	1974
Fieldfare	1981, 1996, 1998, 2000
Redwing	2000
Grasshopper Warbler	1980
Goldcrest	1974, 1986
Coal Tit	1977, 1986, 1995
Jackdaw	1973–1980, 1986, 1987, 1989, 1990, 1991, 1996, 1999, 2002
Rook	1980, 1986, 1987, 1989, 1990, 1996, 1997, 1998, 2000, 2002

Aylestone Meadows

Table 5: Common Birds Census results at the Aylestone Meadows CBC plot 1981–89

	1981	1982	1983	1984	1985	1986	1987	1989
Mallard	4	3	3	5	4	4	4	5
Grey Partridge	2	1	p	1	1	p	–	2
Pheasant	–	p	1	2	3	1	1	4
Little Grebe	p	1	p	p	p	–	–	–
Kestrel	–	1	1	1	1	1	1	1
Moorhen	3	3	5	5	5	6	5	9
Coot	–	–	–	–	–	p	1	1
Stock Dove	–	p	p	1	–	p	p	2
Wood Pigeon	nc	1	nc	nc	nc	nc	7	nc
Collared Dove	nc	nc	1	1	nc	2	3	10
Cuckoo	–	p	p	1	1	1	–	1
Sky Lark	3	2	3	2	2	2	1	p
Meadow Pipit	–	–	–	p	–	–	1	2

Pied Wagtail	p	p	–	p	p	p	–	1
Wren	13	19	19	18	19	21	17	20
Dunnock	8	11	13	12	12	22	8	17
Robin	3	6	11	9	7	10	5	12
Blackbird	13	15	18	18	17	24	21	40
Song Thrush	8	8	8	10	10	8	4	9
Mistle Thrush	1	2	1	2	2	p	p	2
Sedge Warbler	p	2	3	2	2	4	5	10
Blackcap	1	p	1	1	p	1	–	p
Lesser Whitethroat	2	p	–	1	p	p	p	p
Common Whitethroat	3	1	p	p	1	1	2	8
Willow Warbler	3	3	3	4	4	7	4	7
Blue Tit	7	7	7	10	10	13	11	10
Great Tit	4	5	6	7	7	7	2	4
Willow Tit	–	1	p	1	p	p	p	p
Magpie	3	3	6	5	1	2	5	14
Carrion Crow	2	2	2	1	2	2	5	3
Starling	nc	nc	nc	nc	nc	nc	nc	nc
House Sparrow	nc	nc	nc	nc	nc	nc	nc	nc
Tree Sparrow	p	1	p	p	p	1	p	1
Greenfinch	7	8	5	6	6	6	6	9
Goldfinch	4	5	4	4	1	p	p	2
Linnet	4	8	6	5	4	4	2	8
Lesser Redpoll	1	2	2	1	p	2	–	2
Bullfinch	1	3	2	1	3	1	1	2
Yellowhammer	2	2	1	3	2	2	–	–
Reed Bunting	3	7	6	3	4	4	3	5
Total species holding territory	29	32	29	34	30	30	27	34
Total number of territories	105	132	138	143	130	159	125	223

Table 6: Species recorded but not holding territory at the Aylestone Meadows CBC plot 1981–1989

	Years recorded
Mute Swan	1981, 1982, 1983, 1984, 1985, 1986, 1987
Red-legged Partridge	1982, 1983, 1984, 1987
Sparrowhawk	1984
Little Ringed Plover	1987, 1989
Lapwing	1984
Common Snipe	1987
Common Sandpiper	1989
Black-headed Gull	1989
Common Gull	1989
Lesser Black-backed Gull	1989
Turtle Dove	1982, 1983
Tawny Owl	1981
Common Swift	1981, 1982, 1983, 1989
Kingfisher	1981, 1983, 1984, 1984, 1989
Green Woodpecker	1983
Lesser Spotted Woodpecker	1981
Sand Martin	1983
Swallow	1982, 1983, 1984, 1985, 1989

House Martin	1981, 1982, 1989
Yellow Wagtail	1982, 1983, 1984, 1986, 1989
Grey Wagtail	1981
Whinchat	1983, 1985
Norther Wheatear	1983, 1984
Ring Ouzel	1983
Grasshopper Warbler	1982
Reed Warbler	1989
Garden Warbler	1986
Spotted Flycatcher	1983, 1986
Long-tailed Tit	1984, 1985, 1986, 1989
Coal Tit	1982, 1983
Marsh Tit	1982
Treecreeper	1985
Jackdaw	1983
Chaffinch	1981, 1982, 1983, 1984, 1985, 1986, 1989

King's Hill Lodge, Uppingham

Table 7: Common Birds Census results at the King's Hill Lodge, Uppingham CBC plot 1992–2005

	92	93	94	95	96	97	98	99	00	01	02	03	04	05
Common Shelduck	1	–	1	–	–	–	–	–	–	p	–	–	p	–
Mallard	1	p	p	p	p	p	p	1	p	2	2	p	p	p
Red-legged Partridge	1	1	1	1	2	1	1	p	3	1	2	2	2	1
Grey Partridge	–	–	–	1	–	–	p	–	p	–	–	–	–	–
Pheasant	8	5	5	9	3	4	2	4	3	3	7	2	4	3
Sparrowhawk	p	p	p	p	p	1	p	p	1	p	p	p	1	p
Common Buzzard	–	–	–	–	–	p	–	–	–	–	p	p	1	1
Kestrel	–	1	1	1	1	1	p	1	1	1	2	1	1	1
Moorhen	–	–	–	p	–	–	–	p	p	p	1	1	–	–
Lapwing	–	–	–	–	–	–	–	–	–	–	p	1	–	p
Stock Dove	4	4	5	6	3	4	5	6	6	5	5	7	5	6
Wood Pigeon	32	32	32	29	48	40	36	39	31	30	34	39	48	29
Collared Dove	p	1	1	1	1	2	1	1	1	p	p	1	1	p
Cuckoo	–	1	2	p	–	–	–	–	p	p	–	–	–	p
Barn Owl	–	–	–	–	–	–	–	–	–	–	–	–	–	1
Little Owl	1	–	1	1	1	1	1	1	1	1	1	1	1	1
Tawny Owl	–	–	–	p	1	1	1	1	1	2	1	1	–	1
Green Woodpecker	p	1	2	1	2	1	1	2	1	1	1	p	1	1
Great Spotted Woodpecker	1	1	1	p	p	p	p	p	–	1	p	p	1	1
Sky Lark	7	5	4	6	6	5	7	6	7	3	7	5	6	5
Swallow	2	1	1	1	1	p	1	2	1	1	p	2	1	1
Meadow Pipit	–	p	p	p	p	p	1	2	1	2	3	2	1	1
Pied Wagtail	2	2	2	2	2	2	2	2	2	2	2	2	2	2
Wren	8	17	14	16	6	5	11	21	26	20	29	32	17	19
Dunnock	9	15	13	20	16	11	16	16	21	16	21	23	20	12
Robin	8	11	16	18	12	9	12	20	27	29	29	27	27	26
Common Redstart	–	–	2	1	–	–	–	–	–	–	–	–	–	–
Blackbird	10	11	13	20	18	9	21	10	8	18	18	22	28	23
Song Thrush	1	P	1	1	1	P	1	3	3	2	3	2	1	1
Mistle Thrush	1	1	1	2	1	P	1	1	1	1	P	1	p	–
Blackcap	3	1	2	2	2	2	2	5	5	4	2	3	3	6

Garden Warbler	p	2	1	2	1	–	1	1	1	1	–	1	1	–
Lesser Whitethroat	1	p	2	1	p	1	1	2	2	–	2	1	3	1
Common Whitethroat	–	2	1	1	4	2	2	2	3	3	8	4	5	5
Chiffchaff	–	p	p	2	1	1	1	p	2	2	p	1	3	2
Willow Warbler	4	3	2	2	6	1	1	2	p	p	1	–	2	1
Goldcrest	p	–	p	–	–	p	p	p	–	p	p	p	2	p
Spotted Flycatcher	p	–	1	1	1	p	1	1	1	1	1	2	–	1
Long-tailed Tit	1	2	3	4	1	3	1	4	3	1	1	1	2	1
Blue Tit	11	12	13	16	15	16	14	14	11	14	13	18	17	15
Great Tit	6	7	3	4	8	6	8	10	9	9	12	12	11	11
Coal Tit	p	p	1	–	p	p	–	p	p	–	p	p	–	p
Marsh Tit	p	1	p	–	p	p	p	p	–	p	p	p	p	–
Nuthatch	–	–	–	p	–	–	–	–	–	–	–	–	–	1
Treecreeper	–	1	1	2	1	1	p	2	2	p	1	p	p	p
Jay	–	p	p	p	p	1	p	p	p	p	–	p	p	1
Magpie	1	p	1	2	p	1	1	2	3	3	2	2	p	1
Jackdaw	19	26	19	15	11	16	16	16	13	16	14	12	6	16
Rook	13	13	13	10	10	11	14	13	15	14	20	13	13	13
Carrion Crow	1	1	2	1	1	1	1	3	2	1	1	2	1	p
Starling	nc	10	8	10	10	8	8	7	5	8	8	4	3	1
House Sparrow	nc	nc	nc	nc	nc	nc	3	5	7	7	7	7	4	6
Tree Sparrow	–	–	2	1	1	–	–	–	–	p	–	–	–	–
Chaffinch	22	25	27	24	23	22	29	28	36	32	30	43	37	45
Greenfinch	1	1	2	3	4	4	4	4	5	6	7	9	13	11
Goldfinch	1	p	p	1	2	1	1	1	2	2	2	2	1	2
Linnet	1	5	6	7	6	3	4	2	2	5	6	6	3	3
Bullfinch	2	2	2	3	1	1	1	2	1	2	3	2	2	1
Yellowhammer	6	10	16	15	13	10	9	10	16	17	16	19	19	20
Total species holding territory	34	37	44	44	39	38	40	41	41	40	40	41	41	42
Total number of territories	188	236	247	266	247	209	244	275	291	289	280	338	320	301

Table 8: Species recorded but not holding territory at the King's Hill Lodge, Uppingham CBC plot 1992–2005

	Years recorded
Mute Swan	1994, 1999, 2000, 2004
Greater Canada Goose	1992, 1993, 1994, 1996, 1998, 1999, 2000, 2002, 2003, 2004, 2005
Barnacle Goose	1999
Tufted Duck	2005
Cormorant	1996, 1997, 1999, 2000, 2001, 2002, 2003, 2004, 2005
Grey Heron	1992, 1994, 1995, 1997, 1998, 1999, 2001, 2002, 2003, 2005
Red Kite	2001, 2005
Hobby	1999
Woodcock	1994
Black-headed Gull	2004
Common Gull	2002, 2003, 2005
Lesser Black-backed Gull	2002, 2003
Herring Gull	2004
Great Black-backed Gull	2004
Common Tern	2001, 2002
Feral Pigeon	1997, 1999, 2005

Turtle Dove	1994
Common Swift	1995, 1996, 1997, 1998, 1999, 2000, 2002, 2003, 2004, 2005
Lesser Spotted Woodpecker	1997
House Martin	1998, 2004
Yellow Wagtail	1992, 1995, 1996, 1997, 1999, 2000
Fieldfare	1999, 2000, 2001, 2002, 2003, 2004, 2005
Redwing	2001, 2002, 2003, 2005
Willow Tit	2005
Brambling	2002
Lesser Redpoll	1992, 1995
Common Crossbill	1998, 2003
Reed Bunting	1993, 1994, 1995, 1996, 2004

APPENDIX 6:
SPECIMENS AT LEICESTER MUSEUM

The Table presents data for all known extant specimens collected in Leicestershire and Rutland which are held by Leicester Museum. The species listed are either rare in the counties or are interesting for taxonomic reasons.

Species	Accession number	Date	Locality	Source
Greenland White-fronted Goose	L.Z115.1961.0.0	Dec 28th 1960	Eyebrook Reservoir	A. Chapel
Red Grouse	L.Z98.1924.0.0	1878	Noseley	A. Hazelrigg
Storm Petrel	L.Z4732.1892.0.0	Nov 24th 1892	Earl Shilton	T. Macaulay
Storm Petrel	L.Z544.1953.0.0	Sep 22nd 1953	Loughborough	P.R. Dutton
Leach's Petrel	L.Z26.1916.0.0	1876	Sketchley	M. Browne
Leach's Petrel	L.Z1019.1899.0.0	Nov 1899	Cosby	M. Browne
Leach's Petrel	L.Z163.1953.0.0	Oct 30th 1952	Leicester	L. Bingley
Little Bittern	L.Z474.1954.0.0	Aug 21st 1954	Thornton Reservoir	W.J. Lorrimer
Night Heron	L.Z191.1987.0.0	Feb 19th 1985	Rutland Water	T.P. Appleton
Honey Buzzard	L.Z458.1968.17.0	Oct 28th 1841	Martinshaw Wood	W. Chaplin
Honey Buzzard	L.Z99.1924.0.0	1872	Noseley	A. Hazelrigg
Honey Buzzard	L.Z39.1956.0.0	Sep 1881	Twyford	Mr Greasley
Rough-legged Buzzard	L.Z94.1869.35.0	Nov 15th 1839	Bradgate Park	Unknown
Rough-legged Buzzard	L.Z12.1927.0.0	1925	Swithland	A. Turner
Spotted Crake	L.Z100.1984.2	Unknown	Stapleford Park	Lord Gretton
Spotted Crake	L.Z102.1914	Unknown	Sketchley	T. Adcock
Spotted Crake	L.Z11.1946	Sep 1946	Kilby Bridge	A.E. Jolley
Spotted Crake	L.Z444.1963	Oct 6th 1963	Cropston Reservoir	P.J. Cox
Corn Crake (adult and nine juveniles)	L.Z103.1914	Unknown	Leicestershire	T. Adcock
Corn Crake	L.Z14.1985.4	1890–1900	River Soar	W. Broome
Corn Crake	L.Z39.1910	May 22nd 1910	Aylestone	J. White
Corn Crake	L.Z285.1958	Sep 7th 1958	King's Norton	W.D. Allen
Cream-coloured Courser	L.Z458.1968.1.0	Oct 15th 1827	Timberwood Hill	T. Gisborne
Purple Sandpiper (4)	L.Z34–38.1904.0.0	Aug 16th 1904	Abbey Meadows	T. Adcock
Great Snipe	L.Z2081.185.0.0	Sep 2nd 1885	Garthorpe	A. Ross
Pomarine Skua	L.Z2377.1886.0.0	1879	Hinckley	R.W. Chase
Long-tailed Skua	L.Z87.1926.0.0	Oct 3rd 1926	Melton Mowbray	R.E. Peach
Roseate Tern	L.Z291.1954.0.0	May 7th 1954	Hinckley	E. Lambert
Little Auk	L.Z50.1912.0.0	Feb 1902	Kilby Bridge	J. Freer
Little Auk	L.Z87.1929.0.0	Jan 1930	Kibworth	E. Henson
Little Auk	L.Z7.1942.0.0	Nov 18th 1942	Rolleston	H. Dytham
Little Auk	L.Z159.1984.0.0	Nov 10th 1957	Grace Dieu	D. Mortimer
Little Auk	L.Z36.1958.0.0	Nov 12th 1957	Beacon Hill	County Land Agent
Little Auk	L.Z29.1968.0.0	Nov 2nd 1967	Tolethorpe	M. Wells
Little Auk	L.Z879.1978.0.0	Nov 1st 1974	Pickworth	G. Hallam
Little Auk	L.Z644.1976.0.0	Nov 9th 1975	Ashby Magna	A.D. Sims
Little Auk	L.Z189.1987.0.0	Nov 7th 1983	Clipsham	T.P. Appleton
Little Auk	L.Z205.1988.0.0	Nov 7th 1983	Great Glen	S. Witts
Roller	L.Z261.1968.0.0	Jun 21st 1968	Kirby Muxloe	H. Ikin
Wryneck	L.Z100.1984.6	Unknown	Stapleford Park	Lord Gretton

Wryneck	L.Z472.1954	Jun 25th 1954	Kilby Bridge	G.E. Marley
Wryneck	L.Z710.1975.1	Sep 23rd 1974	Queniborough	H.G. Cherry
Wryneck	L.Z199.1990	Sep 14th 1990	Beeby	J. Bland
Aquatic Warbler	L.Z162.1969.321.0	1864	Loughborough	Hewitt collection
Great Grey Shrike	2.OS.157	Feb 8th 1885	Belvoir	W. Ingram
Great Grey Shrike	L.Z2301.1885.0.0	Dec 23rd 1885	Leicester	W.A. Evans
Great Grey Shrike	L.Z411.1891.0.0	Nov 16th 1891	Eaton	J. Young
Great Grey Shrike	L.Z410.1891.0.0	Dec 28th 1891	Leicester	J. Young
Great Grey Shrike	L.Z312.1970.0.0	Nov 7th 1970	Oadby	M. Whitcombe
Great Grey Shrike	L.Z730.1975.1.1	Nov 16th 1974	Bradgate Park	N. Barrett
Red-backed Shrike (male of 'pair')	L.Z25.1904.0.0	May 27th 1885	Barkby	T. Adcock
Common Crossbill	L.Z167.1990.0.0	Jun 29th 1990	Benscliffe Wood	E. Broughton
Common Crossbill	L.Z203.1990.0.0	Sep 9th 1990	Benscliffe Wood	E. Broughton
Common Crossbill (3)	L.Z21.1997.1–3.0	Jul 19th 1997	West Beacon Farm	A. Marmont
Common Crossbill	L.Z21.1997.4.0	Aug 7th 1997	West Beacon Farm	A. Marmont

Notes on Leicester Museum specimens

- The record of four Purple Sandpipers at Abbey Meadows on August 16th 1904 has been rejected by the LROS Records Committee
- Thomas Adcock was a taxidermist who is mentioned in trade directories between 1889 and 1922, after being in America between about 1875 and 1889. The provenance of some specimens which passed through his hands is questionable.
- Several of the dates of Little Auks have been labelled incorrectly at the Museum. Correct dates are: November 12th 1957 (Grace Dieu); November 5th 1974 (Pickworth); November 11th 1975 (Ashby Magna); November 5th 1983 (Clipsham).
- The date of the Wryneck at Kilby Bridge is labelled incorrectly at the Museum, and should read August 25th 1954.
- The Great Grey Shrike at Belvoir in February 1885 shows some characters of 'Siberian' Great Grey Shrike *Lanius excubitor sibiricus*, although further investigation has shown it is most likely to be an atypical *excubitor* or an intergrade (see text on page 593, as well as Browne 1907 and Harrop 2006b).
- The Great Grey Shrike at Leicester on December 28th 1891 shows characters of an 'eastern' Great Grey Shrike, though it is now difficult to trace the exact history of the specimen (Harrop 2006b).
- A progress report on the molecular analysis of Common Crossbills by R. Summers found that DNA obtained from specimens in archival collections (including Leicester) provided no evidence for differences in genetic diversity between contemporary and museum samples.

In general, it should be noted that although the table of specimens is as complete and accurate as possible, others may come to light in future or other species may be of interest to subsequent reviewers.

APPENDIX 7: EGGS AT LEICESTER MUSEUM

The Table presents data about eggs collected in Leicestershire and Rutland which are held by Leicester Museum.

Species	Accession number	Year if known	Locality	Source if known
Red-legged Partridge	L.Z415.1954.216.0	1934	Thurmaston	Barrow
Great Crested Grebe	L.Z2388.1886.0.0	Unknown	Saddington Reservoir	Browne/Macaulay
Sparrowhawk	L.Z232.1983.0.0	1969	Sileby	Unknown
Little Ringed Plover	L.Z442.1987.0.0	1987	Cadeby	Plant
Lapwing	L.Z34.1905.0.0	Unknown	Scraptoft	Horwood
Common Sandpiper	L.Z3799.1888.0.0	1885	Bradgate Park	Unknown
Wood Pigeon	L.Z22.1903.0.0	Unknown	Owston	Unknown
Cuckoo	L.Z240.1904.0.0	Unknown	Narborough	Unknown
Kingfisher	L.Z4.1904.0.0	Unknown	Quorn	Unknown
Sand Martin	L.Z24.1906.0.0	Unknown	Aylestone	Unknown
Sand Martin	L.Z25.1906.0.0	Unknown	Aylestone	Unknown
Swallow	L.Z4398.1892.0.0	Unknown	Loughborough	Unknown
Swallow	L.Z374.1983.0.0	Unknown	Shearsby	Unknown
Swallow	L.Z375.1983.0.0	1968	Thurnby	Unknown
Swallow	L.Z237.1984.0.0	1984	Great Glen	Cook
Tree Pipit	L.Z56.1903.0.0	Unknown	Swithland	Unknown
Tree Pipit	L.Z4397.1892.0.0	1890	Loughborough	Unknown
Pied Wagtail	L.Z352.1891.0.0	Unknown	Leicester	Unknown
Dunnock	L.Z96.1902.0.0	1902	Earl Shilton	Kirk
Dunnock	L.Z372.1983.0.0	1969	Leicester	Unknown
Dunnock	L.Z1999.1885.0.0	Unknown	Stoneygate, Leicester	Unknown
Robin	L.Z78.1904.0.0	Unknown	Narborough	Gunning
Robin	L.Z375.1989.00	1989	Rothley	Preston
Robin	L.Z371.1983.0.0	1965	Loughborough	Ward
Robin	L.Z280.1983.0.0	1968	Oadby	Unknown
Robin	L.Z281.1983.0.0	1968	Anstey	Unknown
Robin	L.Z282.1983.0.0	Unknown	Leicester	Unknown
Robin	L.Z283.1983.0.0	1975	Leicester	Unknown
Blackbird	L.Z70.1905.0.0	Unknown	Scraptoft	Horwood
Blackbird	L.Z61.1904.0.0	Unknown	Narborough	Gunning
Blackbird	L.Z275.1983.0.0	1968	Leicester	Unknown
Blackbird	L.Z277.1983.0.0	1971	Leicester	Unknown
Blackbird	L.Z278.1983.0.0	1956	Leicester	Unknown
Blackbird	L.Z1.1904.0.0	1901	Evington	Unknown
Song Thrush	L.Z71.1905.0.0	Unknown	Scraptoft	Horwood
Song Thrush	L.Z73.1905.0.0	Unknown	Thurnby	Horwood
Song Thrush	L.Z58.1904.0.0	Unknown	Narborough	Gunning
Song Thrush	L.Z3.1905.0.0	1895	Melton Mowbray	Unknown
Song Thrush	L.Z273.1983.0.0	1968	Loughborough	Nix
Mistle Thrush	L.Z74.1905.0.0	Unknown	Scraptoft	Horwood
Mistle Thrush	L.Z26.1903.0.0	Unknown	Owston	Unknown
Grasshopper Warbler	L.Z3553.1887.0.0	1887	Tugby	Unknown
Sedge Warbler	L.Z2021.1885	Unknown	Aylestone	Unknown
Sedge Warbler	L.Z109.1904.0.0	Unknown	Narborough	Gunning
Reed Warbler	L.Z58.1903.0.0	Unknown	Groby Pool	Unknown

Reed Warbler	L.Z285.1983.0.0	1921	Wanlip	Unknown
Reed Warbler	L.Z2033.1885.0.0	Unknown	Leicester	Unknown
Reed Warbler	L.Z157.1881.0.0	Unknown	Leicester	Unknown
Blackcap	L.Z65.1905.0.0	Unknown	South Croxton	Horwood
Blackcap	L.Z66.1905.0.0	Unknown	Scraptoft	Horwood
Blackcap	L.Z60.1903.0.0	Unknown	Swithland	Unknown
Blackcap	L.Z1519.1893.0.0	Unknown	Tugby	Unknown
Garden Warbler	L.Z64.1905.0.0	Unknown	South Croxton	Horwood
Lesser Whitethroat	L.Z88.1904.0.0	Unknown	Narborough	Gunning
Lesser Whitethroat	L.Z67.1905.0.0	Unknown	Quenby	Horwood
Common Whitethroat	L.Z85.1904.0.0	Unknown	Narborough	Gunning
Common Whitethroat	L.Z83.1909.0.0	Unknown	Great Glen	Unknown
Common Whitethroat	L.Z68.1905.0.0	Unknown	Scraptoft	Horwood
Common Whitethroat	L.Z2022.1885.0.0	Unknown	Aylestone	Unknown
Chiffchaff	L.Z68.1902.0.0	Unknown	Swithland	Unknown
Chiffchaff	L.Z16.1902.0.0	Unknown	South Croxton	Unknown
Goldcrest	L.Z62.1985.0.0	1983	Carlton Curlieu	Hames
Spotted Flycatcher	L.Z65.1903.0.0	Unknown	Withcote	Unknown
Spotted Flycatcher	L.Z60.1902.0.0	Unknown	South Croxton	Unknown
Spotted Flycatcher	L.Z55.1905.0.0	Unknown	South Croxton	Unknown
Spotted Flycatcher	L.Z55.1903.0.0	Unknown	Swithland	Unknown
Spotted Flycatcher	L.Z54.1905.0.0	Unknown	South Croxton	Unknown
Spotted Flycatcher	L.Z157.1904.0.0	Unknown	Narborough	Gunning
Spotted Flycatcher	L.Z158.1904.0.0	Unknown	Narborough	Gunning
Blue Tit	L.Z453.1987.0.0	1987	Leicester	Marshall
Blue Tit	L.Z373.1983.0.0	1969	Leicester	Unknown
Blue Tit	L.Z267.1983.0.0	1959	Leicester	Foxwell
Blue Tit	L.Z268.1983.0.0	1969	Thurnby	Unknown
Blue Tit	L.Z269.1983.0.0	1979	Wigston	Towell
Great Tit	L.Z266.1983.0.0	1966	Aylestone	Unknown
Red-backed Shrike	L.Z25.1904.0.0	1885	Barkby	Adcock
Rook	L.Z5.1966.0.0	1964	Great Glen	Fleming
Rook	L.Z2361.1886.0.0	Unknown	Stoughton	Unknown
Rook	L.Z205.1909.0.0	Unknown	Aylestone	Unknown
House Sparrow	L.Z370.1983.0.0	1960	Kirby Muxloe	Unknown
House Sparrow	L.Z185.1904.0.0	Unknown	Narborough	Gunning
House Sparrow	L.Z184.1904.0.0	Unknown	Narborough	Gunning
Chaffinch	L.Z50.1905.0.0	Unknown	South Croxton	Horwood
Chaffinch	L.Z51.1905.0.0	Unknown	South Croxton	Horwood
Chaffinch	L.Z190.1904.0.0	Unknown	Narborough	Gunning
Greenfinch	L.Z62.1902.0.0	Unknown	South Croxton	Horwood
Greenfinch	L.Z298.1983.0.0	1969	Thurnby	Unknown
Greenfinch	L.Z171.1904.0.0	Unknown	Narborough	Gunning
Greenfinch	L.Z172.1904.0.0	Unknown	Narborough	Gunning
Linnet	L.Z64.1902.0.0	Unknown	South Croxton	Horwood
Linnet	L.Z51.1903.0.0	Unknown	Swithland	Unknown
Linnet	L.Z46.1905.0.0	Unknown	Scraptoft	Horwood
Linnet	L.Z48.1905.0.0	Unknown	Scraptoft	Horwood
Linnet	L.Z313.1989.0.0	1989	Shearsby	Heathcote
Linnet	L.Z290.1983.0.0	1966	Leicester	Unknown
Linnet	L.Z291.1983.0.0	1976	Leicester	Unknown
Linnet	L.Z292.1983.0.0	1977	Melton Mowbray	Unknown
Linnet	L.Z193.1904.0.0	Unknown	Narborough	Gunning

Lesser Redpoll	L.Z2006.1885.0.0	1885	Anstey	Unknown
Bullfinch	L.Z295.1983.0.0	1973	Rothley	Unknown
Hawfinch	L.Z32.1910.0.0	Unknown	Groby Road, Leicester	Unknown
Reed Bunting	L.Z209.1904.0.0	Unknown	Narborough	Gunning
Reed Bunting	L.Z79.1905.0.0	Unknown	Keythorpe	Unknown
Reed Bunting	L.Z38.1908.0.0	Unknown	South Croxton	Horwood

Notes on Leicester Museum eggs

- In the majority of cases listed above, the identity of the egg has not been checked.
- Thomas Adcock was a taxidermist who is mentioned in trade directories between 1889 and 1922, after being in America between about 1875 and 1889. The provenance of some specimens which passed through his hands is questionable.

APPENDIX 8: LIST OF ARTICLES PUBLISHED IN LEICESTERSHIRE AND RUTLAND BIRD REPORTS 1941 TO 2005

1941	None
1942	None
1943	The changing status of Leicestershire birds *A. E. Jolley*
	The breeding bird population of The Brand *F. Brady*
1944	Report on the nesting of the Blue-headed Wagtail *R. E. Pochin*
	Report on the Sand Martin Enquiry, 1944 *A. E. Jolley & R. Storer*
1945	The Eye Brook Reservoir *A. E. Jolley*
	The Lesser Whitethroat: some observations on its distribution in Leicestershire *A. Bonner*
1946	The change in bird-life during the growth of a Charnwood conifer plantation *E. A. G. Duffey*
	Great Crested Grebe: from notes compiled over a period of four years at Swithland Reservoir *G. H. Hunt*
1947	Notes and observations on the effect of the severe weather on the counties' wild birds *Anon*
1948	None
1949	None
1950	Some observations on the races of Golden Plover at Lindley Aerodrome *M. K. Howarth*
1951	None
1952	The breeding of the Grey Wagtail in Leicestershire in 1952 *G. Felstead*
	The wintering of gulls in Leicestershire *R. A. O. Hickling*
	A provisional report on visible migration at Croft Hill, 1940–1952 *R. E. Pochin*
1953	The Hobby: its breeding in Leicestershire, 1953 *H. Lapworth*
	Starling roosts in Leicestershire: winter, 1953/4 *R. A. O. Hickling*
	Wild birds within the city of Leicester *R. E. Pochin*
1954	None
1955	None
1956	None
1957	A second year with Greenfinches *C. Gimson*
	Greenfinches and Chaffinches on nut feeders *H. M. Skelton*
	Report on the breeding of Black-headed Gulls in Leicestershire in 1957 *P.W. Jones*
	Buddon: an Ecological Survey *P.H. Gamble*
1958	The distribution of the Nuthatch in the woodland area north and east of Ashby-de-la-Zouch *G. Rowbottom*
	A third year with Greenfinches *C. Gimson*
1959	None
1960	Starling roost: Newnham Paddox, Warwickshire. Some observations on fly lines, 1960–61 *E.R. Ingles*
	A fourth year with Greenfinches *C. Gimson*
1961	None
1962	None
1963	A summary of observations on the effects of the severe weather of the 1962–63 winter on bird-life in Leicestershire and Rutland *P.H. Gamble*
1964	A Common Bird Census at Great Fenney Wood, 1965 *R.G. Gibbs & I.G. Andrew*
	Breeding studies of Great Crested Grebes at Wanlip Gravel Pits, 1965 *R.G. Gibbs*
1965	Ringed Plover nesting in Leicestershire *R.G. Gibbs*
	Rooks in Leicestershire *C.T. Beverley & R. A. O. Hickling*
1966	Breeding birds of Leicestershire granite quarries *D. Holyoak*
	The birds of Leicester City Farms 1944–64 *C. F. Mason & F. C. Pickering*

1967	Black-headed Bunting in Leicestershire *M. Morris*
	Bee-eater in Leicestershire *D. R. Willett*
	Greenfinch feeding House Sparrow *E. R. Ingles*
	Birds in a large Stoneygate garden *J. R. Webster*
	A short survey of the birds of Narborough Bog *E. R. Ingles*
	Some observations on the roosting behaviour of farmland Blackbirds *D. Holyoak*
	Preliminary report on the status of Marsh Tit and Willow Tit in Leicestershire and Rutland *M. E. Griffiths*
	Oral identification of Marsh and Willow Tits *E. M. P. Allsopp*
	An index of bird populations in Leicestershire *M. E. Griffiths*
1968	Night Heron at Welham *K. M. Kirton*
	White-winged Black Tern at Eyebrook Reservoir *Uppingham School Field Club & K. M. Kirton*
	House Sparrows extracting sunflower seeds from shell *E. R. Ingles*
	The birds of Spinney Hill Park, Leicester, 1960–68 *H. Bradshaw*
	Birstall bird survey 1968: Fergusson's Spinney, Loughborough Road and School Lane *M. D. Kirkman*
	Some notes on the distribution of the Tree Pipit in Leicestershire *H. Bradshaw*
	Observations on wildfowl at Cropston and Swithland Reservoirs during 1960–64 *C. F. Mason*
1969	The birds of Narborough Bog *E.R. Ingles*
	Artificial nesting sites of Willow Tits *F. C. Pickering*
	The Meadow Pipit in Leicestershire *H. Bradshaw*
1970	None
1971	Squacco Heron – Eyebrook Reservoir *K. Allsopp*
1972	None
1973	None
1974	Gulls in Leicestershire *R. A. O. Hickling*
1975	Leicestershire and Rutland Breeding Bird Atlas results 1968–1972 *N. E. Baker*
1976	The Hobby – its general status and breeding in Leicestershire *J. C. Metcalf*
	Migration at Frisby Gravel Pit, autumn 1976 *I. Snape*
1977	Bearded Tit movements, 1977 *G. Felstead*
	School Lane Spinney, Birstall, Leicester: a ten-year bird population study 1968–1977 *M. D. Kirkman*
1978	None
1979	The Abbey Park Starling roost in 1979 *G. Felstead*
	The Common Bird Census 1964 to 1979 *T. W. Johnson*
1980	Estimating a Leicestershire Reed Bunting roost *J. A. Fowler*
1981	The Cropston Greenfinch roost *J. A. Fowler*
1982	The Peckleton Hobbies 1982 *D. J. S. Gamble*
	Common Bird Census at Newton Harcourt 1971–1982 *D. J. Scott*
1983	The Mute Swan Census, 1983 *C. Measures & R. A. O. Hickling*
	Gulls in Leicestershire 1983 *R. A. O. Hickling*
1984	The Leicestershire and Rutland Referees' Committee *R. F. Baker*
	Possible Lesser Golden Plover in the Shepshed area, 1984/5 *D. Smallshire*
	Wader migration at Eyebrook Reservoir, 1957–1979 *C. F. Mason*
	The increase of Gadwall and Ruddy Ducks in Leicestershire and Rutland *Anon*
1985	LROS Warbler Survey 1985 *M. Holling*
	Study of Spring Wood, Rough Park, Birch Coppice and adjacent scrub at Lount *D. Smallshire*
1986	The feeding distribution of Cormorants at Rutland Water *D. Smallshire*
	Study of Martinshaw Wood *M. Holling*
	Breeding bird densities in two east Leicestershire woods in 1986 *M. B. Jeeves*
	A review of the occurrence of Rock and Water Pipits in Leicestershire *D. J. S. Gamble*
	Flight-lines to the Abbey Park Starling roost *W. Peach & J. A. Fowler*

The incidence of the parasitic nematode *Sarconema* and the feather louse *Trinoton* in Leicestershire swans *S. Cohen, M. Greenwood & J. A. Fowler*

1987 Common Bird Censuses in Leicestershire, 1987 *Anon*
The distribution of Nuthatches in Leicestershire and Rutland *R. M. Fray*
Rookeries in Leicestershire and Rutland 1986–87 *M. Holling*

1988 Wintering Golden Plovers in Leicestershire and Rutland 1987–89 *A. J. Mackay*
Ring-billed Gull – new to the County List *A. J. Mackay*
Common Bird Censuses in Leicestershire and Rutland, 1988 *Anon*
Common Bird Census Knighton Spinney 1988 *M. Holling*

1989 Siskins feeding in Quorn gardens *I. B. Gamble*
Comparison of the breeding bird communities in Leicester's green spaces: a pilot study *R. M. Fray, D. J. Bullock & J. A. Fowler*

1990 The Society through fifty years *R. A. O. Hickling*
The occurrence of scarce raptors in Leicestershire *C. F. Mason*
Richard's Pipit – new to the County List *S. J. Close*
Tawny Pipit – new to the County List *S. Woollard*
Mute Swan census – spring/summer 1990 *D. J. S. Gamble*

1991 Unusual breeding record of Pochard at Kirby Lakes *D. J. S. Gamble*
Survey of introduced geese, June – July 1991 *D. J. S. Gamble*
Black Storks – new to the County List *N. W. Hagley*
Citrine Wagtail – new to the County List *I. Merrill*

1992 American Wigeons at Eyebrook Reservoir *A. H. J. Harrop*

1993 BTO winter gull roost survey *A. J. Mackay*
Cattle Egret – new to the County List *R. M. Fray*
Lesser Scaup – new to the County List *J. A. Forryan*
Chiffchaffs wintering at Kirby Lakes 1993 *D. J. S. Gamble*
Review of Chiffchaffs wintering in Leicestershire *D. J. S. Gamble*

1994 Leicestershire records review *A. J. Mackay*
Pallid Harrier – new to the County List *D. J. S. Gamble*
White-rumped Sandpiper – new to the County List *R. M. Fray*
Baird's Sandpiper at Eyebrook Reservoir *J. Wright*
Scarce gulls in Leicestershire and Rutland *A. J. Mackay*
Escapes in Leicestershire and Rutland *A. H. J. Harrop*
Observations on the changes in bird populations with the alteration of the management of a Leicester cemetery *D. A. C. McNeil*
Estimating bird populations for small sites in Leicestershire *D. A. C. McNeil*

1995 Laughing Gull – new to the County List *R. M. Fray*
Arctic Redpoll – new to the County List *A. H. J. Harrop*
Potential future additions to the County List *A. J. Mackay*
Corn Buntings in west Leicestershire in July 1995 *D. Dixon*
Bird populations on Leicestershire farmland, part 1 *D. A. C. McNeil*

1996 Common Crane – new to the County List *R. C. Shergold*
American Golden Plover – new to the County List *R. M. Fray*
Attempted breeding by Avocets at Rutland Water *A. H. J. Harrop*
The Leicestershire Garden Bird Survey *K. J. Goodrich & S. Grover*
Bird populations on Leicestershire farmland, part 2 *D. A. C. McNeil*

1997 Redhead – new to the County List *R. Mills*
Long-tailed Skua – new to the County List *A. H. J. Harrop & J. Wright*
Red-flanked Bluetail – new to the County List *R. M. Fray*
Greenish Warbler – new to the County List *M. J. Jarvis*
Greenish Warbler at Priory Water *D. J. S. Gamble*
Potential new breeding birds for Leicestershire and Rutland *R. P. Fray*
Wintering Blackcaps in a Glenfield garden *R. E. Davis*

	Bird populations at two threatened sites *D. A. C. McNeil*
1998	Spotted Sandpiper – new to the County List *D. Summerfield*
	Blue-winged Teal – new to the County List *M. Berriman*
	The Bean Goose in Leicestershire and Rutland *A. H. J. Harrop*
	The Nightjar in Leicestershire and Rutland *A. J. Mackay*
	A Leicestershire Hawfinch in Norway *J. A. Fowler*
	Bird populations in Leicestershire woodland *D. A. C. McNeil*
1999	Crag Martin – new to the County List *S. M. Lister*
	Peregrine Falcons in Leicestershire *C. Baggott*
	The Ashby-de-la-Zouch Yellow-browed Warbler *R. M. Fray & A. H. J. Harrop*
2000	*Aythya* hybrid at Thornton Reservoir *D. Wright*
	Tree Sparrows at Rutland Water – history and current research *G. Anderson*
	Greenland Wheatear at Bagworth Heath *A. Smith*
	Siskin with brood patch ringed in Leicestershire *A. Smith*
	Peregrine Falcons in Leicestershire and Rutland *C. Baggott*
2001	Shore Lark – new to the County List *M. Ketley*
	Colour-ringed Cormorants at Rutland Water in 2001 *S. M. Lister*
	Anglian Water Osprey Project update *H. Dixon*
	Rutland Water Tree Sparrow Project update *R. Field & G. Anderson*
2002	Franklin's Gull – new to the County List *G. Pullan*
	Colour-ringed Cormorants at Rutland Water in 2002 *S. M. Lister*
	Continental Song Thrushes in Leicestershire *N. Judson*
2003	Red-rumped Swallow- new to the County List *A. J. Mackay*
	Leicestershire and Rutland records review *R. M. Fray*
	Colour-ringed Cormorants at Rutland Water in 2003 *S. M. Lister*
2004	Colour-ringed Cormorants at Rutland Water in 2004 *S. M. Lister*
	The Great Snipe in Leicestershire and Rutland *A. H. J. Harrop*
	Two interesting shrike specimens from Leicestershire *A. H. J. Harrop*
	Memories of the formation of the Leicestershire and Rutland Ornithological Society *E. Duffey*
2005	Long-billed Dowitcher – new to the County List *S. M. Lister*
	Visible migration at Deans Lane in autumn 2005 *S. M. Lister*
	Waxwings in Leicestershire and Rutland in 2005 *R. M. Fray*

APPENDIX 9: SELECTED ARTICLES PUBLISHED PREVIOUSLY

OCCURRENCE OF *SYLVIA AQUATICA** FOR THE SECOND TIME, SO FAR AS IS KNOWN, IN ENGLAND

From *The Zoologist* October 1867, pages 946–947.

The occurrence of *Sylvia aquatica* in England was for the first time made known by Professor Newton, who, at a Meeting of the Zoological Society in May, 1866, exhibited a specimen from the collection of Mr. Borrer, of Cowfold, Sussex, which had been obtained near Brighton in October, 1853. I was unfortunately prevented from attending this Meeting, but in November last, while on a visit to Mr. Borrer, I had ample opportunity of examining this specimen.

I was at once struck with its similarity to a bird in my own collection, which I had received from the neighbourhood of Loughborough two years previously, and which I had put aside to be named, not being acquainted with the species.

On my return home I carefully re-examined this specimen and compared it with the plate in Dr. Bree's 'Birds of Europe,' and felt little doubt that it was *S. aquatica*. To be sure, however, that I was not mistaken, I sent the bird for examination to the Rev. H.B. Tristram, who is so well acquainted with the Avifauna of Europe.

To my note which accompanied it, his reply was as follows: 'There is no doubt about your *Salicaria aquatica*. It is not in full plumage, and therefore may be a bird of the year. The mature bird in breeding plumage has not the spots on the breast and flanks. There is no difference between the sexes.'

The specific characters of this bird, as pointed out by Dr. Bree, are as follows: 'A large band of yellowish white or yellow over the eyes; on the head two large longitudinal black bands separated by a reddish yellow band; the under-tail coverts and the rump marked with oblong blackish spots; tarsi flesh-colour.'

To the history of this species which may be found in the work just referred to (vol. ii., p. 80) may be added the following interesting note from Mr. Tristram: 'The nest of *S. aquatica*, which I have several times taken in Africa, is rather like that of *S. luscinoides*, of one material throughout, not suspended like the reed warbler's, but placed in the fork or leaf-joint of a big reed or cane in the centre of a swamp. The nest is small, lined with horse-hair, and interlaced with the stem.'

It only remains for me to add that the subject of this memoir was obtained in the neighbourhood of Loughborough, Leicestershire, during the summer of 1864, and was forwarded to me by a friend under the impression that it was a grasshopper warbler.

When we consider that *S. aquatica* is known to breed on the opposite shores of Holland, and is found in the marshes about Lille and Dieppe, we are only surprised that it is not a more frequent visitor to Great Britain than it appears to be. On the other hand, its general resemblance in size and colour to other well-known species, when seen at a little distance, would naturally cause it to be overlooked.

J.E. HARTING

* '*Sylvia aquatica*' is now known as *Acrocephalus paludicola*, the Aquatic Warbler (see Systematic List).

KENTISH PLOVER ON LEICESTERSHIRE-RUTLAND BORDER

From *British Birds* Volume 39, pages 188–189.

On November 4th, 1945, and subsequently a Kentish Plover (*Leucopolius a. alexandrinus*) was seen and clearly identified by a number of observers at the Eye Valley Reservoir. It was first observed by Messrs. P.O. Summers and H.R. Colman, masters of Kingswood and Uppingham Schools respectively, in company with several boys of the former school, and it was seen again by the majority of these observers on the 6th. On the 12th, Messrs. G. Felstead and P. Gamble, independently of the other observers, also saw the bird, on the 13th it was seen again by Messrs. R.E. Pochin, A.E Jolley, J.L. Petcher, and Felstead, and on the 14th by Messrs A. Bonner,

R. Broughton, and E. Duffey. It allowed a reasonably close approach, sometimes within 12 feet, and when disturbed only flew a few yards.

The details, noted in the field, were as follows. Appeared similar to Ringed Plover in build, but noticeably smaller. Bill dark. Eye set in dark oval patch which did not extend to base of bill; white superciliary stripe; forehead white; crown buffish with no evidence of dark markings; lower ear-coverts rufous; back light olive-buff, feathers light edged at tips. Thin wing-bar in flight, more noticeable when wings were fully outstretched; inconspicuous horizontal buff streak on closed wing. White throat and under-parts; brown-grey patch on either side of breast, running into shoulders. Legs black, appearing longer than in Ringed Plover, particularly from the tarsal joint, which was very prominent. Outer tail feathers white, centre ones very dark, running into khaki-buff upper tail-coverts. Thin nuchal collar. It was never heard to utter any note.

The reservoir is half in Leicestershire and half in Rutland. The bird was seen in both counties and constitutes a first record for both.

A.E. JOLLEY

[The Eye Valley record is exceptionally late, but is fortunately very thoroughly authenticated. After the most thorough examination we are satisfied of the reliability. . . – EDS.]

FERRUGINOUS DUCK IN LEICESTERSHIRE

From *British Birds* Volume 41, pages 215–216.

On November 30th 1947, I saw a Ferruginous Duck on the River Soar between Barrow and Loughborough. It was swimming alone amongst reeds near the side of the river. Although I was somewhat concealed by some willows when I first saw the bird it took alarm and flew up; after circling around several times, however, it landed again a short distance further upstream.

After stalking it to about 30–50 yards, I obtained a tolerably good view with binoculars in a good light for a short time before the bird was unfortunately frightened away by a passing train. During the period of observation I noted the following points: general build much as a Pochard or Tufted Duck; head and neck brownish-chestnut; back dark brownish; flanks light chestnut; under tail-coverts pure white; bill polished slate colour. The irides gleamed lightish, but I could not determine their exact colour. The belly, as seen in flight, was pure white and the broad white wing-bars very noticeable.

P.H. GAMBLE

[A field sketch of the bird and of the appearance of the spread wing confirms the identification – EDS.]

WOODCHAT SHRIKE IN LEICESTERSHIRE

From *British Birds* Volume 45, pages 410–411.

From October 29th to November 3rd 1950, an immature shrike frequented the gardens of a group of houses at Braunstone, on the outskirts of the city of Leicester, and was observed by G.A. Todd and C.W. Holt; the latter also made a cine-film in colour. It was described as being about as big as a Skylark (*Alauda arvensis*); the upper parts were greyish-buff, closely barred with crescentic darker brown, and the rump was light buff-grey. Tail and upper tail-coverts appeared uniform dark grey-brown except for narrow buff edge and more noticeable buff-cream terminal band on tail. Primaries, secondaries and median coverts were dark grey-brown with well marked warm buff edges and tips; primary coverts were dark brown and lesser coverts mottled light grey and brown. The underparts were light greyish, barred all over darker grey, and there was a lightish patch on the scapulars. The most striking feature of the bird was a clearly defined white wing-patch.

The bird seemed to be an immature Woodchat Shrike (*Lanius senator*) from all characters except the wing-patch, which caused great doubt as no ornithologist consulted had any experience of such a wing-patch in an immature bird of this species, nor was there any reference to it in the literature. The record was therefore submitted to

M. Georges Olivier, the French authority on the shrikes. In view of its general interest, a translation of his report is given:

'From examination of the photographs my immediate impression was that the bird was an immature *Lanius senator*. I then studied the written notes and sketches, which confirmed my impression for the following reasons:

1. *Size*: With different proportions the size of a lark and this shrike are about the same.
2. *Colour*: The colours, indicated in the notes by Mr. Holt and Mr. Todd, as well as on the sketches, correspond to those of *L. senator*, even bearing in mind that there are very wide variations of colour in the young of this species. This applies even to birds hatched from the same clutch of eggs.
   L. collurio must be ruled out, because its general colouration is quite different. The rump of the young *senator* is whitish or greyish-white (which is never the case in the young *collurio*). The scapulars are always very visible in *senator*, forming a whitish or greyish-white zone much paler than the rest of the plumage. This characteristic does not occur in *collurio*. In addition the tail pattern is different, the creamy part being larger in *senator* than in *collurio*.
   L. minor in immature plumage has a yellowish colour, and sometimes sandy yellow. It never has the white patch on the scapulars.
   L. excubitor can be eliminated, because of its larger size and its lack of the white patch on the scapulars.
3. *Vermiculations*: In the young *senator* these are dark, and very close, giving to the young birds an added characteristically closely mottled appearance. In *minor* these marks are more widely spaced.
4. *Wing-bar*: I believe that the chief confusion has arisen because the bird observed by Mr. Holt had an abnormally accentuated wing patch. In young *senator* observed in September I have already noticed wide differences in the 'importance' of the wing-bar (and also on the scapulars) in terms of the visibility, but I have never seen specimens in which the wing patch was quite as strongly marked as on the Leicester bird. I should add that I have never seen young *senator* after September in France, Spain or North Africa, though I have seen them in June. It is possible that the Leicester bird had already begun to moult when observed. . .'

It is the first Woodchat Shrike recorded for Leicestershire.

R. A. O. HICKLING

NOTES AND OBSERVATIONS ON THE EFFECT OF THE SEVERE WEATHER ON THE COUNTIES' WILD BIRDS

From *Leicestershire & Rutland County Report of Wild Birds for 1947*, pages 12–16.

During the very severe weather from late January to early March, 1947, considerable concern was felt regarding the counties' resident birds, and in the months following an enquiry was undertaken to collect data regarding mortality, movement and change in behaviour of birds during the severe weather, and to endeavour to assess the effect of the weather on the status of the resident species in the light of breeding data for 1947. Considerable importance was attached to the enquiry in view of the prolonged period of the frost.

A large number of interesting reports relative to mortality, movement, behaviour, changed feeding habits, depredations, etc, were sent in by many observers, and although some of these were naturally conflicting, a careful sifting of the data enabled fairly accurate conclusions to be drawn.

Mortality

Unlike those counties which have tidal waters and estuaries where birds congregate in hard weather, with a consequent high percentage of recovery of victims, Leicestershire and Rutland with purely inland conditions have few assembly places and, as a result, only a very small proportion of casualties were found. Therefore, to arrive at a true estimate of the losses suffered by any particular species during the period, more reliance had to be placed on the consequent breeding status for 1947 than on the actual recovery of dead birds.

However, with regard to certain species, *e.g.* Bullfinch, it was necessary to make allowance for the fact that they were already in decline owing to factors in operation prior to the period under review, and also that mortality of a particular species might vary in different parts of the counties owing to difference in habitat. The following are the species that suffered most, apparently owing to inability to adapt themselves to changed conditions:

Sky Lark. Very marked decrease everywhere.

Thrushes. Very substantial decrease in number of breeding pairs of both Mistle and Song Thrush. In some areas particularly, the numbers of Song Thrush were badly depleted. Indicative of the decrease in Mistle Thrushes is the interesting evidence that the Rowans, which this species usually clear of berries by mid-August, were still carrying full crops at the end of October.

Wren. Serious decrease over practically the whole of the counties.

Kingfisher. Practically wiped out; from the end of the frost until September, only reported five times from four localities.

Green Woodpecker. Very serious decrease. With the exception of Charnwood Forest and certain other small areas, the species has suffered extremely severely. It was completely wiped out over huge areas of the County where previously common, and it was not until the late summer that odd birds began to re-populate these areas.

Owls. Considerable decrease in both Little and Tawny Owls, and a disastrous decrease in Barn Owls.

Coot. Very serious decrease; winter residents were almost entirely wiped out – a typical example being Cropston Reservoir where, on 20th February, 24 dead birds were found and the number of live birds had decreased by 50 on previous counts. By February 27th only one live bird was left, and that too weak to fly, and many more dead birds were seen.

Considerable importance must be attached to the status of these species during 1948 and their occurrence carefully recorded in order that their recovery rate may be assessed.

With regard to mortality among species as a whole, the general inference was that two broad conclusions could be drawn:

(1) Mortality in the Soar Valley was not so heavy as on the higher ground, except in the case of certain ground-nesting birds.
(2) That on the higher ground the birds fared best on Charnwood Forest, where numerous woods with heavy undergrowth furnished food and refuge to both ground and tree-feeding birds, in contrast to the open, hilly districts such as the Wolds, where many species suffered heavily and were practically wiped out.

Movement

Movement during winter being so closely related to feeding, there was, as could be expected, a wholesale migration by several species when they could no longer obtain food. Certain well-defined movements were as follows:

Starling. On February 16th (third week of frost) a large migratory movement was noted at Kegworth – flock after flock flying over, flying south by east.

Thrushes. Whilst a few Mistle Thrushes stayed on, Fieldfares, Song Thrushes and Redwings almost completely disappeared quite early in the frost. The latest date that Fieldfares or Redwings were seen in any number until after the cold spell was January 18th.

Ducks and grebes. The vast majority of these birds left the counties soon after the larger sheets of water became frozen, whilst a small proportion resorted to weir pools and open reaches of the Soar. At Abbey Park, in the City of Leicester, the unfrozen river basin became a refuge for many uncommon species. In addition to the usual Little Grebe, Mallard, Tufted Duck and Great Crested Grebe, Slavonian Grebe, Smew, Pochard and Scaup were all observed during the period.

Behaviour, changed feeding habits and depredations

Crows. The most important change in the feeding habits of the Carrion Crow, Rook and Jackdaw was that they turned their attentions from the fields to the stacks and stackyards. It is certain that much serious damage was done to stacks, and there are authentic cases of stacks being literally torn to pieces and the straw being carried and scattered for hundreds of yards around. Once attacked, it was extremely difficult to keep the birds from a stack, and nothing but complete enclosure by wire-netting was effective. The fact that only a very small proportion of stacks were so attacked raises the question as to whether the stacks had already been broken into by livestock or other agency.

Even more serious were reports in the press of attacks on sheep and cattle – "cattle had to be moved under cover as they were attacked by hungry Magpies which tore flesh from their backs" being a typical example. Great difficulty was experienced in following up these reports as weather conditions prevented immediate investigations, and so it was impossible to obtain "first-hand" evidence. There is, however, good reason to believe that there were examples of this type of attack, but there is equally good reason to believe that this only occurred when the beast was already wounded or suffering from sores. Many reports were received relative to Carrion Crow which, during the snows, lived mainly on dead and ailing birds: Coot, Partridge, Slavonian Grebe and Tawny Owl are all recorded as having been fed upon, the three former species having all been attacked whilst still alive. At Quorn a pair of Magpies came daily to be fed at a kitchen door.

Finches. Generally speaking, when the ground became snow-covered the Finch flocks forsook the stubbles and similar feeding areas for the stacks and stack-bottoms, where they maintained themselves for the duration of the frost.

Buntings. Yellow Buntings, Reed Buntings and the very uncommon Corn Bunting joined the Finches around the chaff heaps and stacks.

Sparrow. The House Sparrow presents a peculiar problem: large flocks, normally haunting fowl-runs in well built-up areas, left, although the food supply was available as usual. The unusual size of the flocks at stackyards would suggest that the "domestic" flocks moved out to these localities, but no theory is advanced for the move. Tree Sparrows joined the Finch flocks in large numbers.

Tits. As can be expected, these came more readily to bird tables. The only other information worth noting is that they, too, were found in far greater numbers than usual around the stacks, Great Tit, Blue Tit, Marsh Tit and Willow Tit all being observed.

Thrushes. Quite early in the frost, Fieldfares and Redwings were driven to foraging in both village and town gardens, but later disappeared.

Robin. In a garden at Quorn where two Robins were holding well-defined territories, the territorial instinct was not evident during the frost.

Owls. Hunger forced both Barn and Tawny Owls to regularly hunt in broad daylight and to ignore human beings. An Owl (probably Tawny) took a Starling in day-time; when disturbed, the Starling escaped under a nearby hedge, but the Owl refused to be driven off and, waiting on a nearby fence, eventually returned and took the bird. Barn Owls became exceptionally tame, and one bird took dead sparrows from the hand.

Hawks. Sparrowhawks naturally followed their food supply, and several instances were recorded of them being regularly attendant at bird tables and stackyards.

Ducks and grebe. Those diving Duck and Grebe that remained were forced to seek food in open water usually not frequented owing to the close proximity of houses. As an example, Abbey Park weir pool, situated in the City of Leicester itself, was frequented by Tufted Duck (max. 70), Pochard (max. 30), Scaup (max. 4), Smew (1), Great Crested Grebe (1), Slavonian Grebe (1), Little Grebe (5+). Seven Goldeneye were reported on the Soar at Kegworth – a very unusual occurrence.

Pigeons. Throughout the frost enormous flocks of Wood Pigeons ravaged all "green" crops on fields, allotments and gardens. Even within the City boundary, flocks of up to 100 were feeding on brussels sprouts, standing on top of the plants and tearing off the top leaves.

Gulls. Black-headed Gulls in large numbers foraged regularly in the City gardens and at refuse tips. At the latter they developed "Skua" tactics against Starlings, forcing the latter to drop their food, which was then picked up from the ground – at no time was the food secured in mid-air. One Gull (?species) was seen to dive upon a House Sparrow in mid-air, carrying it away in its beak. The large flocks of Common Gulls usually present in the Soar Valley in January and February were forced to leave, whilst Herring and Great Black-backed Gulls were reported more frequently than normally – flocks of up to 20 of the former being reported from the Soar Valley, and numbers fed at the Abbey Meadows destructor, where pig-food is sorted.

Moorhen and Coot. During the period, the Moorhen suffered less than the Coot, as the species moved out to every little stream and drain, whereas the Coot remained at the reservoirs and larger sheets of water. Moorhen were present in large numbers at all weir pools on canals and rivers and at every point where open water was to be found. Even under these circumstances, the food supply was meagre, and seven birds regularly feeding on a small watercress bed were all unable to fly by February 2nd.

Unusual visitors

During the cold spell, the following species were reported in the counties, but with the exception of the Bittern, it must be borne in mind that these species are occasionally seen in normal winters:

Waxwing. Several during February and March.

Bittern. One was present at Swithland Reservoir during February and was subsequently picked up dead.

Bewick's Swan. Were reported in far larger numbers than usual – nine at Groby Pool, January 5th; 25, Swithland Reservoir, January 8th; seven, Swithland Reservoir, March 8th; eight, Cropston Reservoir, April 4th.

White-fronted Goose. A flock of 20 was present on the City Sewage Farms on February 16th.

Scaup. Up to four were regularly present on the Abbey Park river basin (Leicester) from February 6th to March 12th. Reports were also received from Kegworth (River Soar) and Cropston Reservoir.

Smew. One bird was present at Abbey Park basin from February 1st to February 16th; four were present at Cropston Reservoir on February 14th.

Red-necked Grebe. A decomposed bird was picked up in a field at Ashby-de-la-Zouch on April 14th, which probably died during the frost.

Slavonian Grebe. Reports of single birds came from Abbey Park basin, February 2nd until 12th; Cropston Reservoir, February 13th; Glen Parva, February 12th; and Kegworth (River Soar) on February 21st, this bird being found dead on February 25th.

Red-throated Diver. One bird was seen on the River Soar at Kegworth on February 19th.

General conclusions

Mention was made earlier in this report of the difficulty of assessing much of the evidence available, but the general conclusion is that many of the pessimistic forecasts of the early months were proved unfounded, for although there was heavy mortality in some species, the effect on the vast majority was not so disastrous as at first feared, and the end of the 1947 breeding season saw many of these species well on the way to recovery.

ANON

A SUMMARY OF OBSERVATIONS ON THE EFFECTS OF THE SEVERE WEATHER OF THE 1962–63 WINTER ON BIRDLIFE IN LEICESTERSHIRE AND RUTLAND

From *The Birds of Leicestershire & Rutland 1963*, pages 3–7.

The Weather

Although December 1962 started with a week of sharp frost, it was not until the 22nd of the month that the exceptionally long period of severe weather really began. Snow fell on the 27th and 28th, when blizzards ranged across the country; however, Leicestershire missed the worst extreme of the snowstorms and blizzards experienced in many parts of the country, and except for some of the higher, more exposed localities, where drifting occurred, the depth of snow cover only amounted to a few inches throughout the period. Whatever was missed with regards to snow amounts was amply made up for in low temperatures and few parts of the country can have had more severe weather as far as frosts were concerned, and on several occasions the temperatures dropped to within the odd degree or so of zero Fahrenheit. The frosts continued, with varying intensity, apart from brief respites of thaw, until early in March, a period of some ten weeks, and constituted the coldest winter recorded in central and southern England since 1740.

Movement

On the whole, little movement directly attributable to the weather was noted and large numbers of many species obviously left the counties without being observed.

Soon after the onset of the bad weather, at the end of December, large numbers of Lapwing were observed passing over, mostly heading in a westerly direction, and during January and February only very small numbers of this species remained in the counties and some of these were found in a very poor condition. During January flocks of up to 30 grey-geese were noticed moving over several localities heading east and south-east. On the 4th January a single White-fronted Goose was noted feeding in a field at Wistow Park, and on the following day a flock of 28 landed in a field at Gaulby and stayed there until the 7th; they fed on rye grass which protruded through the snow. On the night of the 5th, at about midnight, a large flock of geese was heard passing over Quorn, and on the 6th a single White-front was seen at Aylestone. These geese were probably part of a large movement into the southern counties which took place about this time. A large herd of 45 wild swans, thought to be Bewick's, was observed over Spinney Hill Park, Leicester, on the 6th January, and on the same date 20 Bewick's were observed at Eyebrook Reservoir. Early in January a large south-westerly movement of Redwings was noted in various parts of the country and in connection with this it is worth including details of two ringed in Nuneaton: one ringed on the 3rd January was recovered 11 days later at Hayle in Cornwall and another, ringed on the 4th January, was reported three days later on board a ship in mid-Atlantic en route between Greenland and Spain, one of the most dramatic examples of cold weather movement ever recorded.

No other movement, except that involving presumably local populations, such as the now familiar resident winter roosting gulls, was reported until the first few days in March when a return movement, west to east, and south to north, of Lapwing and Golden Plover took place.

Food and Feeding Habits

By early January practically all but the fastest moving stretches of water in the counties were ice-bound, thereby severely limiting and restricting the amount of suitable feeding area for many water-frequenting species. As in the severe winter of 1947 an unusual variety and number of waterfowl were attracted to the open water around the weir at the river basin in the Abbey Park, Leicester, during January and February, including quite a variety of grebes and ducks; similarly, waterfowl also congregated at other localities along the Soar where the river remained free of ice. On the northern edge of Leicestershire, between King's Mills, Castle Donington, and Sawley, the River Trent attracted particularly large numbers of waterfowl, including several rare species. At the local reservoirs a drastic reduction took place in the duck populations during January and February, although small numbers of Mallard and Teal remained during daylight hours resting on ice. Wigeon were noted in several localities grazing in fields well away from their usual feeding places. Moorhens and Coots were driven from most of their usual aquatic haunts and there were several reports of Moorhens frequenting gardens in various places and feeding on household scraps. At Quorn three paid regular visits to one house, entering the porch for food scraps. Both species were particularly numerous along the banks of the Trent in the north of Leicestershire.

During the first half of January large flocks of Redwing and smaller numbers of Fieldfares visited gardens in villages and towns and fed on berries of various decorative shrubs such as Pyracantha spp., Cotoneaster spp. and holly. The last berries to be eaten were from shrubs growing up against house walls but, by about the middle of the month, even these had been consumed and about this time passerine species generally became noticeably scarce in the two counties away from built up areas and a few favoured places like sewage farms, refuse pits and stack yards; indeed, large areas of countryside appeared almost devoid of any small species and it can only be assumed that large numbers had vacated our countryside to hunt for sustenance further afield.

During the latter part of January and throughout February, flocks of Wood Pigeons made widespread raids on Brassica crops in gardens, allotments and fields, and even the presence of men with guns was not sufficient to deter the starving birds, huge numbers of which were shot. They also lost all their usual caution and came close up to houses to feed on anything that was going.

As in previous bad winters both Tawny and Little Owls were observed hunting during daylight hours and there were two reports of Tawny's feeding on sparrows.

Nuthatch seem to be increasingly emulating titmice in adapting themselves to a wide range of man-provided food and during January and February several were noted feeding on bread scraps as well as other things. Amongst the more unusual garden visitors were Skylarks, flocks of which were observed in gardens in various localities; lone Meadow Pipits visited a number of gardens, in both Leicester and various villages during January and February, and fed on bread crumbs, potted meat, 'Swoop', etc, and odd Pied Wagtails were also noted feeding likewise. Large numbers of Greenfinch were reported visiting bird tables in many districts throughout the cold period and during ringing activities at a finch roost at Groby one member discovered that the weight of the Greenfinch was higher during the cold spell than in the period immediately before it – presumably indicative of a change in diet. Goldfinch were welcome visitors to several gardens where they had not been previously seen and Bramblings were seen feeding in gardens at Fenny Drayton, Quorn, Oadby and Leicester during January. Two species noted more frequently in urban gardens than usual were Reed Bunting and Yellow Bunting.

Mortality

Compared with coastal counties the number of birds actually found dead or dying in Leicestershire and Rutland were small. The main reasons for this were presumably that a large proportion of our local bird populations were forced to leave to find food, plus the fact that inland counties, lacking as they do tidal waters and estuaries, do not, as a rule, get such large concentrations of birds feeding in a given area; also, of course, bird carcasses, where undergrowth is present, as in woods and hedgerows, are more unlikely to be found. It must also be remembered that where remains are dotted around here and there during periods of food shortage, most are undoubtedly quickly eaten by any one of a number of carnivorous mammals or birds, and apart from a few feathers, which in any case are soon dispersed, would leave no recognisable remains.

Of the 30 or so species found dead in the two counties the Redwing was easily the most numerous and it was significant that in the case of some of the species most badly affected, e.g., Wren, not a single dead specimen was reported. The corpses of over 20 species were handed in to the Leicester Museum during the cold spell and I.M. Evans (the Keeper of Biology) remarked of these that all lacked obvious cause of death other than low body weight. In many cases the body weights were only approximately half that of birds of the same species brought in to the Museum at roughly the same time of year in previous years.

Few cases of icing were reported, presumably because freezing fog was not a feature of the cold spell hereabouts and few deaths reported were directly attributable to this cause. Dead waterfowl were however found frozen in to the ice of certain reservoirs and rivers but only in small numbers and by no means as many as in the winter of 1947. A few garden birds were noted with small accretions of ice on their legs, and on the 20th January Wood Pigeons arriving to roost in a plantation at Quorn were noted to have large nodules of ice attached to their legs.

Species Most Affected

In some ways it is an advantage to write this article in retrospect, for whereas some of the more vulnerable species remain sedentary even when it costs them their lives, others are sufficiently adaptable to desert their normal terrain to go in search of more favourable quarters. Consequently certain species which appeared to be particularly hard hit, judging by their numbers during and immediately after the cold spell, eventually turned out to be more common than was at first thought when the wanderers returned.

Up to six Little Grebes were seen at the Abbey Park Weir during January and February when numbers were also seen on the River Trent. This species was more adversely affected than the Great Crested Grebe and even now (1965) numbers still seem less than normal; only odd pairs were located during the 1963 breeding season. Although only one or two dead Herons were found during the cold period, the species suffered a severe reduction in numbers and their slow recovery since gives cause for concern. Both Moorhen and Coot suffered heavy losses and quite a number of the former and a few of the latter were found dead and dying; however, far fewer

Coot appeared to have succumbed than during the 1947 winter when very large numbers were found frozen into the ice on local reservoirs. Such Lapwing as remained in the county undoubtedly suffered greatly and it is fortunate for this species that the majority are quick to leave for more favourable quarters when the ground becomes ice-bound and feeding becomes difficult.

Sewage farms play an important role these days in helping certain species to survive in prolonged frosty weather and large numbers of Common Snipe were present at some of our local farms throughout January and February when this species was also present in appreciable numbers on the side of the River Trent near Castle Donington; any species with the feeding habits of the Snipe inevitably suffers in periods of such intense cold and several Snipe were found dead in the Leicester area; many others must have perished.

As already stated, large numbers of Wood Pigeons were shot whilst many others perished to starvation. However, such set-backs are unlikely to prove other than temporary in abundant species blessed with ample breeding habitats like this species. The related Stock Dove, already suffering locally from the felling, during recent decades, of many of its old nesting trees must inevitably find recovery more difficult and although only odd dead birds were reported, the scarcity of this species during the following summer was only too apparent.

Locally Little Owls did not seem to recover fully from the 1947 winter and since the end of this last big freeze-up few have been reported, and its distinctive call is now seldom heard in many districts where it was formerly common. Of all resident species none was more decimated by the arctic weather than the Kingfisher and even now, after three breeding-seasons, the species has failed to return to most of its former haunts; only odd birds have in fact been reported throughout the two counties. Unlike our two native Spotted Woodpeckers the Green Woodpecker is much depleted during prolonged frost and although only one dead bird was reported the species suffered badly this time and its characteristic laughing call was seldom heard during the 1963 breeding season. No doubt the Green Woodpecker suffers on account of its ground feeding habits and it is rather surprising how this species manages to maintain itself so far north on the Continent.

The Long-tailed Tit is a well known victim of severe winters and it was feared that the severity of this winter would completely wipe out this vulnerable little bird; fortunately this proved not to be so, for a small but adequate number survived and numbers are now apparently back to normal. Few of us ever thought that we should find the ubiquitous little Wren so scarce as it was at the termination of this cold spell, for in many localities the species was practically non-existent; in other areas it fared better though, and a few pairs were present and bred the following spring. By the summer of 1964 the species was not obviously less common than normal and the rate of recovery was quicker than many of us would have believed possible. Redwing, and to a lesser extent Fieldfare, suffered greatly and starving birds allowed themselves to be approached to within a few feet. With the disappearance of the last berries, early in January, the majority of those surviving that were strong enough left the two counties, though how many had the strength to reach the safety of distant lands to the south is anybody's guess. As could be expected, both Pied and Grey Wagtails suffered a marked decrease and very few pairs of the former and none of the latter were recorded during the 1963 breeding season. Numbers of breeding Pied Wagtails appeared to be almost back to normal by the spring of 1965, but no breeding Grey Wagtails have been reported as yet, although the species' wintering population now, at last, seems almost back to normal.

Unusual visitors

Most of the species mentioned below probably occurred where they did as a result of the severity of the weather.

A Red-necked Grebe was present throughout January at the Abbey Park river basin at Leicester. A Slavonian Grebe was also seen there and on the River Trent near Castle Donington during January and February. A Bittern was seen in the vicinity of Red Hill Lock near Kegworth in February. Up to four Scaup (three females and one male) were recorded on the River Trent near King's Mills during January and February and a little further to the west, just inside Derbyshire, large numbers of waterfowl including uncommon species such as Velvet Scoter, Red-breasted Merganser and Smew were recorded. Two Smew were also seen on the River Soar at the Abbey Park, Leicester, and single birds on the Soar at Wanlip and Belgrave, and on a small area of open water on a canal at Theddingworth during January and February. Six Smew (four males and two females) were also present at Eyebrook Reservoir on 9th January and one pair at Swithland Reservoir on 5th January. A Water Rail was seen in a very weak state at the Leicester City Sewage Farms on the 19th January, and three were seen together in an open area of a marsh on the side of the River Trent near King's Mills on 10th February. Amongst the waders frequenting the banks of the River Trent near King's Mills in January and February were odd Golden Plover, Curlew and Jack Snipe, up to 20 Redshank and one Knot. A Raven flew over Thurcaston towards Beacon Hill on 6th January and a Hooded Crow was seen the previous week at Kibworth rubbish tip. A Great Grey Shrike was seen near the Laughton-Theddingworth field road on 6th January.

Conclusions

Like most other wild creatures, birds show a marvellous resilience to these infrequent periods of abnormal weather – as they do indeed to most other types of natural phenomena – for, of course, the fact of a species presence here today is proof of its success in surviving all manner of extreme conditions in the past.

Nowadays, however, man is responsible directly or indirectly, for playing an ever increasing part in the natural scheme of things and whilst in some respects this would appear to be beneficial as, for instance, when he feeds birds when natural food is in short supply or when he builds sewage farms where certain species can find food even in the worst weather; yet conversely by his wholesale destruction of habitats, his use of insecticides and pesticides, or his pollution of rivers and streams he may well bring about a decline or even cause the extinction of certain susceptible species. In comparing the effects of this winter with the effects of similar past winters it is possible to detect a difference in the degree of change affecting certain species. For example, during the winter in question many species of garden frequenting birds undoubtedly owed their survival to the liberal quantities of food (and water) that were daily supplied by people both locally and throughout Britain and we have only to compare the large quantity of such food now available with the much smaller amounts of foods available in less prosperous times to realise the extent to which a variety of species must now benefit. In this connection it is obviously a great advantage for a species to have a varied diet and particularly disadvantageous for a species to be solely insectivorous and low feeding. As regards the adverse side of man's actions, the increasing pollution of rivers and streams is doubtless connected with the extremely slow recovery rates of the Kingfisher and Heron compared with the way they recovered from the 1947 winter, and these two species provide a good example of how the status of susceptible species may be jeopardised when an additional hazard has to be met and the scales further tilted.

P. H. GAMBLE

THE ASHBY-DE-LA-ZOUCH YELLOW-BROWED WARBLER

From *The Leicestershire & Rutland Bird Report 1999*, pages 102–103.

Leicestershire's second Yellow-browed Warbler was present on a housing estate in Ashby-de-la-Zouch from January 9th to March 5th 1988. The bird caused quite a stir at the time, being one of the first instances of wintering of this species in Britain, and was seen by many observers during its eight week stay. Several people commented on its overall drab plumage and the subspecies *humei* was mentioned more than once.

Following recent taxonomic developments, Hume's Yellow-browed Warbler *Phylloscopus humei* has now been granted full species status from Yellow-browed Warbler *Phylloscopus inornatus* by the British Ornithologists' Union Records Committee, and interest was rekindled in the Ashby bird. It was therefore considered an opportune moment to reassess the identification of this individual, especially in the light of greater understanding of this species' characteristics.

The Ashby bird, as to be expected in late winter, was very worn, with generally dull greyish upperparts and off-white underparts. The greater covert wingbar was obvious, but the median covert wingbar was virtually absent. It was these features which turned several observers' thoughts to *humei*, but examination of photographs and a video recording of the bird ('Rare Birds in Britain 1987/88' by Alan Shaw) revealed several pro *inornatus* features. The lower mandible was, in the main, pinkish, with darkish colouring restricted to the tip, whilst the supercilia were broad and distinct in front of the eye, meeting above the bill, and wide behind the eye. The ear coverts were dark and mottled. Crucially, the supercilia and greater covert wingbar showed yellowish tones. This combination of features point toward *inornatus*, especially as general plumage tones and lack of median covert wingbar become far less useful features on worn late winter birds. Unfortunately, the bird remained silent for much of the time, although the only first-hand description of the call sounded more like *humei*. However, it is known that several other observers heard calls compatible with *inornatus*. The bird was also trapped, although the measurements taken proved inconclusive in establishing the form involved.

The BBRC has accepted this bird as a Hume's Yellow-browed Warbler, but has been asked to reconsider this decision. As the majority of available evidence points against the identification as *humei*, the LROS Records Committee does not feel that this species can be added to the County List, and it seems safest to treat this bird as either *inornatus* or indeterminate.

R. M. FRAY & A. H. J. HARROP

APPENDIX 10: NOTABLE RECORDS IN 2006, 2007 AND 2008

Records detailed in this Appendix are mainly of two types. Firstly, any additional records of species recorded fewer than ten times up to the end of 2005 are given; secondly, any other records that have a significant bearing on what is written in the main species texts are included. All relevant records for 2006 and 2007 are included. Coverage of 2008 extends to October but excludes any records awaiting acceptance by the relevant Records Committee at that time.

Mute Swan Highest ever count: 588 at Rutland Water on July 18th 2006.

Whooper Swan Largest ever flock away from Rutland Water: 29 at Eyebrook Reservoir on January 26th 2006.

Bean Goose Fourth record: two of the Tundra form *A .f. rossicus* at Rutland Water on November 12th 2008.

European White-fronted Goose Second largest flock ever: 50 at Eyebrook Reservoir on February 4th 2006.

Greylag Goose Highest ever counts: 490 at Rutland Water on June 27th 2006, 535 at Swithland Reservoir on November 16th 2006 and 710 at the latter site on November 22nd 2008.

Egyptian Goose Highest ever count: 98 at Rutland Water on August 19th 2008.

Mandarin Duck Highest ever counts: 43 at Blackbrook Reservoir on September 27th 2006 and 44 at the same site on October 17th 2007.

Green-winged Teal Fifth to eighth records: a male at Eyebrook Reservoir from March 11th to May 4th 2006 and assumed to be the same bird returning March 3rd to April 26th 2007 and February 26th to May 3rd 2008; a second male at the same site from March 24th to April 5th 2008.

Tufted Duck Highest ever count: 9,758 at Rutland Water on September 17th 2006.

Lesser Scaup Fourth to eighth records: adult male at Swithland Reservoir from April 9th to May 4th 2006; adult male at Rutland Water on April 11th 2006; first-summer male at Eyebrook Reservoir from April 24th to May 3rd 2007; adult male at Rutland Water September 16th to 22nd 2007; first-summer male at Swithland Reservoir from March 23rd to 28th 2008.

Goldeneye Highest ever count: 521 at Rutland Water on January 15th 2006.

Great Northern Diver Record numbers in 2006, with 12 individuals found: single birds at Eyebrook Reservoir from March 17th to May 8th and on December 4th, Rutland Water from October 5th to 15th and Cropston Reservoir on December 7th, up to two at Trent Valley Pit from November 26th to March 3rd 2007 and up to six at Rutland Water from November 29th into 2007, when seven were present from February 3rd to March 13th 2007 and the last two on April 29th 2007.

Little Grebe Highest ever count: 116 at Rutland Water on September 14th 2008.

Slavonian Grebe First breeding records for England: in 2006 one paired with a Great Crested Grebe at an undisclosed site in west Leicestershire and hatched two chicks from a clutch of four eggs, but both chicks were predated within a few days (Toon 2007). Further unsuccessful attempts followed at the same site in both 2007 and 2008.

Little Egret Highest ever annual totals: at least 36 individuals recorded during 2006, at least 50 in 2007 and at least 60 by October 2008 including the largest ever flock, 22 roosting at Rutland Water on August 21st 2008.

Great White Egret Ninth to 15th records: Groby Pool on March 24th 2006; Albert Village Lake on July 24th 2006; Exton Park and Rutland Water from October 13th to 17th 2007; in the Cossington Meadows/Wanlip North Lakes area between December 30th 2007 and January 6th 2008; Eyebrook Reservoir on January 6th 2008; Watermead Country Park Birstall on March 13th 2008; Sheepy Parva on April 9th 2008.

Purple Heron Fifth record, and first for Rutland: one at Rutland Water on May 17th and 18th 2008.

Spoonbill Best ever year in 2006: single birds at Rutland Water on March 29th, May 2nd and June 18th and Eyebrook Reservoir on May 4th, and two at Rutland Water on August 8th.

Marsh Harrier Earliest and latest ever records: one at Trent Valley Pit on January 17th 2007 and one at Billesdon on November 10th 2006.

Common Crane Fifth to ninth records: one at Rutland Water on March 25th 2007; one at Rutland Water on May 25th 2007; one near Twycross on June 2nd 2007; two at Woolfox on April 19th 2008; two at Owston on June 29th 2008.

Avocet Record year in 2006: 23 individuals including the second largest flock ever, 19 at Rutland Water on June 10th.

Sanderling Largest ever flock: 16 at Eyebrook Reservoir on May 14th 2007.

Pectoral Sandpiper Latest ever arrival: juvenile at Rutland Water on October 7th 2006.

Stilt Sandpiper ***Calidris himantopus*** First record: adult at Rutland Water on May 27th 2008.

Purple Sandpiper Tenth record: one at Rutland Water on August 22nd 2007.

Black-tailed Godwit Largest ever winter flock: 48 at Rutland Water on November 28th 2006.

Bar-tailed Godwit Large spring numbers in 2007: 43 individuals including largest ever spring flock, 30 over Bushby on April 28th.

Marsh Sandpiper *Tringa stagnatilis* First record: adult at Rutland Water on May 27th 2008.

Long-tailed Skua Third record: juvenile at Rutland Water on August 14th 2006.

Sabine's Gull Fifth and sixth records: adult at Rutland Water on August 21st 2007 and at least three juveniles there between September 27th and 29th 2007.

Ring-billed Gull Fifth record: second-summer at Rutland Water from April 2nd to 12th 2006.

Whiskered Tern Second record: adult at Eyebrook Reservoir on June 18th 2007.

Barn Owl Accurate assessment of population: 53 confirmed breeding pairs in 2007.

Richard's Pipit Second record: one at Bardon Hill on October 16th 2006.

Ring Ouzel Record years: at least 17 individuals in 2006 and 37 in 2007.

Cetti's Warbler First breeding record: at an undisclosed site in 2007.

Icterine Warbler *Hippolais icterina* First record: one trapped and ringed at Stanford Reservoir on June 14th 2008.

Yellow-browed Warbler Fifth and sixth records: single birds at Fosse Meadows on October 10th 2007 and Whetstone on October 14th 2007.

Bonelli's Warbler sp. *Phylloscopus bonelli/orientalis* First record: singing male at Hambleton Wood on May 2nd 2006.

Raven Increase in breeding population: two pairs in 2006, four pairs in 2007, five pairs in 2008.

Rose-coloured Starling Third modern record: a juvenile at Countesthorpe from August to December 2007.

Twite First record since 1996: one at Rutland Water on November 26th and 27th 2006.

Common Redpoll Small influx in early 2006: 33 birds at nine sites.

Arctic Redpoll Sixth or seventh individual: one of the race *exilipes* at Sence Valley Forest Park from January 21st to 23rd 2006.

BIBLIOGRAPHY

Allport, A.M. & Carroll, D. 1989. Little Bitterns breeding in South Yorkshire. *Brit. Birds* 82: 442–446.

Allsopp, K. 1972. Squacco Heron – Eyebrook Reservoir. *Leicestershire & Rutland Bird Report 1971*: 24.

Anderson, G. 2002. Tree Sparrows at Rutland Water – History and Current Research. *The Leicestershire and Rutland Bird Report 2000*: 104–106.

Appleton, T.P. 1978a. *The Birds of Rutland Water*. Leicestershire & Rutland Trust for Nature Conservation, Leicester.

Appleton, T.P. 1978b. *The Birds of Rutland Water 1977–78*. Leicestershire & Rutland Trust for Nature Conservation, Leicester.

Appleton, T.P. 1984. *The Birds of Rutland Water 1983*. Leicestershire & Rutland Trust for Nature Conservation, Leicester.

Appleton, T.P. 1985. *The Birds of Rutland Water 1984*. Leicestershire & Rutland Trust for Nature Conservation, Leicester.

Appleton, T.P. 1986. *The Birds of Rutland Water 1985*. Leicestershire & Rutland Trust for Nature Conservation, Leicester.

Appleton, T.P. 1987a. *The Birds of Rutland Water 1986*. Leicestershire & Rutland Trust for Nature Conservation, Leicester.

Appleton, T.P. 1987b. *The Birds of Rutland Water 1987*. Leicestershire & Rutland Trust for Nature Conservation, Leicester.

Appleton, T.P. 1990. *The Birds of Rutland Water 1988 & 1989*. Leicestershire & Rutland Trust for Nature Conservation, Leicester.

Appleton, T.P. 1991. *The Birds of Rutland Water 1990*. Leicestershire & Rutland Trust for Nature Conservation, Leicester.

Appleton, T.P., Debney, C., Harrop, A.H.J. & Mitcham, T. 1996. *The Birds of Rutland Water 1991–1995*. Leicestershire & Rutland Trust for Nature Conservation, Leicester.

Baillie, S.R., Marchant, J.H., Crick, H.Q.P., Noble, D.G., Balmer, D.E., Coombes, R.H., Downie, I.S., Freeman, S.N., Joys, A.C., Leech, D.I., Raven, M.J., Robinson, R.A. and Thewlis, R.M. 2006. *Breeding Birds in the wider countryside: their conservation status 2005*. BTO Research Report No. 435. BTO, Thetford.

Baillie, S.R., Marchant, J.H., Leech, D.I., Joys, A.C., Noble, D.G., Barimore, C., Grantham, M.J., Risely, K. & Robinson, R.A. (2009). *Breeding Birds in the Wider Countryside: their conservation status 2008*. BTO Research Report No. 516. BTO, Thetford.

Bak, F.A. 1948a. Breeding of Garganey in Leicestershire or Rutland. *Brit. Birds* 41: 154.

Bak, F.A. 1948b. Red-breasted Flycatcher in Leicestershire. *Brit. Birds* 41: 183–184.

Baker, H., Stroud, D.A., Aebischer, J., Cranswick, P.A., Gregory, R.D., McSorley, C.A., Noble, D.G. & Rehfisch, M.M. 2006. Population estimates of birds in Great Britain and the United Kingdom. *Brit. Birds* 99: 25–44.

Batten, L.A. 2001. European Honey-buzzard survey 2000 and 2001: preliminary results and request for further surveys. *Brit. Birds* 94: 143–144.

Bednall, D. (ed) 2006. *Norfolk Ornithologists' Association Annual Report 2005*. Norfolk Ornithologists' Association.

Berriman, M. 1999. Blue-winged Teal – new to the County List. *The Leicestershire & Rutland Bird Report 1998*: 102.

Berthold, P. 1995. Microevolution of migratory behaviour illustrated by the Blackcap *Sylvia atricapilla*. *Bird Study* 42: 89–100.

Bibby, C.J. 1981. Wintering Bitterns in Britain. *Brit. Birds* 74: 1–10.

Blaker, G.B. 1934. *The Barn Owl in England and Wales*. RSPB, London.

Bonner, A. 1946. The Lesser Whitethroat: some observations on its distribution in Leicestershire. *Leicestershire & Rutland County Report of Wild Birds for 1945*: 12–16.

BOURC 2001. British Ornithologists' Union Records Committee: 28th Report (October 2001). *Ibis* 144: 181–184.

Bourne, W.R.P. 2002. The nomenclature and past history in Britain of the Bean and Pink-footed Geese. *Bull. B.O.C.* 122(1): 11–14.

Bourne, W.R.P. 2003. Fred Stubbs, Egrets, Brewes and climatic change. *Brit. Birds* 96: 332–339.

Boyd, H. 1954. The "wreck" of Leach's Petrels in the autumn of 1952. *Brit. Birds* 47: 137–163.

Bradshaw, C. & Wright, J. 2002. From the Rarities Committee's files: A White-winged Black Tern in an unusually advanced state of moult. *Brit. Birds* 95: 449–453.

Bradshaw, H. 1969a. The birds of Spinney Hill Park, Leicester, 1960–1968. *The Birds of Leicestershire & Rutland 1968*: 21–22.

Bradshaw, H. 1969b. Some notes on the distribution of the Tree Pipit *Anthus trivialis* in Leicestershire. *The Birds of Leicestershire & Rutland 1968*: 28–29.

Brady, F. 1944. The breeding bird population of The Brand. *County Report of Wild Birds for 1943*: 9–12.

Brown, A. & Grice P. 2005. *Birds in England.* T. & A.D. Poyser, London.

Browne, M. 1889. *The Vertebrate Animals of Leicestershire and Rutland.* Midland Educational Company Ltd, Birmingham & Leicester.

Browne, M. 1907. 'Birds' in *The Victoria History of the County of Leicester, Volume I.* Archibald Constable & Co Ltd, London.

Butler, C. 2002. Breeding parrots in Britain. *Brit. Birds* 95: 345–348.

Chamberlain, D. & Vickery, J. 2002. Declining farmland birds: evidence from large-scale monitoring studies in the UK. *Brit. Birds* 95: 300–310.

Chamberlain, D.E., Cannon, A.R., Toms, M.P., Leech, D.I., Hatchwell, B.J. & Gaston, K.J. 2009. Avian productivity in urban landscapes: a review and meta-analysis. *Ibis* 151: 1–18.

Chandler, R.J. 1981. Influxes into Britain and Ireland of Red-necked Grebes and other water-birds during winter 1978/79. *Brit. Birds* 74: 55–81.

Chisholm, K. 2007. History of the Wood Sandpiper as a breeding bird in Britain. *Brit. Birds* 100: 112–121.

Clements, R. 2000. Range expansion of the Common Buzzard in Britain. *Brit. Birds* 93: 242–248.

Clements, R. 2001. The Hobby in Britain: a new population estimate. *Brit. Birds* 94: 402–408.

Clements, R. 2002. The Common Buzzard in Britain: a new population estimate. *Brit. Birds* 95: 377–383.

Clergeau, P., Croci, S., Jokimaki, J., Kaisanlahti-Jokimaki, M-L. & Dinetti, M. 2006. Avifauna homogenisation by urbanisation: Analysis at different European latitudes. *Biological Conservation* 127: 336–344.

Close, S. 1991. Richard's Pipit – new to the County List. *The Leicestershire & Rutland Bird Report 1990*: 55.

Collier, M.P., Banks, A.N., Austin, G.E., Girling, T., Hearn, R.D. & Musgrove, A.J. 2005. *The Wetland Bird Survey 2003/04: Wildfowl and Wader Counts.* BTO/WWT/RSPB/JNCC, Thetford.

Combridge, P. & Parr, C. 1992. Influx of Little Egrets in Britain and Ireland in 1989. *Brit. Birds* 85: 16–21.

Cowley, E. 1979. Sand Martin population trends in Britain, 1965–1978. *Bird Study* 26: 113–116.

Dagley, J.R. 1994. Golden Orioles in East Anglia and their conservation. *Brit. Birds* 87: 205–219.

Davenport, D.L. 1982. Influxes into Britain of Hen Harriers, Long-eared Owls and Short-eared Owls in winter 1978/79. *Brit. Birds* 75: 309–316.

Davenport, H.S. 1920. Cirl Bunting nesting in Leicestershire. *Brit. Birds* 14: 39.

Davies, A.K. 1988. The distribution and status of Mandarin Duck in Britain. *Bird Study* 35: 203–208.

Davis, R. 1998. Wintering Blackcaps in a Glenfield garden. *The Leicestershire & Rutland Bird Report 1997*:

96–97.

Dean, A.R. 1984. Origins and distribution of British Glaucous Gulls. *Brit. Birds* 77: 165–166.

Delany, S. 1993. Introduced and escaped geese in Britain in summer 1991. *Brit. Birds* 86: 591–599.

Dixon, D. 1996. Corn Buntings in West Leicestershire in July 1995. *The Leicestershire & Rutland Bird Report 1995*: 86–87.

Dixon, H. 1955. The Leicestershire record of a Wilson's Phalarope. *Brit. Birds* 48: 190–191.

Dixon, H. 2002. Anglian Water Osprey Project Update. *The Leicestershire and Rutland Bird Report 2001*: 104–105.

Dobinson, H.M. & Richards, A.J. 1964. The effects of the severe weather of 1962/63 on birds in Britain. *Brit. Birds* 57: 373–433.

Dudley, S.P. 2005. Changes to Category C of the British List. *Ibis* 147: 803–820.

Dymond, J.N., Fraser, P.A. & Gantlett, S.J.M. 1989. *Rare birds in Britain and Ireland.* T. & A.D. Poyser, Calton.

Felstead, G. 1953. The breeding of the Grey Wagtail in Leicestershire in 1952. *The Birds of Leicestershire & Rutland 1952*: 6.

Felstead, G. 1978. Bearded Tit movements, 1977. *The Birds of Leicestershire and Rutland 1977*: 33–34.

Felstead, G. 1980. The Abbey Park Starling Roost in 1979. *The Birds of Leicestershire and Rutland 1979*: 32.

Field, R. & Anderson, G. 2002. Rutland Water Tree Sparrow Project Update. *The Leicestershire and Rutland Bird Report 2001*: 105–107.

Forryan, A. 1994. Lesser Scaup – new to the County List. *The Leicestershire & Rutland Bird Report 1993*: 72–73.

Fowler, J.A. 1981. Estimating a Leicestershire Reed Bunting roost. *The Birds of Leicestershire and Rutland 1980*: 37–38.

Fowler, J.A. 1982. The Cropston Greenfinch roost. *The Birds of Leicestershire and Rutland 1981*: 36–38.

Fowler, J.A., Blakesley, D. & Miller, C.J. 1984. Red-throated Pipit chasing Swifts. *Brit. Birds* 77: 361–362.

Fowler, J.A. 1999. A Leicestershire Hawfinch in Norway. *The Leicestershire and Rutland Bird Report 1998*: 105.

Fox, A.D. 1988. Breeding status of the Gadwall in Britain and Ireland. *Brit. Birds* 81: 51–66.

Fraser, P.A., Lansdown, P.G. & Rogers, M.J. 1997. Report on scarce migrant birds in Britain in 1995. *Brit. Birds* 90: 413–439.

Fraser, P.A., Lansdown, P.G. & Rogers, M.J. 2000. Report on scarce migrant birds in Britain in 1998. *Brit. Birds* 93: 588–641.

Fraser, P.A. & Rogers, M.J. 2001. Report on scarce migrant birds in Britain in 1999. *Brit. Birds* 94: 560–589.

Fraser, P.A. & Rogers, M.J. 2002. Report on scarce migrant birds in Britain in 2000. *Brit. Birds* 95: 606–630.

Fraser, P.A. & Rogers, M.J. 2003. Report on scarce migrant birds in Britain in 2001. *Brit. Birds* 96: 626–649.

Fraser, P.A. & Rogers, M.J. 2004. Report on scarce migrant birds in Britain in 2002. Part 1: European Bee-eater to Little Bunting. *Brit. Birds* 97: 647–664.

Fraser, P.A. & Rogers, M.J. 2005. Report on scarce migrant birds in Britain in 2002. Part 2: American Wigeon to Ring-billed Gull. *Brit. Birds* 98: 73–88.

Fraser, P.A. & Ryan, J.F. 1992. Scarce migrants in Britain and Ireland Part 1. Numbers during 1986–90: seabirds to waders. *Brit. Birds* 85: 631–635.

Fraser, P.A. & Ryan, J.F. 1994. Scarce migrants in Britain and Ireland Part 1. Numbers during 1986–92: gulls to passerines. *Brit. Birds* 87: 605–612.

Fraser, P.A. & Ryan, J.F. 1995. Status of the Great Grey Shrike in Britain and Ireland. *Brit. Birds* 88: 478–484.

Fray, R.M. 1988. The Distribution of Nuthatches in Leicestershire and Rutland. *The Birds of Leicestershire and Rutland 1987*: 48–51.

Fray, R.M. 1994. Cattle Egret – new to the County List. *The Leicestershire & Rutland Bird Report 1993*: 72.

Fray, R.M. 1995. White-rumped Sandpiper – new to the County List. *The Leicestershire & Rutland Bird Report 1994:* 72.

Fray, R.M. 1996. Laughing Gull – new to the County List. *The Leicestershire & Rutland Bird Report 1995*: 82–83.

Fray, R.M. 1997. American Golden Plover – new to the County List. *The Leicestershire & Rutland Bird Report 1996:* 87.

Fray, R.M. 1998a. Red-flanked Bluetail – new to the County List. *The Leicestershire & Rutland Bird Report 1997*: 91.

Fray, R.M. 2004. *The birds of the Hemington Area.* Privately published.

Fray, R.M. 2005. Leicestershire and Rutland records review. *The Leicestershire & Rutland Bird Report 2003:* 128–133.

Fray, R.M. 2006. Where to watch birds in the East Midlands. Second edition. Christopher Helm, London.

Fray, R.M. (ed.) 2007a. *The Leicestershire & Rutland Bird Report 2005*. Leicestershire & Rutland Ornithological Society.

Fray, R.M. 2007b. Waxwings in Leicestershire and Rutland in 2005. *The Leicestershire & Rutland Bird Report 2005*: 139–144.

Fray, R.M., Bullock, D.J. & Fowler, J.A. 1990. Comparison of the breeding bird communities in Leicester's green spaces: a pilot study. *The Birds of Leicestershire & Rutland 1989*: 44–47.

Fray, R.M. & Harrop, A.H.J. 2000. The Ashby-de-la-Zouch Yellow-browed Warbler. *The Leicestershire & Rutland Bird Report 1999*: 102–103.

Fray, R.P. 1998b. Potential new Breeding Birds for Leicestershire and Rutland. *The Leicestershire & Rutland Bird Report 1997*: 94–95.

Fuller, R.J. & Youngman, R.E. 1979. The utilisation of farmland by Golden Plovers wintering in Southern England. *Bird Study* 26: 37–46.

Gamble, D.J.S. 1991. Mute Swan census – spring/summer 1990. *The Leicestershire & Rutland Bird Report 1990*: 56–58.

Gamble, D.J.S. 1992a. Unusual Breeding Record of Pochard at Kirby Lakes. *The Leicestershire & Rutland Bird Report 1991*: 54.

Gamble, D.J.S. 1992b. Survey of introduced geese, June-July 1991. *The Leicestershire & Rutland Bird Report 1991*: 54–57.

Gamble, D.J.S. 1994. Chiffchaffs wintering at Kirby Lakes 1993. *The Leicestershire & Rutland Bird Report 1993:* 74.

Gamble, D.J.S. 1995. Pallid Harrier – new to the County List. *The Leicestershire & Rutland Bird Report 1994*: 71.

Gamble, D.J.S. 1998. Greenish Warbler at Priory Water. *The Leicestershire & Rutland Bird Report 1997*: 93.

Gamble, I. 2001. *Birdlife of Swithland Reservoir.* Loughborough Naturalists' Club & Kairos Press, Newtown Linford, Leicester.

Gamble, I.B. 1990. Siskins Feeding in Quorn Gardens. *The Birds of Leicestershire & Rutland 1989*: 42–44.

Gamble, P.H. 1948. Ferruginous Duck in Leicestershire. *Brit. Birds* 41: 215–216.

Gamble, P.H. 1965. A summary of observations on the effects of the severe weather of the 1962–63 winter on birdlife in Leicestershire and Rutland. *The Birds of Leicestershire & Rutland 1963*: 3–7.

Gibbons, D.W., Reid, J.B. & Chapman, R.A. (eds.) 1993. *The New Atlas of Breeding Birds in Britain and Ireland: 1988–1991.* T. & A.D. Poyser, London.

Gibbons, D.W., Avery, M.I. & Brown, A.F. 1996. Population trends of breeding birds in the United Kingdom since 1800. *Brit. Birds* 89: 291–305.

Gibbs, R.G. 1967. Ringed Plover nesting in Leicestershire. *The Birds of Leicestershire and Rutland 1965*: 3.

Gilbert, G. 2002. The status and habitat of Spotted Crakes in Britain. *Bird Study* 49: 79–86.

Gill, F. & Wright, M. 2006. *Birds of the World: Recommended English Names.* Christopher Helm. London.

Gillham, E. & Gillham, B. 1996. *Hybrid Ducks.* Wallington, Surrey.

Gimson, C. 1959. A second year with Greenfinches. *The Birds of Leicestershire & Rutland 1957*: 15.

Gregory, R.D., Wilkinson, N.I., Noble, D.G., Robinson, J.A., Brown, A.F., Hughes, J., Proctor, D., Gibbons, D.W. & Galbraith, C.A. 2002. The population status of birds in the United Kingdom, Channel Islands and Isle of Man: an analysis of conservation concern 2002–2007. *Brit. Birds* 95: 410–448.

Griffiths, M.E. 1967. The population density of the Kestrel in Leicestershire. *Bird Study* 14: 184–190.

Griffiths, M.E. 1968. Preliminary report on the status of the Marsh Tit *Parus palustris* and the Willow Tit *P. atricapillus* in Leicestershire and Rutland. *The Birds of Leicestershire & Rutland 1967*: 29–30.

Grover, S. & Goodrich, K. 1997. *Leicestershire Garden Birds.* The LGB Survey, Leicester.

Hagley, N. 1992. Black Storks – new to the County List. *The Leicestershire & Rutland Bird Report 1991*: 58.

Haines, C.R. 1907. *Notes on the Birds of Rutland.* R.H. Porter, London.

Haines, C.R. 1908. 'Birds' in *The Victoria History of the County of Rutland, Volume 1.* Archibald Constable & Co Ltd, London.

Harrison G. & Harrison, J. 2005. *The new Birds of the West Midlands.* West Midlands Bird Club, Worcester.

Harrison, G.R., Dean, A.R., Richards, A.J. & Smallshire, D. 1982. *The Birds of the West Midlands.* West Midlands Bird Club, Studley.

Harrop, A.H.J. 1991. The status of Red-crested Pochard. *Birding World* 4: 171–175.

Harrop, A.H.J. 1993a. American Wigeons at Eyebrook Reservoir. *The Leicestershire & Rutland Bird Report 1992*: 60–61.

Harrop, A.H.J. 1993b. Presumed Red-crested Pochard x Northern Pintail hybrid. *Brit. Birds* 86: 130–131.

Harrop, A.H.J. 1996. Arctic Redpoll – new to the County List. *The Leicestershire & Rutland Bird Report 1995*: 83–84.

Harrop, A.H.J. 1997. Attempted breeding by Avocets at Rutland Water. *The Leicestershire & Rutland Bird Report 1996*: 88.

Harrop, A.H.J. 1998. Successful hybridisation between Ruddy Shelduck and Egyptian Goose. *Brit. Birds* 91: 281–282.

Harrop, A.H.J. 1999. The Bean Goose in Leicestershire and Rutland. *The Leicestershire & Rutland Bird Report 1998*: 103.

Harrop, A.H.J. 2000. Identification of Jackdaw forms in northwestern Europe. *Birding World* 13: 290–295.

Harrop, A.H.J. 2004. The 'North American' Peregrine Falcon in Britain. *Brit. Birds* 97: 130–133.

Harrop, A.H.J. 2006a. The Great Snipe in Leicestershire and Rutland. *The Leicestershire & Rutland Bird Report 2004*: 138–139.

Harrop, A.H.J. 2006b. Two interesting shrike specimens from Leicestershire. *The Leicestershire & Rutland*

Bird Report 2004: 139–140.

Harrop, A.H.J. 2008. A note on the Green Pheasant *Phasianus versicolor* in Leicestershire and elsewhere in the UK. *The Leicestershire & Rutland Bird Report 2006*: 118–119.

Harrop, A.H.J. & Collinson, M. 2003. The 1864 Wiltshire 'Steppe Buzzard'. *Brit. Birds 96*: 247–249.

Harrop, A.H.J. & Wright, J. 1998. Long-tailed Skua – new to the County List. *The Leicestershire & Rutland Bird Report 1997:* 90.

Hickling, R.A.O. 1952. Woodchat Shrike in Leicestershire. *Brit. Birds* 45: 410–411.

Hickling, R.A.O. 1954. Starling roosts in Leicestershire: winter, 1953/4. *The Birds of Leicestershire & Rutland 1953*: 10–12.

Hickling, R.A.O. 1955. Little Ringed Plovers breeding in Leicestershire. *Brit. Birds* 48: 543.

Hickling, R.A.O. 1976. Gulls in Leicestershire. *The Birds of Leicestershire & Rutland 1974*: 26–28.

Hickling, R.A.O. 1978. *Birds in Leicestershire and Rutland.* Leicestershire and Rutland Ornithological Society, Leicester.

Hickling, R.A.O. 1984. Gulls in Leicestershire 1983. *The Birds of Leicestershire and Rutland 1983*: 41–42.

Holling, M. 1987. Study of Martinshaw Wood. *The Birds of Leicestershire & Rutland 1986*: 43–46.

Holling, M. 1988. Rookeries in Leicestershire and Rutland 1986–87. *The Birds of Leicestershire & Rutland 1987*: 51–55.

Holling, M. & the Rare Breeding Birds Panel 2007a. Rare breeding birds in the United Kingdom in 2003 and 2004. *Brit. Birds* 100: 321–367.

Holling, M. & the Rare Breeding Birds Panel 2007b. Non-native breeding birds in the United Kingdom in 2003, 2004 and 2005. *Brit. Birds* 100: 638–649.

Holling, M. & the Rare Breeding Birds Panel 2008. Rare breeding birds in the United Kingdom in 2005. *Brit. Birds* 101: 276–316.

Holloway, S. 1996. *The Historical Atlas of Breeding Birds in Britain and Ireland 1875–1900.* T. & A.D. Poyser, London.

Hollyer, J.N. 1970. The invasion of Nutcrackers in autumn 1968. *Brit. Birds* 63: 353–373.

Howarth, M.K. 1951. Some observations on the races of Golden Plovers at Lindley Aerodrome. *The Birds of Leicestershire & Rutland 1950*: 13–15.

Hume, R.A. 1976. Inland flocks of Kittiwakes. *Brit. Birds* 69: 62–63.

Hume, R.A. 1983. Twites wintering in Midland England. *Brit. Birds* 76: 90.

Hume, R.A. & Christie, D.A. 1989. Sabine's Gulls and other seabirds after the October 1987 storm. *Brit. Birds* 82: 191–208.

Hutchinson, C.D. & Neath, B. 1978. Little Gulls in Britain and Ireland. *Brit. Birds* 71: 563–582.

Jarvis, M.J. 1998. Greenish Warbler – new to the County List. *The Leicestershire & Rutland Bird Report 1997*: 92.

Jeeves, M. 1987. Breeding bird densities in two east Leicestershire woods in 1986. *The Birds of Leicestershire & Rutland 1986*: 47–49.

John, A.W.G. & Roskell, J. 1985. Jay movements in autumn 1983. *Brit. Birds* 78: 611–637.

Jolley, A.E. 1944. The changing status of Leicestershire birds. *County Report of Wild Birds for 1943*: 6–9.

Jolley, A.E. 1946a. Kentish Plover on Leicestershire-Rutland border. *Brit. Birds* 39: 188–189.

Jolley, A.E. 1946b. The Eye Brook Reservoir. *Leicestershire & Rutland County Report of Wild Birds for 1945*: 8–11.

Jolley, A.E. & Storer, R. 1945. Report on the Sand Martin enquiry, 1944. *County Report of Wild Birds for 1944*: 10–21.

Jones, G. 1987. Selection against large size in the Sand Martin *Riparia riparia* during a dramatic population crash. *Ibis* 129: 274–280.

Jones, P.W. 1959. Report on the breeding of Black-headed Gulls in Leicestershire in 1957. *The Birds of*

Leicestershire & Rutland 1957: 18–19.

Judson, N. 2004. Continental Song Thrushes in Leicestershire. *The Leicestershire & Rutland Bird Report 2002*: 114.

Kelsey, M.G., Green, G.H., Garnett, M.C. & Hayman, P.V. 1989. Marsh Warblers in Britain. *Brit. Birds* 82: 239–256.

Ketley, M. 2002. Shore Lark – new to the County List. *The Leicestershire & Rutland Bird Report 2001*: 101–102.

Kirby, J.S., Kirby, K.K. & Woolfall, S.J. 1989. Curlew Sandpipers in Britain and Ireland in autumn 1988. *Brit. Birds* 82: 399–409.

Kirton, K.M. 1969. Night Heron at Welham. *The Birds of Leicestershire & Rutland 1969*: 18–19.

Knox, A.G., Collinson, M., Helbig, A.J., Parkin, D.P. & Sangster, G. 2002. Taxonomic recommendations for British birds. *Ibis* 144: 707–710.

Kramer, D. 1989. Adult Moorhen killing chick. *Brit. Birds* 82: 73.

Lack, P. (ed.) 1986. *The Atlas of Wintering Birds in Britain and Ireland.* T. & A.D. Poyser, Calton.

Lapworth, H. 1954. The Hobby (*Falco subbuteo*): its breeding in Leicestershire, 1953. *The Birds of Leicestershire & Rutland 1953*: 8–9.

Leech, D. 2007. The Effect of Climate Change on Birds. http://www.bto.org/research/advice/ecc

Leigh, A.G. 1910. White-winged Black Tern in Warwickshire. *Brit. Birds* 3: 168.

Leverton, R. 1993. Migrant Ring Ouzels at a stopover site on the South Downs. *Brit. Birds* 86: 253–266.

Lilford 1895. *Birds of Northamptonshire and Neighbouring Counties.* R.H. Porter, London.

Lister, S. 1999. The Crag Martin in Leicestershire. *Birding World* 12: 148–150.

Lister, S. 2000. Crag Martin – new to the County List. *The Leicestershire & Rutland Bird Report 1999*: 98.

Lister, S. 2002. Colour-ringed Cormorants at Rutland Water in 2001. *The Leicestershire & Rutland Bird Report 1999*: 102–103.

Lister, S. 2006. Colour-ringed Cormorants at Rutland Water in 2004. *The Leicestershire & Rutland Bird Report 2004*: 135–137.

Lister, S. 2007a. Long-billed Dowitcher – new to the County List. *The Leicestershire & Rutland Bird Report 2005*: 135–136.

Lister, S. 2007b. Visible migration at Deans Lane in autumn 2005. *The Leicestershire & Rutland Bird Report 2005*: 137–138.

Lock, L. & Cook, K. 1998. The Little Egret in Britain: a successful colonist. *Brit. Birds* 91: 273–280.

Macfarlane, A.M. 2002. European Bee-eaters nesting in Britain. *Brit. Birds* 95: 657.

Mackay, A.J. 1989a. Wintering Golden Plovers in Leicestershire and Rutland 1987–89. *The Leicestershire & Rutland Bird Report 1988*: 47–48.

Mackay, A.J. 1989b. Ring-billed Gull – new to the County list. *The Leicestershire & Rutland Bird Report 1988*: 49.

Mackay, A.J. 1995a. Leicestershire records review. *The Leicestershire & Rutland Bird Report 1994*: 69–70.

Mackay, A.J. 1995b. Scarce gulls in Leicestershire and Rutland. *The Leicestershire & Rutland Bird Report 1994*: 74–82.

Mackay, A.J. (ed.) 1996a. *The Leicestershire & Rutland Bird Report 1995*. Leicestershire & Rutland Ornithological Society.

Mackay, A.J. 1996b. Hybrid wigeon resembling American Wigeon in Leicestershire. *Birding World* 9: 146–147.

Mackay, A.J. 1999. The Nightjar in Leicestershire and Rutland. *The Leicestershire & Rutland Bird Report 1998:* 104–105.

Mackay, A.J. 2005. Red-rumped Swallow – new to the County List. *The Leicestershire & Rutland Bird Report 2003*: 127–128.

Marquiss, M. & Newton, I. 1982. The Goshawk in Britain. *Brit. Birds* 75: 243–260.

Mason, C.F. 1969. Waders and terns in Leicestershire and an index of relative abundance. *Brit. Birds* 62: 523–533.

Mason, C.F. 1970. The arrival of summer migrants in Leicestershire. *The Birds of Leicestershire & Rutland 1969*: 30.

Mason, C.F. 1977. Recent later arrivals of summer migrants in Leicestershire. *Brit. Birds* 70: 342–343.

Mason, C.F. & Pickering, F.C. 1968. The birds of Leicester City Farms 1944–1964. *The Birds of Leicestershire & Rutland 1966*: 21–25.

Mayes, W.E. 1927. Long-tailed Skua in Leicestershire. *Brit. Birds* 20: 276–277.

McInerny, C.J. & Griffin, M. 2007. Regular inland passage of skuas observed in Lothian. *Brit. Birds* 100: 506–507.

Mead, C.J. 1984. Sand Martins slump. *BTO News* 133: 1.

Measures, C. & Hickling, R.A.O. 1984. The Mute Swan Census, 1983. *The Birds of Leicestershire & Rutland 1983*: 39–40.

Mellor, J.E. & Pearce, T. 1981. The Austin Friars, Leicester. *Council for British Archaeology Research Report No. 35.*

Merrill, I. 1992. Citrine Wagtail – new to the County List. *The Leicestershire & Rutland Bird Report 1991*: 59.

Mills, R. 1998. Redhead – new to the County List. *The Leicestershire & Rutland Bird Report 1997*: 89.

Mitcham, T. 1984. *The Birds of Rutland and its Reservoirs.* Sycamore Press, Wymondham.

Mitcham, T. 1992. *Rutland Breeding Bird Atlas.* Spiegl, Stamford.

Mitchell, P.I., Newton, S.F., Ratcliffe, N. & Dunn, T.E. 2004. *Seabird Populations of Britain and Ireland.* Poyser, London.

Morgan, D.H.W. 1993. Feral Rose-ringed Parakeets in Britain. *Brit. Birds* 86: 561–564.

Morris, A., Burges, D., Fuller, R.J., Evans, A.D. & Smith, K.W. 1994. The status and distribution of Nightjars *Caprimulgus europaeus* in Britain in 1992. *Bird Study* 41: 181–191.

Morris, M. 1968. Black-headed Bunting in Leicestershire. *The Birds of Leicestershire & Rutland 1967*: 23.

Moss, S. 1998. Predictions of the effects of global climate change on Britain's birds. *Brit. Birds* 91: 307–325.

Mudge, G.P. & Dennis, R.H. 1995. History of breeding by Temminck's Stints in Britain. *Brit. Birds* 88: 573–577.

Musgrove, A.J. 2002. The non-breeding status of the Little Egret in Britain. *Brit. Birds* 95: 62–80.

Musgrove, A.J., Collier, M.P., Banks, A.N., Calbrade, N.A., Hearn, R.D. & Austin, G.E. 2007. *Waterbirds in the UK 2005/06: The Wetland Bird Survey.* BTO/WWT/RSPB/JNCC, Thetford.

Nightingale, B. & Allsopp, K. 1994. Invasion of Red-footed Falcons in spring 1992. *Brit. Birds* 87: 223–231.

Nightingale, B. & Sharrock, J.T.R. 1982. Seabirds inland in Britain in late April 1981. *Brit. Birds* 75: 558–566.

O'Connor, R.J. & Mead, C.J. 1984. The Stock Dove in Britain. *Brit. Birds* 77: 181–201.

O'Connor, R.J. & Shrubb, M. 1986. *Farming and Birds.* Cambridge University Press, Cambridge.

Ogilvie, M. 1981. The Mute Swan in Britain, 1978. *Bird Study* 28: 87–106.

Ogilvie, M. & the Rare Breeding Birds Panel. 2000. Rare breeding birds in the United Kingdom in 1998. *Brit. Birds* 93: 358–393.

Ogilvie, M. & the Rare Breeding Birds Panel. 2003. Rare breeding birds in the United Kingdom in 2001. *Brit. Birds* 96: 476–519.

Ogilvie, M. & the Rare Breeding Birds Panel. 2004. Rare breeding birds in the United Kingdom in 2002. *Brit. Birds* 97: 492–536.

Otter, J. 1965. *The Birds of East Leicestershire.* Loughborough Naturalists' Club. Loughborough,

Leicestershire.

Ovens, R. & Sleath, S. (eds.) 2007. *The Heritage of Rutland Water.* Rutland Local History & Record Society, Oakham.

Page, W. (ed.) 1907. *The Victoria History of the County of Leicester, Volume 1.* Archibald Constable & Co Ltd, London.

Parslow, J.L.F. 1967. Changes in status among breeding birds in Britain and Ireland. *Brit. Birds* 60: 10–47, 97–123, 177–202, 261–285, 396–404, 493–508.

Parslow, J.L.F. 1968. Changes in status among breeding birds in Britain and Ireland. *Brit. Birds* 61: 49–64, 241–255.

Parslow-Otsu, M. & Elliott, G.D. 1991. Red-necked Grebe breeding in England. *Brit. Birds* 84: 188–191.

Peach, W. & Fowler, J. 1987. Flight-lines to the Abbey Park Starling Roost. *The Birds of Leicestershire and Rutland 1986*: 50–51.

Pennington, M. (ed.) 2006. *Shetland Bird Report 2005.* Shetland Bird Club.

Pennington, M.G. & Meek, E.R. 2006. The 'Northern Bullfinch' invasion of autumn 2004. *Brit. Birds* 99: 2–24.

Pennington, M., Osborn, K., Harvey, P., Riddington, R., Okill, D., Ellis, P. & Heubeck, M. 2004. *The Birds of Shetland.* Christopher Helm, London.

Pochin, R.E. 1945. Report on the nesting of the Blue-headed Wagtail. *County Report of Wild Birds for 1944*: 6–9.

Pochin, R.E. 1953. A provisional report on visible migration at Croft Hill, 1940 to 1952. *The Birds of Leicestershire & Rutland 1952*: 9–11.

Pochin, R.E. 1954. Wild birds within the city of Leicester. *The Birds of Leicestershire & Rutland 1953*: 20–30.

Pullan, G. 2004. Franklin's Gull – new to the County List. *The Leicestershire & Rutland Bird Report 2002*: 110–112.

Pullan, G. & Martin, J. 2004. From the Rarities Committee's files: Presumed hybrid gull resembling adult Franklin's Gull. *Brit. Birds* 97: 264–269.

Riddington, R., Votier, S.C. & Steele, J. 2000. The influx of redpolls into Western Europe, 1995/96. *Brit. Birds* 93: 59–67.

Roadhouse, A. (ed) 2006. *Spurn Wildlife No 15.* Spurn Bird Observatory.

Rock, P. 2005. Urban gulls: problems and solutions. *Brit. Birds* 98: 338–355.

Rose, P.M. & Scott, D.A. 1997 (2nd ed). *Waterfowl Population Estimates.* Wetlands International Publication 44. Wageningen: Wetlands International.

Scott, D.J. 1983. Common Bird Census at Newton Harcourt 1971–1982. *The Birds of Leicestershire & Rutland 1982*: 36–38.

Scott, R.E. 1978. Rough-legged Buzzards in Britain in 1973/74 and 1974/75. *Brit. Birds* 71: 325–338.

Sellers, R.M. 1984. Movements of Coal, Marsh and Willow Tits in Britain. *Ring. Migr.* 5: 79–89.

Sharrock, J.T.R. 1976. *The Atlas of Breeding Birds in Britain and Ireland.* Poyser, Berkhamsted.

Shawyer, C.R. 1994. *The Barn Owl.* Hamlyn, London.

Shergold, R.C. 1997. Common Crane – new to the County List. *The Leicestershire & Rutland Bird Report 1996*: 86.

Shrubb, M. 2003. *Birds, Scythes and Combines.* Cambridge University Press, Cambridge.

Sills, N. 1970. *Birds of Stanford Reservoir 1933–1967.* Rugby Natural History Society, Rugby.

Sim, I., Gibbons, D.W., Bainbridge, I. & Mattingley, W. 2001. Status of the Hen Harrier in the United Kingdom and the Isle of Man in 1998. *Bird Study* 48: 341–353.

Simms, E. (1952). *Bird Migrants; Some Aspects and Observations.* Cleaver-Hume, London.

Sitters, H.P. 1982. The decline of the Cirl Bunting in Britain, 1968–80. *Brit. Birds* 75: 105–108.

Skelton, H.M. 1959. Chaffinches attempting to feed on nut feeders. *The Birds of Leicestershire & Rutland 1957*: 16.

Smallshire, D. 1985. Possible Lesser Golden Plover in the Shepshed area, 1984/5. *The Birds of Leicestershire & Rutland 1984:* 48–49.

Smallshire, D. 1986a. The frequency of hybrid ducks in the Midlands. *Brit. Birds* 79: 87–89.

Smallshire, D. 1986b. Study of Spring Wood, Rough Park, Birch Coppice and adjacent scrub at Lount. *The Birds of Leicestershire & Rutland 1985*: 40–42.

Smith, A. 2002a. Greenland Wheatear at Bagworth Heath. *The Leicestershire & Rutland Bird Report 2000:* 107.

Smith, A. 2002b. Siskin With a Brood Patch Ringed in Leicestershire. *The Leicestershire & Rutland Bird Report 2000:* 108.

Snape, I. 1978. Migration at Frisby Gravel Pit, autumn 1976. *The Birds of Leicestershire & Rutland 1976*: 31–35.

Snow, B.K. 1966. The migration and dispersal of British Blackbirds. *Bird Study* 13: 237–255.

Sparks, T.H. 1999. Phenology and the changing pattern of bird migration in Britain. *International Journal of Biometeorology* 42: 134–138.

Spencer, K.G. 1969. Overland migrations of Common Scoter. *Brit. Birds* 62: 332–333.

Spencer, R. 1989. Rare breeding birds in the United Kingdom in 1987. *Brit. Birds* 82: 477–504.

Spencer, R. 1991. Rare breeding birds in the United Kingdom 1989. *Brit. Birds* 84: 349–392.

Staton, J. 1945. The breeding of Black-winged Stilts in Nottinghamshire in 1945. *Brit. Birds* 38: 322–328.

Stoate, C. 2001. Reversing the declines in farmland birds: a practical demonstration. *Brit. Birds* 94: 302–209.

Stone, B.H., Sears, J., Cranswick, P.A., Gregory, R.D., Gibbons, D.W., Rehfisch, M.M., Aebischer, N.J. & Reid, J.B. 1997. Population estimates of birds in Britain and in the United Kingdom. *Brit. Birds* 90: 1–22.

Summerfield, D. 1999. Spotted Sandpiper – new to the County List. *The Leicestershire & Rutland Bird Report 1998:* 101.

Taylor, M., Seago, M., Allard, P. & Dorling, D. 1999. *The Birds of Norfolk.* Pica Press, Robertsbridge, Sussex.

Thomas, J. 2007. Autumn skua records in Somerset indicating overland passage. *Brit. Birds* 100: 503–505.

Thomas, C. D. & Lennon, J. J. 1999. Birds extend their ranges northwards. *Nature* 399: 213.

Toon, S.J. 2007. Slavonian Grebe breeding with Great Crested Grebe. *Brit. Birds* 100: 381.

Tucker, V. 1985. Origins of British Glaucous Gulls. *Brit. Birds* 78: 355–356.

Uppingham School Field Club & Kirton, K.M. 1969. White-winged Black Tern at Eye Brook Reservoir. *The Birds of Leicestershire & Rutland 1968*: 19–20.

Van Franeker, J.A. 2005. Fulmar wreck in the southern North Sea: preliminary findings. *Brit. Birds* 97: 247–249.

Vincent, K.E. 2005. *Investigating the causes of the decline of the urban House Sparrow Passer domesticus population in Britain.* PhD thesis, De Montfort University, Leicester.

Vinicombe, K.E. 1994. Common Teals showing mixed characters of Eurasian and North American races. *Brit. Birds* 87: 88–89.

Vinicombe, K.E. 2000. Identification of Ferruginous Duck and its status in Britain and Ireland. *Brit. Birds* 93: 4–21.

Vinicombe, K., Marchant, J. & Knox, A. 1993. Review of status and categorisation of feral birds on the British List. *Brit. Birds* 86: 605–614.

Votier, S.C., Harrop, A.H.J. & Denny, M. 2003. A review of the status and identification of American Wigeon in Britain & Ireland. *Brit. Birds* 96: 2–22.

Wanless, S., Murray, S. & Harris, M.P. 2005. The status of Northern Gannet in Britain & Ireland in 2003/04. *Brit. Birds* 98: 280–294.

Warrilow, G.J. 1996. *Atlas of Breeding Birds of Leicestershire and Rutland.* Privately published.

Webster, M. 1997. *Birds of Charnwood.* Kairos Press, Newtown Linford, Leicester.

Weir, D.N., Kitchener, A.C. & McGowan, R. 2000. Hybridisation and changes in the distribution of Iceland Gulls (*Larus glaucoides/kumlieni/thayeri*). *J. Zool.* 252: 517–530.

Wernham, C.V., Toms, M.P., Marchant, J.H., Clark, J.A., Siriwardena, G.M. & Baillie, S.R. (eds.) 2002. *The Migration Atlas: movements of the birds of Britain and Ireland.* T. & A.D. Poyser, London.

White, S.J. & Kehoe, C.V. 2001. Difficulties in determining the age of Common Terns in the field. *Brit. Birds* 94: 268–277.

Willett, D.R. 1968. Bee-eater in Leicestershire. *The Birds of Leicestershire and Rutland 1967*: 23.

Wilson, A.M., Vickery, J.A. & Browne, S.J. 2001. The numbers and distribution of Lapwings *Vanellus vanellus* breeding in England and Wales in 1998. *Bird Study* 48: 2–17.

Wilson, A.M., Henderson, A.C.B. & Fuller, R.J. 2002. Status of the Common Nightingale *Luscinia megarhynchos* in England at the end of the 20th century with particular reference to climate change. *Bird Study* 49: 193–204.

Witherby, H.F., Jourdain, F.C.R., Ticehurst, N.F. & Tucker, B.W. 1938–1946. *The Handbook of British Birds.* 5 volumes. Witherby, London.

Wotton, S., Gibbons, D.W., Dilger, M. & Grice, P.V. 1998. Cetti's Warblers in the United Kingdom and the Channel Islands in 1996. *Brit. Birds* 91: 77–89.

Wotton, S., Rylands, K., Grice, P., Smallshire, D. & Gregory, R. 2004. The status of the Cirl Bunting in Britain and the Channel Islands in 2003. *Brit. Birds* 97: 376–384.

Wotton, S.R. & Gillings, S. 2000. The status of breeding Woodlarks *Lullula arborea* in Britain in 1997. *Bird Study* 47: 212–224.

Wright, D. 2002. *Aythya* hybrid at Thornton Reservoir. *The Leicestershire & Rutland Bird Report 2000:* 103.

Wright, J. 1995. Baird's Sandpiper at Eyebrook Reservoir. *The Leicestershire & Rutland Bird Report 1994:* 73.

INDEX